Best of
Christmas Cheer 1960
to a Swell Guy from
His Brother.

Real Good Reading!

Boris Pasternak
DOCTOR ZHIVAGO

—

PANTHEON

FIRST PUBLISHED SEPTEMBER 1958

TRANSLATED
FROM THE RUSSIAN
BY MAX HAYWARD AND
MANYA HARARI
"THE POEMS OF YURII ZHIVAGO"
BY BERNARD GUILBERT GUERNEY

CONTENTS

PART ONE

PART TWO

THE PRINCIPAL CHARACTERS
IN THIS BOOK

Yurii Andreievich Zhivago (as a child, called _Yura;_ affectionately, _Yurochka_) is the son of Andrei Zhivago, a profligate, and Maria Nikolaievna Zhivago.
Evgraf Andreievich Zhivago, his half brother, is the son of his father and Princess Stolbunova-Enrici.
Nikolai Nikolaievich Vedeniapin (_Uncle Kolia_) is his maternal uncle.

Antonina Alexandrovna Gromeko (_Tonia_) is the daughter of _Alexander Alexandrovich Gromeko_, a professor of chemistry, and his wife _Anna Ivanovna_, whose father was the landowner and ironmaster Ivan Ernestovich Krueger.
As young people, Yurii Andreievich Zhivago and _Misha Gordon_, son of a lawyer, live with the Gromekos.

Larisa Feodorovna Guishar (_Lara_) is the daughter of a Russianized, widowed Frenchwoman, Amalia Karlovna Guishar. Rodion (Rodia) is her younger brother.

Victor Ippolitovich Komarovsky was Andrei Zhivago's lawyer and is Madame Guishar's lover and adviser.

Lavrentii Mikhailovich Kologrivov is a rich industrialist; his wife, Serafima Filippovna; their daughters, Nadia and Lipa.

Pavel Pavlovich Antipov (_Pasha, Pashenka_) is the son of a railway worker, Pavel Ferapontovich Antipov. After his father's exile to Siberia, he lives with the Tiverzins (Kuprian Savelievich and his mother, Marfa Gavrilovna), another revolutionary family of railway workers.

Osip Gimazetdinovich Galiullin (_Yusupka_), son of Gimazetdin, the janitor at the Tiverzins' tenement; he is a Moslem.

Innokentii Dudorov (_Nika_), son of Dementii Dudorov, a revolutionary terrorist, and a Georgian princess.

Markel Shchapov, porter at the Gromekos' house, and his daughter _Marina_ (_Marinka_).

PART ONE

CHAPTER ONE

THE FIVE-O'CLOCK EXPRESS

The funeral of Maria Nikolaieona, the mother of Yura Zhivago

1

On they went, singing "Rest Eternal," and whenever they stopped, their feet, the horses, and the gusts of wind seemed to carry on their singing.

Passers-by made way for the procession, counted the wreaths, and crossed themselves. Some joined in out of curiosity and asked: "Who is being buried?"—"Zhivago," they were told.—"Oh, I see. That's what it is."—"It isn't him. It's his wife."—"Well, it comes to the same thing. May her soul rest in peace. It's a fine funeral."

The last moments slipped by, one by one, irretrievable. "The earth is the Lord's and the fullness thereof, the earth and everything that dwells therein." The priest, with the gesture of a cross, scattered earth over the body of Maria Nikolaievna. They sang "The souls of the righteous." Then a fearful bustle began. The coffin was closed, nailed, and lowered into the ground. Clods of earth rained on the lid as the grave was hurriedly filled by four spades. A little mound formed. A ten-year-old boy climbed on it. Only the state of stupor and insensibility which is gradually induced by all big funerals could have created the impression that he intended to speak over his mother's grave.

He raised his head and from his vantage point absently glanced about the bare autumn landscape and the domes of the monastery. His snub-nosed face became contorted and he stretched out his neck. If a wolf cub had done this, everyone would have thought that it was about to howl. The boy covered his face with his hands and burst into sobs. The wind bearing down on him lashed his hands and face with cold gusts of rain. A man in black with tightly fitting sleeves went up to the grave.

3

This was Nikolai Nikolaievich Vedeniapin, the dead woman's brother and the uncle of the weeping boy; a former priest, he had been unfrocked at his own request.

He went up to the boy and led him out of the graveyard.

Nikolai Nikolaievich Vedeniapin, Yura's uncle.

2

They spent the night at the monastery, where Uncle Nikolai was given a room for old times' sake. It was on the eve of the Feast of the Intercession of the Holy Virgin. The next day they were supposed to travel south to a provincial town on the Volga where Uncle Nikolai worked for the publisher of the local progressive newspaper. They had bought their tickets and their things stood packed in the cell. The station was near by, and they could hear the plaintive hooting of engines shunting in the distance.

It grew very cold that evening. The two windows of the cell were at ground level and looked out on a corner of the neglected kitchen garden, a stretch of the main road with frozen puddles on it, and the part of the churchyard where Maria Nikolaievna had been buried earlier in the day. There was nothing in the kitchen garden except acacia bushes around the walls and a few beds of cabbages, wrinkled and blue with cold. With each blast of wind the leafless acacias danced as if possessed and then lay flat on the path.

During the night the boy, Yura, was wakened by a knocking at the window. The dark cell was mysteriously lit up by a flickering whiteness. With nothing on but his shirt, he ran to the window and pressed his face against the cold glass.

Outside there was no trace of the road, the graveyard, or the kitchen garden, nothing but the blizzard, the air smoking with snow. It was almost as if the snowstorm had caught sight of Yura and, conscious of its power to terrify, roared and howled, doing everything possible to impress him. Turning over and over in the sky, length after length of whiteness unwound over the earth and shrouded it. The blizzard was alone in the world; it had no rival.

When he climbed down from the window sill Yura's first impulse was to dress, run outside, and start doing something. He was afraid that the cabbage patch would be buried so that no one could dig it out and that his mother would helplessly sink deeper and deeper away from him into the ground.

Once more it ended in tears. His uncle woke up, spoke to him of Christ, and tried to comfort him, then yawned and stood thoughtfully by the window. Day was breaking. They began to dress.

The Zhivagos go from wealth to poverty.

3

While his mother was alive Yura did not know that his father had abandoned them long ago, leading a dissolute life in Siberia and abroad and squandering the family millions. He was always told that his father was away on business in Petersburg or at one of the big fairs, usually at Irbit.

His mother had always been sickly. When she was found to have consumption she began to go to southern France and northern Italy for treatment. On two occasions Yura went with her. He was often left with strangers, different ones each time. He became accustomed to such changes, and against this untidy background, surrounded with continual mysteries, he took his father's absence for granted.

He could remember a time in his early childhood when a large number of things were still known by his family name. There was a Zhivago factory, a Zhivago bank, Zhivago buildings, a Zhivago necktie pin, even a Zhivago cake which was a kind of *baba au rhum,* and at one time if you said "Zhivago" to your sleigh driver in Moscow, it was as if you had said: "Take me to Timbuctoo!" and he carried you off to a fairy-tale kingdom. You would find yourself transported to a vast, quiet park. Crows settled on the heavy branches of firs, scattering the hoarfrost; their cawing echoed and re-echoed like crackling wood. Purebred dogs came running across the road out of the clearing from the recently constructed house. Farther on, lights appeared in the gathering dusk.

And then suddenly all that was gone. They were poor.

A visit to Ivan Ivanovich Voskoboinikov at Duplyanka

4

One day in the summer of 1903, Yura was driving across fields in a two-horse open carriage with his Uncle Nikolai. They were on their way to see Ivan Ivanovich Voskoboinikov, a teacher and author of popular textbooks, who lived at Duplyanka, the estate of Kologrivov, a silk manufacturer, and a great patron of the arts.

It was the Feast of the Virgin of Kazan. The harvest was in full swing but, whether because of the feast or because of the midday break, there was not a soul in sight. The half-reaped fields under the glaring sun looked like the half-shorn heads of convicts. Birds were circling overhead. In the hot stillness the heavy-eared wheat stood straight. Neat sheaves rose above the stubble in the distance; if you stared at them long enough they seemed to move, walking along on the horizon like land surveyors taking notes.

"Whose fields are these?" Nikolai Nikolaievich asked Pavel, the publisher's odd-job man who sat sideways on the box, shoulders hunched and legs crossed to show that driving was not his regular job. "The landlord's or the peasants'?"

"These are the master's." Pavel, who was smoking, after a long silence jabbed with the end of his whip in another direction: "And those are the peasants'!—Get along," he shouted at the horses, keeping an eye on their tails and haunches like an engineer watching his pressure gauge. The horses were like horses the world over: the shaft horse pulled with the innate honesty of a simple soul while the off horse arched its neck like a swan and seemed to the uninitiated to be an inveterate idler who thought only of prancing in time to the jangling bells.

Nikolai Nikolaievich had with him the proofs of Voskoboinikov's book on the land question; the publisher had asked the author to revise it in view of the increasingly strict censorship.

"The people are getting out of hand here," he told Pavel. "A merchant in a near-by village has had his throat slit and the county stud farm has been burned down. What do you make of it? Any talk of it in your village?"

But evidently Pavel took an even gloomier view than the censor who urged Voskoboinikov to moderate his passionate views on the agrarian problem.

"Talk of it? The peasants have been spoiled—treated too well. That's no good for the likes of us. Give the peasants rope and God knows we'll all be at each other's throats in no time.—Get along, there!"

This was Yura's second trip with his uncle to Duplyanka. He thought he remembered the way, and every time the fields spread out, forming a narrow border around the woods, it seemed to him he recognized the place where the road would turn right and disclose briefly a view of the six-mile-long Kologrivov estate, with the river gleaming in the distance and the railway beyond it. But each time he was mistaken. Fields followed fields and were in turn lost in woods. These vast expanses gave him a feeling of freedom and elation. They made him think and dream of the future.

Not one of the books that later made Nikolai Nikolaievich famous was yet written. Although his ideas had taken shape, he did not know how close was their expression. Soon he was to take his place among contemporary writers, university professors, and philosophers of the revolution, a man who shared their ideological concern but had nothing in common with them except their terminology. All of them, without exception, clung to some dogma or other, satisfied with words and superficialities, but Father Nikolai had gone through Tolstoyism and revolutionary idealism and was still moving forward. He passionately sought an idea, inspired, graspable, which in its movement would clearly point the way toward change, an idea like a flash of lightning or a roll of thunder capable of speaking even to a child or an illiterate. He thirsted for something new.

Yura enjoyed being with his uncle. He reminded him of his mother. Like hers, his mind moved with freedom and welcomed the unfamiliar. He had the same aristocratic sense of equality with all living creatures and the same gift of taking in everything at a glance and of expressing his thoughts as they first came to him and before they had lost their meaning and vitality.

Yura was glad that his uncle was taking him to Duplyanka. It was a beautiful place, and this too reminded him of his mother, who had been fond of nature and had often taken him for country walks.

He also looked forward to seeing Nika Dudorov again, though

Nika, being two years older, probably despised him. Nika was a schoolboy who lived at the Voskoboinikovs'; when he shook hands with Yura, he jerked his arm downwards with all his might and bowed his head so low that his hair flopped over his forehead and hid half his face.

Ivan & Nikolai revise a manuscript

5

"The vital nerve of the problem of pauperism," Nikolai Nikolaievich read from the revised manuscript.

"Essence would be better, I think," said Ivan Ivanovich, making the correction on the galleys.

They were working in the half-darkness of the glassed-in veranda. Watering cans and gardening tools lay about, a raincoat was flung over the back of a broken chair, mud-caked hip boots stood in a corner, their uppers collapsed on the floor.

"On the other hand, the statistics of births and deaths show," dictated Nikolai Nikolaievich.

"Insert 'for the year under review,'" said Ivan Ivanovich and made a note. There was a slight draft. Pieces of granite lay on the sheets as paperweights.

When they finished Nikolai Nikolaievich wanted to leave at once.

"There's a storm coming. We must be off."

"Nothing of the sort. I won't let you. We're going to have tea now."

"But I must be back in town by night."

"It's no use arguing. I won't hear of it."

From the garden, a whiff of charcoal smoke from the samovar drifted in, smothering the smell of tobacco plant and heliotrope. A maid carried out a tray with clotted cream, berries, and cheese cakes. Then they were told that Pavel had gone off to bathe in the river and had taken the horses with him. Nikolai Nikolaievich had to resign himself to staying.

"Let's go down to the river while they're getting tea ready," suggested Ivan Ivanovich.

On the strength of his friendship with Kologrivov, he had the use of two rooms in the manager's house. The cottage with its

small garden stood in a neglected corner of the park, near
ld drive, now thickly overgrown with grass and no longer
t   except for carting rubbish to the gully, which served as a
dump. Kologrivov, a man of advanced views and a millionaire
who sympathized with the revolution, was abroad with his wife.
Only his two daughters, Nadia and Lipa, with their governess
and a small staff of servants, were on the estate.

A thick hedge of blackthorn separated the manager's house
and garden from the park with its lawns and artificial lakes
which surrounded the main house. As Ivan Ivanovich and Nikolai Nikolaievich skirted the hedge, small flocks of sparrows flew
out at regular intervals. The blackthorn swarmed with them, and
their even chatter accompanied them like water flowing in a
pipe.

They passed the hothouses, the gardener's cottage, and the
ruins of some stone structure. They were talking about new
talent in science and literature.

"Yes, there are gifted men," said Nikolai Nikolaievich; "but
the fashion nowadays is all for groups and societies of every
sort. Gregariousness is always the refuge of mediocrities, whether
they swear by Soloviëv or Kant or Marx. Only individuals seek
the truth, and they shun those whose sole concern is not the
truth. How many things in the world deserve our loyalty? Very
few indeed. I think one should be loyal to immortality, which is
another word for life, a stronger word for it. One must be true
to immortality—true to Christ! Ah, you're turning up your nose,
my poor man. As usual, you haven't understood a thing."

"Hmm," said Ivan Ivanovich. Thin, fair-haired, restless as an
eel, he had a mocking little beard that made him look like an
American of Lincoln's time: he was always bunching it up in his
hand and nibbling the tip. "I say nothing, of course. As you
know, I look at these things rather differently. But while we're
at it, tell me, what was it like when they unfrocked you? I bet
you were scared. They didn't anathematize you, did they?"

"You're trying to change the subject. However, why not. . . .
Anathematize me? No, they don't do that any more. It was unpleasant, and there are certain consequences. For instance, one
is banned from the civil service for quite a long time, and I was
forbidden to go to Moscow or Petersburg. But these are trifles.

As I was saying, one must be true to Christ. I'll explain. What you don't understand is that it is possible to be an atheist, it is possible not to know whether God exists, or why, and yet believe that man does not live in a state of nature but in history, and that history as we know it now began with Christ, and that Christ's Gospel is its foundation. Now what is history? It is the centuries of systematic explorations of the riddle of death, with a view to overcoming death. That's why people discover mathematical infinity and electromagnetic waves, that's why they write symphonies. Now, you can't advance in this direction without a certain faith. You can't make such discoveries without spiritual equipment. And the basic elements of this equipment are in the Gospels. What are they? To begin with, love of one's neighbor, which is the supreme form of vital energy. Once it fills the heart of man it has to overflow and spend itself. And then the two basic ideals of modern man—without them he is unthinkable—the idea of free personality and the idea of life as sacrifice. Mind you, all this is still extraordinarily new. There was no history in this sense among the ancients. They had blood and beastliness and cruelty and pockmarked Caligulas who do not suspect how untalented every enslaver is. They had the boastful dead eternity of bronze monuments and marble columns. It was not until after the coming of Christ that time and man could breathe freely. It was not until after Him that men began to live toward the future. Man does not die in a ditch like a dog—but at home in history, while the work toward the conquest of death is in full swing; he dies sharing in this work. Ouf! I got quite worked up, didn't I? But I might as well be talking to a blank wall."

"That's metaphysics, my dear fellow. It's forbidden by my doctors, my stomach won't take it."

"Oh well, you're hopeless. Let's leave it. Goodness, what a view, you lucky devil. Though I suppose as you live with it every day you don't see it."

It was hard to keep one's eyes on the shimmering river, which, like a sheet of polished metal, reflected the glare of the sun. Suddenly its surface parted in waves. A big ferry loaded with carts, horses, and peasants and their women started for the other shore.

"Just think, it's only a little after five," said Ivan Ivanovich. "There's the express from Syzran. It passes here at five past five."

Far out on the plain, crossing it from right to left, came a neat little yellow and blue train, tiny in the distance. Suddenly they noticed that it had stopped. White puffs of steam flurried over the engine, and then came a prolonged whistle.

"That's strange," said Voskoboinikov. "Something's wrong. It has no business to stop in the middle of the marsh out there. Something must have happened. Let's go and have tea."

Yura day-dreams of his mother

6

Nika was neither in the garden nor in the house. Yura guessed that he was hiding because they bored him, and because Yura was too young for him. When his uncle and Ivan Ivanovich went on the veranda to work, Yura was left to wander aimlessly about the grounds.

How enchanting this place was! Orioles kept making their clear three-note calls, stopping each time just long enough to let the countryside suck in the moist fluting sounds down to the last vibration. A heavy fragrance, motionless, as though having lost its way in the air, was fixed by the heat above the flower beds. This brought back memories of Antibes and Bordighera. Yura turned this way and that. The ghost of his mother's voice was hallucinatingly present in the meadows. He heard it in the musical phrases of the birds and the buzzing of the bees. Now and then he imagined with a start that his mother was calling him, asking him to join her somewhere.

He walked to the gully and climbed from the clear coppice at its edge into the alder thicket that covered its bottom.

Down there among the litter of fallen branches it was dark and dank; flowers were few, and the notched stalks of horsetail looked like the staffs with Egyptian ornaments in his illustrated Bible.

Yura felt more and more lonely. He wanted to cry. He slumped to his knees and burst into tears.

"Angel of God, my holy guardian," he prayed, "keep me firmly on the path of truth and tell Mother I'm all right, she's not to worry. If there is a life after death, O Lord, receive Mother into Your heavenly mansions where the faces of the saints and of the just shine like stars. Mother was so good, she couldn't have been a sinner, have mercy on her, Lord, and please don't let her suffer. Mother!"—in his heart-rending anguish he called to her as though she were another patron saint, and suddenly, unable to bear any more, fell down unconscious.

He was not unconscious for long. When he came to, he heard his uncle calling him from above. He answered and began to climb. Suddenly he remembered that he had not prayed for his missing father, as Maria Nikolaievna had taught him to.

But his fainting spell had left him with a sense of lightness and well-being that he was unwilling to lose. He thought that nothing terrible would happen if he prayed for his father some other time, as if saying to himself, "Let him wait." Yura did not remember him at all.

Misha Gordon & his father Grigory Osipovich Gordon witness the suicide of the elder Zhivago.

7

In a second-class compartment of the train sat Misha Gordon, who was travelling with his father, a lawyer from Orenburg. Misha was a boy of eleven with a thoughtful face and big dark eyes; he was in his second year of gymnasium. His father, Grigory Osipovich Gordon, was being transferred to a new post in Moscow. His mother and sisters had gone on some time before to get their apartment ready.

Father and son had been travelling for three days.

Russia, with its fields, steppes, villages, and towns, bleached lime-white by the sun, flew past them wrapped in hot clouds of dust. Lines of carts rolled along the highways, occasionally lumbering off the road to cross the tracks; from the furiously speeding train it seemed that the carts stood still and the horses were marking time.

At big stations passengers jumped out and ran to the buffet; the sun setting behind the station garden lit their feet and shone under the wheels of the train.

Every motion in the world taken separately was calculated

and purposeful, but, taken together, they were spontaneously intoxicated with the general stream of life which united them all. People worked and struggled, each set in motion by the mechanism of his own cares. But the mechanisms would not have worked properly had they not been regulated and governed by a higher sense of an ultimate freedom from care. This freedom came from the feeling that all human lives were interrelated, a certainty that they flowed into each other—a happy feeling that all events took place not only on the earth, in which the dead are buried, but also in some other region which some called the Kingdom of God, others history, and still others by some other name.

To this general rule Misha was an unhappy, bitter exception. A feeling of care remained his ultimate mainspring and was not relieved and ennobled by a sense of security. He knew this hereditary trait in himself and watched morbidly and self-consciously for symptoms of it in himself. It distressed him. Its presence humiliated him.

For as long as he could remember he had never ceased to wonder why, having arms and legs like everyone else, and a language and way of life common to all, one could be different from the others, liked only by few and, moreover, loved by no one. He could not understand a situation in which if you were worse than other people you could not make an effort to improve yourself. What did it mean to be a Jew? What was the purpose of it? What was the reward or the justification of this impotent challenge, which brought nothing but grief?

When Misha took the problem to his father he was told that his premises were absurd, and that such reasonings were wrong, but he was offered no solution deep enough to attract him or to make him bow silently to the inevitable.

And making an exception only for his parents, he gradually became contemptuous of all grownups who had made this mess and were unable to clear it up. He was sure that when he was big he would straighten it all out.

Now, for instance, no one had the courage to say that his father should not have run after that madman when he had rushed out onto the platform, and should not have stopped the train when, pushing Grigory Osipovich aside, and flinging open the door, he had thrown himself head first out of the express like a diver from a springboard into a swimming pool.

But since it was his father who had pulled the emergency release, it looked as if the train had stopped for such an inexplicably long time because of them.

No one knew the exact cause of the delay. Some said that the sudden stop had damaged the air brakes, others that they were on a steep gradient and the engine could not make it. A third view was that as the suicide was a prominent person, his lawyer, who had been with him on the train, insisted on officials being called from the nearest station, Kologrivovka, to draw up a statement. This was why the assistant engineer had climbed up the telegraph pole: the inspection handcar must be on its way.

There was a faint stench from the lavatories, not quite dispelled by eau de cologne, and a smell of fried chicken, a little high and wrapped in dirty wax paper. As though nothing had happened, graying Petersburg ladies with creaking chesty voices, turned into gypsies by the combination of soot and cosmetics, powdered their faces and wiped their fingers on their handkerchiefs. When they passed the door of the Gordons' compartment, adjusting their shawls and anxious about their appearance even while squeezing themselves through the narrow corridor, their pursed lips seemed to Misha to hiss: "Aren't we sensitive! We're something special. We're intellectuals. It's too much for us."

The body of the suicide lay on the grass by the embankment. A little stream of blood had run across his forehead, and, having dried, it looked like a cancel mark crossing out his face. It did not look like his blood, which had come from his body, but like a foreign appendage, a piece of plaster or a splatter of mud or a wet birch leaf.

Curious onlookers and sympathizers surrounded the body in a constantly changing cluster, while his friend and travelling companion, a thickset, arrogant-looking lawyer, a pure-bred animal in a sweaty shirt, stood over him sullenly with an expressionless face. Overcome by the heat, he was fanning himself with his hat. In answer to all questions he shrugged his shoulders and said crossly without even turning around: "He was an alcoholic. Can't you understand? He did it in a fit of D.T.'s."

Once or twice a thin old woman in a woollen dress and lace kerchief went up to the body. She was the widow Tiverzina, mother of two engineers, who was travelling third class on a pass with her two daughters-in-law. Like nuns with their mother superior, the two quiet women, their shawls pulled low over their foreheads, followed her in silence. The crowd made way for them.

Tiverzina's husband had been burned alive in a railway accident. She stood a little away from the body, where she could see it through the crowd, and sighed as if comparing the two cases. "Each according to his fate," she seemed to say. "Some die by the Lord's will—and look what's happened to him—to die of rich living and mental illness."

All the passengers came out and had a look at the corpse and went back to their compartments only for fear that something might be stolen.

When they jumped out onto the track and picked flowers or took a short walk to stretch their legs, they felt as if the whole place owed its existence to the accident, and that without it neither the swampy meadow with hillocks, the broad river, nor the fine house and church on the steep opposite side would have been there. Even the diffident evening sun seemed to be a purely local feature. Its light probed the scene of the accident timidly, like a cow from a nearby herd come for a moment to take a look at the crowd.

Misha had been deeply shaken by the event and had at first wept with grief and fright. In the course of the long journey the suicide had come several times to their compartment and had talked with Misha's father for hours on end. He had said that he found relief in the moral decency, peace, and understanding which he discovered in him and had asked him endless questions about fine points in law concerning bills of exchange, deeds of settlement, bankruptcy, and fraud. "Is that so?" he exclaimed at Gordon's answers. "Can the law be as lenient as that? My lawyer takes a much gloomier view."

Each time that this nervous man calmed down, his travelling companion came from their first-class coach to drag him off to the restaurant to drink champagne. He was the thickset, arrogant, clean-shaven, well-dressed lawyer who now stood over

his body, showing not the least surprise. It was hard to escap̃
the feeling that his client's ceaseless agitation had somehow beeᴇ
to his advantage.

Misha's father described him as a well-known millionaire,
Zhivago, a good-natured profligate, not quite responsible for his
actions. When he had come to their compartment, he would,
unrestrained by Misha's presence, talk about his son, a boy of
Misha's age, and about his late wife; then he would go on about
his second family, whom he had deserted as he had the first. At
this point he would remember something else, grow pale with
terror, and begin to lose the thread of his story.

To Misha he had shown an unaccountable affection, which
probably reflected a feeling for someone else. He had showered
him with presents, jumping out to buy them at the big stations,
where the bookstalls in the first-class waiting rooms also sold toys
and local souvenirs.

He had drunk incessantly and complained that he had not
slept for three months and that as soon as he sobered up for
however short a time he suffered torments unimaginable to any
normal human being.

At the end, he rushed into their compartment, grasped Gordon
by the hand, tried to tell him something but found he could not,
and dashing out onto the platform threw himself from the
train.

Now Misha sat examining the small wooden box of minerals
from the Urals that had been his last gift. Suddenly there was a
general stir. A handcar rolled up on the parellel track. A
doctor, two policemen, and a magistrate with a cockade in his
hat jumped out. Questions were asked in cold businesslike
voices, and notes taken. The policemen and the guards, slipping
and sliding awkwardly in the gravel, dragged the corpse up
the embankment. A peasant woman began to wail. The passengers were asked to go back to their seats, the guard blew his
whistle, and the train started on.

Nika & Nadia fall in a pond.

8

"Here's old Holy Oil," Nika thought savagely, looking around the room for a way of escape. The voices of the guests were outside the door, and retreat was cut off. The room had two beds, his own and Voskoboinikov's. With scarcely a moment's thought he crept under the first.

He could hear them calling and looking for him in other rooms, surprised at his absence. Finally they entered the bedroom.

"Well, it can't be helped," said Nikolai Nikolaievich. "Run along, Yura. Perhaps your friend will turn up later and you can play with him then." They sat talking about the student riots in Petersburg and Moscow, keeping Nika in his absurd and undignified confinement for about twenty minutes. At last they went out onto the veranda. Nika quietly opened the window, jumped out, and went off into the park.

He had had no sleep the night before and was out of sorts. He was in his fourteenth year and was sick and tired of being a child. He had stayed awake all night and had gone out at dawn. The rising sun had cast the long dewy shadows of trees in loops over the park grounds. The shadow was not black but dark gray like wet felt. The heady fragrance of the morning seemed to come from this damp shadow on the ground, with strips of light in it like a girl's fingers.

Suddenly a streak of quicksilver, as shiny as the dew on the grass, flowed by him a few paces away. It flowed on and on and the ground did not absorb it. Then, with an unexpectedly sharp movement, it swerved aside and vanished. It was a grass snake. Nika shuddered.

He was a strange boy. When he was excited he talked aloud to himself, imitating his mother's predilection for lofty subjects and paradox.

"How wonderful to be alive," he thought. "But why does it always hurt? God exists, of course. But if He exists, then it's me." He looked up at an aspen shaking from top to bottom, its wet leaves like bits of tinfoil. "I'll order it to stop." With an insane intensity of effort, he willed silently with his whole being, with every ounce of his flesh and blood: "Be still," and the tree at once obediently froze into immobility. Nika laughed with joy and ran off to the river to bathe.

His father, the terrorist Dementii Dudorov, condemned to death by hanging but reprieved by the Tsar, was now doing forced labor. His mother was a Georgian princess of the Eristov family, a spoiled and beautiful woman, still young and always infatuated with one thing or another—rebellions, rebels, extremist theories, famous actors, unhappy failures.

She adored Nika, turning his name, Innokentii, into a thousand impossibly tender and silly nicknames such as Inochek or Nochenka, and took him to Tiflis to show him off to her family. There, what struck him most was a straggly tree in the courtyard of their house. It was a clumsy, tropical giant, with leaves like elephant's ears which sheltered the yard from the scorching southern sky. Nika could not get used to the idea that it was a plant and not an animal.

It was dangerous for the boy to bear his father's terrible name. Ivan Ivanovich wished him to adopt his mother's and intended, with her consent, to petition the Tsar for permission to make the change. When lying under the bed, indignant at all the world, he had thought among other things of this. Who did Voskoboinikov think he was to meddle so outrageously with his life? He'd teach him where he got off.

And that Nadia! Just because she was fifteen, did that give her the right to turn up her nose and talk down to him as if he were a child? He'd show her! "I hate her," he said several times to himself. "I'll kill her. I'll take her out in the boat and drown her."

His mother was a fine one, too. Of course she'd lied to him and Voskoboinikov when she went away. She hadn't gone anywhere near the Caucasus, she had simply turned around at the nearest junction and gone north to Petersburg, and was now having a lovely time with the students shooting at the police, while he was supposed to rot alive in this silly dump. But he'd outsmart them all. He'd kill Nadia, quit school, run away to his father in Siberia, and start a rebellion.

The pond had water lilies all around the edge. The boat cut into this growth with a dry rustle; the pond water showed through like juice in a watermelon where a sample wedge has been cut out.

Nika and Nadia were picking the lilies. They both took hold of the same tough rubbery stem; it pulled them together, so that their heads bumped, and the boat was dragged in to shore as by a boathook. There the stems were shorter and more tangled; the white flowers, with their glowing centers looking like blood-specked egg yolks, sank and emerged dripping with water.

Nadia and Nika kept on picking flowers, tipping the boat more and more, lying in it almost side by side.

"I'm sick of school," said Nika. "It's time I began my life—time I went out into the world and earned my living."

"And I meant to ask you about square root equations. My algebra is so bad I nearly had to take another exam."

Nika thought there was a hidden barb in those words. Naturally, she was putting him in his place, reminding him he was a baby. Square root equations! Why, he hadn't even begun algebra.

Feigning indifference to conceal his feelings, he asked, realizing at the same moment how silly it was: "Whom will you marry when you're grown up?"

"That's a very long way off. Probably no one. I haven't thought about it."

"I hope you don't think I'm interested."

"Then why do you ask?"

"You're stupid."

They began to quarrel. Nika remembered his early morning misogyny. He threatened to drown her if she didn't stop calling him names. "Just try," said Nadia. He grabbed her around the waist. They fought, lost their balance, and fell in.

They could both swim, but the lilies caught at their arms and legs and they were out of their depth. Finally, wading through the sticky mud, they climbed out, water streaming from their shoes and pockets. Nika was the more exhausted of the two.

They were sitting side by side, drenched to the skin. No later than last spring, after such an adventure, they would have shouted, cursed, or laughed. But now they were silent, catching their breath, overcome by the absurdity of the whole thing.

Nadia seethed with inner indignation, and Nika ached all over, as if someone had beaten him with a club and cracked his ribs.

In the end Nadia said quietly, like an adult: "You really are mad," and Nika said in an equally adult tone: "I'm sorry."

They walked home dripping water like two water carts. Their way took them up the dusty slope swarming with snakes near the place where Nika had seen the grass snake that morning.

He remembered the magic elation that had filled him in the night, and his omnipotence at dawn when nature obeyed his will. What order should he give it now, he wondered. What was his dearest wish? It struck him that what he wanted most was to fall into the pond again with Nadia, and he would have given much to know if this would ever happen.

CHAPTER TWO

A GIRL FROM A DIFFERENT WORLD

Amalia Karlovna Guishar; Larisa & Rodion
Mme Guishar takes over a dressmaking business

1

The war with Japan was not yet over when it was unexpectedly overshadowed by other events. Waves of revolution swept across Russia, each greater and more extraordinary than the last.

It was at this time that Amalia Karlovna Guishar, the widow of a Belgian engineer and herself a Russianized Frenchwoman, arrived in Moscow from the Urals with her two children—her son Rodion and her daughter Larisa. She placed her son in the military academy and her daughter in a girls' gymnasium, where, as it happened, Nadia Kologrivova was her classmate.

Madame Guishar's husband had left her his savings, stocks which had been rising and were now beginning to fall. To stop the drain on her resources and to have something to do she bought a small business; this was Levitskaia's dressmaking establishment near the Triumphal Arch; she took it over from Levitskaia's heirs together with the firm's good will, its clientele, and all its seamstresses and apprentices.

This she did on the advice of Komarovsky, a lawyer who had been a friend of her husband's and was now the man to whom she turned for counsel and help, a cold-blooded businessman who knew the Russian business world like the back of his hand. It was with him that she had arranged her move by correspondence; he had met her and the children at the station and had driven them to the other end of Moscow, to the Montenegro Hotel in Oruzheiny Pereulok, where he had booked their room. He had also persuaded her to send Rodia to the military academy and Lara to the school of his choice. He joked carelessly with the boy and stared at the girl so that he made her blush.

21

The Guishars move to Moscow

2

They stayed about a month at the Montenegro before moving into the small three-room apartment adjoining the workshop.

This was the most disreputable part of Moscow—slums, cheap bars frequented by cabmen,[1] whole streets devoted to vice, dens of "fallen women."

The children were not surprised by the dirt in the rooms, the bedbugs, and the wretchedness of the furniture. Since their father's death their mother had lived in constant fear of destitution. Rodia and Lara were used to being told that they were on the verge of ruin. They realized that they were different from the children of the street, but, like children brought up in an orphanage, they had a deep-seated fear of the rich.

Their mother was a living example of this fear. Madame Guishar was a plump blonde of about thirty-five subject to spells of palpitation alternating with her fits of silliness. She was a dreadful coward and was terrified of men. For this very reason, out of fear and confusion, she drifted continually from lover to lover.

At the Montenegro the family lived in Room 23; Room 24, ever since the Montenegro had been founded, had been occupied by the cellist Tyshkevich, a bald, sweaty, kindly man in a wig who joined his hands prayerfully and pressed them to his breast when he was trying to be persuasive, and who threw back his head and rolled his eyes in ecstasy when he played at fashionable parties and concert halls. He was rarely in, spending whole days at the Bolshoi Theater or the Conservatory. As neighbors they helped each other out, and this brought them together.

Since the presence of the children sometimes embarrassed Madame Guishar during Komarovsky's visits, Tyshkevich would leave her his key so that she could receive her friend in his room. Soon she took his altruism so much for granted that on several occasions she knocked on his door asking him in tears to protect her from her benefactor.

[1] Cabmen: The Russian expression here is *likhachi*—fashionable cab drivers who had an unsavory reputation as a class.

Madame Guishar's dressmaking establishment

3

The workshop was in a one-story house near the corner of Tverskaia Street. Near by was the Brest railway with its engine depots, warehouses, and lodgings for the employees.

In one of them lived Olia Demina, a clever girl who worked at Madame Guishar's and whose uncle was employed at the freight yard.

She was a quick apprentice. She had been singled out by the former owner of the workshop and was now beginning to be favored by the new one. Olia had a great liking for Lara Guishar.

Nothing had changed since Levitskaia's day. The sewing machines whirred frantically under the tread of tired seamstresses or their flitting hands. Here and there a woman sat on a table sewing quietly with a broad sweep of the arm as she pulled the needle and long thread. The floor was littered with scraps. You had to raise your voice to make yourself heard above the clatter of the machines and the modulated trills of Kirill Modestovich, the canary in its cage in the window (the former owner had carried with her to the grave the secret of the bird's improbable name).

In the reception room the customers clustered in a picturesque group around a table heaped with fashion magazines. Standing, sitting, or bending over the table in the poses they had seen in the pictures, they discussed models and patterns. In the manager's chair at another table sat Faina Silantievna Fetisova, Madame Guishar's assistant and senior cutter, a bony woman with warts in the hollows of her flabby cheeks. A cigarette in a bone holder clamped between her yellowed teeth, squinting her yellowish eyes and blowing a stream of yellow smoke from her nose and mouth, she jotted in a notebook the measurements, orders and addresses, and requests of the thronging clients.

Madame Guishar had no experience of running a workshop. She felt that she was not quite the boss, but the staff were honest and Fetisova was reliable. All the same, these were troubled times and she was afraid to think of the future; she had moments of paralyzing despair.

Komarovsky often went to see them. As he walked through the

workshop on his way to their apartment, startling the fashionable ladies at their fittings so that they darted behind the screens playfully parrying his ambiguous jokes, the seamstresses, disapproving, muttered sneeringly: "Here comes his lordship," "Amalia's heartache," "old goat," "lady-killer."

An object of even greater hatred was his bulldog Jack; he sometimes took it with him on a lead on which it pulled with such violent jerks that Komarovsky followed stumbling and lurching with outstretched hands like a blind man after his guide.

One spring day Jack sank his teeth in Lara's leg and tore her stocking.

"I'll kill that demon," Olia whispered hoarsely into Lara's ear.

"Yes, it really is a horrid dog; but how can you do that, silly?"

"Ssh, don't talk so loud, I'll tell you. You know those stone Easter eggs—the ones on your Mama's chest of drawers. . . ."

"Well, yes, they're made of glass and marble."

"That's it. Bend down and I'll whisper. You take them and dip them in lard—the filthy beast will guzzle them and choke himself, the devil. That'll do it."

Lara laughed and thought of Olia with envy. Here was a working girl who lived in poverty. Such children were precocious. Yet how unspoiled and childlike she was! Jack, the eggs—where on earth did she get all her ideas? "And why is it," thought Lara, "that my fate is to see everything and take it all so much to heart?"

4

"Mother is his—what's the word . . . He's Mother's . . . They're bad words, I won't say them. Then why does he look at me like that? I'm her daughter, after all."

Lara was only a little over sixteen but she was well developed. People thought she was eighteen or more. She had a good mind and was easy to get along with. She was very good-looking.

She and Rodia realized that nothing in life would come to them without a struggle. Unlike the idle and well-to-do, they did not have the leisure for premature curiosity and theorizing about things that were not yet practical concerns. Only the superfluous is sordid. Lara was the purest being in the world.

Brother and sister knew the value of things and appreciated what they had achieved so far. People had to think well of you if you were to get on. Lara worked well at school, not because she had an abstract love of learning but because only the best pupils were given scholarships. She was just as good at washing dishes, helping out in the workshop, and doing her mother's errands. She moved with a silent grace, and all her features—voice, figure, gestures, her gray eyes and her fair hair—formed a harmonious whole.

It was a Sunday in the middle of July. On holidays you could stay in bed a little longer. Lara lay on her back, her hands clasped behind her head.

The workshop was quiet. The window looking out on the street was open. Lara heard the rattle of a droshki in the distance turn into a smooth glide as the wheels left the cobbles for the groove of a trolley track. "I'll sleep a bit more," she thought. The rumble of the town was like a lullaby and made her sleepy.

Lara felt her size and her position in the bed with two points of her body—the salient of her left shoulder and the big toe of her right foot. Everything else was more or less herself, her soul or inner being, harmoniously fitted into her contours and impatiently straining toward the future.

"I must go to sleep," thought Lara, and conjured up in her imagination the sunny side of Coachmakers' Row as it must be at this hour—the enormous carriages displayed on the cleanly swept floors of the coachmakers' sheds, the lanterns of cut glass, the stuffed bears, the rich life. And a little farther down the street, the dragoons exercising in the yard of the Znamensky barracks—the chargers mincing in a circle, the men vaulting into the saddles and riding past, at a walk, at a trot, and at a gallop, and outside, the row of children with nurses and wet-nurses gaping through the railings.

And a little farther still, thought Lara, Petrovka Street. "Good heavens, Lara, what an idea! I just wanted to show you my apartment. We're so near."

It was the name day of Olga, the small daughter of some friends of Komarovsky's who lived in Coachmakers' Row. The grownups were celebrating the occasion with dancing and champagne. He had invited Mother, but Mother couldn't go, she wasn't feeling well. Mother said: "Take Lara. You're always telling me to look after Lara. Well, now you look after her." And look after her he did—what a joke!

It was all this waltzing that had started it. What a crazy business it was! You spun round and round, thinking of nothing. While the music played, a whole eternity went by like life in a novel. But as soon as it stopped you had a feeling of shock, as if a bucket of cold water were splashed over you or somebody had found you undressed. Of course, one reason why you allowed anyone to be so familiar was just to show how grown-up you were.

She could never have imagined that he danced so well. What clever hands he had, what assurance as he gripped you by the waist! But never again would she allow anyone to kiss her like that. She could never have dreamed there could be so much effrontery in anyone's lips when they were pressed for such a long time against your own.

She must stop all this nonsense. Once and for all. Stop playing at being shy, simpering and lowering her eyes—or it would end in disaster. There loomed an imperceptible, a terrifying border-line. One step and you would be hurtled into an abyss. She must stop thinking about dancing. That was the root of the evil. She must boldly refuse—pretend that she had never learned to dance or that she'd broken her leg.

a threatened railway strike

5

That autumn there was unrest among the railway workers on the Moscow network. The men on the Moscow-Kazan line went on strike, and those of the Moscow-Brest line were expected to join them. The decision to strike had been taken, but the strike committee was still arguing about the date. Everyone on the railway knew that a strike was coming and only a pretext was needed for it to begin.

It was a cold overcast morning at the beginning of October, and on that day the wages were due. For a long time nothing was heard from the bookkeeping department; then a boy came into the office with a pay sheet and a pile of records that had been consulted for the deduction of fines. The cashier began handing out the pay. In an endless line, conductors, switchmen, mechanics and their assistants, scrubwomen from the depot, moved across the ground between the wooden buildings of the management and the station with its workshops, warehouses, engine sheds, and tracks.

The air smelled of early winter in town—of trampled maple leaves, melted snow, engine soot, and warm rye bread just out of the oven (it was baked in the basement of the station buffet). Trains came and went. They were shunted, coupled, and uncoupled to the waving of furled and unfurled signal flags. Locomotives hooted, guards tooted their horns, and shunters blew their whistles. Smoke rose in endless ladders to the sky. Hissing engines scalded the cold winter clouds with clouds of boiling steam.

Fuflygin, the Divisional Manager, and Pavel Ferapontovich Antipov, the Track Overseer of the station area, walked up and down along the edge of the tracks. Antipov had been pestering the repair shops about the quality of the spare parts for mending the tracks. The steel was not sufficiently tensile, the rails failed the test for strains, and Antipov thought that they would crack in the frosty weather. The management merely shelved his complaints. Someone was making money on the contracts.

Fuflygin wore an expensive fur coat on which the piping of the railway uniform had been sewn; it was unbuttoned, showing his new civilian serge suit. He stepped cautiously on the embankment, glancing down with pleasure at the line of his lapels, the straight creases on his trousers, and his elegant shoes. What Antipov was saying came in one ear and went out the other. Fuflygin had his own thoughts; he kept taking out his watch and looking at it; he was in a hurry to be off.

"Quite right, quite right, my dear fellow," he broke in impatiently, "but that's only dangerous on the main lines with a lot of traffic. But just look at what you've got. Sidings and dead ends, nettles and dandelions. And the traffic—at most an old shunting engine for sorting the empties. What more do you want? You must be out of your mind! Talk about steel—wooden rails would do here!"

Fuflygin looked at his watch, snapped the lid, and gazed into the distance where a road ran toward the railway. A carriage came into sight at a bend of the road. This was Fuflygin's own turnout. His wife had come for him. The coachman drew in the horses almost at the edge of the tracks, talking to them in a high-pitched womanish voice, like a nursemaid scolding fretful children; they were frightened of trains. In a corner of the carriage sat a pretty woman negligently leaning against the cushions.

"Well, my good fellow, some other time," said the Divisional Manager with a wave of the hand, as much as to say, "I've got more important things than rails to think about." The couple drove off.

Kuprian Tiverzin (Savelich)

6

Three or four hours later, almost at dusk, in a field some distance from the track, where no one had been visible until then, two figures rose out of the ground and, looking back over their shoulders, quickly walked away.

"Let's walk faster," said Tiverzin. "I'm not worried about spies following us, but the moment those slowpokes in their hole in the ground have finished they'll come out and catch up with us. I can't bear the sight of them. What's the point of having a committee if you drag things out like that? You play with fire and then you duck for shelter. You're a fine one yourself—siding with that lot."

"My Daria's got typhus. I ought to be taking her to the hospital. Until I've done that I can't think about anything else."

"They say the wages are being paid today. I'll go around to the office. If it wasn't payday I'd chuck the lot of you, honest to God I would. I'd stop all this myself, I wouldn't wait a minute."

"And how would you do that, if I may ask?"

"Nothing to it. I'd go down to the boiler room and blow the whistle. That's all."

They said goodbye and went off in different directions.

Tiverzin walked across the tracks toward the town. He ran into people coming from the office with their pay. There were a great many of them. By the look of it he reckoned that nearly all the station workers had been paid.

It was getting dark, the lights were on in the office. Idle workers crowded in the square outside it. In the driveway stood Fuflygin's carriage and in it sat Fuflygin's wife, still in the same pose as though she had not moved since morning. She was waiting for her husband, who was getting his money.

Suddenly sleet began to fall. The coachman climbed down from his box to put up the leather hood. While he tugged at the stiff struts, one leg braced against the back of the carriage, Fuflygina sat admiring the silver beads of sleet glittering in the light of the office lamps; her unblinking dreamy eyes were fixed on a point above the heads of the workers in a manner suggesting that her glance could, in case of need, go through them as through sleet or mist.

Tiverzin caught sight of her expression. It gave him a turn. He walked past without greeting her and decided to call for his wages later, so as not to run into her husband at the office. He crossed over to the darker side of the square, toward the workshops and the black shape of the turntable with tracks fanning out from it toward the depot.

"Tiverzin! Kuprik!" Several voices called out of the darkness. There was a little crowd outside the workshops. Inside, someone was yelling and a boy was crying. "Do go in and help that boy, Kuprian Savelievich," said a woman in the crowd.

As usual, the old foreman, Piotr Khudoleiev, was walloping his young apprentice Yusupka.

Khudoleiev had not always been a tormentor of apprentices and a brawling drunkard. There had been a time when, as a dashing young workman, he had attracted the admiring glances of merchants' and priests' daughters in Moscow's industrial suburbs. But the girl he courted, Marfa, who had graduated that year from the diocesan convent school, had turned him down and had married his comrade, the mechanic Savelii Nikitich, Tiverzin's father.

Five years after Savelii's horrible end (he was burned to death in the sensational railway crash of 1888) Khudoleiev renewed his suit, but again Marfa Gavrilovna rejected him. So Khudoleiev took to drink and rowdiness, trying to get even with a world which was to blame, so he believed, for all his misfortunes.

Yusupka was the son of Gimazetdin, the janitor at the block

of tenements where Tiverzin lived. Tiverzin had taken the boy under his wing, and this added fuel to Khudoleiev's hostility.

"Is that the way to hold a file, you Asiatic?" bellowed Khudoleiev, dragging Yusupka by the hair and pummelling the back of his neck. "Is that the way to strip down a casting, you slit-eyed Tartar?"

"Ouch, I won't do it any more, mister, ow, I won't do it any more, ouch, it hurts!"

"He's been told a thousand times: first adjust the mandrel and then screw up the chuck, but no, he must do it his own way! Nearly broke the spindle, the bastard."

"I didn't touch the spindle, honest I didn't."

"Why do you tyrannize the boy?" asked Tiverzin, elbowing his way through the crowd.

"It's none of your business," Khudoleiev snapped.

"I'm asking you why you tyrannize the boy."

"And I'm telling you to move off before there's trouble, you socialist meddler. Killing's too good for him, such scum, he nearly broke my spindle. He should thank his lucky stars he's still alive, the slit-eyed devil—all I did was tweak his ears and pull his hair a bit."

"So you think he should be beheaded for this. You ought to be ashamed of yourself, really, an old foreman like you—you've got gray hair but you still haven't learned sense."

"Move on, move on, I tell you, while you're still in one piece. I'll knock the stuffing out of you, preaching at me, you dog's arse. You were made on the tracks, you jellyfish, under your father's very nose. I know your mother, the slut, the mangy cat, the crumpled skirt!"

What happened next was over in a minute. Both men seized the first thing that came to hand on the lathe benches where heavy tools and pieces of iron were lying about, and would have killed each other if the crowd had not rushed in to separate them. Khudoleiev and Tiverzin stood with their heads bent down, their foreheads almost touching, pale, with bloodshot eyes. They were so angry that they could not utter a word. They were held firmly, their arms gripped from behind. Once or twice they tried to break free, twisting their bodies and dragging their comrades who were hanging on to them. Hooks and buttons went flying, their jackets and shirts slipped off, baring their shoulders. Around them was a ceaseless uproar.

"The chisel! Take the chisel away from him, he'll smash his head in. Easy now, easy now, Piotr old man, or we'll break your arm! What are we playing around with them for! Drag them apart and put them under lock and key and there's an end to it."

With a superhuman effort Tiverzin suddenly shook off the men who clung to him and, breaking loose, dashed to the door. They started after him but, seeing that he had changed his mind, left him alone. He went out, slamming the door, and marched off without turning around. The damp autumn night closed in on him. "You try to help them and they come at you with a knife," he muttered, striding on unconscious of his direction.

This world of ignominy and fraud, in which an overfed lady had the impertinence to stare right through a crowd of workingmen and where a drink-sodden victim of such an order found pleasure in torturing his comrades—this world was now more hateful to him than ever before. He hurried on as though his pace might hasten the time when everything on earth would be as rational and harmonious as it was now inside his feverish head. He knew that all their struggles in the last few days, the troubles on the line, the speeches at meetings, the decision to strike—not carried out yet but at least not cancelled—were separate stages on the great road lying ahead of them.

But at the moment he was so worked up that he wanted to run all the way without stopping to draw breath. He did not realize where he was going with his long strides, but his feet knew very well where they were taking him.

It was not until much later that Tiverzin learned of the decision, taken by the strike committee after he had left the underground shelter with Antipov, to begin the strike that very night. They decided then and there which of them was to go where and which men would be called out. At the moment when the whistle of the engine repair shop blew, as though coming from the very depths of Tiverzin's soul, hoarsely at first and then gradually clearing, a crowd was already moving from the depot and the freight yard. Soon it was joined by the men from the boiler room, who had downed tools at Tiverzin's signal.

For many years Tiverzin thought that it was he alone who had stopped work and traffic on the line that night. Only much later, at the trial, when he was charged with complicity in the strike but not with inciting it, did he learn the truth.

People ran out asking: "Where is everybody going? What's the signal for?"—"You're not deaf," came from the darkness. "It's a fire. They're sounding the alarm. They want us to put it out." —"Where's the fire?"—"There must be a fire or they wouldn't be sounding the alarm."

Doors banged, more people came out. Other voices were heard. "Fire? Listen to the ignorant lout! It's a strike, that's what it is, see? Let them get some other fools to do their dirty work. Let's go, boys."

More and more people joined the crowd. The railway workers were on strike.

Gimazetdin Galfiullin   Prov Afanasievich Sokolov
Marfa Gavrilovna gets the apartment warm for Kuprian

7

Tiverzin went home two days later, unshaven, drawn with lack of sleep, and chilled to the bone. Frost, unusual at this time of year, had set in the night before, and Tiverzin was not dressed for winter. The janitor, Gimazetdin, met him at the gate.

"Thank you, Mr. Tiverzin," he babbled in broken Russian. "You didn't let Yusupka come to harm. I will always pray for you."

"You're crazy, Gimazetdin, who're you calling Mister? Cut it out and say what you have to say quickly, you see how cold it is."

"Why should you be cold? You will soon be warm, Kuprian Savelich. Me and your mother Marfa Gavrilovna brought a whole shedful of wood from the freight station yesterday—all birch—good, dry wood."

"Thanks, Gimazetdin. If there's something else you want to tell me let's have it quickly. I'm frozen."

"I wanted to tell you not to spend the night at home, Savelich. You must hide. The police have been here asking who comes to the house. Nobody comes, I said, my relief comes, I said, the people from the railway but no strangers come, I said, not on your life."

Tiverzin was unmarried and lived with his mother and his younger married brother. The tenements belonged to the neighboring Church of the Holy Trinity. Among the lodgers were some of the clergy and two *artels,* or associations, of street hawkers—one of butchers, the other of greengrocers—but most of them were workers on the Moscow-Brest railway.

It was a stone house. All around the dirty and unpaved courtyard ran a wooden passageway. Out of it rose a number of dirty, slippery outside staircases, reeking of cats and cabbage. On the landings were privies and padlocked storerooms.

Tiverzin's brother had fought as a conscript in the war and had been wounded at Wafangkou. Now he was convalescing at the military hospital in Krasnoyarsk, and his wife and two daughters had gone there to see him and to bring him home (the Tiverzins, hereditary railway workers, travelled all over Russia on official passes). The flat was quiet; only Tiverzin and his mother lived in it at present.

It was on the second floor. On the landing outside there was a water butt, filled regularly by the water carrier. Tiverzin noticed as he came up that the lid of the butt had been pushed sideways and a tin mug stood on the frozen surface of the water. "Prov must have been here," he thought, grinning. "The way that man drinks, his guts must be on fire." Prov Afanasievich Sokolov, the church psalmist, was a relative of Tiverzin's mother.

Tiverzin jerked the mug out of the ice and pulled the handle of the doorbell. A wave of warm air and appetizing vapors from the kitchen came out to him.

"You've got a good fire going, Mother. It's nice and warm in here."

His mother flung herself on his neck and burst into tears. He stroked her head and, after a while, gently pushed her aside.

"Nothing ventured, nothing won, Mother," he said softly. "The line's struck from Moscow to Warsaw."

"I know, that's why I'm crying. They'll be after you, Kuprinka, you've got to get away."

"That nice boy friend of yours, Piotr, nearly broke my head!"
He meant to make her laugh but she said earnestly: "It's a
sin to laugh at him, Kuprinka. You should be sorry for him, the
poor wretch, the drunkard."

"Antipov's been arrested. They came in the night, searched
his flat, turned everything upside down, and took him away this
morning. And his wife Daria's in hospital with the typhus. And
their kid, Pasha, who's at the *Realgymnasium,* is alone in the
house with his deaf aunt. And they're going to be evicted. I
think we should have the boy to stay with us. What did Prov
want?"

"How did you know he came?"

"I saw the water butt was uncovered and the mug on the ice
—sure to have been Prov guzzling water, I said to myself."

"How sharp you are, Kuprinka. Yes, he's been here. Prov—
Prov Afanasievich. Came to borrow some logs—I gave him some.
But what am I talking about, fool that I am. It went clean out of
my head—the news Prov brought. Think of it, Kuprinka! The
Tsar has signed a manifesto and everything's to be changed—
everybody's to be treated right, the peasants are to have land,
and we're all going to be equal with the gentry! It's actually
signed, he says, it's only got to be made public. The Synod's
sent something to be put into the Church service, a prayer of
thanks or something. He told me what it was, but I've forgotten."

Pasha Antipov
The strikers march & are scattered by Cossackes

8

Pasha Antipov, whose father had been arrested as one of the
organizers of the strike, went to live with the Tiverzins. He was
a clean, tidy boy with regular features and red hair parted in
the middle: he was always slicking it down with a brush and
straightening his tunic or the school buckle on his belt. He had a
great sense of humor and an unusual gift of observation and
kept everyone in fits with his clever imitations of everything he
heard and saw.

Soon after the manifesto of October 17th several revolutionary
organizations called for a big demonstration. The route was from
the Tver Gate to the Kaluga Gate at the other end of the town.

But this was a case of too many cooks spoiling the broth. The planners quarrelled and one after the other withdrew from participation. Then, learning that crowds had nevertheless gathered on the appointed morning, they hastily sent representatives to lead the demonstrators.

In spite of Tiverzin's efforts to dissuade her, his mother joined the demonstrators, and the gay and sociable Pasha went with her.

It was a dry frosty November day with a still, leaden sky and a few snowflakes coming down one by one. They spun slowly and hesitantly before settling on the pavement like fluffy gray dust.

Down the street people came pouring in a torrent—faces, faces, faces, quilted winter coats and sheepskin hats, men and women students, old men, children, railwaymen in uniform, workers from the trolley depot and the telephone exchange in knee boots and leather jackets, girls and schoolboys.

For some time they sang the "Marseillaise," the "Varshavianka," and "Victims You Fell." Then a man who had been walking backwards at the head of the procession, singing and conducting with his cap, which he used as a baton, turned around, put his cap on his head, and listened to what the other leaders around him were saying. The singing broke off in disorder. Now you could hear the crunch of innumerable footsteps on the frozen pavement.

The leaders had received a message from sympathizers that Cossacks were waiting to ambush the procession farther down the street. The warning had been given by telephone to a near-by pharmacy.

"What of it?" said the organizers. "We must keep calm and not lose our heads, that's the main thing. We must occupy the first public building we come to, warn the people, and scatter."

An argument began about the best building to go to. Some suggested the Society of Commercial Employees, others the Technical School, and still others the School of Foreign Correspondence.

While they were still arguing they reached the corner of a school building, which offered shelter every bit as good as those that had been mentioned.

When they drew level with the entrance the leaders turned

aside, climbed the steps of the semicircular porch, and motioned the head of the procession to halt. The doors opened and the procession—coat to coat and cap to cap—moved into the entrance hall and up the stairs.

"The auditorium, the auditorium," shouted a few voices in the rear, but the crowd continued to press forward, scattering down corridors and straying into the classrooms. When the leaders at last succeeded in shepherding it into the auditorium, they tried several times to warn it of the ambush, but no one listened to them. Stopping and going inside a building were taken as an invitation to an impromptu meeting, which in fact began at once.

After all the walking and singing people were glad to sit quietly for a while and let others do their work for them, shouting themselves hoarse. The crowd, welcoming the rest, overlooked the minor differences between the speakers, who agreed on all essential points. In the end it was the worst orator of the lot who received the most applause. People made no effort to follow him and merely roared approval at his every word, no one minding the interruptions and everyone agreeing out of impatience to everything he said. There were shouts of "Shame," a telegram of protest was drafted, and suddenly the crowd, bored with the speaker's droning voice, stood up as one man and forgetting all about him poured out in a body—cap to cap and row after row—down the stairs and out into the street. The procession was resumed.

While the meeting was on, it had begun to snow. The street was white. The snow fell thicker and thicker.

When the dragoons charged, the marchers at the rear first knew nothing of it. A swelling noise rolled back to them as of great crowds shouting "Hurrah," and individual screams of "Help!" and "Murder" were lost in the uproar. Almost at the same moment, and borne, as it were, on this wave of sound along the narrow corridor that formed as the crowd divided, the heads and manes of horses, and their saber-swinging riders, rode by swiftly and silently.

Half a platoon galloped through, turned, re-formed, and cut into the tail of the procession. The massacre began.

A few minutes later the avenue was almost deserted. People

were scattering down the side streets. The snow was lighter. The afternoon was dry like a charcoal sketch. Then the sun, setting behind the houses, pointed as though with a finger at everything red in the street—the red tops of the dragoons' caps, a red flag trailing on the ground, and the red specks and threads of blood on the snow.

A groaning man with a split skull was crawling along the curb. From the far end of the street to which the chase had taken them several dragoons were riding back abreast at a walk. Almost at the horses' feet Marfa Tiverzina, her shawl knocked to the back of her head, was running from side to side screaming wildly: "Pasha! Pasha!"

Pasha had been with her all along, amusing her by cleverly mimicking the last speaker at the meeting, but had vanished suddenly in the confusion when the dragoons charged.

A blow from a nagaika had fallen on her back, and though she had hardly felt it through her thickly quilted coat she swore and shook her fist at the retreating horsemen, indignant that they had dared to strike an old woman like herself, and in public at that.

Looking anxiously from side to side, she had the luck finally to spot the boy across the street. He stood in a recess between a grocer's shop and a private stone house, where a group of chance passers-by had been hemmed in by a horseman who had mounted the sidewalk. Amused by their terror, the dragoon was making his horse perform volts and pirouettes, backing it into the crowd and making it rear slowly as in a circus turn. Suddenly he saw his comrades riding back, spurred his mount, and in a couple of bounds took his place in the file.

The crowd dispersed and Pasha, who had been too frightened to utter a sound, rushed to Marfa Gavrilovna.

The old woman grumbled all the way home. "Accursed murderers! People are happy because the Tsar has given them freedom, but these damned killers can't stand it. They must spoil everything, twist every word inside out."

She was furious with the dragoons, furious with the whole world, and at the moment even with her own son. When she was in a temper it seemed to her that all the recent troubles were the fault of "Kuprinka's bunglers and fumblers," as she called them.

"What do they want, the half-wits? They don't know themselves, just so long as they can make mischief, the vipers. Like that chatterbox. Pasha dear, show me again how he went on, show me, darling. Oh! I'll die laughing. You've got him to the life. Buzz, buzz, buzz—a real bumblebee!"

At home she fell to scolding her son. Was she of an age to have a curly-headed oaf on a horse belt her on her behind?

"Really, Mother, who d'you take me for? You'd think I was the Cossack captain or the Chief of Police."

Nikolai in Moscow

9

Nikolai Nikolaievich saw the fleeing demonstrators from his window. He realized who they were and watched to see if Yura were among them. But none of his friends seemed to be there though he thought that he had caught sight of the Dudorov boy—he could not quite remember his name—that desperado who had so recently had a bullet extracted from his shoulder and who was again hanging about in places where he had no business to be.

Nikolai Nikolaievich had arrived from Petersburg that autumn. He had no apartment in Moscow and he did not wish to go to a hotel, so he had put up with some distant relatives of his, the Sventitskys. They had given him the corner room on the second floor.

The Sventitskys were childless, and the two-story house that their late parents had rented from time immemorial from the Princes Dolgoruky was too big for them. It was part of the untidy cluster of buildings in various styles with three courtyards and a garden that stood on the Dolgorukys' property, bounded by three narrow side streets and known by the ancient name of Flour Town.

In spite of its four windows, the study was darkish. It was cluttered up with books, papers, rugs, and prints. It had a balcony forming a semicircle around the corner of the house. The double glass door of the balcony was hermetically sealed for the winter.

The balcony door and two of the windows looked out on an alley that ran into the distance with its sleigh tracks and the irregular line of its houses and fences.

Purple shadows reached into the room from the garden. The trees, laden with hoarfrost, their branches like smoky streaks of candle wax, looked in as if they wished to rest their burden on the floor of the study.

Nikolai Nikolaievich stood gazing into the distance. He thought of his last winter in Petersburg—Gapon,[1] Gorky, the visit to Prime Minister Witte, modern, fashionable writers. From that bedlam he had fled to the peace and quiet of the ancient capital to write the book he had in mind. But he had jumped out of the frying pan into the fire. Lectures every day—University Courses for Women, the Religious Philosophical Society, the Red Cross and the Strike Fund—not a moment to himself. What he needed was to get away to Switzerland, to some remote canton in the woods, to the peace of lakes, mountains, sky, and the echoing, ever-responsive air.

Nikolai Nikolaievich turned away from the window. He felt like going out to call on someone or just to walk about the streets, but he remembered that Vyvolochnov, the Tolstoyan, was coming to see him about some business or other. He paced up and down the room, his thoughts turning to his nephew.

When Nikolai Nikolaievich had moved from his retreat on the Volga to Petersburg he had left Yura in Moscow, where he had many relatives—the Vedeniapins, the Ostromyslenskys, the Seliavins, the Mikhaelises, the Sventitskys, and the Gromekos. At first Yura was foisted on the slovenly old chatterbox Ostromyslensky, known among the clan as Fedka. Fedka lived in sin with his ward Motia and therefore saw himself as a disrupter of the established order and a champion of progressive thought. He did not justify his kinsman's confidence, and even took the money given him for Yura's upkeep and spent it on himself. Yura was transferred to the professorial family of the Gromekos and was still with them.

The atmosphere at the Gromekos' was eminently suitable,

---

[1] A priest who was thought to be a revolutionary leader but also was suspected of being an *agent provocateur*.

Nikolai Nikolaievich thought. They had their daughter, Tonia, who was Yura's age, and Misha Gordon, who was Yura's friend and classmate, living with them.

"And a comical triumvirate they make," thought Nikolai Nikolaievich. The three of them had soaked themselves in *The Meaning of Love* and *The Kreutzer Sonata* and had a mania for preaching chastity. It was right, of course, for adolescents to go through a frenzy of purity, but they were overdoing it a bit, they had lost all sense of proportion.

How childish and eccentric they were! For some reason, they called the domain of the sensual, which disturbed them so much, "vulgar," and used the expression in and out of place. A most ineptly chosen term! "Vulgar" was applied to instinct, to pornography, to exploitation of women, and almost to the whole physical world. They blushed or grew pale when they pronounced the word.

"If I had been in Moscow," thought Nikolai Nikolaievich, "I would not have let it go so far. Modesty is necessary, but within limits . . . Ah! Nil Feoktistovich, come in!" he exclaimed, going out to meet his visitor.

a follower of Tolstoy

10

A fat man in a gray Tolstoyan shirt with a broad leather belt, felt boots, and trousers bagging at the knees entered the room. He looked like a good soul with his head in the clouds. A pince-nez on a wide black ribbon quivered angrily on his nose. He had begun to take his things off in the hall but had not removed his scarf and came in with it trailing on the floor and his round felt hat still in his hand. These encumbrances prevented him from shaking hands with Nikolai Nikolaievich and even from saying How-do-you-do.

"Um-m-m," he mooed helplessly, looking around the room.

"Put them down anywhere," said Nikolai Nikolaievich, restoring Vyvolochnov's power of speech and self-possession.

Here was one of those followers of Tolstoy in whom the ideas of the genius who had never known peace had settled down to enjoy a long, unclouded rest, growing hopelessly shallow in the process. He had come to ask Nikolai Nikolaievich to speak at a meeting in aid of political deportees that was to be held at some school or other.

"I've spoken at that school already."

"In aid of our exiles?"

"Yes."

"You'll have to do it again."

Nikolai Nikolaievich balked a little and then gave in.

The business dealt with, Nikolai Nikolaievich did not attempt to delay his guest. Nil Feoktistovich could have left at once but he evidently felt that it would be unseemly and was looking for something lively and natural to say by way of parting. The conversation became strained and awkward.

"So you've become a Decadent? Going in for mysticism?"

"What do you mean?"

"It's a waste, you know. Do you remember the county council?"

"Of course. Didn't we canvass for it together?"

"And we did some good work fighting for the village schools and teachers' colleges. Remember?"

"Of course. It was a splendid battle."

"And then you became interested in public health and social welfare, didn't you?"

"For a time, yes."

"Hmm. And now it's all this highbrow stuff—fauns and nenuphars and ephebes and 'Let's be like the sun.' I can't believe it, bless me if I can—an intelligent man like you, and with your sense of humor and your knowledge of the people. . . . Come, now. . . . Or am I intruding into the holy of holies?"

"Why all this talk? What are we arguing about? You don't know my ideas."

"Russia needs schools and hospitals, not fauns and nenuphars."

"No one denies it."

"The peasants are in rags and famished. . . ."

So the conversation dragged on. Knowing how useless it was, Nikolai Nikolaievich tried nevertheless to explain what attracted him to some of the writers of the Symbolist school. Then, turning to Tolstoyan doctrines, he said:

"Up to a point I am with you, but Tolstoy says that the more a man devotes himself to beauty the further he moves away from goodness. . . ."

"And you think it's the other way round—the world will be saved by beauty, is that it? Dostoievsky, Rozanov,[1] mystery plays, and what not?"

"Wait, let me tell you what I think. I think that if the beast who sleeps in man could be held down by threats—any kind of threat, whether of jail or of retribution after death—then the highest emblem of humanity would be the lion tamer in the circus with his whip, not the prophet who sacrificed himself. But don't you see, this is just the point—what has for centuries raised man above the beast is not the cudgel but an inward music: the irresistible power of unarmed truth, the powerful attraction of its example. It has always been assumed that the most important things in the Gospels are the ethical maxims and commandments. But for me the most important thing is that Christ speaks in parables taken from life, that He explains the truth in terms of everyday reality. The idea that underlies this is that communion between mortals is immortal, and that the whole of life is symbolic because it is meaningful."

"I haven't understood a word. You should write a book about it!"

After Vyvolochnov had left, Nikolai Nikolaievich felt extremely cross. He was angry with himself for having blurted out some of his most intimate thoughts to that fool, without impressing him in the least. Then his annoyance, as sometimes happens, changed its target. He recalled another incident.

He did not keep a diary, but once or twice a year he would record in a thick notebook some thought which struck him particularly. He got out the notebook now and began to write in a large, legible hand. This is what he wrote.

"Upset all day by that silly Shlesinger woman. She came in the morning, stayed till lunchtime, and for two solid hours bored me reading out that gibberish—a libretto in verse by the Symbolist A— to the cosmogonic symphony by the composer B— with the spirits of the planets, voices of the four elements, etc., etc. I listened with impatience, then I couldn't stand it and begged her to stop.

[1] A writer of the period who was an exceptional stylist.

"And suddenly I understood everything. I understood why this stuff is so deadly, so insufferably false, even in *Faust*. The whole thing is artificial, no one is genuinely interested in it. Modern man has no need of it. When he is overcome by the mysteries of the universe he turns to physics, not to Hesiod's hexameters.

"And it isn't just that the form is an anachronism, or that these spirits of earth and air only confuse what science has unravelled. The fact is that this type of art is wholly out of keeping with the spirit, the essence, the motivating force of contemporary art.

"These cosmogonies were natural in the ancient world—a world settled so sparsely that nature was not yet eclipsed by man. Mammoths still walked the earth, dragons and dinosaurs were still fresh in people's memory. Nature hit you in the eye so plainly and grabbed you so fiercely and so tangibly by the scruff of the neck that perhaps it really was still full of gods. Those were the first pages of the chronicle of mankind, it was only just beginning.

"This ancient world ended with Rome, because of overpopulation.

"Rome was a flea market of borrowed gods and conquered peoples, a bargain basement on two floors, earth and heaven, a mass of filth convoluted in a triple knot as in an intestinal obstruction. Dacians, Herulians, Scythians, Sarmatians, Hyperboreans, heavy wheels without spokes, eyes sunk in fat, sodomy, double chins, illiterate emperors, fish fed on the flesh of learned slaves. There were more people in the world than there have ever been since, all crammed into the passages of the Coliseum, and all wretched.

"And then, into this tasteless heap of gold and marble, He came, light and clothed in an aura, emphatically human, deliberately provincial, Galilean, and at that moment gods and nations ceased to be and man came into being—man the carpenter, man the plowman, man the shepherd with his flock of sheep at sunset, man who does not sound in the least proud, man thankfully celebrated in all the cradle songs of mothers and in all the picture galleries the world over."

Victor Komarovsky takes a walk

11

The Petrovka looked like a corner of Petersburg in Moscow, with its matching houses on both sides of the street, the tastefully sculptured house entrances, the bookshop, the library, the cartographer's, the elegant tobacco shop, the excellent restaurant, its front door flanked by two gaslights in round frosted shades on massive brackets.

In winter the street frowned with a forbidding surliness. Its inhabitants were solid, self-respecting, prosperous members of the liberal professions.

Here Victor Ippolitovich Komarovsky rented his magnificent third-floor apartment, reached by a wide staircase with massive oak banisters. His housekeeper, or rather the châtelaine of his quiet retreat, Emma Ernestovna, took care of everything without meddling in his private life; she ran the place unseen and unheard. He repaid her with the knightly delicacy to be expected of so fine a gentleman, and never tolerated visitors, male or female, whose presence would have disturbed her peaceful, spinsterish world. A monastic stillness reigned in their home; the blinds were drawn, and everything was spotlessly clean, as in an operating room.

On Sunday mornings Victor Ippolitovich, accompanied by his bulldog, usually took a leisurely walk down the Petrovka and along Kuznetsky Most, and at one of the street corners they were joined by the actor and gambler Constantine Illarionovich Satanidi.

They walked together along Kuznetsky Most, telling each other dirty stories, snorting with contempt, and laughing shamelessly in deep, loud voices that filled the air with sounds no more significant than the howling of a dog.

Lara sees herself as a fallen woman.

12

The weather was on the mend. Plop-plop-plop went the water drops on the metal of the drainpipes and the cornices, roof tapping messages to roof as if it were spring. It was thawing.

Lara walked all the way in a daze and realized what had happened to her only when she reached home.

Everyone was asleep. She fell back into her trance and in this abstracted state sat down at her mother's dressing table, still in her pale mauve, almost white, lace-trimmed dress and long veil borrowed for the evening from the workshop, like a costume. She sat before her reflection in the mirror, and saw nothing. Then, folding her arms, she put them on the dressing table and buried her head in them.

If Mother learned about it she would kill her. She would kill her and then she would kill herself.

How had it happened? How could it possibly have happened? It was too late now, she should have thought of it earlier.

Now she was—what was it called?—a fallen woman. She was a woman out of a French novel, and tomorrow she would go to school and sit side by side with those other girls who were like little children compared with her. O God, O God, how did it happen?

Some day, many, many years later, when it would be possible, Lara would tell Olia Demina, and Olia would hug her and burst into tears.

Outside the window the water drops plopped on and on, the thaw muttered its spells. Down the road someone was banging on a neighbor's door. Lara did not raise her head. Her shoulders quivered. She was weeping.

Komarovsky fears that Lara may become an obsession.

13

"Ah, Emma Ernestovna, that's unimportant. I'm sick and tired of it." He kept opening and shutting drawers, turning things out, throwing cuffs and collars all over the rug and the sofa, without knowing what he was looking for.

He needed her desperately, and there was no way of seeing her that Sunday. He paced up and down the room frantically like a caged animal.

Nothing equalled her spiritual beauty. Her hands were stunning like a sublime idea. Her shadow on the wall of the hotel room was like the outline of her innocence. Her slip was stretched over her breast, as firmly and simply as linen on an embroidery frame.

His fingers drummed on the windowpane in time to the un-hurried thud of horses' hoofs on the asphalt pavement below. "Lara," he whispered, shutting his eyes, and he had a vision of her head resting on his hands; her eyes were closed, she was asleep, unconscious that he watched her sleeplessly for hours on end. Her hair was scattered and its beauty stung his eyes like smoke and ate into his heart.

His Sunday walk was not being a success. He strolled a few paces with Jack, stopped, thought of Kuznetsky Most, of Sata-nidi's jokes, of the acquaintances he met on the street—no, it was more than he could bear. He turned back. The dog, startled, looked up disapprovingly and waddled after him reluctantly.

"What can it all mean?" thought Komarovsky. "What has come over me?" Could it be his conscience, a feeling of pity, or re-pentance? Or was he worried about her? No, he knew she was safe at home. Then why couldn't he get her out of his head?

He walked back to his house, up the stairs, and past the first landing. The stained-glass ornamental coats of arms at the corners of the window threw colored patches of light at his feet. Halfway up the second flight he stopped.

He must not give in to this exhausting, nagging, anxious mood. He was not a schoolboy, after all. He must realize what would happen if instead of being just a toy this girl—a mere child, the daughter of his dead friend—turned into an obsession. He must come to his senses. He must be true to himself and to his habits. Otherwise everything would go up in smoke.

Komarovsky gripped the oak railing until it hurt his hand, shut his eyes a moment, then turned back resolutely and went down. On the landing, with its patches of light, the dog was waiting for him. It lifted its head like a slobbering old dwarf with hanging jowls and looked up at him adoringly.

The dog hated the girl, tore her stockings, growled at her, bared its teeth. It was jealous of her as if fearing that she would infect its master with something human.

"Ah, I see! You have decided that everything is going to be just as before—Satanidi, mean tricks, dirty jokes? All right then,

take this, and this, and this." He struck the bulldog with his
stick and kicked it. Jack squealed, howled, waddled up the
stairs shaking his behind, and scratched at the door to complain
to Emma Ernestovna.

Days and weeks went by.

*although filled with disgust, but is flattered that a handsome,
successful man is interested in a schoolgirl.*

14

What an inescapable spell it was! If Komarovsky's intrusion
into Lara's life had merely filled her with disgust, she would
have rebelled and broken free. But it was not so simple as that.

The girl was flattered that a handsome man whose hair was
turning gray, a man old enough to be her father, a man who
was applauded at meetings and written up in the newspapers,
should spend his time and money on her, should take her out to
concerts and plays, and tell her that he worshipped her, and
should, as they say, "improve her mind."

After all, she was still a girl in a brown uniform who enjoyed
harmless plots and pranks at school. Komarovsky's lovemaking
in a carriage behind the coachman's back or in an opera box in
full view of the audience fascinated her by its daring and
aroused the little devil slumbering in her to imitate him.

But this mischievous, girlish infatuation was short-lived. A
nagging depression and horror at herself were taking permanent
hold of her. And all the time she wanted to sleep—because (she
told herself) she did not get enough sleep at night, because she
cried so much, because she had constant headaches, because
she worked hard at school, and because she was physically exhausted.

Lara's whole life has become so terrifying!

15

He was the curse of her life; she hated him. Every day she returned to these thoughts.

She has become his slave for life. How has he subjugated her?
How does he force her to submit, why does she surrender, why

does she gratify his wishes and delight him with her quivering unconcealed shame? Because of his age, her mother's financial dependence on him, his cleverness in frightening her, Lara? No, no, no! That is all nonsense.

It is she who has a hold on him. Doesn't she see how much he needs her? She has nothing to be afraid of, her conscience is clear. It is he who should be ashamed, and terrified of her giving him away. But that is just what she will never do. To do this she does not have the necessary ruthlessness—Komarovsky's chief asset in dealing with subordinates and weaklings.

This is precisely the difference between them. And it is this that makes the whole of life so terrifying. Does it crush you by thunder and lightning? No, by oblique glances and whispered calumny. It is all treachery and ambiguity. Any single thread is as fragile as a cobweb, but just try to pull yourself out of the net, you only become more entangled.

And the strong are dominated by the weak and the ignoble.

Would marriage with Komarovsky really change anything?

16

What if she were married, she asked herself, what difference would it make? She entered the path of sophistry. But at times she was overtaken by a hopeless anguish.

How can he not be ashamed to grovel at her feet and plead with her? "We can't go on like this. Think what I have done to you! You will end up in the gutter. We must tell your mother. I'll marry you." He wept and insisted as though she were arguing and refusing. But all this was just words, and Lara did not even listen to these tragic, hollow protestations.

And he continued taking her, veiled, to dinner in the private rooms of that ghastly restaurant where the waiters and the clients undressed her with their eyes as she came in. And she merely wondered: "Does one always humiliate those one loves?"

Once she had a dream. She was buried, and there was nothing left of her except her left shoulder and her right foot. A tuft of grass sprouted from her left breast and above the ground people were singing "Black eyes and white breast" and "Masha must not go to the river."

17

Lara was not religious. She did not believe in ritual. But sometimes, to be able to bear life, she needed the accompaniment of an inner music. She could not always compose such a music for herself. That music was God's word of life, and it was to weep over it that she went to church.

Once, early in December, she went to pray with such a heavy heart that she felt as if at any moment the earth might open at her feet and the vaulted ceiling of the church cave in. It would serve her right, it would put an end to the whole thing. She only regretted that she had taken that chatterbox, Olia Demina, with her.

"There's Prov Afanasievich," whispered Olia.

"Sh-sh. Leave me alone. What Prov Afanasievich?"

"Prov Afanasievich Sokolov. The one who's chanting. He's our cousin twice removed."

"Oh, the psalmist. Tiverzin's relative. Sh-sh. Stop talking. Don't disturb me, please."

They had come in at the beginning of the service. They were singing the psalm "Bless the Lord, O my soul: and all that is within me, bless His holy name."

The church was half empty, and every sound in it echoed hollowly. Only in front was there a crowd of worshippers standing close together. The building was new. The plain glass of the window added no color to the gray, snow-bound, busy street outside and the people who walked or drove through it. Near that window stood a church warden paying no attention to the service and loudly reproving a deaf, half-witted beggarwoman in a voice as flat and commonplace as the window and the street.

In the time it took Lara, clutching her pennies in her fist, to make her way to the door past the worshippers without disturbing them, buy two candles for herself and Olia, and turn back, Prov Afanasievich had rattled off nine of the beatitudes at a pace suggesting that they were well enough known without him.

Blessed are the poor in spirit. . . . Blessed are they that mourn. . . . Blessed are they which do hunger and thirst after righteousness. . . .

Lara started and stood still. This was about her. He was saying: Happy are the downtrodden. They have something to tell about themselves. They have everything before them. That was what He thought. That was Christ's judgment.

The Presnia uprising. Building a barricade

18

It was the time of the Presnia uprising. The Guishars' flat was in the rebel area. A barricade was being built in Tver Street a few yards from their house. People carried buckets of water from their yards in order to cement the stones and scrap iron with ice.

The neighboring yard was used by the workers' militia as an assembly point, something between a Red Cross post and a soup kitchen.

Lara knew two of the boys who went to it. One was Nika Dudorov, a friend of her school friend Nadia. He was proud, straightforward, taciturn. He was like Lara and did not interest her.

The other was Pasha Antipov, the gymnasium student, who lived with old Tiverzina, Olia Demina's grandmother. Lara noticed the effect she had on the boy when she met him at the Tiverzins'. He was so childishly simple that he did not conceal his joy at seeing her, as if she were some summer landscape of birch trees, grass, and clouds, and could freely express his enthusiasm about her without any risk of being laughed at.

As soon as she realized the kind of influence she had on him, she began unconsciously to make use of it. However, it was not until several years later and at a much further stage in their relationship that she took his malleable, easygoing character seriously in hand. By then Pasha knew that he was head over heels in love with her and that it was for life.

The two boys were playing the most terrible and adult of games, war; moreover, participation in this particular war was punishable by deportation and hanging. Yet the way their woollen caps were tied at the back suggested that they were children, that they still had fathers and mothers who looked after them. Lara thought of them as a grownup thinks of children. Their dangerous amusements had a bloom of innocence that they communicated to everything—to the evening, so shaggy with hoarfrost that it seemed more black than white, to the dark blue shadows in the yard, to the house across the road where the boys were hiding, and, above all, to the continual revolver shots which came from it. "The boys are shooting," thought Lara. This was how she thought not only of Nika and Pasha but of the whole fighting city. "Good, decent boys," she thought. "It's because they are good that they are shooting."

Although they have no grievances, Mme Guishar's seamstresses join the strike. The Guishars move to Hotel Montenegro for safety.

19

They learned that the barricade might be shelled and that their house would be in danger. It was too late to think of going to stay with friends in some other part of Moscow, the quarter was surrounded; they had to find shelter in the neighborhood, within the ring. They thought of the Montenegro.

It turned out that they were not the first to think of it. The hotel was full. There were many others who shared their predicament. For old time's sake the proprietor promised to put them up in the linen room.

Not to attract attention by carrying suitcases, they packed the most necessary things into three bundles; then they put off moving from day to day.

Because the employees of the workshop were treated rather like family members, they had continued to work despite the strike. But one dull, cold afternoon there was a ring at the door. Someone had come to complain and to argue. The owner was asked for. Fetisova went instead to pour oil on the troubled waters. A few moments later she called the seamstresses into the hall and introduced them to the visitor. He shook hands all round, clumsily and with emotion, and went away having apparently reached an agreement with Fetisova.

The seamstresses came back into the workroom and began tying on their shawls and putting on their shabby winter coats.

"What has happened?" asked Madame Guishar, hurrying in.

"They're calling us out, Madam, we're on strike."

"But . . . Have I ever wronged you?" Madame Guishar burst into tears.

"Don't be upset, Amalia Karlovna. We've got nothing against

you. We're very grateful to you. It's not just you and us. Everybody's doing the same, the whole world. You can't go against everybody, can you?"

They all went away, even Olia Demina and Fetisova, who whispered to Madame Guishar in parting that she agreed to the strike for the good of the owner and the establishment. But Amalia Karlovna was inconsolable.

"What black ingratitude! To think that I was so mistaken in these people! The kindness I've lavished on that brat! Well, admittedly she's only a child, but that old witch!"

"They can't make an exception just for you, Mother, don't you see?" Lara said soothingly. "No one bears you any malice. On the contrary. All that's being done now is done in the name of humanity, in defense of the weak, for the good of women and children. Yes, it is. Don't shake your head so skeptically. You'll see, one day you and I will be better off because of it."

But her mother could not understand. "It's always like this," she sobbed. "Just when I can't think straight you come out with something that simply astounds me. People play a dirty trick on me, and you say it's all for my good. No, really, I must be out of my mind."

Rodia was at school. Lara and her mother wandered about aimlessly, alone in the empty house. The unlit street stared emptily into the rooms, and the rooms returned its stare.

"Let's go to the hotel, Mother, before it gets dark," Lara begged. "Do come, Mother. Don't put it off, let's go now."

"Filat, Filat," they called the janitor. "Take us to the Montenegro, be a good boy."

"Very good, Madam."

"Take the bundles over. And keep an eye on the house, Filat, until things sort themselves out. And please don't forget the bird seed for Kirill Modestovich, and to change his water. And keep everything locked up. That's all, I think, and please keep in touch with us."

"Very well, Madam."

"Thank you, Filat. God keep you. Well, let's sit down[1] and then we must be off."

[1] A superstitious Russian custom: before a move or a journey people sit down a few moments for luck.

When they went out the fresh air seemed as unfamiliar as after weeks of illness. Noises, rounded, as if turned on a lathe, rolled echoing lightly through the crisp, frosty, nut-clean space. Shots and salvoes smacked, thudded, and plopped, flattening the distances into a pancake.

However much Filat tried to convince them to the contrary, Lara and Amalia Karlovna insisted that the shots were blanks.

"Don't be silly, Filat. Think it out for yourself. How could they be anything but blanks when you can't see anyone shooting? Who d'you think is shooting, the Holy Ghost or what? Of course they're blanks."

At one of the crossroads they were stopped by a patrol of grinning Cossacks who searched them, insolently running their hands over them from head to foot. Their visorless caps with chin straps were tilted jauntily over one ear; it made all of them look one-eyed.

"Wonderful," thought Lara as she walked on. She would not see Komarovsky for as long as the district was cut off from the rest of the town. Because of her mother it was impossible for her to break with him. She could not say: "Mother, please stop seeing him." If she did that, it would all come out. And what if it did? Why should that frighten her? Oh, God! Anything, anything, if only it would end! God! God! She would fall down in a faint with disgust. What was it she had just remembered? What was the name of that frightful picture? There was a fat Roman in it. It hung in the first of those private rooms, the one where it all began. "The Woman or the Vase"—yes, that was it. Of course. It was a famous picture. The woman or the vase. When she first saw it she was not yet a woman, she was not yet comparable to an expensive work of art. That came later. The table was splendidly set for a feast.

"Where do you think you are running like that? I can't keep up with you," panted Madame Guishar. Lara walked swiftly, some unknown force swept her on as though she were striding on air, carried along by this proud, quickening strength.

"How splendid," she thought, listening to the gun shots. "Blessed are the downtrodden. Blessed are the deceived. God speed you, bullets. You and I are of one mind."

Alexander A.
Anna G.
Antonina G.
The house of the Gromekos, 1906. A musical soirée

20

The brothers Gromeko had a house at the corner of Sivtsev Vrazhok and another small street. Alexander Alexandrovich and Nikolai Alexandrovich Gromeko were professors of chemistry, the one at the Peter's Academy, the other at the University. Nikolai was unmarried. Alexander had a wife, Anna Ivanovna, Née Krueger. Her father was an ironmaster; he owned an enormous estate in the Urals, near Yuriatin, on which there were several abandoned, unprofitable mines.

The Gromekos' house had two stories. On the top floor were the bedrooms, the schoolroom, Alexander Alexandrovich's study and his library, Anna Ivanovna's boudoir, and Tonia's and Yura's rooms. The ground floor was used for receptions. Its pistachio-colored curtains, gleaming piano top, aquarium, olive-green upholstery, and potted plants resembling seaweed made it look like a green, sleepily swaying sea bed.

The Gromekos were cultivated, hospitable, and great connoisseurs and lovers of music. They often held receptions and evenings of chamber music at which piano trios, violin sonatas, and string quartets were performed.

Such a musical evening was to be held in January, 1906. There was to be a first performance of a violin sonata by a young composer, a pupil of Taneiev's, and a trio by Tchaikovsky.

The preparations were begun the day before. The furniture was moved around in the ballroom. In one corner the piano tuner struck the same chord dozens of times and scattered arpeggios like handfuls of beads. In the kitchen, chickens were being plucked, vegetables cleaned, and mustard mixed with olive oil for sauces and salad dressings.

Shura Shlesinger, Anna's bosom friend and confidante, had come first thing in the morning, making a nuisance of herself.

She was a tall thin woman with regular features and a rather masculine face which recalled the Emperor's, especially when she wore her gray astrakhan hat set at an angle; she kept it on in the house, only slightly raising the veil pinned to it.

In times of sorrow or anxiety the two friends lightened each other's burdens. They did this by saying unpleasant things to each other, their conversation becoming increasingly caustic until an emotional storm burst and soon ended in tears and a reconciliation. These periodic quarrels had a tranquillizing effect on both, like the application of leeches for high blood pressure.

Shura Shlesinger had been married several times, but she forgot her husbands as soon as she divorced them, and despite her many marriages there was a certain coldness, like that of a spinster, about her.

She was a theosophist, but she was also an expert on the ritual of the Orthodox Church, and even when she was *toute transportée*, in a state of utter ecstasy, could not refrain from prompting the officiating clergy. "Hear, O Lord," "Now and ever shall be," "glorious cherubim" she muttered ceaselessly in her hoarse, staccato patter.

Shura Shlesinger knew mathematics, esoteric Indian doctrine, the addresses of the best-known teachers at the Moscow Conservatory, who was living with whom, and God only knows what else. For this reason she was called in, as arbiter and organizer, on all important occasions in life.

At the appointed time the guests began to arrive. There came Adelaida Filippovna, Gints, the Fufkovs, Mr. and Mrs. Basurman, the Verzhitskis, Colonel Kavkaztsev. It was snowing, and whenever the front door was opened you could see the swirling air rush past, as though tangled in a thousand knots by the flickering snow. The men came in out of the cold in high clumsy snow boots, and every one of them, without exception, did his best to look like a country bumpkin; but their wives, on the contrary, their faces glowing from the frost, coats unbuttoned, shawls pushed back and hair spangled with rime, looked like hardened coquettes, cunning itself. "Cui's nephew," the whisper went round as the new pianist came in.

Beyond the open side doors of the ballroom the supper table gleamed, white and long as a winter road. The play of light on frosted bottles of red rowanberry cordial caught the eye. The crystal cruets on silver stands and the picturesque arrangement of game and *zakuski*[1] captured the imagination. The napkins folded into stiff pyramids and the baskets of mauve cineraria smelling of almonds seemed to whet the appetite.

Not to delay the pleasure of earthly food too long, the com-

[1] Hors d'oeuvres, including various kinds of cold meat and fish.

pany got down hastily to their spiritual repast. They sat down in rows. "Cui's nephew," they whispered again as the musician took his place at the piano. The concert began.

The sonata was known to be dry, labored, and boring. The performance confirmed this belief, and the work turned out to be terribly long as well.

During the interval the critic Kerimbekov and Alexander Gromeko had an argument about it, Kerimbekov running it down and Gromeko defending it. All around them people smoked, talked, and moved their chairs, till the glittering tablecloth in the adjoining room once again attracted attention. All proposed that the concert be resumed without delay.

The pianist cast a sideways glance at the audience, and signalled his partners to begin. The violinist and Tyshkevich flourished their bows. The music rose plaintively.

Yura, Tonia, and Misha Gordon, who spent half his time at the Gromekos', were sitting in the third row.

"Egorovna is making signs at you," Yura whispered to Alexander Alexandrovich, who sat directly in front of him.

Egorovna, the Gromekos' white-haired old servant, stood in the doorway and by staring desperately at Yura and nodding with equal energy at Alexander Alexandrovich tried to make Yura understand that she needed urgently to speak to the master.

Alexander Alexandrovich turned, gave her a reproachful look, and shrugged his shoulders, but she stood her ground. Soon they were talking across the room by signs, like a couple of deaf-mutes. People were looking. Anna Ivanovna cast devastating glances at her husband. He got up. Something had to be done. Blushing, he tiptoed around the edge of the room.

"How can you do such a thing, Egorovna! Really now, what's all the fuss? Well, hurry up, what is it?"

Egorovna whispered in his ear.

"What Montenegro?"

"The hotel."

"Well, what about it?"

"They're asking for him to go back at once. There's a relative of his dying."

"So now they're dying! I can imagine. . . . It can't be done,

Egorovna. When they've finished this piece I'll tell them. Until then I can't."

"They've sent the hotel waiter with a cab. They're waiting. Somebody's dying, I tell you, can't you understand? It's a lady."

"And I tell you it's impossible. As if a few minutes could make all that difference." He tiptoed back to his place with a worried frown, rubbing the bridge of his nose.

At the end of the first movement, before the applause had died down, he went up to the musicians and told Tyshkevich that he was needed at home, there had been some accident, they would have to stop playing. Then he turned to the audience and held up his hands for silence:

"Ladies and gentlemen, I am afraid the trio has to be interrupted. The cellist has just received some bad news. All our sympathy is with him. He has to leave us. I wouldn't like him to go by himself at such a moment. He may need help. I'll go with him. Be a good boy, Yurochka, go and tell Semion to bring the carriage around, he's had it ready for some time. Ladies and gentlemen, I won't say goodbye—I beg you all to stay—I won't be long."

The boys asked to go with him for the sake of the drive through the frosty night.

21

Although the normal flow of life had been restored since December, shooting could still be heard, and the houses burned down as the result of ordinary fires looked like the smoldering ruins of those destroyed during the uprising.

The boys had never been for such a long drive before. In reality the Montenegro was a stone's throw away—down the Smolensky Boulevard, along the Novinsky, and halfway up Sadovaia Street—but the savage frost and fog separated space into disconnected fragments, as if space were not homogeneous the world over. The shaggy, ragged smoke of bonfires,[1] the crunch of footsteps and the whine of sleigh runners, contributed to give the impression that they had been travelling

[1] Fires are lit at crossroads in very cold weather.

for God knows how long and had arrived at some terrifyingly remote place.

Outside the hotel entrance stood a narrow, elegant-looking sleigh; the horse was covered with a cloth and had bandaged fetlocks. The driver sat hunched up in the passengers' seat, trying to keep warm, his swathed head buried in his huge gloved paws.

It was warm in the hotel lobby. Behind the cloakroom counter the porter dozed, lulled by the hum of the ventilator, the roar of the blazing stove, and the whistle of the boiling samovar, to be wakened occasionally by one of his own snores.

A thickly made-up woman with a face like a dumpling stood by the looking glass on the left. Her fur jacket was too light for the weather. She was waiting for someone to come down; her back to the glass, she turned her head over each shoulder to make sure that she looked attractive behind.

The frozen cab driver came in. His bulging coat made him look like a twisted bun on a baker's sign, and the clouds of steam he gave off increased the likeness. "How much longer will you be, Mam'zel?" he asked the woman by the looking glass. "Why I ever get mixed up with your sort, I don't know. I don't want my horse to freeze to death."

The incident in No. 23 was only one more nuisance added to the daily vexations of the hotel staff. Every minute the bells shrilled and numbers popped up inside the long glass box on the wall showing which guest in which room was going frantic and pestering the servants without knowing what he wanted.

At the moment the doctor was giving an emetic to that old fool Guisharova and washing out her guts. Glasha, the maid, was run off her feet mopping up the floor and carrying dirty buckets out and clean ones in. But the storm now raging in the service room had started well before this hullabaloo, before Tirashka had been sent in a cab to fetch the doctor and that wretched fiddler, before Komarovsky had arrived and so many people had cluttered up the corridor outside the door.

The trouble had started that afternoon, when someone had turned clumsily in the narrow passage leading from the pantry to the landing and had accidentally pushed the waiter Sysoi just as he was rushing out, bending slightly with a fully loaded tray balanced on his right hand. The tray clattered to the floor, the soup was spilled, and two soup plates and one meat plate were smashed.

Sysoi insisted that it had been the dishwasher, she was answerable and she should pay for the damage. By now it was nearly eleven o'clock and half the staff were due to go off duty shortly, but the row was still going on.

"He's got the shakes, can't keep his hands and feet steady. All he cares about is sitting with a bottle, you'd think it was his wife, getting pickled like a herring, and then he asks who pushed him, who spilled his soup, who smashed his crockery. Now who do you think pushed you, you devil, you Astrakhan pest, you shameless creature?"

"I have told you already, Matriona Stepanovna, watch your language."

"And who's the one that all the fuss is about now, I ask you? You'd think it was somebody worth smashing crockery for. But it's that slut, that streetwalker giving herself airs, that damned madam, innocence in retirement, done so well for herself she's swigging arsenic. Of course, living at the Montenegro, she wouldn't know an alley cat if she met one."

Misha and Yura walked up and down the corridor outside Madame Guishar's room. It had all turned out quite differently from anything Alexander Alexandrovich had expected. He had imagined a clean and dignified tragedy in a musician's life. But this was sordid and scandalous, and certainly not for children.

The boys were waiting in the corridor.

"Go in to the lady now, young gentlemen." The valet came up to them and for the second time tried to persuade them in his soft unhurried voice. "You go in, don't worry. The lady's all right, you needn't be afraid. She's quite recovered. You can't stand here. There was an accident here this afternoon, valuable china was smashed. You can see we have to run up and down serving meals, and it's a bit narrow. You go in there."

The boys complied.

Inside the room, a lighted kerosene lamp which ordinarily hung over the table had been taken out of its bracket and carried behind the wooden screen, where it stank of bedbugs. This was a sleeping alcove separated from the rest of the room and strangers' eyes by a dusty curtain, but the curtain had been flung over the screen and in the confusion no one had thought of drawing it. The lamp stood on a bench and lit the alcove harshly from below as though by a footlight.

Madame Guishar had tried to poison herself not with arsenic, as the dishwasher thought, but with iodine. The room had the tart, astringent smell of green walnuts when their husks are still soft and blacken at a touch.

Behind the screen the maid was mopping up the floor, and lying on the bed was a half-naked woman; drenched with water, tears, and sweat, her hair stuck together, she was holding her head over a bucket and crying loudly.

The boys turned away at once, so embarrassing and unmannerly did they feel it was to look in her direction. But Yura had seen enough to be struck by the fact that in certain clumsy, tense positions, in moments of strain and exertion, a woman ceases to be such as she is represented in sculpture and looks more like a wrestler with bulging muscles, stripped down to his shorts and ready for the match.

At last someone behind the screen had the sense to draw the curtain.

"Fadei Kazimirovich, my dear, where's your hand? Give me your hand," the woman was saying, choking with tears and nausea. "Oh, I have been through such horrors. I had such terrible suspicions. . . . Fadei Kazimirovich . . . I imagined . . . but happily it has all turned out to be nonsense, just my disordered imagination. . . . Just think what a relief. And the upshot of it all . . . here I am . . . here I am alive. . . ."

"Calm yourself, Amalia Karlovna, I beg you . . . How awkward all this is, I must say, how very awkward."

"We'll be off home now," said Alexander Alexandrovich gruffly to the children. Excruciatingly embarrassed, they stood in the doorway, and as they did not know where to look they stared straight in front of them into the shadowy depth of the main room, from which the lamp had been removed. The walls were hung with photographs, there was a bookshelf filled with music scores, a desk piled with papers and albums, and beyond the dining table with a crocheted cover a girl was asleep in an armchair, clasping its back and pressing her cheek against it. She must have been dead tired to be able to sleep in spite of all the noise and excitement.

"We'll be off now," Alexander Alexandrovich said again. There had been no sense in their coming, and to stay any longer would be indecent. "As soon as Fadei Kazimirovich comes out . . . I must say goodbye to him."

It was not Tyshkevich who came out from behind the screen, but a thickset, portly, self-confident man. Carrying the lamp above his head, he went over to the table and replaced it in its bracket. The light woke up the girl. She smiled at him, squinting her eyes and stretching.

At sight of the stranger, Misha gave a start and stared at him intently. He pulled Yura's sleeve and tried to whisper to him, but Yura would not have it. "You can't whisper in front of people. What will they think of you?"

Meanwhile a silent scene took place between the girl and the man. Not a word passed their lips, only their eyes met. But the understanding between them had a terrifying quality of magic, as if he were the master of a puppet show and she were a puppet obedient to his every gesture.

A tired smile puckered her eyes and loosened her lips, but in answer to his sneering glance she gave him a sly wink of complicity. Both of them were pleased that it had all ended so well —their secret was safe and Madame Guishar's attempted suicide had failed.

Yura devoured them with his eyes. Unseen in the half darkness, he kept staring into the circle of lamplight. The scene between the captive girl and her master was both ineffably mysterious and shamelessly frank. His heart was torn by contradictory feelings of a strength he had never experienced before.

Here was the very thing which he, Tonia, and Misha had endlessly discussed as "vulgar," the force which so frightened and attracted them and which they controlled so easily from a safe distance by words. And now here it was, this force, in front of Yura's very eyes, utterly real, and yet troubled and haunting, pitilessly destructive, and complaining and calling for help— and what had become of their childish philosophy and what was Yura to do now?

"Do you know who that man was?" said Misha when they

went out into the street. Yura, absorbed in his thoughts, did not reply.

"He's the one who encouraged your father to drink and drove him to his death. In the train—you remember—I told you."

Yura was thinking about the girl and the future, not about his father and the past. At first he could not even understand what Misha was saying. It was too cold to talk.

"You must be frozen, Semion," Alexander Alexandrovich said to the coachman. They drove home.

CHAPTER THREE

THE SVENTITSKYS' CHRISTMAS PARTY

Anna G. has an accident

1

One winter Alexander Alexandrovich gave Anna Ivanovna an antique wardrobe, which he had picked up somewhere or other. It was made of ebony and was so enormous that it would not go through any door in one piece. It was taken into the house in sections; the problem then was where to put it. It would not do for the reception rooms because of its function nor for the bedrooms because of its size. In the end, a part of the landing was cleared for it outside the master bedroom.

Markel, the porter, came to put it together. He brought with him his six-year-old daughter Marinka. She was given a stick of barley sugar. Sniffling, and sucking the candy and her moist fingers, she stood intently watching her father.

At first everything went smoothly. The wardrobe grew in front of Anna Ivanovna's eyes; when only the top remained to be put on, she took it into her head to help Markel. She climbed onto the raised floor of the wardrobe, slipped, and fell against the sides, which were held in place only by tenons. The rope that Markel had tied loosely around them came undone. Anna Ivanovna fell on her back together with the boards as they clattered to the ground, and bruised herself painfully.

Markel rushed to her. "Oh, Madam, mistress," he said. "What made you do that, my dear? You haven't broken any bones? Feel your bones. It's the bones that matter, the soft part doesn't matter at all, the soft parts mend in God's good time, and, as the saying goes, they're only for pleasure anyway.—Don't bawl, you stupid!" he reprimanded the crying Marinka. "Wipe your nose and go to your mother.—Ah, Madam, couldn't you trust me to set up that clothes chest without you? Of course, to you I'm

63

only a porter, you can't think otherwise, but the fact is, I was a cabinetmaker, yes, Ma'am, cabinetmaking was my trade. You wouldn't believe how many cupboards and sideboards of all kinds, lacquer and walnut and mahogany, passed through my hands. Or, for that matter, how many well-to-do young ladies passed me by, and vanished from under my nose, if you'll forgive the expression. And it all comes from drink, strong liquor."

Markel pushed over an armchair, and with his help Anna Ivanovna sank into it groaning and rubbing her bruises. Then he set about restoring the wardrobe. When he put the top on he said, "Now the doors, and it'll be fit for an exhibition."

Anna Ivanovna did not like the wardrobe. Its appearance and size reminded her of a catafalque or a royal tomb and filled her with a superstitious dread. She nicknamed it the tomb of Askold;[1] she meant the horse of Prince Oleg,[2] which had caused its master's death. She had read a great deal, but haphazardly, and she tended to confuse related ideas.

After that accident Anna Ivanovna developed a pulmonary weakness.

Yura studies medicine

2

Throughout November, 1911, Anna Ivanovna stayed in bed with pneumonia.

Yura, Misha Gordon, and Tonia were due to graduate the following spring, Yura in medicine, Tonia in law, and Misha, who studied at the Faculty of Philosophy, in philology.

Everything in Yura's mind was still helter-skelter, but his views, his habits, and his inclinations were all distinctly his own. He was unusually impressionable, and the originality of his vision was remarkable.

Though he was greatly drawn to art and history, he scarcely hesitated over the choice of a career. He thought that art was no more a vocation than innate cheerfulness or melancholy was a profession. He was interested in physics and natural science,

[1] Askold, one of the founders of the Russian state, was buried in Kiev.
[2] Oleg, another Prince of Kiev, was killed by a snake that came out of the skull of his favorite horse.

and believed that a man should do something socially useful in his practical life. He settled on medicine.

In the first year of his four-year course he had spent a term in the dissecting room, situated in the cellars of the university. You went down the winding staircase. There was always a crowd of dishevelled students, some poring over their tattered textbooks surrounded by bones, or quietly dissecting, each in his corner, others fooling about, cracking jokes and chasing the rats that scurried in swarms over the stone floors. In the half darkness of the mortuary the naked bodies of unidentified young suicides and drowned women, well preserved and untouched by decay, shone like phosphorus. Injections of alum solutions rejuvenated them, giving them a deceptive roundness. The corpses were cut open, dismembered, and prepared, yet even in its smallest sections the human body kept its beauty, so that Yura's wonder before some water nymph brutally flung onto a zinc table continued before her amputated arm or hand. The cellar smelled of carbolic acid and formaldehyde, and the presence of mystery was tangible in everything, from the obscure fate of these spread-out bodies to the riddle of life and death itself—and death was dominant in the underground room as if it were its home or its headquarters.

The voice of this mystery, silencing everything else, haunted Yura, disturbing him in his anatomical work. He had become used to such distracting thoughts and took them in his stride.

Yura had a good mind and was an excellent writer. Ever since his schooldays he had dreamed of composing a book about life which would contain, like buried explosives, the most striking things he had so far seen and thought about. But he was too young to write such a book; instead, he wrote poetry. He was like a painter who was always making sketches for a big canvas he had in mind.

He was indulgent toward these immature works on account of their vigor and originality. These two qualities, vigor and originality, in his opinion gave reality to art, which he otherwise regarded as pointless, idle, unnecessary.

Yura realized the great part his uncle had played in molding his character.

Nikolai Nikolaievich now lived in Lausanne. In his books,

published there in Russian and in translations, he developed his old view of history as another universe, made by man with the help of time and memory in answer to the challenge of death. These works were inspired by a new interpretation of Christianity, and led directly to a new conception of art.

Misha Gordon was influenced by these ideas even more than Yura. They determined him to register at the Faculty of Philosophy. He attended lectures on theology, and even considered transferring later to the theological academy.

Yura advanced and became freer under the influence of his uncle's theories, but Misha was fettered by them. Yura realized that his friend's enthusiasms were partly accounted for by his origin. Being tactful and discreet, he made no attempt to talk him out of his extravagant ideas. But he often wished that Misha were a realist, more down-to-earth.

Anna G. thinks she is dying. Yura explains to her his understanding of consciousness & death.

3

One night at the end of November Yura came home late from the university; he was exhausted and had eaten nothing all day. He was told that there had been a terrible alarm that afternoon. Anna Ivanovna had had convulsions. Several doctors had seen her; at one time they had advised Alexander Alexandrovich to send for the priest, but later they had changed their minds. Now she was feeling better; she was fully conscious and had asked for Yura to be sent to her the moment he got back.

Yura went up at once.

The room showed traces of the recent commotion. A nurse, moving noiselessly, was rearranging something on the night table. Towels that had been used for compresses were lying about, damp and crumpled. The water in the slop basin was pinkish with expectorated blood, and broken ampoules and swollen tufts of cotton wool floated on its surface.

Anna Ivanovna lay drenched in sweat, with parched lips. Her face had become haggard since morning.

"Can the diagnosis be wrong?" Yura wondered. "She has all

the symptoms of lobar pneumonia. It looks like the crisis." After greeting her and saying the encouraging, meaningless things that are always said on such occasions, he sent the nurse out of the room, took Anna Ivanovna's wrist to feel her pulse, and reached into his coat pocket for his stethoscope. She moved her head to indicate that this was unnecessary. He realized that she wanted him for some other reason. She spoke with effort.

"They wanted to give me the last sacraments. . . . Death is hanging over me. . . . It may come any moment. . . . When you go to have a tooth out you're frightened, it'll hurt, you prepare yourself. . . . But this isn't a tooth, it's everything, the whole of you, your whole life . . . being pulled out. . . . And what is it? Nobody knows. . . . And I am sick at heart and terrified."

She fell silent. Tears were streaming down her cheeks. Yura said nothing. A moment later Anna Ivanovna went on.

"You're clever, talented. . . . That makes you different. . . . You surely know something. . . . Comfort me."

"Well, what is there for me to say?" replied Yura. He fidgeted on his chair, got up, paced the room, and sat down again. "In the first place, you'll feel better tomorrow. There are clear indications—I'd stake my life on it—that you've passed the crisis. And then—death, the survival of consciousness, faith in resurrection . . . You want to know my opinion as a scientist? Perhaps some other time? No? Right now? Well, as you wish. But it's difficult like that, all of a sudden." And there and then he delivered a whole impromptu lecture, astonished that he could do it.

"Resurrection. In the crude form in which it is preached to console the weak, it is alien to me. I have always understood Christ's words about the living and the dead in a different sense. Where could you find room for all these hordes of people accumulated over thousands of years? The universe isn't big enough for them; God, the good, and meaningful purpose would be crowded out. They'd be crushed by these throngs greedy merely for the animal life.

"But all the time, life, one, immense, identical throughout its innumerable combinations and transformations, fills the universe and is continually reborn. You are anxious about whether you will rise from the dead or not, but you rose from the dead when you were born and you didn't notice it.)

"Will you feel pain? Do the tissues feel their disintegration? In other words, what will happen to your consciousness? But what is consciousness? Let's see. A conscious attempt to fall asleep is sure to produce insomnia, to try to be conscious of one's own digestion is a sure way to upset the stomach. Consciousness is a poison when we apply it to ourselves. Consciousness is a light directed outward, it lights up the way ahead of us so that we don't stumble. It's like the headlights on a locomotive—turn them inward and you'd have a crash.

"So what will happen to your consciousness? *Your* consciousness, yours, not anyone else's. Well, what are *you*? There's the point. Let's try to find out. What is it about you that you have always known as yourself? What are you conscious of in yourself? Your kidneys? Your liver? Your blood vessels? No. However far back you go in your memory, it is always in some external, active manifestation of yourself that you come across your identity—in the work of your hands, in your family, in other people. And now listen carefully. You in others—this is your soul. This is what you are. This is what your consciousness has breathed and lived on and enjoyed throughout your life—your soul, your immortality, your life in others. And what now? You have always been in others and you will remain in others. And what does it matter to you if later on that is called your memory? This will be you—the you that enters the future and becomes a part of it.

"And now one last point. There is nothing to fear. There is no such thing as death. Death has nothing to do with us. But you said something about being talented—that it makes one different. Now, that does have something to do with us. And talent in the highest and broadest sense means talent for life.

"There will be no death, says St. John. His reasoning is quite simple. There will be no death because the past is over; that's almost like saying there will be no death because it is already done with, it's old and we are bored with it. What we need is something new, and that new thing is life eternal."

He was pacing up and down the room as he was talking.

Now he walked up to Anna Ivanovna's bed and putting his hand on her forehead said, "Go to sleep." After a few moments she began to fall asleep.

Yura quietly left the room and told Egorovna to send in the nurse. "What's come over me?" he thought. "I'm becoming a regular quack—muttering incantations, laying on the hands. . . ."

Next day Anna Ivanovna was better.

Anna G recovers. Yura renounces all claims to his dead father's estate.

4

Anna Ivanovna continued to improve. In the middle of December she tried to get up but she was still weak. The doctors told her to stay in bed and have a really good rest.

She often sent for Yura and Tonia and for hours on end talked to them of her childhood, spent on her grandfather's estate, Varykino, on the river Rynva, in the Urals. Neither Yura nor Tonia had ever been there, but listening to her, Yura could easily imagine those ten thousand acres of impenetrable virgin forest as black as night, and, thrusting into it like a curved knife, the bends of the swift stream with its rocky bed and steep cliffs on the Krueger side.

For the first time in their lives Yura and Tonia were getting evening clothes, Yura a dinner jacket and Tonia a pale satin party dress with a suitably modest neckline.

They were going to wear them at the traditional Christmas party at the Sventitskys' on the twenty-seventh. When the tailor and the seamstress delivered the clothes, Yura and Tonia tried them on, were delighted, and had not yet taken them off when Egorovna came in asking them to go to Anna Ivanovna.

They went to her room in their new clothes. On seeing them, she raised herself on her elbow, looked them over, and told them to turn around.

"Very nice," she said. "Charming. I had no idea they were ready. Let me have another look, Tonia. No, it's all right, I thought the yoke puckered a bit. Do you know why I've called you? But first I want a word with you, Yura."

"I know, Anna Ivanovna, I know you've seen the letter, I had it sent to you myself. I know you agree with Nikolai Nikolaievich. You both think I should not have refused the legacy. But wait a moment. It's bad for you to talk. Just let me explain—though you know most of it already.

"Well, then, in the first place, it suits the lawyers that there should be a Zhivago case because there is enough money in Father's estate to cover the costs and to pay the lawyers' fees. Apart from that there is no legacy—nothing but debts and muddle—and a lot of dirty linen to be washed. If there really had been anything that could be turned into money, do you think I'd have made a present of it to the court and not used it myself? But that's just the point—the whole case is trumped up. So rather than rake up all that dirt it was better to give up my right to a nonexistent property and let it go to all that bunch of false rivals and pretenders who were after it. One claimant, as you know, is a certain Madame Alice, who calls herself Zhivago and lives with her children in Paris—I've known about her for a long time. But now there are various new claims—I don't know about you, but I was told of them quite recently.

"It appears that while Mother was still alive, Father became infatuated with a certain dreamy, eccentric Princess Stolbunova-Enrici. This lady has a son by him, Evgraf; he is ten years old.

"The Princess is a recluse. She lives—God knows on what—in her house just outside Omsk, and she never goes out. I've seen a photograph of the house. It's very handsome, with five French windows and stucco medallions on the cornices. And recently I've been having the feeling that the house was staring at me nastily, out of all its five windows, right across all the thousands of miles between Siberia and Moscow, and that sooner or later it would give me the evil eye. So what do I want with all this—imaginary capital, phony claimants, malice, envy? And lawyers."

"All the same, you shouldn't have renounced it," said Anna Ivanovna. "Do you know why I called you?" she asked again and immediately went on, "His name came back to me. You remember the forest guard I was telling you about yesterday? He was called Bacchus. Extraordinary, isn't it! A real bogeyman, black as the devil, with a beard growing up to his eyebrows, and calls himself Bacchus! His face was all disfigured, a bear had mauled him but he had fought it off. And they're all like that out there. Such names—striking, sonorous! Bacchus or Lupus or Faustus. Every now and then somebody like that would be announced—perhaps Auctus or Frolus—somebody with a name like a shot from your grandfather's gun—and we would all immediately troop downstairs from the nursery to the kitchen. And there—you can't think what it was like—you'd find a charcoal dealer with a live bear cub, or a prospector from the far end of the province with a specimen of the ore. And your grandfather would always give them a credit slip for the office. Some were given money, some buckwheat, others cartridges. The forest came right up to the windows. And the snow, the snow! Higher than the roofs!" Anna Ivanovna had a coughing fit.

"That's enough, it's bad for you," Tonia and Yura urged her.

"Nonsense, I'm perfectly all right. That reminds me. Egorovna told me that you two are worrying about whether you should go to the party the day after tomorrow. Don't let me hear anything so silly again, you ought to be ashamed of yourselves! And you call yourself a doctor, Yura! So that's settled, you'll go, and that's that. But to return to Bacchus. He used to be a blacksmith when he was young. He got into a fight and was disembowelled. So he made himself a set of iron guts. Now, Yura, don't be silly. Of course I know he couldn't. You mustn't take it literally! But that's what the people out there said."

She was interrupted by another coughing fit, a much longer one than the last. It went on and on; she could not get her breath.

Yura and Tonia hurried across to her simultaneously. They stood shoulder to shoulder by her bedside. Their hands touched. Still coughing, Anna Ivanovna caught their hands in hers and kept them joined awhile. When she was able to speak she said: "If I die, stay together. You're meant for each other. Get married. There now, you're engaged," she added and burst into tears.

To escape from Komarovsky, Lara takes a tutoring job with the Kologrivovs.

5

As early as the spring of 1906—only a few months before she would begin her last year in the gymnasium—six months of Lara's liaison with Komarovsky had driven her beyond the limits of her endurance. He cleverly turned her wretchedness to his advantage, and when it suited him subtly reminded her of her shame. These reminders brought her to just that state of confusion that a lecher requires in a woman. As a result, Lara felt herself sinking ever deeper into a nightmare of sensuality which filled her with horror whenever she awoke from it. Her nocturnal madness was as unaccountable as black magic. Here everything was topsy-turvy and flew in the face of logic; sharp pain manifested itself by peals of silvery laughter, resistance and refusal meant consent, and grateful kisses covered the hand of the tormentor.

It seemed that there would be no end to it, but that spring, as she sat through a history lesson at the end of term, thinking of the summer when even school and homework would no longer keep her from Komarovsky, she came to a sudden decision that altered the course of her life.

It was a hot morning and a storm was brewing. Through the open classroom windows came the distant droning of the town, as monotonous as a beehive, and the shrieks of children playing in the yard. The grassy smell of earth and young leaves made her head ache, like a Shrovetide surfeit of pancakes and vodka.

The lesson was about Napoleon's Egyptian campaign. When the teacher came to the landing at Fréjus, the sky blackened and was split by lightning and thunder, and clouds of dust and sand swept into the room together with the smell of rain. Two teacher's pets rushed out obligingly to call the handyman to shut the windows, and as they opened the door, the wind sent all the blotting paper flying off the desks.

The windows were shut. A dirty city rain mingled with dust began to pour. Lara tore a page out of an exercise book, and wrote a note to her neighbor, Nadia Kologrivova:

"Nadia, I've got to live away from Mother. Help me to find a tutoring job, as well paid as possible. You know lots of rich people."

Nadia wrote back:

"We are looking for a governess for Lipa. Why not come to us —it would be wonderful! You know how fond my parents are of you."

he K's treat Lara as a member of the family. She borrows 700 rubles from them to pay a gambling 6 debt for her brother.

Lara spent three years at the Kologrivovs' as behind stone walls. No one bothered her, and even her mother and brother, from whom she had become estranged, kept out of her way.

Lavrentii Mikhailovich Kologrivov was a big businessman, a brilliant and intelligent practitioner of the most modern methods. He hated the decaying order with a double hatred, as a man rich enough to outbid the treasury, and as a member of the lower classes who had risen to fabulous heights. In his house he sheltered revolutionaries sought by the police, and he paid the defense costs in political trials. It was a standing joke that he was so keen on subsidizing the revolution that he expropriated himself and organized strikes at his own plants. An excellent marksman and a passionate hunter, he went to the Serebriany woods and Losin Island in the winter of 1905, giving rifle training to workers' militia.

He was a remarkable man. His wife, Serafima Filippovna, was a worthy match. Lara admired and respected both of them, and the whole household loved her and treated her as a member of the family.

For more than three years Lara led a life free from worries. Then one day her brother Rodia went to see her. Swaying affectedly on his long legs and drawling self-importantly, he told her that the cadets of his class had collected money for a farewell gift to the head of the Academy and entrusted it to him, asking him to choose and buy the gift. This money he had gambled away two days ago down to the last kopek. Having told his story, he flopped full length in an armchair and burst into tears.

Lara sat frozen while Rodia went on through his sobs:

"Last night I went to see Victor Ippolitovich. He refused to talk about it with me, but he said if you wished him to . . . He said that although you no longer loved any of us, your power over him was still so great . . . Lara darling . . . One word from you would be enough. . . . You realize what this means to me, what a disgrace it is . . . the honor of my uniform is at stake. Go to see him, that's not too much to ask, speak to him . . . You can't want me to pay for this with my life."

"Your life . . . The honor of your uniform." Lara echoed him indignantly, pacing the room. "I am not a uniform. I have no honor. You can do what you like with me. Have you any idea of what you are asking? Do you realize what he is proposing to you? Year after year I slave away, and now you come along and don't care if everything goes smash. To hell with you. Go ahead, shoot yourself. What do I care? How much do you need?"

"Six hundred and ninety odd rubles. Say seven hundred in round figures," he added after a slight pause.

"Rodia! No, you're out of your mind! Do you know what you are saying? You've gambled away seven hundred rubles! Rodia! Rodia! Do you realize how long it takes an ordinary person like me to earn that much by honest work?"

She broke off and after a short silence said coldly, as if to a stranger, "All right. I'll try. Come tomorrow. And bring your revolver—the one you were going to shoot yourself with. You'll hand it over to me, for good. And with plenty of bullets, remember."

She got the money from Kologrivov.

Lara graduates from the gymnasium, & goes to the university. Pasha & Lara plan to marry & become teachers.

7

Her work at the Kologrivovs' did not prevent Lara from graduating from the gymnasium, and taking university courses. She did well, and was to obtain her diploma the following year, 1912.

In the spring of 1911 her pupil Lipa graduated from the gymnasium. She was already engaged to a young engineer, Friesendank, who came of a good, well-to-do family. Lipa's parents approved of her choice but were against her marrying so young, and urged her to wait. This led to scenes. Lipa, the spoiled and willful darling of the family, shouted at her parents and stamped her feet.

In this rich household where Lara was accepted as a member of the family, no one reminded her of her debt or indeed remembered it. She would have paid it back long before, if she had not had secret expenses.

Unknown to Pasha, she sent money to his father, who had been deported to Siberia, helped his querulous and ailing mother, and reduced his own expenses by paying part of his board and lodging directly to his landlady. It was she who had found him his room in a new building in Kamerger Street near the Art Theater.

Pasha, who was a little younger than Lara, loved her madly and obeyed her slightest wish. After graduating from the *Real-gymnasium,* he had, at her urging, taken up Greek and Latin. It was her dream that after they had passed their state examinations the following year they would marry and go out as gymnasium teachers to some provincial capital in the Urals.

In the summer of 1911 Lara went for the last time with the Kologrivovs to Duplyanka. She adored the place, and was even fonder of it than its owners. They knew this, and every summer on their arrival the same scene was enacted as though by an unwritten agreement. When the hot, grimy train left them at the station, Lara, overwhelmed by the infinite silence and heady fragrance of the countryside, and speechless with emotion, was allowed to walk alone from the railroad station to the estate. Meanwhile, the luggage was loaded onto a cart, and the family climbed into their barouche and listened to the Duplyanka coachman in his scarlet shirt and sleeveless coat telling them the latest local news.

Lara walked along the tracks following a path worn by pilgrims and then turned into the fields. Here she stopped and, closing her eyes, took a deep breath of the flower-scented air of the broad expanse around her. It was dearer to her than her kin, better than a lover, wiser than a book. For a moment she rediscovered the purpose of her life. She was here on earth to grasp the meaning of its wild enchantment and to call each thing by its right name, or, if this were not within her power, to give birth out of love for life to successors who would do it in her place.

That summer she had arrived exhausted by the many duties she had undertaken. She was easily upset. Generous and understanding by nature, she developed a new suspiciousness and a tendency to nurse petty grievances.

The Kologrivovs were as fond of her as ever and wanted her to stay on with them, but now that Lipa had grown up she felt that she had become useless to them. She refused her salary. They had to press it on her. At the same time she needed the money, and it would have been embarrassing and unfeasible to earn it independently while she was their guest.

Lara felt that her position was false and unendurable. She imagined that they all found her a burden and were only putting a good face on it. She was a burden to herself. She longed to run away from herself and from the Kologrivovs—anywhere —but according to her standards, she must first repay the money she had borrowed, and at the moment she had no means of doing it. She felt that she was a hostage—all through Rodia's stupid fault—and was trapped in impotent exasperation.

She suspected slights at every turn. If the Kologrivovs' friends were attentive to her she was sure that they regarded her as a submissive "ward" and an easy prey. If they left her alone, that proved that she did not exist for them.

Her fits of moodiness did not prevent her from sharing in the amusements of the many house guests. She swam, went boating, joined in night picnics by the river, and danced and let off fireworks with the rest. She took part in amateur theatricals and with even more zest in shooting competitions. Short Mauser rifles were used in these contests, but she preferred Rodia's light revolver and became very skillful in its use. "Pity I'm a woman," she said, laughing, "I'd have made an expert duellist." But the more she did to distract herself, the more wretched she felt and the less she knew what she wanted.

When they went back to town it was worse than ever, for to her other troubles were now added her tiffs with Pasha (she was careful not to quarrel with him seriously; she regarded him as her last refuge). Pasha was beginning to show a certain self-assurance. His tone was becoming a little didactic, and this both amused and irritated her.

Pasha, Lipa, the Kologrivovs, money—everything whirled inside her head. She was disgusted with life. She was beginning to lose her mind. She was obsessed with the idea of breaking with everything she had ever known or experienced, and starting on something new. In this state, at Christmastime in the year 1911, she arrived at a fatal decision. She would leave the Kologrivovs now, at once, and become independent, and she would get the money for this from Komarovsky. It seemed to her that after all there had been between them and the years of independence she had won for herself, he must help her chivalrously, disinterestedly, without explanations or disgraceful conditions.

With this in mind she set out for Petrovka Street on the night of the twenty-seventh. Rodia's revolver, loaded and with the safety catch off, was inside her muff. Should Komarovsky refuse or humiliate her in any way, she intended to shoot him.

She walked through the festive streets in a terrible excitement, seeing nothing. The intended revolver shot had already gone off in her heart—and it was a matter of complete indifference whom the shot was aimed at. This shot was the only thing that she was conscious of. She heard it all the way to Petrovka Street, and it was aimed at Komarovsky, at herself, at her own fate, and at the wooden target on the Duplyanka oak tree.

Lara travels thru Moscow at Xmas time.

8

"Don't touch my muff!"

Emma Ernestovna had put out her hand to help her off with her coat; she had received her with Oh's and Ah's, telling her that Victor Ippolitovich was out but she must stay and wait for him.

"I can't. I'm in a hurry. Where is he?"

He was at a Christmas party. Clutching the scrap of paper with the address on it, Lara ran down the familiar gloomy staircase with its stained-glass coats of arms and started off for the Sventitskys' house in Flour Town.

Only now, when she came out for the second time, did she take a look around her. It was winter. It was the city. It was night.

It was bitter cold. The streets were covered with a thick, black, glassy layer of ice, like the bottom of beer bottles. It hurt her to breathe. The air was dense with gray sleet and it tickled and pricked her face like the gray frozen bristles of her fur cape. Her heart thumping, she walked through the deserted streets past the steaming doors of cheap teashops and restaurants. Faces as red as sausages and horses' and dogs' heads with beards of icicles emerged from the mist. A thick crust of ice and snow covered the windows, and the colored reflections of lighted Christmas trees and the shadows of merrymakers moved across their chalk-white opaque surfaces as on magic lantern screens; it was as though shows were being given for the benefit of pedestrians.

In Kamerger Street Lara stopped. "I can't go on. I can't bear it." The words almost slipped out. "I'll go up and tell him everything." Pulling herself together, she went in through the heavy door.

Lara visits Pasha

9

Pasha, his face red from the effort, his tongue pushing out his cheek, stood in front of the mirror struggling with a collar, a stud, and the starched buttonhole of his shirt front. He was going to a party. So chaste and inexperienced was he that Lara embarrassed him by coming in without knocking and finding him with this minor incompleteness in his dress. He at once noticed her agitation. She could hardly keep on her feet. She advanced pushing the hem of her skirt aside at each step as if she were fording a river.

He hurried toward her. "What's the matter?" he said in alarm. "What has happened?"

"Sit down beside me. Sit down, don't bother to finish dressing. I'm in a hurry, I must go in a minute. Don't touch my muff. Wait, turn the other way for a minute."

He complied. Lara was wearing a tailored suit. She took off her coat, hung it up, and transferred Rodia's revolver from the muff to a pocket. Then she went back to the sofa.

"Now you can look," she said. "Light a candle, and turn off the electricity."

She liked to sit in the dim light of candles, and Pasha always kept a few spare ones. He replaced the stump in the candlestick with a new candle, put it on the window sill, and lit it. The flame choked and spluttered, shooting off small stars, and sharpened to an arrow. A soft light filled the room. In the sheet of ice

covering the windowpane a black eyelet began to form at the
level of the flame.

"Listen, Pasha," said Lara. "I am in trouble. You must help me.
Don't be frightened and don't question me. But don't ever think
we can be like other people. Don't take it so lightly. I am in constant danger. If you love me, if you don't want me to be destroyed, we must not put off our marriage."

"But that's what I've always wanted," broke in Pasha. "Just
name the day. I'm ready when you are. Now tell me plainly
what is worrying you. Don't torment me with riddles."

But Lara evaded his question, imperceptibly changing the
subject. They talked a long time about a number of things that
had nothing to do with her distress.

Yura passed thru the same streets that Lara has travelled

10

That winter Yura was preparing a scientific paper on the nervous
elements of the retina for the University Gold Medal competition. Though he had qualified only in general medicine, he had a
specialist's knowledge of the eye. His interest in the physiology
of sight was in keeping with other sides of his character—his
creative gifts and his preoccupation with imagery in art and the
logical structure of ideas.

Tonia and Yura were driving in a hired sleigh to the Sventitskys' Christmas party. After six years of late childhood and early
adolescence spent in the same house they knew everything
there was to know about each other. They had habits in common,
their own special way of snorting at each other's jokes. Now
they drove in silence, their lips tightly closed against the cold,
occasionally exchanging a word or two, and absorbed in their
own thoughts.

Yura was thinking about the date of his competition and that
he must work harder at his paper. Then his mind, distracted by
the festive, end-of-the-year bustle in the streets, jumped to other
thoughts. He had promised Gordon an article on Blok for the
mimeographed student paper that he edited; young people in
both capitals were mad about Blok, Yura and Gordon particularly. But not even these thoughts held his mind for long. He

and Tonia rode on, their chins tucked into their collars, rubbing their frozen ears, and each of them thinking of something else. But on one point their thoughts converged.

The recent scene at Anna Ivanovna's bedside had transformed them. It was as though their eyes had opened, and they appeared to each other in a new light.

Tonia, his old friend, who had always been taken for granted and had never needed explaining, had turned out to be the most inaccessible and complicated being he could imagine. She had become a woman. By a stretch of imagination he could visualize himself as an emperor, a hero, a prophet, a conqueror, but not as a woman.

Now that Tonia had taken this supreme and most difficult task on her slender and fragile shoulders (she seemed slender and fragile to him, though she was a perfectly healthy girl), he was filled with the ardent sympathy and timid wonder that are the beginning of passion.

Tonia's attitude to Yura underwent a similar change.

It occurred to Yura that perhaps they should not, after all, have gone out. He was worried about Anna Ivanovna. They had been on the point of leaving when, hearing that she was feeling less well, they had gone to her room, but she had ordered them off to the party as sharply as before. They had gone to the window to have a look at the weather. As they came out, the net curtains had clung to Tonia's new dress, trailing after her like a wedding veil. They all noticed this and burst out laughing.

Yura looked around him and saw what Lara had seen shortly before. The moving sleigh was making an unusually loud noise, which was answered by an unusually long echo coming from the ice-bound trees in the gardens and streets. The windows, frosted and lighted from inside, reminded him of precious caskets made of smoky topaz. Behind them glowed the Christmas life of Moscow, candles burned on trees, and guests in fancy dress milled about playing hide-and-seek and hunt-the-ring.

It suddenly occurred to Yura that Blok reflected the Christmas spirit in all domains of Russian life—in this northern city and in the newest Russian literature, under the starry sky of this modern street and around the lighted tree in a twentieth-century drawing room. There was no need to write an article on

Blok, he thought, all you had to do was to paint a Russian version of a Dutch Adoration of the Magi with snow in it, and wolves, and a dark fir forest.

As they drove through Kamerger Street Yura noticed that a candle had melted a patch in the icy crust on one of the windows. The light seemed to look into the street almost consciously, as if it were watching the passing carriages and waiting for someone.

"A candle burned on the table, a candle burned . . . ," he whispered to himself—the beginning of something confused, formless; he hoped that it would take shape of itself. But nothing more came to him.

The Sventitsky's Xmas party.

11

From time immemorial the Sventitskys' Christmas parties followed the same pattern. At ten, after the children had gone home, the tree was lit a second time for the others, and the party went on till morning. The more staid people played cards all night long in the "Pompeiian" sitting room, curtained off from the ballroom by a heavy portiere on bronze rings. Before daybreak they would all have supper together.

"Why are you so late?" asked the Sventitskys' nephew, Georges, running through the entrance hall on his way to his uncle's and aunt's rooms. Yura and Tonia took off their things and looked in at the ballroom door before going to greet their hosts.

Rustling their dresses and treading on each other's toes, those who were not dancing but walking and talking moved like a black wall past the hotly breathing Christmas tree with its several tiers of lights.

In the center of the room the dancers twirled and spun dizzily. They were paired off or formed into chains by a young law school student, Koka Kornakov, son of an assistant public prosecutor who was leading the cotillion. "*Grand rond!*" he bellowed at the top of his voice across the room, or "*Chaîne chinoise!*"—and they all followed his orders. "*Une valse, s'il vous plaît,*" he shouted to the pianist as he led his partner at the

head of the first round, whirling away with her and gradually
slowing down in ever smaller and smaller circles until they
were barely marking time in what was still the dying echo of a
waltz. Everyone clapped, and ices and cool drinks were carried around the noisy, milling, shuffling crowd. Flushed boys and
girls never stopped shouting and laughing as they greedily drank
cold cranberry juice and lemonade, and the moment they put
down their glasses on the trays the noise was ten times louder,
as if they had gulped down some exhilarating mixture.

Without stopping in the ballroom, Tonia and Yura went
through to their hosts' rooms in the back.

Yura & Tonia at the S's Xmas party

12

The living rooms of the Sventitskys were cluttered up with
furniture that had been moved out of the ballroom and the
drawing room. Here was the Sventitskys' magic kitchen, their
Christmas workshop. The place smelled of paint and glue, and
there were piles of colored wrappings and boxes of cotillion
favors and spare candles.

The Sventitskys were writing names on cards for presents
and for seats at the supper table and numbers on tickets for a
lottery. They were helped by Georges, but he kept losing count
and they grumbled at him irritably. They were overjoyed at
Tonia's and Yura's coming; they had known them as children
and unceremoniously set them to work.

"Feliciata Semionovna cannot understand that this should
have been done in advance, not right in the middle of the party
when the guests are here. Look what you've done now, Georges
—the empty *bonbonnières* go on the sofa and the ones with
sugared almonds on the table—now you've mixed up everything."

"I am so glad Annette is better. Pierre and I were so worried."

"Except that she's worse, not better, darling—worse, do you
understand? You always get things *devant-derrière*."

Yura and Tonia spent half the evening backstage with Georges
and the old couple.

Lara does not find the S's party so entertaining.

13

All this time Lara was in the ballroom. She was not in evening dress and did not know anyone there, but she stayed on, either waltzing with Koka Kornakov like a sleepwalker or wandering aimlessly around the room.

Once or twice she stopped and stood hesitating outside the sitting room, in the hope that Komarovsky, who sat facing the doorway, might see her. But he did not take his eyes from his cards, which he held in his left hand and which shielded his face, and he either really did not notice her or pretended not to. She was choking with mortification. A girl whom she did not know went in from the ballroom. Komarovsky looked at her in the way Lara remembered so well. The girl was flattered and flushed and smiled with pleasure. Lara crimsoned with shame and nearly screamed. "A new victim," she thought. Lara saw, as in a mirror, herself and the whole story of her liaison. She did not give up her plan to speak to him but decided to do it later, at a more convenient moment; forcing herself to be calm, she went back to the ballroom.

Komarovsky was playing with three other men. The one on his left was Kornakov, the father of the elegant young man with whom Lara was dancing again, so she understood from the few words she exchanged with him. And the young man's mother was the tall dark woman in black with fiercely burning eyes and an unpleasantly snakelike neck who went back and forth between the ballroom and the sitting room, watching her son dancing and her husband playing cards. And finally Lara learned that the girl who had aroused such complicated feelings in her was the young man's sister and that her suspicions had been groundless.

She had not paid attention to Koka's surname when he had first introduced himself, but he repeated it as he swept her in the last gliding movement of the waltz to a chair and bowed himself off. "Kornakov. Kornakov." It reminded her of something. Of something unpleasant. Then it came back to her. Kornakov was the assistant public prosecutor at the Moscow central court who had made a fanatical speech at the trial of the group of railway men which had included Tiverzin. At

Lara's wish, Kologrivov had gone to plead with him, but without success. "So that's it. . . . Well, well, well. . . . Interesting. . . . Kornakov. Kornakov."

Lara shoots Kornakov

14

It was almost two in the morning. Yura's ears were ringing. There had been an interval with tea and petits fours and now the dancing had begun again. No one bothered any more to replace the candles on the tree as they burned down.

Yura stood uneasily in the middle of the ballroom, watching Tonia dancing with a stranger. She swept up to him, flounced her short satin train—like a fish waving its fin—and vanished in the crowd.

She was very excited. During the interval, she had refused tea and had slaked her thirst with innumerable tangerines, peeling them and wiping her fingers and the corners of her mouth on a handkerchief the size of a fruit blossom. Laughing and talking incessantly, she kept taking the handkerchief out and unthinkingly putting it back inside her sash or her sleeve.

Now, as she brushed past the frowning Yura, spinning with her unknown partner, she caught and pressed his hand and smiled eloquently. The handkerchief she had been holding stayed in his hand. He pressed it to his lips and closed his eyes. The handkerchief smelled equally enchantingly of tangerines and of Tonia's hand. This was something new in Yura's life, something he had never felt before, something sharp that pierced him from top to toe. This naïvely childish smell was as intimate and understandable as a word whispered in the dark. He pressed the handkerchief to his eyes and lips, breathing through it. Suddenly a shot rang out inside.

Everyone turned and looked at the portiere that hung between the ballroom and the sitting room. There was a moment's silence. Then the uproar began. Some people rushed about screaming, others ran after Koka into the sitting room from which the sound of the shot had come; others came out to meet them, weeping, arguing and all talking at once.

"What has she done, what has she done!" Komarovsky kept saying in despair.

"Boria, Boria, tell me you're alive," Mrs. Kornakov was scream-ing hysterically. "Where is Doctor Drokov? They said he's here. Oh, but where, where is he?—How can you, how can you say it's nothing but a scratch! Oh, my poor martyr, that's what you get for exposing all those criminals! There she is, the scum, there she is, I'll scratch your eyes out, you slut, you won't get away this time! What did you say, Komarovsky? You? She shot at you? No, I can't bear it, this is a tragic moment, Komarovsky, I haven't time to listen to jokes. Koka, Kokochka! Can you be-lieve it? She tried to kill your father. . . . Yes. . . . But Provi-dence . . . Koka! Koka!"

The crowd poured out of the sitting room into the ballroom. At the head of it came Kornakov, laughingly assuring everyone that he was quite all right and dabbing with a napkin at a scratch on his left hand. Another group, somewhat apart, was leading Lara by the arms.

Yura was dumfounded. This girl again! And again in such extraordinary circumstances! And again that gray-haired man. But this time Yura knew who he was—the prominent lawyer, Komarovsky, who had had something to do with his father's estate. No need to greet him. They both pretended not to know each other. And the girl . . . So it was the girl who had fired the shot? At the prosecutor? Must be for political reasons. Poor thing. She was in for a bad time. How haughtily beautiful she was! And those louts, twisting her arms, as if she were a com-mon thief!

But at once he realized that he was mistaken. Lara's legs gave way under her, they were holding her up and almost carrying her to the nearest armchair, where she collapsed.

Yura was about to rush up to her to bring her around but thought it proper first to show some interest in the victim. He walked up to Kornakov.

"I am a doctor," he said. "Let me see your hand. Well, you've been lucky. It's not even worth bandaging. A drop of iodine wouldn't do any harm, though. There's Feliciata Semionovna, we'll ask her."

Mrs. Sventitskaia and Tonia, who were coming toward him, were white-faced. They told him to leave everything and quickly get his coat. There had been a message from home, they were to go back at once.

Yura, imagining the worst, forgot everything else and ran for his things.

Anna G. dies.

15

They did not find Anna Ivanovna alive. When they ran up the stairs to her room she had been dead for ten minutes. The cause of death had been an attack of suffocation resulting from acute edema of the lungs; this had not been diagnosed in time. For the first few hours Tonia screamed, sobbed convulsively, and recognized no one. On the following day she calmed down but could only nod in answer to anything that Yura and her father said to her; each time she tried to speak, her grief overpowered her and she began to scream again as if she were possessed.

In the intervals between the services she knelt for hours beside the dead woman, her large, fine hands clasping a corner of the coffin standing on its dais, covered with wreaths. She was oblivious of the people around her. But whenever her eyes met those of her friends she would quickly get up and hurry from the room and up the stairs, repressing her sobs until she fell on the bed and buried her bursts of despair in the pillow.

Sorrow, standing for many hours on end, lack of sleep, the deep-toned singing and the dazzling candles by night and day as well as the cold he had caught, filled Yura's soul with a sweet confusion, a fever of grief and ecstasy.

When his mother had died ten years earlier he had been a child. He could still remember how he had cried, grief-stricken and terrified. In those days he had not been primarily concerned with himself. He could hardly even realize that such a being as Yura existed on its own or had any value or interest. What mattered then was everything outside and around him. From every side the external world pressed in on him, dense, indisputable, tangible as a forest. And the reason he had been so shaken by his mother's death was that, at her side, he had lost himself in the forest, suddenly to find her gone and himself alone in it. The forest was made up of everything in the world —clouds and shop signs and the golden balls on fire towers and the bare-headed riders who went as escort before the holy image of the Mother of God carried in a coach. Shop fronts were in it, and arcades, and the inaccessibly high star-studded sky, and the Lord God and the saints.

This inaccessibly high sky once came all the way down to his nursery, as far as his nurse's skirt when she was talking to him about God; it was close and within reach like the tops of hazel trees in the gullies when you pulled down their branches and picked the nuts. It was as if it dipped into the gilt nursery wash-basin and, having bathed in fire and gold, re-emerged as the morning service or mass at the tiny church where he went with his nurse. There the heavenly stars became the lights before the icons, and the Lord God was a kindly Father, and everything more or less fell into its right place. But the main thing was the real world of the grownups and the city that loomed up all around him like a forest. At that time, with the whole of his half-animal faith, Yura believed in God, who was the keeper of that forest.

Now it was quite different. In his twelve years at gymnasium and university, Yura had studied the classics and Scripture, legends and poets, history and natural science, which had become to him the chronicles of his house, his family tree. Now he was afraid of nothing, neither of life nor of death; everything in the world, all the things in it were words in his vocabulary. He felt he was on an equal footing with the universe. And he was affected by the services for Anna Ivanovna differently than he had been by the services for his mother. Then he had prayed in confusion, fear, and pain. Now he listened to the services as if they were a message addressed to him and concerning him directly. He listened intently to the words, expecting them, like any other words, to have a clear meaning. There was no religiosity in his reverence for the supreme powers of heaven and earth, which he worshipped as his progenitors.

Anna's funeral.

16

"Holy God, holy and mighty, holy and deathless, have mercy on us." What was it? Where was he? They must be taking out the coffin. He must wake up. He had fallen asleep in his clothes on the sofa at six in the morning. Now they were hunting for him all over the house, but no one thought of looking in the far corner of the library behind the bookshelves.

"Yura! Yura!" Markel was calling him. They were taking out the coffin. Markel would have to carry the wreaths, and nowhere could he find Yura to help him; to make matters worse he had got stuck in the bedroom where the wreaths were piled up, because the door of the wardrobe on the landing had swung open and blocked that of the bedroom.

"Markel! Markel! Yura!" people were shouting from downstairs. Markel kicked open the door and ran downstairs carrying several wreaths.

"Holy God, holy and mighty, holy and deathless," the words drifted softly down the street and stayed there; as if a feather duster had softly brushed the air, everything was swaying— wreaths, passers-by, plumed horses' heads, the censer swinging on its chain from the priest's hand, and the white earth under foot.

"Yura! My God! At last." Shura Shlesinger was shaking his shoulder. "What's the matter with you? They're carrying out the coffin. Are you coming with us?"

"Yes, of course."

17

The funeral service was over. The beggars, shuffling their feet in the cold, closed up in two ranks. The hearse, the gig with wreaths on it, and the Kruegers' carriage stirred and swayed slightly. The cabs drew up closer to the church. Out of it came Shura Shlesinger, crying; lifting her veil, damp with tears, she cast a searching glance at the crowd, spotted the pallbearers, beckoned to them, and went back into the church. More and more people were pouring out.

"Well, so now it's Anna Ivanovna's turn. She sends her best regards. She took a ticket to a far place, poor soul."

"Yes, her dance is over, poor cricket, she's gone to her rest."

"Have you got a cab or are you going to walk?"

"I need to stretch my legs after all that standing. Let's walk a bit and then we'll take a cab."

"Did you see how upset Fufkov was? Looking at her, tears pouring down his face, blowing his nose, staring at her face. Standing next to her husband at that."

"He always had his eye on her."

They slowly made their way to the cemetery at the other end of town. That day the hard frost had broken. It was a still, heavy day; the cold had gone and the life had gone too—it was a day as though made for a funeral. The dirty snow looked as if it shone through crêpe, and the firs behind the churchyard railings, wet and dark like tarnished silver, seemed to be in deep mourning.

It was in this same churchyard that Yura's mother lay buried. He had not been to her grave in recent years. He glanced in its direction and whispered, "Mother," almost as he might have done years before.

They dispersed solemnly, in picturesque groups, along the cleared paths, whose meanderings did not harmonize with the sorrowful deliberation of their step. Alexander Alexandrovich led Tonia by the arm. They were followed by the Kruegers. Black was very becoming to Tonia.

Hoarfrost, bearded like mold, sprouted on the chains with crosses hanging from the domes and on the pink monastery walls. In the far corner of the monastery yard, washing hung on lines stretching from wall to wall—shirts with heavy sodden sleeves, peach-colored tablecloths, badly wrung out and crookedly fastened sheets. Yura realized that this, altered in appearance by the new buildings, was the part of the monastery grounds where the blizzard had raged that night.

He walked on alone, ahead of the others, stopping occasionally to let them catch up with him. In answer to the desolation brought by death to the people slowly pacing after him, he was drawn, as irresistibly as water funnelling downward, to dream, to think, to work out new forms, to create beauty. More vividly than ever before he realized that art has two constant, two unending concerns: it always meditates on death and thus always creates life. All great, genuine art resembles and continues the Revelation of St. John.

With joyful anticipation he thought of the day or two which he would set aside and spend alone, away from the university and from his home, to write a poem in memory of Anna Ivanovna. He would include all those random things that life had sent his way, a few descriptions of Anna Ivanovna's best characteristics, Tonia in mourning, street incidents on the way back from the funeral, and the washing hanging in the place where, many years ago, the blizzard had raged in the night and he had wept as a child.

CHAPTER FOUR

THE HOUR OF THE INEVITABLE

*In reaction to the shooting, Lara is feverish, & only half conscious.
She is put to bed in the Sventitsky home. He Komarovsky rents a
room for Lara with Ruffina 1 Onisimovna Voit - Voithovsky, a
woman lawyer.*

Lara lay feverish and half conscious in Feliciata Semionovna's
bed; the Sventitskys, the servants, and Dr. Drokov were talking
in whispers around her.

The rest of the house was dark and empty. Only in one small
sitting room did a lamp on a bracket cast its dim light up and
down the long suite of rooms.

Here Komarovsky strode with angry, resolute steps, as if he
were at home and not a visitor. He would look into the bedroom
for news and tear back to the other end of the house, past the
tree with its tinsel, and through the dining room where the
table stood laden with untasted dishes and the greenish crystal
wineglasses tinkled every time a cab drove past the windows or
a mouse scurried over the tablecloth among the china.

Komarovsky thrashed about in a fury. Conflicting feelings
crowded in his breast. The scandal! The disgrace! He was beside himself. His position was threatened, his reputation would
suffer from the incident. At whatever cost he must prevent the
gossip or, if the news had already spread, stop the rumors, nip
them in the bud.

Another reason for his agitation was that he had once again
experienced the irresistible attraction of this crazy, desperate
girl. He had always known that she was different. There had always been something unique about her. But how deeply, painfully, irreparably had he wounded her and upset her life, and
how rebellious and violent she was in her determination to re-
shape her destiny and start afresh!

It was clear that he must help her in every way. Take a room
for her, perhaps. But in no circumstances must he come near

her; on the contrary, he must keep away, stand aside so as not to be in her way, or with her violent nature there was no knowing what she might do.

And what a lot of trouble ahead! This wasn't the sort of thing for which they patted you on the head! The law didn't wink at it. It was not yet morning, and hardly two hours had passed since it happened but already the police had been twice and he, Komarovsky, had had to go to the kitchen and see the inspector and smooth things over.

And the further it went the more complications there would be. They would have to have proof that Lara had meant to shoot at him and not at Kornakov. And even that wouldn't be the end of it; she would only be cleared of one part of the charge, but she would still be liable to prosecution.

Naturally, he would do everything to prevent it. If the case came to court he would get expert evidence from a psychiatrist that she had not been responsible for her actions at the moment when she fired the shot and would see to it that the proceedings were dropped.

With these reflections he began to calm down. The night was over. Streaks of light probed from room to room and dived under the chairs and tables like thieves or appraisers.

After a last look in the bedroom, where he was told that Lara was no better, Komarovsky left and went to see a friend of his, Ruffina Onissimovna Voit-Voitkovsky, a woman lawyer who was the wife of a political émigré. Her eight-room apartment was now too large for her, she could not afford to keep it all up, so she let two of the rooms. One of them had recently become vacant, and Komarovsky took it for Lara. There she was taken a few hours later, only half conscious with brain fever.

Ruffina takes a dislike to Lara. As Lara is recovering, Kologrivov forces her to accept a gift of 10,000 rubles & finds a studio apartment for her.

2

Ruffina Onissimovna was a woman of advanced views, entirely unprejudiced, and well disposed toward everything that she called "positive and vital."

On top of her chest of drawers she kept a copy of the Erfurt Program with a dedication by the author. One of the photographs on the wall showed her husband, "her good Voit," at a rally in Switzerland, together with Plekhanov, both in alpaca jackets and panama hats.

Ruffina Onissimovna took a dislike to her sick lodger the moment she saw her. She considered Lara a malingerer. The girl's feverish ravings seemed to her nothing but play-acting. She was ready to swear that Lara was impersonating Gretchen gone mad in her dungeon.

She expressed her contempt for Lara by being brisker than usual. She banged doors, sang in a loud voice, tore through her part of the apartment like a hurricane, and kept the windows open all day long.

The apartment was on the top floor of a building in the Arbat. After the winter solstice its windows filled to overflowing with blue sky as wide as a river in flood. Through half the winter it was full of the early signs of the coming spring.

A warm wind from the south blew in through the casements. Locomotives at their distant stations roared like sea lions. Lara, lying ill in bed, filled her leisure with recollections.

She often thought of the night of her arrival in Moscow from the Urals, seven or eight years before, in the unforgettable days of her childhood. She was riding in a cab from the station through gloomy alleys to the hotel at the other end of town. One by one the street lamps threw the humpbacked shadow of the coachman on the walls. The shadow grew and grew till it became gigantic and stretched across the roofs, and was cut off. Then it all began again from the beginning. The bells of Moscow's countless churches clanged in the darkness overhead, and the trolleys rang as they scurried through the streets, but Lara was also deafened by the gaudy window displays and glaring lights, as if they too emitted sounds of their own, like the bells and wheels.

In their hotel room she was staggered at the sight of a watermelon of incredible size. It was Komarovsky's housewarming gift, and to her it was a symbol of his power and wealth. When he thrust a knife into this marvel, and the dark green globe split in half, revealing its icy, sugary heart, she was frightened, but she dared not refuse a slice. The fragrant pink mouthfuls stuck in her throat, but she forced herself to swallow them.

Just as she was intimidated by expensive food and by the

night life of the capital, so she was later intimidated by Komarovsky himself—this was the real explanation of everything.

But now he had changed beyond recognition. He made no demands, never reminded her of the past, and never even came.
And all that time he kept at a distance from her, and most
nobly offered to help her.

Kologrivov's visit was something entirely different. She was
overjoyed when he came. Not because he was tall and handsome,
but because of his overflowing vitality, her visitor with his shining eyes and intelligent smile filled half the space in her room,
making it seem crowded.

He sat by her bed rubbing his hands. On the occasions when
he was summoned to attend a ministerial meeting in Petersburg
he spoke to the old dignitaries as if they were schoolboys; but
now he saw before him a girl who till recently had been part of
his household, something like a daughter to him, with whom,
as with all other members of his family, he had exchanged
words and glances only casually (this constituted the characteristic charm of their closeness, and both he and his family were
aware of this). He could not treat Lara as an adult, with gravity
and indifference. He did not know how to speak to her without
offending her. "What's the big idea?" he said smilingly, as if she
were a child. "Who wants these melodramas?"

He paused, and glanced at the damp stains on the walls
and ceiling. Then, shaking his head reproachfully, he went on:

"There's an international exhibition opening at Düsseldorf—
painting, sculpture, gardening. I'm going. You know, it's a bit
damp here. And how long do you think you're going to wander
about from pillar to post without a proper place to live in? This
Voit woman, between ourselves, is no good, I know her. Why
don't you move out? You've been ill in bed long enough—time
you got up. Change your room, take up something, finish your
studies. There's a painter, a friend of mine, who's going to Turke-
stan for two years. He's got partitions up in his studio—it's more
like a small flat. I think he'd turn it over furnished to somebody
who'd look after it. How about my fixing it up? And there's another thing. I've been meaning to do it for a long time, it's a
sacred duty . . . since Lipa . . . Here's a small sum, a bonus

for her graduation. No, please . . . No, I beg you, don't be stubborn . . . no, really you'll have to . . ."

And in spite of her protests, her tears, and her struggles, he forced her, before he left, to accept a check for ten thousand rubles.

When she recovered, Lara moved to the lodgings Kologrivov had recommended, near the Smolensky Market. The flat was at the top of an old-fashioned two-story house. There were teamsters living in the other part of it, and there was a warehouse on the ground floor. The cobbled yard was always littered with spilled oats and hay. Pigeons strutted about cooing and fluttered up noisily to the level of Lara's window whenever a drove of rats scurried down the stone gutter.

Lara marries Pavel Antipov (Pasha)

3

Lara was greatly troubled about Pasha. So long as she was seriously ill he had not been allowed to see her, and what could he be expected to think? Lara had tried to kill a man who, as he saw it, was no more than an acquaintance of hers, and this same man, the object of her unsuccessful attempt at murder, had afterwards shielded her from its consequences. And all that after their memorable conversation at Christmas, by candlelight. If it had not been for this man, Lara would have been arrested and tried. He had warded off the punishment that hung over her. Thanks to him she was able to continue her studies, safe and unharmed. Pasha was puzzled and tormented.

When she was better Lara sent for him and said: "I am a bad woman. You don't know me, someday I'll tell you. I can't talk about it now, you can see for yourself, every time I try I start crying. But enough, forget me, I'm not worthy of you."

There followed heart-rending scenes, each more unbearable than the last. All this went on while Lara was still living in Arbat Street, and Voitkovskaia, meeting Pasha in the corridor with his tear-stained face, would rush off to her room and collapse on her sofa laughing herself sick. "Oh, I can't, I can't, it's too much!" she exclaimed. "Really! The hero! Ha, ha, ha!"

To deliver Pasha from a disgraceful attachment, to tear out his love for her by the roots and put an end to his torment, Lara told him that she had decided to give him up because she did not love him, but in making this renunciation she sobbed so much that it was impossible to believe her. Pasha suspected her of all the deadly sins, disbelieved every word she said, was ready to curse and hate her, but he loved her to distraction and was jealous of her very thoughts, and of the mug she drank from and of the pillow on which she lay. If they were not to go insane they must act quickly and firmly. They made up their minds to get married at once, before graduation. The idea was to have the wedding on the Monday after Low Sunday. At Lara's wish it was again put off.

They were married on Whit Monday; by then it was quite clear that they had passed their examinations. All the arrangements were made by Liudmila Kapitonovna Chepurko, the mother of Lara's fellow student Tusia. Liudmila was a handsome woman with a high bosom, a fine low-pitched singing voice, and a head full of innumerable superstitions, some of them picked up and others invented by herself.

The day Lara was to be "led to the altar" (as Liudmila purred in her gypsy voice while helping her to dress) it was terribly hot. The golden domes of churches and the freshly sanded paths in the town gardens were a glaring yellow. The green birch saplings cut on Whitsun Eve hung over the church railings, dusty, their leaves rolled up into little scrolls and as though scorched. There was hardly a breath of air, and the sunshine made spots before your eyes. It was as though a thousand weddings were to be held that day, for all the girls were in white dresses like brides and had curled their hair and all the young men were pomaded and wore tight-fitting black suits. Everyone was excited and everyone was hot.

As Lara stepped on the carpet leading to the altar, Lagodina, the mother of another friend, threw a handful of small silver coins at her feet to ensure the future prosperity of the couple; and with the same intention Liudmila told her that, when the wedding crown was held over her head, she must not make the sign of the cross with her bare fingers but cover them with the edge of her veil or a lace frill. She also told Lara to hold her candle high in order to have the upper hand in her house. Lara, sacrificing her future to Pasha's, held her candle as low as she could, but all in vain, because however low she held it Pasha held his lower still.

Straight from the church they drove to the wedding breakfast at the studio to which the couple moved. The guests shouted, "It's bitter!" and others responded unanimously from the end of the room, "Make it sweet!" and the bride and bridegroom smiled shyly and kissed. Liudmila sang "The Vineyard" in their honor, with the double refrain "God give you love and concord," and a song that began "Undo the braid, scatter the fair hair."

When all the guests had gone and they were left alone, Pasha felt uneasy in the sudden silence. A street lamp shone from across the road, and however tightly Lara drew the curtains, a streak of light, narrow as a board, reached into the room. This light gave Pasha no rest, he felt as if they were being watched. He discovered to his horror that he was thinking more of the street lamp than of Lara or of himself or of his love for her.

During this night, which lasted an eternity, Antipov ("Stepanida," or "the fair maiden," as he was called by his fellow students) reached the heights of joy and the lowest depths of despair. His suspicious guesses alternated with Lara's confessions. He questioned her, and with each of her answers his spirit sank as though he were hurtling down a void. His wounded imagination could not keep up with her revelations.

They talked till morning. In all Pasha's life there had not been a change in him so decisive and abrupt as in the course of this night. He got up a different man, almost astonished that he was still called Pasha Antipov.

Nine days later Pasha & Lara travel to the Urals to teach school. The tipsy farewell party.

4

Nine days later their friends arranged a farewell party for them, in that same room. Both Pasha and Lara had graduated with flying colors, and both had been offered jobs in the same town in the Urals. They were setting out for it next day.

Again they drank and sang and were boisterous, but this time there were only young people present.

Behind the partition that separated the living quarters from the studio, there stood a big wicker hamper and another, smaller one of Lara's, a suitcase, a box of crockery, and several sacks. There was a lot of luggage. Part of it was being sent next day by freight. Almost everything was packed, but there was still a little room left in the box and in the hampers. Every now and then Lara thought of something else she meant to take and put it into one of the hampers, rearranging things to make it tidy.

Pasha was at home entertaining guests by the time Lara got back from the university office where she had gone for her birth certificate and other papers. She came up followed by the janitor with a bundle of sacking and a thick rope for those pieces that were going by freight. After he left, Lara made the round of the guests, shaking hands with some and kissing others, and went behind the partition to change. When she came back, they greeted her with applause, sat down, and a noisy party began, like the one a few days earlier. The more enterprising poured vodka for their neighbors; hands armed with forks stretched toward the center of the table where bread, appetizers, and cooked dishes were set out. There were speeches, toasts, and constant joking. Some got drunk.

"I'm dead tired," said Lara, who was sitting next to her husband. "Did you manage to get everything done?"

"Yes."

"All the same, I'm feeling wonderful. I'm so happy. Are you?"

"I too. I feel fine. But there's a lot to talk about."

As an exception Komarovsky had been allowed to join the young people's party. At the end of the evening he started to say how bereaved he would feel when his two young friends left Moscow—the town would be like a desert, a Sahara; but he became so sentimental that he began to sob, and he had to start all over from the beginning.

He asked the Antipovs' permission to write to them and to visit them at Yuriatin, if he missed them too much.

"That's quite unnecessary," Lara said loudly and nonchalantly. "And in general it's all quite pointless—writing, Sahara, and all that. As for coming, don't think of it. With God's help you'll manage without us, we aren't as important as all that. Don't you think so, Pasha? I'm sure you'll find other young friends."

Then suddenly forgetting with whom she was talking and what she was saying she hurried off to the kitchen. There she took the meat grinder apart and packed the parts into the corners of the crockery case, padding them with tufts of straw. In doing this she scratched herself on the edge of the box and nearly ran a splinter into her hand.

She was suddenly reminded of her guests by a particularly loud outburst of laughter on the other side of the partition. It occurred to her that when people were drunk they always tried to impersonate drunkards, and the drunker they were the more they overacted.

At this moment she became aware of another peculiar sound, coming from the yard, through the open window. She pulled the curtains and leaned out.

A hobbled horse was moving across the yard with short, limping jumps. Lara did not know whose it was or how it had strayed into the yard. It was completely light though a long way to sunrise. The sleeping city seemed dead. It was bathed in the gray-blue coolness of the early hours. Lara closed her eyes. The characteristic sound of the hobbled horse's steps, so unlike anything else, transported her to some wonderful, remote village.

There was a ring at the door. Lara pricked up her ears. Someone got up from the table to open. It was Nadia! Lara ran to meet her. Nadia had come straight from the train, so fresh and enchanting that it seemed as if she brought with her the scent of the lilies of the valley of Duplyanka. The two friends stood speechless with emotion and, hugging each other, could only cry.

Nadia had brought Lara the congratulations and good wishes of the whole family and a present from her parents. She took a jewel case out of her travelling bag, snapped it open, and held out a very beautiful necklace.

There were gasps of delight and astonishment. A guest who had been drunk but had recovered a little said:

"It's pink hyacinth. Yes, yes, pink, believe it or not. That's what it is. It's just as valuable as diamonds."

But Nadia said that the stones were yellow sapphires.

Lara put Nadia next to her at table and made her eat and drink. The necklace lay beside her plate, and she could not stop looking at it. The stones had rolled into a hollow on the mauve-cushioned lining of the case and looked now like dew and now like a cluster of small grapes.

Meanwhile those of the guests who had sobered up were again drinking to keep company with Nadia, whom they soon made tipsy.

Soon everyone in the flat was fast asleep. Most of them, planning to go to the station with Lara and Pasha in the morning, stayed the night. A good many had been snoring before Nadia came, and Lara herself never knew afterwards how she came to be lying fully dressed on the sofa next to Ira Lagodina.

She was wakened by the sound of loud voices near by. They were the voices of strangers who had come into the yard to recover their horse. As she opened her eyes she said to herself: "What on earth can Pasha be doing pottering about in the middle of the room?" But when the man she had taken for Pasha turned his head she saw a pockmarked scarecrow whose face was cut by a deep scar from brow to chin. She realized it was a burglar and tried to shout but could not utter a sound. She remembered her necklace and raising herself cautiously on her elbow looked where she had left it on the table.

The necklace was still there among the bread crumbs and unfinished pieces of caramel; the thief hadn't noticed it among the litter. He was only rummaging in the suitcase she had packed so carefully and making a mess of her work. That was all she could think of at the moment, half asleep and still tipsy as she was. Indignant, she tried to shout and again found she couldn't. Then she dug her knee into Ira's stomach, and when Ira yelped with pain she too began to scream. The thief dropped everything and ran. Some of the men jumped up and tried to chase him without quite knowing what it was all about, but by the time they got outside the door he had vanished.

The commotion woke everyone up, and Lara, whose tipsiness had suddenly gone, did not allow them to go back to sleep. She made them coffee and packed them off home until it was time to go to the station.

Then she set to work feverishly stuffing the bed linen into the hampers, strapping up the luggage and tying it with ropes, and begging Pasha and the janitor's wife just not to bother her by trying to help.

Everything got done in time. The Antipovs did not miss their train. It started smoothly, as though wafted away by the hats their friends were waving after them. When they stopped waving and bellowed something three times—probably "Hurrah!"—the train put on speed.

Dr Z works as a gynecologist in a Moscow hospital as wounded soldiers pour in. His wife, Tonia, gives birth to a son.

5

For the third day the weather was wretched. It was the second autumn of the war. The successes of the first year had been followed by reverses. Brusilov's Eighth Army, which had been concentrated in the Carpathians ready to pour down the slopes into Hungary, was instead drawing back, caught by the ebb of the general retreat. The Russians were evacuating Galicia, which they had occupied in the first months of the fighting.

Dr. Zhivago, until recently known as Yura but now addressed more and more often as Yurii Andreievich, stood in the corridor of the gynecological section of the hospital, outside the door of the maternity ward to which he had just brought his wife Tonia—Antonina Alexandrovna. He had said goodbye to her and was waiting for the midwife, to tell her where she could reach him in case of need and to ask her how he could get in touch with her.

He was in a hurry: he had to visit two patients and get back to his hospital as soon as possible, and there he was, wasting precious time, staring out of the window at the slanting streaks of rain buffeted by the autumn wind like a cornfield in a storm.

It was not yet very dark. He could see the back yards of the hospital, the glassed-in verandas of the private houses in Devichie Pole, and the branch trolley line leading to one of the hospital blocks.

The rain poured with a dreary steadiness, neither hurrying nor slowing down for all the fury of the wind, which seemed enraged by the indifference of the water. Gusts of wind shook the creeper on one of the houses as if intending to tear it up by the roots, swung it up into the air, and dropped it in disgust like a discarded rag.

A truck with two trailers drove past the veranda to the hospital entrance. Wounded men were carried in.

The Moscow hospitals were desperately overcrowded, especially since the battle of Lutsk. The wounded were put in the passages and on landings. The general overcrowding was beginning to affect the women's wards.

Yurii Andreievich turned away from the window yawning with fatigue. He had nothing to think about. Suddenly he remembered an incident at the Hospital of the Holy Cross, where he worked. A woman had died a few days earlier in the surgical ward. Yurii Andreievich had diagnosed echinococcus of the liver, but everyone thought he was wrong. An autopsy was to be made today, but their prosector was a habitual drunkard and you never could tell how careful he would be.

Night fell suddenly. Nothing more was visible outside. As at the waving of a magic wand, lights sprang up in all the windows.

The head gynecologist came out of Tonia's ward through the narrow lobby separating it from the corridor. He was of mammoth size, and always responded to questions by shrugging his shoulders and staring at the ceiling. These silent gestures were meant to suggest that, whatever the advances of science, there were more things in heaven and earth, friend Horatio, than science ever dreamt on.

He passed Yurii Andreievich with a nod and a smile, flipped his podgy hands a few times to intimate that there was nothing for it but patience, and went off down the corridor to have a smoke in the waiting room.

After him came his assistant, who was as garrulous as her superior was taciturn.

"If I were you I'd go home," she told Yurii Andreievich. "I'll call you up tomorrow at the Holy Cross. It's most unlikely that anything will happen between now and then. There's every reason to expect a natural birth; there shouldn't be any need for surgical intervention. But of course the pelvis is narrow, the child's head is in the occipito-posterior position, there are no pains, and the contractions are slight. All this gives grounds for anxiety. However, it's too soon to say. It all depends on how the pains develop once labor begins. Then we'll know."

When he telephoned the following day, the hospital porter who took the call told him to wait while he made inquiries; after keeping him in misery for a good ten minutes he came back with the following inadequate and crudely worded information: "They say, tell him he's brought his wife too soon, he's to take her back."

Infuriated, Yurii Andreievich told him to get the nurse on the telephone. "The symptoms may be misleading," the nurse said. "We'll know more in a day or two."

On the third day he was told that labor had begun the night before, the water had broken at dawn, and there had been strong pains with short intervals since the early morning.

He rushed headlong to the hospital. As he walked down the passage to the door, which by mistake had been left half open, he heard Tonia's heart-rending screams; she screamed like the victims of an accident dragged with crushed limbs from under the wheels of a train.

He was not allowed to see her. Biting his knuckle until he drew blood, he went over to the window; the same slanting rain was pouring down as on the two preceding days.

A nurse came out of the ward, and he heard the squealing of a newborn child. "She's safe, she's safe," Yurii Andreievich muttered joyfully to himself.

"It's a son. A little boy. Congratulations on a safe delivery," said the nurse in a singsong. "You can't go in yet. When they're ready we'll show you. Then you'll have to give her a nice present. She's had a bad time. It's the first one. There's always trouble with the first."

"She's safe, she's safe." Yurii Andreievich was happy. He did not understand what the nurse was telling him, and why she was including him in her congratulations as if he had played a part in what had happened. For what had he actually had to do with it? Father—son; he did not see why he should be proud of this unearned fatherhood, he felt that this son was a gift

out of the blue. He was scarcely aware of all this. The main
thing was that Tonia—Tonia, who had been in mortal danger—
was now happily safe.

He had a patient living near the hospital. He went to see him
and was back in half an hour. Both the door of the lobby and that
of the ward were again ajar. Without knowing what he was doing, Yurii Andreievich slipped into the lobby.

The huge gynecologist, in his white coat, rose as though from
under the ground in front of him, barring the way.

"Where do you think you're going?" he whispered breath-
lessly so that the new mother should not hear. "Are you out of
your mind? After she lost all that blood, risk of sepsis, not to
speak of psychological shock! And you call yourself a doctor!"

"I didn't mean to . . . Do let me have just a glance. Just from
here, through the crack."

"Oh, well, that's different. All right, if you must. But don't
let me catch you . . . If she sees you, I'll wring your neck."

Inside the ward two women in white uniforms stood with
their backs to the door; they were the midwife and the nurse.
Squirming on the palm of the nurse's hand lay a tender, squealing, tiny human creature, stretching and contracting like a dark
red piece of rubber. The midwife was putting a ligature on the
navel before cutting the cord. Tonia lay on a surgical bed of ad-
justable height in the middle of the room. She lay fairly high.
Yurii Andreievich, exaggerating everything in his excitement,
thought that she was lying, say, at the level of one of those
desks at which you write standing up.

Raised higher, closer to the ceiling than ordinary mortals usually
are, Tonia lay exhausted in the cloud of her spent pain. To Yurii
Andreievich she seemed like a barque lying at rest in the middle
of a harbor after putting in and being unloaded, a barque that
plied between an unknown country and the continent of life
across the waters of death with a cargo of immigrant new souls.
One such soul had just been landed, and the ship now lay at
anchor, relaxed, its flanks unburdened and empty. The whole of
her was resting, her strained masts and hull, and her memory
washed clean of the image of the other shore, the crossing and
the landing.

And as no one had explored the country where she was registered, no one knew the language in which to speak to her.

At Yurii Andreievich's hospital everyone congratulated him. He was astonished to see how fast the news had travelled.

He went into the staff room, known as the Rubbish Dump. With so little space in the overcrowded hospital, it was used as a cloakroom; people came in from outside wearing their snow boots, they forgot their parcels and littered the floor with papers and cigarette ends.

Standing by the window, the flabby, elderly prosector was holding up a jar with some opaque liquid against the light and examining it over the top of his glasses.

"Congratulations," he said, without looking around.

"Thank you. How kind of you."

"Don't thank me. I've had nothing to do with it. Pichuzhkin did the autopsy. But everyone is impressed—echinococcus it was. That's a real diagnostician, they're all saying. That's all everyone is talking about."

Just then the medical director came in, greeted them both, and said: "What the devil is happening to this place? What a filthy mess it is! By the way, Zhivago, it was echinococcus after all! We were wrong. Congratulations. There's another thing. It's a nuisance. They've been reviewing the lists of exemptions again. I can't stop them this time. There's a terrible shortage of medical personnel. You'll be smelling gunpowder before long."

Lara is happy to be back in Yuriatin her native town. Pasha takes advantage of their isolated town & his degree in Classics to read widely. He wants to take a degree in mathematics. Pasha decides he & Lara do not really love one another. How to resolve the dilemma?

The Antipovs had done much better in Yuriatin than they had hoped to. The Guishars were remembered well. This had helped Lara over the difficulties of setting up house in a new place.

Lara had her hands full and plenty to think about. She took care of the house and of their three-year-old daughter, Katenka. Marfutka, their red-haired maid, did her best but could not get all the work done. Larisa Feodorovna shared all her husband's interests. She herself taught at the girls' gymnasium. She worked without respite and was happy. This was exactly the kind of life she had dreamed of.

She liked Yuriatin. It was her native town. It stood on the big river Rynva, navigable except in its upper reaches, and one of the Ural railways passed through it.

The approach of winter in Yuriatin was always heralded by the owners of boats, when they took them from the river and transported them on carts to the town, to be stored in back yards. There they lay in the open air waiting for the spring. The boats with their light upturned bottoms in the yards meant in Yuriatin what the migration of storks or the first snow meant in other places. Such a boat lay in the yard of the house rented by the Antipovs. Katenka played in the shelter of its white hull as in a summerhouse.

Larisa Feodorovna liked Yuriatin's provincial ways, the long vowels of its northern accent, and the naïve trustfulness of its intelligentsia, who wore felt boots and gray flannel sleeveless coats. She was drawn to the land and to the common people.

Paradoxically, it was her husband, Pavel Pavlovich, the son of a Moscow railway worker, who turned out to be an incorrigible urbanite. He judged the people of Yuriatin much more harshly than she. Their crudeness and ignorance irritated him.

He had an extraordinary capacity, it now appeared, for reading quickly and storing up the knowledge he picked up. He had read a great deal in the past, partly thanks to Lara. During the years of his provincial seclusion, he became so well read that even Lara no longer seemed to him well-informed. He towered high above his fellow teachers and complained that he felt stifled among them. Now in wartime, their standard, commonplace, and somewhat stale patriotism was out of tune with his own, more complicated feelings about his country.

Pavel Pavlovich had graduated in classics. He taught Latin and ancient history. But from his earlier *Realgymnasium* days he had kept a half-forgotten passion for the exact sciences, physics and mathematics, and it had now suddenly revived in him. Teaching himself at home, he had reached university standard in these subjects, and dreamed of taking his degree, specializing in some branch of mathematics, and moving with his family to Petersburg. Studying late into the night had affected his health. He began to suffer from insomnia.

His relations with his wife were good but lacked simplicity. Her kindness and her fussing over him oppressed him, but he would not criticize her for fear that she might take some quite innocent word of his for a reproach—a hint, perhaps, that her blood was bluer than his, or that she had once belonged to someone else. His anxiety lest she suspect him of having some absurdly unfair idea about her introduced an element of artificiality into their life. Each tried to behave more nobly than the other, and this complicated everything.

One night they had guests—the headmistress of Lara's school, several fellow teachers of her husband's, the member of an arbitration court on which Pavel Pavlovich too had recently served, and a few others. They were all, from Pavel Pavlovich's point of view, complete fools. He was amazed at Lara's amiability toward them, and he could not believe that she sincerely liked any of them.

After the visitors had gone, Lara took a long time airing and tidying the rooms and washing dishes in the kitchen with Marfutka. Then she made sure that Katenka was properly tucked up and Pasha asleep, quickly undressed, turned off the light, and lay down next to him as naturally as a child getting into bed with its mother.

But Antipov was only pretending that he was asleep. As so often recently, he had insomnia. He knew that he would lie awake for three or four hours. To walk himself to sleep, and to escape from the still smoky air of the room, he got up quietly, put on his fur coat and cap over his night clothes, and went outside.

It was a clear, frosty autumn night. Thin sheets of ice crumbled under his steps. The sky, shining with stars, threw a pale blue flicker like the flame of burning alcohol over the black earth with its clumps of frozen mud.

The Antipovs lived at the other end of town from the river harbor. The house was the last in the street, and beyond it lay a field cut by a railway with a grade crossing and a guard's shelter.

Antipov sat down on the overturned boat and looked at the stars. The thoughts to which he had become accustomed in the past few years assailed him with alarming strength. It seemed to him that sooner or later they would have to be thought out to the end, and that it might as well be done now.

This can't go on, he thought. He could have foreseen it long ago, before they were married. He had caught on late. Even as a child he had been fascinated by her, and she could make him do whatever she liked. Why hadn't he had the sense to renounce her in time, that winter before their marriage, when she herself had insisted on it? Wasn't it clear that it was not he whom she loved, but the noble task she had set herself in relation to him, and that for her he was the embodiment of her own heroism? But what had her mission, however meritorious or inspired, to do with real family life? The worst of it was that he loved her as much as ever. She was stunningly beautiful. And yet—was he sure that it was love even on his side? Or was it a bewildered gratitude for her beauty and magnanimity? Who could possibly sort it all out! The devil himself would be stumped.

So what was he to do? He must set his wife and daughter free from this counterfeit life. This was even more important than to liberate himself. Yes, but how? Divorce? Drown himself? What disgusting rubbish! He rebelled against the very thought. "As if I'd ever do anything of the sort! So why rehearse this melodrama even in my mind?"

He looked up at the stars as if asking them for advice. They flickered on, small or large, quick or slow, some blue and some in all the hues of the rainbow. Suddenly they were blotted out, and the house, the yard, and Antipov sitting on his boat were thrown into relief by a harsh, darting light, as though someone were running from the field toward the gate waving a torch. An army train, puffing clouds of yellow, flame-shot smoke into the sky, rolled over the grade crossing going westward, as countless others had rolled by, night and day, for the past year.

Pavel Pavlovich smiled, got up, and went to bed. He had found a way out of his dilemma.

Pasha volunteers for the army, & is sent to officer-candidate school. He soon realizes the army is a mistake, & misses his wife & daughter. He is shipped to the front. His letters stop coming. Lara trains as a nurse, & gets a job in a hospital train.

7

When Larisa Feodorovna learned of Pasha's decision, she was stunned and at first would not believe her ears. "It's absurd," she thought, "a whim. I won't take any notice, and he'll forget it."

But it appeared that he had been getting ready for the past two weeks. He had sent in his papers to the recruiting office, the gymnasium had found a substitute teacher, and he had been notified that he was admitted to the military school at Omsk.

Lara wailed like a peasant woman and, grabbing Pasha's hands, threw herself at his feet. "Pasha, Pashenka," she screamed, "don't leave us. Don't do it, don't. It isn't too late, I'll see to everything. You haven't even had a proper medical examination, and with your heart . . . You're ashamed to change your mind? And aren't you ashamed to sacrifice your family to some crazy notion? You, a volunteer! All your life you've laughed at Rodia, and now you're jealous of him. You have to swagger about in an officer's uniform too, you have to do your own bit of saber-rattling. Pasha, what's come over you? I don't recognize you. What's changed you like this? Tell me honestly, for the love of Christ, without any fine phrases, is this really what Russia needs?"

Suddenly she realized that it wasn't that at all. Though she could not understand all of it, she grasped the main thing. Pasha misunderstood her attitude to him. He rebelled against the motherly feeling that all her life had been a part of her affection for him and could not see that such a love was something more, not less, than the ordinary feeling of a woman for a man.

She bit her lip and, shrinking as if she had been beaten, and swallowing her tears, set about silently packing his things.

After he had left, it seemed to her that the whole town was silent, and even that there were fewer crows flying about in the sky. "Madam, madam," Marfutka would say reproachfully, trying to call her back to herself. "Mama, Mama," Katenka babbled, pulling at her sleeve. This was the greatest defeat of her life. Her best, brightest hopes had collapsed.

Her husband's letters from Siberia told her all about his moods. He had seen his mistake. He badly missed his wife and daughter. After a few months he was commissioned lieutenant before term and then, just as unexpectedly, was sent to the front. His journey took him nowhere near Yuriatin, and he was not in Moscow long enough to see anyone there.

His letters from the front were less depressed than those from the Omsk school had been. He wanted to distinguish himself so that, as a reward for some military exploit or as a result of some light wound, he could go home on leave and see his family. Soon his opportunity was within sight. Brusilov's forces had broken through and were attacking. Antipov's letters stopped coming. At first Lara was not worried. She put down his silence to the military operations: he could not write when his regiment was on the move. But in the autumn the advance slowed down, the troops were digging themselves in, and there was still no word from him. His wife began to be worried, and to make inquiries, at first locally, in Yuriatin, then by mail in Moscow and at his old field address. There was no reply; nobody seemed to know anything.

Like other local ladies, Larisa Feodorovna had been giving a hand at the military ward attached to the town hospital. Now she trained seriously and qualified as a nurse, got leave of absence from her school for six months, and, putting the house in Marfutka's care, took Katenka to Moscow. She left her with Lipa, whose husband, Friesendank, was a German subject and had been interned with other enemy civilians at Ufa.

Convinced of the futility of trying to get any news by mail, she had decided to go and look for Pasha. With this in mind, she got a job as a nurse on a hospital train going to Mezo-Laborch, on the Hungarian border, the last address Pasha had given her.

8

A Red Cross train, equipped through voluntary contributions collected by the Tatiana Committee for Aid to the Wounded, arrived at divisional headquarters. It was a long train mostly made up of shabby, short freight cars; the only first-class coach carried prominent people from Moscow with presents for the troops. Among them was Gordon. He knew that his childhood friend Zhivago was attached to the divisional hospital; hearing that it was in a near-by village, he obtained the necessary permit to travel in the area just behind the lines, and got a lift in a carriage going to the village.

The driver was a Byelorussian or a Lithuanian who spoke broken Russian. The current spy scare reduced his conversation to a stale official patter. Discouraged by his ostentatious loyalty, Gordon travelled most of the way in silence.

At headquarters, where they were used to moving armies and measured distances in hundred-mile stages, he had been told that the village was quite near—within fifteen miles at most; in reality, it was more like fifty.

All along the way, an unfriendly grunting and grumbling came from the horizon on their left. Gordon had never been in an earthquake, but he decided (quite rightly) that the sullen, scarcely distinguishable, distant sound of enemy artillery could best be compared to volcanic tremors and rumblings. Toward evening, a pink glow flared up over the skyline on that side and went on flickering until dawn.

They passed ruined villages. Some were abandoned; in others people were living in cellars deep underground. Piles of refuse and rubble were aligned as the houses had been. These gutted settlements could be encompassed in a glance, like barren desert. Old women scratched about in the ashes, each on the ruins of her own home, now and then digging something up and putting it away, apparently feeling as sheltered from the eyes of strangers as if their walls were still around them. They looked up at Gordon and gazed after him as he drove past, seeming to ask him how soon the world would come to its senses and peace and order be restored to their lives.

After dark the carriage ran into a patrol and was ordered off the main road. The driver did not know the new by-pass. They drove about in circles for a couple of hours without getting anywhere. At dawn they came to a village that had the name they were looking for, but nobody knew anything about a hospital. It turned out that there were two villages of the same name. At last, in the morning, they found the right one. As they drove down the village road, which smelled of camomile and iodoform, Gordon decided not to stay the night but to spend the day with Zhivago and go back that evening to the railway station where he had left his other friends. But circumstances kept him there for more than a week.

9

During those days the front line began to move. To the south of the village where Gordon found himself, Russian forces succeeded in breaking through the enemy positions. Supporting units followed, widening the gap, but they fell behind and the advance units were cut off and captured. Among the prisoners was Lieutenant Antipov, who was obliged to give himself up when his platoon surrendered.

There were false rumors about him. He was believed to have been killed by a shell and buried by the explosion. This was told on the authority of his friend, Lieutenant Galiullin, who had been watching through field glasses from an observation post when Antipov led the attack.

What Galiullin had seen was the usual picture of an attacking unit. The men advanced quickly, almost at a run, across the no man's land, an autumn field with dry broom swaying in the wind and motionless, spiky gorse. Their object was either to flush the Austrians out of their trenches and engage them with bayonets or to destroy them with hand grenades. To the running men the field was endless. The ground seemed to slip under their feet like a bog. Their lieutenant was running, first in front of them, then beside them, waving his revolver above his head, his mouth split from ear to ear with hurrahs which neither he nor they could hear. At intervals they threw themselves onto the ground, got up all together, and ran on shouting. Each time one or two who had been hit fell with the rest but in a different way, toppling like trees chopped down in a wood, and did not get up again.

"They're shooting long! Get the battery," Galiullin said anxiously to the artillery officer who stood next to him. "No, wait. It's all right."

The attackers were on the point of engaging the enemy. The artillery barrage stopped. In the sudden silence the observers heard their own hearts pounding as if they were in Antipov's place, had brought their men to the edge of the enemy trench, and were expected within the next few minutes to perform wonders of resourcefulness and courage. At that moment two German sixteen-inch shells burst in front of the attackers. Black clouds of dust and smoke hid what followed. "Ya Allah! Finished. They're done for," whispered Galiullin, white-lipped, believing that the lieutenant and his men had been killed. Another shell came down close to the observation post. Bent double, the observers hurried to a safer distance.

Galiullin had shared Antipov's dugout. After Antipov's comrades resigned themselves to the idea that he was dead, Galiullin, who had known him well, was asked to take charge of his belongings and keep them for his widow, a large number of whose photographs had been found among his things.

An enlisted man recently promoted to lieutenant, the mechanic Galiullin, son of Gimazetdin, the janitor of Tiverzin's tenement, was that very Yusupka whom, as an apprentice in the distant past, the foreman Khudoleiev had beaten up. It was to his old tormentor that he was now indebted for his promotion.

On getting his commission, he had found himself, against his will and for no reason that he knew of, in a soft job in a small-town garrison behind the lines. There he commanded a troop of semi-invalids whom instructors as decrepit as themselves took every morning through the drill they had forgotten. Galiullin supervised the changing of the guard in front of the commissary. Nothing else was expected of him. He did not have a care in the world when, among the replacements consisting of older reservists sent from Moscow and put under his orders, there turned up the all too familiar figure of Piotr Khudoleiev.

"Well, well, an old friend," said Galiullin, grinning sourly.

"Yes, sir," said Khudoleiev, standing at attention and saluting.

It was impossible that this should be the end of it. The very first time the lieutenant caught the private in a fault at drill he bawled him out, and when it seemed to him that his subordinate was not looking him straight in the eye but somehow sideways, he hit him in the jaw and put him on bread and water in the guardhouse for two days.

From now on every move of Galiullin's smacked of revenge. But this game, in their respective positions and with rules enforced by the stick, struck Galiullin as unsporting and mean. What was to be done? Both of them could not be in the same place. But what pretext could an officer find for transferring a private from his unit, and where, if it were not for disciplinary reasons, could he transfer him? On the other hand, what grounds could Galiullin think of to apply for his own transfer? Giving the boredom and uselessness of garrison duty as his reasons, he asked to be sent to the front. This earned him a good mark, and when, at the first engagement, he showed his other qualities it turned out that he had the makings of an excellent officer and he was quickly promoted to first lieutenant.

Galiullin had met Antipov in 1905, when Pasha Antipov spent six months with the Tiverzins and Yusupka went to play with him on Sundays. There too he had once or twice met Lara. He had heard nothing of either of them since. When Antipov came from Yuriatin and joined the regiment, Galiullin was struck by the change in his old friend. The shy, mischievous, and girlish child had turned into an arrogant, know-it-all misanthrope. He was intelligent, very brave, taciturn, and sarcastic. Sometimes, looking at him, Galiullin could have sworn that he saw in his gloomy eyes, as inside a window, something beyond, an idea that had taken firm hold of him: a longing for his daughter or for the face of his wife. Antipov seemed like one bewitched, as in a fairy tale. And now Antipov was gone, and Galiullin was left with his papers, his photographs, and the unsolved secret of his transformation on his hands.

As was bound to happen sooner or later, Lara's inquiries for her husband reached Galiullin. He meant to write to her, but he was busy, he had no time to write properly, yet he wished to prepare her for the blow. He kept postponing a long, detailed letter to her until he heard that she was somewhere at the front as a nurse. And he did not know where to address his letter to her now.

10

"Will there be horses today?" Gordon asked every time Dr. Zhivago came home to his midday meal. They were living in a Galician peasant house.

"Not a chance. Anyway, where would you go? You can't go anywhere. There's a terrible muddle. Nobody knows what's what. To the south we have outflanked or broken through the German lines in several places, and I am told some of our overextended units were encircled. To the north, the Germans have crossed the Sventa, at a point that was supposed to be impassable. That is their cavalry, about a corps in strength. They are blowing up railways, destroying supply stores, and in my opinion trying to surround us. That's the picture, and you talk about horses. Come on, Karpenko," he said, turning to his orderly, "set the table, and make it quick. What are we having for dinner? Calves' feet? Good!"

The Medical Unit, with its hospital and its dependencies, was scattered all over the village, which by a miracle was still unharmed. The houses glittered with Western-style lattice windows stretching from wall to wall, and not so much as a pane was damaged.

The end of a hot, golden autumn had turned into an Indian summer. In the daytime the doctors and officers opened windows, swatted at the black swarms of flies along the sills and the low white ceilings, unbuttoned their tunics and hospital coats, and, dripping with sweat, sipped scalding-hot soup or tea. At night they squatted in front of the open stove, blew on the damp logs which kept going out, their eyes smarting with smoke, and cursed the orderlies for not knowing how to build a fire.

It was a still night. Gordon and Zhivago lay on two bunks facing each other. Between them were the dinner table and the low window running the whole length of the wall. The room was overheated and filled with tobacco smoke. They had opened the two end lattices to get a breath of the fresh autumn night air, which made the panes sweat. They were talking, as they had done all these nights and days, and as usual the horizon in the direction of the front was flickering with a pink glow. When the even, incessant chatter of gunfire was occasionally interrupted by a deep bang that shook the ground as though a heavy steel-bound trunk were being dragged across the floor, scraping the paint, Zhivago interrupted the conversation as if out of respect for the sound, paused for a while, and said, "That's a Bertha, a German sixteen-inch. A little fellow that weighs twenty-four hundred pounds." And then, resuming the conversation, he would forget what they had been talking about.

"What's that smell that hangs over the whole village?" asked

Gordon. "I noticed it as soon as I arrived. It's a nauseatingly sweet, cloying smell, rather like mice."

"I know what you mean. That's hemp—they grow a lot of it here. The plant itself has that nagging, clinging, carrion smell. And then in the battle zone, the dead often remain undiscovered in the hemp fields for a long time and begin to decay. Of course the smell of corpses is everywhere. That's only natural. Hear that? It's the Bertha again."

In the past few days they had talked of everything in the world. Gordon had learned his friend's ideas about the war and its effect on people's thinking. Zhivago had told him how hard he found it to accept the ruthless logic of mutual extermination, to get used to the sight of the wounded, especially to the horror of certain wounds of a new sort, to the mutilation of survivors whom the technique of modern fighting had turned into lumps of disfigured flesh.

Going about with him day after day, Gordon too had seen terrible sights. Needless to say, he was aware of the immorality of being an idle spectator of other men's courage, of how they mastered, by an inhuman effort, their fear of death, of the sacrifices they made and the risks they ran. But he did not think that merely crying over them was any less immoral. He believed in behaving simply and honestly according to the circumstances in which life placed him.

That it was possible to faint at the sight of wounds he learned from his own experience when they visited a first-aid station run by a mobile Red Cross unit just behind the front line.

They drove to a clearing in a wood that had been badly damaged by artillery fire. Twisted gun carriages lay upside down in the broken and trampled undergrowth. A riding horse was tethered to a tree. A little farther in the wood was the frame structure of the forester's house; half its roof had been blown away. The first-aid station was in the house and in two big gray tents across the way.

"I shouldn't have brought you," said Zhivago. "The trenches are within half a mile and our batteries are just over there, behind the wood. You can hear what's going on. So don't play the hero, I wouldn't believe you if you did. You're bound to be scared stiff, it's only natural. Any moment the situation may change, and shells will be dropping here."

Tired young soldiers in enormous boots and dusty tunics which were black with sweat on the chest and shoulder-blades sprawled on their backs or on their stomachs by the side of the road. They were the survivors of a decimated unit that had been taken out of the front line after four days of heavy fighting and was being sent to the rear for a short rest. They lay as if they were of stone, without the strength to smile or to swear, and no one turned his head when several carts came rumbling swiftly down the road. They were ammunition carts, without springs, loaded with wounded men whom they jolted, cracking their bones and twisting their guts, as they jogged along at a trot to the first-aid station. There the wounded would be hastily bandaged and the most urgent cases operated on. They had been picked up in appalling numbers on the battlefield in front of the trenches half an hour ago during a short lull in the artillery fire. A good half of them were unconscious.

When the carts stopped in front of the porch, orderlies came down the steps with stretchers and unloaded them. A nurse raised the flap on one of the tents and stood looking out; she was off duty. Two men who had been arguing loudly in the wood behind the tents, their voices echoing among the tall young trees, but their words indistinguishable, came out and walked along the road toward the house. One of them, an excited young lieutenant, was shouting at the Medical Officer of the mobile unit: there had been an artillery park in the clearing and he wanted to know where it had been moved. The doctor did not know, it was not his business; he asked the lieutenant to leave him alone and to stop shouting—there were wounded men here and he was busy. But the little lieutenant went on cursing the Red Cross, the artillery command, and everybody else. Zhivago walked up to the doctor; they greeted each other and went into the house. The lieutenant, still swearing loudly with a slight Tartar accent, untied his horse, vaulted into the saddle, and galloped down the road into the woods. The nurse was still looking on.

Suddenly her face was distorted with horror. "What are you

doing? You're out of your minds!" she shouted at two lightly
wounded soldiers who were walking without assistance between
the stretchers. She ran out toward them.

On one stretcher lay a man who had been mutilated in a
particularly monstrous way. A large splinter from the shell
that had mangled his face, turning his tongue and lips into a
red gruel without killing him, had lodged in the bone structure
of his jaw, where the cheek had been torn out. He uttered short
groans in a thin inhuman voice; no one could take these sounds
for anything but an appeal to finish him off quickly, to put an
end to his inconceivable torment.

The nurse had got the impression that the two lightly wounded
men who were walking beside the stretcher had been so moved
by his cries that they were about to pull out the terrible piece
of iron with their bare hands.

"What's the matter with you? You can't do that. The surgeon
will do it, he has special instruments . . . if it has to be done."
(O God, O God, take him away, don't let me doubt that You
exist.)

Next moment, as he was carried up the steps, the man
screamed, and with one great shudder he gave up the ghost.

The man who had just died was Private Gimazetdin; the excited officer who had been shouting in the wood was his son,
Lieutenant Galiullin; the nurse was Lara. Gordon and Zhivago
were the witnesses. All these people were there together, in one
place. But some of them had never known each other, while
others failed to recognize each other now. And there were things
about them which were never to be known for certain, while
others were not to be revealed until a future time, a later meeting.

11

In this area the villages had been miraculously preserved. They
constituted an inexplicably intact island in the midst of a sea
of ruins. One day at sunset Gordon and Zhivago were driving
home. In one village they saw a young Cossack surrounded by
a crowd laughing boisterously, as the Cossack tossed a copper

coin into the air, forcing an old Jew with a gray beard and a long caftan to catch it. The old man missed every time. The coin flew past his pitifully spread-out hands and dropped into the mud. When the old man bent to pick it up, the Cossack slapped his bottom, and the onlookers held their sides, groaning with laughter: this was the point of the entertainment. For the moment it was harmless enough, but no one could say for certain that it would not take a more serious turn. Every now and then, the old man's wife ran out of the house across the road, screaming and stretching out her arms to him, and ran back again in terror. Two little girls were watching their grandfather out of the window and crying.

The driver, who found all this extremely comical, slowed down so that the passengers could enjoy the spectacle. But Zhivago called the Cossack, bawled him out, and ordered him to stop baiting the old man.

"Yes, sir," he said readily. "We meant no harm, we were only doing it for fun."

Gordon and Zhivago drove on in silence.

"It's terrible," said Yurii Andreievich when they were in sight of their own village. "You can't imagine what the wretched Jewish population is going through in this war. The fighting happens to be in their Pale. And as if punitive taxation, the destruction of their property, and all their other sufferings were not enough, they are subjected to pogroms, insults, and accusations that they lack patriotism. And why should they be patriotic? Under enemy rule, they enjoy equal rights, and we do nothing but persecute them. This hatred for them, the basis of it, is irrational. It is stimulated by the very things that should arouse sympathy —their poverty, their overcrowding, their weakness, and this inability to fight back. I can't understand it. It's like an inescapable fate."

Gordon did not reply.

12

Once again they were lying on their bunks on either side of the long low window, it was night, and they were talking.

Zhivago was telling Gordon how he had once seen the Tsar at the front. He told his story well.

It was his first spring at the front. The headquarters of his regiment was in the Carpathians, in a deep valley, access to which from the Hungarian plain was blocked by this army unit.

At the bottom of the valley was a railway station. Zhivago described the landscape, the mountains overgrown with mighty firs and pines, with tufts of clouds catching in their tops, and sheer cliffs of gray slate and graphite showing through the forest like worn patches in a thick fur. It was a damp, dark April morning, as gray as the slate, locked in by the mountains on all sides and therefore still and sultry. Mist hung over the valley, and everything in it steamed, everything rose slowly—engine smoke from the railway station, gray vapors from the fields, the gray mountains, the dark woods, the dark clouds.

At that time the sovereign was making a tour of inspection in Galicia. It was learned suddenly that he would visit Zhivago's unit, of which he was the honorary Colonel. He might arrive at any moment. A guard of honor was drawn up on the station platform. They waited for about two oppressive hours, then two trains with the imperial retinue went by quickly one after the other. A little later the Tsar's train drew in.

Accompanied by the Grand Duke Nicholas, the Tsar inspected the grenadiers. Every syllable of his quietly spoken greeting produced an explosion of thunderous hurrahs whose echoes were sent back and forth like water from swinging buckets.

The Tsar, smiling and ill at ease, looked older and more tired than on the rubles and medals. His face was listless, a little flabby. He kept glancing apologetically at the Grand Duke, not knowing what was expected of him, and the Grand Duke, bending down respectfully, helped him in his embarrassment not so much by words as by moving an eyebrow or a shoulder.

On that warm gray morning in the mountains, Zhivago felt sorry for the Tsar, was disturbed at the thought that such diffident reserve and shyness could be the essential characteristics of an oppressor, that a man so weak could imprison, hang, or pardon.

"He should have made a speech—'I, my sword, and my people'—like the Kaiser. Something about 'the people'—that was essential. But you know he was natural, in the Russian way, tragically above these banalities. After all, that kind of theatricalism is unthinkable in Russia. For such gestures are theatrical, aren't they? I suppose that there were such things as 'peoples' under the Caesars—Gauls or Scythians or Illyrians and so on. But ever since, they have been mere fiction, which served only as subjects for speeches by kings and politicians: 'The people, my people.'

"Now the front is flooded with correspondents and journalists. They record their 'observations' and gems of popular wisdom, they visit the wounded and construct new theories about the people's soul. It's a new version of Dahl [1] and just as bogus—linguistic graphomania, verbal incontinence. That's one type—and then there's the other: clipped speech, 'sketches and short scenes,' skepticism and misanthropy. I read a piece like that the other day: 'A gray day, like yesterday. Rain since morning, slush. I look out of the window and see the road. Prisoners in an endless line. Wounded. A gun is firing. It fires today as yesterday, tomorrow as today and every day and every hour.' Isn't that subtle and witty! But what has he got against the gun? How odd to expect variety from a gun! Why doesn't he look at himself, shooting off the same sentences, commas, lists of facts day in, day out, keeping up his barrage of journalistic philanthropy as nimble as the jumping of a flea? Why can't he get it into his head that it's for him to stop repeating himself —not for the gun—that you can never say something meaningful by accumulating absurdities in your notebook, that facts don't exist until man puts into them something of his own, a bit of free human genius—of myth."

"You've hit the nail on the head," broke in Gordon. "And now I'll tell you what I think about that incident we saw today. That Cossack tormenting the poor patriarch—and there are thousands of incidents like it—of course it's an ignominy—but there's no point in philosophizing, you just hit out. But the Jewish question as a whole—there philosophy does come in—and then we discover something unexpected. Not that I'm going to tell you anything new—we both got our ideas from your uncle.

[1] Vladimir Ivanovich Dahl, author of a *Dictionary of the Living Russian Tongue.*

"You were saying, what is a nation? . . . And who does more for a nation—the one who makes a fuss about it or the one who, without thinking of it, raises it to universality by the beauty and greatness of his actions, and gives it fame and immortality? Well, the answer is obvious. And what are the nations now, in the Christian era? They aren't just nations, but converted, transformed nations, and what matters is this transformation, not loyalty to ancient principles. And what does the Gospel say on this subject? To begin with, it does not make assertions: 'It's like this and like that.' It is a proposal, naïve and timid: 'Do you want to live in a completely new way? Do you want spiritual happiness?' And everybody accepted, they were carried away by it for thousands of years. . . .

"When the Gospel says that in the Kingdom of God there are neither Jews nor Gentiles, does it merely mean that all are equal in the sight of God? No—the Gospel wasn't needed for that— the Greek philosophers, the Roman moralists, and the Hebrew prophets had known this long before. But it said: In that new way of living and new form of society, which is born of the heart, and which is called the Kingdom of Heaven, there are no nations, there are only individuals.

"You said that facts are meaningless, unless meanings are put into them. Well, Christianity, the mystery of the individual, is precisely what must be put into the facts to make them meaningful.

"We also talked about mediocre publicists who have nothing to say to life and the world as a whole, of petty second-raters who are only too happy when some nation, preferably a small and wretched one, is constantly discussed—this gives them a chance to show off their competence and cleverness, and to thrive on their compassion for the persecuted. Well now, what more perfect example can you have of the victims of this mentality than the Jews? Their national idea has forced them, century after century, to be a nation and nothing but a nation—and they have been chained to this deadening task all through the centuries when all the rest of the world was being delivered from it by a new force which had come out of their own midst! Isn't that extraordinary? How can you account for it? Just think! This glorious holiday, this liberation from the curse of mediocrity, this soaring flight above the dullness of a humdrum existence, was first achieved in their land, proclaimed in their language, and belonged to their race! And they actually saw and heard it and let it go! How could they allow a spirit of such over-whelming power and beauty to leave them, how could they think that after it triumphed and established its reign, they would remain as the empty husk of that miracle they had re-pudiated? What use is it to anyone, this voluntary martyrdom? Whom does it profit? For what purpose are these innocent old men and women and children, all these subtle, kind, humane people, mocked and beaten up throughout the centuries? And why is it that all these literary friends of 'the people' of all nations are always so untalented? Why didn't the intellectual leaders of the Jewish people ever go beyond facile *Weltschmerz* and ironical wisdom? Why have they not—even if at the risk of bursting like boilers with the pressure of their duty—disbanded this army which keeps on fighting and being massacred no-body knows for what? Why don't they say to them: 'Come to your senses, stop. Don't hold on to your identity. Don't stick to-gether, disperse. Be with all the rest. You are the first and best Christians in the world. You are the very thing against which you have been turned by the worst and weakest among you.'"

13

The following day when Zhivago came home to dinner, he said: "Well, you were so anxious to leave, now your wish has come true. I won't say 'Just your luck' because it isn't lucky that we are being hard-pressed and beaten again. The way east is open; the pressure is from the west. All the medical units are under orders to get out. We'll be going tomorrow or the next day. Where to, I don't know. And I suppose, Karpenko, Mikhail Grigorievich's linen still hasn't been washed. It's always the same thing. Karpenko will tell you he has given it to his girl to wash, but if you ask him who and where she is, he doesn't know, the idiot."

He paid no attention to Karpenko's excuses nor to Gordon's apologies for borrowing his host's shirts.

"That's army life for you," he went on. "As soon as you get used to one place you're moved to another. I didn't like anything here when we came. It was dirty, stuffy, the stove was in the wrong place, the ceiling was too low. And now, even if you killed me I couldn't remember what it was like where we came from. I feel as if I wouldn't mind spending my life in this place, staring at that corner of the stove with the sunshine on the tiles and the shadow of that tree moving across."

They packed without haste.

During the night they were roused by shouts, gunfire, and running footsteps. There was a sinister glow over the village. Shadows flickered past the window. The landlord and his wife were getting up behind the partition. Yurii Andreievich sent the orderly to ask what the commotion was about.

He was told that the Germans had broken through. Zhivago hurried off to the hospital and found that it was true. The village was under fire. The hospital was being moved at once, without waiting for the evacuation order.

"We'll all be off before dawn," Zhivago told Gordon. "You're going in the first party, the carriage is ready now, but I've told them to wait for you. Well, good luck. I'll see you off and make sure you get your seat."

They ran down the village street, ducking and hugging the walls. Bullets whizzed past them, and from the crossroads they could see shrapnel explosions like umbrellas of fire opening over the fields.

"And what about you?" asked Gordon as they ran.

"I'll follow with the second party. I have to go back and collect my things."

They separated at the edge of the village. The carriage and several carts that made up the convoy started, bumping into one another and gradually spacing out. Yurii Andreievich waved to his friend, who saw him for a few moments longer by the light of a burning barn.

Again keeping to the shelter of the houses, Yurii Andreievich hurried back. A few yards from his house he was knocked off his feet by the blast of an explosion and hit by a shell splinter. He fell in the middle of the road, bleeding and unconscious.

14

The hospital where Yurii Andreievich was recovering in the officers' ward had been evacuated to an obscure, small town on a railway line close to the G.H.Q. It was a warm day at the end of February. The window near his bed was open at his request.

The patients were killing time before dinner as best they could. They had been told that a new nurse had joined the hospital staff and would be doing her first round that day. In the bed opposite Zhivago's, Galiullin was looking at the newspapers that had just arrived and exclaiming indignantly at the blanks left by the censorship. Yurii Andreievich was reading Tonia's letters, which had accumulated in one great batch. The breeze rustled the letters and the papers. At the sound of light footsteps he looked up. Lara came into the ward.

Zhivago and Galiullin each recognized her without realizing that the other knew her. She knew neither of them. She said: "Hello. Why is the window open? Aren't you cold?" Going up to Galiullin, she asked him how he felt and took his wrist to feel his pulse, but immediately let go of it and sat down by his bed, looking at him with a puzzled expression.

"This is indeed unexpected, Larisa Feodorovna," he said. "I knew your husband. We were in the same regiment. I've kept his things for you."

"It isn't possible," she kept saying, "it isn't possible. You knew him! What an extraordinary coincidence. Please tell me quickly how it happened. He was killed by a shell, wasn't he, and buried by the explosion? You see I know, please don't be afraid of telling me."

Galiullin's courage failed him. He decided to tell her a comforting lie.

"Antipov was taken prisoner," he said. "He advanced too far with his unit. They were surrounded and cut off. He was forced to surrender."

But she did not believe him. Shaken by the unexpectedness of the meeting and not wishing to break down in front of strangers, she hurried out into the corridor.

A few moments later she came back, outwardly collected; afraid of crying again if she spoke to Galiullin, she deliberately avoided looking at him and went over to Yurii Andreievich. "Hello," she said absentmindedly and mechanically. "What's the trouble with you?"

Yurii Andreievich had seen her agitation and her tears. He wanted to ask her why she was so upset and to tell her that he had seen her twice before in his life, once as a schoolboy and once as a university student, but it occurred to him that he would sound too familiar and she would misinterpret his meaning. Then he suddenly remembered the coffin with Anna Ivanovna's body in it and Tonia's screams, and said instead:

"Thank you. I am a doctor. I am looking after myself. I don't need anything."

"How have I offended him?" Lara wondered. She looked in surprise at the stranger with his snub nose and unremarkable face.

For several days the weather was variable, uncertain, with a warm, constantly murmuring wind in the night, smelling of damp earth.

During those days there came strange reports from G.H.Q., and there were alarming rumors from the interior. Telegraphic communications with Petersburg were cut off time and again. Everywhere, at every corner, people were talking politics.

Nurse Antipova did her rounds morning and evening, exchanging a few words with each patient, including Galiullin and Zhivago. "What a curious creature," she thought. "Young and gruff. You couldn't call him handsome with his turned-up nose. But he is intelligent in the best sense of the word, alive and with an attractive mind. However, that's unimportant. What is important is to finish my job here as soon as possible and get transferred to Moscow to be near Katenka, and then to apply for my discharge and go home to Yuriatin, back to the gymnasium. It's quite clear now what happened to poor Pasha, there isn't any hope, so the sooner I stop playing the heroine the better. I wouldn't be here if I hadn't come to look for Pasha."

How was Katenka getting on out there, she wondered, poor orphan, and this always made her cry.

She had noticed a sharp change around her recently. Before, there had been obligations of all kinds, sacred duties—your duty to your country, to the army, to society. But now that the war was lost (and that was the misfortune at the bottom of all the rest) nothing was sacred any more.

Everything had changed suddenly—the tone, the moral climate; you didn't know what to think, whom to listen to. As if all your life you had been led by the hand like a small child and suddenly you were on your own, you had to learn to walk by yourself. There was no one around, neither family nor people whose judgment you respected. At such a time you felt the need of committing yourself to something absolute—life or truth or beauty—of being ruled by it in place of the man-made rules that had been discarded. You needed to surrender to some such ultimate purpose more fully, more unreservedly than you had ever done in the old familiar, peaceful days, in the old life that was now abolished and gone for good. But in her own case, Lara reminded herself, she had Katenka to fulfill her need for an absolute, her need of a purpose. Now that she no longer had Pasha, Lara would be nothing but a mother, devoting all her strength to her poor orphaned child.

Yurii Andreievich heard from Moscow that Gordon and Dudorov had published his book without his permission, and that it was praised and regarded as showing great literary promise; that Moscow was going through a disturbed, exciting time and was on the eve of something important, that there was growing discontent among the masses, and that grave political events were imminent.

It was late at night. Yurii Andreievich was terribly sleepy. He dozed intermittently and imagined that the excitement of the past days was keeping him awake. A drowsy, sleepily breathing wind yawned and stirred outside the window. The wind wept and complained, "Tonia, Sasha, I miss you, I want to go home, I want to go back to work." And to the muttering of the wind Yurii Andreievich slept and woke and slept again in a quick, troubled alternation of joy and suffering, as fleeting and disturbing as the changing weather, as the restless night.

It occurred to Lara that after all the devotion Galiullin had shown to Pasha's memory, the pains he had taken to look after his things, she had not so much as asked him who he was and where he came from.

To make up for her omission and not seem ungrateful she asked him all about himself when she made her next morning round.

"Merciful heaven," she wondered aloud. Twenty-eight Brest Street, the Tiverzins, the revolution of 1905, that winter! Yusupka? No, she couldn't remember having met him, he must forgive her. But that year, that year, and that house! That's true, there had really been such a house and such a year! How vividly it all came back to her! The gunfire and—what was it she had called it then?—"Christ's judgment"! How strong, how piercingly sharp were the feelings you experienced for the first time as a child! "Forgive me, do forgive me, Lieutenant, what did you say your name is? Yes, yes, you did tell me once. Thank you, Osip Gimazetdinovich, I can't thank you enough for reminding me, for bringing it all back to my mind."

All day long she went about thinking of "that house" and kept talking to herself.

To think of it, Brest Street, No. 28! And now they were shooting again, but how much more frightening it was now! You couldn't say, "The boys are shooting" this time. The children had all grown up, the boys were all here, in the army, all those humble people who had lived in that house and in others like it and in villages that also were like it. Extraordinary, extraordinary!

All the patients who were not bedridden rushed in from the other rooms, hobbling noisily on crutches or running, or walking with canes, and shouted vying with each other:

"Big news! Street fighting in Petersburg! The Petersburg garrison has joined the insurgents! The revolution!"

PART TWO

PART TWO

CHAPTER FIVE

FAREWELL TO THE OLD

Dr Zhivago & Nurse Antipova are thrown together.

1

The small town was called Meliuzeievo and lay in the fertile, black-soil country. Black dust hung over its roofs like a cloud of locusts. It was raised by the troops and convoys passing through the town; they moved in both directions, some going to the front and others away from it, and it was impossible to tell whether the war were still going on or had ceased.

Every day newly created offices sprang up like mushrooms. And they were elected to everything—Zhivago, Lieutenant Galiullin, and Nurse Antipova, as well as a few others from their group, all of them people from the big cities, well-informed and experienced.

They served as temporary town officials and as minor commissars in the army and the health department, and they looked upon this succession of tasks as an outdoor sport, a diversion, a game of blindman's buff. But more and more they felt that it was time to stop and to get back to their ordinary occupations and their homes.

Zhivago and Antipova were often brought together by their work.

Zhivago writes to his wife & reminds her of their previous contacts with Larisa. Tonia becomes very jealous.

2

The rain turned the black dust into coffee-colored mud and the mud spread over the streets, most of them unpaved.

The town was small. At the end of almost every street you could see the steppe, gloomy under the dark sky, all the vastness of the war, the vastness of the revolution.

Yurii Andreievich wrote to his wife:

131

"The disintegration and anarchy in the army continue. Measures are being taken to improve discipline and morale. I have toured units stationed in the neighborhood.

"By way of a postscript, though I might have mentioned it much earlier, I must tell that I do a lot of my work with a certain Antipova, a nurse from Moscow who was born in the Urals.

"You remember the girl student who shot at the public prosecutor on that terrible night of your mother's death? I believe she was tried later. I remember telling you that Misha and I had once seen her, when she was still a schoolgirl, at some sordid hotel where your father took us. I can't remember why we went, only that it was a bitterly cold night. I think it was at the time of the Presnia uprising. Well, that girl was Antipova.

"I have made several attempts to go home, but it is not so simple. It is not so much the work—we could hand that over easily enough—the trouble is the trip. Either there are no trains at all or else they are so overcrowded that there is no way of finding a seat.

"But of course it can't go on like this forever, and some of us, who have resigned or been discharged, including Antipova, Galiullin, and myself, have made up our minds that whatever happens we shall leave next week. We'll go separately; it gives us a better chance.

"So I may turn up any day out of the blue, though I'll try to send a telegram."

Before he left, however, he received his wife's reply. In sentences broken by sobs and with tear stains and ink spots for punctuation, she begged him not to come back to Moscow but to go straight to the Urals with that wonderful nurse whose progress through life was marked by portents and coincidences so miraculous that her own, Tonia's, modest life could not possibly compete with it.

"Don't worry about Sasha's future," she wrote. "You will never need to be ashamed of him. I promise you to bring him up in those principles which as a child you saw practiced in our house."

Yurii Andreievich wrote back at once: "You must be out of your mind, Tonia! How could you imagine such a thing? Don't you know, don't you know well enough, that if it were not for you, if it were not for my constant, faithful thoughts of you and of our home, I would never have survived these two terrible, devastating years of war? But why am I writing this—soon we'll be together, our life will begin again, everything will be cleared up.

"What frightens me about your letter is something else. If I really gave you cause to write in such a way, my behavior must have been ambiguous and I am at fault not only before you but before that other woman whom I am misleading. I'll apologize to her as soon as she is back. She is away in the country. Local councils, which formerly existed only in provincial capitals and county seats, are being set up in the villages, and she has gone to help a friend of hers who is acting as instructor in connection with these legislative changes.

"It may interest you to know that although we live in the same house I don't know to this day which is Antipova's room. I've never bothered to find out."

...y bushino declares itself an independent republic. It lasts 2 weeks

3

Two main roads ran from Meliuzeievo, one going east, the other west. One was a mud track leading through the woods to Zybushino, a small grain center that was administratively a subdivision of Meliuzeievo although it was ahead of it in every way. The other was gravelled and went through fields, boggy in winter but dry in summer, to Biriuchi, the nearest railway junction.

In June Zybushino became an independent republic. It was set up by the local miller Blazheiko and supported by deserters from the 212th Infantry who had left the front at the time of the upheavals, kept their arms, and come to Zybushino through Biriuchi.

The republic refused to recognize the Provisional Government and split off from the rest of Russia. Blazheiko, a religious dissenter who had once corresponded with Tolstoy, proclaimed a new millennial Zybushino kingdom where all work and property were to be collectivized, and referred to the local administration as an Apostolic Seat.

Zybushino had always been a source of legends and exaggerations. It is mentioned in documents dating from the Times of Troubles[1] and the thick forests surrounding it teemed with robbers even later. The prosperity of its merchants and the fabulous fertility of its soil were proverbial. Many popular beliefs, customs, and oddities of speech that distinguished this whole western region near the front originated in Zybushino.

Now amazing stories were told about Blazheiko's chief assistant. It was said that he was deaf and dumb, that he acquired the gift of speech at moments of inspiration, and then lost it again.

The republic lasted two weeks. In July a unit loyal to the Provisional Government entered the town. The deserters fell back on Biriuchi. Several miles of forest had once been cleared along the railway line on both sides of the junction, and there, among the old tree stumps overgrown with wild strawberries, the piles of timber depleted by pilfering, and the tumble-down mud huts of the seasonal laborers who had cut the trees, the deserters set up their camp.

4

The hospital in which Zhivago convalesced and later served as a doctor, and which he was not preparing to leave, was housed in the former residence of <u>Countess Zhabrinskaia.</u> She had offered it to the Red Cross at the beginning of the war.

It was a two-story house on one of the best sites of the town, at the corner of the main street and the square, known as the *Platz,* where soldiers had drilled in the old days and where meetings were held now.

Its position gave it a good view of the neighborhood; in addition to the square and the street it overlooked the adjoining farm (owned by a poor, provincial family who lived almost like peasants) as well as the Countess's old garden at the back.

The Countess had a large estate in the district, Razdolnoie, and had used the house only for occasional business visits to

---

[1] Period of interregnum and civil war in the seventeenth century.

the town and as a rallying point for the guests who came from
near and far to stay at Razdolnoie in summer.

Now the house was a hospital, and its owner was in prison
in Petersburg, where she had lived.

Of the large staff, only two women were left, Ustinia, the
head cook, and Mademoiselle Fleury, the former governess of
the Countess's daughters, who were now married.

Gray-haired, pink-cheeked, and dishevelled, Mademoiselle
Fleury shuffled about in bedroom slippers and a floppy, worn-
out housecoat, apparently as much at home in the hospital as
she had been in the Zhabrinsky family. She told long stories in
her broken Russian, swallowing the ends of her words in the
French manner, gesticulated, struck dramatic poses, and burst
into hoarse peals of laughter that ended in coughing fits.

She believed that she knew Nurse Antipova inside out and
thought that the nurse and the doctor were bound to be attracted to each other. Succumbing to her passion for match-
making, so deep-rooted in the Latin heart, she was delighted
when she found them in each other's company, and would shake
her finger and wink slyly at them. This puzzled Antipova and
angered the doctor; but, like all eccentrics, Mademoiselle cherished her illusions and would not be parted from them at any
price.

Ustinia was an even stranger character. Her clumsy, pear-
shaped figure gave her the look of a brood hen. She was dry
and sober to the point of maliciousness, but her sober-minded-
ness went hand in hand with an imagination unbridled in everything to do with superstition. Born in Zybushino and said to be
the daughter of the local sorcerer, she knew countless spells
and would never go out without first muttering over the stove
and the keyhole to protect the house in her absence from fire and
the Evil One. She could keep quiet for years, but once she
was roused nothing would stop her. Her passion was to defend
the truth.

After the fall of the Zybushino republic, the Meliuzeievo
Executive Committee launched a campaign against the local
anarchistic tendencies. Every night peaceful meetings were held
at the *Platz*, attended by small numbers of citizens who had
nothing better to do and who, in the old days, used to gather

for gossip outside the fire station. The Meliuzeievo cultural soviet encouraged them and invited local and visiting speakers to guide the discussions. The visitors believed the tales about the talking deaf-mute to be utter nonsense and were anxious to say so. But the small craftsmen, the soldiers' wives, and former servants of Meliuzeievo did not regard these stories as absurd and stood up in his defense.

One of the most outspoken of his defenders was Ustinia. At first held back by womanly reserve, she had gradually become bolder in heckling orators whose views were unacceptable in Meliuzeievo. In the end she developed into an expert public speaker.

The humming of the voices in the square could be heard through the open windows of the hospital, and on quiet nights even fragments of speeches. When Ustinia took the floor, Mademoiselle often rushed into any room where people were sitting and urged them to listen, imitating her without malice in her broken accent: "Disorder . . . Disorder . . . Tsarist, bandit . . . Zybushi- . . . deaf-mute . . . traitor! traitor!"

Mademoiselle was secretly proud of the spirited and sharp-tongued cook. The two women were fond of each other although they never stopped bickering.

5

Yurii Andreievich prepared to leave, visiting homes and offices where he had friends, and applying for the necessary documents.

At that time the new commissar of the local sector of the front stopped at Meliuzeievo on his way to the army. Everybody said he was completely inexperienced, a mere boy.

A new offensive was being planned and a great effort was made to improve the morale of the army masses. Revolutionary courts-martial were instituted, and the death penalty, which had recently been abolished, was restored.

Before leaving, the doctor had to obtain a paper from the local commandant.

Usually crowds filled his office, overflowing far out into the street. It was impossible to elbow one's way to the desks and no one could hear anything in the roar caused by hundreds of voices.

But this was not one of the reception days. The clerks sat writing silently in the peaceful office, disgruntled at the growing complication of their work, and exchanging ironic glances. Cheerful voices came from the commandant's room; it sounded as if, in there, people had unbuttoned their tunics and were having refreshments.

Galiullin came out of the inner room, saw Zhivago, and vigorously beckoned to him.

Since the doctor had in any case to see the commandant, he went in. He found the room in a state of artistic disorder.

The center of the stage was held by the new commissar, the hero of the day and the sensation of the town, who, instead of being at his post, was addressing the rulers of this paper kingdom quite unconnected with staff and operational matters.

"Here's another of our stars," said the commandant, introducing the doctor. The commissar, completely self-absorbed, did not look around, and the commandant turned to sign the paper that the doctor put in front of him and waved him politely to a low ottoman in the center of the room.

The doctor was the only person in the room who sat normally. All the rest were lolling eccentrically with an air of exaggerated and assumed ease. The commandant almost lay across his desk, his cheek on his fist, in a thoughtful, Byronic pose. His aide, a massive, stout man, perched on the arm of the sofa, his legs tucked on the seat as if he were riding side saddle. Galiullin sat astride a chair, his arms folded on its back and his head resting on his arms, and the commissar kept hoisting himself up by his wrists onto the window sill and jumping off and running up and down the room with small quick steps, buzzing about like a wound-up top, never still or silent for a moment. He talked continuously; the subject of the conversation was the problem of the deserters at Biriuchi.

The commissar was exactly as he had been described to Zhivago. He was thin and graceful, barely out of his teens, aflame with the highest ideals. He was said to come of a good family (the son of a senator, some people thought) and to have been one of the first to march his company to the Duma in

February. He was called Gints or Gintse—the doctor had not quite caught the name—and spoke very distinctly, with a correct Petersburg accent and a slight Baltic intonation.

He wore a tight-fitting tunic. It probably embarrassed him to be so young, and in order to seem older he assumed a sneer and an artificial stoop, hunching his shoulders with their stiff epaulettes and keeping his hands deep in his pockets; this did in fact give him a cavalryman's silhouette which could be drawn in two straight lines converging downward from the angle of his shoulders to his feet.

"There is a Cossack regiment stationed a short distance down the railway," the commandant informed him. "It's Red, it's loyal. It will be called out, the rebels will be surrounded, and that will be the end of the business. The corps commander is anxious that they should be disarmed without delay."

"Cossacks? Out of the question!" flared the commissar. "This is not 1905. We're not going back to prerevolutionary methods. On this point we don't see eye to eye. Your generals have outsmarted themselves."

"Nothing has been done yet. This is only a plan, a suggestion."

"We have an agreement with the High Command not to interfere with operational matters. I am not cancelling the order to call out the Cossacks. Let them come. But I, for my part, will take such steps as are dictated by common sense. I suppose they have a bivouac out there?"

"I guess so. A camp, at any rate. Fortified."

"So much the better. I want to go there. I want to see this menace, this nest of robbers. They may be rebels, gentlemen, they may even be deserters, but remember, they are the people. And the people are children, you have to know them, you have to know their psychology. To get the best out of them, you must have the right approach, you have to play on their best, most sensitive chords.

"I'll go, and I'll have a heart-to-heart talk with them. You'll see, they'll go back to the positions they have deserted. You don't believe me? Want to bet?"

"I wonder. But I hope you're right."

"I'll say to them, 'Take my own case, I am an only son, the hope of my parents, yet I haven't spared myself. I've given up

everything—name, family, position. I have done this to fight
for your freedom, such freedom as is not enjoyed by any other
people in the world. This I did, and so did many other young
men like myself, not to speak of the old guard of our glorious
predecessors, the champions of the people's rights who were sent
to hard labor in Siberia or locked up in the Schlüsselburg Fortress. Did we do this for ourselves? Did we have to do it? And
you, you who are no longer ordinary privates but the warriors
of the first revolutionary army in the world, ask yourselves
honestly: Have you lived up to your proud calling? At this moment when our country is being bled white and is making a
supreme effort to shake off the encircling hydra of the enemy,
you have allowed yourselves to be fooled by a gang of nobodies,
you have become a rabble, politically unconscious, surfeited
with freedom, hooligans for whom nothing is enough. You're
like the proverbial pig that was allowed in the dining room
and at once jumped onto the table.' Oh, I'll touch them to the
quick, I'll make them feel ashamed of themselves."

"No, that would be risky," the commandant objected half-
heartedly, exchanging quick, meaningful glances with his aide.

Galiullin did his best to dissuade the commissar from his insane idea. He knew the reckless men of the 212th, they had
been in his division at the front. But the commissar refused to
listen.

Yurii Andreievich kept trying to get up and go. The commissar's naïveté embarrassed him, but the sly sophistication of
the commandant and his aide—two sneering and dissembling
opportunists—was no better. The foolishness of the one was
matched by the slyness of the others. And all this expressed
itself in a torrent of words, superfluous, utterly false, murky,
profoundly alien to life itself.

Oh, how one wishes sometimes to escape from the meaningless
dullness of human eloquence, from all those sublime phrases,
to take refuge in nature, apparently so inarticulate, or in the
wordlessness of long, grinding labor, of sound sleep, of true
music, or of a human understanding rendered speechless by
emotion!

The doctor remembered his coming talk with Antipova. Though
it was bound to be unpleasant, he was glad of the necessity

of seeing her, even at such a price. She was unlikely to be back. But he got up as soon as he could and went out, unnoticed by the others.

6

She was back. Mademoiselle, who gave him the news, added that she was tired, she had had a quick meal and had gone up to her room saying she was not to be disturbed. "But I should go up and knock if I were you," Mademoiselle suggested. "I am sure she is not asleep yet."—"Which is her room?" the doctor asked. Mademoiselle was surprised beyond words by his question. Antipova lived at the end of the passage on the top floor, just beyond several rooms in which all of the Countess's furniture was kept locked, and where the doctor had never been.

It was getting dark. Outside, the houses and fences huddled closer together in the dusk. The trees advanced out of the depth of the garden into the light of the lamps shining from the windows. The night was hot and sticky. At the slightest effort one was drenched with sweat. The light of the kerosene lamps streaking into the yard went down the trees in a dirty, vaporous flow.

The doctor stopped at the head of the stairs. It occurred to him that even to knock on Antipova's door when she was only just back and tired from her journey would be discourteous and embarrassing. Better leave the talk for tomorrow. Feeling at a loss as one does when one changes one's mind, he walked to the other end of the passage, where a window overlooked the neighboring yard, and leaned out.

The night was full of quiet, mysterious sounds. Next to him, inside the passage, water dripped from the washbasin regularly and slowly. Somewhere outside the window people were whispering. Somewhere in the vegetable patch they were watering cucumber beds, clanking the chain of the well as they drew the water and poured it from pail to pail.

All the flowers smelled at once; it was as if the earth, unconscious all day long, were now waking to their fragrance. And from the Countess's centuries-old garden, so littered with fallen branches that it was impenetrable, the dusty aroma of old linden trees coming into bloom drifted in a huge wave as tall as a house.

Noises came from the street beyond the fence on the right— snatches of a song, a drunken soldier, doors banging.

An enormous crimson moon rose behind the crows' nest in the Countess's garden. At first it was the color of the new brick mill in Zybushino, then it turned yellow like the water tower at Biriuchi.

And just under the window, the smell of new-mown hay, as perfumed as jasmine tea, mixed with that of belladonna. Below there a cow was tethered; she had been brought from a distant village, she had walked all day, she was tired and homesick for the herd and would not yet accept food from her new mistress.

"Now, now, whoa there, I'll show you how to butt," her mistress coaxed her in a whisper, but the cow crossly shook her head and craned her neck, mooing plaintively, and beyond the black barns of Meliuzeievo the stars twinkled, and invisible threads of sympathy stretched between them and the cow as if there were cattle sheds in other worlds where she was pitied.

Everything was fermenting, growing, rising with the magic yeast of life. The joy of living, like a gentle wind, swept in a broad surge indiscriminately through fields and towns, through walls and fences, through wood and flesh. Not to be overwhelmed by this tidal wave, Yurii Andreievich went out into the square to listen to the speeches.

7

By now the moon stood high. Its light covered everything as with a thick layer of white paint. The broad shadows thrown by the pillared government buildings that surrounded the square in a semicircle spread on the ground like black rugs.

The meeting was being held across the square. Straining one's ears, one could hear every word. But the doctor was stunned by the beauty of the spectacle; he sat down on the bench outside the fire station and instead of listening looked about him.

Narrow dead-end streets ran off the square, as deep in mud as country lanes and lined with crooked little houses. Fences of plaited willows stuck out of the mud like bow nets in a pond, or lobster pots. You could see the weak glint of open windows. In the small front gardens, sweaty red heads of corn with oily whiskers reached out toward the rooms, and single pale thin hollyhocks looked out over the fences, like women in night clothes whom the heat had driven out of their stuffy houses for a breath of air.

The moonlit night was extraordinary, like merciful love or the gift of clairvoyance. Suddenly, into this radiant, legendary still-ness, there dropped the measured, rhythmic sound of a fa-miliar, recently heard voice. It was a fine ardent voice and it rang with conviction. The doctor listened and recognized it at once. Commissar Gints was addressing the meeting on the square.

Apparently the municipality had asked him to lend them the support of his authority. With great feeling he chided the peo-ple of Meliuzeievo for their disorganized ways and for giving in to the disintegrating influence of the Bolsheviks, who, he said, were the real instigators of the Zybushino disorders. Speak-ing in the same spirit as at the Commandant's, he reminded them of the powerful and ruthless enemy, and of their country's hour of trial. Then the crowd began to heckle.

Calls of protest alternated with demands for silence. The in-terruptions grew louder and more frequent. A man who had come with Gints, and who now assumed the role of chairman, shouted that speeches from the floor were not allowed and called the audience to order. Some insisted that a citizeness who wished to speak should be given leave.

A woman made her way through the crowd to the wooden box that served as a platform. She did not attempt to climb on the box but stood beside it. The woman was known to the crowd. Its attention was caught. There was a silence. This was Ustinia.

"Now you were saying, Comrade Commissar, about Zybush-ino," she began, "and about looking sharp—you told us to look sharp and not to be deceived—but actually, you yourself, I

heard you, all you do is to play about with words like 'Bolsheviks, Mensheviks,' that's all you talk about—Bolsheviks,
Mensheviks. Now all that about no more fighting and all being
brothers, I call that being godly, not Menshevik, and about
the works and factories going to the poor, that isn't Bolshevik,
that's just human decency. And about that deaf-mute, we're fed
up hearing about him. Everybody goes on and on about the
deaf-mute. And what have you got against him? Just that he
was dumb all that time and then he suddenly started to talk
and didn't ask your permission? As if that were so marvellous!
Much stranger things than that have been known to happen.
Take the famous she-ass, for instance. 'Balaam, Balaam,' she
says, 'listen to me, don't go that way, I beg you, you'll be sorry.'
Well, naturally, he wouldn't listen, he went on. Like you saying,
'A deaf-mute,' he thought, 'a she-ass, a dumb beast, what's the
good of listening to her.' He scorned her. And look how sorry
he was afterwards. You all know what the end of it was."

"What?" someone asked curiously.

"That's enough," snapped Ustinia. "If you ask too many questions you'll grow old before your time."

"That's no good. You tell us," insisted the heckler.

"All right, all right, I'll tell you, you pest. He was turned into
a pillar of salt."

"You've got it wrong, that was Lot. That was Lot's wife," people shouted. Everyone laughed. The chairman called the meeting to order. The doctor went to bed.

8

He saw Antipova the following evening. He found her in the
pantry with a pile of linen, straight out of the wringer; she was
ironing.

The pantry was one of the back rooms at the top, looking out
over the garden. There the samovars were got ready, food was
dished out, and the used plates were stacked in the dumb-
waiter to be sent down to the kitchen. There too the lists of
china, silver, and glass were kept and checked, and there people
spent their moments of leisure, using it as a meeting place.

The windows were open. In the room, the scent of linden blossoms mingled, as in an old park, with the caraway-bitter smell of dry twigs and the charcoal fumes of the two flatirons that Antipova used alternately, putting them each in turn in the flue to keep them hot.

"Well, why didn't you knock last night? Mademoiselle told me. But it's a good thing you didn't. I was already in bed. I couldn't have let you in. Well, how are you? Look out for the charcoal, don't get it on your suit."

"You look as if you've been doing the laundry for the whole hospital."

"No, there's a lot of mine in there. You see? You keep on teasing me about getting stuck in Meliuzeievo. Well, this time I mean it, I'm going. I'm getting my things together, I'm packing. When I've finished I'll be off. I'll be in the Urals and you'll be in Moscow. Then one day somebody will ask you: 'Do you happen to know a little town called Meliuzeievo?' and you'll say: 'I don't seem to call it to mind.'—'And who is Antipova?'—'Never heard of her.'"

"That's unlikely. Did you have a good trip? What was it like in the country?"

"That's a long story. How quickly these irons cool! Do hand me the other, do you mind? It's over there, look, just inside the flue. And could you put this one back? Thanks. Every village is different, it depends on the villagers. In some the people are industrious, they work hard, then it isn't bad. And in others I suppose all the men are drunks. Then it's desolate. A terrible sight."

"Nonsense! Drunks? A lot you understand! It's just that there is no one there, all the men are in the army. What about the new councils?"

"You're wrong about the drunks, I don't agree with you at all. The councils? There's going to be a lot of trouble with the councils. The instructions can't be applied, there's nobody to work with. All the peasants care about at the moment is the land question. . . . I stopped at Razdolnoie. What a lovely place, you should go and see it. . . . It was burned a bit and looted last spring, the barn is burned down, the orchards are charred, and there are smoke stains on some of the houses. Zybushino I didn't see, I didn't get there. But they all tell you the deaf-mute really exists. They describe what he looks like, they say he's young and educated."

"Last night Ustinia stood up for him on the square."

"The moment I got back there was another lot of old furniture from Razdolnoie. I've asked them a hundred times to leave it alone. As if we didn't have enough of our own. And this morning the guard from the commandant's office comes over with a note—they must have the silver tea set and the crystal glasses, it's a matter of life and death, just for one night, they'll send it back. Half of it we'll never see again. It's always a loan—I know these loans. They're having a party—in honor of some visitor or something."

"I can guess who that is. The new commissar has arrived, the one who's appointed to our sector of the front. They want to tackle the deserters, have them surrounded and disarmed. The commissar is a greenhorn, a babe in arms. The local authorities want to call out the Cossacks, but not he—he's planning to speak to their hearts. The people, he says, are like children, and so on; he thinks it's a kind of game. Galiullin tried to argue with him, he told him to leave the jungle alone, not to rouse the wild beast. 'Leave us to deal with it,' he said. But you can't do anything with a fellow like that once he's got a thing in his head. I do wish you'd listen to me. Do stop ironing a minute. There will be an unimaginable mess here soon; it's beyond our power to avert it. I do wish you'd leave before it happens."

"Nothing will happen, you're exaggerating. And anyway, I am leaving. But I can't just snap my fingers and say goodbye. I have to hand in a properly checked inventory. I don't want it to look as if I've stolen something and run away. And who is to take over? That's the problem, I can't tell you what I've been through with that miserable inventory, and all I get is abuse. I listed Zhabrinskaia's things as hospital property, because that was the sense of the decree. Now they say I did it on purpose to keep them for the owner! What a dirty trick!"

"Do stop worrying about pots and rugs. To hell with them. What a thing to fuss about at a time like this! Oh, I wish I'd seen you yesterday. I was in such good form that I could have told you all about everything, explained the whole celestial mechanics, answered any accursed question! It's true, you know, I'm not joking, I really did want to get it all off my chest. And I wanted to tell you about my wife, and my son, and myself. . . . Why the hell can't a grown-up man talk to a grown-up woman without being at once suspected of some ulterior motive? Damn all motives—ulterior ones and others.

"Please, go on with your ironing, make the linen nice and smooth, don't bother about me, I'll go on talking. I'll talk a long time.

"Just think what's going on around us! And that you and I should be living at such a time. Such a thing happens only once in an eternity. Just think of it, the whole of Russia has had its roof torn off, and you and I and everyone else are out in the open! And there's nobody to spy on us. Freedom! Real freedom, not just talk about it, freedom, dropped out of the sky, freedom beyond our expectations, freedom by accident, through a misunderstanding.

"And how great everyone is, and completely at sea! Have you noticed? As if crushed by his own weight, by the discovery of his greatness.

"Go on ironing, I tell you. Don't talk. You aren't bored. Let me change your iron for you.

"Last night I was watching the meeting in the square. An extraordinary sight! Mother Russia is on the move, she can't stand still, she's restless and she can't find rest, she's talking and she can't stop. And it isn't as if only people were talking. Stars and trees meet and converse, flowers talk philosophy at night, stone houses hold meetings. It makes you think of the Gospel, doesn't it? The days of the apostles. Remember St. Paul? You will speak with tongues and you will prophesy. Pray for the gift of understanding."

"I know what you mean about stars and trees holding meetings. I understand that. It's happened to me too."

"It was partly the war, the revolution did the rest. The war was an artificial break in life—as if life could be put off for a time—what nonsense! The revolution broke out willy-nilly, like a sigh suppressed too long. Everyone was revived, reborn, changed, transformed. You might say that everyone has been through two revolutions—his own personal revolution as well as the general one. It seems to me that socialism is the sea, and all these separate streams, these private, individual revolutions, are flowing into it—the sea of life, the sea of spontaneity. I said life, but I mean life as you see it in a great picture, transformed by genius, creatively enriched. Only now people have decided to experience it not in books and pictures but in themselves, not as an abstraction but in practice."

The sudden trembling of his voice betrayed his rising agitation. Antipova stopped ironing and gave him a grave, astonished look. It confused him and he forgot what he was saying. After a moment of embarrassed silence he rushed on, blurting out whatever came into his head.

"These days I have such a longing to live honestly, to be productive. I so much want to be a part of all this awakening. And then, in the middle of all this general rejoicing, I catch your mysterious, sad glance, wandering God knows where, far away. How I wish it were not there! How I wish your face to say that you are happy with your fate and that you need nothing from anyone. If only someone who is really close to you, your friend or your husband—best of all if he were a soldier—would take me by the hand and tell me to stop worrying about your fate and not to weary you with my attentions. But I'd wrest my hand free and take a swing. . . . Ah, I have forgotten myself. Please forgive me."

Once again the doctor's voice betrayed him. He gave up struggling and, feeling hopelessly awkward, got up and went to the window. Leaning on the sill, his cheek on his hand, he stared into the dark garden with absent, unseeing eyes, trying to collect himself.

Antipova walked round the ironing board, propped between the table and the other window, and stopped in the middle of the room a few steps behind him. "That's what I've always been afraid of," she said softly, as if to herself. "I shouldn't have . . . Don't, Yurii Andreievich, you mustn't. Oh, now just look at what you've made me do!" she exclaimed. She ran back to the board, where a thin stream of acrid smoke came from under the iron that had burned through a blouse.

She thumped it down crossly on its stand. "Yurii Andreievich," she went on, "do be sensible, go off to Mademoiselle for a minute, have a drink of water and come back, please, as I've always

known you till now and as I want you to be. Do you hear, Yurii
Andreievich? I know you can do it. Please do it, I beg you."

They had no more talks of this kind, and a week later Larisa
Feodorovna left.

9

Some time later, Zhivago too set out for home. The night before
he left there was a terrible storm. The roar of the gale merged
with that of the downpour, which sometimes crashed straight
onto the roofs and at other times drove down the street with the
changing wind as if lashing its way step by step.

The peels of thunder followed each other uninterruptedly,
producing a steady rumble. In the blaze of continual flashes of
lightning the street vanished into the distance, and the bent
trees seemed to be running in the same direction.

Mademoiselle Fleury was waked up in the night by an urgent knocking at the front door. She sat up in alarm and listened. The knocking went on.

Could it be, she thought, that there wasn't a soul left in the
hospital to get up and open the door? Did she always have to
do everything, poor old woman, just because nature had made
her reliable and endowed her with a sense of duty?

Well, admittedly, the house had belonged to rich aristocrats,
but what about the hospital—didn't that belong to the people,
wasn't it their own? Whom did they expect to look after it?
Where, for instance, had the male nurses got to, she'd like to
know. Everyone had fled—no more orderlies, no more nurses, no
doctors, no one in authority. Yet there were still wounded in the
house, two legless men in the surgical ward where the drawing
room used to be, and downstairs next to the laundry the storeroom full of dysentery cases. And that devil Ustinia had gone
out visiting. She knew perfectly well that there was a storm
coming, but did that stop her? Now she had a good excuse to
spend the night out.

Well, thank God the knocking had stopped, they realized
that nobody would answer, they'd given it up. Why anybody
should want to be out in this weather . . . Or could it be Us-

tinia? No, she had her key. Oh God, how terrible, they've started again.

What pigs, just the same! Not that you could expect Zhivago to hear anything, he was off tomorrow, his thoughts were already in Moscow or on the journey. But what about Galiullin? How could he sleep soundly or lie calmly through all this noise, expecting that in the end she, a weak, defenseless old woman, would go down and open for God knows whom, on this frightening night in this frightening country.

Galiullin!—she remembered suddenly. No, such nonsense could occur to her only because she was half asleep, Galiullin wasn't there, he should be a long way off by now. Hadn't she herself, with Zhivago, hidden him, and disguised him as a civilian, and then told him about every road and village in the district to help him to escape after that horrible lynching at the station when they killed Commissar Gints and chased Galiullin all the way from Biriuchi to Meliuzeievo, shooting at him and then hunting for him all over the town!

If it hadn't been for those automobiles, not a stone would have been left standing in the town. An armored division happened to be passing through, and stopped those evil men.

The storm was subsiding, moving away. The thunder was less continuous, duller, more distant. The rain stopped occasionally, when the water could be heard splashing softly off the leaves and down the gutters. Noiseless reflections of distant lightning lit up Mademoiselle's room, lingering as though looking for something.

Suddenly the knocking at the front door, which had long since stopped, was resumed. Someone was in urgent need of help and was knocking repeatedly, in desperation. The wind rose again and the rain came down.

"Coming," shouted Mademoiselle to whoever it was, and the sound of her own voice frightened her.

It had suddenly occurred to her who it might be. Putting down her feet and pushing them into slippers, she threw her dressing gown over her shoulders and hurried to wake up Zhivago, it would be less frightening if he came down with her. But he had heard the knocking and was already coming down with a lighted candle. The same idea had occurred to both of them.

"Zhivago, Zhivago, they're knocking on the front door, I'm afraid to go down alone," she called out in French, adding in Russian: "You will see, it's either Lar or Lieutenant Gaiul."

Roused by the knocking, Yurii Andreievich had also felt certain that it was someone he knew—either Galiullin, who had been stopped in his flight and was coming back for refuge, or Nurse Antipova, prevented from continuing her journey for some reason.

In the hallway the doctor gave the candle to Mademoiselle, drew the bolts, and turned the key. A gust of wind burst the door open, putting out the candle and showering them with cold raindrops.

"Who is it? Who is it? Anybody there?"

Mademoiselle and the doctor shouted in turn into the darkness but there was no reply. Suddenly the knocking started again in another place—was it at the back door, or, as they now thought, at the French window into the garden?

"Must be the wind," said the doctor. "But just to make sure, perhaps you'd have a look at the back. I'll stay here in case there really is someone."

Mademoiselle disappeared into the house while the doctor went out and stood under the entrance roof. His eyes had become accustomed to the darkness, and he could make out the first signs of dawn.

Above the town, clouds raced dementedly as if pursued, so low that their tatters almost caught the tops of the trees, which bent in the same direction so that they looked like brooms sweeping the sky. The rain lashed the wooden wall of the house, turning it from gray to black.

Mademoiselle came back. "Well?" said the doctor.

"You were right. There's no one." She had been all around the house; a branch knocking on the pantry window had broken one of the panes and there were huge puddles on the floor, and the same thing in what used to be Lara's room—there was a sea, a real sea, an ocean. "And on this side, look, there's a broken shutter knocking on the casement, do you see it? That's all it was."

They talked a little, locked the door, and went back to their rooms, both regretting that the alarm had been a false one.

They had been sure that when they opened the door Antipova

would come in, chilled through and soaked to the skin, and they would ask her dozens of questions while she took off her things, and she would go and change and come down and dry herself in front of the kitchen stove, still warm from last night, and would tell them her adventures, pushing back her hair and laughing.

They had been so sure of it that after locking the front door they imagined that she was outside the house in the form of a watery wraith, and her image continued to haunt them.

10

It was said that the Biriuchi telegrapher, Kolia Frolenko, was indirectly responsible for the trouble at the station.

Kolia, the son of a well-known Meliuzeievo clockmaker, had been a familiar figure in Meliuzeievo from his earliest childhood. As a small boy he had stayed with some of the servants at Razdolnoie and had played with the Countess's daughters. It was then that he learned to understand French. Mademoiselle Fleury knew him well.

Everyone in Meliuzeievo was used to seeing him on his bicycle, coatless, hatless, and in canvas summer shoes in any weather. Arms crossed on his chest, he free-wheeled down the road, glancing up at the poles and wires to check the condition of the network.

Some of the houses in Meliuzeievo were connected by a branch line with the exchange at the station. The calls were handled by Kolia at the station switchboard. There he was up to his ears in work, for not only the telephone and telegraph were in his charge, but, if the stationmaster Povarikhin was absent for a few moments, also the railway signals, which were operated from the same control room.

Having to look after several mechanical instruments at once, Kolia had evolved a special style of speech, obscure, abrupt, and puzzling, which enabled him, if he chose, to avoid answering questions or getting involved in a conversation. He was said to have abused the advantage this gave him on the day of the disorders.

It is true that, by suppressing information, he had defeated Galiullin's good intentions and, perhaps unwittingly, had given a fatal turn to the events.

Galiullin had called up from town and asked for Commissar Gints, who was somewhere at the station or in its vicinity, in order to tell him that he was on his way to join him and to ask him to wait for him and do nothing until he arrived. Kolia, on the pretext that he was busy signalling an approaching train, refused to call the commissar. At the same time he did his utmost to delay the train, which was bringing up the Cossacks summoned to Biriuchi.

When the troops arrived nevertheless he did not conceal his dismay.

The engine, crawling slowly under the dark roof of the platform, stopped in front of the huge window of the control room. Kolia drew the green serge curtain with the initials of the Company woven in yellow into the border, picked up the enormous water jug standing on the tray on the window ledge, poured some water into the plain, thick, straight-sided glass, drank a few mouthfuls, and looked out.

The engineer saw him from his cab and gave him a friendly nod.

"The stinker, the louse," Kolia thought with hatred. He stuck out his tongue and shook his fist. The engineer not only understood him but managed to convey by a shrug of the shoulders and a nod in the direction of the train: "What was I to do? I'd like to know what you'd have done in my place. He's the boss." —"You're a filthy brute all the same," Kolia replied by gestures.

The horses were taken, balking, out of the freight cars. The thud of their hoofs on the wooden gangways was followed by the ring of their shoes on the stone platform. They were led, rearing, across the tracks.

At the end of the tracks were two rows of derelict wooden coaches. The rain had washed them clean of paint, and worms and damp had rotted them from inside, so that now they were reverting to their original kinship with the wood of the forest, which began just beyond the rolling stock, with its lichen, its birches, and the clouds towering above it.

Varykino

Krueger, former owner   Father of Tonia's
mother

Commissar Strelnikov

Juriatin

...ikulitzyn, Mik, 260   present owners
of Varykino (270)

...na Prokloova, Mik's wife 270

...cchus Mekhonoshin drove Zhivagos
...m the station.

...ndeviatov

...sha   Zhivago's son

...usha, Sasha's nurse 273

...tinia, Mik's maid

At the word of command, the Cossacks mounted their horses and galloped to the clearing.

The rebels of the 212th were surrounded. In woods, horsemen always seem taller and more formidable than in an open field. They impressed the infantrymen, although they had rifles in their mud huts. The Cossacks drew their swords.

Within the ring formed by the horses, some timber was piled up. Gints mounted it and addressed the surrounded men.

As usual, he spoke of soldierly duty, of the fatherland, and many other lofty subjects. But these ideas found no sympathy among his listeners. There were too many of them. They had suffered a great deal in the war, they were thick-skinned and exhausted. They had long been fed up with the phrases Gints was giving them. Four months of wooing by the Left and Right had corrupted these unsophisticated men, who, moreover, were alienated by the speaker's foreign-sounding name and Baltic accent.

Gints felt that his speech was too long and was annoyed at himself, but he thought that he had to make himself clear to his listeners, who instead of being grateful rewarded him with expressions of indifference or hostile boredom. Gradually losing his temper, he decided to speak straight from the shoulder and to bring up the threats he had so far held in reserve. Heedless of the rising murmurs, he reminded the deserters that revolutionary courts-martial had been set up, and called on them, on pain of death, to disarm and give up their ringleaders. If they refused, he said, they would prove that they were common traitors, an irresponsible swollen-headed rabble. The men had become unused to being talked to in such a tone.

Several hundred voices rose in an uproar. Some were low-pitched and almost without anger: "All right, all right. Pipe down. That's enough." But hate-filled, hysterical trebles predominated:

"The nerve! Just like in the old days! These officers still treat us like dirt. So we're traitors, are we? And what about you yourself, Excellency? Why bother with him? Obviously he's a German, an infiltrator. Show us your papers, blueblood. And what are you gaping at, pacifiers?" They turned to the Cossacks. "You've come to restore order, go on, tie us up, have your fun."

But the Cossacks, too, liked Gints' unfortunate speech less and less. "They are all swine to him," they muttered. "Thinks himself the lord and master!" At first singly, and then in ever-growing numbers, they began to sheathe their swords. One after another they got off their horses. When most of them had dismounted, they moved in a disorderly crowd toward the center of the clearing, mixed with the men of the 212th, and fraternized.

"You must vanish quietly," the worried Cossack officers told Gints. "Your car is at the station, we'll send for it to meet you. Hurry."

Gints went, but he felt that to steal away was beneath his dignity, so he turned quite openly toward the station. He was terribly agitated but out of pride forced himself to walk calmly and unhurriedly.

He was close to the station. At the edge of the woods, within sight of the tracks, he looked back for the first time. Soldiers with rifles had followed him. "What do they want?" he wondered. He quickened his pace.

So did his pursuers. The distance between them remained unchanged. He saw the double wall of derelict coaches, stepped behind them, and ran. The train that had brought the Cossacks had been shunted. The lines were clear. He crossed them at a run and leapt onto the steep platform. At the same moment the soldiers ran out from behind the old coaches. Povarikhin and Kolia were shouting and waving to him to get into the station building, where they could save him.

But once again the sense of honor bred in him for generations, a city-bred sense of honor, which impelled him to self-sacrifice and was out of place here, barred his way to safety. His heart pounding wildly, he made a supreme effort to control himself. He told himself: "I must shout to them, 'Come to your senses, men, you know I'm not a spy.' A really heart-felt word or two will bring them to their senses."

In the course of the past months his feeling for a courageous exploit or a heart-felt speech had unconsciously become associated with stages, speakers' platforms, or just chairs onto which you jumped to fling an appeal or ardent call to the crowds.

At the very doors of the station, under the station bell, there stood a water butt for use in case of fire. It was tightly covered. Gints jumped up on the lid and addressed the approaching soldiers with an incoherent but gripping speech. His unnatural voice and the insane boldness of his gesture, two steps from the door where he could so easily have taken shelter, amazed them and stopped them in their tracks. They lowered their rifles.

But Gints, who was standing on the edge of the lid, suddenly pushed it in. One of his legs slipped into the water and the other hung over the edge of the butt.

Seeing him sitting clumsily astride the edge of the butt, the soldiers burst into laughter and the one in front shot Gints in the neck. He was dead by the time the others ran up and thrust their bayonets into his body.

11

Mademoiselle called up Kolia and told him to find Dr. Zhivago a good seat in the train to Moscow, threatening him with exposure if he did not.

Kolia was as usual conducting another conversation and, judging by the decimal fractions that punctuated his speech, transmitting a message in code over a third instrument.

"Pskov, Pskov, can you hear me? What rebels? What help? What are you talking about, Mademoiselle? Ring off, please. Pskov, Pskov, thirty-six point zero one five. Oh hell, they've cut me off. Hello, hello, I can't hear. Is that you again, Mademoiselle? I've told you, I can't. Ask Povarikhin. All lies, fictions. Thirty-six . . . Oh hell . . . Get off the line, Mademoiselle."

And Mademoiselle was saying:

"Don't you throw dust in my eyes, Pskov, Pskov, you liar, I can see right through you, tomorrow you'll put the doctor on the train, and I won't listen to another word from any murdering little Judases."

12

The day Yurii Andreievich left, it was sultry. A storm like the one that had broken two days earlier was brewing. Near the station, at the outskirts of the town, littered with the shells of sunflower seeds, the clay huts and the geese looked white and frightened under the still menace of the black sky.

The grass on the wide field in front of the station and stretching to both sides of it was trampled and entirely covered by a countless multitude who had for weeks been waiting for trains.

Old men in coarse gray woollen coats wandered about in the hot sun from group to group in search of news and rumors. Glum fourteen-year-old boys lay on their elbows twirling peeled twigs, as if they were tending cattle, while their small brothers and sisters scuttled about with flying shirts and pink bottoms. Their legs stretched straight in front of them, their mothers sat on the ground with babies packed into the tight shapeless bosoms of their brown peasants coats.

"All scattered like sheep as soon as the shooting began. They didn't like it," the stationmaster told the doctor unsympathetically as they walked between the rows of bodies lying on the ground in front of the entrance and on the floors inside the station. "In a twinkling everybody cleared off the grass. You could see the ground again; we hadn't seen it in four months with all this gypsy camp going on, we'd forgotten what it looked like. This is where he lay. It's a strange thing, I've seen all sorts of horror in the war, you'd think I'd be used to anything. But I felt so sorry somehow. It was the senselessness of it. What had he done to them? But then they aren't human beings. They say he was the favorite son. And now to the right, if you please, into my office. There isn't a chance on this train, I'm afraid, they'd crush you to death. I'm putting you on a local one. We are making it up now. But not a word about it until you're ready to get on it, they'd tear it apart before it was made up. You change at Sukhinichi tonight."

13

When the "secret" train backed into the station from behind the railway sheds, the whole crowd poured onto the tracks. People rolled down the hills like marbles, scrambled onto the embankment, and, pushing each other, jumped onto the steps and buffers or climbed in through the windows and onto the roofs. The train filled in an instant, while it was still moving, and by the time it stood by the platform, not only was it crammed but passengers hung all over it, from top to bottom. By a miracle, the doctor managed to get onto a platform and from there, still more unaccountably, into the corridor.

There he stayed, sitting on his luggage, all the way to Sukhinichi.

The stormy sky had cleared. In the hot, sunny fields, crickets chirped loudly, muffling the clatter of the train.

Those passengers who stood by the windows shaded the rest from the light. Their double and triple shadows streaked across the floor and benches. Indeed, these shadows went beyond the cars. They were crowded out through the opposite windows, and accompanied the moving shadow of the train itself.

All around people were shouting, bawling songs, quarrelling, and playing cards. Whenever the train stopped, the noise of the besieging crowds outside was added to this turmoil. The roar of the voices was deafening, like a storm at sea, and, as at sea, there would be a sudden lull. In the inexplicable stillness you could hear footsteps hurrying down the platform, the bustle and arguments outside the freight car, isolated words from people, farewells spoken in the distance, and the quiet clucking of hens and rustling of trees in the station garden.

Then, like a telegram delivered on the train, or like greetings from Meliuzeievo addressed to Yurii Andreievich, there drifted in through the windows a familiar fragrance. It came from somewhere to one side and higher than the level of either garden or wild flowers, and it quietly asserted its excellence over everything else.

Kept from the windows by the crowd, the doctor could not see the trees; but he imagined them growing somewhere very near, calmly stretching out their heavy branches to the carriage roofs, and their foliage, covered with dust from the passing trains and thick as night, was sprinkled with constellations of small, glittering waxen flowers.

This happened time and again throughout the trip. There were roaring crowds at every station. And everywhere the linden trees were in blossom.

This ubiquitous fragrance seemed to be preceding the train on its journey north as if it were some sort of rumor that had reached even the smallest, local stations, and which the passengers always found waiting for them on arrival, heard and confirmed by everyone.

14

That night at Sukhinichi a porter who had preserved his prewar obligingness took the doctor over the unlit tracks to the back of some unscheduled train that had just arrived, and put him in a second-class carriage.

Hardly had he unlocked it with the conductor's key and heaved the doctor's luggage inside when the conductor came and tried to throw it out. He was finally appeased by Yurii Andreievich and withdrew and vanished without a trace.

The mysterious train was a "special" and went fairly fast, stopping only briefly at stations, and had some kind of armed guard. The carriage was almost empty.

Zhivago's compartment was lit by a guttering candle that stood on the small table, its flame wavering in the stream of air from the half-open window.

The candle belonged to the only other occupant of the compartment, a fair-haired youth who, judging by the size of his arms and legs, was very tall. His limbs seemed to be attached too loosely at the joints. He had been sprawling nonchalantly in a corner seat by the window, but when Zhivago came in he politely rose and sat up in a more seemly manner.

Something that looked like a floor cloth lay under his seat. One corner of it stirred and a flop-eared setter scrambled out. It sniffed Yurii Andreievich over and ran up and down the compartment throwing out its paws as loosely as its lanky master crossed his legs. Soon, at his command, it scrambled back under the seat and resumed its former likeness to a floor rag.

It was only then that Yurii Andreievich noticed the double-barrelled gun in its case, the leather cartridge belt, and the hunter's bag tightly packed with game that hung on a hook in the compartment.

The young man had been out shooting.

He was extremely talkative, and, smiling amiably, at once engaged the doctor in conversation, looking, as he did so, fixedly at his mouth.

He had an unpleasant, high-pitched voice that now and then rose to a tinny falsetto. Another oddity of his speech was that, while he was plainly Russian, he pronounced one vowel, *u*, in a most outlandish manner, like the French *u*. To utter even this garbled *u*, he had to make a great effort, and he pronounced it louder than any other sound, accompanying it each time with a slight squeal. At moments, apparently by concentrating, he managed to correct this defect but it always came back.

"What is this?" Zhivago wondered. "I'm sure I've read about it, as a doctor I ought to know, but I can't think what it is. It must be some brain trouble that causes defective speech." The squeal struck him as so funny that he could hardly keep a straight face. "Better go to bed," he told himself.

He climbed up onto the rack which was used as a berth. The young man offered to blow out the candle lest it keep him awake. The doctor accepted, thanking him, and the compartment was plunged into darkness.

"Shall I close the window?" Yurii Andreievich asked. "You are not afraid of thieves?"

There was no reply. He repeated his question louder, but there was still no answer.

He struck a match to see if his neighbor had gone out during the brief interval. That he had dropped off to sleep in so short a time seemed even more improbable.

He was there, however, sitting in his place with his eyes open. He smiled at the doctor, leaning over him from his berth.

The match went out. Yurii Andreievich struck another, and while it was alight repeated his question for the third time.

"Do as you wish," the young man replied at once. "I've got nothing a thief would want. But perhaps leave it open. It's stuffy."

"What an extraordinary character!" thought Zhivago. "An eccentric, evidently. Doesn't talk in the dark. And how distinctly he pronounced everything now, without any slur. It's beyond me."

15

Tired out by the events of the past week, the preparations for the trip, and the early start, the doctor expected to go to sleep the moment he had stretched comfortably, but he was mistaken. His exhaustion made him sleepless. Only at daybreak did he fall asleep.

His thoughts swarmed and whirled in the dark. But they all fell clearly into two distinct groups, as it were, two main threads that kept getting tangled and untangled.

One group of thoughts centered around Tonia, their home, and their former, settled life where everything, down to the smallest detail, had an aura of poetry and was permeated with affection and warmth. The doctor was concerned about this life, he wanted it safe and whole and in his night express was impatient to get back to it after two years of separation.

In the same group were his loyalty to the revolution and his admiration for it. This was the revolution in the sense in which it was accepted by the middle classes and in which it had been understood by the students, followers of Blok, in 1905.

These familiar, long-held ideas also included the anticipations and promises of a new order which had appeared on the horizon before the war, between 1912 and 1914, which had emerged in Russian thinking, in Russian art, in Russian life, and which had a bearing on Russia as a whole and on his own future.

It would be good to go back to that climate, once the war was over, to see its renewal and continuation, just as it was good to be going home.

New things were also in the other group of his thoughts, but how different, how unlike the first! These new things were not familiar, not led up to by the old, they were unchosen, determined by an ineluctable reality, and as sudden as an earthquake.

Among these new things was the war with its bloodshed and its horrors, its homelessness and savagery, its ordeals and the practical wisdom that it taught. So, too, were the lonely little towns to which the war washed you up, and the people you met in them. And among these new things too was the revolution—not the idealized intellectuals' revolution of 1905, but this new upheaval, today's, born of the war, bloody, ruthless, elemental, the soldiers' revolution led by those professional revolutionaries, the Bolsheviks.

And among the new thoughts, too, was Nurse Antipova, stranded by the war God knows where, about whose past he knew nothing, who never blamed anyone but whose very silence seemed to be a complaint, who was mysteriously reserved and so strong in her reserve. And so was Yurii Andreievich's honest endeavor not to love her, as wholehearted as his striving throughout his life until now to love everyone, not only his family and his friends, but everyone else as well.

The train rushed on at full speed. The head wind, coming through the open window, ruffled and blew dust on Yurii Andreievich's hair. At every station, by night as by day, the crowds stormed and the linden trees rustled.

Sometimes carts or gigs rattled up to the station out of the darkness, and voices and rumbling wheels mingled with the rustling of trees.

At such moments Yurii Andreievich felt he understood what it was that made these night shadows rustle and put their heads together, and what it was they whispered to each other, lazily stirring their leaves heavy with sleep, like faltering, lisping tongues. It was the very thing he was thinking of, turning restlessly in his berth—the tidings of the ever-widening circles of unrest and excitement in Russia, the tidings of the revolution, of its difficult and fateful hour and its probable ultimate greatness.

16

The doctor did not wake up until after eleven. "Prince, Prince," his neighbor was calling softly to his growling dog. To Yurii Andreievich's astonishment, they still had the compartment to themselves; no other passenger had got in.

The names of the stations were familiar to him from childhood. They were out of the province of Kaluga and well into that of Moscow.

He washed and shaved in prewar comfort and came back to

the compartment in time for breakfast, to which his strange companion had invited him. Now he had a better look at him.

What struck him most were his extreme garrulousness and restlessness. He liked to talk, and what mattered to him was not communicating and exchanging ideas but the function of speech itself, pronouncing words and uttering sounds. As he spoke he kept jumping up as if he were on springs; he laughed deafeningly for no reason, briskly rubbing his hands with contentment, and, when all this seemed inadequate to express his delight, he slapped his knees hard, laughing to the point of tears.

His conversation had the same peculiarities as the night before. He was curiously inconsistent, now indulging in uninvited confidences, now leaving the most innocent questions unanswered. He poured out incredible and disconnected facts about himself. Perhaps he lied a little; he obviously was out to impress by his extremism and by his rejection of all commonly accepted opinions.

It all reminded Zhivago of something long familiar to him. Similar radical views were advanced by the nihilists of the last century, and a little later by some of Dostoievsky's heroes, and still more recently by their direct descendants, the provincial educated classes, who were often ahead of the capitals because they still were in the habit of going to the root of things while in the capitals such an approach was regarded as obsolete and unfashionable.

The young man told him that he was the nephew of a well-known revolutionary, but that his parents were incorrigible reactionaries, real dodoes, as he called them. They had a fairly large estate in a place near the front, where he had been brought up. His parents had been at swords' points with his uncle all their lives, but the uncle did not bear them a grudge and now used his influence to save them a good deal of unpleasantness.

His own views were like his uncle's, the talkative man informed Zhivago; he was an extremist in everything, whether in life, politics, or art. This too reminded the doctor of Piotr Verkhovensky[1]—not so much the leftism as the frivolity and the shallowness. "He'll be telling me he's a futurist next," thought

1 Character in Dostoievsky's *The Possessed.*

Yurii Andreievich, and indeed they spoke of modern art. "Now it'll be sport—race horses, skating rinks, or French wrestling." And the conversation turned to shooting.

The young man had been shooting in his native region. He was a crack shot, he boasted, and if it had not been for the physical defect that had kept him out of the army he would have distinguished himself by his marksmanship. Catching Zhivago's questioning glance, he exclaimed: "What? Haven't you noticed anything? I thought you had guessed what was the matter with me."

He took two cards out of his pocket and handed them to Yurii Andreievich. One was his visiting card. He had a double name; he was called Maxim Aristarkhovich Klintsov-Pogorevshikh—or just Pogorevshikh, as he asked Zhivago to call him, in honor of his uncle who bore this name.

The other card showed a table with squares, each containing a drawing of two hands variously joined and with fingers differently folded. It was an alphabet for deaf-mutes. Suddenly everything became clear. Pogorevshikh was a phenomenally gifted pupil of the school of either Hartman or Ostrogradov, a deaf-mute who had reached an incredible facility in speaking and understanding speech by observing the throat muscles of his teachers.

Putting together what he had told him of the part of the country he came from and of his shooting expedition, the doctor said:

"Forgive me if this is indiscreet; you needn't tell me. Did you have anything to do with setting up the Zybushino republic?"

"But how did you guess . . . Do you know Blazheiko? Did I have anything to do with it? Of course I did!" Pogorevshikh burst forth joyfully, laughing, rocking from side to side, and frenziedly slapping his knees. And once again he launched on a long and fantastic discourse.

He said that Blazheiko had provided the opportunity and Zybushino the place for the application of his own theories. Yurii Andreievich found it hard to follow his exposition of them. Pogorevshikh's philosophy was a mixture of the principles of anarchism and hunter's tall stories.

Imperturbable as an oracle, he prophesied disastrous upheavals in the near future. Yurii Andreievich inwardly agreed that this was not unlikely, but the calm, authoritative tone in which this unpleasant boy was making his forecasts angered him.

"Just a moment," he said hesitantly. "True, all this may happen. But it seems to me that with all that's going on—the chaos, the disintegration, the pressure from the enemy—this is not the moment to start dangerous experiments. The country must be allowed to recover from one upheaval before plunging into another. We must wait till at least relative peace and order are restored."

"That's naïve," said Pogorevshikh. "What you call disorder is just as normal a state of things as the order you're so keen about. All this destruction—it's a natural and preliminary stage of a broad creative plan. Society has not yet disintegrated sufficiently. It must fall to pieces completely, then a genuinely revolutionary government will put the pieces together and build on completely new foundations."

Yurii Andreievich felt disturbed. He went out into the corridor.

The train, gathering speed, was approaching Moscow. It ran through birch woods dotted with summer houses. Small roofless suburban stations with crowds of vacationers flew by and were left far behind in the cloud of dust raised by the train, and seemed to turn like a carrousel. The engine hooted repeatedly, and the sound filled the surrounding woods and came back in long, hollow echoes from far away.

All at once, for the first time in the last few days, Yurii Andreievich understood quite clearly where he was, what was happening to him, and what awaited him in an hour or so.

Three years of changes, moves, uncertainties, upheavals; the war, the revolution; scenes of destruction, scenes of death, shelling, blown-up bridges, fires, ruins—all this turned suddenly into a huge, empty, meaningless space. The first real event since the long interruption was this trip in the fast-moving train, the fact that he was approaching his home, which was intact, which still existed, and in which every stone was dear to him. This was real life, meaningful experience, the actual goal of all quests, this was what art aimed at—homecoming, return to one's family, to oneself, to true existence.

The woods had been left behind. The train broke out of the leafy tunnels into the open. A sloping field rose from a hollow to a wide mound. It was striped horizontally with dark green potato beds; beyond them, at the top of the mound, were cold frames. Opposite the field, beyond the curving tail of the train, a dark purple cloud covered half the sky. Sunbeams were breaking through it, spreading like wheel spokes and reflected by the glass of the frames in a blinding glare.

Suddenly, warm, heavy rain, sparkling in the sun, fell out of the cloud. The drops fell hurriedly and their drumming matched the clatter of the speeding train, as though the rain were afraid of being left behind and were trying to catch up.

Hardly had the doctor noticed this when the Church of Christ the Savior showed over the rim of the hill, and a minute later the domes, chimneys, roofs, and houses of the city.

"Moscow," he said, returning to the compartment. "Time to get ready."

Pogorevshikh jumped up, rummaged in his hunter's bag, and took out a fat duck. "Take it," he said. "As a souvenir. I have rarely spent a day in such pleasant company."

Zhivago's protests were unavailing. In the end he said: "All right, I'll take it as a present from you to my wife."

"Splendid, splendid, your wife," Pogorevshikh kept repeating delightedly, as though he had heard the word for the first time, jerking and laughing so much that Prince jumped out and took part in the rejoicing.

The train drew into the station. The compartment was plunged into darkness. The deaf-mute held out the wild duck, wrapped in a torn piece of some printed poster.

CHAPTER SIX

THE MOSCOW ENCAMPMENT

1

In the train it had seemed to Zhivago that only the train was moving but that time stood still and it was not later than noon.

But the sun was already low by the time his cab had finally made its way through the dense crowd in Smolensky Square.

In later years, when the doctor recalled this day, it seemed to him—he did not know whether this was his original impression or whether it had been altered by subsequent experiences —that even then the crowd hung about the market only by habit, that there was no reason for it to be there, for the empty stalls were shut and not even padlocked and there was nothing to buy or sell in the littered square, which was no longer swept.

And it seemed to him that even then he saw, like a silent reproach to the passers-by, thin, decently dressed old men and women shrinking against the walls, wordlessly offering for sale things no one bought and no one needed—artificial flowers, round coffee pots with glass lids and whistles, black net evening dresses, uniforms of abolished offices.

Humbler people traded in more useful things—crusts of stale rationed black bread, damp, dirty chunks of sugar, and ounce packages of coarse tobacco cut in half right through the wrapping.

And all sorts of nondescript odds and ends were sold all over the market, going up in price as they changed hands.

The cab turned into one of the narrow streets opening from the square. Behind them, the setting sun warmed their backs. In front of them a draft horse clattered along, pulling an empty, bouncing cart. It raised pillars of dust, glowing like bronze in the rays of the low sun. At last they passed the cart which had blocked their way. They drove faster. The doctor was struck by the piles of old newspapers and posters, torn down from the walls and fences, littering the sidewalks and streets. The wind pulled them one way and hoofs, wheels, and feet shoved them the other.

They passed several intersections, and soon the doctor's house appeared at a corner. The cab stopped.

Yurii Andreievich gasped for breath and his heart hammered loudly as he got out, walked up to the front door, and rang the bell. Nothing happened. He rang again. As there was still no reply, he went on ringing at short, anxious intervals. He was still ringing when he saw that the door had been opened by Antonina Alexandrovna and that she stood holding it wide open. The unexpectedness of it so dumfounded them both that neither of them heard the other cry out. But as the door held wide open by Tonia was in itself a welcome and almost an embrace, they soon recovered and rushed into each other's arms. A moment later they were both talking at once, interrupting each other.

"First of all, is everybody well?"

"Yes, yes, don't worry. Everything is all right. I wrote you a lot of silly nonsense, forgive me. But we'll talk about that later. Why didn't you send a telegram? Markel will take your things up. I suppose you got worried when Egorovna didn't let you in! She is in the country."

"You're thinner. But how young you look, and so pretty! Wait a minute, I'll pay the driver."

"Egorovna has gone to get some flour. The other servants have been discharged. There's only one girl now, Niusha, you don't know her, she's looking after Sashenka, there's no one else. Everybody has been told you're coming, they're all longing to see you—Gordon, Dudorov, everyone."

"How is Sashenka?"

"All right, thank God. He's just waked up. If you weren't still dirty from the train we could go to him at once."

"Is Father at home?"

"Didn't anyone write to you? He's at the borough council from morning till night, he's the chairman. Yes, can you believe it! Have you settled with the driver? Markel! Markel!"

They were standing in the middle of the street with wicker hamper and suitcase blocking the way, and the passers-by, as they walked around them, looked them over from head to foot, and stared at the cab as it pulled away from the curb and at the wide-open front door, to see what would happen next.

But Markel was already running up from the gate to welcome the young master, his waistcoat over his cotton shirt and his porter's cap in his hand, shouting as he ran:

"Heavenly powers, if it isn't Yurochka! It's our little falcon in person! Yurii Andreievich, light of our eyes, so you haven't forgotten us and our prayers, you've come home! And what do you want?" he snapped at the curious. "Be off with you. What's there to goggle at?"

"How are you, Markel? Let's embrace. Put your cap on, you eccentric. Well, what's new? How's your wife? How are the girls?"

"How should they be? They're growing, thanks be to God. As for news, you can see for yourself, while you were busy at the front we were not idle either. Such a mess they made, such bedlam, the devil couldn't sort it out! The streets unswept, roofs unrepaired, houses unpainted, bellies empty as in Lent. Real peace there—no annexations and no reparations, as they say."

"I'll tell on you, Markel. He's always like that, Yurochka. I can't stand that foolishness. He's talking like that only because he thinks you like it, but he's a sly one. All right, all right, Markel, don't argue with me, I know you. You're a deep one, Markel. Time you were sensible. After all, you know what kind of people we are."

They went in. Markel carried the doctor's things inside, shut the front door behind him, and went on confidentially:

"Antonina Alexandrovna is cross, you heard what she said. It's always like that. She says, You're all black inside, Markel, she says, like that stovepipe. Nowadays, she says, every little child, maybe even every spaniel or any other lap dog knows what's what. That, of course, is true, but all the same, Yurochka, believe it or not, those who know have seen the book, the Mason's prophecies, one hundred and forty years it's been lying under a stone, and now, it's my considered opinion, Yurochka, we've been sold down the river, sold for a song. But can I say a word? See for yourself, Antonina Alexandrovna is making signs to me, she wants me to go."

"Do you wonder? That's enough, Markel, put the things down, and that will be all, thank you. If Yurii Andreievich wants anything, he'll call you."

2

"At last we've got rid of him! All right, all right, you can listen to him if you like, but I can tell you, it's all make-believe. You talk to him and you think he's the village idiot, butter wouldn't melt in his mouth, and all the time he's secretly sharpening his knife—only he hasn't quite decided yet whom he'll use it on, the charming fellow."

"Isn't that a bit far-fetched? I expect he's just drunk, that's all."

"And when is he sober, I'd like to know. Anyway, I've had enough of him. What worries me is, Sasha might go to sleep again before you've seen him. If it weren't for typhus on trains . . . You haven't any lice on you?"

"I don't think so. I travelled comfortably—the same as before the war. I'd better have a quick wash, though; I'll wash more thoroughly afterwards. Which way are you going? Don't we go through the drawing room any more?"

"Oh, of course, you don't know. Father and I thought and thought and we decided to give up a part of the ground floor to the Agricultural Academy. It's too much to heat in winter, anyway. Even the top floor is too big. So we've offered it to them. They haven't taken it over yet, but they've moved in their libraries and their herbariums and their specimens of seed. I only hope we don't get rats—it's grain, after all. But at the moment they're keeping the rooms spick-and-span. By the way, we don't say 'rooms' any more, it's called 'living space' now. Come on, this way. Aren't you slow to catch on! We go up the back stairs. Understand? Follow me, I'll show you."

"I'm very glad you've given up those rooms. The hospital I've been in was also in a private house. Endless suites of rooms,

here and there the parquet flooring still left. Potted palms sticking out their paws like ghosts over the beds—some of the
wounded from the battle zone used to wake up screaming—
they weren't quite normal, of course—shell-shocked—we had
to remove the plants. What I mean is, there really was something unhealthy in the way rich people used to live. Masses of
superfluous things. Too much furniture, too much room, too much
emotional refinement, too many circumlocutions. I'm very glad
we're using fewer rooms. We should give up still more."

"What's that parcel you've got? There's something sticking
out of it, it looks like a bird's beak. It's a duck! How lovely!
A wild drake! Where did you get it? I can't believe my eyes.
It's worth a fortune these days."

"Somebody made me a present of it on the train. I'll tell you
later, it's a long story. What shall I do? Shall I leave it in the
kitchen?"

"Yes, of course. I'll send Niusha down at once to pluck and
clean it. They say there will be all sorts of horrors this winter,
famine, cold."

"Yes, that's what they are saying everywhere. Just now, I
was looking out of the window in the train—I thought, what is
there in the whole world worth more than a peaceful family
life and work? The rest isn't in our hands. It does look as if there
is a bad time coming for a lot of people. Some are trying to get
out, they talk of going south, to the Caucasus, or farther still.
I wouldn't want to do that, myself. A grown-up man should
share his country's fate. To me it's obvious. But for you it's different. I wish you didn't have to go through it all. I'd like to
send you away to some safe place—to Finland, perhaps. But if
we stand gossiping half an hour on every step we'll never get
upstairs."

"Wait a minute. I forgot to tell you. I've got news for you—
and what news! Nikolai Nikolaievich is back."

"What Nikolai Nikolaievich?"

"Uncle Kolia."

"Tonia! It can't be! Is it really true?"

"It is true. He was in Switzerland. He came all the way
around through London and Finland."

"Tonia! You're not joking? Have you seen him? Where is he? Can't we get him now, at once?"

"Don't be so impatient. He's staying with someone in the country. He promised to be back the day after tomorrow. He's changed a lot. You'll be disappointed. He stopped in Petersburg on the way, he's got Bolshevized. Father gets quite hoarse arguing with him. But why do we stop on every step. Let's go. So you too have heard there's a bad time ahead—hardships, dangers, anything might happen."

"I think so myself. Well, what of it? We'll manage, it can't be the end of everything. We'll wait and see, the same as other people."

"They say there won't be any firewood, or water, or light. They'll abolish money. No supplies will be coming in. Now we've stopped again! Come along. Listen, they say there are wonderful iron stoves for sale in the Arbat. Small ones. You can burn a newspaper and cook a meal. I've got the address. We must get one before they're all gone."

"That's right. We'll get one. Good idea. But just think of it, Uncle Kolia! I can't get over it."

"Let me tell you what I want to do. We'll set aside a corner somewhere on the top floor, say two or three rooms, communicating ones, and we'll keep those for ourselves and Father and Sashenka and Niusha, and we'll give up all the rest of the house. We'll put up a partition and have our own door, and it will be like a separate apartment. We'll put one of those iron stoves in the middle room, with a pipe through the window, and we'll do all our laundry, and our cooking, and our entertaining, all in this one room. That way we'll get the most out of the fuel, and who knows, with God's help, we'll get through the winter."

"Of course we'll get through it. There's no question. That's a fine idea. And you know what? We'll have a housewarming. We'll cook the duck and we'll invite Uncle Kolia."

"Lovely. And I'll ask Gordon to bring some drink. He can get it from some laboratory or other. Now look, this is the room I was thinking of. All right? Put your suitcase down and go get your hamper. We could ask Dudorov and Shura Shlesinger to the housewarming as well. You don't mind? You haven't for-

gotten where the washroom is? Spray yourself with some dis-
infectant. In the meantime I'll go in to Sashenka, and send
Niusha down, and when we're ready I'll call you."

3

The most important thing for him in Moscow was his little
boy. He had been mobilized almost as soon as Sashenka was
born. He hardly knew him.

One day, while Tonia was still in hospital, he went to
see her; he was already in uniform and was about to leave
Moscow. He arrived at the babies' feeding time and was not
allowed in.

He sat down in the waiting room. From the nursery, at the
end of the passage beyond the maternity ward, came the squealing chorus of ten or twelve babies' voices. Several nurses came
down the corridor, hurrying so that the newborn babies should
not catch cold, taking them to their mothers, bundled up like
shopping parcels, one under each arm.

"Wa, wa," yelled the babies all on one note, almost impas-
sively, without feeling, as if it were all in the day's work.
Only one voice stood out from the others. It was also yelling
"wa, wa," and it did not express any more suffering than
the rest, but it was deeper and seemed to shout less out of
duty than with a deliberate, sullen hostility.

Yurii Andreievich had already decided that his child was to
be called Alexander in honor of his father-in-law. For some reason he imagined that the voice he had singled out was that of
his son; perhaps it was because this particular cry had its own
character and seemed to foreshadow the future personality and
destiny of a particular human being; it had its own sound-
coloring, which included the child's name, Alexander, so Yurii
Andreievich imagined.

He was not mistaken. It turned out later that this had in
fact been Sashenka's voice. It was the first thing he had known
about his son.

The next thing was the photographs Tonia sent to him at the
front. They showed a cheerful, handsome, chubby little fellow

with a cupid's-bow mouth, standing up on a blanket, bandy-legged and with its fist up as if it were doing a peasant dance. Sashenka had been a year old at the time and trying to take his first steps; now he was two and was beginning to talk.

Yurii Andreievich picked up his suitcase, put it on to the card table by the window, and began to unpack. What had the room been used for in the past, he wondered. He could not recognize it. Tonia must have changed the furniture or the wall-paper or redecorated it in some way.

He took out his shaving kit. A bright full moon rose between the pillars of the church tower exactly opposite the window. When it lit up the top layer of clothes and books inside the suitcase, the light in the room changed and he realized where he was.

It had been Anna Ivanovna's storeroom, where she used to put broken chairs and tables and old papers. Here she had kept her family archives and, in the summer, the trunks of winter clothes. During her lifetime the corners were cluttered up to the ceiling with junk, and the children were not allowed in. Only at Christmas or Easter, when huge crowds of children came to parties and the whole of the top floor was thrown open to them, was it unlocked and they played bandit in it, hiding under the tables, dressing up, and blackening their faces with cork.

The doctor stood thinking of all this, then he went down the back stairs to get his wicker hamper from the hall.

In the kitchen Niusha squatted in front of the stove, plucking the duck on a piece of newspaper. When he came in carrying his hamper she jumped up with a shy, graceful movement, blushing crimson, shook the feathers from her apron, and, after greeting him respectfully, offered to help him. He thanked her, saying he could manage, and went up. His wife called him from a couple of rooms farther on: "You can come in now, Yura."

He went into the room, which was Tonia's and his old class-room. The boy in the crib was not nearly so handsome as in his photograph, but he was the exact image of Yurii Andreievich's mother, Maria Nikolaievna Zhivago, a more striking like-ness than any of her portraits.

"Here's Daddy, here's your Daddy, wave your hand like a good boy," Antonina Alexandrovna was saying. She lowered the net of the crib to make it easier for the father to kiss the boy and pick him up.

Sashenka, though doubtless frightened and repelled, let the unshaven stranger get quite close and bend over him, then he jerked himself upright, clutching the front of his mother's dress with one hand, and angrily swung the other arm and slapped him in the face. Terrified by his own daring, he then threw himself into his mother's arms and burst into bitter tears.

"No, no," Tonia scolded him. "You mustn't do that, Sashenka. What will Daddy think? He'll think Sasha is a bad boy. Now, show how you can kiss, kiss Daddy. Don't cry, silly, it's all right."

"Let him be, Tonia," the doctor said. "Don't bother him, and don't upset yourself. I know the kind of nonsense you are thinking—that it's not accidental, it's a bad sign—but that's all rubbish. It's only natural. The boy has never seen me. Tomorrow he'll have a good look at me and we'll become inseparable."

Yet he went out of the room depressed and with a feeling of foreboding.

4

Within the next few days he realized how alone he was. He did not blame anyone. He had merely got what he had asked for.

His friends had become strangely dim and colorless. Not one of them had preserved his own outlook, his own world. They had been much more vivid in his memory. He must have overestimated them in the past. Under the old order, which enabled those whose lives were secure to play the fools and eccentrics at the expense of the others while the majority led a wretched existence, it had been only too easy to mistake the foolishness and idleness of a privileged minority for genuine character and originality. But the moment the lower classes had risen, and the privileges of those on top had been abolished, how quickly had those people faded, how unregretfully had they renounced independent ideas—apparently no one had ever had such ideas!

The only people to whom Yurii Andreievich now felt close were his wife, her father, and two or three of his colleagues, modest rank-and-file workers, who did not indulge in grandiloquent phrases.

The party with duck and vodka was given as planned, a few days after his return. By then he had seen all those who came to it, so that the dinner was not in fact the occasion of their reunion.

The large duck was an unheard-of luxury in those already hungry days, but there was no bread with it, and because of this its splendor was somehow pointless—it even got on one's nerves.

The alcohol (a favorite black-market currency) had been brought by Gordon in a medicine bottle with a glass stopper. Antonina Alexandrovna never let go of the bottle, and now and then diluted a small portion of the alcohol with more or less water, according to her inspiration. It was discovered that it is easier to hold a number of consistently strong drinks than ones of varying strength. This, too, was annoying.

But the saddest thing of all was that their party was a kind of betrayal. You could not imagine anyone in the houses across the street eating or drinking in the same way at the same time. Beyond the windows lay silent, dark, hungry Moscow. Its shops were empty, and as for game and vodka, people had even forgotten to think about such things.

And so it turned out that only a life similar to the life of those around us, merging with it without a ripple, is genuine life, and that an unshared happiness is not happiness, so that duck and vodka, when they seem to be the only ones in town, are not even duck and vodka. And this was most vexing of all.

The guests too inspired unhappy reflections. Gordon had been all right in the days when he was given to gloomy thoughts and expressed them sullenly and clumsily. He was Zhivago's best friend, and in the gymnasium many people had liked him.

But now he had decided to give himself a new personality,

and the results of his efforts were unfortunate. He played the merry fellow, he was jovial, cracked jokes, and often exclaimed, "What fun!" and "How amusing!"—expressions that did not belong to his vocabulary, for Gordon had never looked upon life as an entertainment.

While they were waiting for Dudorov he told the story of Dudorov's marriage, which he thought was comical, and which was circulating among his friends. Yurii Andreievich had not yet heard it.

It turned out that Dudorov had been married for about a year and then divorced his wife. The improbable gist of this story consisted in the following:

Dudorov had been drafted into the army by mistake. While he was serving and his case was being investigated, he was constantly punished for absent-mindedly forgetting to salute officers in the street. For a long time after his discharge he would raise his arm impulsively whenever an officer came in sight, and often he imagined epaulettes where there were none.

In this latter period his behavior was erratic in other ways as well. At one point—so the rumor went—while waiting for a steamer at a Volga port, he made the acquaintance of two young women, sisters, who were waiting for the same steamer. Confused by the presence of a large number of army men and the memories of his misadventures as a soldier, he fell in love with the younger sister, and proposed to her on the spot. "Amusing, isn't it?" Gordon said. But he had to interrupt his story when its hero was heard at the door. Dudorov entered the room.

Like Gordon, he had become the opposite of what he had been. He had always been flippant and featherbrained: now he was a serious scholar. As a schoolboy he had been expelled for helping political prisoners escape; he had then tried several art schools, but in the end had become a student of the humanities. During the war he graduated from the university a few years behind his schoolmates. Now he held two chairs—those of Russian history and of general history. He was even the author of two books, one on the land policies of Ivan the Terrible, the other a study of Saint-Just.

Here at the party he spoke amiably about everyone and everything, in a voice that was muffled as though by a cold, staring dreamily at a certain fixed point in the distance like a man delivering a lecture.

Toward the end of the evening, when Shura Shlesinger burst in and added to the general noise and excitement, Dudorov, who had been Zhivago's childhood friend, asked him several times, addressing him with the formal "you" rather than the usual "thou," whether he had read Mayakovsky's *War and the World* and *Flute-Spine*.

Missing Yurii Andreievich's reply in all the noise, he asked him again a little later: "Have you read *Flute-Spine* and *Man?*"

"I told you, Innokentii. It's not my fault that you don't listen. Well, all right, I'll say it again. I've always liked Mayakovsky. He is a sort of continuation of Dostoievsky. Or rather, he's a Dostoievsky character writing lyrical poems—one of his young rebels, the 'Raw Youth' or Hippolyte or Raskolnikov. What an all-devouring poetic energy! And his way of saying a thing once and for all, uncompromisingly, straight from the shoulder! And above all, with what daring he flings all this in the face of society and beyond, into space!"

But the main attraction of the evening was, of course, Uncle Kolia. Antonina Alexandrovna had been mistaken in thinking that he was out of town; he had come back the day of his nephew's return. They had met a couple of times already and had got over their initial exclamations and had talked and laughed together to their heart's content.

The first time had been on a dull, gray night with a drizzle, fine as watery dust. Yurii Andreievich went to see him at his hotel. The hotels were already refusing to take people in except at the recommendation of the town authorities, but Nikolai Nikolaievich was well known and had kept some of his old connections.

The hotel looked like a lunatic asylum abandoned by its staff —the stairways and corridors empty, everything in a state of chaos.

Through the large window of his unswept room the huge

square of those mad days looked in, deserted and frightening, more like a square in a nightmare than the one plainly to be seen in front of the hotel.

For Yurii Andreievich the encounter was a tremendous, unforgettable event. He was seeing the idol of his childhood, the teacher who had dominated his mind as a boy.

His gray hair was becoming to him, and his loose foreign suit fitted him well. He was very young and handsome for his years.

Admittedly, he was overshadowed by the grandeur of the events; seen beside them, he lost in stature. But it never occurred to Yurii Andreievich to measure him by such a yardstick.

He was surprised at Nikolai Nikolaievich's calm, at his light and detached tone in speaking of politics. He was more self-possessed than most Russians could be at that time. It marked him as a new arrival, and it seemed old-fashioned and a little embarrassing.

But it was something very different from politics that filled those first few hours of their reunion, that made them laugh and cry and throw their arms around each other's necks, and punctuated their first feverish conversation with frequent moments of silence.

Theirs was a meeting of two artists, and although they were close relatives, and the past arose and lived again between them and memories surged up and they informed each other of all that had happened during their separation, the moment they began to speak of the things that really matter to creative minds, all other ties between them vanished, their kinship and difference of age were forgotten, all that was left was the confrontation of elemental forces, of energies and principles.

For the last ten years Nikolai Nikolaievich had had no opportunity to speak about the problems of creative writing as freely and intimately as now. Nor had Yurii Andreievich ever heard views as penetrating, apt, and inspiring as on that occasion.

Their talk was full of exclamations, they paced excitedly up and down the room, marvelling at each other's perspicacity, or stood in silence by the window drumming on the glass, deeply moved by the exalting discovery of how completely they understood each other.

Such was their first meeting, but later the doctor had seen his uncle a few times in company, and then Nikolai Nikolaievich was completely different, unrecognizable.

He felt that he was a visitor in Moscow and persisted in acting like one. Whether it was Petersburg that he regarded as his home, or some other place, remained uncertain. He enjoyed his role of a social star and political oracle, and possibly he imagined that Moscow would have political salons in the style of Madame Roland's in Paris on the eve of the Convention.

Calling on his women friends at their hospitable apartments in quiet Moscow back streets, he amiably teased them and their husbands on their backwardness and parochialism. He showed off his familiarity with newspapers, as he had done formerly with books forbidden by the Church, and Orphic texts.

It was said that he had left a new young love, much unfinished business, and a half-written book in Switzerland, and had only come for a dip into the stormy waters of his homeland, expecting, if he came out safe and sound, to hasten back to his Alps.

He was pro-Bolshevik, and often mentioned two left-wing Social Revolutionaries who shared his views, a journalist who wrote under the pseudonym of Miroshka Pomor and a pamphleteer, Sylvia Koteri.

"It's frightful, what you've come down to, Nikolai Nikolaievich," Alexander Alexandrovich chided him. "You and your Miroshkas! What a cesspool! And then that Lydia Pokori."

"Koteri," corrected Nikolai Nikolaievich, "and Sylvia."

"Pokori or Potpourri, who cares. Names won't change anything."

"All the same, it happens to be Koteri," Nikolai Nikolaievich insisted patiently. They had dialogues of this sort:

"What are we arguing about? It's so obvious that it makes you blush to have to prove it. It's elementary. For centuries the mass of the people have lived impossible lives. Take any history textbook. Whatever it was called—feudalism and serfdom or capitalism and industrial workers, it was unnatural and unjust. This has been known for a long time, and the world has been preparing for an upheaval that would bring enlightenment to the people and put everything in its proper place.

"You know perfectly well that it's quite useless tinkering with the old structure, you have to dig right down to the foundations. I don't say the whole building mayn't collapse as a result. What of it? The fact that it's frightening doesn't mean it won't happen. It's a question of time. How can you dispute it?"

"That's not the point, that's not what I was talking about," Alexander Alexandrovich said angrily, and the argument flared up. "Your Potpourris and Miroshkas are people without a conscience. They say one thing and do another. Anyway, where's your logic? It's a complete nonsequitur. No, wait a minute, I'll show you something," and he would begin hunting for some newspaper with a controversial article, banging the drawers of his desk and stimulating his eloquence with this noisy fuss.

Alexander Alexandrovich liked something to get in his way when he was talking; the distraction served as an excuse for his mumbling and his hems and haws. His fits of talkativeness came on him when he was looking for something he had lost—say, hunting for a matching snow boot in the dimly lighted cloakroom—or when he stood at the bathroom door with a towel over his arm, or when he was passing a heavy serving dish or pouring wine into the glasses of his friends.

Yurii Andreievich enjoyed listening to his father-in-law. He adored the familiar, old-Moscow singsong and the soft, purring Gromeko *r*'s.

Alexander Alexandrovich's upper lip with its little cropped mustache protruded above the lower lip in just the same way as his butterfly tie stuck out from his neck. There was something in common between the lip and the tie, and it somehow gave him a touching, childishly trusting look.

On the night of the party Shura Shlesinger appeared very late. She had come straight from a meeting and was wearing a suit and a worker's cap. She strode into the room and, shaking everyone's hand in turn, at once burst into complaints and accusations.

"How are you, Tonia? Hello, Alexander. You must admit it's disgusting. The whole of Moscow knows he's back, everyone is talking about it, and I am the last to be told. Well, I suppose I'm not good enough. Where is he, anyway? Let me get at him, you surround him like a wall. Well, how are you? I've read it, I don't understand a word, but it's brilliant, you can tell at once. How are you, Nikolai Nikolaievich? I'll be back in a moment, Yurochka, I've got to talk to you. Hello, young men. You're here too, Gogochka, Goosey-Goosey-Gander" (this to a distant relative of the Gromekos', an enthusiastic admirer of all rising talents, known as Goosey because of his idiot laugh and as the Tapeworm on account of his lankiness). "So you're eating and drinking? I'll soon catch up with you. Well, my friends, you've simply no idea what you're missing. You don't know anything, you haven't seen a thing. If you only knew what's going on! You go and have a look at a real mass meeting, with real workers, real soldiers, not out of books. Just try to let out a squeak to them about fighting the war to a victorious end! They'll give you a victorious end! I've just been listening to a sailor—Yurochka, you'd simply rave! What passion! What single-mindedness!"

Shura was interrupted time and again. Everyone shouted. She sat next to Yurii Andreievich, took his hand in hers, and, moving her face close to his, shouted like a megaphone above the din:

"Let me take you along someday, Yurochka. I'll show you real people. You must, you simply must get your feet on the ground, like Antaeus. Why are you staring at me like that? I'm an old war horse, didn't you know? An old Bestuzhevist.[1] I've seen the inside of a prison, I've fought on the barricades.—Well of course, what did you think? Oh, we don't know the people at all. I've just come from there, I was right in the thick of it. I'm collecting a library for them."

She had had a drink and was obviously getting tipsy. But Yurii Andreievich's head was also spinning. He never noticed how it happened that Shura was now at one end of the room and he at the other; he was standing at the head of the table and apparently, quite unexpectedly to himself, making a speech. It took him some time to get silence.

"Ladies and gentlemen . . . I should like . . . Misha! Gogochka! Tonia, what am I to do, they won't listen! Ladies and gentlemen, let me say a word or two. Unprecedented, extraor-

[1] A student taking the Bestuzhev university courses for women. Many of the students were left-wing.

dinary events are approaching. Before they burst upon us, here is what I wish you: May God grant us not to lose each other and not to lose our souls. Gogochka, you can cheer afterwards, I haven't finished. Stop talking in the corners and listen carefully.

"In this third year of the war the people have become convinced that the difference between those on the front line and those at the rear will sooner or later vanish. The sea of blood will rise until it reaches every one of us and submerge all who stayed out of the war. The revolution is this flood.

"During the revolution it will seem to you, as it seemed to us at the front, that life has stopped, that there is nothing personal left, that there is nothing going on in the world except killing and dying. If we live long enough to read the chronicles and memoirs of this period, we shall realize that in these five or ten years we have experienced more than other people do in a century. I don't know whether the people will rise of themselves and advance spontaneously like a tide, or whether everything will be done in the name of the people. Such a tremendous event requires no dramatic proof of its existence. I'll be convinced without proof. It's petty to explore causes of titanic events. They haven't any. It's only in a family quarrel that you look for beginnings—after people have pulled each other's hair and smashed the dishes they rack their brains trying to figure out who started it. What is truly great is without beginning, like the universe. It confronts us as suddenly as if it had always been there or had dropped out of the blue.

"I too think that Russia is destined to become the first socialist state since the beginning of the world. When this comes to pass, the event will stun us for a long time, and after awakening we shall have lost half our memories forever. We'll have forgotten what came first and what followed, and we won't look for causes. The new order of things will be all around us and as familiar to us as the woods on the horizon or the clouds over our heads. There will be nothing else left."

He said a few more things, and by then he had sobered up completely. As before, he could not hear clearly what people were saying, and answered them pointlessly. He saw that they liked him, but could not rid himself of the sadness that oppressed him. He said:

"Thank you, thank you. I appreciate your feelings, but I don't deserve them. It's wrong to bestow love in a hurry, as though otherwise one would later have to give much more of it."

They all laughed and clapped, taking it for a deliberate witticism, while he did not know where to escape from his forebodings of disaster and his feeling that despite his striving for the good and his capacity for happiness, he had no power over the future.

The guests began to leave. They had long, tired faces. Their yawns, snapping and unsnapping their jaws, made them look like horses.

Before going, they drew the curtains and pushed the windows open. There was a yellowish dawn in the wet sky filled with dirty, pea-colored clouds. "Looks as if there's been a storm while we were chattering," said someone. "I was caught in the rain on my way here, I only just made it," Shura confirmed.

In the deserted street it was still dark and the drip-drip of the water from the trees alternated with the insistent chirruping of drenched sparrows.

There was a roll of thunder, as if a plow had been dragged right across the sky. Then silence. Then four loud, delayed thuds, like overgrown potatoes in autumn being flung out with a shovel from the soft ground.

The thunder cleared the dusty, smoke-filled room. Suddenly the element of life became distinguishable, as apprehensible as electric currents, air and water, desire for happiness, earth, sky.

The street filled with the voices of the departing guests. They had begun a heated argument in the house and continued arguing just as hotly in the street. Gradually the voices grew fainter in the distance and died out.

"How late it is," said Yurii Andreievich. "Let's go to bed. The only people I love in the world are you and Father."

5

August had gone by and now September was almost over. The inevitable was approaching. Winter was near and, in the human world, something like a state of suspended animation, which was in the air, and which everyone was talking about.

This was the time to prepare for the cold weather, to store up food and wood. But in those days of the triumph of materialism, matter had become a disembodied idea, and the problems of alimentation and fuel supply took the place of food and firewood.

The people in the cities were as helpless as children in the face of the unknown—that unknown which swept every established habit aside and left nothing but desolation in its wake, although it was itself the offspring of the city and the creation of city-dwellers.

All around, people continued to deceive themselves, to talk endlessly. Everyday life struggled on, by force of habit, limping and shuffling. But the doctor saw life as it was. It was clear to him that it was under sentence. He looked upon himself and his milieu as doomed. Ordeals were ahead, perhaps death. Their days were counted and running out before his eyes.

He would have gone insane had he not been kept busy by the details of daily life. His wife, his child, the necessity to earn money, the humble daily ritual of his practice—these were his salvation.

He realized that he was a pygmy before the monstrous machine of the future; he was anxious about this future, and loved it and was secretly proud of it, and as though for the last time, as if in farewell, he avidly looked at the trees and clouds and the people walking in the streets, the great Russian city struggling through misfortune—and was ready to sacrifice himself for the general good, and could do nothing.

He most often saw the sky and the people from the middle of the street when he crossed the Arbat at the corner of Old Coachyard Row, near the pharmacy of the Russian Medical Society.

He resumed his duties at his old hospital. It was still called the Hospital of the Holy Cross, although the society of that name had been dissolved. So far no one had thought of a new name for the hospital.

The staff had already divided up into camps. To the moderates, whose obtuseness made the doctor indignant, he seemed dangerous; to those whose politics were advanced, not Red enough. Thus he belonged to neither group, having moved away from the former and lagging behind the latter.

In addition to his normal duties, the medical chief had put him in charge of general statistics. Endless questionnaires and forms went through his hands. Death rate, sickness rate, the earnings of the staff, the degree of their political consciousness and of their participation in the elections, the perpetual shortage of fuel, food, medicines, everything had to be checked and reported.

Zhivago worked at his old table by the staff-room window, stacked with charts and forms of every size and shape. He had pushed them to one side; occasionally, in addition to taking notes for his medical works, he wrote in snatches his "Playing at People, a Gloomy Diary or Journal Consisting of Prose, Verse, and What-have-you, Inspired by the Realization that Half the People Have Stopped Being Themselves and Are Acting Unknown Parts."

The light, sunny room with its white painted walls was filled with the creamy light of the golden autumn days that follow the Feast of the Assumption, when the mornings begin to be frosty and titmice and magpies dart into the bright-leaved, thinning woods. On such days the sky is incredibly high, and through the transparent pillar of air between it and the earth there moves an icy, dark-blue radiance coming from the north. Everything in the world becomes more visible and more audible. Distant sounds reach us in a state of frozen resonance, separately and clearly. The horizons open, as if to show the whole of life for years ahead. This rarefied light would be unbearable if it were not so short-lived, coming at the end of the brief autumn day just before the early dusk.

Such was now the light in the staff room, the light of an early autumn sunset, as succulent, glassy, juicy as a certain variety of Russian apple.

The doctor sat at his desk writing, pausing to think and to dip his pen while some unusually quiet birds flew silently past the tall windows, throwing shadows on his moving hands, on the table with its forms, and on the floor and the walls, and just as silently vanished from sight.

The prosector came in; he was a stout man who had lost so much weight that his skin hung on him in bags. "The maple leaves are nearly all gone," he said. "When you think how they stood up to all the rain and wind, and now a single morning frost has done it."

The doctor looked up. The mysterious birds darting past the window had in fact been wine-red maple leaves. They flew away from the trees, gliding through the air, and covered the hospital lawn, looking like bent orange stars.

"Have the windows been puttied up?" the prosector asked.

"No," Yurii Andreievich said, and went on writing.

"Isn't it time they were?"

Yurii Andreievich, absorbed in his work, did not answer.

"Pity Taraska's gone," went on the prosector. "He was worth his weight in gold. Patch your boots or repair your watch—he'd do anything. And he could get you anything in the world. Now we'll have to do the windows ourselves."

"There's no putty."

"You can make some. I'll give you the recipe." He explained how you made putty with linseed oil and chalk. "Well, I'll leave you now. I suppose you want to get on with your work."

He went off to the other window and busied himself with his bottles and specimens. "You'll ruin your eyes," he said a minute later. "It's getting dark. And they won't give you any light. Let's go home."

"I'll work another twenty minutes or so."

"His wife is a nurse here."

"Whose wife?"

"Taraska's."

"I know."

"Nobody knows where he is himself. He prowls about all over the country. Last summer he came twice to see his wife, now he's in some village. He's building the new life. He's one of those soldier-Bolsheviks, you see them everywhere, walking about in the streets, travelling in trains. And do you know what makes them tick? Take Taraska. He can turn his hand to anything. Whatever he does, he has to do it well. That's what happened to him in the army—he learned to fight, just like any other trade. He became a crack rifleman. His eyes and hands—first-class! All his decorations were awarded him, not for courage, but for always hitting the mark. Well, anything he takes up becomes a passion with him, so he took to fighting in a big way. He could see what a rifle does for a man—it gives him power, it brings him distinction. He wanted to be a power himself. An armed man isn't just a man like any other. In the old days such men turned from soldiers into brigands. You just try to take Taraska's rifle away from him now! Well, then came the slogan 'Turn your bayonets against your masters,' so Taraska turned. That's the whole story. There's Marxism for you."

"That's the most genuine kind—straight from life. Didn't you know?"

The prosector went back to his test tubes.

"How did you make out with the stove specialist?" he asked after a while.

"I'm most grateful to you for sending him. A most interesting man. We spent hours talking about Hegel and Croce."

"Naturally! Took his doctorate in philosophy at Heidelberg. What about the stove?"

"That's not so good."

"Still smoking?"

"Never stops."

"He can't have fixed the stovepipe right. It ought to be connected with a flue. Did he let it out through the window?"

"No, the flue, but it still smokes."

"Then he can't have found the right air vent. If only we had Taraska! But you'll get it right in the end. Moscow wasn't built in a day. Getting a stove to work isn't like playing the piano, it takes skill. Have you laid in your firewood?"

"Where am I to get it from?"

"I'll send you the church janitor. He's an expert at stealing wood. Takes fences to pieces and turns them into firewood. But you'll have to bargain with him. No, better get the exterminator."

They went down to the cloakroom, put their coats on, and went out.

"Why the exterminator? We don't have bedbugs."

"That's got nothing to do with it. I'm talking about wood. The exterminator is an old woman who is doing a big business in wood. She's got it all set up on a proper business footing—buys up whole houses for fuel. It's dark, watch your step. In the old

days I could have taken you blindfold anywhere in this district.
I knew every stone. I was born near here. But since they've
started pulling down the fences I can hardly find my way about,
even by day. It's like being in a strange town. On the other hand,
some extraordinary places have come to light. Little Empire
houses you never knew were there, with round garden tables
and half-rotten benches. The other day I passed a place like
that, a sort of little wilderness at an intersection of three streets,
and there was an old lady poking about with a stick—she must
have been about a hundred. 'Hello, Granny,' I said, 'are you
looking for worms to go fishing?' I was joking, of course, but she
took it quite seriously. 'No, not worms,' she said, 'mushrooms.'
And it's true, you know, the town is getting to be like the woods.
There's a smell of decaying leaves and mushrooms."

"I think I know where you mean—between Serebriany and
Molchanovka, isn't it? The strangest things are always happening to me there—either I meet someone I haven't seen in twenty
years, or I find something. They say it's dangerous, and no wonder, there's a whole network of alleys leading to the old thieves'
dens near Smolensky. Before you know where you are, they've
stripped you to the skin and vanished."

"And look at those street lamps—they don't shine at all. No
wonder they call bruises shiners. Be careful you don't bump
yourself."

6

All sorts of things did indeed happen to the doctor at that place.
One cold dark night, shortly before the October fighting, he
came across a man lying unconscious on the sidewalk, his arms
flung out, his head against a curbstone, and his feet in the
gutter. Occasionally he uttered weak groans. When the doctor
tried to rouse him he muttered a few words, something about a
wallet. He had been attacked and robbed. His head was bat-
tered and covered with blood, but a casual examination revealed that the skull was intact.

Zhivago went to the pharmacy in the Arbat, telephoned for
the cab that the hospital used in emergencies, and took the patient to the emergency ward.

The wounded man proved to be a prominent political leader. The doctor treated him till he recovered, and for years afterwards this man acted as his protector, getting him out of trouble several times in those days that were so heavy with suspicion.

7

Antonina Alexandrovna's plan had been adopted and the family had settled for the winter in three rooms on the top floor.

It was a cold, windy Sunday, dark with heavy snow clouds. The doctor was off duty.

The fire was lit in the morning, and the stove began to smoke. Niusha struggled with the damp wood. Antonina Alexandrovna, who knew nothing about stoves, kept giving her absurd and bad advice. The doctor, who did know, tried to interfere, but his wife took him gently by the shoulders and pushed him out of the room, saying: "Don't you meddle in this. You'll only pour oil on the fire."

"Oil wouldn't be so bad, Toniechka, the stove would be ablaze at once! The trouble is, there is neither oil nor fire."

"This is no time for jokes. There are moments when they are out of place."

The trouble with the stove upset everyone's plans. They had all hoped to get their chores done before dark and have a free evening, but now dinner would be late, there was no hot water, and various other plans might have to be dropped.

The fire smoked more and more. The strong wind blew the smoke back into the room. A cloud of black soot stood in it like a fairy-tale monster in a thick wood.

Finally Yurii Andreievich drove everyone out into the two other rooms, and opened the top pane of the window. He removed half the wood from the stove, and spaced out the rest with chips and birchwood shavings between them.

Fresh air rushed in through the window. The curtain swayed and flew up. Papers blew off the desk. A door banged somewhere down the hall, and the wind began a cat-and-mouse game with what was left of the smoke.

The logs flared up and crackled. The stove was ablaze. Its

iron body was covered with red-hot spots like a consumptive flush. The smoke in the room thinned out and soon vanished.

The room grew lighter. The windows, which Yurii Andreievich had recently fixed according to the prosecutor's recipe, gave off the warm, greasy smell of putty. An acrid smell of charred fir bark and the fresh, toilet-water scent of aspen came from the wood drying by the stove.

Nikolai Nikolaievich burst into the room as impetuously as the wind coming through the open window.

"They're fighting in the street," he reported. "There is a regular battle between the cadets who support the Provisional Government and the garrison soldiers who support the Bolsheviks. There is skirmishing all over the city. I got into trouble coming here—once at the corner of Bolshaia Dmitrovka and once at the Nikitsky Gate. Now you can't get through directly, you have to go around. Hurry up, Yura! Put your coat on, let's go. You've got to see it. This is history. This happens once in a lifetime."

But he stayed talking for a couple of hours. Then they had dinner, and by the time he was ready to go home and was dragging the doctor out, Gordon burst in, in exactly the same way as Nikolai Nikolaievich and with much the same news.

Things had progressed, however. There were new details. Gordon spoke of increasing rifle fire and of passers-by killed by stray bullets. According to him, all traffic had stopped. He had got through by a miracle, but now the street was cut off.

Nikolai Nikolaievich refused to believe him and dashed out but was back in a minute. He said bullets whistled down the street knocking chips of brick and plaster off the corners. There was not a soul outside. All traffic had stopped.

That week Sashenka caught a cold.

"I've told you a hundred times, he's not to play near the stove," Yurii Andreievich scolded. "It's much worse to let him get too hot than cold."

Sashenka had a sore throat and a fever. He had a special, overwhelming terror of vomiting, and when Yurii Andreievich tried to examine his throat he pushed away his hand, clenching his teeth, yelling and choking. Neither arguments nor threats had the slightest effect on him. At one moment, however, he inadvertently yawned, and the doctor quickly took advantage of this to insert a spoon into his son's mouth and hold down his tongue for long enough to get a look at his raspberry-colored larynx and swollen tonsils covered with alarming white spots.

A little later, by means of a similar maneuver, he got a specimen and, as he had a microscope at home, was able to examine it. Fortunately, it was not diphtheria.

But on the third night Sashenka had an attack of nervous croup. His temperature shot up and he could not breathe. Yurii Andreievich was helpless to ease his suffering and could not bear to watch it. Antonina Alexandrovna thought the child was dying. They carried him about the room in turn, and this seemed to make him feel better.

They needed milk, mineral water, or soda water for him. But the street fighting was at its height. Gun and rifle fire never ceased for a moment. Even if Yurii Andreievich had crossed the battle zone at the risk of his life, he would not have found anyone about in the streets beyond it. All life in the city was suspended until the situation would be definitively clarified.

Yet there could be no doubt about the outcome. Rumors came from all sides that the workers were getting the upper hand. Small groups of cadets were fighting on, but they were cut off from each other and from their command.

The Sivtzev quarter was held by soldiers' units who were pressing on toward the center. Soldiers who had fought against Germany and young working boys sat in a trench they had dug down the street; they were already getting to know the people who lived in the neighborhood and joked with them as they came and stood outside their gates. Traffic in this part of the town was being restored.

Gordon and Nikolai Nikolaievich, who had got stuck at the Zhivagos', were released from their three days' captivity. Zhivago had been glad of their presence during Sashenka's illness, and his wife forgave them for adding to the general disorder. But they had felt obliged to repay the kindness of their hosts by entertaining them with ceaseless talk. Yurii Andreievich was so exhausted by three days of pointless chatter that he was happy to see them go.

8

They learned that their guests had got home safely. But military operations continued, several streets were still closed, and the doctor could not yet go to his hospital. He was impatient to return to his work and the manuscript he had left in the drawer of the staff-room desk.

Only here and there did people come out in the morning and walk a short distance to buy bread. When they saw a passer-by carrying a milk bottle, they would surround him trying to find out where he had got it.

Occasionally the firing resumed all over the town, and the streets were cleared again. It was said that the two sides were engaged in negotiations, whose course, favorable or unfavorable, was reflected in the varying intensity of the firing.

At about 10 P.M. one evening in late October (Old Style) Yurii Andreievich went without any particular necessity to call on one of his colleagues. The streets he passed were deserted. He walked quickly. The first thin powdery snow was coming down, scattered by a rising wind.

He had turned down so many side streets that he had almost lost count of them when the snow thickened and the wind turned into a blizzard, the kind of blizzard that whistles in a field covering it with a blanket of snow, but which in town tosses about as if it had lost its way.

There was something in common between the disturbances in the moral and in the physical world, near and far on the ground and in the air. Here and there resounded the last salvoes of islands of resistance. Bubbles of dying fires rose and broke on the horizon. And the snow swirled and eddied and smoked at Yurii's feet, on the wet streets and pavements.

A newsboy running with a thick batch of freshly printed papers under his arm and shouting "Latest news!" overtook him at an intersection.

"Keep the change," said the doctor. The boy peeled a damp sheet off the batch, thrust it into his hand, and a minute later was engulfed in the snowstorm.

The doctor stopped under a street light to read the headlines. The paper was a late extra printed on one side only; it gave the official announcement from Petersburg that a Soviet of People's Commissars had been formed and that Soviet power and the dictatorship of the proletariat were established in Russia. There followed the first decrees of the new government and various brief news dispatches received by telegraph and telephone.

The blizzard lashed at the doctor's eyes and covered the printed page with gray, rustling pellets of snow. But it was not the snowstorm that prevented him from reading. The historic greatness of the moment moved him so deeply that it took him some time to collect himself.

To read the rest of the news he looked around for a better lit, sheltered place. He found that he was standing once again at that charmed spot, the intersection of Serebriany and Molchanovka, in front of a tall, five-story building with a glass door and a spacious, well-lit lobby.

He went in and stood under the electric light, next to the staircase, reading the news.

Footsteps sounded above him. Someone was coming down the stairs, stopping frequently, as though hesitating. At one point, he actually changed his mind and ran up again. A door opened somewhere and two voices welled out, so distorted by echoes that it was impossible to tell whether men or women were speaking. Then the door banged and the same steps ran down, this time resolutely.

Yurii Andreievich was absorbed in his paper and had not meant to look up, but the stranger stopped so suddenly at the foot of the stairs that he raised his head.

Before him stood a boy of about eighteen in a reindeer cap and a stiff reindeer coat worn, as in Siberia, fur side out. He was dark and had narrow Kirghiz eyes. His face had an aristocratic quality, the fugitive spark and reticent delicacy that give an impression of remoteness and are sometimes found in people of a complex, mixed parentage.

The boy obviously mistook Yurii Andreievich for someone else. He looked at him, puzzled and shy, as if he knew him but could not make up his mind to speak. To put an end to the misunderstanding Yurii Andreievich measured him with a cold, discouraging glance.

The boy turned away confused and walked to the entrance.

There he looked back once again before going out and banging the heavy glass door shut behind him.

Yurii Andreievich left a few minutes after him. His mind was full of the news; he forgot the boy and the colleague he had meant to visit, and set out straight for home. But he was distracted on the way by another incident, one of those details of everyday life that assumed an inordinate importance in those days.

Not far from his house he stumbled in the dark over an enormous pile of timber near the curb. There was an institution of some sort in the street, to which the government had probably supplied fuel in the form of boards from a dismantled house in the outskirts of the town. Not all of it would go into the yard, and the rest had been left outside. A sentry with a rifle was on duty by this pile; he paced up and down the yard and occasionally went out into the street.

Without thinking twice, Yurii Andreievich took advantage of a moment when the sentry's back was turned and the wind had raised a cloud of snow into the air to creep up on the dark side, avoiding the lamplight, carefully loosen a heavy beam from the very bottom, and pull it out. He loaded it with difficulty on his back, immediately ceasing to feel its weight (your own load is not a burden), and, hugging the shadow of the walls, took the wood safely home.

Its arrival was timely; they had run out of firewood. The beam was chopped up, and the pieces were stacked. Yurii Andreievich lit the stove and squatted in front of it in silence, while Alexander Alexandrovich moved up his armchair and sat warming himself.

Yurii Andreievich took the newspaper out of the side pocket of his coat and held it out to him.

"Seen that? Have a look."

Still squatting on his heels and poking the fire, he talked to himself.

"What splendid surgery! You take a knife and with one masterful stroke you cut out all the old stinking ulcers. Quite simply, without any nonsense, you take the old monster of injustice, which has been accustomed for centuries to being bowed and scraped and curtsied to, and you sentence it to death.

"This fearlessness, this way of seeing the thing through to the end, has a familiar national look about it. It has something of Pushkin's uncompromising clarity and of Tolstoy's unwavering faithfulness to the facts."

"Pushkin, you said? Wait a second. Let me finish. I can't read and listen at the same time," said Alexander Alexandrovich under the mistaken impression that his son-in-law was addressing him.

"And the real stroke of genius is this. If you charged someone with the task of creating a new world, of starting a new era, he would ask you first to clear the ground. He would wait for the old centuries to finish before undertaking to build the new ones, he'd want to begin a new paragraph, a new page.

"But here, they don't bother with anything like that. This new thing, this marvel of history, this revelation, is exploded right into the very thick of daily life without the slightest consideration for its course. It doesn't start at the beginning, it starts in the middle, without any schedule, on the first weekday that comes along, while the traffic in the street is at its height. That's real genius. Only real greatness can be so unconcerned with timing and opportunity."

9

Winter came, just the kind of winter that had been foretold. It was not as terrifying as the two winters that followed it, but it was already of the same sort, dark, hungry, and cold, entirely given to the breaking up of the familiar and the reconstruction of all the foundations of existence, and to inhuman efforts to cling to life as it slipped out of your grasp.

There were three of them, one after the other, three such terrible winters, and not all that now seems to have happened in 1917 and 1918 really happened then—some of it may have been later. These three successive winters have merged into one and it is difficult to tell them apart.

The old life and the new order had not yet come in contact. They were not yet openly hostile to each other, as when the civil war broke out a year later, but there was no connection between the two. They stood apart, confronting each other, incompatible.

There were new elections everywhere—in administration of buildings, organizations of all kinds, government offices, public services. Commissars invested with dictatorial powers were appointed to each, men of iron will in black leather jackets, armed with means of intimidation and guns, who shaved rarely and slept even more rarely.

They knew the slinking bourgeois breed, the ordinary holders of cheap government bonds, and they spoke to them without the slightest pity and with Mephistophelean smiles, as to petty thieves caught in the act.

These were the people who reorganized everything in accordance with the plan, and company after company, enterprise after enterprise became Bolshevized.

The Hospital of the Holy Cross was now known as the Second Reformed. Many things had changed in it. Part of the staff had been dismissed and others had resigned because they did not find the work sufficiently rewarding. These were doctors with a fashionable practice and high fees, and glib talkers. They left out of self-interest but asserted that they had made a civic gesture of protest and looked down on those who had stayed on, almost boycotting them. Zhivago had stayed.

In the evenings husband and wife had conversations of this sort:

"Don't forget Wednesday, at the Doctors' Union; they'll have two sacks of frozen potatoes for us in the basement. I'll let you know what time I can get away. We'll have to go together and take the sled."

"All right, Yurochka, there's plenty of time. Why don't you go to bed now, it's late. I wish you'd rest, you can't do everything."

"There's an epidemic. Exhaustion is lowering resistance. You and Father look terrible. We must do something. If only I knew what. We don't take enough care of ourselves. Listen. You aren't asleep?"

"No."

"I'm not worried about myself, I've got nine lives, but if by any chance I should get ill, you will be sensible, won't you, you mustn't keep me at home. Get me into the hospital at once."

"Don't talk like that. Pray God you'll keep well. Why play Cassandra?"

"Remember, there aren't any honest people left, or any friends. Still less any experts. If anything should happen don't trust anyone except Pichuzhkin. That is if he's still there, of course. You aren't asleep?"

"No."

"The pay wasn't good enough, so off they went; now it turns out they had principles and civic sentiments. You meet them in the street, they hardly shake hands, just raise an eyebrow: 'So you're working for *them?*'—'I am,' I said, 'and if you don't mind, I am proud of our privations and I respect those who honor us by imposing them on us.'"

10

For a long time most people's daily food consisted of thin millet boiled in water and soup made of herring heads; the herring itself was used as a second course. A sort of kasha was also made of unground wheat or rye.

A woman professor who was a friend of Antonina Alexandrovna's taught her to bake bread in an improvised Dutch oven. The idea was to sell some of the bread and so cover the cost of heating the tile stove as in the old days, instead of using the iron stove, which continued to smoke and gave almost no heat.

Antonina Alexandrovna's bread was good but nothing came of her commercial plans. They had to go back to the wretched iron stove. The Zhivagos were hard up.

One morning, after Yurii Andreievich had gone to work, Antonina Alexandrovna put on her shabby winter coat—she was so run down that she shivered in it even in warm weather—and went out "hunting." There were only two logs left. For about half an hour she wandered through the alleys in the neighborhood where you could sometimes catch a peasant from one of the villages outside Moscow selling vegetables and potatoes. In the main streets, peasants with loads were liable to be arrested. Soon she found what she was looking for. A sturdy young fellow in a peasant's coat walked back with her, pulling a sleigh that looked as light as a toy, and followed her cautiously into the yard.

Covered up by sacking inside the sleigh was a load of birch logs no thicker than the balusters of an old-fashioned country house in a nineteenth-century photograph. Antonina Alexandrovna knew their worth—birch only in name, the wood was of the poorest sort and too freshly cut to be suitable for burning. But as there was no choice, it was pointless to argue.

The young peasant carried five or six armloads up to the living room and took in exchange Tonia's small mirror wardrobe. He carried it down and packed it in his sleigh to take away as a present for his bride. In discussing a future deal in potatoes, he asked the price of the piano.

When Yurii Andreievich came home he said nothing about his wife's purchase. It would have been more sensible to chop up the wardrobe, but they could never have brought themselves to do it.

"There's a note for you on the table, did you see it?" she said.

"The one sent on from the hospital? Yes, I've had the message already. It's a sick call. I'll certainly go. I'll just have a little rest first. But it's pretty far. It's somewhere near the Triumphal Arch, I've got the address."

"Have you seen the fee they are offering you? You'd better read it. A bottle of German cognac or a pair of stockings! What sort of people are they, do you imagine? Vulgar. They don't seem to have any idea of how we live nowadays. *Nouveaux riches,* I suppose."

"Yes, that's from a supplier."

Suppliers, concessionnaires, and authorized agents were names then given to small businessmen to whom the government, which had abolished private trade, occasionally made concessions at moments of economic difficulties, charging them with the procurement of various goods.

They were not former men of substance or dismissed heads of old firms—such people did not recover from the blow they had received. They were a new category of businessmen, people without roots who had been scooped up from the bottom by the war and the revolution.

Zhivago had a drink of hot water and saccharin whitened with milk and went off to see his patient.

Deep snow covered the street from wall to wall, in places up to the level of the ground-floor windows. Silent half-dead shadows moved all over this expanse carrying a little food or pulling it along on sleds. There was almost no other traffic.

Old shop signs still hung here and there. They had no relation to the small new consumer shops and co-operatives, which were all empty and locked, their windows barred or boarded up.

The reason they were locked and empty was not only that there were no goods but that the reorganization of all aspects of life, including trade, had so far remained largely on paper and had not yet affected such trifling details as the boarded-up shops.

11

The house to which the doctor went was at the end of Brest Street near the Tver Gate.

It was an old barracklike stone building with an inside courtyard, and three wooden staircases rose along the courtyard walls.

That day the tenants were at their general meeting, in which a woman delegate from the borough council participated, when a military commission suddenly turned up to check arms licenses and to confiscate unlicensed weapons. The tenants had to go back to their flats, but the head of the commission asked the delegate not to leave, assuring her that the search would not take long and the meeting could be resumed within a short time.

When the doctor arrived, the commission had almost finished but the flat where he was going had not yet been searched. Zhivago was stopped on the landing by a soldier with a rifle, but the head of the commission heard them arguing and ordered the search to be put off until after the doctor had examined his patient.

The door was opened by the master of the house, a polite young man with a sallow complexion and dark, melancholy eyes.

He was flustered by a number of things—because of his wife's illness, the impending search, and his profound reverence for medical science and its representatives.

To save the doctor time and trouble he tried to be as brief as possible, but his very haste made his speech long and incoherent.

The flat was cluttered with a mixture of expensive and cheap furniture, hastily bought as an investment against the rapid inflation. Sets were supplemented by odd pieces.

The young man thought his wife's illness had been caused by nervous shock. He explained with many digressions that they had recently bought an antique clock. It was a broken-down chiming clock, and they had bought it for a song merely as a remarkable example of the clockmaker's art (he took the doctor into the next room to see it). They had even doubted whether it could be repaired. Then, one day, suddenly the clock, which had not been wound for years, had started of itself, played its complicated minuet of chimes, and stopped. His wife was terrified, the young man said; she was convinced that her last hour had struck, and now there she was delirious, refused all food, and did not recognize him.

"So you think it's nervous shock," Yurii Andreievich said doubtfully. "May I see her now?"

They went into another room, which had a porcelain chandelier, a wide double bed, and two mahogany bedside tables. A small woman with big black eyes lay near the edge of the bed, the blanket pulled up above her chin. When she saw them she freed one arm from under the bedclothes and waved them back, the loose sleeve of her dressing gown falling back to her armpit. She did not recognize her husband, and as if she were alone in the room, she began to sing something sad in a low voice, which upset her so much that she cried, whimpering like a child and begging to "go home." When the doctor went up to the bed she turned her back on him and refused to let him touch her.

"I ought to examine her," he said, "but it doesn't really matter. It's quite clear that she's got typhus—a severe case, poor thing; she must be feeling pretty wretched. My advice to you is to put her in a hospital. I know you'd see to it that she had everything she needed at home, but it's most important that she should have constant medical supervision in the first few weeks.

Could you get hold of any sort of transportation—a cab or even a cart? Of course she'll have to be well wrapped up. I'll give you an admission order."

"I'll try, but wait a moment. Is it really typhus? How horrible!"

"I am afraid so."

"Look, I know I'll lose her if I let her go—couldn't you possibly look after her here? Come as often as you possibly can—I'll be only too happy to pay you anything you like."

"I am sorry—I've told you: what she needs is constant supervision. Do as I say—I really am advising you for her good. Now, get a cab at any cost and I'll write out the order. I'd better do it in your house committee room. The order has to have the house stamp on it, and there are a few other formalities."

12

One by one the tenants, in shawls and fur coats, had returned to the unheated basement, which had once been a wholesale egg store and was now used by the house committee.

An office desk and several chairs stood at one end of it. As there were not enough chairs, old empty egg crates turned upside down had been placed in a row to form a bench. A pile of them as high as the ceiling towered at the far end of the room; in a corner was a heap of shavings stuck into lumps with frozen yolk that had dripped from broken eggs. Rats scurried noisily inside the heap, making an occasional sortie into the middle of the stone floor and darting back.

Each time this happened a fat woman climbed squealing onto a crate and, holding up her skirt daintily and tapping her fashionable high shoes, shouted in a deliberately hoarse, drunken voice:

"Olia, Olia, you've got rats all over the place. Get away, you filthy brute. Ai-ai-ai! look at it, it understands, it's mad at me. Ai-ai-ai! it's trying to climb up, it'll get under my skirt, I'm so frightened! Look the other way, gentlemen. Sorry, I forgot, you're comrade citizens now, not gentlemen."

Her astrakhan cape hung open over the three quaking layers

of her double chin and rich, silk-swathed bosom and stomach. She had once been the belle of her circle of small tradesmen and salesmen, but now her little pig eyes with their swollen lids could scarcely open. A rival had once tried to splash her with vitriol but had missed and only a drop or two had plowed traces on her cheek and at the corner of her mouth, so slight as to be almost becoming.

"Stop yelling, Khrapugina. How can we get on with our work?" said the delegate of the borough council, who had been elected chairman and was sitting behind the desk.

The delegate had known the house and many of the tenants all her life. Before the meeting she had had an unofficial talk with Aunt Fatima, the old janitress who had once lived with her husband and children in a corner of the filthy basement but had now only her daughter with her and had been moved into two light rooms on the first floor.

"Well, Fatima, how are things going?" the delegate asked.

Fatima complained that she could not cope with such a big house and so many tenants all by herself and that she got no help because, although each family was supposed to take turns cleaning the yard and the sidewalks, not one of them did it.

"Don't worry, Fatima, we'll show them. What kind of committee is this, anyway? They're hopeless. Criminal elements are given shelter, people of doubtful morals stay on without registration. We'll get rid of them and elect another. I'll make you house-manageress, only don't make a fuss."

The janitress begged to be let off, but the delegate refused to listen.

Looking around the room and deciding that enough people were present, she called for quiet and opened the meeting with a short introductory speech. She condemned the committee for slackness, proposed that candidates should be put up for the election of a new one, and went on to other business.

In conclusion she said:

"So that's how it is, comrades. Frankly speaking, this is a big house, it's suitable for a hostel. Look at all the delegates who come to town to attend conferences, and we don't know where to put them. It's been decided to take over the building for a district soviet hostel for visitors from the country and to call it the Tiverzin Hostel, in honor of Comrade Tiverzin, who lived here before he was deported, as everyone knows. No objections! Now, as to dates. There's no hurry, you've got a whole year. Working people will be rehoused; others must find accommodations for themselves and are given a year's notice."

"We're all working people! Every one of us! We're all workers," people shouted from every side, and one voice sobbed out: "It's Great-Russian chauvinism! All the nations are equal now! I know what you're hinting at."

"Not all at once, please. Whom am I to answer first? What have nations got to do with it, Citizen Valdyrkin? Look at Khrapugina, you can't think there's a question of nationality involved in her case, and we are certainly evicting her."

"You are, are you! Just you try and evict me, we'll see about that! You crushed sofa! You crumpled bedsheet!" Khrapugina screamed, calling the delegate every meaningless name she could think of in the heat of the quarrel.

"What a she-devil!" The janitress was indignant. "Haven't you any shame?"

"Don't you meddle in this, Fatima, I can look after myself," said the delegate. "Stop it, Khrapugina, I know all about you. Shut up, I tell you, or I'll hand you over at once to the authorities before they catch you brewing vodka and running an illegal bar."

The uproar was at its height when the doctor came into the room. He asked the first man he ran into at the door to point out to him a member of the house committee. The other held up his hands like a trumpet in front of his mouth and shouted above the noise:

"Ga-li-iul-li-na! Come here. You're wanted."

The doctor could not believe his ears. A thin elderly woman with a slight stoop, the janitress, came up to him. He was struck by her likeness to her son. He did not, however, identify himself at once, but said: "One of your tenants has got typhus" (he told her the name). "There are various precautions that have to be taken to prevent its spreading. Moreover, the patient must go to the hospital. I'll make out an admission order, which the house committee has to certify. How and where can we get that done?"

She thought he meant "How is the patient to get to the hospital?" and replied: "There's a cab coming from the soviet for Comrade Demina, that's the delegate. She's very kind, Comrade Demina, I'll tell her, she's sure to let your patient have the cab. Don't worry, Comrade Doctor, we'll get her there all right."

"That's wonderful. Actually, I only meant where could I write out the order. But if there's a cab as well . . . May I ask you, are you the mother of Lieutenant Galiullin? We were in the same unit at the front."

Galiullina started violently and grew pale. She grasped the doctor's hand. "Come outside," she said. "We'll talk in the yard."

As soon as they were outside the door she said quickly: "Talk softly, for God's sake. Don't ruin me. Yusupka's gone wrong. Judge for yourself—what is he? He was an apprentice, a worker. He ought to understand—simple people are much better off now, a blind man can see that, nobody can deny it. I don't know what you feel yourself, maybe it would be all right for you, but it's a sin for Yusupka, God won't forgive him. Yusupka's father was a private, he was killed, they say his face was shot off, and his arms and legs."

Her voice broke, she waited till she was more calm, then she went on: "Come. I'll get you the cab. I know who you are. He was here for a couple of days. He told me. He said you knew Lara Guishar. She was a good girl, I remember her, she used to come and see us. What she's like now, I don't know—who can tell with you people? After all, it's natural for the masters to stick together. But for Yusupka it's a sin. Come, let's ask for the cab. I'm sure Comrade Demina will let you have it. You know who Comrade Demina is? She's Olia Demina, a seamstress she was, worked for Lara's mother, that's who she is, and she's from this house. Come along."

13

Night had fallen. All around them was darkness. Only the small round patch of light from Demina's pocket flashlight jumped from snowdrift to snowdrift four or five paces ahead, confusing more than lighting the way. The darkness was all around them, and they had left behind them the house where so many people had known Lara, where she had often come as a girl, and where, they said, Antipov, her husband, had grown up.

"Will you really find your way without a flashlight, Comrade Doctor?" Demina was facetiously patronizing. "If not, I'll lend you mine. It's a fact, you know, I had a real crush on her when we were little girls. They had a dressmaking establishment, I was an apprentice in the workshop. I've seen her this year. She stopped on her way through Moscow. I said, 'Where are you off to, silly? Stay here. Come and live with us. We'll find you a job.' But it wasn't any good, she wouldn't. Well, it's her business. She married Pasha with her head, not with her heart, she's been crazy ever since. Off she went."

"What do you think of her?"

"Careful—it's slippery. I don't know how many times I've told them not to throw the slops out of the door—might as well talk to a wall. What do I think of her? How do you mean, think? What should I think? I haven't any time to think. Here's where I live. One thing I didn't tell her—her brother, who was in the army, I think they've shot him. As for her mother, my mistress she used to be—I'll save her, I'm seeing to it. Well, I've got to go in, goodbye."

They parted. The light of Demina's little flashlight shot into the narrow stone entrance and ran on, lighting up the stained walls and the dirty stairs while the doctor was left surrounded by the darkness. On his right lay Sadovaia Triumphalnaia Street, on his left Sadovaia Karetnaia Street. Running into the black snowy distance, they were no longer streets but cuttings in the jungle of stone buildings, like cuttings through the impassable forests of Siberia or the Urals.

At home it was light and warm.

"Why are you so late?" asked Antonina Alexandrovna. "An extraordinary thing happened while you were out," she went on before he could reply. "Really quite unaccountable. Yesterday Father broke the alarm clock—I forgot to tell you—he was terribly upset, it was our only clock. He tried to repair it, he tinkered and tinkered with it, but he got nowhere. The clockmaker around the corner wanted a ridiculous price—three pounds

of bread. I didn't know what to do and Father was completely
dejected. Well, about an hour ago—can you believe it—there
was a sudden ringing—such a piercing, deafening noise, we were
all frightened out of our wits. It was the alarm clock! Can you
imagine such a thing? It had started up again, all by itself."

"My hour for typhus has struck," said Yurii Andreievich,
laughing. He told her about his patient and the chiming clock.

14

But he did not get typhus until much later. In the meantime the
Zhivagos were tried to the limits of endurance. They had nothing and they were starving. The doctor went to see the Party
member he had once saved, the one who had been the victim
of a robbery. This man did everything he could for the doctor,
but the civil war was just beginning and he was hardly ever in
Moscow; moreover, he regarded the privations people had to
suffer in those days as only natural, and he himself went hungry,
though he concealed it.

Yurii Andreievich tried to get in touch with the supplier in
Brest Street. But in the intervening months the young man had
disappeared and nothing was known about his wife, who had
recovered. Galiullina was out when Yurii Andreievich called,
most of the tenants were new, and Demina was at the front.

One day he received an allocation of wood at the official
price. He had to bring it from the Vindava Station. Walking
home along the endless stretches of Meshchanskaia Street—
keeping an eye on the cart loaded with his unexpected treasure
—he noticed that the street looked quite different; he found that
he was swaying from side to side, his legs refusing to carry him.
He realized that he was in for a bad time, that he had typhus.
The driver picked him up when he fell down and slung him on
top of the wood. The doctor never knew how he got home.

15

He was delirious off and on for two weeks. He dreamed that
Tonia had put two streets on his desk, Sadovaia Karetnaia on his

left and Sadovaia Triumphalnaia on his right, and had lit the
table lamp; its warm orange glow lit up the streets and now he
could write. So he was writing.

He was writing what he should have written long ago and had
always wished to write but never could. Now it came to him
quite easily, he wrote eagerly and said exactly what he wanted
to say. Only now and then a boy got in his way, a boy with narrow Kirghiz eyes, in an unbuttoned reindeer coat worn fur side
out, as in the Urals or Siberia.

He knew for certain that this boy was the spirit of his death
or, to put it quite plainly, that he was his death. Yet how could
he be his death if he was helping him to write a poem? How
could death be useful, how was it possible for death to be a help?

The subject of his poem was neither the entombment nor the
resurrection but the days between; the title was "Turmoil."

He had always wanted to describe how for three days the
black, raging, worm-filled earth had assailed the deathless in-
carnation of love, storming it with rocks and rubble—as waves
fly and leap at a seacoast, cover and submerge it—how for three
days the black hurricane of earth raged, advancing and retreating.

Two lines kept coming into his head:
"We are glad to be near you," and "Time to wake up."

Near him, touching him, were hell, dissolution, corruption,
death, and equally near him were the spring and Mary Magdalene and life. And it was time to awake. Time to wake up and
to get up. Time to arise, time for the resurrection.

16

He began to get better. At first he took everything for granted,
like a halfwit. He remembered nothing, he could see no connection between one thing and another and was not surprised at
anything. His wife fed him on white bread and butter and
sugared tea; she gave him coffee. He had forgotten that such
things did not exist, and he enjoyed their taste like poetry or
like fairy tales, as something right and proper for a convalescent.
Soon, however, he began to think and wonder.

"How did you get all this?" he asked his wife.

"Your Grania got it for us."

"What Grania?"

"Grania Zhivago."

"Grania Zhivago?"

"Well, yes, your brother Evgraf, from Omsk. Your half brother. He came every day while you were ill."

"Does he wear a reindeer coat?"

"That's right. So you did see him. You were unconscious nearly all the time. He said he had run into you on the stairs in some house or other. He knew you—he meant to speak to you, but apparently you frightened him to death! He worships you, he reads every word you write. The things he got for us! Rice, raisins, sugar! He's gone back now. He wants us to go there too. He's a strange boy, a bit mysterious. I think he must have some sort of connection with the government out there. He says we ought to get away for a year or two, get away from the big towns, 'go back to the land' for a bit, he says. I thought of the Krueger place and he said it was a very good idea. We could grow vegetables and there's the forest all around. There isn't any point in dying without a struggle, like sheep."

In April that year Zhivago set out with his whole family for the former Varykino estate, near the town of Yuriatin, far away in the Urals.

CHAPTER SEVEN

TRAIN TO THE URALS

1

The end of March brought the first warm days of the year, false heralds of spring which were always followed by a severe cold spell.

The Zhivagos were hurriedly getting ready to leave. To disguise the bustle, the tenants—there were more of them now than sparrows in the street—were told that the apartment was having a spring cleaning for Easter.

Yurii Andreievich had opposed the move. So far, he had thought that it would come to nothing and had not interfered with the preparations, but they had advanced and were about to be completed. The time had come to discuss the matter seriously.

He reiterated his doubts at a family council made up of himself, his wife, and his father-in-law. "Do you think I'm wrong?" he asked them after stating his objections. "Do you still insist on going?"

"You say that we must manage as best we can for the next couple of years," said his wife, "until land conditions are settled, then we might get a vegetable garden near Moscow. But how are we to endure until then? That's the crucial point, and you haven't told us."

"It's sheer madness to count on such things," her father backed her up.

"Very well then, you win," Yurii Andreievich said. "What bothers me is that we are going blindfold, to a place we know nothing about. Of the three people who lived at Varykino, Mother and Grandmother are dead, and Grandfather Krueger is being held as a hostage—that is, if he is still alive.

"You know he made a fictitious sale in the last year of the war, sold the forests and the factories or else put the title deeds in the name of someone else, a bank or a private person, I don't know. We don't know anything, in fact. To whom does the estate belong now? I don't mean whose property it is, I don't care if we lose it, but who is in charge there? Who runs it? Is the timber being cut? Are the factories working? And above all, who is in power in that part of the country, or rather, who will be by the time we get there?

"You are relying on the old manager, Mikulitsyn, to see us through, but who is to tell us if he is still there? Or whether he is still alive? Anyway what do we know about him except his name—and that we only remember because Grandfather had such difficulty in pronouncing it.

"However, what is there to argue about? You have made up your minds, and I've agreed. Now we must find out exactly what one does about travelling these days. There is no point in putting it off."

2

Yurii Andreievich went to the Yaroslavsky Station to make inquiries.

Endless queues of passengers moved along raised gangways between wooden handrails. On the stone floors lay people in gray army coats who coughed, spat, shifted about, and spoke in voices that resounded incongruously loudly under the vaulted ceilings.

Most of these people had recently had typhus and been discharged from the overcrowded hospitals as soon as they were off the critical list. Yurii Andreievich, as a doctor, knew the necessity for this, but he had had no idea that there could be so many of these unfortunates or that they were forced to seek refuge in railway stations.

"You must get a priority," a porter in a white apron told him. "Then you must come every day to ask if there is a train. Trains are rare nowadays, it's a question of luck. And of course" (he rubbed two fingers with his thumb) "a little flour or something . . . Wheels don't run without oil, you know, and what's more" (he tapped his Adam's apple) "you won't get far without a little vodka."

3

About that time Alexander Alexandrovich was asked several times to act as consultant to the Higher Economic Council, and Yurii Andreievich to treat a member of the government who was dangerously ill. Both were paid in what was then the highest currency—credit slips for an allotment of articles from the first of the newly opened distribution centers.

The center was an old army warehouse next to the Simonov Monastery. The doctor and his father-in-law went through the monastery and the barrack yard and straight through a low stone door into a vaulted cellar. It sloped down and widened at its farther end, where a counter ran across from wall to wall; behind it stood an attendant, weighing, measuring, and handing out goods with calm unhurried movements, crossing off the items on the list with broad pencil strokes and occasionally replenishing his stock from the back of the store.

There were not many customers. "Containers," said the storekeeper, glancing at the slips. The professor and the doctor held out several large and small pillowcases and, with bulging eyes, watched them being filled with flour, cereals, macaroni, sugar, suet, soap, matches, and something wrapped in paper that was later found to be Caucasian cheese.

Overwhelmed by the storekeeper's generosity and anxious not to waste his time, they hurriedly stuffed their bundles into big sacks and slung them over their shoulders.

They came out of the vault intoxicated not by the mere thought of food but by the realization that they too were of use in the world and did not live in vain and had deserved the praise and thanks that Tonia would shower on them at home.

4

While the men disappeared for whole days into government offices, seeking travel documents and registering the apartment so that they should be able to go back to it on their return to

Moscow, Antonina Alexandrovna sorted the family belongings.

Walking up and down the three rooms now officially assigned to the Zhivagos, she weighed even the smallest article twenty times in her hand before deciding whether to put it into the pile of things they were taking with them. Only a small part of their luggage was intended for their personal use; the rest would serve as currency on the way and in the first weeks after their arrival.

The spring breeze came in through the partly open window, tasting faintly of newly cut white bread. Cocks were crowing and children playing and shouting in the yard. The more the room was aired the more noticeable became the smell of moth-balls from the open trunks in which the winter clothes had been packed.

As for the choice of things to be taken or left behind, there existed a whole theory, developed by those who had left earlier and communicated their observations to friends at home. The simple, indisputable rules of this theory were so distinctly present in Antonina Alexandrovna's mind that she imagined hearing them repeated by some secret voice coming from outside with the chirruping of sparrows and the cries of playing children.

"Lengths for dresses," she pondered, "but luggage is checked on the way, so this is dangerous unless they are tacked up to look like clothes. Materials and fabrics, clothes, preferably coats if they're not too worn. No trunks or hampers (there won't be any porters); be sure to take nothing useless and tie up everything in bundles small enough for a woman or a child to carry. Salt and tobacco have been found very useful but risky. Money in Kerenkas.[1] Documents are the hardest thing to carry safely." And so on and so on.

5

On the day before they left there was a snowstorm. Gray clouds of spinning snow swept into the sky and came back to earth as

[1] Kerenkas: paper money introduced by the Kerensky government and still in circulation at that time.

a white whirlwind, which ran off into the black depths of the street and covered it with a white shroud.

All the luggage was packed. The apartment, with such things as remained in it, was being left in the care of an elderly former salesclerk and his wife, relatives of Egorovna's who, the preceding winter, had helped Antonina Alexandrovna to trade old clothes and furniture for potatoes and wood.

Markel could not be trusted. At the militia post which he had selected as his political club he did not actually say that his former masters sucked his blood, but he accused them, instead, of having kept him in ignorance all these years and deliberately concealed from him that man is descended from apes.

Antonina Alexandrovna took the couple on a final survey of the house, fitting keys to locks, opening and shutting drawers and cupboards, and giving them last-minute instructions.

The chairs and tables had been pushed against the walls, the curtains taken down, and there was a pile of bundles in the corner. The snowstorm, seen through the bare windows of the rooms stripped of their winter comfort, reminded each of them of past sorrows. Yurii Andreievich thought of his childhood and his mother's death, and Antonina Alexandrovna and her father of the death and funeral of Anna Ivanovna. They felt that this was their last night in the house, that they would never see it again. They were mistaken on this point, but under the influence of their thoughts, which they kept to themselves in order not to upset each other, they looked back over the years spent under this roof, struggling against the tears that came to their eyes.

In spite of all this, Antonina Alexandrovna kept within the rules of propriety in the presence of strangers. She talked endlessly with the woman in whose care she was leaving everything. She overestimated the favor the couple were doing her. Anxious not to seem ungrateful, she kept apologizing, going next door and coming back with presents for the woman—blouses and lengths of cotton and silk prints. And the dark materials, with their white check or polka-dot patterns, were like the dark snow-bound street checkered with bricks and covered with

white dots which, that farewell night, looked in through the
uncurtained windows.

6

They left for the station at dawn. The other tenants were usually
asleep at this hour, but one of them, Zevorotnina, incurably
fond of organizing any social occasion, roused them all shouting: "Attention! Attention! Comrades! Hurry up! The Gromeko
people are going. Come and say goodbye!"

They all poured out onto the back porch (the front door was
kept boarded up) and stood in a semicircle as though for a
photograph. They yawned and shivered and tugged at the
shabby coats they had thrown over their shoulders and stamped
about in the huge felt boots they had hastily pulled on over
their bare feet.

Markel had already managed to get drunk on some murderous
brew he had succeeded in obtaining even in those dry days, and
he hung like a corpse over the worn porch railings, which
threatened to collapse under him. He insisted on carrying the
luggage to the station and was offended when his offer was refused. At last they got rid of him.

It was still dark. The wind had fallen and the snow fell
thicker than the night before. Large, fluffy flakes drifted down
lazily and hung over the ground, as though hesitating to settle.

By the time they had left the street and reached the Arbat it
was lighter. Here the snow came down like a white, slowly
descending stage curtain as wide as the street, its fringe swinging around the legs of the passers-by so that they lost the sense
of moving forward and felt they were marking time.

There was not a soul about except the travellers, but soon
they were overtaken by a cab with a snow-white nag and a
driver who looked as if he had been rolled in dough. For a
fabulous sum (worth less than a kopek in those days) he took
them to the station with their luggage, except for Yurii Andreievich, who at his own request was allowed to walk.

7

He found Antonina Alexandrovna and her father standing in one of the endless queues squeezed between the wooden handrails. Niusha and Sashenka were walking about outside and occasionally looking in to see if it were time to join the grownups. They gave off a strong smell of kerosene, which had been thickly smeared on their necks, wrists, and ankles as a protection against lice.

The queues went up to the gates of the platforms, but in fact the passengers had to board the train a good half mile farther down the line. With not enough cleaners, the station was filthy and the tracks in front of the platforms were unusable because of dirt and ice. The trains stopped farther out.

Antonina Alexandrovna waved to her husband and when he was close enough shouted instructions as to where he was to get their travel papers stamped.

"Show me what they've put," she said when he came back. He held out a batch of papers across the handrail.

"That's for the special coach," said the man behind her in the queue, reading over her shoulder.

The man in front of her was more explicit. He was one of those sticklers for form who seem to be familiar with and accept without question every regulation in the world.

"This stamp," he explained, "gives you the right to claim seats in a classified coach, that is to say a passenger coach, if there is a passenger coach on the train."

The whole queue joined in at once.

"Passenger coach indeed! If you can get a seat on the buffers you must be thankful nowadays!"

"Don't listen to them," said the other. "I'll explain, it's quite simple. Today there is only one type of train, and it always includes army, convict, cattle, and passenger cars. Why mislead the man?" he said, turning to the crowd. "Words don't cost anything, you can say what you like, but you should say it clearly so that he can understand."

"A lot you've explained." He was shouted down. "A lot you've said when you've told him he's got stamps for the special coach! You should look at a man first, before you start explaining.

How can anyone with such a face go in the special coach? The special coach is full of sailors. A sailor has a trained eye and a gun. He takes a look at him and what does he see? A member of the propertied classes—worse than that: a doctor, former quality. He pulls out his gun—and goodbye."

There is no knowing to what lengths the sympathy aroused by the doctor's case would have gone if the crowd had not turned its attention to something else.

For some time people had been looking curiously through the enormous plate-glass windows at the tracks, which were roofed in for several hundred yards. The falling snow could be seen only beyond the far end of the roofs; seen so far away, it looked almost still, sinking to the ground as slowly as bread crumbs thrown to fishes sink through water.

For some time, figures had been strolling into the distance along the tracks, singly or in groups. At first they were taken for railwaymen attending to their duties, but now a whole mob rushed out, and from the direction in which they were running there appeared a small cloud of smoke.

"Open up the gates, you scoundrels," yelled voices in the queue. The crowd stirred and swung against the gates, those at the back pushing those in front.

"Look what's going on! They've locked us in here and through there some people have found a way around and jumped the queue. Open up, you bastards, or we'll smash the gates. Come on, let's give it a push."

"They needn't envy that lot, the fools," said the know-it-all stickler for form. "Those men are conscripts, called up for forced labor from Petrograd. They were supposed to be sent to Vologda, but now they're being taken to the eastern front. They're not travelling of their own choice. They're under escort. They'll be digging trenches."

8

They had been travelling three days but had not got far from Moscow. The landscape was wintry. Tracks, fields, woods, and village roofs—everything was covered with snow.

The Zhivagos had been lucky enough to get a corner to themselves on the upper bunks, right up against the long bleary window close under the ceiling.

Antonina Alexandrovna had never travelled in a freight car before. The first time they got in Yurii Andreievich lifted her up to the high floor and pushed open the heavy sliding doors for her, but later she learned to climb in and out by herself.

The car looked to Antonina Alexandrovna no better than a pigsty on wheels, and she had expected it to fall apart at the first jar. But for three days now they had been jolted back and forth and from side to side as the train had changed speed or direction, for three days the wheels had rattled underneath them like the sticks on a mechanical toy drum, and there had been no accident. Her fears had been groundless.

The train had twenty-three cars (the Zhivagos were in the fourteenth). When it stopped at country stations, only a few front, middle, or end cars stood beside the short platform.

Sailors were in front, civilian passengers in the middle, and the labor conscripts in eight cars at the back. There were about five hundred of the latter, people of all ages, conditions, and professions.

They were a remarkable sight—rich, smart lawyers and stockbrokers from Petrograd side by side with cab drivers, floor polishers, bath attendants, Tartar ragpickers, escaped lunatics, shopkeepers, and monks, all lumped in with the exploiting classes.

The lawyers and stockbrokers sat on short thick logs in their shirt sleeves around red-hot iron stoves, told endless stories, joked, and laughed. They were not worried, they had connections, influential relatives were pulling strings for them at home, and at the worst they could buy themselves off later on.

The others, in boots and unbuttoned caftans, or barefoot and in long shirts worn outside their trousers, with or without beards, stood at the half-open doors of the airless cars, holding on to the sides or to the boards nailed across the openings, and gazed sullenly at the peasants and villages by the wayside, speaking to no one. These had no influential friends. They had nothing to hope for.

There were too many conscripts for the cars allotted to them.

and the overflow had been put among the civilian passengers, including those of the fourteenth car.

9

Whenever the train stopped, Antonina Alexandrovna sat up cautiously to avoid knocking her head on the ceiling and looked down through the slightly open door to see if it were worth while to go out. This depended on the size of the station, the probable length of the halt, and the consequent likelihood of profitable barter.

So it was on this occasion. The train had wakened her from a doze by slowing down. The number of switches over which it bumped and rattled suggested that the station was fairly large, and that they would stop for a long time.

She rubbed her eyes, tidied her hair, and after rummaging at the bottom of a bundle pulled out a towel embroidered with cockerels, oxbows, and wheels.

The doctor, who had waked up in the meantime, jumped down first from his bunk, and helped his wife to get to the floor. Guards' shelters and lampposts drifted past the door, followed by trees bending under heavy piles of snow, which they held out toward the train as though in sign of welcome. Long before it had stopped, sailors jumped off into the untrodden snow and raced around the corner of the station building where peasant women were usually to be found trading illegally in food.

Their black uniforms with bell-bottom trousers and ribbons fluttering from their visorless caps gave an air of reckless speed to their advance and made other people give way as before the onrush of racing skiers or skaters.

Around the corner, girls and women from near-by villages, as excited as if they were at the fortuneteller's, stood one behind the other in single file in the shelter of the station wall selling cucumbers, cottage cheese, and platters of boiled beef and rye pancakes kept hot and tasty by quilted napkins. Muffled up in shawls tucked inside their sheepskins, the women blushed a fiery red at the sailors' jokes but at the same time were terrified of them, for it was generally sailors who formed the units organized to fight against speculation and the forbidden free market.

The apprehensions of the peasant women were soon dispelled. When the train stopped and civilian passengers joined the crowd, trade became brisk.

Antonina Alexandrovna walked down the line inspecting the wares, her towel flung over her shoulder as if she were going to the back of the station to wash in the snow. Several women had called out: "Hey, what do you want for your towel?" but she continued on her way, escorted by her husband.

At the end of the row there was a woman in a black shawl with a scarlet pattern. She saw the towel and her bold eyes lit up. Glancing around cautiously, she sidled up to Antonina Alexandrovna and, uncovering her wares, whispered eagerly: "Look at this. Bet you haven't seen that in a long while. Tempting, isn't it? Don't think about it too long or it will be gone. Like to give me your towel for a half?"

Antonina Alexandrovna missed the last word.

"What do you mean, my good woman?"

The woman meant half a hare, roasted whole from head to tail and cut in two. She held it up. "I'm telling you, I'll give you a half for your towel. What are you staring at? It isn't dog meat. My husband is a hunter. It's hare, all right."

They exchanged their goods. Each believed that she had had the best of the bargain. Antonina Alexandrovna felt as ashamed as if she had swindled the peasant woman, while she, delighted with her deal, called a friend who had also sold out her wares and made off with her, home to their village, striding down the snowy path into the distance.

At this moment there was an uproar in the crowd. An old woman was screaming: "Hey, you! Where are you off to? Where's my money? When did you pay me, you cheat? Look at him, greedy pig, you call him and he doesn't even bother to turn around. Stop! Stop, I tell you, Mister Comrade! I've been robbed! Stop, thief! There he goes, that's him, catch him!"

"Which one?"

"That one, the one who's clean-shaven and grinning."

"Is that the one with the hole in his sleeve?"

"Yes, yes, catch him, the heathen!"

"The one with the patched elbow?"

"Yes, yes. Oh, I've been robbed."

"What's going on here?"

"Fellow over there bought some milk and pies, stuffed himself, and went off without paying, so the old woman is crying."

"That shouldn't be allowed. Why don't they go after him?"

"Go after him! He's got straps and cartridge belts all over him. He'll go after you."

10

There were several labor conscripts in car fourteen. With them was their guard, Private Voroniuk. Three of the men stood out from the rest. They were Prokhor Kharitonovich Prituliev, who had been cashier in a government liquor store in Petrograd—the cashier, as he was called in the car; Vasia Brykin, a sixteen-year-old boy apprenticed to an ironmonger; and Kostoied-Amursky, a gray-haired revolutionary co-operativist, who had been in all the forced-labor camps of the old regime and was now discovering those of the new.

The conscripts, who had all been strangers when they were impressed, were gradually getting to know each other. It turned out that the cashier and Vasia, the apprentice, came from the same part of the country, the Viatka government, and also that the train would be going through their native villages.

Prituliev came from Malmyzh. His hair was cropped and he was pockmarked, squat, and hideous. His gray sweater, black with sweat under the arms, fitted him snugly like a fleshy woman's blouse. He would sit for hours as silent as a statue, lost in thought, scratching the warts on his freckled hands until they bled and suppurated.

One day last autumn, he was going down the Nevsky when he walked into a militia roundup at the corner of Liteiny Street. He had to show his papers and was found to hold a fourth-class ration book, the kind issued to nonworkers, on which nothing could ever be bought. He was consequently detained, with many others who were arrested for the same reason, and taken under escort to barracks. His group was to be sent, like the one preceding it, to dig trenches on the Archangel front, but was diverted on its way and sent east through Moscow.

Prituliev had a wife in Luga, where he had worked before the war. She heard indirectly of his misfortune and rushed off to Vologda (the junction for Archangel) to look for him and obtain his release. But the unit had not gone there, her labors had been in vain, and she lost track of him.

In Petrograd Prituliev lived with a certain Pelagia Nilovna Tiagunova. At the time he was arrested he had just said good-bye to her, preparing to go in a different direction to keep an appointment, and looking down Liteiny Street he could still see her back disappearing among the crowd.

She was a plump woman with a stately carriage, beautiful hands, and a thick braid which she tossed from time to time, with deep sighs, over her shoulder. She was now with the convoy, having volunteered to accompany Prituliev.

It was difficult to know what it was that attracted women to such an ugly man, but certainly they clung to him. In a car farther forward there was another woman friend of his, Ogryzkova, a bony girl with white eyelashes who had somehow made her way onto the train and whom Tiagunova called "the squirt," "the nozzle," and many other insulting names. The rivals were at swords' points and took good care to avoid each other. Ogryzkova never went to the other's car. It was a mystery to know how she ever met the object of her passion. Perhaps she contented herself with seeing him from afar, when the engine was being refuelled with the help of all the passengers.

11

Vasia's story was quite different. His father had been killed in the war and his mother had sent him to Petrograd to be apprenticed to his uncle.

The uncle kept a private shop in Apraksin Yard. One day last winter he had been summoned by the local soviet to answer a few questions. He mistook the door and walked into the office of the labor corps selection board. The room was full of conscripts; after a while soldiers came in, surrounded the men, and took them to the Semenov barracks for the night, and escorted them to the Vologda train in the morning.

The news of so many arrests spread and the prisoners' families came to say goodbye to them at the station. Among them were Vasia and his aunt. His uncle begged the guard (Voroniuk, who was now in car fourteen) to let him out for a minute to see his wife. The guard refused without a guarantee that he would return. The uncle and aunt offered Vasia as a hostage. Voroniuk agreed. Vasia was brought in and his uncle was let out. This was the last he ever saw of his aunt or uncle.

When the fraud was discovered, Vasia, who had suspected nothing, burst into tears. He threw himself at Voroniuk's feet, kissed his hands, and begged him to let him go, but to no avail. The guard was inexorable not because he was cruel, but discipline was very strict in those troubled times. The guard answered for the number of his charges with his life, and the numbers were checked by roll call. That was how Vasia came to be in the labor corps.

The co-operativist, Kostoied-Amursky, who had enjoyed the respect of his jailors under both Tsarism and the present government and who was always on good terms with them, repeatedly spoke to the head of the convoy about Vasia's predicament. The officer admitted that it was a terrible misunderstanding but said there were formal difficulties in the way of examining the case until they arrived; he promised to do his best at that moment.

Vasia was an attractive boy with regular features who looked like a royal page or an angel of God in a picture. He was unusually innocent and unspoiled. His favorite occupation was to sit on the floor at the feet of his elders, looking up at them, his hands clasped around his knees, and listen to their discussions and stories. By watching the muscles of his face, as he just barely restrained himself from tears or choked with laughter, you could almost follow the conversation.

12

The Zhivagos had invited the co-operativist Kostoied to dinner. He sat in their corner sucking a leg of hare with a loud wheezing noise. He dreaded drafts and chills, and changed his place several times, looking for a sheltered spot. At last he found a place where he did not feel the draft. "That's better," he said. He finished his bone, sucked his fingers clean, wiped them on his handkerchief, thanked his hosts, and said: "It's your window. It has to be cemented. But to go back to our discussion: You're mistaken, Doctor. Roast hare is an excellent thing, but to conclude that the peasants are prosperous is rash, to say the least, if you'll forgive my saying so."

"Oh, come," said Yurii Andreievich. "Look at all these stations. The trees aren't cut, the fences are intact. And these markets! These women! Think how wonderful! Somewhere life is still going on, some people are happy. Not everyone is wretched. This justifies everything."

"It would be good if that were true. But it isn't. Where did you get all those ideas? Take a trip to any place that is fifty miles from the railway. You'll find that there are peasant rebellions everywhere. Against whom? you'll ask. Well, they're against the Reds or against the Whites, whoever happens to be in power. You'll say, Aha, that's because the peasants are enemies of all authority, they don't know what they want. Allow me to differ. The peasant knows very well what he wants, better than you or I do, but he wants something quite different.

"When the revolution woke him up, he decided that his century-old dream was coming true—his dream of living on his own land by the work of his hands, in complete independence and with no obligations to anyone. Instead, he found he had only exchanged the oppression of the former state for the new, much harsher yoke of the revolutionary superstate. Can you wonder that the villages are restless and can't settle down? And you say they are prosperous! No, there are a lot of things you don't know, my dear fellow, and as far as I can see you don't want to know them."

"All right, it's true, I don't. Why on earth should I know and worry myself sick over every blessed thing? History hasn't con-

sulted me. I have to put up with whatever happens, so why
shouldn't I ignore the facts? You tell me my ideas don't correspond to reality. But where is reality in Russia today? As I see
it, reality has been so terrorized that it is hiding. I want to believe that the peasants are better off and flourishing. If it is an
illusion, what am I to do? What am I to live by; whom am I
to believe? And I have to go on living, I've got a family."

He made a despairing gesture and, leaving the argument to
his father-in-law, moved away, and hung his head over the
edge of the bunk to look at what was going on below.

Prituliev, Tiagunova, Vasia, and Voroniuk were talking together. As the train was approaching his native province, Prituliev
recalled the way to his village, the station, and the road you took
according to whether you went by horse or on foot, and at the
mention of familiar village names, Vasia repeated them with
shining eyes, as if they were a marvellous fairy tale.

"You get off at Dry Ford?" he asked, choking with excitement.
"Our station! Of course! And then you go on to Buisky, right?"

"That's right, you take the Buisky road."

"That's what I say—Buisky—Buisky village. Of course I know
it, that's where you get off the main road, you turn right and
right again. That's to get to us, to Veretenniki. And your way
must be left, away from the river, isn't it? You know the river
Pelga? Well, of course! That's our river. You keep following the
river, on and on, and away up on the cliff on the right, overhanging that same river Pelga, there's our village, Veretenniki!
It's right up on the edge, and it's stee-eep! It makes you giddy,
honest to God it does. There's a quarry down below, for mill-
stones. That's where my mother lives, in Veretenniki, and my
two little sisters. Alenka and Arishka . . . Mother is a bit like
you, Aunt Pelagia, she's young and fair. Uncle Voroniuk! Please,
Uncle Voroniuk, for the love of Christ, please, I beg you, for
God's sake . . . Uncle Voroniuk!"

"Well, what? Uncle, uncle, I know I'm not your aunt. What
do you expect me to do? Am I mad? If I let you go that would
be the end of me, amen, they'd put me up against a wall."

Pelagia Tiagunova sat looking thoughtfully out of the window,
stroking Vasia's reddish hair. Now and then she bent down to
him and smiled as if she were telling him: "Don't be silly.

This isn't something to talk to Voroniuk about in front of everyone. Don't worry, have patience, it will be all right."

13

Peculiar things began to happen when they left Central Russia behind on their way east. They were going through a restless region infested with armed bands, past villages where uprisings had recently been put down.

The train stopped frequently in the middle of nowhere and security patrols checked the passengers' papers and luggage.

Once they stopped at night, but no one came in and no one was disturbed. Yurii Andreievich wondered if there had been an accident and went out to see.

It was dark. For no apparent reason the train had stopped between two stations, in a field, with a row of firs on either side of the track. Other passengers who had come out and were stamping their feet in the snow told Yurii Andreievich that there was nothing wrong, but that the engineer refused to go on, saying that this stretch was dangerous and should first be inspected by handcar. Spokesmen of the passengers had gone to reason with him and if necessary to grease his palm. It was said that sailors were also taking a hand in it and would undoubtedly get their way.

The snow at the head of the train was lit up at intervals, as from a bonfire, by fiery flashes from the smokestack or the glowing coals in the firebox. By this light several dark figures were now seen running to the front of the engine.

The first of them, presumably the engineer, reached the far end of the running board, leapt over the buffers, and vanished as if the earth had swallowed him. The sailors who were chasing him did exactly the same thing: they too flashed for a moment through the air and vanished.

Curious about what was going on, several passengers including Yurii Andreievich went to see.

Beyond the buffers, where the track opened out before them, they were met with an astonishing sight. The engineer stood in the snow up to his waist. His pursuers surrounded him in a semicircle, like hunters around their quarry; like him, they were buried in snow up to the waist.

"Thank you, comrades, fine stormy petrels you are," [1] the engineer was shouting. "A fine sight, sailors chasing a fellow worker with guns! All because I said the train must stop. You be my witnesses, comrade passengers, you can see what kind of place this is. Anybody might be roaming around unscrewing the bolts. Do you think I'm worrying about myself, you God-damned bastards? To hell with you. It's for you I was doing it, so that nothing should happen to you, and that's all the thanks I get for my trouble! Go on, go on, why don't you shoot? Here I am. You be my witnesses, comrade passengers, I'm not running away."

Bewildered voices rose from the group. "Pipe down, old man . . . They don't mean it . . . Nobody would let them . . . They don't really mean it . . ." Others urged him on: "That's right, Gavrilka, stand up for yourself! Don't let them bully you!"

The first sailor to scramble out of the snow was a red-haired giant with a head so huge that it made his face look flat. He turned to the passengers and spoke in a deep, quiet, unhurried voice with a Ukrainian accent, like Voroniuk's, his composure oddly out of keeping with the scene.

"Beg pardon, what's all this uproar about? Be careful you don't catch a chill in this cold, citizens. It's windy. Why not go back to your seats and keep warm?"

The crowd gradually dispersed. The giant went to the engineer, who was still worked up, and said:

"Enough hysterics, comrade engineer. Get out of the snow, and let's get going."

14

Next day the train, creeping at a snail's pace lest it run off the tracks, powdered by the wind with unswept snow, pulled up

---

[1] Stormy petrels: The reference is to the sailors in the *Potemkin* mutiny and is also an allusion to Gorky's story of that name.

beside a lifeless, burned-out ruin. This was all that was left of the station, Nizhni Kelmes, its name still faintly legible on its blackened façade.

Beyond it lay a deserted village blanketed in snow. This too was damaged by fire. The end house was charred, the one next to it sagged where its corner timbers had fallen in; broken sleighs, fences, rusty pieces of metal, and smashed furniture were scattered all over the street; the snow was dirty with soot, and black patches of earth showed through the frozen puddles with half-burnt logs sticking out of them—all evidence of the fire and of the efforts to put it out.

The place was not in fact as dead as it looked; there were a few people still about. The stationmaster rose out of the ruins and the guard jumped down from the train and commiserated with him. "The whole place was burned down?"

"Good day to you, and welcome. Yes, we certainly had a fire, but it was worse than that."

"I don't follow."

"Better not try."

"You don't mean Strelnikov!"

"I do."

"Why? What had you done?"

"We didn't do anything, it was our neighbors; we got it too for good measure. You see that village over there? Nizhni Kelmes is in the Ust-Nemdinsk county—it was all because of them."

"And what crime had they committed?"

"Just about all the seven deadly sins: Dissolved their Poor Peasants' Committee, that's one; refused to supply horses to the Red Army, that's two (and they're all Tartars, mind you, horsemen); resisted the mobilization decree, that makes three. Well, there you are."

"Yes, I see. I quite see. So they were shelled?"

"Naturally."

"From the armored train?"

"Of course."

"That's bad. All our sympathy. Still, it's none of our business."

"Besides, it's an old story. And the news I have isn't very good either. You'll have to stop here for a couple of days."

"You're joking! I'm taking replacements to the front. This is an urgent matter."

"I'm not joking at all. We've had a blizzard for a solid week—snowdrifts all along the line, and no one to clear it. Half the village has run away. I'll put the rest of them on the job, but it won't be enough."

"Damn. What am I to do?"

"We'll get it cleared, somehow."

"How deep is the snow?"

"Not too bad. It varies. The worst patch is in the middle—about two miles long; we'll certainly have trouble there. Farther on the forest has kept the worst of the snow off the tracks. And on this side it's open country, so the wind has blown away some of it."

"Hell, what a pain in the neck! I'll mobilize all the passengers."

"That's what I was thinking."

"We mustn't use the sailors and Red Army men. But there's a whole corps of labor conscripts—including the other passengers, there are about seven hundred in all."

"That's more than enough. We'll start the moment we get the shovels. We're a bit short of them, so we've sent to the near-by villages for more. We'll manage."

"God, what a blow! Do you think we can do it?"

"Of course we can. With plenty of troops you can take a city, they say, and this is only a bit of tracks. Don't worry."

15

Clearing the line took three days, and all the Zhivagos, even Niusha, took part in it. They were the best three days of their journey.

The landscape had a withdrawn, secretive quality. It made one think of Pushkin's story about the Pugachev uprising and of some places described by Aksakov. The ruins added to the air of mystery; so did the wariness of the remaining villagers, who, afraid of informers, avoided the passengers and were silent even among themselves.

The workers were divided into gangs, with the labor conscripts and the civilians kept apart. Armed soldiers guarded each working group.

The tracks were cleared in several places at the same time by separate gangs. Mounds of snow between the sections hid the gangs from one another and were left untouched until the last.

The workers spent all day in the open, going back only to sleep. The days were clear and frosty, and the shifts were short because there were not enough shovels. It was sheer pleasure.

Zhivago's section of the track had a fine view. The country to the east dipped down into a valley and rose in gentle hills as far as the horizon.

On the top of a hill there was a house exposed to all the winds; its park must have been luxuriant in summer but could not give it any shelter now with its frosty lacework.

The snow smoothed and rounded all contours. It could not quite conceal the winding bed of a stream which in spring would rush down to the viaduct below the railway bank but at present was tucked up in the snow like a child in its cot with its head under the eiderdown.

Was anyone living in the house on the hill, Zhivago wondered, or was it standing empty and falling into ruins, held by some land committee? What had happened to the people who had once lived there? Had they fled abroad? Or been killed by the peasants? Or had they been popular and were they allowed to settle in the district as technical specialists? If they had stayed, had they been spared by Strelnikov or shared the fate of the kulaks?

The house teased his curiosity but kept its sorrowful silence. Questions were not in order in these days, and no one ever answered them. But the sun sparkled on the pure whiteness with a glare that was almost blinding. How cleanly his shovel cut into its smooth surface! How dry, how iridescent, like diamonds, was each shovelful. He was reminded of the days when, as a child in their yard at home, dressed in a braided hood and a black sheepskin fastened with hooks and eyes sewn in the curly fleece, he cut the dazzling snow into cubes and pyramids and cream puffs and fortresses and the cities of cave dwellers. Life had had zest in those far-off days, everything was a feast for the eyes and the stomach!

But these three days in the air, too, gave the impression of a feast. And no wonder! At night the workers received loaves of hot fresh bread, which was brought no one knew from where or by whose orders. The bread had a tasty crisp crust, shiny on top, cracked at the side, and with bits of charcoal baked into it underneath.

16

They became fond of the ruined station, as one becomes attached to a shelter used for a few days on a climbing trip in a snow-bound mountain. Its shape, its site, the details of its damage, remained imprinted in their memory.

They returned to it every evening just as the sun, as if out of loyalty to the past, set at its usual place behind an old birch tree outside the telegrapher's window.

At that spot the wall had caved into the room, but the corner facing the window had remained intact, with its coffee-colored wallpaper, the tiled stove with the round vent and the copper lid closed with a chain, and the inventory of the office furniture hanging on the wall in a black frame. As before the collapse, the setting sun brushed the tiles, brought out the warm brown glow on the wallpaper, and hung the shadow of the birch on the wall as if it were a woman's scarf.

At the rear of the building, on the nailed door to the ruins of the waiting room, there was still an announcement, put up in the first days of the February revolution, or shortly before it, which said:

"Sick passengers are temporarily requested not to bother about medicines and bandages. For obvious reasons, am sealing door, of which am giving notice hereby.

"Medical Assistant
"Ust-Nemdinsk District"

When finally the last piles of snow between the cleared tracks were levelled, the entire line of rails came into view, fly-

ing into the distance like an arrow. On each side stretched white
mountains of shovelled snow, bordered all along by the black
walls of the forest.

As far as the eye could reach, groups of people with shovels
in hand stood at intervals along the line. Seeing themselves
for the first time in full force, they were astonished at their
numbers.

17

It was learned that the train would leave shortly, despite the
lateness of the hour and the approaching night. Yurii Andreievich and Antonina Alexandrovna went out to enjoy the sight
of the cleared line once again. No one else was on the tracks.
The doctor and his wife stood a while, gazing into the distance,
exchanged a few words, and turned back to their car.

On the way they heard the angry voices of two quarrelling
women. They recognized them at once as those of Ogryzkova
and Tiagunova, who were walking in the same direction as
they were, from the head to the end of the train, but on the
station side, while the doctor and his wife walked on the
wooded side. The endless line of cars screened the two couples
from each other. The women seemed hardly ever to be abreast
of the doctor and Antonina Alexandrovna, but always to be
ahead of them or falling behind.

They seemed to be in a state of great agitation, and it was as
though their strength failed them. Judging from the way their
voices rose to a shriek or died down to a whisper, either their
legs refused to carry them or else they kept stumbling and falling into snowdrifts. Tiagunova seemed to be chasing Ogryzkova,
perhaps belaboring her with her fists whenever she caught up
with her. She showered her rival with choice abuse, and her
genteel, melodious voice made the insults sound infinitely
more obscene than the coarse and unmusical swearing of men.

"You slut, you drag-tailed whore," Tiagunova screamed. "I
can't move an inch without seeing you flouncing up and down,
and ogling. Isn't my old fool enough for you without your having
to make eyes at a babe in arms, to seduce a minor?"

"So Vasia too is your legal husband?"

"I'll give you legal husband, you filthy plague! One more word from you, and I'll kill you, don't tempt me."

"Now, now, keep your hands to yourself. What do you want of me?"

"I want to see you dead, you lecherous louse, you cat in heat, you shameless bitch!"

"That's what I am, is it? Naturally, I'm nothing but a cat, a bitch, compared with such a grand lady as you! Born in the gutter, married in a ditch, a rat in your belly, and a hedgehog for a brat! . . . Help! Help! She'll kill me! Help a poor orphan, help a poor defenseless girl!"

"Come along," Antonina Alexandrovna urged her husband. "I can't bear to listen to it, it's too disgusting. It will end badly."

18

Suddenly everything changed—the weather and the landscape. The plains ended, and the track wound up hills through mountain country. The north wind that had been blowing all the time dropped, and a warm breath came from the south, as from an oven.

Here the woods grew on escarpments projecting from the mountain slopes, and when the track crossed them, the train had to climb sharply uphill until it reached the middle of the wood, and then go steeply down again.

The train creaked and puffed on its way into the wood, hardly able to drag itself along, as if it were an aged forest guard walking in front and leading the passengers, who turned their heads from side to side and observed whatever was to be seen.

But there was nothing yet to see. The woods were still deep in their winter sleep and peace. Only here and there a branch would rustle and shake itself free of the remaining snow, as though throwing off a choker.

Yurii Andreievich was overcome with drowsiness. All these days he lay in his bunk and slept and woke and thought and listened. But there was nothing yet to hear.

19

While Yurii Andreievich slept his fill, the spring was heating and melting the masses of snow that had fallen all over Russia, first in Moscow on the day they had left and since then all along the way—all that snow they had spent three days clearing off the line at Ust-Nemdinsk, all that thick, deep layer of snow that had settled over the immense distances.

At first the snow thawed quietly and secretly from within. But by the time half the gigantic labor was done it could not be hidden any longer and the miracle became visible. Waters came rushing out from below with a roar. The forest stirred in its impenetrable depth, and everything in it awoke.

There was plenty of room for the water to play. It flung itself down the rocks, filled every pool to overflowing, and spread. It roared and smoked and steamed in the forest. It streaked through the woods, bogging down in the snow that tried to hinder its movement, it ran hissing on level ground or hurtled down and scattered into a fine spray. The earth was saturated. Ancient pine trees perched on dizzy heights drank the moisture almost from the clouds, and it foamed and dried a rusty white at their roots like beer foam on a mustache.

The sky, drunk with spring and giddy with its fumes, thickened with clouds. Low clouds, drooping at the edges like felt, sailed over the woods and rain leapt from them, warm, smelling of soil and sweat, and washing the last of the black armor-plating of ice from the earth.

Yurii Andreievich woke up, stretched, raised himself on one elbow, and looked and began to listen.

20

As they approached the mining region, there were more and more settlements, the runs were shorter, the stations more frequent. More people got on and off at the small stations. Instead of settling down and going to sleep, those who had only a short way to go found seats anywhere—near the door or in the middle of the car—and sat up arguing in low voices about local matters intelligible only to themselves.

From the hints dropped by such local passengers in the past three days Yurii Andreievich gathered that in the north the Whites were getting the upper hand and had seized or were about to occupy Yuriatin. Moreover, unless he had misheard the name or his old friend had a namesake, the White forces were led by Galiullin, whom he had last seen in Meliuzeievo.

Not to worry his family, he said nothing to them about these unconfirmed rumors.

21

Yurii Andreievich woke up shortly after midnight brimming with a vague feeling of happiness, which was, however, strong enough to have aroused him. The train was standing still. The station bathed in the glassy dusk of a white night. Something subtle and powerful in this luminous darkness suggested a vast and open landscape and that the station was situated high up.

People walked along the platform past the carriage speaking softly and treading as silently as shadows. Zhivago was touched by this evidence of a prewar consideration for the sleeping passengers.

The doctor was mistaken. There was the same din of shouting voices and stamping boots on this platform as on any other. But there was a waterfall near by. It widened the expanse of the white night by a breath of freshness and freedom; that was what had filled him with happiness in his sleep. Its incessant noise dominated all other sounds and gave an illusion of stillness.

Knowing nothing of its existence but soothed and braced by it, the doctor fell fast asleep.

Two men were talking underneath his bunk.

"Well, have they had their tails twisted yet? Are they keeping quiet now?"

"The shopkeepers, you mean?"

"That's right. The grain merchants."

"Feed out of your hand! As soon as a few were bumped

off by way of example, all the others piped down. A fine has been imposed on the district."

"How much?"

"Forty thousand."

"You're lying!"

"Why should I lie?"

"Forty thousand—that isn't even chicken feed!"

"Not forty thousand rubles, of course—forty thousand bushels."

"That was smart!"

"Forty thousand of the finest ground."

"Well, that's not such a miracle, after all. It's rich soil. Right in the thick of the corn belt. From here on, along the Rynva till you get to Yuriatin, it's village to village, harbor to harbor, one wholesaler after another."

"Don't shout. You'll wake people up."

"All right." He yawned.

"How about going to sleep? Looks as if we're moving."

The train, however, stayed where it was. But the rumble of another train came from behind, bursting into a deafening thunder and obliterating the sound of the waterfall as it approached, and an old-fashioned express rushed past at full speed on the parallel track, roared, hooted, winked its tail lights, and vanished into the distance ahead.

The conversation was resumed.

"Well, we're in for it. Now we'll never go."

"Yes. It won't be soon."

"It's an armored express—must be Strelnikov."

"Must be him."

"He's a wild beast when it comes to counterrevolutionaries."

"He's after Galeiev."

"Who's that?"

"Hetman Galeiev. They say he's outside Yuriatin with a Czech covering force. He's seized the harbors, the pest, and he's hanging on. Hetman Galeiev."

"Never heard of him."

"Or it may be Prince Galileiev. I can't quite remember the name."

"There aren't any such princes. Must be Ali Kurban. You've mixed them up."

"May be Kurban."

"That's more like it."

22

Toward morning Yurii Andreievich woke up a second time. He
had had a pleasant dream. The feeling of bliss and liberation
was still with him. Again the train was standing still, perhaps at
the same station as before, possibly at another. Once more there
was the sound of the waterfall, perhaps a different waterfall
but more probably the same one.

He went back to sleep almost at once, and as he was dozing
off he dimly heard the sound of running feet and of some commotion. Kostoied was quarrelling with the commander of the
convoy and they were shouting at each other. The air was even
more pleasant than before. It had a breath of something new
in it, something that had not been there earlier—something
magical, springlike, white, blackish, thin and insubstantial, like
a snow flurry in May when the wet, melting flakes falling on the
earth make it seem black rather than white. It was something
transparent, blackish-white, sweet-smelling—"Wild cherry," Yurii
Andreievich decided in his sleep.

23

Next morning Antonina Alexandrovna said:

"Really, Yura, you're extraordinary, you're a mass of contradictions. Sometimes a fly will wake you up and you can't get
back to sleep till morning, and here you slept through all this
row and I simply couldn't get you to wake up. Prituliev and
Vasia have escaped, just think of it! And so have Tiagunova
and Ogryzkova! Can you imagine such a thing! Wait, that isn't
all. Voroniuk as well. It's true, I tell you, he's run away. Now
listen. How they managed it, together or separately, and in
what order—it's all a complete mystery. Voroniuk, of course, I
understand—once he found the others had gone, he would have
to try to save his skin. But what about the rest? Did they really
all vanish of their own free will, or was somebody done away

with? For instance, if the women are to be suspected, did Tiagunova kill Ogryzkova or was it the other way around? Nobody knows. The commander of the escort has been running up and down the train like a lunatic. 'You're not to start the train. I order you in the name of the law not to move till I've caught my prisoners.' And the commanding officer shouts back: 'I'm taking replacements up to the front, I'm not waiting for your lousy crew. What an idea!' Then they both went for Kostoied. 'You, a syndicalist, an educated man, how could you sit by and let a simple soldier, an ignorant child of nature, act in such a reckless manner! And you a populist!'[1] And Kostoied gave them as good as he got. 'That's interesting,' he says. 'The prisoner has to look after his guard, does he? Well, really, the day that happens the hens will start to crow.' I was shaking you as hard as I could. 'Yura,' I cried, 'get up, there's been an escape.' But nothing doing. If a gun had gone off in your ear you wouldn't have heard it. . . . But I'll tell you more later. . . . Look! Father, Yura, look, isn't the view superb!"

Through the opening in the window they could see the country covered with spring floods as far as eye could reach. Somewhere a river had overflowed its banks and the water had come right up to the embankment. In the foreshortened view from the bunk it looked as if the train were actually gliding on the water.

Only here and there was its smoothness broken by streaks of a metallic blue, but over all the rest of its surface the hot morning sun was chasing glassy patches of light as smooth and oily as melted butter that a cook brushes with a feather on a pie crust.

In this shoreless flood were sunk the shafts of the white clouds, their pediments submerged together with the fields, the hollows, and the bushes.

And somewhere in the middle of the flood there was a narrow strip of land with a row of doubled trees going up and down and suspended between earth and sky.

"Look, a family of ducks!" Alexander Alexandrovich cried out. "Where?"

"Near the island. More to the right. Damn, they've flown. We've frightened them."

[1] Left-wing idealists who devoted themselves to work among the people.

"Yes, I see them now," said Yurii Andreievich. "I must have a talk with you, Alexander Alexandrovich. Some other time. . . . As for our labor conscripts and the women, good for them. And I'm sure there wasn't any murder. They just broke free like the water."

24

The white northern night was ending. Everything could be seen clearly—the mountain, the thicket, and the ravine—but seemed unreal, as though made up.

The wood, which had several blossoming wild cherries in it, was just coming into leaf. It grew under an overhanging cliff, on a narrow ledge above another precipice.

The waterfall, though not far away, could be seen only from the edge of the ravine beyond the thicket. Vasia was tired from walking to see it, to experience the joy and terror of the spectacle.

The waterfall had no equal anywhere around, nothing that could match it. This uniqueness endowed it with an awesome quality; it was like a living and conscious creature, a local dragon or winged serpent who levied tribute and preyed upon the countryside.

Halfway down, it broke on a sharp rock and divided in two. The top was almost motionless, but the two lower columns weaved slightly from side to side as if the water were continually slipping and righting itself, shaken but always recovering.

Vasia had spread his sheepskin on the ground and was lying at the edge of the thicket. When it grew lighter, a large bird with heavy wings flew down from the mountain, soared in a smooth circle around the wood, and settled on a pine close to where he lay. He looked up enchanted at its dark blue throat and gray-blue breast and whispered its Urals name, *ronzha*. Then he got up, picked up his sheepskin, flung it over his shoulders, and crossed the clearing to speak to his companion.

"Come on, Auntie Polia. Goodness, how cold you are! I can hear your teeth chattering. Well, what are you staring at, why are you so frightened? We've got to go, I'm telling you, we must

get to a village. They'll hide us, they won't harm their own kind.
If we go on like this we'll die of starvation. We've had nothing to
eat for two days. Uncle Voroniuk must have raised a terrible
hullabaloo, they must all be out looking for us. We have to go,
Auntie; to put it plainly, we've got to run. I don't know what to
do with you, Auntie, not a word out of you for two whole days.
You worry too much, honest to God, you do. What are you so
unhappy about? It isn't as if you'd meant to push Auntie Katia
Ogryzkova off the train, you just caught her sideways, by accident, I saw you. She picked herself up off the grass—I saw
her with my own eyes—and she got up and ran away. She and
Uncle Prokhor, Prokhor Kharitonovich, are sure to catch up
with us, we'll all be together again. The main thing is to stop
worrying, then you'll find your tongue again."

Tiagunova got up, took Vasia's hand, and said softly:
"All right, let's go, lamb."

25

Their timbers creaking, the cars climbed up the steep hill. Below the bank there was a thicket, its top not quite reaching the
level of the track. Lower still were fields. The floods had just
withdrawn and the grass was strewn with sand and pieces of
timber. The boards must have been washed down from somewhere higher up the hill where they had been stacked preparatory to floating them downstream.

The young wood below the embankment was still almost as
bare as in winter. Only in the buds that spotted it all over like
drops of candle grease there was something not in accord with
the rest, something superfluous, some disturbance, perhaps
dirt or an inflammation causing them to swell, and the disturbance, superfluity, and dirt were the signs of life, which had
already set the most forward of the trees on fire with its green
leafy flame.

Here and there a birch stretched itself like a martyr pierced
by the barbs and arrows of its opening shoots, and you knew its
smell by just looking at it, the smell of its glistening resin, which
is used for making varnish.

Soon the tracks drew level with the place where the logs washed down by the flood might have come from. A cutting through the wood showed at a bend of the tracks; it was littered all over with chips and shavings, and there was a pile of timber in the middle. The engine braked and the train shuddered and stopped on the curve of the hill, bending slightly in a wide arc.

A few short barking hoots and shouts came from the engine, but the passengers did not need these signals to know that the engineer had stopped to take in a supply of fuel.

The freight-car doors rolled open, and a crowd the size of the population of a small town poured out. Only the sailors stayed in the front cars; they were excused from all chores.

There was not enough small firewood in the clearing to fill the tender, and some of the large timber had to be cut down to the right size. The engine crew had saws as part of their equipment and these were issued to volunteers, one to each pair, the doctor and his father-in-law among them.

Grinning sailors stuck their heads out of their doors. They were a curious mixture of middle-aged workingmen, straight from their emergency training, and boys just out of naval college who looked as if they had got in by mistake among the staid fathers of families and who joked and played the fool with the older sailors to keep themselves from thinking. All of them felt that their hour of trial was at hand.

Jokes and guffaws followed the work parties.

"Hey, Grandfather! I'm not shirking, I'm too young to work, my nanny won't let me." "Hey, Marva, don't saw off your skirt, you'll catch cold!" "Hey, young one, don't go to the wood, come and be my wife instead!"

26

There were several trestles in the clearing. Yurii Andreievich and Alexander Alexandrovich went up to one of them and began to saw.

This was the moment of spring when the earth emerges from the snow looking much as when the snow had trapped it six months earlier. The wood smelled of damp and was heaped with last year's leaves like an unswept room where people have been tearing up letters, bills, and receipts for years.

"Don't go so fast, you'll tire yourself," said the doctor, giving a slower and more even movement to the saw. "What about a rest?"

The wood echoed to the hoarse ringing of other saws; somewhere, very far away, a nightingale was trying out its voice, and at longer intervals a blackbird whistled as if blowing dust out of a flute. Even the engine steam rose into the sky warbling like milk boiling up on a nursery alcohol stove.

"What did you want to speak to me about?" asked Alexander Alexandrovich. "Do you remember? We were going past the island, the ducks flew away, and you said you wanted to speak to me."

"Oh, yes. . . . Well, I don't quite know how to put it briefly. I was thinking that we are going farther and farther. The whole of this region is in ferment. We don't know what we'll find when we get there. Perhaps we ought to talk things over just in case . . . I don't mean about our convictions—it would be absurd to try to define them in five minutes in a spring wood. Besides, we know each other well. You and I and Tonia and many others like us, we make up our own world these days, the only difference between us is in the degree of our awareness of it. But that's not what I want to talk about. What I meant was that perhaps we ought to agree in advance on how to behave under certain circumstances, so that we need never blush for one another or make each other feel ashamed."

"I know what you mean. I like the way you put it. Now this is what I'll tell you. Do you remember that night you brought me the paper with the first government decrees in the winter, in a snowstorm? You remember how unbelievably uncompromising they were? It was that single-mindedness that carried us away. But such things retain their original purity only in the minds of those who have conceived them, and then only on the day they are first made public. Next day, the casuistry of politics has turned them inside out. What can I say to you? Their philosophy is alien to me, their regime is hostile to us, I have not been asked if I consent to all this change. But I have been trusted, and my own actions, even if they were not freely chosen, put me under a certain obligation.

"Tonia keeps asking if we'll arrive in time to plant our vegetables. I don't know. I don't know the soil or the climate in the Urals; the summer is so short I can't imagine how anything ever ripens in time.

"But after all, it is not for the sake of gardening that we are going all this enormous distance. No, we had better face things honestly, our object is quite different. We are going to try to subsist in the modern fashion, taking our share in the squandering of old Krueger's properties, his factories and machines. We are not going to rebuild his fortune, but like everyone else and in the same incredibly chaotic way we'll fritter it away and lend a hand in the collective squandering of thousands for the sake of earning a kopek's worth of living. Not that I would take back the estate on the old terms, even if you showered me with gold. That would be as foolish as to start running about naked or trying to forget the alphabet. No, the age of private property in Russia is over, and anyway, we Gromekos lost our acquisitive passion a generation ago."

27

It was too hot and stuffy in the car to sleep. The doctor's pillow was soaked in sweat. Carefully, so as not to wake the others, he got down from his bunk and pushed open the car doors.

Sticky damp heat struck him in the face as if he had walked into a cobweb in a cellar. "Mist," he guessed. "Tomorrow will be scorching hot. That's why it is so airless and so heavy and oppressive now."

It was a big station, possibly a junction. Besides the mist and the stillness, there was a feeling of emptiness, of neglect, as if the train had been lost and forgotten. It must be standing at the farthest end of the station, and so great was the maze of tracks separating it from the station buildings that if, at the other end of the yard, the earth were to open and swallow up the station, no one in the train would have noticed it.

Two faint sounds could be heard in the distance.

Behind him, where they had come from, there was a rhythmic splashing, as if clothes were being rinsed or the wind were flapping a heavy, damp flag against a pole.

From ahead there came an even rumbling, which made the doctor, who had been at the front, prick up his ears. "Long-range guns," he decided after listening to the calmly echoing, low, sustained note.

"That's it, we're right at the front." He shook his head and jumped down from the car. He walked a few steps forward. Two cars farther up, the train ended; the rest had been uncoupled and had gone away with the engine.

"So that was why they were so keyed up yesterday," the doctor thought. "They had a feeling they would be thrown in as soon as we arrived."

He walked around the front car, meaning to cross the rails and look for the main part of the station, but a sentry with a rifle rose in his path.

"Where you going? Got a pass?"

"What is this station?"

"Never mind. Who are you?"

"I am a doctor from Moscow. My family and I are passengers on this train. Here are my papers."

"To hell with your papers. I'm not such a fool as to try to read in the dark. There's a mist—can't you see? I don't need any papers to know what kind of doctor you are. Those are more of your doctors shooting twelve-inch guns at us. Put an end to you, I would, but it's too soon for that. Get back now, while you're still in one piece."

"He's taking me for someone else," thought Zhivago. Clearly, it was no use arguing, better follow his advice before it was too late. He turned and walked the other way.

The gunfire was now at his back. There, behind him, was the east. There the sun had risen in a drift of mist and was peering dully through floating shadows, like a naked man through clouds of steam at the baths.

Zhivago walked down the length of the train and passed the end car. His feet sank deeper and deeper into soft sand.

The even sound of splashing came nearer. The ground sloped

down steeply. He stopped, trying to make out the indistinct shapes in front of him; the mist made them unnaturally large. One more step, and the hulls of beached boats came up out of the dark. Before him was a wide river, its lazy ripples splashing slowly, wearily against the sides of the fishing smacks and the planks of landing stages along the shore.

A figure rose from the beach.

"Who gave you permission to prowl around?" asked another sentry with a rifle.

"What is this river?" shot out Yurii Andreievich, though he had firmly resolved not to ask any more questions.

By way of answer the sentry put his whistle to his mouth, but he was saved the trouble, for the first sentry, whom it was meant to summon, had evidently been following the doctor without a sound, and now joined his comrade. They stood talking.

"There's no doubt about it. You can tell this kind of bird at a glance. 'What's this station?' 'What's this river?' There's dust in your eyes! What do you say? Shall we take him straight to the jetty or to train first?"

"I say to the train. See what the boss says.—Your documents," he barked. Grabbing the bunch of papers in his fist and calling back to someone: "Keep an eye on him," he strode away with the first sentry toward the station.

The third figure, whom Zhivago had not so far made out, was evidently a fisherman. He had been lying on the beach, but he now grunted, stirred, and set about enlightening the doctor on his position.

"It's lucky for you they're taking you to the boss. That may save your skin. But you mustn't blame them. They're only doing their duty. The people are on top nowadays. Perhaps it's even for the best in the long run, though there isn't much to be said for it now. They've made a mistake, you see. They've been hunting, hunting all the time, for a certain man. So they thought it was you. That's him, they thought, that's the enemy of the workers' state, we've got him. A mistake, that's all it is. If anything happens, insist on seeing the boss. Don't you let those two get away with anything. They're politically conscious, it's a misfortune, God help us. They'd think nothing of doing away with you. So, if they say 'Come along,' see you don't go. Say you must see the boss."

From the fisherman Yurii Andreievich learned that the river was the famous waterway, the Rynva, and that the station by the river served Razvilie, an industrial suburb of the town of Yuriatin. He also learned that Yuriatin, which lay a couple of miles upstream, seemed now to have been recaptured from the Whites. And that there had been troubles in Razvilie and that they too seemed to have been put down, the reason for the great stillness all around being that the station area had been cleared of civilians and strictly cordoned off. He learned finally that among the trains at the station which were used as military offices was the special train of Army Commissar Strelnikov, to whom the two sentries had gone to report.

A third sentry now came from the direction in which the two others had gone; he was distinguished from them chiefly by the fact that he pulled his rifle after him, the butt trailing on the ground, or propped it up in front of him like a tipsy friend who needed his support. This guard took the doctor to the commissar.

28

Sounds of laughter and movement came from one of the two coupled parlor cars to which the guard, after giving the pass-word to the sentry, took the doctor, but they ceased the moment the two men went in.

The guard led the doctor down a narrow passage to a wide central compartment. It was a clean, comfortable room where tidy, well-dressed people worked in complete silence. The doctor had had a very different idea of the background of Strelnikov, the famous non-Party military expert who was the pride and terror of the region.

But undoubtedly the real center of his activities lay elsewhere, closer to the staff H.Q. and to the field of military operations. This could only be his personal suite, his private office and sleeping quarters.

Hence the stillness, rather like that in a steam bath with cork floors and attendants in soft slippers.

The office was in the former dining car, carpeted and with several desks in it.

"One moment," said a young officer whose desk was by the door. He nodded absent-mindedly, dismissing the guard who left, rattling his rifle butt on the metal strips nailed across the floor of the passage. After this, everyone felt free to forget the doctor and paid no more attention to him.

From where he stood at the entrance he could see his papers lying on a desk at the far end of the room. The desk was occupied by a man who was older than the rest and who looked like an old-style colonel. He was an army statistician of some sort. Mumbling to himself, he consulted reference books, studied field maps, checked, compared, cut out, and pasted things in. After looking around at every window in the room he announced: "It's going to be hot," as though forced to this conclusion only by the examination of all the windows.

An army electrician was crawling about on the floor mending a broken wire. When he reached the desk by the door the young officer got up to make room for him. At the next table a typist in an army leather jacket was struggling with her typewriter; its carriage had slipped and got stuck. The young officer stood over her and examined the cause of the mishap from above while the electrician crawled in under her desk and examined it from below. The old-style colonel got up and joined them, and all four busied themselves with the typewriter.

This made Yurii Andreievich feel better. These people must know his fate better than he did; it was hardly likely that they would be so unconcerned and so busy with trifles in the presence of a man whom they considered doomed.

"And yet who knows?" he reflected. "Why are they so unconcerned? Guns are going off and people are dying, and they calmly prognosticate heat—not the heat of the battle but of the weather. Perhaps, after all, they have seen so much that they have no sensibility left."

To occupy himself, he stared across the room through the window opposite.

29

He could see the edge of the tracks and higher up the hill the station and the suburb of Razvilie.

Three flights of unpainted wooden steps led from the platforms to the station building.

At the end of the tracks there was a large graveyard for old engines. Locomotives without tenders, with smokestacks shaped like the tops of knee boots or like beakers, stood smokestack to smokestack amid piles of scrap.

The engine graveyard below and the human graveyard above, the crumpled iron on the tracks and the rusty iron of the roofs and shop signs of the suburb, composed a single picture of neglect and age under the white sky scalded by the early morning heat.

Living in Moscow, Yurii Andreievich had forgotten how many shop signs there still were in other towns and how much of the façades they covered. Some of those he was seeing now were so large that he could read them easily from where he stood, and they came down so low over the crooked windows of the sagging one-story buildings that the squat little houses were almost hidden by them like the faces of village children in their fathers' caps.

The mist had gone from the west, and now what remained of it in the east stirred, swayed, and parted like the curtain of a stage.

And there, on a hill above Razvilie and a mile or two beyond it, stood a large town, the size of a provincial capital. The sun warmed its colors and the distance simplified its lines. It clung to the summit of the hill in tiers, house by house and street by street, with a big church in the middle on the top, as in a cheap color print of a desert monastery or of Mount Athos.

"Yuriatin," the doctor thought excitedly. "The town I used to hear about so often from Anna Ivanovna and from Nurse Antipova. How strange that I should see it in these circumstances!"

At that moment the attention of the military was diverted from the typewriter to something they could see from one of the other windows, and the doctor looked around.

A group of prisoners was being taken under guard up the

station steps. Among them was a boy in a school uniform who was wounded in the head. He had received first aid, but a trickle of blood seeped through the bandage and he kept smudging it with his hand over his dark sweaty face. Walking between two Red Army men at the tail of the procession, he attracted notice not only by his resolute air, his good looks, and the pathos of so young a rebel's plight, but by the utter absurdity of his own and his two companions' gestures. They were doing exactly the opposite of what they should have done.

He was still wearing his school cap. It slithered continually from his bandaged head, and instead of taking it off and carrying it in his hand he rammed it back each time, disturbing the bandage and the wound, and in this his two guards assisted him readily.

In this absurdity, so contrary to common sense, the doctor saw a profound symbol. He longed to rush out and address the boy in words that were impatiently welling up inside him. He longed to shout to him and to the people in the railway coach that salvation lay not in loyalty to forms but in throwing them off.

He turned away. Strelnikov came in with long, vigorous strides and stood in the middle of the room.

How was it possible that he, a doctor, with his countless acquaintances, had never until this day come across anything so definite as this man's personality? How was it that they had never been thrown together, that their paths had not crossed?

In some inexplicable way it was clear at once that this man was entirely a manifestation of the will. So completely was he the self he resolved to be that everything about him seemed inevitable, exact, perfect—his well-proportioned, handsomely set head, his impetuous step, his long legs, his knee boots which may well have been muddy but looked polished, and his gray serge tunic which may have been creased but looked as if it were made of the best linen and had just been pressed.

Such was the irresistible effect of his brilliance, his unaffected ease, and his sense of being at home in any conceivable situation on earth.

He must certainly, Yurii Andreievich thought, be possessed of a remarkable gift, but it was not necessarily the gift of originality. This talent, which showed itself in his every movement, might well be the talent of imitation. In those days everyone modelled himself on someone else—they imitated heroes of history, or the men who had struck their imagination by winning fame in the fighting at the front or in the streets, or those who had great prestige with the people, or this or that comrade who had won distinction, or simply one another.

Strelnikov politely concealed any surprise or annoyance he may have felt at the presence of a stranger. He addressed his staff, treating him as if he belonged among them.

He said: "Congratulations. We have driven them back. It all seems more like playing at war than serious business, because they are as Russian as we are, only stuffed with nonsense—they won't give it up, so we have to beat it out of them. Their commander was my friend. His origin is even more proletarian than mine. We grew up in the same house. He has done a great deal for me in my life and I am deeply indebted to him. And here I am rejoicing that we have thrown them back beyond the river and perhaps even farther. Hurry up with that connection, Gurian, we need the telephone, we can't possibly manage with only messengers and the telegraph. Have you noticed how hot it is? I managed to get in an hour's sleep, just the same. Oh, yes!" He turned to the doctor, remembering that he had been waked up to deal with some nonsense in connection with this man.

"This man?" Strelnikov thought, looking him over sharply. "Nonsense! He's nothing like him. Fools!" He laughed, and said to Yurii Andreievich:

"My apologies, comrade. They mistook you for someone else. My sentries got mixed up. You are free to go. Where are the comrade's work papers? Ah, here are your documents. May I just have a glance . . . Zhivago . . . Zhivago . . . Doctor Zhivago . . . Moscow . . . How about going to my place for a moment? This is the secretariat, I'm in the next car. This way, I won't keep you long."

30

Who, in fact, was Strelnikov?

That he should have reached and held his position was re-

markable, for he was a non-Party man. He had been totally unknown because, though born in Moscow, he had gone straight
from the university to the provinces as a teacher, and in the war
had been taken prisoner, reported missing, believed killed, and
had only recently come back from German captivity.

He was recommended and vouched for by Tiverzin, a railway
worker of advanced political views in whose family he had
lived as a child. Those who controlled appointments were impressed by him: in those days of inordinate rhetoric and political
extremism his revolutionary fervor, equally unbridled, was remarkable for its genuineness. His fanaticism was not an imitation
but was his own, a natural consequence of all his previous life.

Strelnikov justified the confidence of the authorities.

His fighting record over the past few months included the
actions at Nizhni Kelmes and Ust-Nemdinsk, the suppression of
the Gubysov peasants who had put up armed resistance to food
levies, and of the men of the 14th Infantry who had plundered a
food convoy. He had also dealt with Stenka Razin soldiers, who
had started an uprising in the town of Turkatui and gone over to
the Whites, and with the mutiny at Chirkin Us, where a loyal
commander had been killed.

In each case, he had taken his enemies by surprise and had
investigated, tried, sentenced, and enforced his sentence with
speed, severity, and resolution.

He had brought the epidemic of desertions in this whole
region under control and had successfully reorganized the recruiting bodies. As a result, conscription went ahead and the
Red Army reception centers were working overtime.

Finally, when the White pressure from the north increased
and the position became admittedly grave, Strelnikov was entrusted with new responsibilities, military, strategic, and operational. His interventions produced immediate results.

Strelnikov ("the shooter") knew that rumor had nicknamed
him Razstrelnikov, the Executioner. He took this in his stride; he
was disturbed by nothing.

He was a native of Moscow, and his father was a worker
who had been sent to prison for taking part in the revolution of
1905. He did not participate in the revolutionary movement in
those years, first because he was too young, and at the university

because young men who come from a poor background value higher education more and work harder than the children of the rich. The ferment among other students left him uninvolved. He absorbed an immense amount of information and after taking his degree in the humanities trained himself later in science and mathematics.

Exempted from the army, he enlisted voluntarily, was commissioned, sent to the front, and captured, and on hearing of the revolution in Russia he escaped in 1917 and came home. He had two characteristic features, two passions: an unusual power of clear and logical reasoning, and a great moral purity and sense of justice; he was ardent and honorable.

But he would not have made a scientist of the sort who break new ground. His intelligence lacked the capacity for bold leaps into the unknown, the sudden flashes of insight that transcend barren, logical deductions.

And if he were really to do good, he would have needed, in addition to his principles, a heart capable of violating them—a heart which knows only of particular, not of general, cases, and which achieves greatness in little actions.

Filled with the loftiest aspirations from his childhood, he had looked upon the world as a vast arena where everyone competed for perfection, keeping scrupulously to the rules. When he found that this was not so, it did not occur to him that his conception of the world order might have been oversimplified. He nursed his grievance and with it the ambition to judge between life and the dark forces that distorted it, and to be life's champion and avenger.

Embittered by his disappointment, he was armed by the revolution.

31

"Zhivago," repeated Strelnikov when they were settled in his room. "Zhivago . . . Trade, I think. Or upper class . . . Well, of course, a Moscow doctor . . . Going to Varykino. That's strange, why should you leave Moscow for such a provincial hole?"

"That's just the idea. In search of quiet, seclusion, and obscurity."

"Well, well, how romantic! Varykino? I know most of the places around here. That used to be Krueger's estate. You aren't related to him, by any chance? You don't happen to be his heir?"

"Why the irony? Being his 'heir' has nothing to do with it. Though it is true that my wife . . ."

"Ah, so you see! But if you're feeling nostalgic for the Whites I'm going to disappoint you. You're too late. We've cleared the district."

"You're still making fun of me?"

"And then, a doctor. An army medical officer. And we're at war. That really is my business. You're a deserter. The Greens[1] are also seeking refuge in the woods. Your reasons?"

"I have been wounded twice and discharged as an invalid."

"Next you'll be handing me a reference from the People's Commissariat of Education or Health to prove that you are a Soviet citizen, a 'sympathizer,' 'entirely loyal.' These are apocalyptic times, my dear sir, this is the Last Judgment. This is a time for angels with flaming swords and winged beasts from the abyss, not for sympathizers and loyal doctors. However, I told you you were free, and I won't go back on my word. But remember, it's for this once. I have a feeling that we'll meet again, and then our conversation will be quite different. Watch out."

Neither the threat nor the challenge disturbed Yurii Andreievich. He said: "I know what you think of me. From your point of view you are right. But the issue you wish me to discuss with you is one I have been arguing with an imaginary accuser all my life, and it would be odd if I had not by now reached some conclusion. Only I could not put it into a couple of words. So if I am really free, permit me to leave without having it out with you. If I am not, then you must decide what to do with me. I have no excuses to make to you."

They were interrupted by the telephone. The line was repaired. Strelnikov picked up the receiver.

"Thanks, Gurian. Now be a good fellow and send somebody along to see Comrade Zhivago to his train; I don't want any more accidents. And give me the Razvilie Cheka Transport Department."

---

[1] Greens: Anarchistic elements, chiefly peasants, who fought both Reds and Whites.

When Zhivago had gone, Strelnikov telephoned the railway station.

"There's a schoolboy they've brought in, keeps pulling his cap over his ears and he's got a bandaged head, it's disgraceful. —That's right.—He's to have medical aid if he needs it.—Certainly.—Yes, like the apple of your eye, you'll be responsible to me personally.—Food, too, if necessary. That's right. Now, let's get down to business. . . . I'm still talking, don't cut me off. Damn, there's somebody else on the line. Gurian! Gurian! They've cut me off."

He gave up trying to finish his conversation for the time being. "It could be one of my former pupils," he thought. "Fighting us, now he's big." He counted up the years since he had stopped teaching to see if the boy could have been his pupil. Then he looked out of the window toward the panorama of the horizon, and searched for the part of Yuriatin where they had lived. Suppose his wife and daughter were still there! Couldn't he go to them? Why not now, this very minute? Yes, but how could he? They belonged to another life. First he must see this one through, this new life, then he could go back to the one that had been interrupted. Someday he would do it. Someday. But when, when?

CHAPTER EIGHT

ARRIVAL

1

The train that had brought the Zhivago family was still on a siding behind several other trains that screened it from the station, yet they had a feeling that their connection with Moscow —which till now had remained unbroken—snapped that morning, that it had come to an end. Here began another territory, a different, provincial world, which had a center of gravity of its own.

Here people were closer together than in the capitals. Although the station area was cleared of civilians and surrounded by Red Army units, passengers for the local trains managed in some unaccountable way to get to the tracks, to "infiltrate," as we would say today. They had already crammed the cars, thronging in the open sliding doors, and they walked back and forth along the train and stood in small groups on the embankment.

All of them, without exception, were acquainted; they waved and called out as soon as they caught sight of each other, and they exchanged greetings as they passed. Their speech and dress, their food and manners, were all a little different from those of people in the capitals.

"How do they earn their living?" the doctor wondered. What were their interests and their material resources, how did they cope with the difficulties of the times, how did they evade the laws?

All these questions were soon answered in the most vivid way.

2

Escorted by the sentry who dragged his rifle after him or used it as a walking stick, the doctor went back to his carriage. It was

a sultry day. The hot sun beat down on the rails and the roofs
of the cars. The black puddles of oil on the ground blazed with
a yellow shimmer, like gold leaf.

The sentry's rifle butt plowed a furrow in the sand. It clinked
against the ties.

"The weather has settled," he was saying. "Time for the spring
sowing—oats, wheat, millet—it's the best time. It's too early for
the buckwheat, though. Where I come from we sow the buckwheat on the Feast of Akulina. I'm not from these parts, I come
from Morshansk, in the Tambov government. Eh, Comrade Doctor, if it wasn't for this here civil war and this plague of a
counterrevolution, do you think I'd be wasting my time in strange
parts at this season? The class war has run between us like the
black cat of discord, and just look at what it's doing."

3

Hands stretched out of the carriage to help him up.

"Thanks, I can manage."

Yurii Andreievich hoisted himself into the car, and after re-
gaining his balance embraced his wife.

"At last! Thank God, it's ended well," she said. "Actually, we
knew you were all right."

"What do you mean, you knew?"

"We knew everything."

"How?"

"The sentries told us. How could we have stood it otherwise?
As it is, Father and I nearly went out of our minds. There he is,
he's fast asleep, you can't wake him, sleeping like a log after all
the excitement. There are several new passengers, I'll introduce
you in a moment, but listen to what everybody's talking about
—they are all congratulating you on your lucky escape. Here
he is," she said suddenly, turning and introducing her husband
over her shoulder to one of the new passengers who was hemmed
in by the crowd at the back of the freight car.

"Samdeviatov," the stranger introduced himself, raising his soft
hat over other people's heads and pushing his way forward
through the press of bodies.

"Samdeviatov," thought the doctor. "With a name like that he ought to have come straight out of an old Russian ballad, complete with a bushy beard, a smock, and a studded belt. But he makes you think of the local Arts Club, with his graying curls, mustache, goatee . . ."

"Well, did Strelnikov give you a fright?" said Samdeviatov. "Tell the truth."

"No, why? We had an interesting talk. Certainly he has a powerful personality."

"I should think so. I've got some idea of what he's like. He's not from these parts. He's one of you Moscow people. Like all our newfangled things. They too are imported from the capital. We wouldn't have thought of them ourselves."

"Yurochka, this is Anfim Efimovich, he knows everything," Antonina Alexandrovna said. "He's heard about you and about your father, and he knew my grandfather—he knows everyone, absolutely everyone!—I suppose you must have met the schoolteacher, Antipova?" she slipped in casually, and Samdeviatov replied just as casually: "What about Antipova?" Yurii Andreievich heard this exchange but did not say anything, and his wife went on: "Anfim Efimovich is a Bolshevik. Be on your guard, Yurochka. You must watch your tongue when he is around."

"Really? I'd never have thought so. I'd have taken him for an artist of some sort."

"My father kept an inn," said Samdeviatov. "He had seven troikas on the road. But I went to the university, and it's true that I'm a Social Democrat."

"Listen to what Anfim Efimovich told me, Yurochka, and by the way, if you don't mind my saying so, Anfim Efimovich, your name is a real tongue-twister!—So, listen, Yurochka, we've been terribly lucky. We can't change at Yuriatin—part of the town is on fire and the bridge has been blown up, you can't get through. Our train will be switched to another line, and that line happens to be just the one we need to get to Torfianaia. Isn't it wonderful! We don't have to change and lug all our stuff from one station to another. On the other hand, we'll be shunted back and forth for hours before we really start off. Anfim Efimovich told me all that."

4

Antonina Alexandrovna was right. Cars were coupled and uncoupled, and the train was shifted endlessly from one congested
line to another where other trains blocked its way into the open
country.

The town lay in the distance partly hidden by the rolling
countryside. Only now and then did its roofs, the chimneys of
its factories, and the crosses on its belfries emerge above the
horizon. One of its suburbs was on fire. The smoke drifted across
the sky looking like a gigantic horse's mane blowing in the wind.

The doctor and Samdeviatov sat on the floor of the freight car,
their legs dangling over the side. Samdeviatov kept pointing into
the distance and explaining what they saw to Yurii Andreievich.
Every now and then the train would jerk noisily and drown
his voice, and he would lean across bringing his mouth close to
the doctor's ear and repeat what he had said, shouting himself
hoarse.

"That's a movie house, the 'Giant,' they've set on fire. The
cadets were holding it, though they'd surrendered earlier. Otherwise, the fighting isn't over yet. You see those black dots on the
belfry? Those are our people, sniping at the Czechs."

"I can't see a thing. How can you see them at such a distance?"

"That's the artisans' quarter, Khokhriki, burning over there.
Kholodeievo, the shopping center, is farther on. I'm interested
because our inn is there. Luckily, it's only a small fire, it hasn't
spread. So far the center has remained intact."

"What did you say? I can't hear you."

"I said the center, the center of the town—the cathedral, the
library . . . Our name, Samdeviatov, is a garbled Russian form
of San Donato. We're supposed to be descended from the
Demidovs."

"I still can't hear."

"I said Samdeviatov is a form of San Donato. They say we are
a branch of the Demidov family, the Princess Demidov San
Donato. But it may be just a family legend. This place here is
called Spirka's Dell. It's full of summer houses and amusement
parks. Strange name, isn't it?"

Before them extended a field crisscrossed by branch tracks. Telegraph poles strode away to the horizon like giants in seven-league boots, and the broad winding ribbon of a highway competed in beauty with the tracks. It vanished beyond the horizon, reappeared in a broad arc at a turn, and again vanished.

"That's our famous highway. It runs right across Siberia. The convicts used to sing songs about it. Now it's the operational base of the partisans. . . . You'll like it here, you know, it's not at all bad. You'll get used to it. You'll get to like the curiosities of the town. Our water pumps, for instance. The women queue up for water at the intersections, it's their open-air club through the winter."

"We are not going to live in town. We're going to Varykino."

"I know. Your wife told me. Still, you'll be coming in to town on business. I guessed who your wife was the moment I saw her. She's the living image of Krueger—eyes, nose, forehead—just like her grandfather. Everyone here remembers him."

There were round red oil tanks in the field, and large advertisements on wooden billboards. One of them caught the doctor's eye twice. It bore the inscription: "Moreau & Vetchinkin. Mechanical seeders. Threshing machines."

"That was a good firm. Their agricultural machinery was first-rate."

"I can't hear. What did you say?"

"A good firm, I said. Can you hear? A good firm. They made agricultural machinery. It was a corporation. My father was a stockholder."

"I thought you said he kept an inn."

"He did. That didn't mean he couldn't have stock. Very shrewd investments he made, too. He had money in the 'Giant.'"

"You sound as if you were proud of it."

"Of my father being shrewd? Of course I am."

"But what about your socialism?"

"Good Lord, what has that got to do with it? Why on earth should a man, because he is a Marxist, be a drivelling idiot? Marxism is a positive science, a theory of reality, a philosophy of history."

"Marxism a science? Well, it's taking a risk, to say the least, to argue about that with a man one hardly knows. However—

Marxism is too uncertain of its ground to be a science. Sciences are more balanced, more objective. I don't know a movement more self-centered and further removed from the facts than Marxism. Everyone is worried only about proving himself in practical matters, and as for the men in power, they are so anxious to establish the myth of their infallibility that they do their utmost to ignore the truth. Politics doesn't appeal to me. I don't like people who don't care about the truth."

Samdeviatov took the doctor's words for the fooling of a witty eccentric. He listened with a smile, and did not contradict him.

The train was still being shunted. Every time it reached the "go" signal, an elderly woman with a milk can tied to her belt, who was on duty at the switch, shifted her knitting, bent down, and moved the lever, sending the train back. As it slowly rolled away she sat up and shook her fist at it.

Samdeviatov took this personally. "Why does she do that?" he wondered. "Her face is familiar. Can it be Tuntseva? No, I don't think it can be Glasha. She looks too old. Anyway, what has she got against me? I suppose, what with Mother Russia in the throes of her upheavals and the railways in a muddle, the poor old thing is having a bad time, so she is taking it out on me. Oh, to hell with her!—Why should I rack my brains about her?"

At long last the woman waved her flag, shouted something to the engineer, and let the train past the signals, out into the open; but as the fourteenth car sped by she stuck her tongue out at the two men chatting on the floor, who had got on her nerves. Once again Samdeviatov wondered.

5

When the outskirts of the burning town, the round oil tanks, telegraph poles, and advertisements had vanished in the distance, giving way to a landscape of woods and low hills with occasional glimpses of the winding road, Samdeviatov said:

"Let's go back to our seats. I have to get off soon and your station is the one after the next. Be careful you don't miss it."

"I suppose you know all this area very well?"

"Like my own back yard. Up to a hundred-mile radius. I'm a lawyer, you know. Twenty years of practice. I'm always travelling about on business."

"Even now?"

"Certainly."

"But what kind of business can there be, these days?"

"Anything you please. Old unfinished deals, business operations, breaches of contract. I'm up to my ears in it."

"But haven't all such activities been abolished?"

"Of course they have, nominally. But in practice people are asked to do all sorts of things, sometimes mutually exclusive. There's the nationalization of all enterprises, but the municipal soviet needs fuel, and the Provincial Economic Council wants transportation. And everyone wants to live. This is a transitional period, when there is still a gap between theory and practice. At a time like this you need shrewd, resourceful people like myself. Blessed is the man who doesn't see too much. Also an occasional punch on the jaw doesn't come amiss, as my father used to say. Half the province depends on me for its livelihood. I'll be dropping in at Varykino about timber one of these days. Not just yet, though. You can't get there except by horse, and my horse is lame. Otherwise you wouldn't catch me jolting along on this pile of scrap. Look at the way it crawls. Calls itself a train! I might be useful to you in Varykino. I know those Mikulitsyns of yours inside out."

"Do you know why we are going there, what we want to do?"

"More or less. I have an idea. Man's eternal longing to go back to the land. The dream of living by the sweat of your brow."

"What's wrong with it? You sound disapproving."

"It's naïve and idyllic, but why not? Good luck to you. Only I don't believe in it. It's utopian. Arts and craftsy!"

"How do you think Mikulitsyn will receive us?"

"He won't let you in, he'll drive you out with a broomstick, and he'll be quite right! He's in a fine pickle as it is. Idle factories, workers gone, no means of livelihood, no food, and then you turn up. If he murders you, I won't blame him!"

"There you are. You are a Bolshevik, and yet you yourself don't deny that what's going on isn't life—it's madness, an absurd nightmare."

"Of course it is. But it's historically inevitable. It has to be gone through."

"Why is it inevitable?"

"Are you a baby, or are you just pretending? Have you dropped from the moon? Gluttons and parasites sat on the backs of the starving workers and drove them to death, and you imagine things could stay like that? Not to mention all the other forms of outrage and tyranny. Don't you understand the rightness of the people's anger, of their desire for justice, for truth? Or do you think a radical change was possible through the Duma, by parliamentary methods, and that we can do without dictatorship?"

"We are talking at cross-purposes, and even if we argued for a hundred years we'd never see eye to eye. I used to be very revolutionary, but now I think that nothing can be gained by brute force. People must be drawn to good by goodness. But let's drop the subject. To return to Mikulitsyn—if that's what is in store for us, then why are we going? We should turn back."

"Nonsense. To begin with, Mikulitsyn is not the only pebble on the beach. And second, Mikulitsyn is kind to excess, almost criminally kind. He'll make a fuss and refuse and resist, and then he'll relent. He'll give you the shirt off his back and share his last crust of bread with you." And Samdeviatov told Yurii Andreievich Mikulitsyn's story.

6

"Mikulitsyn arrived here twenty-five years ago from Petersburg. He had been a student at the Technological Institute. He was deported and put under police supervision. He came here, got a job as manager at Krueger's, and married. There were four sisters here in those days—one more than in Chekhov's play—the Tuntsevas, Agrippina, Avdotia, Glafira, and Serafima. All the young men were after them. Mikulitsyn married the eldest.

"Before long they had a son. His fool of a father, who worshipped freedom, gave him the unusual name Liberius. Liberius —Livka, for short—grew up a bit wild but he had all sorts of unusual talents. When the war came he was fifteen. He faked the date on his birth certificate and made off to the front as a volunteer. His mother, a sickly woman, couldn't stand the shock. She took to her bed and didn't get up again. She died the year before last, just before the revolution.

"At the end of the war Liberius came back as a lieutenant hero with three medals, and of course he was a thoroughly indoctrinated Bolshevik delegate from the front. Have you heard about the 'Forest Brotherhood'?"

"No, I'm afraid not."

"In that case there's no sense in telling you the story, half the point would be lost. And there isn't any point in your staring out of the window at the highway either. What's so remarkable about the highways these days? The partisans. And what are the partisans? They are the backbone of the revolutionary army in the civil war. Two things account for the power of this army: the political organization that has taken over the leadership of the revolution, and the common soldier who after the last war refused to obey the old authorities. The partisan army was born of the union of the two. Most of them are middle peasants, but you find all sorts of people—poor peasants, unfrocked monks, sons of kulaks up in arms against their fathers. There are ideological anarchists, riffraff without identity papers, and highschool boys expelled for precocious skirt chasing. And then there are German and Austrian prisoners of war lured by the promise of freedom and repatriation. Well, one of the units of this great people's army is called the Forest Brotherhood, and the Forest Brotherhood is commanded by Comrade Forester, and Comrade Forester is Livka, Liberius Averkievich, the son of Averkii Stepanovich Mikulitsyn."

"You don't mean it!"

"I do indeed. But to go on with my story. After his wife's death, Averkii Stepanovich married again. His second wife, Elena Proklovna, went straight from school to the altar. Naïve by nature, she also affects naïveté; and although she is still quite young, she already pretends to be younger still, prattles, twitters, plays the ingénue, the little foolish girl, the pure field lily. The moment she sees you, she puts you through an exam: 'When was Suvorov born? Enumerate the conditions of equality of triangles.' And if she can trip you, she's overjoyed. But you'll see for yourself in a few hours.

"The old man has his own peculiarities. He was going to be a sailor. He studied marine engineering. He's clean-shaven, never takes his pipe out of his mouth, talks through his teeth in a slow, friendly voice, has the pipe smoker's jutting lower jaw, and cold gray eyes. Oh, and a detail I almost forgot—he's a Social Revolutionary and was elected regional deputy to the Constituent Assembly."

"That is surely very important! So father and son are at swords' points? Political enemies?"

"In theory, of course they are. But in practice the Forest doesn't make war against Varykino. However, to go on with the story. The three remaining Tuntsevas—Mikulitsyn's sisters-in-law by his first marriage—live in Yuriatin to this day, all confirmed spinsters—but times have changed and so have the girls.

"The oldest, Avdotia, is librarian at the public library. Dark, pretty, desperately shy, blushes scarlet at the slightest provocation. She has a terrible time at the library. It's as quiet as the tomb, and the poor girl has a chronic cold—gets sneezing fits and looks as if she'd like to drop through the floor. All nerves.

"The next one, Glafira Severinovna, is the family's blessing. Terrific drive, a wonderful worker, doesn't mind what she does. Livka, Comrade Forester, is supposed to take after her. One day she's a seamstress or she's working in a stocking factory, then before you know where you are she's turned herself into a hairdresser. You saw the woman at the switch, who shook her fist at us? Bless me, I thought, if it isn't Glafira gone to work on the railway. But I don't think it was Glafira, she looked too old.

"And then there's the youngest, Simushka. She's their cross, she gives them no end of trouble. She's an educated girl, well read, used to go in for poetry and philosophy. But since the revolution, what with all the general uplift, speeches, demonstrations, she's become a bit touched in the head, she's got religious mania. The sisters lock her up when they go to work, but she gets out of the window and off she goes down the street, collecting crowds, preaching the Second Coming and the end of the world. Well, it's time I stopped talking, we're nearly there. This is my station. Yours is next. You'd better get ready."

After Samdeviatov had gone Antonina Alexandrovna said: "I don't know about you but I feel he's a godsend. I think he'll play some good sort of part in our lives."

"Very possible, Toniechka. But it worries me that everybody recognizes you as Krueger's granddaughter and that Krueger is so well remembered here. Even Strelnikov, the moment I said 'Varykino,' asked me sarcastically if we were Krueger's heirs.

"I am afraid that after leaving Moscow to escape notice, we are going to be even more conspicuous here. Not that there is anything to be done about it, and there certainly isn't any sense in crying over spilt milk. But we'd better stay in the background and keep quiet. Generally speaking, I'm not too happy about the whole thing. . . . But we must be nearly there. Let's wake up the others and get ready."

7

Antonina Alexandrovna stood on the platform at the Torfianaia station counting her family and her luggage over and over to make sure that nothing had been left on the train. The well-trodden sand of the platform was firm under her feet, but the anxiety lest they miss the station remained with her and the clatter of the wheels was still in her ears although the train was standing motionless before her eyes. This prevented her from seeing, hearing, or thinking properly.

Passengers who were continuing their journey were calling out goodbye and waving to her from the car but she never noticed them. Nor did she notice that the train was leaving and realized that it had gone only when she found herself looking at the green fields and the blue sky across the empty track.

The station was built of stone and had benches on either side of the entrance. The Zhivagos were the only travellers who had got out at Torfianaia. They put their luggage down and sat on one of the benches.

They were struck by the silence, emptiness, and tidiness of the station. It seemed strange not to be surrounded by a milling, cursing mob. History had not caught up with this remote provincial life. It had not yet relapsed into savagery, as at the capitals.

The station nestled in a birch wood. When the train drew in, the cars were plunged into darkness. Now the shadows of the scarcely stirring trees moved lightly over their hands and faces, over the ground and the station walls and roofs, and over the platform with its clean, damp, yellow sand. It was cool in the grove, and the singing of the birds in it had an equally cool sound. Candid and pure as innocence, it pierced and carried through the wood from end to end. Two roads cut through the grove—the railroad and a country road—and both were shaded by branches, which swayed like long sleeves.

Suddenly Antonina Alexandrovna's eyes and ears opened. She became aware of everything at once—the ringing bird calls, the pure woodland solitude, and the flowing, unruffled stillness. She had prepared a speech in her mind: "I couldn't believe that we would really get here safely. Your Strelnikov, you know, could quite easily have made a display of magnanimity, and then sent a telegram telling them to arrest all of us as soon as we got off the train. I don't believe in their noble sentiments, my dear, it's all a sham." But quite different words broke from her at sight of the enchanting scene before her. "How lovely!" she cried out. She could not say any more. Tears choked her, and she began to weep.

At the sound of her crying a little old man in a stationmaster's uniform came out and shuffled across to them. Touching the peak of his red-topped cap, he asked politely:

"Would the young lady like a sedative? We have some in the station medicine chest."

"It's nothing. Thank you. She'll be all right in a moment," said Alexander Alexandrovich.

"It's the anxiety and the worry of the journey that does it, it's well known. And then this African heat, which is so rare in this latitude. Not to mention the events in Yuriatin."

"We saw the fire from the train as we went by."

"You're from Central Russia, if I'm not mistaken?"

"From the very heart of it."

"From Moscow! Little wonder, then, that the lady's nerves are upset. They say there isn't a stone left standing."

"Not quite as bad as that. People exaggerate. But we've certainly seen plenty. This is my daughter, and that's her husband, and that's their little boy. And this is his nurse, Niusha."

"How do you do. How do you do. Delighted. I was rather expecting you. Anfim Efimovich Samdeviatov telephoned from Sakma. Dr. Zhivago is coming with his family from Moscow, he said, and would I please give them every possible assistance. So that's who you are, am I right?"

"No, Dr. Zhivago is my son-in-law, there he is. I'm a professor of agronomy and my name is Gromeko."

"Pardon me. My mistake. I am very glad to make your acquaintance."

"So you know Samdeviatov?"

"Who doesn't know him, the wonder-worker! I don't know what we would have done without him—we'd have all been dead long ago. Give them every possible assistance, he said. Very good, I said. I promised I would. So if you need a horse or anything . . . ? Where are you bound for?"

"We want to get to Varykino. Is it far from here?"

"Varykino! That's why I've kept wondering whom your daughter reminds me of! So it's Varykino you want! That explains everything! Old man Krueger and I built this road together. I'll see to the horse right away, I'll call one of the men and we'll see about a cart.—Donat! Donat! Take these things into the waiting room for the time being. And how about a horse? Run over to the tearoom and see what can be done. Bacchus was hanging around here this morning. See if he's still there. Tell them four passengers for Varykino. They're new arrivals. They've got hardly any luggage, tell them. And make it snappy. And now, lady, may I give you a piece of fatherly advice? I purposely didn't ask you how closely you were related to Ivan Ernestovich. Be very careful what you say about it. You can't talk too much with everyone in times like these."

At the mention of Bacchus the travellers looked at each other in amazement. They remembered Anna Ivanovna's tales about the fabulous blacksmith who had made himself an indestructible set of iron guts and the many other local legends she had told them.

8

The horse was a white mare that had recently foaled, and their driver was a lop-eared old man with dishevelled white hair. For some reason everything about him was white: his new birch-bark shoes had not had time to grow dark, and his linen shirt and trousers had faded with age.

The foal, with a short, curly mane, and black as night, like a painted toy, ran after its mother kicking out its soft-boned legs.

The travellers clung to the sides of the cart as it jolted over the ruts. Their hearts were at peace. Their dream was coming true, they were almost at the end of their journey. The last hours of the clear day lingered generously, as though eager to prolong its splendor.

Their way led sometimes through woods and sometimes across open fields. Driving through the forest, each time they were jolted violently when the cart wheel hit a root; they scowled, hunched their shoulders, and pressed close to each other. Every time they came out into the open, where the space seemed exuberantly to toss its cap into the air, they sat up straight and more comfortably, and breathed sighs of relief.

It was hilly country. The hills, as always, had their own expression. They rose huge and dark in the distance, like proud shadows, silently scrutinizing the travellers. A comfortingly rosy light followed them across the fields, soothing them and giving them hope.

They liked and they marvelled at everything, most of all at the unceasing chatter of their quaint old driver, in whose speech archaic Russian forms, Tartar idioms, and local oddities of diction were punctuated with obscurities of his own invention.

Whenever the foal lagged behind, the mare stopped and waited. The foal would catch up with her in graceful, wavelike bounds, and then, walking up to the cart clumsily on its long legs set too close together, it would stretch its long neck and push its tiny head under the shaft to nurse.

"But I don't understand," Antonina Alexandrovna shouted to her husband, slowly, for fear that her teeth, which chattered with the shaking of the cart, should bite off the tip of her tongue at some sudden jolt. "Can this be the same Bacchus that Mother used to tell us about? You remember all that stuff about the blacksmith who was disembowelled in a fight and made himself a set of new bowels? Bacchus Iron-Belly. Of course I know it's only a story, but can it have been told about him? Is he the same Bacchus?"

"No, of course not. To begin with, as you say, it's only a story, a legend, and then Mother told us that even the legend was over a hundred years old when she heard it. But don't talk so loud. You don't want to hurt the old man's feelings."

"He won't hear anything, he's deaf. And if he did, he wouldn't understand—he's not quite right in the head."

"Hey, Feodor Nefeodich!" the old man shouted to his horse, addressing it for some reason by a male name and patronymic, although he knew as well as his passengers did that it was a mare. "Curse this heat! Like unto the children of Abraham in the Persian furnace! Gee-up, you unredeemed devil! It's you I'm talking to, you bungler."

Sometimes, he would suddenly burst into snatches of old songs composed in the former Krueger factories.

> "Goodbye, main office,
> Goodbye, shaft and mine.
> The master's bread is stale to me
> And I am sick of drinking water.
> A swan is swimming past the shores,
> He makes furrows in the water.
> It isn't wine that makes me sway
> It is because Vania is going into the army.
> But I, Masha, I won't blunder.
> But I, Masha, am not a fool,
> I'll go to the town of Seliaba,
> And work for Sentetiurikha."

"Eh, you Godforsaken beast. Look at that carrion. I give her the whip and she gives me the lip! Eh, Fedia Nefedia, are you making up your mind to go?—That forest, it's called the taiga, there's no end to it. And there's no end of peasant folk inside it, the Forest Brotherhood is there.—Eh, Fedia Nefedia, have you stopped again, you devil?"

All at once he turned and looked Antonina Alexandrovna
straight in the eye.

"Do you really think, young woman, that I didn't know who
you were? You're simple-minded, young lady, that I can see.
May I fall dead if I didn't recognize you! Certainly I recognized
you! Couldn't believe my eyes—you're the living image of
Grigov." (This was his version of Krueger's name.) "You wouldn't
be his granddaughter, would you? Who could tell a Grigov if
not me! I've spent my life working for him. Did every kind of job
for him—worked in the mines as a woodman, and at the winch
above ground, and in the stables.—Gee-up, get a move on!
Stopped again, like she had no legs! Angels in China! Can't you
hear I'm talking to you?

"Well now, you were asking if I'm that same blacksmith
Bacchus. What a simpleton you are, little mother, such big eyes
and a lady, but a fool. Your Bacchus—he was called Postanogov,
Postanogov Iron-Belly—he went to his grave more than fifty
years ago. But my name is Mekhonoshin. Our Christian names
are the same but our surnames are different."

Little by little, the old man told them in his own words what
they had already heard from Samdeviatov about the Mikulitsyns.
He called them Mikulich and Mikulichna. He spoke of the latter
as the manager's second wife and of his first wife as an "angel,"
a "white cherub." When he came to the partisan leader, Liberius,
and learned that his fame had not yet reached Moscow and that
the Forest Brotherhood was unknown there, he could hardly
believe it.

"They haven't heard? They haven't heard of Comrade Forester?
Angels in China, then what has Moscow got ears for?"

Evening was coming on. Their shadows, growing longer and
longer, ran ahead of them. They were driving through a flat,
treeless stretch. Here and there, in lonely clusters, stood tall
stringy stalks of goosefoot, of willow herb and thistle tipped with
flowering tufts. Their ghostlike contours, widely spaced, loomed
like mounted guards keeping watch over the plain.

Far ahead of them, the plain abutted a tall range of hills. They
stood across the road like a wall, beyond which there was perhaps
a ravine or a stream. It was as though the sky over there were
enclosed by a rampart, and the road were leading to its gate.

A long, one-story white house emerged at the top of the ridge.

"See the lookout up on the hill?" said Bacchus. "That's where your Mikulich and Mikulichna live. And down below there's a gully, Shutma it's called."

Two rifle shots rang out from the hills, followed by rolling echoes.

"What's that? It wouldn't be partisans shooting at us, would it, little grandfather?"

"Bless you, no! Partisans! That's Stepanych scaring the wolves away in the Shutma."

9

Their first meeting with the Mikulitsyns took place in the yard of the manager's house. It was a painful scene that began in silence and became noisily confused.

Elena Proklovna was coming home across the yard from a walk in the woods. The rays of the setting sun, as golden as her golden hair, trailed behind her from tree to tree through the wood. She wore a light summer dress. She was hot from her walk and was wiping her face with her handkerchief. Her straw hat hung at her back from an elastic around her bare throat.

Her husband was coming to meet her from the ravine; he had just climbed up from it with his gun, which he meant to clean because he had noticed that there was something wrong with it.

Suddenly, into this peaceful setting Bacchus rolled up smartly with a loud clatter of cart wheels over the cobbles, bringing his surprise.

The passengers got out, and Alexander Alexandrovich, hemming and hawing and taking off and putting on his hat, began to explain.

Their hosts were struck dumb with amazement. Their genuine speechlessness lasted for several minutes; so did the sincere and appalled confusion of their miserable guests, who were burning with shame. The situation could not have been plainer, whatever might have been said, not only to those directly involved but also to Sashenka, Niusha, and Bacchus. Their painful embarrassment seemed to communicate itself even to the mare, the foal, the golden rays of the setting sun, and the gnats that swarmed around Elena Proklovna and settled on her face and neck.

The silence was finally broken by Mikulitsyn. "I don't understand. I don't understand a thing and I never will. What do you think this is? The south, where the Whites are, and plenty of bread? Why did you pick on us? What on earth has brought you here—here, of all places?"

"Has it occurred to you, I wonder, what a responsibility this is for Averkii Stepanovich?"

"Don't interrupt, Lenochka. Yes, she's quite right. Did you stop to think what a burden you would be imposing on us?"

"But heavens above! You misunderstand us. There is no question of intruding on you, of upsetting your peaceful existence. All we want is a very small thing, a corner in any old empty, tumble-down building and a strip of land that happens to be going to waste because nobody wants it, so that we can grow vegetables. And a cartload of firewood from the forest when there's no one to see us take it. Is this really asking so much, is it such an imposition?"

"True, but the world is a big place. What does this have to do with us? Why should we be chosen for this honor, rather than anyone else?"

"Because we've heard of you and we hoped that you'd have heard of us, so that we would not be coming to complete strangers."

"Ah! So it's because of Krueger! Because you are related to him! But how can you even bring yourselves to admit such a thing at a time like this?"

"I wonder, do you understand? Precisely because you're related to Krueger you should have spared us the pleasure of your acquaintance."

"Lenochka, don't meddle. My wife is absolutely right. Precisely because you're related."

Yurii Andreievich had had no time to compare Samdeviatov's portrait with the original. During the awkward scene the doctor forgot Samdeviatov's description. Later, after things had calmed down, he was struck by the likeness and the aptness of the portrait. However, Anfim Efimovich's characterization of the manager was incomplete. Yurii Andreievich supplemented it later.

Averkii Stepanovich pronounced the sound *l* in the Polish manner, like a *w*. He actually never was separated from his pipe, which was an integral part of his face and which contributed to his style of speech, because he composed his words and ideas while relighting it and making it draw.

He had regular features. He tossed his hair back and took great strides, planting his feet squarely on the ground. In summer he wore a Russian shirt tied with a silk tasselled cord. He was the kind of man who, in the old days, might have become a pirate on the Volga. In more recent times such people have created the type of the eternal student, the dreamer turned schoolmaster.

Mikulitsyn had devoted his youth to the movement for emancipation, to the revolution, and his only fear had been that he would not live to see it or that when it came it would be too moderate, not bloody enough for him. Now it had come, surpassing his wildest dreams, but he, the born and faithful champion of the proletariat who had been among the first to set up a Factory Committee in the Sviatogor Bogatyr, and to hand the place over to the workers, had been left high and dry; instead of being in the thick of things, he was in a remote village from which the workers—some of whom were Mensheviks—had fled! And now what was this ridiculous nonsense on top of everything? These uninvited remnants of Krueger's family seemed to him fate's crowning joke, a deliberate trick, which was more than he could bear.

"This is beyond all reason. Do you realize the danger you will put me in? I suppose I must be mad. I don't understand. I don't understand a thing and never will."

"I wonder if you realize what a volcano we are sitting on even without you here?"

"Just a moment, Lenochka. My wife is quite right. Things are bad enough without you. It's a dog's life, a madhouse. I am caught between two fires. Between those who make my life a misery because my son is a Red, a Bolshevik, the people's favorite, and those who want to know why I was elected to the Constituent Assembly. Nobody is pleased, I have no one to turn to. And now you! A nice thought, to have to face a firing squad on your account!"

"Oh, come! Be sensible. What's the matter with you!"

A little later he relented.

"Well, there isn't any point in squabbling in the yard. We can go inside. Not, of course, that I can see any good coming of it, but 'we see as in a glass darkly.' Still, we aren't Janizaries, we aren't heathens, we won't drive you out into the forest to be eaten by bears. I think, Lenochka, we'd better put them in the palm room for the moment, next to the study. We'll see later where they can settle down, we might find them some place in the park. Do come inside. Bring their things in, Bacchus, give the guests a hand."

Bacchus did as he was told, muttering: "Mother of God! They've got no more stuff than pilgrims! Nothing but little bundles, not a single trunk."

10

The night was cold. They washed, and the women got the room ready for the night. Sashenka, who from long custom expected to have his childish utterances greeted with raptures and therefore prattled obligingly, was upset because for once he had no success, no one took any notice of him. He was disappointed that the black foal had not been brought into the house, and when he was told sharply to be quiet he burst into tears, afraid that he might be sent back to the baby shop where, he believed, his parents had bought him. His fear was genuine, and he wanted to share it with everyone around him, but his charming absurdities on this occasion failed to produce the usual effect. Ill at ease in a strange house, the grownups seemed to him to be in more than their usual hurry as they went about silently absorbed in their tasks. Sashenka was offended, and he sulked. He was made to eat and put to bed with difficulty. When at last he was asleep, Ustinia, the Mikulitsyns' maid, took Niusha to her room to give her supper and initiated her into the secrets of the household. Antonina Alexandrovna and the men were invited to tea with the Mikulitsyns.

Alexander Alexandrovich and Yurii Andreievich first went out on the veranda for a breath of air.

"What a lot of stars!" said Alexander Alexandrovich.

It was very dark. Standing only a few steps apart, the two men could not see each other. Lamplight streamed from a window behind them into the ravine. In its shaft shrubs, trees, and other vague shapes rose cloudily in the cold mist. But the two men were outside this light, which only thickened the darkness around them.

"First thing tomorrow we must have a look at the annex he's got in mind for us, and if it's any good we must start repairing it at once. Then, by the time we've got it fitted up the ground will have thawed out and we can start digging the beds without losing any time. Didn't he say he'd let us have some seed potatoes?"

"He certainly did. He promised us other seed as well. I heard him say so with my own ears. As for the place he offers us, we saw it as we were crossing the park. You know where it is? It's the annex behind the main house, you can hardly see it for thistles. It's wooden, though the house is of stone. I pointed it out to you, do you remember? I thought it would be a good place for the seedbeds. It looked to me as if there might have been a flower garden once, at least it looked like that from a distance, but I may have been mistaken. The soil in the old flower beds must have been well manured; I imagine it might still be pretty good."

"I don't know, we'll have a look tomorrow. I should think it's rank with weeds and hard as stone by now. There must have been a kitchen garden somewhere for the house. Possibly we can use it. We'll find out tomorrow. Probably there's still frost in the mornings. There's sure to be a frost tonight. Anyway, what bliss to be here at last—that's something to be thankful for. It's a good place. I like it."

"They are nice people. He especially. She's a bit affected. There is something she doesn't like about herself. That's why she talks such a lot and why she makes herself sillier than she is. It's as if she were in a hurry to distract your attention from her looks, before you've had time to get a bad impression. And her forgetting to take off her hat and wearing it around her neck isn't absent-mindedness either—it really is becoming to her."

"Well, we'd better go back or they'll think we're rude."

On their way to the dining room, where their hosts and Antonina Alexandrovna were having tea at the round table under the hanging lamp, they went through Mikulitsyn's dark study.

It had an enormous window the length of the wall, overlooking the ravine. Earlier, while it was still light, the doctor had noticed the view from it over the gully and the plain beyond, which they had crossed with Bacchus. At the window stood a draftsman's table which also took up the width of the wall. A gun lying lengthways on it and leaving plenty of room at either end further emphasized the great width of the table.

Now, as they went through, Yurii Andreievich once more thought with envy of the window with its vast view, the size and position of the table, and the spaciousness of the well-furnished room, and it was the first thing he spoke of to his hosts as he entered the dining room.

"What a wonderful place you have! What a splendid study, it must be a perfect place to work in, a real inspiration."

"A glass or a cup? And do you like it strong or weak?"

"Yurochka, do look at this. It's a stereoscope, Averkii Stepanovich's son made it when he was a child."

"He still hasn't grown up and settled down, even though he has captured district after district for the Soviets from Komuch."

"What's Komuch?"

"It's the army of the Siberian Government; it's fighting to restore the Constituent Assembly."

"We've been hearing praise of your son all day long. You must be very proud of him."

"Those stereoscopic photographs of the Urals—they are his work too, and he took them with a homemade camera."

"Wonderful cookies! Are they made with saccharin?"

"Good gracious, no! Where would we get saccharin in our wilderness? It's honest to God sugar. Didn't you see me putting sugar in your tea?"

"Of course it is! I was looking at the photographs. And it's real tea, isn't it?"

"Certainly! It's jasmine tea."

"How on earth do you get it?"

"We have a sort of magician. A friend of ours. He's a public figure of the new sort. Very left-wing. He's the official representative of the Provincial Economic Council. He takes our timber to town and gets us flour and butter through his friends. Pass me the sugar bowl, Siverka" (that was what she called Averkii). "And now, I wonder, can you tell me the year of Griboiedov's death?"

"He was born in 1795, I think. But just when he was killed, I don't remember."

"More tea?"

"No, thank you."

"Now here's something for you. Tell me the date of the Treaty of Nimwegen and which countries signed it."

"Don't torment them, darling. They've hardly recovered from their journey."

"And now this is what I'd like to know. How many kinds of lenses are there, and when are the images real, reversed, natural, or inverted?"

"How do you come to know so much about physics?"

"We had an excellent science teacher in Yuriatin, he taught both in the boys' school and in ours. I can't tell you how good he was. He was a wonder. It was all so clear when he explained it to you! His name was Antipov. He was married to a teacher too. All the girls were mad about him, they all fell in love with him. He went off to the war as a volunteer and was killed. Some people say this scourge of ours, Commissar Strelnikov, is Antipov risen from the dead. But that's only a silly rumor, of course. It's most unlikely. Though, who can tell, anything is possible. Another cup?"

CHAPTER NINE

VARYKINO

1

In the winter, when Yurii Andreievich had more time, he began a notebook. He wrote: "How often, last summer, I felt like saying with Tiutchev:

'What a summer, what a summer!
This is magic indeed.
And how, I ask you, did it come
Just like that, out of the blue?'

What happiness, to work from dawn to dusk for your family and for yourself, to build a roof over their heads, to till the soil to feed them, to create your own world, like Robinson Crusoe, in imitation of the Creator of the universe, and, as your own mother did, to give birth to yourself, time and again.

"So many new thoughts come into your head when your hands are busy with hard physical work, when your mind has set you a task that can be achieved by physical effort and that brings its reward in joy and success, when for six hours on end you dig or hammer, scorched by the life-giving breath of the sky. And it isn't a loss but a gain that these transient thoughts, intuitions, analogies are not put down on paper but forgotten. The town recluse whipping up his nerves and his imagination with strong black coffee and tobacco doesn't know the strongest drug of all —good health and real necessity.

"I am not going further than this. I am not preaching Tolstoyan austerity and the return to the land, I am not trying to improve on socialism and its solution to the agrarian problem. I am merely stating a fact, I am not building a system on the basis of our own accidental experience. Our example is debatable and unsuitable for deductions. Our economy is too mixed. What we produce ourselves—potatoes and vegetables—is only a small part of what we need; the rest comes from other sources.

"Our use of the land is illegal. We have taken the law into our own hands, and we conceal what we are doing from the state. The wood we cut is stolen, and it is no excuse that we steal from the state or that the property once belonged to Krueger. We can do all this thanks to Mikulitsyn's tolerant attitude (he lives in much the same way as we do), and we can do it safely because we are far from the town, where, fortunately, nothing is known, for the time being, about our illegal activities.

"I have given up practicing medicine, and I don't tell anyone that I am a physician, because I don't want to restrict my freedom. But there are always some good souls who get wind of the fact that there is a doctor in Varykino. So they trudge twenty miles to consult me, and bring a chicken or eggs, or butter, or something. And there is no way to persuade them that I don't want to be paid, because people don't believe in the effectiveness of free medical advice. So my practice brings in a little. But our chief mainstay, Mikulitsyn's and ours, is Samdeviatov.

"He is a fantastically complicated character. I can't make him out. He is a genuine supporter of the revolution and he fully deserves the confidence that the Yuriatin Soviet has in him. With all the powers they have given him he could requisition the Varykino timber without so much as telling Mikulitsyn or us, and he knows that we wouldn't protest. On the other hand, if he felt like robbing the state, he could fill his pocket and again no one would say a word. He has no need to bribe or share with anybody. What, then, is it that makes him take care of us; help the Mikulitsyns, and everyone in the district, for instance, the stationmaster at Torfianaia? All the time he is on the road, getting hold of something to bring us. He is just as familiar with Dostoievsky's *Possessed* as with the Communist Manifesto, and he talks about them equally well. I have the impression that if he didn't complicate his life so needlessly, he would die of boredom."

2

A little later the doctor wrote:

"We are living in two rooms in a wooden annex at the back of the old house. When Anna Ivanovna was a child Krueger used it for special servants—the dressmaker, the housekeeper, and the retired nurse.

"It was pretty dilapidated when we came, but we repaired it fairly quickly. With the help of experts we rebuilt the stove, which serves both rooms. We have rearranged the flues and it gives more heat.

"In this part of the grounds the old garden has vanished, obliterated by new growth. But now, in winter, when everything is inanimate, living nature no longer covers the dead; in snowy outline the past can be read more clearly.

"We have been lucky. The autumn was dry and warm. It gave us time to dig up the potatoes before the rains and the cold weather. Not counting those we gave back to Mikulitsyn, we had twenty sacks. We put them in the biggest bin in the cellar and covered them with old blankets and hay. We also put down two barrels of salted cucumbers and two of sauerkraut prepared by Tonia. Fresh cabbages hang in pairs from the beams. There are carrots buried in dry sand, and radishes and beets and turnips, and plenty of peas and beans are stored in the loft. There is enough firewood in the shed to last us till spring.

"I love the warm, dry winter breath of the cellar, the smell of earth, roots, and snow that hits you the moment you raise the trap door as you go down in the early hours before the winter dawn, a weak, flickering light in your hand.

"You come out; it is still dark. The door creaks or perhaps you sneeze or the snow crunches under your foot, and hares start up from the far cabbage patch and hop away, leaving the snow crisscrossed with tracks. In the distance dogs begin to bark and it is a long time before they quiet down. The cocks have finished their crowing and have nothing left to say. Then dawn breaks.

"Besides the tracks of hares, the endless snowy plain is patterned by those of lynxes, stretching across it neatly, like strings of beads. The lynx walks like a cat, putting one paw down in front of the other, and they say it travels many miles in a night.

"Traps are set for them, but instead of the lynxes the wretched hares get caught, half buried in the snow, and are taken out, frozen stiff.

"At the beginning, during spring and summer, we had a very hard time. We drove ourselves to the utmost. But now we can relax in the winter evenings. Thanks to Samdeviatov, who supplies us with kerosene, we sit around a lamp. The women sew or knit, Alexander Alexandrovich or I read aloud. The stove is hot, and I, as the appointed stoker, watch it for the right moment to close the damper so as not to waste any heat. If a charred log prevents the fire from drawing properly, I remove it and run out with it smoking and fling it as far as possible into the snow. It flies through the air like a torch, throwing off sparks and lighting up the white rectangular lawns of the sleeping park and then buries itself, hissing, in a snowdrift.

"We read and reread *War and Peace, Evgenii Onegin* and Pushkin's other poems, and Russian translations of Stendhal's *The Red and the Black,* Dickens's *Tale of Two Cities,* and Kleist's short stories."

3

As spring approached, the doctor wrote:

"I believe Tonia is pregnant. I told her and she doesn't believe it, but I feel sure of it. The early symptoms are unmistakable to me, I don't have to wait for the later, more certain ones.

"A woman's face changes at such a time. It isn't that she becomes less attractive, but her appearance is no longer quite under her control. She is now ruled by the future which she carries within her, she is no longer alone. Her loss of control over her appearance makes her seem physically at a loss; her face dims, her skin coarsens, her eyes shine in a different way, not as she wants them to, it is as if she couldn't quite cope with all these things and has neglected herself.

"Tonia and I have never drifted apart, but this year of work has brought us even closer together. I have noticed how efficient,

strong, and tireless she is, how cleverly she plans her work, so
as to waste as little time as possible between one job and another.

"It has always seemed to me that every conception is immaculate and that this dogma, concerning the Mother of God, expresses the idea of all motherhood.

"At childbirth, every woman has the same aura of isolation, as
though she were abandoned, alone. At this vital moment the
man's part is as irrelevant as if he had never had anything to
do with it, as though the whole thing had dropped from heaven.

"It is the woman, by herself, who brings forth her progeny, and
carries it off to some remote corner of existence, a quiet, safe
place for a crib. Alone, in silence and humility, she feeds and
rears the child.

"The Mother of God is asked to 'pray zealously to her Son
and her God,' and the words of the psalm are put into her
mouth: 'My soul doth magnify the Lord, and my spirit hath rejoiced in God my Saviour. For He hath regarded the low estate
of his handmaiden: for, behold, from henceforth all generations
shall call me blessed.' It is because of her child that she says this,
He will magnify her ('For He that is mighty hath done to me
great things'): He is her glory. Any woman could say it. For
every one of them, God is in her child. Mothers of great men must
have been familiar with this feeling, but then, all women are
mothers of great men—it isn't their fault if life disappoints them
later."

4

"We go on endlessly rereading *Evgenii Onegin* and the poems.
Samdeviatov came yesterday and brought presents—nice things
to eat and kerosene for the lamps. We have endless discussions
about art.

"I have always thought that art is not a category, not a realm
covering innumerable concepts and derivative phenomena, but
that, on the contrary, it is something concentrated, strictly
limited. It is a principle that is present in every work of art, a
force applied to it and a truth worked out in it. And I have never
seen art as form but rather as a hidden, secret part of content.

All this is as clear to me as daylight. I feel it in every bone of my body, but it's terribly difficult to express or to define this idea.

"A literary creation can appeal to us in all sorts of ways—by its theme, subject, situations, characters. But above all it appeals to us by the presence in it of art. It is the presence of art in *Crime and Punishment* that moves us deeply rather than the story of Raskolnikov's crime.

"Primitive art, the art of Egypt, Greece, our own—it is all, I think, one and the same art through thousands of years. You can call it an idea, a statement about life, so all-embracing that it can't be split up into separate words; and if there is so much as a particle of it in any work that includes other things as well, it outweighs all the other ingredients in significance and turns out to be the essence, the heart and soul of the work."

5

"A slight chill, a cough, probably a bit of temperature. Gasping all day long, the feeling of a lump in my throat. I am in a bad way. It is my heart. The first symptoms that I have inherited my poor mother's heart—she suffered from it all her life. Can it really be that? So soon? If so, my tenure in this world is short.

"A faint smell of charcoal in the room. A smell of ironing. Tonia is ironing, every now and then she gets a coal out of the stove and puts it in the iron, and the lid of the iron snaps over it like a set of teeth. It reminds me of something, but I can't think of what. Must be my condition.

"To celebrate Samdeviatov's gift of soap we have had two washing days and Sashenka has been running wild. As I write he sits astride the crosspiece under the table and, imitating Samdeviatov, who takes him out in his sleigh whenever he comes, pretends that he is giving me a ride.

"As soon as I feel better I must go to the town library and read up on the ethnography and history of the region. They say the library has had several important donations and is exceptionally good. I have an urge to write. But I'll have to hurry. It will be spring before we know where we are—and then there'll be no time for reading or writing.

"My headache gets worse and worse. I slept badly. Had a muddled dream of the kind you forget as you wake up. All that remained in my memory was the part that woke me up. It was a woman's voice, I heard it in my dream, sounding in the air. I remembered it and kept hearing it in my mind and going through the list of our women friends—I tried to think of someone who spoke in that deep, soft, husky voice. It didn't belong to any of them. I thought it might be Tonia's, and that I had become so used to her that I no longer heard the tone of her voice. I tried to forget that she was my wife and to become sufficiently detached to find out. But it wasn't her voice either. It remains a mystery.

"About dreams. It is usually taken for granted that you dream of something that has made a particularly strong impression on you during the day, but it seems to me it's just the contrary.

"Often it's something you paid no attention to at the time—a vague thought that you didn't bother to think out to the end, words spoken without feeling and which passed unnoticed—these are the things that return at night, clothed in flesh and blood, and they become the subjects of dreams, as if to make up for having been ignored during waking hours."

6

"A clear, frosty night. Unusual brilliance and perfection of everything visible. Earth, sky, moon, and stars, all seem cemented, riveted together by the frost. Shadows of trees lie across the paths, so sharp that they seem carved in relief. You keep thinking you see dark figures endlessly cross the road at various places. Big stars hang in the woods between branches like blue lanterns. Small ones are strewn all over the sky like daisies in a summer field.

"We go on discussing Pushkin. The other night we talked about the early poems he wrote as a schoolboy. How much depended on his choice of meter!

"In the poems with long lines, his ambition did not extend beyond the Arzamas Literary Circle; he wanted to keep up with the grownups, impress his uncle with mythologism, bombast, faked epicureanism and sophistication, and affected a precocious worldly wisdom.

"But as soon as he stopped imitating Ossian and Parny and changed from 'Recollections of Tsarskoie Selo' to 'A Small Town' or 'Letter to My Sister' or 'To My Inkwell' (written later in Kishinev), or 'To Yudin,' the future Pushkin was already there.

"Air, light, the noise of life, reality burst into his poetry from the street as through an open window. The outside world, everyday things, nouns, crowded in and took possession of his lines, driving out the vaguer parts of speech. Things and more things lined up in rhymed columns on the page.

"As if this, Pushkin's tetrameter, which later became so famous, were a measuring unit of Russian life, a yardstick, as if it had been patterned after the whole of Russia's existence, as you draw the outline of a foot or give the size of a hand to make sure that the glove or the shoe will fit.

"Later in much the same way, the rhythm of spoken Russian, the intonations of ordinary speech were expressed in Nekrassov's trimeters and dactyls."

7

"I should like to be of use as a doctor or a farmer and at the same time to be gestating something lasting, something fundamental, to be writing some scientific paper or a literary work.

"Every man is born a Faust, with a longing to grasp and experience and express everything in the world. Faust became a scientist thanks to the mistakes of his predecessors and contemporaries. Progress in science is governed by the laws of repulsion, every step forward is made by refutation of prevalent errors and false theories. Faust was an artist thanks to the inspiring example of his teachers. Forward steps in art are governed by the law of attraction, are the result of the imitation of and admiration for beloved predecessors.

"What is it that prevents me from being a doctor and a writer? I think it is not our privations or our wanderings or our unsettled lives, but the prevalent spirit of high-flown rhetoric, which has spread everywhere—phrases such as 'the dawn of the future,' 'the building of a new world,' 'the torch-bearers of mankind.' The first time you hear such talk you think 'What breadth of imagination, what richness!' But in fact it's so pompous just because it is so unimaginative and second-rate.

"Only the familiar transformed by genius is truly great. The best object lesson in this is Pushkin. His works are one great hymn to honest labor, duty, everyday life! Today, 'bourgeois' and 'petty bourgeois' have become terms of abuse, but Pushkin fore-stalled the implied criticism in his 'Family Tree,' where he says proudly that he belongs to the middle class, and in 'Onegin's Travels' we read:

> 'Now my ideal is the housewife,
> My greatest wish, a quiet life
> And a big bowl of cabbage soup.'

"What I have come to like best in the whole of Russian litera-ture is the childlike Russian quality of Pushkin and Chekhov, their modest reticence in such high-sounding matters as the ul-timate purpose of mankind or their own salvation. It isn't that they didn't think about these things, and to good effect, but to talk about such things seemed to them pretentious, presumptuous. Gogol, Tolstoy, Dostoievsky looked restlessly for the meaning of life, and prepared for death and balanced accounts. Pushkin and Chekhov, right up to the end of their lives, were absorbed in the current, specific tasks imposed on them by their vocation as writers, and in the course of fulfilling these tasks they lived their lives, quietly, treating both their lives and their work as private, individual matters, of no concern to anyone else. And these in-dividual things have since become of concern to all, and their works, like apples picked while they are green, have ripened of themselves, mellowing gradually and growing richer in mean-ing."

8

"First signs of spring. Thaw. The air smells of buttered pancakes and vodka, as at Shrovetide. A sleepy, oily sun blinking in the forest, sleepy pines blinking their needles like eyelashes, oily puddles glistening at noon. The countryside yawns, stretches, turns over, and goes back to sleep.

"Chapter Seven of *Evgenii Onegin* describes the spring, One-

gin's house deserted in his absence, Lensky's grave by the stream
at the foot of the hill.

> *'The nightingale, spring's lover,*
> *Sings all night. The wild rose blooms.'*

Why 'lover'? The fact is, the epithet is natural, apt: the nightingale *is* spring's lover. Moreover, he needed it for the rhyme.
I wonder whether the nickname Nightingale, for the brigand son
of Odikmantii, in the well-known Russian folk epic, is not a meta-
phor based on similarity of sound. How well the song character-
izes him!

> *'At his nightingale whistle,*
> *At his wild forest call,*
> *The grass is all a-tremble,*
> *The flowers shed their petals,*
> *The dark forest bows down to the ground,*
> *And all good people fall down dead.'*

We came to Varykino in early spring. Soon the trees grew green
—alder and nut trees and wild cherry—especially in the Shutma,
the ravine below Mikulitsyn's house. And soon after that the
nightingales began to sing.

"Once again, as though hearing them for the first time, I
wondered at the difference between their song and that of all
other birds, at the sudden jump, without transitions, that nature
makes to the richness and uniqueness of their trills. Such variety
and power and resonance! Turgenev somewhere describes these
whistling, fluting modulations. There were two phrases that stood
out particularly. One was a luxurious, greedily repetitive tiokh-
tiokh-tiokh, in response to which the vegetation, all covered with
dew, trembled with delight. The other was in two syllables, grave,
imploring, an appeal or a warning: 'Wake up! Wake up!' "

9

"Spring. We are preparing for the spring sowing. No time for a
diary. It was pleasant to write. I'll have to stop until next winter.

"The other day—and now it really was Shrovetide—right in the middle of the spring floods, a sick peasant drove his sleigh into the yard through the mud and slush. I refused to examine him. 'I've given up practicing,' I said. 'I have neither medicines nor equipment.' But he persisted. 'Help me. My skin is bad. Have pity on me. I'm sick.' What could I do? I don't have a heart of stone. I told him to undress. He had lupus. As I was examining him I glanced at the bottle of carbolic acid on the window sill (don't ask me where it comes from—that and a few other things I couldn't do without—everything comes from Samdeviatov). Then I saw there was another sleigh in the yard. I thought at first it was another patient. But it was my brother, Evgraf, who had dropped in on us out of the blue. The family took charge of him—Tonia, Sashenka, Alexander Alexandrovich. Later I went out and joined them. We showered him with questions. Where had he come from? How had he come? As usual, he was evasive, he smiled, shrugged, spoke in riddles.

"He stayed about two weeks, went often to Yuriatin, and then vanished suddenly as if the earth had swallowed him. I realized while he was staying with us that he had even more influence than Samdeviatov and that his work and his connections were even more mysterious. What is he? What does he do? Why is he so powerful? He promised to make things easier for us so that Tonia should have more time for Sashenka and I for practicing medicine and writing. We asked him how he proposed to do this. He merely smiled. But he has been as good as his word. There are signs that our living conditions are really going to change.

"It is truly extraordinary. He is my half brother. We bear the same name. And yet I know virtually nothing about him.

"For the second time he has burst into my life as my good genius, my rescuer, resolving all my difficulties. Perhaps in every life there has to be, in addition to the other protagonists, a secret, unknown force, an almost symbolic figure who comes unsummoned to the rescue, and perhaps in mine Evgraf, my brother, plays the part of this hidden benefactor?"

At this point Yurii Andreievich's diary breaks off. He never went on with it.

10

Yurii Andreievich looked through the books he had ordered at the reading room of the Yuriatin public library. The reading room had several windows and could seat about a hundred people. Long tables stood in rows that ended by the windows. The library closed at sunset; in the spring the town had no lighting. Zhivago always left before dark, however, and never stayed in town later than the dinner hour. He would leave the horse that Mikulitsyn lent him at Samdeviatov's inn, read all morning, and ride back to Varykino in the afternoon.

Before he began visiting the library Yurii Andreievich had only rarely been to Yuriatin; he had nothing in particular to do there, and he hardly knew it. Now, as the reading room gradually filled with local people, some sitting down near to him and others farther away, he felt as if he were getting to know the town by standing at one of its bustling intersections, and as if not only the people but also the houses and the streets in which they lived were coming into the room.

However, from the windows one could also see the actual Yuriatin, real and not imagined. In front of the central, largest window was a tank of boiled water. Readers who wanted a break went out to the landing to smoke or gathered around the tank for a drink and, after emptying the cup into the basin, stood at the window, admiring the view over the town.

The readers were of two kinds. The majority were elderly members of the local intelligentsia; the rest were of more humble origin.

The former, mostly women, were poorly dressed and had a neglected, hangdog look and long, sickly faces which for one reason or another—whether through hunger, jaundice, or dropsy—were puffy. They were habitués of the library, and knew the attendants personally and felt at home here.

The common people looked well and handsome and were neatly dressed in their best clothes; they came in timidly as though they were entering a church; they made more noise than the others, not because they did not know the rules but because in their anxiety not to make a sound they could not control their vigorous steps and voices.

The librarian and his two assistants sat on a dais in a recess in the wall opposite the window, separated from the rest of the room by a high counter. One of the assistants was a cross-looking woman who wore a woollen shawl and kept putting on her pince-nez and taking it off, apparently in accordance with mood rather than need. The other, in a black silk blouse, seemed to have a weak chest, for she breathed and spoke through her handkerchief and never took it away from her nose and mouth.

The staff had the same long, puffy, flabby faces as most of the readers, and the same loose skin, earthy and greenish like pickled cucumbers or gray mold. The three of them took turns explaining the rules in whispers to new readers, sorted the order slips, handed out books and took them back, and in the intervals worked on some report or other.

Through an unaccountable association of ideas started by the sight of the real town outside the window and the imagined one inside the room, as well as by the swollen faces around him, which made it seem as though everyone had goiter and somehow recalled the face of the sulky woman in charge of the Yuriatin railway switch on the morning of his arrival, Yurii Andreievich remembered the distant panorama of the town and Samdeviatov beside him on the floor of the car, and his comments and explanations. He tried to connect these explanations, given him so far outside the town, with his immediate surroundings now that he was at the center of the picture. But he did not remember what Samdeviatov had told him, and he did not get anywhere.

11

Yurii Andreievich sat at the far end of the room. In front of him were several reports on local land statistics and some reference books on the ethnography of the region. He had also asked for two books on the history of the Pugachev rebellion, but the librarian in the silk blouse had whispered through her handkerchief that no one reader could have so many volumes at the same time and that he would have to give back some of the journals and reference books before taking out the others that interested him.

So he applied himself to his unsorted pile of books with more haste and industry than before in order to set aside those that he really needed and exchange the rest for the historical books he wanted. He was leafing through the manuals and going over the chapter headings, wholly concentrated on his work and not looking about him. The crowd of readers did not distract him. He had had a good look at his neighbors; those on his left and right were fixed in his mind, he knew they were there without raising his eyes and he had the feeling that they would not leave before him, just as the houses and churches outside the window would not move from their places.

The sun, however, did move. It had shifted from the east corner of the room and was now shining through the windows in the south wall straight into the eyes of the nearest readers.

The librarian who had a cold came down from her dais and went over to the windows. They had pleated white curtains that softened the light pleasantly. She drew them all except at the last window, which was still in the shade. Coming to it, she pulled the cord to open the transom and had a fit of sneezing.

After she had sneezed ten or twelve times Yurii Andreievich realized that she was Mikulitsyn's sister-in-law, one of the Tuntseva girls mentioned by Samdeviatov. Like other readers, he raised his head and looked in her direction.

Now he noticed a change in the room. At its farther end there was a new reader. Yurii Andreievich recognized Antipova at once. She was sitting with her back to him, speaking in a low voice with the sneezing librarian, who stood leaning over her. The conversation seemed to have a good effect on the librarian. It cured her instantly, not only of her annoying cold but of her nervous tenseness. With a warm, grateful glance at Antipova, she took the handkerchief she had been ceaselessly pressing to her mouth away from her face, put it in her pocket, and went back to her place behind the partition, happy, self-confident, and smiling.

The incident marked by this touching detail was noticed by several people in different parts of the room; they too smiled, looking at Antipova with approval. From these trivial signs Yurii Andreievich gathered that Antipova was known and liked in the town.

12

His first impulse was to get up and speak to her. But a shyness and lack of simplicity, entirely alien to his nature, had, in the past, crept into his relationship with her and now held him back. He decided not to disturb her and not to interrupt his work. To keep away from the temptation of looking at her he turned his chair sideways, so that its back was almost against his table; he tried to concentrate on his books, holding one in his hand and another on his knees.

But his thoughts had wandered far from his studies. Suddenly he realized that the voice he had once heard in a dream on a winter night in Varykino had been Antipova's. The discovery dumfounded him, and startling his neighbors he jerked his chair back to be able to see Antipova. He began to look at her.

He saw her in a quarter view from the rear. She wore a light checked blouse with a belt and read with complete absorption, like a child, her head bent slightly over her right shoulder. Occasionally she stopped to think, looked up at the ceiling or straight in front of her, then again propped her cheek on her hand and copied excerpts from the volume she was reading, writing with a swift, sweeping movement of her pencil in her notebook.

Yurii Andreievich noticed again what he had observed long ago in Meliuzeievo. "She does not want to please or to look beautiful," he thought. "She despises all that aspect of a woman's nature; it's as though she were punishing herself for being lovely. But this proud hostility to herself makes her ten times more irresistible.

"How well she does everything! She reads not as if reading were the highest human activity, but as if it were the simplest possible thing, a thing that even animals could do. As if she were carrying water from a well, or peeling potatoes."

These reflections calmed him. A rare peace descended upon his soul. His mind stopped darting from subject to subject. He could not help smiling; Antipova's presence affected him the same way as it had affected the nervous librarian.

No longer worrying about the angle of his chair nor afraid of distractions, he worked for an hour or so with even greater concentration than before her arrival. He went through the whole pile of books in front of him, setting aside those he needed most, and even had time to read two important articles he found in them. Then, deciding that he had done enough for the day, he collected his books and took them back to the desk. With an easy conscience and without any ulterior motive, he reflected that after his hard morning's work he deserved to take time off to see an old friend and that he could legitimately allow himself this pleasure. But when he stood up and looked around the room, Antipova was no longer there.

The books she had just returned were still lying on the counter where he had put his own. They were textbooks of Marxism. She must be re-educating herself politically before going back to her teaching job.

On her order slips, which stuck out from between the pages of the books, was her address. Yurii Andreievich took it down, surprised by its oddity: "Merchant Street, opposite the house with sculptures." He asked another reader what this meant and was told that the expression "house with sculptures" was as familiar in Yuriatin as in Moscow the designation of a street by the name of its parish church, or the phrase "the Five Corners" in Petersburg.

The name referred to a dark, steel-gray house decorated with Caryatides and statues of the Muses holding cymbals, lyres, and masks. A merchant had built it in the last century as his private theater. His heirs had sold it to the Merchants' Guild, which gave its name to the street, and the whole neighborhood was known by the name of the house. It was now used by the Party's Town Committee, and the lower part of its façade, where posters and programs had been displayed in the old days, was now covered with government proclamations and decrees.

13

It was a cold, windy afternoon at the beginning of May. Yurii Andreievich, having finished what he had to do in town and having looked in at the library, suddenly changed his plans and decided to go see Antipova.

The wind often held him up, barring his way with clouds of dust and sand. He averted his head, closed his eyes, waited for the dust to stop blowing, and continued on his way.

Antipova lived at the corner of Merchant Street opposite the dark, blue-gray house with sculptures, which he now saw for the first time. It did indeed live up to its name, and there was something strange and disturbing about it.

Its entire top floor was surrounded by female mythological figures half as big again as human beings. Between two gusts of the dust storm it seemed to him as if all the women in the house had come out on the balcony and were looking down at him over the balustrade.

There were two doors into Antipova's house, one from Merchant Street, the other around the corner from the alley. Not having noticed the front entrance, Yurii Andreievich went in from the side street.

As he turned in at the gate the wind whirled scraps and trash up into the sky, screening the yard from the doctor. Through this black curtain, hens, chased by a cock, fled clucking from under his feet.

When the dust settled the doctor saw Antipova by the well. She had filled two buckets and hung them on a yoke across her left shoulder. Her hair was hastily tied in a kerchief knotted in front to protect it from the dust, and she was holding her billowing skirt down between her knees. She started for the house, but was stopped by another gust that tore the kerchief from her head and carried it off to the far end of the fence where the hens were still cackling.

Yurii Andreievich ran after it, picked it up, and took it back to her at the well. Preserving her usual natural air, she did not, even by an exclamation, betray her amazement or embarrassment. All she said was: "Zhivago!"

"Larisa Feodorovna!"

"What on earth are you doing here?"

"Put your buckets down. I'll carry them for you."

"I never stop halfway, I never leave what I do unfinished. If it's me you've come to see, let's go."

"Who else?"

"How should I know?"

"Anyway, let me take those buckets. I can't just stand by while you work."

"You call that work? Leave them alone. You'd only splash the stairs. Better tell me what brought you here. You've been around more than a year and you never found a moment to come till now."

"How do you know?"

"Things get around. Moreover, I saw you in the reading room."

"Why didn't you speak to me?"

"Don't tell me you didn't see me."

Swaying a little under the weight of the lightly swinging buckets, she walked in front of him through the low arch of the entrance. Here she squatted quickly, setting the pails on the earth floor, took the yoke off her shoulder, straightened up, and dried her hands with a small handkerchief.

"Come, I'll take you through the inside passage to the front hall. It's lighter. You'll have to wait there a moment. I'll take the buckets up the back stairs and tidy up a bit. I won't be long. Look at our smart stairs—cast-iron steps with an open-work pattern. You can see everything through them from the top. It's an old house. The shelling has shaken it up a bit, you can see where the masonry has come loose. See this crack in the brick-work? That's where Katenka and I leave the key to the flat when we go out. Keep it in mind. You might come someday when I'm out—you can open the door and make yourself at home till I come back. You see, there it is, but I don't need to use it now. I'll go in the back way and open the door from inside. Our only trouble is rats. There are swarms and swarms of them, and you can't get rid of them. It's these old walls. Cracks and crevices all over the place. I stop up all the ratholes I can, but it doesn't do much good. Perhaps you'd come one day and help me? The cracks between the skirting and the floor boards need stopping up. Yes? Well, you stay here in the hall and think about something. I won't be long, I'll call you in a minute."

While waiting, he looked around at the peeling walls and the cast-iron steps. He told himself: "In the reading room I thought she was absorbed in her reading with the ardor she would give to a real, hard physical task. Now I see that the reverse is also true: she carries water from the well as lightly and effortlessly as if she were reading. There is the same gracefulness in everything she does, as if she had taken a flying start early in life, way back in her childhood, and now everything she does follows this momentum, easily, naturally. This quality is in the line of her back when she bends down and in her smile as it parts her lips and rounds her chin, and in her words and thoughts."

"Zhivago!" Antipova called down from the top landing.

He went up.

14

"Give me your hand and do as I tell you. We have to go through two dark rooms piled with furniture. You might bump into something and hurt yourself."

"True. It is like a labyrinth. I'd never have found my way. Why is it like this? Is the flat being redecorated?"

"Oh no, nothing like that. It belongs to someone else, I don't even know who it is. I had my own flat in the school building. When the school was taken over by the Town Housing Department, Katenka and I were given part of this house. The owners had gone away, leaving all their furniture. There was an awful lot of it. I don't want other people's things, so I put it all into these two rooms and whitewashed the windows to keep out the sun. Don't let go of my hand or you'll get lost. Here we are, we turn right, now we're out of the maze, here's my door. It will be lighter in a second. Watch the step."

As he followed her into the room he was struck by the view from the window facing the door. It looked out on the yard and over the low roofs of the houses beyond it to the vacant lots by the river. Goats and sheep grazed there, and their long woolly coats swept the ground like long skirts. There too was the familiar billboard: "Moreau & Vetchinkin. Mechanical seeders. Threshing machines."

Reminded by it of the day of his arrival from Moscow, the doctor proceeded to describe it to Larisa Feodorovna. Forgetting there was a rumor that Strelnikov was her husband, he told her of his meeting with the commissar in the train. This part of his story made a deep impression on her.

"You saw Strelnikov?" she asked eagerly. "I won't tell you now, but really it is extraordinary. It's as if you were predestined to meet. I'll tell you all about it sometime, you'll be amazed. If I'm not mistaken, he made a good rather than a bad impression on you?"

"Yes, on the whole. He ought to have repelled me. We had actually passed through the country where he had brought death and destruction. I expected to see a brutal soldier or a revolutionary Jack-the-Ripper, but he was neither. It's a good thing when a man is different from your image of him. It shows he isn't a type. If he were, it would be the end of him as a man. But if you can't place him in a category, it means that at least a part of him is what a human being ought to be. He has risen above himself, he has a grain of immortality."

"They say he is not a Party member."

"Yes, I think that's true. What is it that makes one like him? He is a doomed man. I believe that he'll come to a bad end. He will atone for the evil he has done. Revolutionaries who take the law into their own hands are horrifying not because they are criminals, but because they are like machines that have got out of control, like runaway trains. Strelnikov is as mad as the others, only his madness does not spring from theories, but from the ordeals he has gone through. I don't know his secret, but I am sure he has one. His alliance with the Bolsheviks is accidental. So long as they need him, they put up with him, and he happens to be going their way. The moment they don't need him they'll throw him overboard with no regret, and crush him, as they have done with other military experts."

"You think so?"

"I am sure of it."

"Is there no escape for him? Couldn't he run away?"

"Where could he run, Larisa Feodorovna? You could do that in the old days, under the Tsars. But just you try nowadays!"

"Too bad. You've made me feel sorry for him. You've changed, you know. You used to speak more calmly about the revolution, you were less harsh about it."

"That's just the point, Larisa Feodorovna. There are limits to everything. In all this time something definite should have been achieved. But it turns out that those who inspired the revolution aren't at home in anything except change and turmoil, they aren't happy with anything that's on less than a world scale. For them transitional periods, worlds in the making, are an end in themselves. They aren't trained for anything else, they don't know anything except that. And do you know why these never-ending preparations are so futile? It's because these men haven't any real capacities, they are incompetent. Man is born to live, not to prepare for life. Life itself, the phenomenon of life, the gift of life, is so breath-takingly serious! So why substitute this childish harlequinade of immature fantasies, these schoolboy escapades? But enough of this. It's my turn to ask questions. We arrived on the morning of the local upheaval. Were you in it?"

"I should say I was! There were fires all around us, it's a wonder the house didn't burn down. It was pretty badly shaken, as I told you. To this day there's an unexploded shell in the yard just inside the gate. Looting, bombardment, all kinds of horrors —as at every change of government. But by then we were used to it, it wasn't the first time. And the things that went on under the Whites! Murders to settle old accounts, extortions, blackmail —a real orgy! But I haven't told you the most extraordinary thing. Our Galiullin! He turned up with the Czechs as a most important personage—a sort of Governor-General."

"I know. I heard about it. Did you see him?"

"Very often. You can't think how many people I managed to save, thanks to him, how many I hid. In all fairness, he behaved perfectly, chivalrously, not like all those small fry—little Cossack captains, policemen, and what not. Unfortunately, it was the small fry who set the tone, not the decent people. Galiullin helped me a lot, bless him. We are old friends, you know. When I was a little girl I often went to the house where he grew up. Most of the tenants were railway workers. I saw a lot of poverty as a child. That's why my attitude to the revolution is different from yours. It's closer to me. There's a lot of it I understand from the inside. But that Galiullin, that the son of a janitor should become a White Colonel—perhaps even a General! There aren't any soldiers in my family, I don't know much about army ranks. And by profession I am a history teacher. . . . Anyway, that's how it was. Between us, we managed to help quite a lot of people. I used to go and see him.

We talked about you. I've always had friends and connections in every government—and also sorrows and disappointment from all of them. It's only in mediocre books that people are divided into two camps and have nothing to do with each other. In real life everything gets mixed up! Don't you think you'd have to be a hopeless nonentity to play only one role all your life, to have only one place in society, always to stand for the same thing?— Ah, there you are!"

A little girl of about eight came in, her hair done up in finely braided pigtails. Her narrow eyes had a sly, mischievous look and went up at the corners when she laughed. She knew her mother had a visitor, having heard his voice outside the door, but she thought it necessary to put on an air of surprise. She curtsied and looked at the doctor with the fearless, unblinking stare of a lonely child who had begun to think early in life.

"My daughter, Katenka. I hope you'll be friends!"

"You showed me her photograph in Meliuzeievo. How she's grown and changed since then!"

"I thought you were out. I didn't hear you come in."

"I took the key out of the crack and there was an enormous rat in it—as big as this! You should have seen me jump! I nearly died of fright."

She made an absurd face, opening her eyes wide and rounding her mouth like a fish out of water.

"Off you go now. I'll get Uncle to stay to dinner, and call you when the kasha is ready."

"Thank you, I wish I could stay. But we have dinner at six since I've started coming to town and I try not to be late. It takes me over three hours to get home—nearly four. That is why I came so early. I'm afraid I'll have to go soon."

"You can stay another half hour."

"I'd love to."

15

"And now, since you have been so frank with me, I'll be frank with you. The Strelnikov you met is my husband, Pasha, Pavel Pavlovich Antipov, whom I went to look for at the front and in whose death I so rightly refused to believe."

"What you say does not come as a surprise. I was prepared for something of the sort. I heard that rumor, but I didn't believe it for a moment. That's why I spoke about him to you so freely, ignoring the rumor, which is sheer nonsense. I've seen this man. How could anyone connect him with you? What do you have in common with him?"

"And yet it's true. Strelnikov is Antipov, my husband. I share the general belief. Katenka knows it and is proud of her father. Strelnikov is his pseudonym—he has an assumed name, like all active revolutionaries. For some reason he must live and act under an alias.

"It was he who took Yuriatin, and shelled us, knowing that we were here, and never once tried to find out if we were alive, in order not to reveal his identity. Of course it was his duty. If he had asked me I would have told him to do just that. You might say that my being safe and the Town Soviet's giving me a reasonable place to live in shows that he is secretly looking after us. But that he should actually have been here and resisted the temptation to have a look at us—it's inconceivable! It's beyond me, it isn't natural, it's like the ancient Roman virtue, one of those newfangled ideas. But I mustn't let myself be influenced by your way of looking at things. You and I don't really think alike. When it comes to the intangible, the marginal choices, we understand each other. But when it comes to the big issues, to one's outlook on life, we don't see eye to eye. But to go back to Strelnikov. . . .

"Now he's in Siberia, and you are right—I have heard him accused of things that make my blood run cold. He is out there, in command of one of our most advanced positions, and he is fighting and beating poor old Galiullin, his childhood friend and his comrade in arms in the German war. Galiullin knows who he is, and he knows that I am his wife, but he has had the delicacy—I can't value it too highly—never to refer to it, though goodness knows he goes mad with rage at the sound of Strelnikov's name.

"Yes, that's where he is now, in Siberia. But he was here for a long time, living in that railway car where you saw him. I kept hoping I'd run into him by accident. Sometimes he went to the staff headquarters, which were in the building where Komuch

—the Constituent Assembly Army—used to have its headquarters. And by an odd coincidence, the entrance was through the wing where Galiullin used to see me. I was always going there to ask him to help somebody or to stop some horrible business or other. For instance, there was that affair at the military academy, which made a lot of noise at the time. If an instructor was unpopular the cadets ambushed him and shot him, saying he was a Bolshevik sympathizer. And then there was the time when they started beating up the Jews. Incidentally, if you do intellectual work of any kind and live in a town, as we do, half of your friends are bound to be Jews. Yet in times when there are pogroms, when all these terrible, despicable things are done, we don't only feel sorry and indignant and ashamed, we feel wretchedly divided, as if our sympathy came more from the head than from the heart and had an aftertaste of insincerity.

"It's so strange that these people who once liberated mankind from the yoke of idolatry, and so many of whom now devote themselves to its liberation from injustice, should be incapable of liberating themselves from their loyalty to an obsolete, antediluvian identity that has lost all meaning, that they should not rise above themselves and dissolve among all the rest whose religion they have founded and who would be so close to them, if they knew them better.

"Of course it's true that persecution forces them into this futile and disastrous attitude, this shamefaced, self-denying isolation that brings them nothing but misfortune. But I think some of it also comes from a kind of inner senility, a historical centuries-long weariness. I don't like their ironical whistling in the dark, their prosaic, limited outlook, the timidity of their imagination. It's as irritating as old men talking of old age or sick people about sickness. Don't you think so?"

"I haven't thought about it much. I have a friend, Misha Gordon, who thinks as you do."

"Well, I used to go to this place hoping to catch Pasha on his way in or out. In Tsarist times the Governor-General used to have his office in that part of the building. Now there is a notice on the door: 'Complaints.' Have you seen it? It's the prettiest place in town. The square in front of it is paved with wooden blocks, and across the square there is the town park, full of maples,

hawthorn, honeysuckle. There was always a line in the street
outside the door. I used to stand there and wait. Of course I
didn't try to crash the door, I didn't say I was his wife. After all,
our names are different. And don't think that an appeal to senti-
ment would move them! Their ways are quite different. Do you
know, his own father, Pavel Ferapontovich Antipov, a former
political exile, an old worker, is quite near here, in a settlement
along the highway, where he lived as an exile. And his friend
Tiverzin is there too. They are both members of the local revolutionary court. Well, can you believe it, Pasha hasn't been to
see his father and he hasn't told him who he is. And his father
takes it for granted, he isn't a bit hurt. If his son wants to remain
incognito, then that's as it should be, he can't see him and that's
all there is to it. They are made of stone, these people, they
aren't human, with all their discipline and principles.

"Even if I had managed to prove that I was his wife, it
wouldn't have done me any good! What do wives matter to them
at a time like this? The workers of the world, the remaking of
the universe—that's something! But a wife, just an individual
biped, is of no more importance than a flea or a louse!

"His aide-de-camp used to come out and ask people what they
wanted to see him for and let some of them in. But I never told
him my name and when he asked me what my business was I
always said it was personal. Of course, I knew I was wasting my
time. The aide would shrug his shoulders and give me a suspicious look. I never once saw him.

"I suppose you think he can't be bothered with us, he doesn't
love us, he's forgotten us? Well, you are wrong. I know him too
well. I know just what he wants, and it's just because he loves
us. He can't bear to come back to us empty-handed. He wants
to come back as a conqueror, full of honor and glory, and lay
his laurels at our feet. To immortalize us, to dazzle us! Just like
a child."

Katenka came in again. Larisa Feodorovna snatched her up
and, to the girl's astonishment, started swinging her around and
tickling and hugging her.

16

Yurii Andreievich was riding back to Varykino. He had been over this stretch of country countless times. He was so used to the road that he was no longer aware of it, he hardly saw it.

Soon he would come to the crossroad in the forest where the way ahead led to Varykino and another path turned off to the fishing village of Vasilievskoie on the river Sakma. Here stood yet a third billboard advertising agricultural machinery. As usual he reached the crossroad at dusk.

Two months had now elapsed since the day when, instead of going home from Yuriatin, he spent the night at Larisa Feodorovna's and told his family that he had been kept on business and had stayed at Samdeviatov's inn. He had long been calling her Lara and addressing her as "thou," though she still called him Zhivago. Yurii Andreievich was betraying Tonia, and his involvement was becoming ever more serious. This was shocking, impossible.

He loved Tonia, he worshipped her. Her peace of mind meant more to him than anything in the world. He would defend her honor more devotedly than her father or herself. He would have torn apart with his own hands anyone who would hurt her pride. And yet he himself was now the offender.

At home he felt like a criminal. His family's ignorance of the truth and their unchanged affection were a mortal torment to him. In the middle of a conversation he would suddenly be numbed by the recollection of his guilt and cease hearing a word of what was being said around him.

If this happened during a meal, his food stuck in his throat and he put down his spoon and pushed away his plate. He choked, repressing his tears. "What is wrong with you?" Tonia would ask, puzzled. "You must have had some bad news when you were in town. Has anyone been arrested? Or shot? Do tell me. Don't be afraid of upsetting me. You'll feel better when you've told me."

Had he been unfaithful because he preferred another woman? No, he had made no comparison, no choice. The idea of "free love," terms like "the legitimate demands of love," were alien to him. To think or speak in such terms seemed to him degrading.

He had never "sown wild oats," nor did he regard himself as a superman with special rights and privileges. Now he was crushed by the weight of his guilty conscience.

"What next?" he had sometimes wondered, and hoped wretchedly for some impossible, unexpected circumstance to solve his problem for him.

But now he no longer wondered. He had decided to cut the knot, and he was going home with a solution. He would confess everything to Tonia, beg her to forgive him, and never see Lara again.

Not that everything was quite as it should be. He felt now that he had not made it clear enough to Lara that he was breaking with her for good, forever. He had announced to her that morning that he wished to make a clean breast of it with Tonia and that they must stop seeing each other, but now he had the feeling that he had softened it all down and not made it sufficiently definite.

Larisa Feodorovna had realized how unhappy he felt and had no wish to upset him further by painful scenes. She tried to hear him out as calmly as she could. They were talking in one of the empty front rooms. Tears were running down her cheeks, but she was no more conscious of them than the stone statues on the house across the road were of the rain running down their faces. She kept saying softly: "Do as you think best, don't worry about me. I'll get over it." She was saying it sincerely, without any false magnanimity, and as she did not know that she was crying she did not wipe away her tears.

At the thought that Lara might have misunderstood him, and that he had left her with a wrong impression and false hopes, he nearly turned and galloped straight back, to say what he had left unsaid and above all to take leave of her much more warmly, more tenderly, in a manner more suitable to a last farewell. Controlling himself with difficulty, he continued on his way.

As the sun went down, the forest was filled with cold and darkness. It smelled of damp leaves. Swarms of mosquitoes hung in the air as still as buoys, humming sadly on a constant, high-pitched note. They settled on his sweating face and neck, and he kept swatting them, his noisy slaps keeping time with the sounds of riding—the creaking of the saddle, the heavy thud of hoofs on the squelching mud, and the dry, crackling salvoes as the horse broke wind. In the distance, where the sunset glow seemed to endure forever, a nightingale began to sing.

"Wake up! Wake up!" it called persuasively; it sounded almost like the summons on the eve of Easter Sunday: "Awake, O my soul, why dost thou slumber?"

Suddenly Yurii Andreievich was struck by a very simple thought. What was the hurry? He would not go back on his promise to himself; the confession would be made, but who had said that it must be made that day? He had not said anything to Tonia yet, it was not too late to put it off till his next trip to town. He would finish his conversation with Lara, with such warmth and depth of feeling that it would make up for all their suffering. How splendid, how wonderful! How strange that it had not occurred to him before!

At the thought of seeing Lara once more his heart leapt for joy. In anticipation he lived through his meeting with her.

The wooden houses and pavements on the outskirts of the town . . . He is on his way to her. In a moment he will leave the wooden sidewalks and vacant lots for the paved streets. The small suburban houses flash by like the pages of a book, not as when you turn them over one by one with your forefinger but as when you hold your thumb on the edge of the book and let them all swish past at once. The speed is breath-taking. And over there is her house at the far end of the street, under the white gap in the rain clouds where the sky is clearing, toward the evening. How he loves the little houses in the street that lead to her! He could pick them up and kiss them! Those one-eyed attics with their roofs pulled down like caps. And the lamps and icon lights reflected in the puddles and shining like berries! And her house under the white rift of the sky! There he will again receive the dazzling, God-made gift of beauty from the hands of its Creator. A dark muffled figure will open the door, and the promise of her nearness, unowned by anyone in the world and guarded and cold as a white northern night, will reach him like the first wave of the sea as you run down over the sandy beach in the dark.

Yurii Andreievich dropped his reins, leaned forward in his saddle, flung his arms around the horse's neck, and buried his face in its mane. Taking this display of affection for an appeal to its strength, the horse broke into a gallop.

As it bounded smoothly, its hoofs barely touching the ground, it seemed to Yurii Andreievich that, besides the joyful thudding of his own heart, he heard shouts, but he thought he was imagining it.

Suddenly a deafening shot was fired very close to him. He sat up, snatched at the reins, and pulled. Checked in full flight, the horse side-stepped, backed, and went down on its haunches ready to rear.

In front of him was the crossroad. The sign, "Moreau & Vetchinkin. Mechanical seeders, Threshing machines," glowed in the rays of the setting sun. Three armed horsemen blocked his way: a boy in a school cap and a tunic with two cartridge belts, a cavalryman in an officer's overcoat and fur cap, and a fat man oddly clothed as for a fancy-dress ball in quilted trousers and a wide-brimmed clerical hat pulled low over his forehead.

"Don't move, Comrade Doctor," said the cavalryman in the fur cap, who was the oldest of the three. "If you obey orders, we guarantee that you will not be harmed. If you don't—no offense meant—we'll shoot you. The surgeon attached to our unit has been killed and we are conscripting you as a medical worker. Get down from your horse and hand the reins over to this young man. And let me remind you: if you try to escape we'll give you short shrift."

"Are you Comrade Forester, Mikulitsyn's son Liberius?"

"No, I am his chief liaison officer."

CHAPTER TEN

THE HIGHWAY

1

There were towns, villages, and Cossack settlements along the highway. It was the ancient post road, the oldest highway in Siberia. It cut through the towns like a knife, slicing them like a loaf of bread along the line of their main streets. As for the villages, it swept through them without a backward glance, scattering them right and left, leaving the rows of houses far behind it, or going around them in a broad arc or a sharp turn.

In the distant past, before the railway came to Khodatskoie, the mail was rushed along the highway by troikas. Caravans of tea, bread, and pig iron travelled one way, and convicts under guard, on foot, were driven the other. They walked in step, jangling their fetters—lost souls, desperadoes who filled one's heart with terror. And around them the forests rustled, dark, impenetrable.

Those who lived along the highway were as one family. Friendships and marriages linked village to village and town to town. Khodatskoie stood at a crossing of the road and the railway; it had engine repair shops and other workshops connected with the upkeep of the line, and there, crowded into barracks, the poorest of the poor lived and wasted away and died. Political exiles who had technical qualifications and had served their term of hard labor came to work as skilled mechanics, and settled here.

The original Soviets, which had been set up all along the line, had long since been overthrown. For some time the region had been under the Siberian Provisional Government, but now it

had fallen to Admiral Kolchak, who had given himself the title
of "Supreme Ruler."

2

At one stretch the road had a long uphill climb disclosing an ever
broader panorama. It seemed as if there would be no end to the
slow ascent and to the widening of the horizon, but when the
tired horses and passengers stopped for a rest they found that
they had reached the summit of the hill. The road went on over
a bridge and the river Kezhma swirled beneath it.

Beyond the river, on an even steeper rise, they could see the
brick walls of the Vozdvizhensky Monastery. The road circled
the hill of the monastery and zigzagged on through the outskirts
of the town.

When it reached the center of the town it skirted the monastery grounds once again, for the green-painted iron door of the
monastery gave on to the main square. The icon over the arched
gate was framed by the legend in gold letters: "Rejoice, life-
giving Cross, unconquerable victory of piety."

It was Holy Week, the end of Lent, and winter was almost
over. The snow on the roads was turning black, betraying the
beginning thaw, but on the roofs it was still white, and covered
them as with tall hats.

To the boys who had climbed up to the belfry to watch the
bell ringers, the houses below looked like small caskets and
boxes jumbled close together. Little black people, hardly bigger
than dots, walked toward the houses. Some could be recognized
from the belfry by the way they moved. They stopped to read
the decree of the Supreme Ruler, posted on the walls, announcing that three age groups were drafted.

3

Many unexpected things had happened in the night. It had
turned unusually warm for the time of year. A drizzle was com-

ing down, so fine and airy that it seemed to drift away in mist before it reached the earth. But this was an illusion. In reality there was enough rain water to stream, warm and swift, along the ground—which had turned black all over and glistened as if it sweated—and to wash it clean of the remaining snow.

Stunted apple trees, covered with buds, reached miraculously across the garden fences. Drops of water fell from them, and their arhythmic drumming on the wooden pavements could be heard throughout the town.

Tomik, the puppy, chained up for the night in the photographer's yard, squealed and yelped, and in the Galuzins' garden the crow, perhaps irritated by the noise, cawed loud enough to keep the whole town awake.

In the lower part of the town, three cartloads of goods had been taken to the merchant, Liubeznov, who refused to accept delivery, saying it was a mistake, he had never ordered the stuff. The draymen, arguing the lateness of the hour, begged him to put them up for the night, but he cursed and sent them to the devil and refused to open the gate. This row, too, could be heard from one end of the town to the other.

At the seventh canonical hour, at one in the morning by the clock, a dark low sweet humming drifted from the deepest of the monastery bells, which hardly stirred. It mixed with the dark drizzle in the air. It drifted from the bell, sinking and dissolving in the air, as a clump of earth, torn from the riverbank, sinks and dissolves in the water of the spring floods.

It was the night of Maundy Thursday. Almost indistinguishable in the distance, behind the network of rain, candles, lighting a face here, a forehead or a nose there, stirred and moved across the monastery yard. The fasting congregation was going to mass.

A quarter of an hour later, steps sounded on the wooden sidewalk coming from the church. This was Galuzina, the grocer's wife, going home, although the service had only begun. She went at an uneven pace, now running, now slowing down and stopping, her kerchief over her head and her fur coat unbuttoned. She had felt faint in the stuffy church and had come out into the fresh air, but now she was ashamed and sorry that she had not stayed to the end, and because, for the second year now, she was not fasting in Lent. But this was not the chief cause of her worry. The mobilization order posted that day affected her poor, silly boy, Terioshka. She tried to drive the thought of it from her head, but the white patches in the darkness were there to remind her at every turn.

Her house was just around the corner, but she felt better out of doors and was not in a hurry to go back into the airless rooms.

She was upset by gloomy thoughts. Had she tried to think them all out aloud, one by one, she would not have had sufficient words or time enough till dawn. But out here, in the street, these comfortless reflections flew at her in clusters, and she could deal with all of them together, in the short while it took her to walk a few times from the monastery gate to the corner of the square and back.

It was almost Easter and there was not a soul in the house; they had all gone away, leaving her alone. Well, wasn't she alone? Of course she was. Her ward Ksiusha didn't count. Who was she, anyway? Could you ever know anyone's heart? Perhaps she was a friend, or perhaps she was an enemy or a secret rival. She was supposed to be the daughter of her husband's first wife by another marriage. Her husband, Vlas, said that he had adopted her. But suppose she was his natural daughter? Or suppose she wasn't his daughter but something else? Could you ever see into a man's heart? Though, to give Ksiusha her due, there was nothing wrong with her. She had brains, looks, manners— much more brains than either poor stupid Terioshka or her adoptive father!

So here she was, deserted for Holy Week. They had all scattered, everyone had gone his way.

Her husband was travelling up and down the highway making speeches to the new recruits, exhorting them to mighty feats of arms. Instead of looking after his own son, the fool, and saving him from his mortal peril!

And Terioshka too had dashed away from home on the eve of the great feast. He had gone to their relatives in Kuteiny village to amuse himself and forget his troubles. The poor boy had been expelled from school. They had kept him back an extra year in almost every other grade, and now that he was in the eighth they had to kick him out!

Oh, how depressing it all was! Oh, Lord! Why had everything gone so wrong? It was so disheartening, she felt like giving up, she had no wish to live. What had caused all this misery? Was it the revolution? No, oh no! It was the war. The war had killed off the flower of Russia's manhood, now there was nothing but rotten, good-for-nothing rubbish left.

How different it had been in her father's time! Her father had been a contractor. Sober, literate. They had lived off the fat of the land. She and her two sisters, Polia and Olia, as fine a pair of girls as you could hope to meet and as well matched as their names. And master carpenters had called on their father, every one a fine, upstanding man, and a good match. At one time, she and her sisters—things they would think of!—had got it into their heads to knit scarves in wool of six colors. And believe it or not, such good knitters were they that their scarves had become famous all over the province! And everything in those days had been fine and rich and seemly—church services and dances and people and manners—everything had rejoiced her heart, for all that her own family were simple people who came of peasant and worker stock. And Russia too had been a marriageable girl in those days, courted by real men, men who would stand up for her, not to be compared with this rabble nowadays. Now everything had lost its glamour, nothing but civilians left, lawyers and Yids clacking their tongues day and night. Poor old Vlas and his friends thought they could bring back those golden days by toasts and speeches and good wishes! But was this the way to win back a lost love? For that you had to move mountains!

4

By now she had crossed the square and walked as far as the market place more than once. From there her house was down the street on the left, but every time she came to it she changed her mind about going in and turned back into the maze of alleys adjoining the monastery.

The market place of Krestovozdvizhensk was as big as a field. In times gone by, it had been crowded on market days with peasants' carts. At one end of it was Eleninskaia Street; the other formed a sharp arc lined with one- or two-story buildings used for warehouses, offices, and workshops.

There, she remembered, in more peaceful times, Brukhianov, a boorish misogynist in spectacles and a long frock coat, who dealt in leather, oats and hay, cart wheels and harness, would read the penny paper as he sat importantly on a chair outside his great, four-panelled iron door.

And there, in a small dim window, a few pairs of beribboned wedding candles and posies in cardboard boxes gathered dust for years, while in the small room at the back, empty of either furniture or goods except for a pile of large round cakes of wax, thousand-ruble deals were made by the unknown agents of a millionaire candle manufacturer who lived nobody knew where.

There, in the middle of the row of shops, was the Galuzins' large grocery store with its three windows. Its bare, splintery floor was swept morning, noon, and night with used tea leaves: Galuzin and his assistants drank tea all day long. And here Galuzina as a young married woman had often and willingly sat at the cash box. Her favorite color was a violet mauve, the color of church vestments on certain solemn days, the color of lilac in bud, the color of her best velvet dress and of her set of crystal wine glasses. It was the color of happiness and of her memories, and Russia too, in her prerevolutionary virginity, seemed to her to have been the color of lilac. She had enjoyed sitting at the cash box because the violet dusk in the shop, fragrant with starch, sugar, and purple black-currant caramels in glass jars, had matched her favorite color.

Here at the corner, beside the timber yard, stood an old, gray frame house which had settled on all four sides like a dilapidated coach. It had two stories and two entrances, one at either end. Each floor was divided in two; downstairs were Zalkind's pharmacy on the right and a notary's office on the left. Above the pharmacist lived old Shmulevich, a ladies' tailor, with his big family. The flat across the landing from Shmulevich, and above the notary, was crammed with lodgers whose trades and professions were stated on cards and signs covering the whole of the door. Here watches were mended and shoes cobbled; here Kaminsky, the engraver, had his workroom and two photographers, Zhuk and Shtrodakh, worked in partnership.

As the first-floor premises were overcrowded, the photographers' young assistants, Blazhein, a student, and Magidson, who retouched the photographs, had fixed up a darkroom at one end of the large woodshed in the yard. To judge by the angry red eye of the lamp winking blearily in the darkroom window, they were working there now. It was underneath this window that the puppy, Tomik, sat on his chain and yelped, so that you could hear him all along Eleninskaia Street.

"There they all are in a pack, the whole Kehillah," thought Galuzina as she passed the gray house. "It's a den of filthy beggars." And yet, she reflected at once, her husband carried his Jew-hating too far. After all, these people were not important enough to affect Russia's destinies. Though, if you asked old Shmulevich why he thought the country was in such turmoil and disorder, he would twist and turn and contort his ugly face into a grin and say: "That's Leibochka up to his tricks."

Oh, but what nonsense was she wasting her time thinking about! Did they matter? Were they Russia's misfortune? Her misfortune was the towns. Not that the country stood or fell by the towns. But the towns were educated, and the country people had had their heads turned, they envied the education of the towns and tried to copy their ways and could not catch up with them, so now they were neither one thing nor the other.

Or perhaps it was the other way around, perhaps ignorance was the trouble? An educated man can see through walls, he knows everything in advance, while the rest of us are like people in a dark wood. We only miss our hats when our heads have been chopped off. Not that the educated people were having an easy time now. Look at the way the famine was driving them out of the towns! How confusing all this was! Even the devil couldn't make head or tail of it!

And yet, it was the country people who knew how to live. Look at her relatives, the Selitvins, Shelaburins, Pamphil Palykh, the brothers Nestor and Pankrat Modykh. They relied on their own hands and their own heads, they were their own masters. The new farmsteads along the highway were a lovely sight. Forty acres of arable land, with sheep, horses, pigs, cows, and enough corn in the barns for three years ahead! And their farming machines! They even had harvesters! Kolchak was buttering them up, trying to get them on his side, and so were the commissars, to get them into the forest army. They had come back from the war with St. George Crosses and everyone was after them, wanting to employ them as instructors. Epaulettes or no epaulettes, if you knew your job you were always in demand. You would always land on your feet.

But it was time she went home. It wasn't decent for a woman to be wandering about the streets so late. It wouldn't have mattered so much if she had been in her own garden. But it was so muddy, it was like a bog. Anyway, she thought, she felt a little better now.

Thus entangled in her reflections and having quite lost the thread of them, Galuzina went home. But before she went inside, she stood for a moment in front of the porch, going over a few more things in her mind.

She thought of the people who were lording it in Khodatskoie now; she knew more or less what they were like, they were former political exiles from the capitals, Tiverzin, Antipov, the anarchist "Black Banner" Vdovichenko, the local locksmith "Mad Dog" Gorsheny. They were cunning and they knew their own minds, they had stirred up plenty of trouble in their day, they were sure to be plotting something again now. They couldn't live unless they were up to something. They spent their lives dealing with machines, and they were cold and merciless as machines. They went about in sweaters under their jackets, they smoked through bone cigarette holders, and they drank boiled water for fear of catching something. Poor Vlas was wasting his time, these men would turn everything upside down, they would always get their way.

Then she thought about herself. She knew she was a fine woman, with a mind of her own, intelligent and well preserved; all in all, she was not a bad person. But none of her qualities was appreciated in this Godforsaken hole—nor anywhere else, for all she knew. The indecent song about the silly old woman Sentetiurikha, which was well known throughout the Urals, came into her mind, but only the first two lines could be quoted:

> *"Sentetiurikha sold her cart*
> *And bought a balalaika. . . ."*

After this came nothing but obscenities. They sang it in Krestovozdvizhensk, aiming it, she suspected, at herself.

She sighed bitterly and went into the house.

5

She went straight to her bedroom, without stopping in the hall to take off her coat. The room looked out into the garden. Now, at night, the massed shadows on this side of the window and outside it almost repeated each other. The limp, drooping shapes of the curtains were like the limp, drooping shapes of the bare, dark trees in the garden with their uncertain outlines. The velvety darkness in the garden, where the winter was almost over, was being warmed by the dark purple heat of the coming spring bursting out of the ground. And there was a similar interaction of two elements inside the room with its dusty curtains, where the airless darkness was softened by the warm dark violet tones of the coming Feast.

The Virgin in the icon, freeing her dark, narrow hands from the silver covering, held them up, seeming to hold in each the first and last letters of her Greek name, Μήτηρ Θεοῦ, Mother of God. The garnet-colored icon lamp, dark as an inkwell in its gold bracket, scattered its star-shaped light, splintered by the cut glass, on the bedroom carpet.

Taking off her coat and kerchief, Galuzina made an awkward movement and felt her old pain, a stitch in the side under her shoulder blade. She gave a frightened cry and murmured: "Mighty protectress of the sorrowful, chaste Mother of God, help of the afflicted, shelter of the universe . . ." Halfway through the prayer she burst into tears. When the pain died down, she began to undo her dress, but the hooks at the back slipped through her fingers and got lost in the soft crinkled stuff. She had difficulty in finding them.

Her ward Ksiusha woke up and came into the room.

"Why are you in the dark, Mother? Shall I bring a lamp?"

"No, don't. There's enough light."

"Let me undo your dress, Mother. Don't tire yourself."

"My fingers are all thumbs, I could cry. And that tailor didn't have the sense to sew the hooks on so that you can get at them. I've got a notion to rip them all off and throw them at his ugly face."

"How well they sang at the monastery! It's so still, you could hear it from the house."

"The singing was all right, but I'm not feeling so well, my girl. I've got that stitch again—here and here. Everywhere. . . . It's such a nuisance, I don't know what to do."

"The homeopath, Stydobsky, helped you the last time."

"He's always telling you to do something impossible. He's a quack, your homeopath. That's one thing. And the other thing is that he's gone away. He's gone, I tell you, he's left town. And he isn't the only one, they've all rushed off just before the holiday—as if they expected an earthquake or something."

"Well, then, what about that Hungarian doctor, the one who is a prisoner of war? His treatment did you good."

"That's no use either. I tell you, there isn't a soul left. Kerenyi Lajos is with the other Hungarians beyond the demarcation line. They've conscripted him for the Red Army."

"But you know, Mother, you're imagining a lot of it. A nervous heart. In a case like yours suggestion can do wonders; it's what the peasants do, after all. Do you remember that soldier's wife who conjured away your pain? What was her name?"

"Well, really! You take me for an ignorant fool! It wouldn't surprise me if you sang 'Sentetiurikha' behind my back."

"Mother! How can you say such a thing! It's a sin. You ought to be ashamed of yourself. You'd do much better to help me remember that woman's name. It's on the tip of my tongue. I won't have any peace till it comes back to me."

"She has more names than petticoats. I don't know which is the one you're thinking of. They call her Kubarikha and Medvedikha and Zlydarikha and I don't know how many other names besides. She isn't around here any more. No more guest appearances. She's gone. Vanished. They locked her up in the Kezhemsk jail for practicing abortion and making pills and powders of some sort. But sooner than be bored in jail she escaped and got away somewhere to the Far East. I tell you, everyone has run away—Vlas and Terioshka and your Aunt Polia—Aunt Polia of the loving heart. Apart from the two of us,

fools that we are, there isn't an honest woman left in town, I'm
not joking. And no medical help of any sort. If anything happened, you couldn't get a doctor. They say there's one in
Yuriatin, some famous professor from Moscow, the son of a Siberian merchant who committed suicide. But just when I was
thinking of sending for him, the Reds cut the road in twelve
places. . . . Now, off to bed with you, and I'll try to get some
sleep too. By the way, that student of yours, Blazheïn, he's
turned your head. What's the good of saying no?—you're getting
red as a beet. He'll be sweating all night long over some photographs I gave him to develop, poor boy. They don't sleep in that
house, and they keep everyone else awake as well. Their Tomik
is barking, you can hear him all over town, and our wretched
crow is cawing its head off up in the apple tree. Looks as if I'll
have another sleepless night. . . . Now what are you so cross
about? Don't be so touchy. What are students for if not for girls
to fall in love with!"

6

"What's that dog howling for? Go and see what's the matter with
it, it can't be making all that noise for nothing. Wait a minute,
Lidochka, quiet, hold it! We've got to find out what's what or
we'll have the police on us before we know it. Stay here, Ustin,
and you, Sivobluy. They'll manage without you."

Lidochka, the representative of the Central Committee, did
not hear the partisan leader asking him to stop and continued
his tired patter:

"By its policy of looting, requisitioning, violence, shooting, and
torture the bourgeois militarist regime in Siberia is bound to
open the eyes of the gullible. It is hostile not only to the working
class but, in fact, to the whole of the toiling peasantry. The toiling peasantry of Siberia and the Urals must understand that
only in alliance with the city proletariat and the soldiers, only
in alliance with the poor Kirghiz and Buriat peasants . . ."

At last he became aware of the interruptions, stopped, wiped
his sweaty face with his handkerchief, and wearily shut his
puffy eyes.

"Have a rest. Have a drink of water," whispered those who were standing closest to him.

The worried partisan leader was reassured.

"What's all the fuss about? Everything is in order. The signal lamp is in the window and the lookout, if I may use a picturesque expression, has his eyes glued to space. I don't see why we shouldn't go on with the discussion of the report. Go on, Comrade Lidochka."

The wood kept in the large barn in the photographers' yard had been moved aside, and the illegal meeting was being held in the cleared space screened from the small darkroom at the entrance by a wall of logs as high as the ceiling. In case of emergency there was a way of escape through a trap door to an underground passage that came out in a lonely alley at the back of the monastery.

The speaker, who had a sallow complexion, a beard from ear to ear, and a black cotton cap on his bald head, suffered from nervous perspiration and sweated profusely. He kept relighting the stump of his cigarette in the stream of hot air over the kerosene lamp, puffing greedily. Bending low over his scattered papers, he looked them over nervously with his near-sighted eyes, as if he were sniffing them, and continued in his flat, tired voice:

"Only through the Soviets can this alliance of the poor in town and country be achieved. Willy-nilly, the Siberian peasant will now pursue the end for which the workers of Siberia began to fight long ago. Their common goal is the overthrow of the hateful autocracy of hetmans and admirals, and the establishment, by means of an armed uprising, of the power of the peasants' and soldiers' Soviets. In fighting the officer and Cossack hirelings of the bourgeoisie, who are armed to the teeth, the insurgents will have to wage a full-fledged war. The struggle will be long and stubborn."

Once again he stopped, wiped his face, and shut his eyes. In defiance of the rules, someone in the audience got up and raised his hand, signifying his intention to make a comment.

The partisan leader, or, to be more exact, the commander of the Kezhemsk group of the trans-Ural partisan units, sat in a provocatively nonchalant attitude under the speaker's very nose;

he kept interrupting him rudely and disrespectfully. It was hard to believe that so young a soldier—little more than a boy—could be in charge of whole armies and that his men obeyed him and looked up to him with veneration. He sat with his hands and feet wrapped in the skirts of his cavalry overcoat; its top, thrown back over his chair, showed his ensign's tunic with dark patches on the shoulders where the epaulettes had been removed.

On either side of him stood a silent bodyguard of his own age, in a white sheepskin grown a little gray, with a curly lamb's-wool edging. Their handsome, stony faces revealed nothing except blind loyalty to their chief and readiness to do anything for him. Taking no part in the discussion and unmoved by any of the issues raised in it, they neither spoke nor smiled.

There were a dozen or so other people in the room. Some were standing, others sitting on the floor; they leaned against the walls of calked logs, their legs stretched out in front of them or their knees drawn up under their chins.

Three or four were guests of honor and sat on chairs. They were old workers, veterans of the revolution of 1905. Among them were Tiverzin, morose and greatly changed since his Moscow days, and his friend, old Antipov, who always agreed with every word he said. Counted among the gods at whose feet the revolution laid its gifts and its burnt offerings, they sat silent and grim as idols. They had become dehumanized by political conceit.

There were other noteworthy figures in the shed, such as that pillar of Russian anarchism, "Black Banner" Vdovichenko, who, never resting a moment, kept sitting down on the floor and getting up again or pacing back and forth and stopping in the middle of the shed. A fat giant of a man, with a big head, a big mouth, and a lion's mane of hair, who had been an officer in the war with Japan if not in the one with Turkey, he was a dreamer eternally absorbed in his fantasies.

Because of his excessive good nature and colossal size, which kept him from noticing anything smaller than himself, he did not pay sufficient attention to what was going on, misunderstood everything, and, mistaking the views of his opponents for his own, agreed with everything they said.

Next to him on the floor sat his friend Svirid, a trapper. Although he was not a tiller of the soil, his earthy nature showed through the collar of his opened dark cloth shirt, which he bunched in his hand together with the cross he wore around his neck, pulling it about and scratching his chest with it. He was half Buriat, warm-hearted and illiterate; his hair was plaited in thin braids, and he had a sparse mustache and a still sparser beard. His Mongol features aged his face, which was always creased in a sympathetic smile.

The speaker, who was touring Siberia on a military mission from the Central Committee, mentally surveyed the vast expanses he had still to cover. He was uninterested in most of the men he was addressing. But as an old revolutionary and from childhood a champion of the people, he gazed with adoration at the young commander who sat facing him. Not only did he forgive him his lack of manners, which he regarded as the expressions of a genuinely revolutionary temperament, but he delighted in his insolence as an infatuated woman may be pleased by the arrogant ways of a masterful lover.

The partisan commander was Mikulitsyn's son, Liberius. The speaker was a former member of the co-operative labor movement, Kostoied-Amursky, who had once been a Social Revolutionary. He had recently revised his views, admitted his past errors, and recanted them in several detailed statements, and he had not only been received into the Communist Party but had soon afterwards been entrusted with his present responsible task.

He was chosen for it—though he was anything but a soldier —partly as a tribute to his long years of revolutionary service and his ordeals in Tsarist prisons, and partly on the assumption that, as a former member of the co-operative movement, he knew the mood of the peasant masses in insurgent western Siberia. For the purpose of his mission his knowledge was regarded as more important than military training.

His change of political convictions had altered his looks and manners beyond recognition. No one could remember him as either bald or bearded in the old days. But then, perhaps it was all merely a disguise. He was under strict orders from the Party not to reveal his former identity. His underground names were Berendey and Comrade Lidochka.

There was a moment of commotion when Vdovichenko prematurely said that he agreed with the instructions just read. When calm was restored, Kostoied went on:

"In order to keep up with the growing movement of the peasant masses, it is essential to establish contact at once with all the partisan units operating in the territory of the Party Provincial Committee."

He then spoke of arrangements for secret meeting places, passwords, codes, and means of communication and went over the whole ground in detail.

"The units must be informed of the location of the stores of arms, food, and equipment belonging to the Whites and of the places where they keep large sums of money, as well as of their means of safeguarding it.

"It is essential to work out to the last detail all questions concerning the organization of partisan detachments, their commanders, proletarian discipline, conspiratorial work, contact with the outside world, behavior toward the local population, revolutionary courts-martial, and sabotage in enemy territory—for example, the destruction of bridges, railway lines, steamships, barges, stations, workshops with all their technical equipment, telegraph offices, mines, and food supplies."

Liberius could bear it no longer. All that had been said seemed to him to be irrelevant and amateurish.

"A very fine lecture," he said. "I shall take it to heart. I suppose we must accept all this without a word of protest, lest we lose the support of the Red Army?"

"Of course you must."

"And what am I to do with your childish recitation, my wonderful Lidochka, when my forces, damn it—three regiments, including artillery and cavalry—have been campaigning for months and routing the enemy?"

"What a marvel! What strength!" thought Kostoied.

The argument was interrupted by Tiverzin, who disliked Liberius's impertinent tone.

"Pardon me, Comrade Speaker, there is something that I don't understand. I may have put down one of the points in the instructions incorrectly. May I read it out—I should like to be sure. 'It is most desirable that war veterans who were at the front and belonged to soldiers' organizations at the time of the revolution should be drawn into the committee. It is desirable that the membership of the committee should include one or two N.C.O.s and one military technician.' Have I put it down correctly, Comrade Speaker?"

"Perfectly. Word for word."

"Then allow me to say this. I find the point concerning military specialists disquieting. We workers who took part in the revolution of 1905 are not used to trusting army people. There are always counterrevolutionary elements among them."

There were cries of "That's enough! The resolution! Let's have a resolution! It's time to go home, it's late."

"I am in agreement with the majority," said Vdovichenko in a deep rumbling voice. "To put it poetically, civic institutions should be founded on democracy, they should grow up from below, like seedlings that are planted and take root in the soil. You can't hammer them in from above like stakes for a fence. This was precisely the mistake of the Jacobin dictatorship and the reason why the Convention was crushed by the Thermidorians."

"It's as clear as daylight," Svirid, his friend and fellow vagabond, backed him up. "Any child can see it. We should have thought of it earlier, now it's too late. Now our business is just to fight and to push on for all we're worth. How can we turn back, now we've started? We've cooked our soup, so now we must eat it. We've jumped into the water, and we mustn't complain."

"The resolution! The resolution!" people were repeating on all sides. They talked on a little longer, but what they said made less and less sense, and finally, at dawn, the meeting broke up. They went home one by one, taking the usual precautions.

7

There was a picturesque place along the highway, where the swift little river Pazhinka divided the two villages of Kuteiny Posad and Maly Ermolaï, the one extending down a steep hill and the other spread in the valley below it. In Kuteiny a farewell party was being given for the new recruits, and in Ermolaï the medical board under Colonel Strese had resumed, after the Easter break, its examination of the draftees of that area. Mounted militia and Cossacks were stationed in the village for the occasion.

It was the third day of an unusually late Easter and an unusually early spring, warm and without a breath of wind. Tables spread with food and drink for the recruits stood in a street in Kuteiny, some distance from the highway. Placed end to end but not quite in a straight line and covered with white cloths hanging to the ground, they stretched down the street like a long hose.

The villagers had pooled their resources to provide the treat. The main dishes were the remnants of the Easter food, two smoked hams, several *kulich* buns, two or three large paskha cakes. Spread over the tables were bowls of pickled mushrooms, cucumbers, and sauerkraut, plates of home-baked bread cut into thick slices, and dishes piled with Easter eggs; most of them were colored pink or light blue.

Broken eggshells, pink and light blue with white insides, littered the new grass around the tables. Pink and light blue were the shirts of the young men and the dresses of the girls. And pink clouds sailed in the blue sky, slowly and gracefully, and it seemed as if the sky were sailing with them.

Wearing a pink shirt with a silk sash and pointing his toes right and left, Vlas Pakhomovich Galuzin clattered down the steps of Pafnutkin's house on the slope above the highway and the tables, ran down to the tables, and began his speech:

"For want of champagne, I drink to you, my boys, in our own home-brewed vodka. A long life and happy years to you young men who are setting forth today. I should like to make you many other toasts. Gentlemen recruits! May I have your attention! The calvary that stretches out before you is the road of defense of our motherland against the ravishers who flood her fields with fratricidal blood. The people cherished the hope of enjoying the conquests of the revolution in peace, but the party of the Bolsheviks, in the pay of foreign capital, dispersed the Constituent Assembly, which was the people's highest hope, by brute force of bayonets, and now the blood of the defenseless flows in rivers. Young men who are setting forth today, to you is entrusted the outraged honor of Russian arms! We have covered ourselves with shame and we are in debt to our gallant Allies. For not only the Reds but also Germany and Austria are raising their brazen heads once again. God is with us, boys. . . ." He was still speaking when his voice was drowned in a roar of hurrahs. He raised the glass of weak, poorly distilled vodka to his lips and sipped. It gave him no pleasure. He was used to vintage wines. But the thought that he was making a sacrifice to the public good filled him with satisfaction.

"He's a fine one for speeches, your old man! Deputy Miliukov is nothing to him," said Goshka Riabikh to his friend Terentii Galuzin, who sat next to him, in a tipsy voice amidst the loud, drunken voices at the table. "He certainly is a fine fellow! But I suppose it's not for nothing he's working so hard. I expect he'll earn you an exemption from the draft with his speeches."

"Shame on you, Goshka! How can you think such a thing! Get me exempted indeed. I'd like to see him try! I'll get my notification the same day you get yours, and that'll be that. We'll serve in the same unit. They've kicked me out of school, the bastards. Mother's eating her heart out. I suppose I won't get a commission now. . . . As for Father, he certainly knows how to make a speech. He hits it off every time. And the extraordinary thing is, it's a natural gift he has. He's had no formal education."

"Have you heard about Sanka Pafnutkin?"

"Yes. Is it really such a terrible disease?"

"Incurable. He'll end up with it in his spine. It's his own fault. We warned him not to go. You have to be very careful whom you get mixed up with."

"What will happen to him now?"

"It's tragic. He wanted to shoot himself. He's been called up, he's having his medical now in Ermolaï. I suppose they'll take him. He said he'd join the partisans—'to avenge the ills of society,' he said."

"You know, Goshka, you talk about infectious diseases, but if you don't go to them you might get another disease."

"I know what you mean. I suppose you know it from personal experience. But that isn't a disease, it's a secret vice."

"I'll punch your nose for saying things like that, Goshka. That's a nice way to talk to a friend, you rotten liar!"

"Calm down, it was only a joke. What I wanted to tell you was this—I went to Pazhinsk for Easter, and there was a visiting lecturer there, an anarchist, very interesting he was. He talked about the Liberation of the Personality. I liked that, it was good stuff. I'll join the anarchists, damned if I won't. There's an inner force in us, he said. Sex, he said, and character are the manifestations of animal electricity. How do you like that? A genius, he was. . . . But I'm pretty loaded. People bawling their heads off all around, it's enough to deafen a man. I can't stand it any longer, so shut up, Terioshka, dry up, I tell you."

"What you were saying about that electric force—I've heard about that. I was thinking of ordering an electric truss from Petersburg—cash on delivery—I saw it in an advertisement. 'To increase your vigor,' it said. But then there was another revolution, so there were other things to think about."

Terentii did not finish his sentence. The roar of drunken voices was drowned by a loud, rumbling explosion not far away. For a moment the din at the table stopped. Then it broke out much louder and more confused. Some people jumped up from their seats, and those who were least unsteady remained on their feet. Others tried to stagger away but slumped under the table and at once began to snore. Women screamed. There was a general uproar.

Vlas Pakhomovich stood looking around for the culprit. At first he thought that the rumble had come from somewhere in the village, perhaps even from somewhere quite close to the tables. The veins in his neck stood out, his face went purple, and he bawled: "Who is the Judas in our ranks? Who has committed this outrage? Who's been throwing hand grenades around? I'll throttle him with my own hands, the reptile, even if it's my own son. Citizens, we will not allow anyone to play such jokes on us. We must cordon off the village. We'll find the provocateur, we won't let him get away."

At first they listened to him, then their attention was distracted by a pillar of black smoke slowly rising up into the sky from the county office building in Maly Ermolaï, and they all rushed to the edge of the ravine to see what was happening in the valley.

The building was on fire. Several recruits—one of them bare-

foot and naked except for his trousers—ran out of the building
with Colonel Strese and the other officers of the draft board.
Mounted Cossacks and militiamen, leaning low out of their saddles and swinging their nagaikas, their horses writhing under
them like snakes, galloped back and forth through the village,
hunting for someone. Many people were running up the road
to Kuteiny, pursued by the urgent flurry of the church bells ringing the alarm.

Event followed event with terrifying speed. At dusk Colonel
Strese, apparently convinced that his quarry had left Ermolaï,
rode up with his Cossacks to Kuteiny, surrounded the village
with guards, and began to search every house and every farm.

Half the recruits were by now dead drunk. They had stayed
on at the party and were snoring slumped on the ground or with
their heads on the tables. By the time it became known that the
militia were in the village it was already dark.

Several young men took to their heels, made their way
through back yards to the nearest barn, and, kicking and jostling
each other, crawled underneath the floor through a narrow opening at the bottom of the wall. In the dark and the commotion
they had not been able to make out whose barn it was, but now,
judging by the smell of fish and kerosene, it seemed to be one
used as a warehouse by the village shop.

The young men had nothing on their conscience and it was
foolish of them to hide; most of them had merely run away on
the spur of the moment, because they were drunk and had lost
their heads. A few, however, had kept company that now seemed
to them compromising and might, they were afraid, lead to their
undoing if it were known. It was true that their friends were
nothing worse than hooligans, but you never knew. They knew
that everything had a political angle in those days. Hooliganism
was considered a sign of black reaction in the Soviet zone, while
in the White zone it was regarded as Bolshevism.

They found that they were not alone in the barn; others had
got in before them. The space between the ground and the floor
was crammed with people from both villages. Those from Kuteiny were dead drunk. Some were snoring and grinding their
teeth and moaning in their sleep, and others were being sick. It
was pitch-dark and airless, and the stench was terrible. To con-

ceal their hide-out, those who had come last had plugged the
opening through which they had crowded with stones and earth.
After a time the snores and grunts ceased. There was complete
silence. The drunks had settled down to sleep quietly. Only in
one corner was there an urgent, persistent whispering, where
Terentii and Goshka huddled in panic with Koska Nekhvalenykh, a quarrelsome, heavy-handed bully from Ermolaï.

"Not so loud," Koska was saying. "You'll give us all away, you
devil. Can't you hear—Strese's crowd are prowling up and
down. They've been to the end of the street, now they're coming
back. There they are. Don't breathe or I'll strangle you. . . .
Lucky for you they've gone by. . . . What the devil did you
have to come here for? What did you have to hide for, block-
head? Who on earth would have laid a finger on you?"

"I heard Goshka yelling 'Hide,' so I crawled in here."

"Goshka's got good reason to hide. His whole family is in
trouble, they're all under suspicion. They've got relatives working at the railway yards in Khodatskoie, that's why. . . . Don't
fidget, keep still, you fool. People have been throwing up and
crapping all over the place; if you move you'll get the mess all
over us. Can't you smell the stink? Do you know why Strese is
racing around the village? He's looking for people from outside,
from Pazhinsk, that's what he's doing."

"How did all this happen, Koska? How did it all begin?"

"Sanka started it—Sanka Pafnutkin. We were all at the recruiting office, lined up naked waiting for the doctor. When
Sanka's turn came he wouldn't get undressed. He was a bit
drunk when he came into the office. The clerk told him politely
to take his clothes off, even saying 'you' to him. Sanka snapped
his head off. 'I won't undress,' he says, 'I won't show my private
parts to everybody.' As if he were ashamed. And then he sidles
up to the clerk and hits him in the jaw. And then, believe it or
not, before you could so much as blink, Sanka bends down,
grabs the office table by the leg, and turns it over. Bang it goes
on the floor with everything that's on it, inkstand and army lists
and all! Then Strese comes in shouting: 'I'm not putting up with
hooligans. I'm not having any bloodless revolution here. I'll
teach you to be disrespectful to the law in an official place.
Who's the ringleader?' "

"Sanka yells: 'Grab your things, comrades. We're in for it,' and he goes to the window and puts his fist through it. I pick up my things and run after him, putting them on as I run. Out he runs into the street and goes like the wind. I went after him, and so did one or two others. We all ran as fast as our legs would carry us, and they came after us yelling and shouting. But if you ask me what it's all about—nobody can make head or tail of it."

"But what about the bomb?"

"What about it?"

"Well, who threw it? The bomb or the grenade or whatever it was."

"My God! You don't think we did?"

"Who did, then?"

"How should I know? It must have been someone else. Somebody sees all this hullabaloo going on and says to himself: 'Why shouldn't I blow the place up while the racket is going on—they'll suspect the others.' It must have been someone political, one of those politicals from Pazhinsk, the place is full of them. . . . Quiet! Shut up! Can't you hear—Strese's men are coming back. That'll be the end of us. Keep quiet, I tell you."

Voices could be heard approaching from down the street; boots creaked, spurs clanked.

"Don't argue. You can't fool me," came the crisp commanding voice of the Colonel speaking with Petrograd distinctness. "I am certain that there was somebody talking over there."

The Mayor of the village of Ermolaï, an old fisherman, Otviazhistin, said:

"You might have imagined it, Your Excellency. And why should people not be talking in a village? It isn't a churchyard. Maybe they were talking. People aren't dumb animals. Or perhaps the devil was shaking someone in his sleep."

"Come, come! Stop playing the village idiot! The devil indeed! You've all been getting too big for your boots here. You'll get so clever you'll talk yourselves into Bolshevism next."

"Merciful goodness, how can you say that, Your Excellency, Mr. Colonel! Our village yokels are so ignorant, they can't read the prayerbook, what would they want with Bolshevism!"

"That's how you all talk, until you're caught. Have the shop searched from top to bottom. Turn everything inside out, and see that you look under the counters."

"Yes, Your Excellency."

"I want Pafnutkin, Riabikh, and Nekhvalenykh, dead or alive. I don't care if you have to dredge them up from the bottom of the sea. And that Galuzin puppy as well. I don't care how many patriotic speeches his Papa makes. He can talk the hind leg off a donkey, but he won't catch us napping. There's bound to be something fishy when a shopkeeper goes around making speeches. It's suspicious. It's unnatural. We have information that the Galuzins hide political criminals and hold illegal meetings in their house in Krestovozdvizhensk. Get me the brat. I haven't yet decided what to do with him, but if there's anything against him, I won't think twice about stringing him up as a lesson to the others."

The searchers moved away. When they were quite far away, Koska whispered to Terioshka, who was nearly dead with fright:

"Hear that?"

"Yes," he whispered in a changed voice.

"Well, there's only one place for me and you and Sanka and Goshka now; that's the forest. I don't mean we'll have to stay there for good—just until they calm down. Then we'll see, we might come back."

CHAPTER ELEVEN

THE FOREST BROTHERHOOD

1

It was more than a year since Yurii Andreievich had been taken prisoner by the partisans. The limits of his freedom were very ill defined. The place of his captivity was not surrounded by walls; he was not under guard, and no one watched his movements. The partisan force was constantly on the move, and Yurii Andreievich moved with it. It did not remain apart from the local population through whose lands and settlements it passed; it mixed and indeed dissolved in it.

On the surface, this captivity, this dependence, seemed to be nonexistent, as though the doctor were free and merely failed to take advantage of his freedom. His captivity, his dependence, were not different from other forms of compulsion in life, which are often equally invisible and intangible, and seem to be nonexistent and merely a figment of the imagination, a chimera. But although he was not fettered, chained, or watched, the doctor had to submit to his unfreedom, imaginary though it appeared.

Each of his three attempts at escaping from the partisans had ended in capture. He did not suffer any penalties, but he was playing with fire, and he did not try again.

He was favored by the partisan chief, Liberius Mikulitsyn, who liked his company and made him sleep in his tent. Yurii Andreievich found this enforced companionship irksome.

2

During this period, the partisans were constantly moving eastward. At times this movement was part of the general campaign to drive Kolchak from western Siberia; at other times, when the Whites struck from the rear, threatening to encircle the partisans, the same eastward marches turned into retreats. For a long time the doctor could not understand these subtleties.

The partisans moved parallel to the highway and occasionally they made use of it. The villages and small towns along it were Red or White according to the fortunes of war. It was difficult to tell from their outward appearance in whose power they were at any particular moment.

While the peasant army was passing through the villages or small towns, everything else in them sank into insignificance. The houses on both sides of the road seemed to shrink into the ground, and the riders, horses, guns, and big jostling riflemen splashing through the mud loomed higher than the houses.

One day, in one such small town, the doctor was ordered to take over a stock of British medical supplies abandoned by the White officers' unit under General Kappel and now seized by the partisans.

It was a bleak, rainy afternoon with only two colors: wherever the light fell it was white, everywhere else it was black; and the doctor's mood was of the same bleak simplification unsoftened by transitions and half-tones.

The road, completely destroyed by the frequent movements of troops, was nothing but a river of black mud. It could be forded in only a few places, which could be reached by hugging the houses for hundreds of yards. It was in these circumstances, at Pazhinsk, that the doctor met Pelagia Tiagunova, who had been his fellow passenger in the train from Moscow.

She recognized him first. It took him some moments to remember the woman who kept looking at him from across the street, as from the opposite bank of a canal, with an expression suggesting a readiness to greet him if he knew her or to remain anonymous if he did not.

Finally he did remember her, and, together with the picture of the overcrowded freight car, the labor conscripts and their guards, and the woman with a braid over her shoulder, there flashed into his mind an image of his family. Sharp details of the journey crowded in on him, and the faces of his dear ones, whom he missed desperately, rose vividly in his memory.

He nodded to her to go farther up the street to a place where it could be crossed on stones protruding from the mud and, walking in the same direction, went over and greeted her.

She told him many things about the past two years. Reminding him of Vasia, the boy with the handsome, unspoiled face, who had been unlawfully conscripted and who had shared their car, she described her stay with his mother in their village, Veretenniki. She had been very happy among them, but the village treated her as an outsider. She had been falsely accused of having a love affair with Vasia and in the end had had to leave if she were not to be pecked to death. She had settled with her married sister, Olga Galuzina, in Krestovozdvizhensk. Rumors that Prituliev had been seen in the neighborhood had brought her to Pazhinsk. The rumors had proved false and she had found herself stranded in the little town, where she had later got work.

In the meanwhile, misfortune had overtaken her friends. Veretenniki had been raided in reprisal for withholding food supplies. It was said that Vasia's house had been burned down and that a member of his family had perished. And at Krestovozdvizhensk, Pelagia's brother-in-law, Vlas Galuzin, had either been put in jail or been shot, and her nephew had vanished without a trace. Her sister had starved for some time but was now working for her keep in the village of Zvonarskaia as a servant in a family of peasants who were related to her.

It so happened that Tiagunova had a job as assistant at the Pazhinsk pharmacy, whose stock the doctor was about to requisition. All the pharmacist's dependents, including herself, were faced with ruin by this measure. But the doctor was powerless to call it off. Tiagunova was present at the taking over of the stock.

The doctor's cart pulled up at the back of the shop. Sacks, cases, and bottles packed in wickerware were carried out.

The employees watched the operation dejectedly, and their feelings seemed to infect the pharmacist's thin, mangy mare watching sadly from her stable. The rainy day was drawing to its close. The sky cleared a little. Hemmed in by the clouds, the setting sun peered out and splashed the yard with dark bronze rays, casting a sinister glow on the puddles of liquid manure.

The wind did not stir them; the muddy slops were too heavy.
But the rain water on the road rippled and glistened with cin-
nabar reflections.

The troops moved on along the street, walking or riding
around the deeper pools. The requisitioned supplies were found
to contain a whole jar of cocaine, to which the partisan chief
had recently become addicted.

3

The doctor was up to his neck in work. In winter there was
typhus and in summer dysentery, and on top of all that there
were the wounded, whose numbers kept increasing now that
the fighting was renewed.

In spite of setbacks and frequent retreats, the ranks of the
partisans were continually swollen by new insurgents from
the settlements through which the peasant hordes passed and
by deserters from the enemy. In the eighteen months the doctor
had spent with the partisans, their army had increased tenfold,
actually reaching the number of which Liberius Averkievich had
boasted at the underground meeting at Krestovozdvizhensk.

Yurii Andreievich had several newly appointed medics and
two chief assistants, both former prisoners of war—Kerenyi Lajos,
a Hungarian Communist who had been a doctor in the Austrian
army, and the Croat, Angelar, who had had some medical
training. With the former, Yurii Andreievich spoke in German;
the latter more or less understood Russian.

4

According to the Red Cross International Convention, the army
medical personnel must not take part in the military operations
of the belligerents. But on one occasion the doctor was forced
to break this rule. He was in the field when an engagement
began and he had to share the fate of the combatants and shoot
in self-defense.

The front line, where he was caught by enemy fire, was at

the edge of a forest. He threw himself down on the ground next to the unit's telephonist. The forest was at their back, in front of them was a field, and across this open, undefended space the Whites were attacking.

The Whites were now close enough for the doctor to see their faces. They were boys, recent volunteers from the civilian population of the capitals, and older men mobilized from the reserve. The tone was set by the youngsters, first-year students from the universities and last-year students from gymnasiums.

None of them were known to the doctor, yet half the faces looked familiar. Some of them reminded him of former classmates and he wondered if they were their younger brothers; others he felt he had noticed in a theater crowd or in the street in years gone by. Their expressive, handsome faces seemed to belong to people of his own kind.

Responding to duty as they understood it, they displayed enthusiasm and a reckless courage that was entirely out of place. Advancing in extended formation and excelling the parade ground smartness of the Imperial Guards, they walked defiantly upright, neither running nor throwing themselves to the ground, ignoring the irregularities of the terrain behind which they might easily have taken cover. The bullets of the partisans mowed them down.

In the middle of the wide, bare field there was a dead tree, blasted by lightning or charred by fire, or scorched and splintered in the course of some earlier battles. Each of the advancing volunteers glanced at it, fighting the temptation to stop behind it for shelter and a surer aim, then, casting the thought aside, walked on.

The partisans had a limited supply of cartridges and were under orders to fire only at short range and at clearly visible targets.

Yurii Andreievich had no rifle; he lay on the grass watching the course of the engagement. All his sympathies were on the side of these heroically dying children. With all his heart he wished them success. They belonged to families who were probably akin to him in spirit, in education, in moral discipline and values.

It occurred to him to run out into the field and give himself up, thus obtaining his release. But that was dangerous, too dangerous. While he was running with his arms raised above his head he could be shot down from both sides, struck in the breast and in the back—by the partisans in punishment for his betrayal and by the Whites in misunderstanding of his motives. He knew this kind of situation, he had been in it before, he had considered all the possibilities of such escape plans and had rejected them as unfeasible. So resigning himself to his divided feelings, he lay on his belly on the grass, his face toward the clearing, and watched, unarmed, the course of the battle.

But to look on inactively while the mortal struggle raged all around was impossible, it was beyond human strength. It was not a question of loyalty to the side that held him captive or of defending his own life, but of submitting to the order of events, to the laws governing what went on around him. To remain an outsider was against the rules. You had to do what everyone was doing. A battle was going on. He and his comrades were being shot at. He had to shoot back.

So when the telephonist at his side jerked convulsively and then lay still, he crept over to him, took his cartridge bag and rifle, and, going back to his place, emptied the gun, shot after shot.

But as pity prevented him from aiming at the young men whom he admired and with whom he sympathized, and simply to shoot into the air would be too silly, he fired at the blasted tree, choosing those moments when there was no one between his sights and his target. He followed his own technique.

Setting the sights and gradually improving his aim as he pressed the trigger slowly and not all the way down, as if not in fact intending to release the bullet, so that in the end the shot went off of itself and as it were unexpectedly, he fired with the precision of old habit at the dead wood of the lower branches, lopping them off and scattering them around the tree.

But alas!—however carefully he tried to avoid hitting anyone, every now and then a young attacker would move into his firing line at the crucial moment. Two of them he wounded, and one who fell near the tree seemed to have lost his life.

At last the White command, convinced of the futility of the attack, ordered a retreat.

The partisans were few. Part of their main force was on a march and others had engaged a larger enemy detachment some way off. Not to disclose their weakness, they refrained from pursuing the retreating Whites.

Angelar joined the doctor in the clearing with two medics carrying stretchers. Telling him to attend to the wounded, the doctor bent over the telephonist in the vague hope that he might still be breathing and could be revived. But when he undid his shirt and felt his heart, he found that it had stopped.

An amulet hung by a silk cord from the dead man's neck. The doctor took it off. It contained a sheet of paper, worn and rotted at the folds, sewn into a piece of cloth.

Written on the paper, which almost fell apart in the doctor's fingers when he unfolded it, were excerpts from the Ninety-first Psalm with such changes in the wording as often creep into popular prayers through much repetition, making them deviate increasingly from the original. The Church Slavonic text was transliterated into Russian script.

The words of the psalm, "He that dwelleth in the secret place of the Most High," had become the title, "Dwell High." The verse "Thou shalt not be afraid for the terror by night nor for the arrow that flieth by day" was changed into the exhortation: "Do not be afraid of the arrows of flying war." Where the psalm says: "He hath known my name," the paper said: "He postpones my name," and "I will be with him in trouble: I will deliver him" was garbled into "I will relieve him from darkness."

The text was believed to be miraculous and a protection against bullets. It had been worn as a talisman by soldiers in the last imperialist war. Decades later prisoners were to sew it into their clothes and mutter its words in jail when they were summoned at night for interrogation.

Leaving the telephonist, Yurii Andreievich went out into the field to the young White Guardsman whom he had killed. The boy's handsome face bore the marks of innocence and of all-forgiving suffering. "Why did I kill him?" thought the doctor.

He undid the boy's coat and opened it. Some careful hand—probably his mother's—had embroidered his name and surname, Seriozha Rantsevich, in carefully traced cursive letters on the lining. From the opening of Seriozha's shirt there slipped out and hung suspended by a chain a cross, a locket, and some other small flat gold case, rather like a snuffbox, dented as if a nail had been driven into it. A paper fell out. The doctor unfolded it and could not believe his eyes. It was the same Ninety-first Psalm but this time printed in its full and original Slavonic text.

At this moment Seriozha groaned and stirred. He was alive. It appeared afterward that he had only been stunned as the result of a slight internal injury. The bullet had been stopped by his mother's amulet and this had saved him. But what was to be done with this unconscious man now?

It was a time when savagery was at its height. Prisoners did not reach headquarters alive and enemy wounded were knifed in the field.

In the existing state of the partisan force, with its high turnover of deserters to and from the enemy, it was possible, if the strictest secrecy were kept, to pass Rantsevich off as a recently enlisted ally.

Yurii Andreievich took off the outer clothing of the dead telephonist and, with the help of Angelar, in whom he confided, exchanged it for that of the boy.

He and Angelar nursed Seriozha back to health. When he was well they released him, although he did not conceal from them that he meant to go back to Kolchak's army and continue fighting the Reds.

5

In the autumn the partisans took up quarters in Fox's Thicket, a small wood on a steep hill with a swift stream foaming around three sides of it and biting into the shores.

The Whites had wintered in it the year before and had dug themselves in with the help of the neighboring villagers, but they had left in the spring without destroying their fortifications. Now their dugouts and communication trenches were used by the partisans.

The doctor shared a dugout with Liberius Mikulitsyn, who had kept him awake by chattering for two nights running.

"I wonder what my esteemed parent, my respected Papa, is doing at this moment."

"God, how I hate this buffoonery," the doctor thought, with a sigh. "And yet he's the living image of his father."

"Judging from our previous talks, you got to know him quite well. You seem to have formed a not unfavorable opinion of him. What can you say on the subject, my dear sir?"

"Liberius Averkievich, tomorrow we have the pre-election meeting. And there is the trial of the medics who have been brewing vodka coming up—Lajos and I have still got to go through the evidence. I have to see him tomorrow for that purpose. And I haven't slept for two nights. Can't we put this conversation off? I'm dead tired."

"Well, anyway, just tell me what you think of the old bird."

"To begin with, your father is quite young. I don't know why you refer to him that way. Well, all right, I'll tell you. As I've often said to you, I am very bad at sorting out the various shades of socialism, and I can't see much difference between Bolsheviks and other socialists. Your father is one of those to whom Russia owes its recent disorders and disturbances. He is a revolutionary type, a revolutionary character. Like yourself, he represents the principle of ferment in Russian life."

"Is that meant as praise or blame?"

"Once again, I beg you to put off this discussion to a more convenient time. And I must really draw your attention to your excessive consumption of cocaine. You have been willfully depleting the stock of which I am in charge. You know perfectly well that it is needed for other purposes, as well as that it is a poison and I am responsible for your health."

"You cut the study group again last night. You have an atrophied social sense, just like an illiterate peasant woman or a bourgeois diehard. And yet you are a doctor, you are well read, I believe you even write. How do you explain it?"

"I don't. Apparently it can't be helped. You should be sorry for me."

"Why the mock modesty? If instead of using that sarcastic tone you took the trouble to find out what we do in our classes, you wouldn't be so supercilious."

"Heavens, Liberius Averkievich. I'm not being supercilious. I have the utmost respect for your educational work. I've read the discussion notes you circulate. I know your ideas on the moral improvement of the soldier, they're quite excellent. All you say about what the soldier's attitude should be to the people's army, to his fellows, to the weak, the helpless, to women, and about honor and chastity—it's almost the teaching of the Dukhobors. All that kind of Tolstoyism I know by heart. My own adolescence was full of those aspirations toward a better life. How could I laugh at such things?

"But, first, the idea of social betterment as it is understood since the October revolution doesn't fill me with enthusiasm. Second, it is so far from being put into practice, and the mere talk about it has cost such a sea of blood, that I'm not sure that the end justifies the means. And last—and this is the main thing —when I hear people speak of reshaping life it makes me lose my self-control and I fall into despair.

"Reshaping life! People who can say that have never understood a thing about life—they have never felt its breath, its heartbeat—however much they have seen or done. They look on it as a lump of raw material that needs to be processed by them, to be ennobled by their touch. But life is never a material, a substance to be molded. If you want to know, life is the principle of self-renewal, it is constantly renewing and remaking and changing and transfiguring itself, it is infinitely beyond your or my obtuse theories about it."

"And yet, you know, if you came to our meetings, if you kept in touch with our splendid, our magnificent people, you wouldn't feel half so low. You wouldn't suffer from this melancholia. I know what it comes from. You see us being beaten and you can't see a ray of hope ahead. But one should never panic, my friend. I could tell you much worse things—to do with me personally, not to be made public for the moment—and yet I don't lose my head. Our setbacks are purely temporary, Kolchak is bound to lose in the end. You mark my words. You'll see, we'll win in the long run. So cheer up!"

"It's unspeakable," thought the doctor. "How can anyone be so dense, so childish! I spend my time dinning into him that our ideas are diametrically opposed, he has captured me by force, he is keeping me against my will, and yet he imagines that his setbacks fill me with dismay and that his hopes can cheer me up! How can anyone be as blind as this? For him the fate of the universe is less important than the victory of the revolution."

Yurii Andreievich said nothing, merely shrugging his shoulders and making no secret of his almost uncontrollable exasperation at Liberius's naïveté. Nor did this escape Liberius's notice.

"You are angry, Jupiter, therefore you must be wrong," he said.

"Do, for God's sake, understand once and for all that none of this means anything to me. 'Jupiter' and 'Never panic' and 'Anyone who says A must say B' and 'The Moor has done his work, the Moor can go'—none of these clichés, these vulgar commonplaces, appeal to me. I'll say A but I won't say B—whatever you do. I'll admit that you are Russia's liberators, the shining lights, that without you it would be lost, sunk in misery and ignorance, and I still don't give a damn for any of you, I don't like you and you can all go to the devil.

"The people you worship go in for proverbs, but they've forgotten one proverb—'You can lead a horse to water but you can't make it drink'—and they've got into the habit of liberating and of showering benefits on just those people who haven't asked for them. I suppose you think I can't imagine anything in the world more pleasant than your camp and your company. I suppose I have to bless you for keeping me a prisoner and thank you for liberating me from my wife, my son, my home, my work, from everything I hold dear and that makes life worth living for me!

"There is a rumor going around that some unknown force—not Russian—has raided and sacked Varykino. Kamennodvorsky doesn't deny it. They say your people and mine managed to escape. Apparently some sort of mythical slit-eyed warriors in padded coats and fur hats crossed the Rynva in a terrible frost, and calmly shot every living soul in the place and vanished as mysteriously as they had come. Do you know anything about it? Is it true?"

"Nonsense. All lies. Groundless rumors."

"If you are as kind and generous as you claim to be when you lecture on the moral improvement of the soldiers, then let me go. I'll go and look for my family—I don't know where they are, I don't even know whether they are alive or dead. And if you won't do that, then shut up, for heaven's sake, and leave me alone, because I am not interested in anything else and I won't answer for myself if you go on. Anyway, the devil take it, haven't I the right to go to sleep?"

Yurii Andreievich lay down flat on his bunk, his face in his pillow, doing his utmost not to listen to Liberius justifying himself and comforting him once more with the prospect of a final victory over the Whites by the spring. The civil war would be over, there would be peace, liberty, and prosperity, and no one would dare to detain the doctor a moment longer. But until then he must be patient. After all they had gone through, and all the sacrifices they had made, and all that time they had been waiting, a few months mattered little, and anyhow, where could the doctor go at present? For his own good he must be prevented from going anywhere alone.

"Just like a phonograph record, the devil!" Yurii Andreievich raged in silent indignation. "He can't stop. Why isn't he ashamed of chewing on the same cud all these years? How can he go on listening to the sound of his own voice, the wretched dope-fiend? Day and night he goes on. God, how I hate him! As God is my witness, I'll murder him someday!

"Tonia, my darling, my poor child! Where are you? Are you alive? Dear Lord, she was to have her baby long ago. How did she get through the confinement? Have we got a son or a daughter? My dear ones, what is happening to all of you? Tonia, you are my everlasting reproach. Lara, I daren't speak your name for fear of gasping out my life. O God! God!—And that loathsome, unfeeling brute is still talking! One day he'll go too far and I'll kill him, I'll kill him."

6

The Indian summer was over. It was a clear, golden autumn day. At the western end of Fox's Thicket the wooden turret of a blockhouse built by the Whites showed above the ground. Here Yurii Andreievich had arranged to meet Dr. Lajos, to discuss various service matters. He arrived on time and, waiting for his friend, strolled along the edge of the crumbling earthworks, climbed into the watchtower, and looked out of the slits in front of the now empty machine-gun nests at the wooded distance beyond the river.

The autumn had already clearly marked the frontiers between the coniferous and the deciduous trees. Between the gloomy, bristling walls of almost black pines the leafy thickets shone flame- and wine-colored like medieval towns with painted and gold-roofed palaces built of the timber cut down in the thickness of the forest.

The earth at the doctor's feet, inside the trench and in the ruts of the forest road, was hard with ground frost and heaped with small dry willow leaves, curled up in little scrolls. The autumn smelled of these brown, bitter leaves and of many other things. Greedily he breathed in the mixed peppery smell of frostbitten apples, bitter dry twigs, sweetish damp earth, and the blue September mist that smoked like the fumes of a recently extinguished fire.

He did not hear Lajos come up behind him.

"How are you, colleague?" Lajos said in German. They discussed their business.

"There are three points. First, the court-martial of the vodka brewers; second, the reorganization of the field ambulance and the pharmacy; and third, my proposal for the treatment of mental illnesses. I don't know whether you agree with me, my dear Lajos, but from what I observe we are going mad, and modern forms of insanity spread like an epidemic.

"It's a very interesting question. I'll come to it in a moment. But first I'd like to mention something else. There is unrest in the camp. There is sympathy with the vodka brewers. Moreover, the men are worried about their families who are fleeing from the Whites. As you know, there's a convoy coming, with wives, children, and old people, and many of the partisans have refused to leave the camp until it comes."

"I know. We'll have to wait for them."

"And all this on the eve of the election of a joint commander for our unit and several others, so far independent of us. I think the only candidate is Comrade Liberius. But some of the young people are putting Vdovichenko forward. He is supported by a group, alien to us in spirit, connected with the vodka brewers—sons of shopkeepers and kulaks, deserters from Kolchak. They are particularly restless."

"What do you think will happen to the vodka brewers?"

"I think they will be sentenced to be shot and be reprieved."

"Well, let's get down to business. First, the field ambulance."

"All right. But I must tell you that I am not surprised at your suggestion for preventive psychiatry. I believe in it myself. We are faced with the rise and spread of a form of psychic illness that is typical of our time and is directly related to the contemporary upheavals. We have a case of it in the camp—Pamphil Palykh, a former private in the Tsarist army with a highly developed class instinct and devoted to the revolution. The cause of his trouble is precisely his anxiety for his family in the event of his being killed and of their falling into the hands of the Whites and being made to answer for him. It's a very complex case. I believe his family is one of those who are coming in the convoy. I don't know enough Russian to question him properly. You could find out from Angelar or Kamennodvorsky. He ought to be examined."

"I know Palykh very well. At one time we often came across each other in the army soviet. Swarthy and cruel with a low forehead. I can't think what good you find in him. He was always for extreme measures, harshness, execution. I've always found him repellent. All right, I'll see what I can do about it."

7

It was a clear, sunny day; the weather had been still and dry for a whole week.

The usual rumble of noise hung over the large camp, like the distant roar of the sea. There were footsteps, voices, axes chopping wood, the ringing of anvils, the neighing of horses, the barking of dogs, the crowing of cocks. Crowds of sunburned, smiling men with shining white teeth moved through the forest. Those who knew the doctor nodded to him, others passed him by without a greeting.

The men had refused to leave Fox's Thicket until their families had caught up with them, but now the fugitives were expected shortly and preparations for the move were being made. Things were being cleaned and mended, crates nailed down, carts counted and checked over.

There was a large clearing in the middle of the wood where meetings were often held. It was a sort of mound or barrow on which the grass had been trodden down. A general meeting had been called that day for an important announcement.

Many of the trees in the forest had not yet turned; in its depths they were still fresh and green. The afternoon sun was setting behind the forest, piercing it with its rays, and the leaves, letting them through, glowed green like transparent bottle glass.

In an open space outside his tent Kamennodvorsky, the chief liaison officer, was burning papers, discarded rubbish from General Kappel's records that had fallen into his hands, as well as papers from his own partisan files. The fire with the setting sun behind it was as transparent as the leaves; the flames were invisible and only the waves of shimmering heat showed that something was burning.

Here and there the woods were brilliant with ripe berries—bright tassels of lady's smock, brick-red alderberries, and clusters of viburnum, shimmering from white to purple. Whirring their glassy wings, dragonflies as transparent as the flames and the leaves sailed slowly through the air.

Ever since his childhood Yurii Andreievich had been fond of woods seen at evening against the setting sun. At such moments he felt as if he too were being pierced by shafts of light. It was as though the gift of the living spirit were streaming into his breast, piercing his being and coming out at his shoulders like a pair of wings. The archetype that is formed in every child for life and seems for ever after to be his inward face, his personality, awoke in him in its full primordial strength, and compelled nature, the forest, the afterglow, and everything else visible to be transfigured into a similarly primordial and all-embracing likeness of a girl. Closing his eyes, "Lara," he whispered and thought, addressing the whole of his life, all God's earth, all the sunlit space spread out before him.

But everyday, current reality was still there, Russia was going through the October revolution, and he was a prisoner of the partisans. Absent-mindedly he went up to Kamennodvorsky's bonfire.

"Burning your records? Not finished yet?"

"There's enough of this stuff to burn for days."

The doctor kicked a heap of papers with his foot. It was the White staff headquarters' correspondence. It occurred to him that he might come across some mention of Rantsevich. But all he saw were boring, out-of-date communiqués in code. He kicked another heap. It proved to be an equally dull collection of minutes of partisan meetings. A paper on top of the pile said: "Extra urgent. Re furloughs. Re-election of members of draft board. Current business. In view of the fact that the charges against the schoolmistress of the village Ignatodvortsy have not been substantiated, the army soviet proposes . . ."

Kamennodvorsky took a piece of paper from his pocket and handed it to the doctor.

"Here are your marching orders for the medical unit. The convoy with the partisans' families is quite near and the dissensions inside the camp will be settled by this evening, so we can expect to move any day now."

The doctor glanced at the paper and groaned:

"But you're giving me less transportation than last time and there are all those extra wounded. Those who can will have to walk; there are only a few of these. What am I to do with the stretcher cases? And the stores and the bedding and the equipment?"

"You'll have to manage somehow. We must adjust ourselves to circumstances. Now another thing. It's a request from all of us. Will you have a look at a comrade of ours—tried, tested, devoted to the cause and a splendid soldier. There's something wrong with him."

"Palykh? Lajos told me."

"Yes. Go to see him. Examine him."

"He's a mental case?"

"I suppose so. He says he sees will-o'-the-wisps. Hallucinations, evidently. Insomnia. Headaches."

"All right, I might as well go and see him now, since I'm free at the moment. When does the meeting begin?"

"I think they're coming now. But why bother? As you see, I'm not going either. They'll manage without us."

"Then I'll go and see Pamphil. Though I can hardly keep my eyes open, I'm so sleepy. Liberius Averkievich likes to philosophize at night, and he's worn me out with his talk. Where do I find Pamphil?"

"You know the birch grove beyond the rubbish pit?"

"Yes, I think I know it."

"You'll find some commanders' tents in a clearing. We've put one of them at Pamphil's disposal. He's got his family coming, they're in the convoy. That's where you'll find him—in one of the tents—he's got battalion commander status as a reward for revolutionary merit."

8

On his way to see Pamphil, the doctor was overcome with fatigue. It was the cumulative effect of several sleepless nights. He could go back to his dugout and lie down, but he was afraid of staying there, for at any moment Liberius might come in and disturb him. He stopped in a glade scattered with golden leaves from the surrounding woods. They lay in a checkerboard pattern, and so did the low rays of the sun falling on their golden carpet. This double, crisscross brightness made your head spin and sent you to sleep like small print or a monotonous murmur.

The doctor lay down on the silkily rustling leaves, his head on his arm and his arm on a pillow of moss at the foot of a tree. He dozed off at once. The dazzle of light and shadow that had put him to sleep now covered him with its patchwork so that his body, stretched on the ground, was indistinguishable from the kaleidoscopic brilliance of the rays and leaves, invisible as if he had put on a magic cap.

But soon the very force of his desire and need for sleep aroused him. Direct causes operate only within certain limits; beyond them they produce the opposite effect. His wakeful consciousness, not finding any rest, worked feverishly of its own momentum. Thoughts whirled and wheeled inside his head, his mind was knocking like a faulty engine. This inner confusion worried and exasperated him. "That swine Liberius," he thought indignantly. "As if there weren't enough things in the world to drive people mad, he has to take a sane man and turn him deliberately into a neurotic by keeping him a prisoner and boring him with his friendship and chatter. Someday I'll kill him."

Folding and unfolding like a scrap of colored stuff, a brown speckled butterfly flew across the sunny side of the clearing. The doctor watched it sleepily. Choosing a background with a color like its own, it settled on the brown speckled bark of a pine and became indistinguishable from it, vanishing as completely as Yurii Andreievich, hidden by the play of light and shadow, had vanished.

His mind turned to its accustomed round of thoughts—he had touched on them indirectly in many medical works—concerning will and purposefulness as superior forms of adaptation; mimicry and protective coloring; the survival of the fittest; and the hypothesis that the path of natural selection is the very path leading to the formation and emergence of consciousness. And what was subject? What was object? How was their identity to be defined? In the doctor's reflections, Darwin was next to Schelling, the butterfly that had just flown by next to modern painting and Impressionist art. He thought of creation, the creature, creativeness, the instincts of creation and simulation.

Once again he fell asleep but woke up a moment later. A soft, muffled conversation near by had disturbed him. The few words he overheard were enough to tell him that it concerned some secret and illicit plan. He had not been seen, the conspirators had no suspicion of his presence. The slightest movement that would betray it now might cost him his life. Yurii Andreievich remained quiet and listened.

Some of the voices he recognized. They were those of the scum of the partisans, hangers-on such as Goshka, Sanka, Koska, and their usual follower Terentii Galuzin, young good-for-nothings who were at the bottom of every kind of outrage and disorder. Zakhar Gorazdykh was also there, an even more sinister personality who was mixed up in the affair of the vodka brewing but was not being prosecuted just now because he had denounced the chief offenders. What surprised Yurii Andreievich was the presence of Sivobluy, a partisan of the crack "Silver Company" who was one of the commander's bodyguards. In keeping with a tradition going back to Stenka Razin and Pugachev, this favorite, known to be in the confidence of the chief, was nicknamed "The Hetman's Ear." And yet he too seemed to be in the conspiracy.

The plotters were negotiating with delegates from the advanced positions of the enemy. The delegates were inaudible, so softly did they speak to the traitors, and Yurii Andreievich could only guess that they were speaking when an occasional silence seemed to interrupt the whispering.

Zakhar Gorazdykh, the drunkard, was doing most of the talking, cursing every other moment in his hoarse, wheezing voice. He seemed to be the ringleader.

"Now, you others, listen. The chief thing is, we've got to keep it quiet. If anybody talks—you see this knife?—I'll rip his guts. Is that clear? Now you know as well as I do—we're stuck. There's no way out for us. We've got to earn our pardon. We've got to work such a trick as nobody's seen before. They want him taken alive. Now they say their boss Gulevoy is coming." (They corrected him—"Galiullin"—but he did not catch the name and said "General Galeiev.") "That's our chance. There won't be another like it. Here're their delegates. They'll tell you all about it. They say we've got to take him alive. Now you tell them, you others."

Now the others, the delegates, began to speak. Yurii Andreievich could not catch a word, but from the length of the pause he judged that they explained the proposal in detail. Then Gorazdykh spoke again.

"Hear that, boys? You see what a nice fellow he is. Why should we pay for him? He isn't even a man—he's a half-wit of some sort, a monk or a hermit. You stop grinning, Terioshka. I'll give you something to grin about, you stupid ass. I wasn't talking about you. I'm telling you—he's a hermit, that's what he is. Let him have his way and he'll turn you all into monks—eunuchs. What does he tell you? No cursing, no getting drunk, all this stuff about women. How can you live like that? Tonight we'll get him down to the ford. I'll see that he comes. Then we'll all fall on him together. It won't be hard. That's nothing. What's difficult is that they want him alive. Tie him up, they say. Well, if it doesn't work out that way I'll deal with him myself, I'll finish him off with my own hands. They'll send their people along to help."

He went on explaining the plan, but gradually they moved away and the doctor ceased to hear them.

"That's Liberius they're plotting to hand over to the Whites or to kill, the swine," he thought with horror and indignation, forgetting how often he had himself wished his tormentor dead. How was it to be prevented? He decided to go back to Kamennodvorsky and tell him of the plot without mentioning any names, and also to warn Liberius.

But when he got back, Kamennodvorsky had gone; only his assistant was keeping an eye on the smoldering fire to prevent its spreading.

The crime did not take place. It was forestalled. The conspiracy, as it turned out, was known. That day the details were disclosed and the plotters seized. Sivobluy had played the role of *agent provocateur*. Yurii Andreievich felt even more disgusted.

9

It was learned that the partisans' families were now within two days' journey of the camp. The partisans were getting ready to welcome them and soon afterwards to move on. Yurii Andreievich went to Pamphil Palykh.

He found him at the entrance to his tent, an ax in his hand. In front of him was a tall heap of birch saplings; he had cut them down but had not yet stripped them. Some had fallen where they stood and, toppling with their whole weight, had dug the sharp ends of their broken branches into the damp ground. Others he had dragged from a short distance and piled on top of the rest. Shuddering and swaying on their springy branches, these trees lay neither on the ground nor close together. It seemed as though with outstretched arms they were fending off Pamphil, who had cut them down, and that their tangled green foliage was barring his way to his tent.

"It's for my dear guests," explained Pamphil. "My wife and children. The tent is too low. And the rain comes through. I've cut these down for joints to make a roof."

"I shouldn't count on their allowing you to have them in your tent, Pamphil. Who has ever heard of civilians, women and children, being allowed to live inside a camp? They'll stay with the wagons somewhere just outside, you'll be able to see them as much as you like in your spare time, but I shouldn't think they'd be allowed to live in your tent. But that isn't what I've come about. They tell me you're getting thin, you can't eat or sleep. Is that true? I must say you look all right. Though you could do with a haircut."

Pamphil was a huge man with black tousled hair and beard and a bumpy forehead that looked double; a thickening of the frontal bone, like a ring or a steel band pressed over his temples, gave him a beetling, glowering look.

When at the beginning of the revolution it had been feared that, as in 1905, the upheaval would be a short-lived episode in the history of the educated upper classes and leave the deeper layers of society untouched, everything possible had been done to spread revolutionary propaganda among the people to upset them, to stir them up and lash them into fury.

In those early days, men like Pamphil Palykh, who needed no encouragement to hate intellectuals, officers, and gentry with a savage hatred, were regarded by enthusiastic left-wing intellectuals as a rare find and greatly valued. Their inhumanity seemed a marvel of class-consciousness, their barbarism a model of proletarian firmness and revolutionary instinct. By such qualities Pamphil had established his fame, and he was held in great esteem by partisan chiefs and Party leaders.

To Yurii Andreievich this gloomy and unsociable giant, soulless and narrow-minded, seemed subnormal, almost a degenerate.

"Come into the tent," said Pamphil.

"No, why? It's pleasanter out in the open. Anyway, I couldn't get in."

"All right. Have it your own way. After all, it is a stinking hole. We can sit on the trees."

They sat down on the springy birch saplings, and Pamphil told the doctor the story of his life. "They say a tale is soon told.

But mine is a long story. I couldn't tell it in three years. I don't know where to begin.

"Well, I'll try. My wife and I, we were young. She looked after the house. I worked in the fields. It wasn't a bad life. We had children. They drafted me into the army. They sent me to the war. Well, the war. What should I tell you about the war? You've seen it, Comrade Doctor. Then the revolution. I saw the light. The soldiers' eyes were opened. Not the Fritzes, who are Germans, were the enemies, but some of our own people. 'Soldiers of the world revolution, down your rifles, go home, get the bourgeois!' And so on. You know it all yourself, Comrade Army Doctor. Well, to go on. Then came the civil war. I joined the partisans. Now I'll have to leave out a lot or I'll never end. After all that, what do I see now, at the present moment? That parasite, he's brought up the two Stavropolsky regiments from the Russian front, and the first Orenburg Cossack as well. I'm not a child am I? Don't I understand? Haven't I served in the army? We're in trouble, Doctor, it's all up with us. What he wants to do, the swine, is to fall on us with all that scum. He wants to surround us.

"But I've got a wife and children. If he comes out on top, how will they get away? They're innocent, of course, they have nothing to do with it, but this won't stop him. He'll tie up my wife with a rope and he'll torture her to death on my account, my wife and my children, he'll break every bone in their bodies, he'll tear them apart. And you ask, why don't I sleep. A man could be made of iron, but a thing like that is to make you lose your mind."

"What an odd fellow you are, Pamphil. I can't make you out. For years you've been away from them, you didn't even know where they were and you didn't worry. Now you're going to see them in a day or two, and instead of being happy about it you act as though it were their funeral."

"That was before, now it's different. He's beating us, the White bastard. Anyway, it isn't me we're talking about. I'll soon be dead. But I can't take my little ones with me into the next world, can I? They'll stay and they'll fall into his dirty paws. He'll squeeze the blood out of them, drop by drop."

"Is that why you see will-o'-the-wisps? I was told you keep seeing things."

"Well, Doctor, I haven't told you everything. I've kept back the most important thing. Now, I'll tell you the whole truth if you want it, I'll say it to your face, but you mustn't hold it against me.

"I've done away with a lot of your kind, there's a lot of officers' blood on my hands. Officers, bourgeois. And it's never worried me. Spilled it like water. Names and numbers all gone out of my head. But there's one little fellow I can't get out of my mind. I killed that youngster and I can't forget it. Why did I have to kill him? He made me laugh, and I killed him for a joke, for nothing, like a fool.

"During the February revolution that was. Under Kerensky. We were having a mutiny. We were near a railway station. We'd left the front. They sent a young fellow, an agitator, to talk us into going back. To fight on to victory. Well, that little cadet came to talk us into being good. Just like a chicken, he was. 'Fight on to victory'—that was his slogan. He got up on a water butt shouting that slogan, the water butt was on the railway platform. He got up there, you see, so as to make his call to battle come from higher up, and suddenly the lid turned upside down under him and he fell right in. Right into the water. You can't think how funny he looked. Made me split my sides laughing! I was holding a rifle. And I was laughing my head off. Couldn't stop. It was just as if he was tickling me. And then, I aimed and fired and killed him on the spot. I can't think how it happened. Just as though somebody had pushed me.

"Well, that's my will-o'-the-wisp. I see that station at night. At the time it was funny, but now I'm sorry."

"Was that at Biriuchi station near the town of Meliuzeievo?"

"Can't remember."

"Were you in the Zybushino rebellion?"

"Can't remember."

"Which front were you at? Was it the western front? Were you in the west?"

"Somewhere like that. It could have been in the west. I can't remember."

CHAPTER TWELVE

THE ROWAN TREE

1

The convoy with the partisans' families, complete with children and belongings, had long been following the main partisan force. After it, behind the wagons, came vast herds of cattle, mainly cows—several thousand of them.

With the arrival of the womenfolk a new figure appeared in the camp. This was Zlydarikha or Kubarikha, a soldier's wife who was a cattle healer, a veterinarian, and also, secretly, a witch. She went about in a little pancake hat cocked on her head and a pea-green Royal Scots Fusiliers overcoat, which formed part of the British equipment supplied to the Supreme Ruler, and she assured everyone that she had made them out of a prisoner's cap and uniform. She said that the Reds had liberated her from the Kezhemsk jail where for some unknown reason Kolchak had kept her.

The partisans had now moved to a new campground. They were supposed to stay there only until the neighborhood had been reconnoitered and suitable winter quarters found. But as a result of unforeseen developments they were to spend the winter there.

This new camp was quite unlike the old one. The forest around it was a dense, impenetrable taiga. On one side, away from the camp and the highway, there was no end to it. In the early days, while the tents were being pitched and Yurii Andreievich had more leisure, he had explored the forest in several directions and found that one could easily get lost in it. Two places had struck him in the course of these excursions and remained in his memory.

One was at the edge of the taiga, just outside the camp. The forest was autumnally bare, so that you could see into it as through an open gate; here a splendid, solitary, rust-colored rowan tree had alone kept its leaves. Growing on a mound that rose above the low, squelchy, hummocky marsh, it reached into the sky holding up the flat round shields of its hard crimson berries against the leaden, late-autumn sky. Small birds with feathers as bright as frosty dawns—bullfinches and tomtits—settled on the rowan tree and picked the largest berries, stretching out their necks and throwing back their heads to swallow them.

There seemed to be a living intimacy between the birds and the tree, as if it had watched them for a long time refusing to do anything, but in the end had had pity on them and given in and fed them like a nurse unbuttoning her blouse to give breast to a baby. "Well, all right, all right," it seemed to be saying with a smile, "eat me, have your fill."

The other place was even more remarkable. This was on a height that fell off steeply on one side. Looking down, you felt that at the bottom of the escarpment there should be something different from what was on top—a stream or a hollow or a wild field overgrown with seedy, uncut grass. But in fact it was a repetition of the same thing, only at a giddy depth, as if the forest had simply sunk to a lower level with all its trees, so that the treetops were now underfoot. There must have been a landslide there at some time.

It was as if the grim, gigantic forest, marching at cloud level, had stumbled, lost its footing, and hurtled down, all in one piece, and would have dropped right through the earth if it had not, by a miracle, saved itself at the last moment—so that there it was now, safe and sound, rustling below.

But what made the high place in the forest remarkable was something else. All along its edge it was locked in by granite boulders standing on end, looking like the flat stones of prehistoric dolmens. When Yurii Andreievich came across this stony platform for the first time, he was ready to swear that it was not of natural origin, that it bore the mark of human hands. It might well have been the site of an ancient pagan shrine, where prayers and sacrifices had once been offered by unknown worshippers.

It was here that the death sentence against eleven ringleaders of the conspiracy and two male nurses condemned for brewing vodka was executed one cold, sullen morning.

Twenty of the most loyal partisans, including a core of the commander's bodyguard, brought the condemned men to the spot. Then the escort closed around them in a semicircle, rifle in hand, and advancing at a quick, jostling pace drove them to the edge of the platform, where there was no way out except over the precipice.

As a result of questioning, long imprisonment, and maltreatment they had lost their human appearance. Black, hairy, and haggard, they were as terrible as ghosts.

They had been disarmed when they were arrested, and it had not even occurred to anyone to search them again before the execution. Such a search would have seemed superfluous and vile, a cruel mockery of men so close to death.

But now, suddenly, Rzhanitsky, a friend of Vdovichenko, who walked beside him and who, like him, was an old anarchist, fired three shots at the guards, aiming at Sivobluy. He was an excellent marksman but his hand shook in his excitement and he missed. Once again, tactfulness and pity for their former comrades kept the guards from falling on him or shooting him down at once for his attempt. Rzhanitsky had three unspent bullets left in his revolver, but maddened by his failure and perhaps, in his agitation, forgetting that they were there, he flung his Browning against the rocks. It went off a fourth time, wounding one of the condemned men, Pachkolia, in the foot.

Pachkolia cried out, clutched his foot, and fell, screaming with pain. The two men nearest him, Pafnutkin and Gorazdykh, raised him and dragged him by the arms, so that he should not be trampled to death by his comrades, who no longer knew what they were doing. Unable to put down his wounded foot, Pachkolia hopped and limped toward the rocky ledge where the doomed men were being driven, and he screamed without stopping. His inhuman shrieks were infectious. As though at a given signal, everyone lost his self-control. An indescribable scene followed. The men swore loudly, begged for mercy, prayed and cursed.

The young Galuzin, who still wore his yellow-braided school cap, removed it, fell on his knees, and, still kneeling, edged backward following the rest of the crowd toward the terrible stones. Bowing repeatedly to the ground before the guards and crying loudly, he chanted, quite beside himself:

"Forgive me, comrades, I'm sorry, I won't do it again, please let me off. Don't kill me. I haven't lived yet. I want to live a little longer, I want to see my mother just once more. Please let me off, comrades, please forgive me. I'll do anything for you. I'll kiss the ground under your feet. Oh, help, help, Mother, I'm done for!"

Someone else, hidden in the crowd, chanted:

"Good comrades, kind comrades! Is this possible? In two wars we fought together! We stood up and fought for the same things! Let us off, comrades, have pity on us. We'll repay your kindness, we'll be grateful to you all our lives, we will prove it to you. Are you deaf, or what? Why don't you answer? Aren't you Christians?"

Others screamed at Sivobluy:

"Judas! Christ-killer! If we are traitors, you are a traitor three times over, you dog, may you be strangled. You killed your lawful Tsar, to whom you took your oath, you swore loyalty to us and you betrayed us. Go ahead, kiss your Forester, that devil, before you betray him! You'll betray him too!"

Even at the edge of the grave Vdovichenko remained true to himself. His head high, his gray hair streaming in the wind, he spoke to Rzhanitsky as one fellow anarchist to another, in a voice loud enough to be heard by all:

"Don't humble yourself! Your protest will not reach them. These new *oprichniki*,[1] these master executioners of the new torture chambers, will never understand you! But don't lose heart. History will tell the truth. Posterity will pillory the Bourbons of the commissarocracy together with their dirty deeds. We die as martyrs for our ideals at the dawn of the world revolution. Long live the revolution of the spirit! Long live world anarchy!"

A volley of twenty shots, discharged at some inaudible command caught only by the riflemen, mowed down half the condemned men, killing most of them outright. The rest were shot

---

[1] *Oprichniki*—security troops of Ivan the Terrible.

down by another salvo. The boy, Terioshka Galuzin, twitched longest, but finally he too lay still.

2

The idea of moving to another place, farther east, for the winter was not given up easily. Patrols were sent out to survey the country beyond the highway, along the Vytsk-Kezhemsk watershed. Liberius was often absent, leaving the doctor to himself.

But it was too late for the partisans to move and they had nowhere to go to. This was the time of their worst setbacks. Shortly before they were finally crushed, the Whites, resolving to destroy the irregular forest units once and for all, had encircled them and were pressing them from every side. The position would have been catastrophic for the partisans had the radius of the encirclement been smaller. They were saved by its size, for the approaching winter made the taiga impenetrable and prevented the enemy from pulling his ring tighter.

To move, however, had become impossible. They could, indeed, have broken through to new positions had any plan offered specific military advantages. But no such definite plan had been worked out. The men were at the end of their tether. The junior officers lost heart and with it their influence over their subordinates. Senior commanders met nightly in council and proposed conflicting solutions. The idea of shifting camp had finally to be abandoned in favor of fortifying the present positions in the heart of the taiga. Their advantage was that the deep snow made them inaccessible, particularly because the Whites were ill supplied with skis. The immediate task was to dig in and lay in large supplies.

Bisiurin, the camp quartermaster, reported an acute shortage of flour and potatoes. Cattle, however, were plentiful and he foresaw that the staple food in winter would be milk and meat.

There was a shortage of winter clothing; many of the partisans went about half dressed. All the dogs in the camp were strangled, and people with experience as furriers were set to making dogskin jackets, to be worn fur side out.

The doctor was denied the use of transportation. The carts

were kept for more important needs. The last time the partisans had moved camp the wounded were carried thirty miles on stretchers.

The only medicines he had left were quinine, Glauber's salts, and iodine. The iodine was in the form of crystals and had to be dissolved in alcohol before it could be used for dressings or operations. The destruction of the vodka still was now regretted, and those of the brewers who had been acquitted at the trial as less guilty than the rest were told to mend it or construct a new one. The manufacture of alcohol was resumed for medical purposes. When this became known in the camp, people exchanged meaningful glances and shook their heads. Drunkenness broke out again, and contributed to the general demoralization.

The alcohol produced was almost 100 proof. At this strength it was suitable for dissolving crystals and also for preparing tincture of quinine, which was used in the treatment of typhus when it reappeared at the onset of the cold weather.

3

At this time the doctor went to see Pamphil and his family. His wife and children had spent the whole of the past summer as fugitives on dusty roads under the open sky. They were thoroughly frightened by the horrors they had gone through, and they anticipated new ones. Their endless wanderings had marked them indelibly. Pamphil's wife, two daughters, and little son had light hair, faded to a flaxen color by the sun, and bristling eyebrows, white against their tanned and weather-beaten faces. But while the children were too young to bear the marks of their experiences, the mother's face had become lifeless. Strain and fear had narrowed her lips to a thread and frozen her dry, regular features in a rigid expression of suffering and defensiveness.

Pamphil was devoted to all of them and loved his children to distraction. He surprised the doctor by his skill in carving toy rabbits, cocks, and bears for them, using a corner of his finely sharpened ax blade.

With the arrival of his family he had cheered up and begun

to recover. But now the news had got about that the presence
of the families was considered bad for discipline, and they were
going to be sent, under proper escort, to winter quarters at some
distance from the camp, which would thus be relieved of its
burden of civilian refugees. There was more talk about this
plan than actual preparation, and the doctor thought it would
never be carried out, but Pamphil's spirits fell and his hallucinations came back.

4

Before winter finally set in, the camp went through a period of
disturbances—anxieties, uncertainties, confused, threatening situations, and a number of weird incidents.

The Whites had completed the encirclement according to
plan. They were headed by Generals Vitsyn, Quadri, and Bassalygo, who were known far and wide for their harshness and
unyielding resolution, and whose names alone terrified the
refugees inside the camp as well as the peaceful population remaining in its native villages at the rear of the encircling troops.

As we have said, the enemy had no means of tightening his
grip, so the partisans had no reason to worry on this account;
on the other hand, it was impossible for them to remain inactive.
They realized that passive acceptance of their plight would
strengthen enemy morale. However safe they were inside their
trap, they had to attempt a sortie, even if only as a military
demonstration.

A strong force was set aside for this purpose and concentrated
against the western arc of the circle. After several days' hard
fighting, the partisans defeated the Whites and broke through
to their rear.

This breach opened a way to the camp in the taiga, and
through it poured a stream of new refugees. Not all of these
were related to the partisans. Terrified by the punitive measures
of the Whites, all the peasants of the surrounding countryside
had fled from their homes and now sought to join the partisans,
whom they regarded as their natural protectors.

But the camp, anxious to get rid of its own dependents, had
no place for newcomers and strangers. Men were sent to meet

the fugitives and to divert them to a village on the river Chilimka. The village was called Dvory ("farms") because of the farmsteads that had grown up around its mill. There it was proposed to settle the refugees for the winter and to send the supplies that were allotted to them.

While these steps were being taken, however, events followed their own course and the camp command could not always cope with them.

The enemy had closed the breach in his positions and the partisan unit that had broken through was now unable to get back into the taiga.

Also, the women refugees were getting out of hand. It was easy to lose one's way in the taiga. The men sent out to turn back the refugees often missed them, and the women flooded into the forest, chopping down trees, building roads and bridges, and achieving prodigies of resourcefulness.

All this was counter to the intentions of the partisan command, working havoc with the plan made by Liberius.

5

That was why he was in such a temper as he stood talking to the trapper, Svirid, near the highway, which came close to the edge of the taiga at this point. Several of his officers stood on the highway, arguing about whether to cut the telegraph line that ran along the road. Liberius would have the final word, but he was deep in conversation with the trapper and kept signalling to the others to wait for him.

Svirid had been deeply shocked by the shooting of Vdovichenko, whose only crime had been that his influence rivalled that of Liberius and brought dissension into the camp. Svirid wished he could leave the partisans and go back to his old, private, independent life. But this was out of the question. He had made his choice, and were he to leave his Forest Brothers now he would be executed as a deserter.

The weather was the worst imaginable. A sharp, scudding wind swept torn, low clouds as black as flying soot before it. Snow would suddenly fall from them with a convulsive, insane haste. In a moment the broad expanse of the earth was covered with a white blanket. The next minute, the white blanket was consumed, melted completely, and the earth emerged as black as coal under the black sky splashed with slanting streaks of distant showers. The earth could not absorb any more water. Then the clouds would part like windows, as though to air the sky, which shimmered with a cold, glassy white brilliance. The stagnant, unabsorbed water on the ground responded by opening the windows of its pools and puddles, shimmering with the same brilliance. The vapors skidded like smoke over the pine woods; their resinous needles were as waterproof as oilcloth. Raindrops were strung on the telegraph wires like beads one next to the other without ever falling.

Svirid was one of those who had been sent to meet the women refugees. He wanted to tell his chief about the things he had seen, about the confusion resulting from conflicting orders, none of which could be carried out, and about the atrocities committed by the weakest elements of the female hordes, the first to succumb to despair. Trudging on foot, loaded with sacks, bundles, and babies, young mothers who had lost their milk, driven out of their minds by the horrors of the journey, abandoned their children, shook the corn out of their sacks onto the ground, and turned back. A quick death, they had decided, was preferable to a slow death by starvation. Better to fall into the clutches of the enemy than to be torn to pieces by some beast in the forest.

Other women, the strongest, were models of courage and selfcontrol, unsurpassed by men. Svirid had many other things to tell his chief. He wanted to warn him of an impending new rebellion, more dangerous than the one that had been put down, but Liberius, by hurrying him, deprived him of the power of speech. Liberius kept interrupting Svirid not only because his friends were calling and waving to him from the highway, but because during the past two weeks he had been given similar warnings time and again, and by now he knew them by heart.

"Give me time, Comrade Chief. I am no good at finding words. They stick in my throat, they choke me. What I say is this, go to the refugee camp and tell those women to stop their nonsense. Otherwise, I ask you, what is this supposed to be—'All against Kolchak!' or a civil war among the women?"

"Get on with it, Svirid. You see I'm wanted. Don't spin it out."

"And now there's that she-devil, Zlydarikha, God only knows what she is. She says: 'Put me down as a woman ventilator to look after the cattle. . . .'"

"Veterinary, you mean."

"That's what I say—a woman ventilator to cure cattle of wind. But she's not looking after cattle now, such a heretic, devil's reverend mother she has turned out to be, she says cows' masses, and turns young refugee wives from their duty. 'You've only yourselves to blame for your miseries,' she says to them. 'That's what comes of hitching up your skirts and running after the Red flag. Don't do it again.'"

"What refugees are you talking about—ours, from the camp, or some other kind?"

"The others, of course. The new ones, the strangers."

"But they had orders to go to Dvory. How have they got here?"

"Dvory! That's a good one. Your Dvory's burned out, mill and all, nothing left of it but cinders. That's what they saw when they came by—not a living thing. Half of them went crazy, yelled and howled and turned straight back to the Whites, and the other half turned this way."

"But how do they get through the taiga, through the swamps?"

"What are saws and axes for? Some of our men, who were sent to guard them, helped them a bit. Twenty miles of road they've cut, they say. Bridges and all, the brutes! Talk about women! They've done things that would take us a month of Sundays!"

"That's a fine thing, twenty miles of road! And what are you looking so pleased about, you jackass? That's just what the Whites want, a highway into the taiga! Now all they have to do is to roll in their artillery!"

"Send a force to guard the road."

"I can do my own thinking, thank you."

6

The days were getting shorter; it was dark by five. Toward dusk Yurii Andreievich crossed the highway at the very place

where Liberius had stood talking to Svirid a few days earlier. He
was on his way back to the camp. Near the clearing where the
mound and the rowan tree marked the camp boundary, he
heard the bold, challenging voice of Kubarikha, his "rival" as
he jokingly called the cattle healer. She was singing a gay
jingle and her voice had a raucous, boisterous screech in it.
Judging by the peals of approving laughter that kept interrupting her, there was a crowd of men and women listening.
Then came silence. The people must have dispersed.

Thinking herself alone, Kubarikha sang a different song,
softly, as if to herself. Yurii Andreievich, who was cautiously
making his way in the dusk along the footpath that skirted the
swamp in front of the rowan tree, stopped in his tracks. Kubarikha was singing an old Russian song, but he did not know it.
Or she was improvising it?

An old Russian folk song is like water held back by a dam. It
looks as if it were still and were no longer flowing, but in its
depths it is ceaselessly rushing through the sluice gates and the
stillness of its surface is deceptive. By every possible means, by
repetitions and similes, the song slows down the gradual unfolding of its theme. Then at some point it suddenly reveals itself
and astounds us. That is how the song's sorrowing spirit comes to
expression. The song is an insane attempt to stop time by means
of its words.

Kubarikha half sang and half recited:

> "As a hare was running about the wide world,
> About the wide world, over the white snow,
> He ran, the lop-eared hare, past a rowan tree,
> Past a rowan tree, and complained to it:
> Have I not, he said, a timorous heart,
> A timorous heart, so faint and weak?
> I am frightened, he said, of the wild beast's tracks,
> Wild beast's tracks, the wolf's hungry belly.
> Pity me, O rowan bush! O fair rowan tree!
> Do not give thy beauty to the wicked enemy,
> The wicked enemy, the wicked raven.
> Scatter thy red berries to the wind,
> To the wind, over the wide world, over the white snow.

Fling them, roll them to my native town,
To the far end of the street, the last house,
The last house in the street, the last window, the room
Where she has shut herself in,
My beloved, my longed-for love.
Whisper to my grieving love, my bride,
A warm, an ardent word.
I, a soldier, languish in captivity,
Homesick, I am, poor soldier, kept in foreign parts.
I'll break from durance bitter,
I'll go to my red berry, to my lovely bride."

7

Agafia Fotievna, Pamphil's wife, had brought her sick cow to Kubarikha. The cow had been separated from the herd and tethered to a tree by a rope tied to her horns. Her mistress sat on a tree stump by the cow's forelegs and Kubarikha, on a milking stool, by her hind legs.

The rest of the countless herd was crammed into a glade, hemmed in all around by the dark forest of triangular firs, as tall as hills and rising from their spreading lower branches as if they were squatting on fat bottoms on the ground.

The cows were mostly black with white spots and belonged to some Swiss breed popular in Siberia. They were exhausted, no less exhausted than their owners by privations, endless wandering, and intolerable crowding. Rubbing flank to flank and maddened by the lack of space, they forgot their sex and reared and climbed on top of one another, pulling up their heavy udders with an effort and roaring like bulls. The heifers who were covered by them broke away from underneath and rushed off into the forest, tails in the air and trampling shrubs and branches. Their herdsmen—old men and children—ran shrieking after them.

And as if they too were hemmed in by the tight circle of treetops in the winter sky above the glade, the black and white clouds reared and piled and toppled as chaotically as the cows.

The knot of curious onlookers who stood at a distance annoyed the witch, and she measured them from top to toe with a hostile look. But, vain as an artist, she felt that it was beneath her dignity to admit that they embarrassed her. She pretended not to notice them. The doctor watched her from the back of the crowd, where she could not see him.

This was the first time he took a good look at her. She wore her usual English cap and pea-green overcoat with its crumpled collar. But the haughty and passionate expression that gave a youthful fire and darkness to this aging woman's eyes showed plainly that she did not care in the least what she was wearing or not wearing.

What astonished Yurii Andreievich was the change in Pamphil's wife. He could scarcely recognize her. In the last few days she had aged terribly. Her goggling eyes were almost ready to pop out of their sockets and her neck was as thin and long as a cart shaft. Such was the effect upon her of her secret fears.

"She doesn't give any milk, my dear," she was saying. "I thought she might be in calf, but then she would have had milk by now and she still hasn't any."

"Why should she be in calf? You can see the scab of anthrax on her udder. I'll give you some herb ointment to rub it with. And of course I'll cast a spell on her."

"My other trouble is my husband."

"I'll charm him back, so he won't stray. That's easy. He'll stick to you so you won't be able to get rid of him. What's your third trouble?"

"It isn't that he strays. That would be nothing. The misfortune is that he clings to me and the children with all his might, and that breaks his heart. I know what he thinks. He thinks they'll separate the camps, that they will send us one way and him another. And that we'll fall into the hands of Bassalygo's men and he won't be there and we won't have anyone to stand up for us. And that they'll torture us, they'll rejoice in our torments. I know his thoughts. I'm afraid he'll do away with himself."

"I'll think about it. I'll find a way to end your grief. What's your third trouble?"

"I haven't a third one. That's all there is—my cow and my husband."

"Well, you are poor in sorrows, my dear. See how merciful God has been to you! Such as you are hard to find. Only two sorrows in your poor heart, and one of them a fond husband! Well, let's begin. What will you give me for the cow?"

"What will you take?"

"I'll have a loaf of bread and your husband."

The onlookers burst out laughing.

"Are you joking?"

"Too much, is it? All right, I'll do without the loaf. We'll settle for your husband."

The laughter grew louder.

"What's the name? Not your husband's, your cow's."

"Beauty."

"Half the herd is called that. All right. We'll start with God's blessing."

She recited the spell for the cow. At first she was indeed concerned with the cow, but after a while she got carried away and gave Agafia a whole set of instructions on witchcraft. Yurii Andreievich listened spellbound, just as, when he first arrived in Siberia from European Russia, he had listened to the florid chatter of the driver, Bacchus.

The woman was saying:

"Aunt Margesta, come and be our guest. Come on Wednesday, take away the pest, take away the spell, take away the scab. Ringworm, leave the heifer's udder. Stand still, Beauty, do your duty, don't upset the pail. Stand still as a hill, let milk run and rill. Terror, terror, show your mettle, take the scab, throw them in the nettle. Strong as a lord is the sorcerer's word.

"You see, Agafia, you have to know everything—bidding and forbidding, the word for escaping and the word for safekeeping. Now you, for example, you look over there and you say to yourself: 'There's a forest.' But what there is over there is the forces of evil fighting the angelic hosts—they're at war like your men with Bassalygo's.

"Or take another example, look over there where I'm pointing. You're looking the wrong way, my dear, use your eyes, not the back of your head, look where my finger is pointing. That's right! Now, what do you think that is? You think it's two twigs that the wind has tangled together? Or a bird building its nest?

Well, it isn't either. That thing is a real devil's work, a garland the water spirit started weaving for her daughter. She heard people coming by, that frightened her, so she left it half done, but she'll finish it one of these nights, you will see.

"Or again, take your red banner. You think it's a flag, isn't that what you think? Well, it isn't a flag. It's the purple kerchief of the death woman, she uses it for luring. And why for luring? She waves it and she nods and winks and lures young men to come and be killed, then she sends famine and plague. That's what it is. And you went and believed her. You thought it was a flag. You thought it was: 'Come to me, all ye poor and proletarians of the world.'

"You have to know everything these days, Agafia my girl, every single thing. What every bird is and every stone and every herb. That bird, for example, that's a starling. And that beast is a badger.

"Now, another thing, suppose you take a fancy to someone, you just tell me. I'll make him pine for you, whoever he is—your Forester, the one who is your chief, if you like, or Kolchak or Ivan Tsarevich—anyone. You think I'm boasting? I am not. Now look, I'll tell you. When winter comes with blizzards and whirlwinds and snowspouts chasing each other in the fields, I will stick a knife into such a pillar of snow, right up to the hilt, and when I take it out of the snow, it will be red with blood. Have you ever heard of such a thing? Well, there you are! And you thought I was boasting. Now, how can it be, you tell me, that blood should come out of a snowspout that is made only of wind and snow? That's just it, my dear, that whirlwind isn't just wind and snow, it's a werewolf, a changeling that's lost its little bewitched child and is looking for it, it goes about the fields crying and looking for it. That is what I struck with my knife, that is why there is blood on it. Now, with that knife I can cut away the footprint of any man, and I can sew it with a silk thread to your skirt, and that man—whoever he is, Kolchak, or Strelnikov, or any new Tsar they set up—will follow you step by step wherever you go. And you thought I was telling lies! You thought it was: 'Come to me, all ye poor and proletarians of the world.'

"And many other things there are, such as stones raining from heaven, so that a man may go forth out of his house and the stones rain upon him. Or, as some have seen, horsemen riding through the sky, the horses' hoofs hitting the tops of the houses. Or as sorcerers prophesied of old, saying: 'In this woman there is corn, in that one honey, in a third marten fur.' And the knight opened the shoulder of the woman, as if it were a casket, and with his sword took out of her shoulder blade a measure of corn or a squirrel or a honeycomb."

Occasionally we experience a deep and strong feeling. Such a feeling always includes an element of pity. The more we love, the more the object of our love seems to us to be a victim. In the case of some men, compassion for a woman exceeds all measure and transports her to an unreal, entirely imaginary world. Such men are jealous of the very air she breathes, of the laws of nature, of everything that happened in the world before she was born.

Yurii Andreievich was sufficiently well read to suspect that Kubarikha's last words repeated the opening passage of an ancient chronicle, either of Novgorod or Epatievo, but so distorted by copyists and the sorcerers and bards who had transmitted them orally for centuries that its original meaning had been lost. Why, then, had he succumbed so completely to the tyranny of the legend? Why did this gibberish, this absurd talk, impress him as if it were describing real events?

Lara's left shoulder had been cut open. Like a key turning in the lock of a secret safe, the sword unlocked her shoulder blade and the secrets she had kept in the depths of her soul came to light. Unfamiliar towns, streets, rooms, countrysides unrolled like a film, whole reels of film, unfolding, discharging their contents.

How he loved her! How beautiful she was! In exactly the way he had always thought and dreamed and wanted! Yet what was it that made her so lovely? Was it something that could be named and analyzed? No, a thousand times no! She was lovely by virtue of the matchlessly simple and swift line that the Creator had, at a single stroke, drawn all around her, and in this divine form she had been handed over, like a child tightly wrapped in a sheet after its bath, into the keeping of his soul.

And what had happened to him now, where was he? In a Siberian forest with the partisans, who were encircled and whose fate he was to share. What an unbelievable, absurd predicament! Once again everything in his head and before his eyes became confused, blurred. At that moment, instead of snowing as had been expected, it began to drizzle. Like a huge banner stretching across a city street, there hung before him in the air, from one side of the forest glade to the other, a blurred, greatly magnified image of a single, astonishing, idolized head. The apparition wept, and the rain, now more intense, kissed and watered it.

"Go along now," said the witch to Agafia. "I have charmed your cow, she will get well. Pray to the Mother of God, who is the abode of light and the book of the living word."

8

There was fighting on the western border of the taiga. But the taiga was so immense that the battles were like border warfare on the edges of a great kingdom, and the camp hidden in its heart was so full of people that however many went away to fight, there seemed always to be more people left.

The rumble of the distant battle hardly ever reached the camp. Suddenly, several shots rang out in the forest. They followed one another at very close intervals, and all at once turned into a quick, ragged fusillade. People started up and ran quickly to their tents or wagons, and a general commotion began. Everyone got ready for battle.

It proved to be a false alarm. But then a growing crowd streamed toward the place where the shots had been fired.

They stood around a bleeding stump of a man lying on the ground. His right arm and left leg had been chopped off. It was inconceivable how, with his remaining arm and leg, he had crawled to the camp. The chopped-off arm and leg were tied in terrible bleeding chunks onto his back with a small wooden board attached to them; a long inscription on it said, with many words of abuse, that the atrocity was in reprisal for similar atrocities perpetrated by such and such a Red unit—a unit that had no connection with the Forest Brotherhood. It also said that the same treatment would be meted out to all the partisans unless, by a given date, they submitted and gave up their arms to the representatives of General Vitsyn's army corps.

Fainting repeatedly from loss of blood, the dying man told them in a faltering voice of the tortures and atrocities perpetrated by Vitsyn's investigating and punitive squads. His own sentence of death had been allegedly commuted; instead of hanging him, they had cut off his arm and leg in order to send him into the camp and strike terror among the partisans. They had carried him as far as the outposts of the camp, where they had put him down and ordered him to crawl, urging him on by shooting into the air.

He could barely move his lips. To make out his almost unintelligible stammering, the crowd around him bent low. He was saying: "Be on your guard, comrades. He has broken through."

"Patrols have gone out in strength. There's a big battle going on. We'll hold him."

"There's a gap. He wants to surprise you. I know. . . . I can't go on, men. I am spitting blood. I'll die in a moment."

"Rest a bit. Keep quiet.—Can't you see it's bad for him, you heartless beasts!"

The man started again: "He went to work on me, the devil. He said: You will bathe in your own blood until you tell me who you are. And how was I to tell him, a deserter is just what I am? I was running from him to you."

"You keep saying 'he.' Who was it that got to work on you?"

"Let me just get my breath. . . . I'll tell you. Hetman, Bekeshin. Colonel, Strese. Vitsyn's men. You don't know out here what it's like. The whole town is groaning. They boil people alive. They cut strips out of them. They take you by the scruff of the neck and push you inside, you don't know where you are, it's pitch black. You grope about—you are in a cage, inside a freight car. There are more than forty people in the cage, all in their underclothes. From time to time they open the door and grab whoever comes first—out he goes. As you grab a chicken to cut its throat. I swear to God. Some they hang, some they shoot, some they question. They beat you to shreds, they put salt on the wounds, they pour boiling water on you. When you vomit or relieve yourself they make you eat it. As for children and women—O God!"

The unfortunate was at his last gasp. He cried out and died without finishing the sentence. Somehow they all knew it at once and took off their caps and crossed themselves.

That night, the news of a far more terrible incident flew around the camp.

Pamphil had been in the crowd surrounding the dying man. He had seen him, heard his words, and read the threatening inscription on the board.

His constant fear for his family in the event of his own death rose to a new climax. In his imagination he saw them handed over to slow torture, watched their faces distorted by pain, and heard their groans and cries for help. In his desperate anguish— to forestall their future sufferings and to end his own—he killed them himself, felling his wife and three children with that same, razor-sharp ax that he had used to carve toys for the two small girls and the boy, who had been his favorite.

The astonishing thing was that he did not kill himself immediately afterward. What could he be thinking of? What could he look forward to? What intentions could he have, what plans? It was a clear case of insanity, and nothing could save him now.

While Liberius, the doctor, and the members of the army soviet debated what to do with him, he roamed freely about the camp, his head hung low over his chest, his dirty-yellow eyes glowering unseeingly. An obtuse vague grimace of inhuman, unconquerable suffering never left his face.

No one was sorry for him. Everyone avoided him. Some people said he should be lynched, but they were not heeded.

There was nothing in the world left for him to do. At dawn he vanished from the camp, fleeing from himself like a dog with rabies.

9

High winter came with its severe frosts. Torn, seemingly disconnected sounds and shapes rose out of the icy mist, stood still, moved, and vanished. The sun was not the sun to which the earth was used, it was a changeling. Its crimson ball hung in the forest and from it, stiffly and slowly as in a dream or in a fairy tale, amber-yellow rays of light as thick as honey spread and, catching in the trees, froze to them in midair.

Invisible feet in felt boots, touching the ground softly with padded soles, yet making the snow screech angrily at each step, moved in all directions, while the hooded and fur-jacketed torsos belonging to them sailed separately through the upper air, like heavenly bodies.

Friends stopped and talked, their faces close together, flushed as at the steam baths, with beards bristling like iced loofahs. Clouds of dense, clammy steam puffed out of their mouths, too large for the clipped, frost-bitten words they accompanied.

Walking along the footpath, the doctor ran into Liberius.

"Hello, stranger! Come to my dugout this evening. Spend the night. We'll have a good talk. There is news."

"Is the courier back? Any news from Varykino?"

"Not a word about your people or mine. This, however, leads me to the comforting conclusion that they must have got away in time, otherwise we would be sure to have heard something. We'll talk about it tonight. I'll expect you."

Going into the dugout that evening, the doctor repeated his question: "What have you heard about our families? Just tell me that."

"You never want to see further than your nose. So far as I know, they are safe and sound. But the point is that the news is first-rate. Have some cold veal."

"No, thanks. Come on now, don't change the subject."

"Are you sure you won't? Well, I'll have a bite. Though bread and vegetables are what we really need. There's a lot of scurvy about. We should have got in more nuts and berries last autumn when the women were there to pick them. Well, as I was saying, our affairs are in excellent shape. What I've always prophesied is coming true. The worst is over. Kolchak's forces are retreating all along the line. It's a complete rout. Now do you see? What did I always tell you? Do you remember how you used to moan?"

"When did I moan?"

"All the time. Especially when we were being pressed by Vitsyn."

The doctor recalled the autumn, the shooting of the rebels, Pamphil's killing of his wife and children, the whole senseless murderous mess to which there seemed to be no end. White and Red atrocities rivalled each other in savagery, outrage breeding outrage. The smell of blood was in his nose and throat, it choked him, it nauseated him, it mounted to his head, it made his eyes swim. That wasn't moaning, that was something entirely different, but how could he explain it to Liberius?

The dugout was lit by torches made of sticks stuck into a metal holder. They gave off an aromatic smell of charcoal. As a stick burned down, the cinder dropped into a bowl of water standing underneath, and Liberius lit a fresh one.

"See what I have to burn? There's no more oil. And the wood is too dry, it burns too quickly. Sure you won't have some veal? About the scurvy. What are you waiting for to call a staff meeting and give us a lecture on scurvy and the means of dealing with it?"

"Stop tormenting me, for God's sake. What exactly do you know about our people?"

"I've told you. There is nothing certain in the report. But I didn't finish telling you what I've learned from the latest communiqués. The civil war is over. Kolchak's forces are smashed. The main part of the Red Army is in pursuit, it is driving him eastward, along the railway, into the sea. Another part of it is hurrying over this way, and we are joining forces to mop up the considerable scattered numbers of Whites in the rear. The whole of southern Russia is clear of the enemy. Well, why aren't you glad? Isn't that enough for you?"

"I am glad. But where are our families?"

"Not in Varykino, and that's a very lucky thing. Not that there is any confirmation of that crazy business Kamennodvorsky told you about—you remember that rumor last summer about mysterious strangers raiding Varykino? I always thought it was nonsense. But the village is deserted. So it looks as if something did happen after all, and it's a very good thing they got out in time, as they evidently did. That is what the few remaining inhabitants think, according to my source."

"And Yuriatin? What happened there? Who is holding it?"

"That's another absurdity. It can't possibly be true."

"What's that?"

"They say the Whites are still there, but that's a sheer impossibility. I'll prove it to you, you'll see for yourself."

He put another stick in the holder and, getting out a tattered map and folding it so that the district he was talking about was on top, explained the position, pencil in hand.

"Look. All these are sectors where the Whites have been thrown back—here, and here, and here, all over this region. Do you follow?"

"Yes."

"So they can't possibly be anywhere near Yuriatin, because if they were, with their communications cut, they couldn't avoid being captured. Even their commanders must realize this, however incompetent they may be. Why are you putting on your coat? Where are you going?"

"I'll be back in a moment. There's a lot of smoke here, and I've got a headache. I'll just go out for a breath of air."

When he was outside, the doctor swept the snow off the wooden block that served as a seat at the entrance to the dugout and sat down, his elbows on his knees and his head propped on his fists.

The taiga, the camp, his eighteen months among the partisans, went right out of his head. He forgot all about them. Memories of his dear ones filled his mind and crowded out all else. He tried to guess their fate, and images rose before him, each more frightening than the last.

Here is Tonia walking through a field in a blizzard with Sasha in her arms. She keeps wrapping him up in a blanket, her feet sinking into the deep snow. She can barely drag along, using all her strength, but the blizzard knocks her down, she stumbles and falls and gets up, too weak to stand on her feet, the wind buffeting her and the snow covering her up. Oh, but he is forgetting. She has two children with her, and she nurses the little one. Both her hands are busy, like the fugitives at Chilimka who broke down and went mad with grief and strain.

She has both her hands full and there is no one near to help her. Sasha's father has vanished, no one knows where he is. He

is away, he has always been away, all his life he has remained
apart from them. What kind of father is he? Is it possible for a
real father always to be away? And what about her own father?
Where is Alexander Alexandrovich? And Niusha? And the others? Better not ask, better not think about it.

The doctor got up and turned to go back into the dugout. Suddenly his thoughts took a different direction and he changed his
mind about returning to Liberius.

Long ago he had cached a pair of skis, a bag of biscuits, and
other things he would need if a chance to make his escape
should ever come. He had buried them in the snow just outside
the camp, at the foot of a tall pine. To make doubly sure of
finding it he had marked the tree with a notch. Now he turned
and walked along the footpath trodden between the snowdrifts
in the direction of his buried treasure. It was a clear night with
a full moon. He knew where the sentries were posted and at
first avoided them successfully. But when he came to the clearing with the mound and rowan tree a sentry hailed him from a
distance, took a run on his skis, and standing straight up on
them glided swiftly toward him.

"Halt or I shoot! Who are you? Password."

"What's come over you, man? Don't you know me? I'm the
camp doctor, Zhivago."

"Sorry, Comrade Zhelvak. I didn't recognize you, no offense
meant. All the same, Zhelvak or not, I'm not letting you go any
farther. Orders are orders."

"As you wish. The password is 'Red Siberia,' and the reply,
'Down with the Interventionists.'"

"That's better. Go ahead. What are you chasing after at this
time of night? Anyone sick?"

"I was thirsty and I couldn't sleep. I thought I'd go out for a
breath of air and eat some snow. Then I saw the rowan tree
with iced berries on it. I want to go and pick a few."

"If that isn't just like a gentleman's notion! Who's ever heard
of picking berries in winter! Three years we've been beating the
nonsense out of you others but you're still the same. All right,
go and pick your berries, you lunatic. What do I care."

And as swiftly as he had come, the sentry took a run, stood
straight up on his long skis, and whistled over the untrodden

snow into the distance beyond the bare winter shrubs as thin as thinning hair.

The footpath brought the doctor to the foot of the rowan tree, whose name he had just spoken. It was half in snow, half in frozen leaves and berries, and it held out two white branches toward him. He remembered Lara's strong white arms and seized the branches and pulled them to him. As if in answer, the tree shook snow all over him. He muttered without realizing what he was saying, and completely beside himself: "I'll find you, my beauty, my love, my rowan tree, my own flesh and blood."

It was a clear night with a full moon. He made his way farther into the taiga, to the marked tree, unearthed his things, and left the camp.

CHAPTER THIRTEEN

OPPOSITE THE HOUSE OF SCULPTURES

1

Merchant Street rambled crookedly downhill, overlooked by the houses and churches of the upper part of Yuriatin.

At the corner there was the dark gray house with sculptures. The huge square stones of the lower part of its façade were covered with freshly posted sheets of government newspapers and proclamations. Small groups of people stood on the sidewalk, reading in silence.

After the recent thaw it was dry and frosty. Now it was light at a time of day when only a few weeks before it had been dark. The winter had just gone, and the emptiness it had left was filled by the light that lingered on into the evenings. The light made one restless, it was like a call from afar that was disturbing, it put one on one's guard.

The Whites had recently left the town, surrendering it to the Reds. The bombardment, bloodshed, and wartime anxieties had ceased. This too was disturbing, and put one on one's guard, like the going of the winter and the lengthening of the spring days.

One of the proclamations pasted on the wall and still readable by the light of the longer day announced:

"Workbooks are obtainable by those qualified at the cost of 50 rubles each, at the Food Office, Yuriatin Soviet, 5 October Street (formerly Governor Street), Room 137.

"Anyone without a workbook, or filling it in incorrectly, or (still worse) fraudulently, will be prosecuted with the utmost rigor of the wartime regulations. Detailed instructions for the correct use of workbooks are printed in I.Y.I.K. No. 86 (1013) for the current year and are posted at the Yuriatin Food Office, Room 137."

Another proclamation stated that the town had ample food supplies. These, it said, were merely being hoarded by the bourgeoisie with the object of disorganizing distribution and creating chaos. It ended with the words:

"Anyone found hoarding food will be shot on the spot."

A third announcement read:

"Those who do not belong to the exploiting class are admitted to membership in Consumer Associations. Details are obtainable at the Food Office, Yuriatin Soviet, 5 October Street (formerly Governor Street), Room 137."

Former members of the military were warned:

"Anyone who fails to surrender his arms or who continues carrying them without having the appropriate new permit will be prosecuted with the utmost severity of the law. New permits are obtainable at the Office of the Yuriatin Revolutionary-Military Committee, 6 October Street, Room 63."

2

The group in front of the building was joined by a wild-looking, emaciated man, black with grime, with a bag flung over his shoulder, and carrying a stick. There was not yet any white in his long, shaggy hair, but his bristly, dark-blond beard was graying. This was Yurii Andreievich. His fur coat must have been taken from him on the road or perhaps he had bartered it for food. His thin, tattered, short-sleeved coat, which did not keep him warm, was the result of an exchange.

All he had left in his bag was the remnant of a crust of bread that someone had given him out of charity, in a village near the town, and a piece of suet. He had reached Yuriatin somewhat earlier, but it had taken him a whole hour to trudge from the outskirts through which the railway ran to this corner of Merchant Street, so great was his weakness and so much had the last few days of the journey exhausted him. He had often stopped, and he had barely restrained an impulse to fall to his knees and kiss the stones of the town, which he had despaired of ever seeing again, and the sight of which filled him with happiness, like the sight of a friend.

For almost half his journey on foot he had followed the railway track. All of it was out of use, neglected and covered with snow. He had passed train after train abandoned by the Whites; they stood idle, stopped by the defeat of Kolchak, by lack of fuel, and by snowdrifts. Immobilized and buried in the snow, they stretched almost uninterruptedly for miles on end. Some of them served as strongholds for armed bands of highwaymen or as hideouts for escaping criminals or political fugitives—the involuntary vagrants of those days—but most of them had become mortuaries and mass graves for the victims of the cold and of the typhus raging all along the line and mowing down whole villages.

That period confirmed the ancient proverb, "Man is a wolf to man." Traveller turned off the road at the sight of traveller, stranger meeting stranger killed for fear of being killed. There were isolated cases of cannibalism. The laws of human civilization were suspended. The jungle law was in force. Man dreamed the prehistoric dreams of the cave dweller.

Every now and then Yurii Andreievich would see lonely shadows stealing along the ditch or scurrying across the road ahead of him. He avoided them carefully whenever he could, but many of them seemed familiar. He imagined that he had seen them all at the partisan camp. In most cases he was mistaken, but once his eyes did not deceive him. The boy who darted out of a snowdrift that concealed a train of *wagons-lits*, relieved himself, and darted back had indeed been a member of the Forest Brotherhood. It was Terentii Galuzin, who was believed to have been shot dead. In reality he had only been wounded and had lost consciousness. When he came to he had crawled away from the place of execution, hidden in the forest until he recovered from his wounds, and was now making his way home to Krestovozdvizhensk under an assumed name, hiding in the buried trains and running at the sight of human beings.

These scenes and incidents had the strangeness of the transcendental, as if they were snatches torn from lives on other planets that had somehow drifted to the earth. Only nature had remained true to history and appeared in the guise it assumed in modern art.

Now and then there was a quiet, pale gray, dark rose evening, with birches, black and fine as script against the afterglow, and black streams faintly clouded over with gray ice flowing between steep white banks of snow blackened at the edges where the running water had eroded them. Such, in an hour or two, would be the evening in Yuriatin: frosty, gray, transparent, and as soft as pussy willows.

The doctor meant to read the notices posted on the house of sculptures, but his eyes kept wandering to the third-floor windows of the house across the street. These were the windows of the rooms in which the furniture left by the previous occupants had been stored. Now, although the frost had filmed them at the edges, it was clear that the glass was transparent; the whitewash had evidently been removed. What did this mean? Had the former occupants returned? Or had Lara moved out and new tenants moved in, rearranging everything?

The uncertainty was unbearable. The doctor crossed the street, went in, and climbed the front staircase he knew so well and which was so dear to him. How often at the camp he had recalled the openwork pattern of the cast-iron steps down to the last scroll. In one place you could look through into the lumber room in the basement where broken chairs and old pails and tin tubs had been stacked. They were still there; nothing had changed. The doctor was almost grateful to the staircase for its loyalty to the past.

There had been a doorbell once, but it had broken and stopped ringing even before the doctor had been captured by the partisans. He was about to knock when he noticed that there was now a padlock on the door, hanging from two rings roughly screwed into the old oak panels with their fine carving, which in places had come away. Such destructiveness would have been inconceivable in the old days. There would have been a fitted lock, and if it had been out of order there were locksmiths to repair it. This trifling detail was eloquent of the general deterioration of things, which had gone a great deal further in his absence.

The doctor was sure that Lara and Katenka were not at home.

Perhaps they were not even in Yuriatin, and perhaps they were not even alive. He was prepared for the worst. It was only in order not to leave a stone unturned that he decided to look for the key in the hollow between the bricks, where a rat had so greatly frightened Katenka. He kicked at the wall, to make sure of not putting his hand on one now. He had not the slightest hope of finding anything. The hollow was closed by a brick. He removed it and felt inside. Oh, miracle! A key and a note! It was a long note covering a large sheet of paper. He took it to the window on the landing. Another miracle, even more unbelievable! The note was addressed to him! He read it quickly:

"Lord, what happiness! They say you are alive and have turned up. Someone saw you near the town and rushed over to tell me. I take it you'll go straight to Varykino, so I'm going there with Katenka. But just in case, I'm leaving the key in the usual place. Wait for me, don't move. You'll see I am using the front rooms now. The flat is rather empty, I've had to sell some of the furniture. I've left a little food, boiled potatoes mostly. Put the lid back on the saucepan with a weight on it, to keep the rats out. I'm mad with joy."

He read to the bottom of the page, and did not notice that the letter continued on the back. He pressed it to his lips, folded it, and put it into his pocket with the key. Mixed with his immense joy, he felt a sharp, stabbing pain. Since Lara was going to Varykino, and not even bothering to explain, it must be that his family were not there. He felt not only anxious because of this, but unbearably aggrieved and sad about them. Why hadn't she said a single word of how and where they were?—as if they didn't exist at all!

But it was getting darker, and he had still many things to do while it was light. One of the most urgent was to read the texts of the decrees posted in the street. It was no trifling matter in those days to be ignorant of the regulations; it might cost you your life. Without going into the flat or taking off his bag, he went down and crossed the street, to the wall thickly covered with various announcements.

3

There were newspaper articles, texts of speeches at meetings, and decrees. Yurii Andreievich glanced at the headings. "Requisitioning, assessment, and taxation of members of the propertied classes." "Establishment of workers' control." "Factory and plant committees." These were the regulations the new authorities had issued on entering the town in place of those that had been in force. No doubt, Yurii Andreievich thought, they were intended as a reminder of the uncompromising nature of the new regime, in case it had been forgotten under the Whites. But these monotonous, endless repetitions made his head go around. What period did they belong to? That of the first upheaval, or of some later re-establishment of the regime after a White rebellion? Had they been composed last year? The year before? Only once in his life had this uncompromising language and single-mindedness filled him with enthusiasm. Was it possible that he must pay for that rash enthusiasm all his life by never hearing, year after year, anything but these unchanging, shrill, crazy exclamations and demands, which became progressively more impractical, meaningless, and unfulfillable as time went by? Was it possible that because of one moment of overgenerous response he had been enslaved forever?

His eyes lit on a fragment of a speech:

"The reports on the famine disclose the unbelievable inactivity of the local organizations. There are glaring abuses, there is speculation on a gigantic scale, but what are our regional and municipal factory committees doing? Only mass searches in the commercial districts of Yuriatin and Razvilie, only terror applied in all its harshness, down to the shooting of speculators on the spot, can deliver us from famine."

"What an enviable blindness!" thought the doctor. "To be able to talk of bread when it has long since vanished from the face of the earth! Of propertied classes and speculators when they have long since been abolished by earlier decrees! Of peasants and villages that no longer exist! Don't they remember their own plans and measures, which long since turned life upside down? What kind of people are they, to go on raving with this never-cooling, feverish ardor, year in, year out, on nonexistent, long-vanished subjects, and to know nothing, to see nothing around them?"

The doctor's head was spinning. He fainted and fell down unconscious on the sidewalk. When he came to and people helped him to get up and offered to take him where he wished to go, he thanked them and refused, saying he had only to cross the street.

4

He went up again, and this time he unlocked the door of Lara's flat. It was still light on the landing, no darker than before he had gone out. He was glad that the sun was not hurrying him.

The creaking of the door touched off a commotion inside. The uninhabited flat greeted him with the clang and rattle of falling tin pans. Rats, scuttling off the shelves, plopped onto the floor and scattered. They must have bred here by the thousands. The doctor felt sick and helpless to deal with this abomination and decided to barricade himself for the night in one room with a closely fitting door, where he could stop the ratholes with broken glass.

He turned left to the part of the flat that he did not know, crossed a dark passage, and came into a light room with two windows facing the street. Directly opposite the window was the gray building with the statues; groups of people stood with their back to him, reading the announcements.

The light in the room was of the same quality as outside, it was the same new, fresh evening light of early spring. This seemed to make the room a part of the street; the only difference was that Lara's bedroom, where he was standing, was colder than the street.

His sudden weakness earlier that afternoon as he approached the town and walked through it an hour or two ago had made Yurii Andreievich think that he was ill, and had filled him with fears. Now, the sameness of the light in the house and in the street exhilarated him. Bathed in the same chilled air as the passers-by, he felt a kinship with them, an identity with the mood of the town, with life in the world. This dispelled his fears. He no longer thought he would be ill. The transparency of the spring evening, the all-penetrating light were a good omen, a promise of generous fulfillment of distant and far-reaching hopes. All would be well, he would achieve all he wanted in life, he would find and reunite and reconcile them all, he would think everything out and find all the right words. He waited for the joy of seeing Lara as an immediate proof that all the rest would follow.

A wild excitement and an uncontrollable restlessness supplanted his earlier fatigue. In reality this animation was an even surer symptom of approaching illness than his recent weakness. Yurii Andreievich could not sit still. Once again he felt the urge to go out.

He wanted, before he settled down, to have a haircut and get rid of his beard. He had looked for a barber earlier, on his way through town. But some of the barbershops he had known before stood empty, others had changed hands and were used for other purposes, and those still in business were locked. He had no razor of his own. Scissors would have done the job, but though he turned everything upside down on Lara's dressing table, in his haste he did not find any.

Now it occurred to him that there had once been a tailor's workshop in Spassky Street; if it still existed and he got to it before closing time, he might borrow a pair of scissors. He walked out.

5

His memory had not failed him. The workshop was still there, with its entrance from the street and a window running the width of the front. The seamstresses worked in full view of the passers-by. You could see right into the back of the room.

It was packed with sewing women. In addition to the seamstresses there were probably aging local ladies who knew how to sew and had obtained jobs in order to become entitled to the workbooks mentioned in the proclamation on the wall of the gray building.

It was easy to tell them from the professionals. The work shop made nothing but army clothes, padded trousers and jackets and parti-colored fur coats, made of the skins of dogs of different breeds, such as Yurii Andreievich had seen on the partisans. This work, more suitable for furriers, was particularly hard on the amateurs, whose fingers looked all thumbs as they pushed the stiffly folded hems through the sewing machines.

Yurii Andreievich knocked on the window and made signs that he wished to be let in. The women replied by signs that no private orders were accepted. He persisted. The women motioned him to go away and leave them alone, they had urgent work to do. One of them made a puzzled face, held up her hand, palm out, like a little boat, in a gesture of annoyance, and questioned with her eyes what on earth he wanted. He snipped two fingers like scissor blades. This was not understood. They decided it was some impertinence, that he was mimicking them and making fun of them. Standing out there, torn and tattered and behaving so oddly, he looked like a madman. The girls giggled and waved him on. At last he thought of going around the house, through the yard, and knocking on the back door.

6

It was opened by a dark, elderly, stern woman in a dark dress who might have been the head seamstress.

"What a pest you are. Can't you leave us alone? Well, get on with it, what is it you want?"

"I want scissors. Don't be so surprised. I'd like to borrow a pair of scissors to cut my hair and my beard. I could do it here and give them back to you at once, it wouldn't take a minute. I'd be terribly grateful."

The woman looked astonished and mistrustful. She clearly doubted his sanity.

"I've just arrived from a long journey. I wanted to get a haircut but there isn't a single barbershop open. So I thought I'd do it myself, but I haven't any scissors. Would you kindly lend me some?"

"All right. I'll give you a haircut. But I warn you. If you've got something else in mind—any tricks such as changing your appearance to disguise yourself for political reasons—don't blame us if we report you. We are not risking our lives for you."

"For heaven's sake! What an idea!"

She let him in and took him into a side room little bigger than a closet; next moment he was sitting in a chair with a sheet wrapped around him and tucked under his chin as at the barber's. The seamstress went out of the room and came back with a pair of scissors, a comb, clippers, a strap, and a razor.

"I've done every kind of job in my life," she explained, noticing her client's astonishment. "At one time I was a hairdresser. I learned haircutting and shaving when I was a nurse in the other war. Now we'll snip off that beard and then we'll have a shave."

"Could you cut my hair very short, please?"

"I'll do my best. Why are you pretending to be so ignorant, an educated man like you? As if you didn't know that we now count time by the decade and not by the week, and today is the seventeenth of the month and the barbers have their day off on every date with a seven in it."

"Honestly I didn't know. I've told you, I've just come from a long way off. Why should I pretend anything?"

"Don't fidget or you'll get cut. So you've just arrived. How did you come?"

"On my feet."

"Along the highway?"

"Partly that, partly along the railway track. I don't know how many trains I've seen, all buried in the snow. Luxury trains, special trains, every kind of train you can think of."

"There, just this little bit to snip off and it's finished. Family business?"

"Heavens, no! I worked for a former union of credit co-operatives as their travelling inspector. They sent me on an inspection tour to eastern Siberia and there I got stuck. No chance of a train, as you know. There was nothing for it but to walk. Six weeks, it took me. I can't begin to tell you all I've seen on the way."

"If I were you, I wouldn't begin. I see I'll have to teach you a thing or two. Have a look at yourself first. Here's a mirror. Get your hand out from under the sheet and hold it. All right?"

"I don't think it's quite short enough. Couldn't you take off a bit more?"

"It won't stay tidy if it's any shorter. As I was saying, don't start telling anything at all. It's better to keep your mouth shut. Credit co-operatives, luxury trains, inspection tours—forget all about such things. It isn't the moment for them. You could get into no end of trouble. Better pretend you are a doctor or a schoolteacher. There now—beard cut off, now we'll shave it clean. Just a spot of lather and you'll be ten years younger. I'll go and boil the kettle."

"Whoever can she be?" Yurii Andreievich wondered. He had a feeling he had some connection with her—something he had seen or heard, someone she reminded him of—but he could not think who it was.

She came back with the hot water.

"Now we'll have a shave. As I was telling you, it's much better not to say a word. Speech is of silver, silence is gold. That has always been true. And your special trains and credit co-operatives—better think of something else, say you are a doctor or a teacher. As for seeing sights, keep that to yourself. Whom are you going to impress these days? Am I hurting you?"

"A little."

"It scrapes a bit, I know, it can't be helped. Just a little bit of patience, my dear man. Your skin isn't used to the razor and your beard is very coarse. It won't take a minute. Yes. There's nothing people haven't seen. They've been through everything. We've had our troubles, too. The things that went on under the Whites! Murder, rape, abduction, man hunts. There was one little lordling who took a dislike to an ensign. He sent soldiers to ambush him in a wood outside the town, near Krapulsky's house. They got him and disarmed him and took him under guard to Razvilie. In those days Razvilie was the same as the regional Cheka is nowadays—a place of execution. Why are you jerking your head like that? It scrapes, does it? I know, my dear, I know. It can't be helped. Your hair is just like bristles. There's just this one tough place. Well, the ensign's wife was in hysterics. 'Kolia! Kolia! What will become of my Kolia!' Off she went, straight to the top, to General Galiullin. That's in a

manner of speaking, of course. She couldn't get straight to him.
You had to pull strings. There was somebody in the next
street over there who knew how to reach him, an exceptionally
kind person, very sensitive, not like anyone else, always stood
up for people. You can't think what went on all over the place,
lynchings, atrocities, dramas of jealousy. Just as in Spanish
novels."

"That's Lara she's talking about," thought Yurii Andreievich.
But he kept prudently silent and did not ask for details. Her
absurd remark about the Spanish novels again oddly reminded
him of something—precisely by its absurdity and irrelevance—
but he still couldn't think what it was.

"Now, of course, it's all quite different. Admittedly there's
any amount of investigations, informing, shooting, and so on.
But the idea is quite different. To begin with, it's a new
government, it's only just come into power, it hasn't got into its
stride yet. And then, whatever you say, they are on the side of
the common people, that's their strength. In our family we are
four sisters, counting myself, all working women. It's natural
that we should be drawn to them. One sister died. Her husband
was a political exile, worked as manager at one of the local
factories. Their son—my nephew, that is—he's at the head of the
peasant forces—he's quite a celebrity."

"So that's who she is," Yurii Andreievich realized. "Liberius's
aunt, Mikulitsyn's sister-in-law, the one who is a local legend,
barber—seamstress—signal woman—Jack of all trades!" But he
decided to say nothing so as not to give himself away.

"My nephew was always drawn to the people, ever since his
childhood. He grew up among the workers at the factory. Perhaps you've heard of the Varykino factories? Now look at what
I've done, fool that I am. Half your chin is smooth and the other
half is bristly. That's what comes of talking. Why didn't you
stop me? Now the lather's dry and the water is cold. I'll go and
warm it up."

When she came back, Yurii Andreievich asked: "Varykino,
that's somewhere miles out in the country, isn't it? That should
have been safe enough in all these upheavals."

"Well, it wasn't exactly safe. They had it worse than we did
in some ways. They had some sort of armed bands out there,

nobody quite knows what they were. They didn't speak our language. They went through the place, house by house, shot everyone they found and went off again, without a by-your-leave. The corpses just stayed in the snow. That was in the winter, of course. Do stop jerking your head, I nearly cut you."

"You were saying your brother-in-law lived in Varykino. Was he there when all this happened?"

"No. God is merciful. He and his wife got out in time—that's his second wife. Where they are, nobody knows, but it's certain that they escaped. There were some new people there as well, strangers from Moscow. They left even earlier. The younger of the two men, a doctor, the head of the family, he's missing. That's in a manner of speaking, of course; it was called 'missing' to spare their feelings. Actually he must be dead—sure to have been killed. They kept looking and looking for him, but he never turned up. In the meantime the other one, the older of the two, he was called back home. A professor he was, an agronomist. The government called him back, I was told. They all stopped in Yuriatin on their way to Moscow, just before the Whites came back. Now you're at it again, twisting and jerking. You really make me cut your throat. You get your money's worth out of your barber, my dear man."

So they were in Moscow!

7

"In Moscow! In Moscow!" The words echoed in his heart at every step of the cast-iron stairs, as he climbed them for the third time. The empty flat again met him with the hellish din of scampering, flopping, racing rats. It was clear to Yurii Andreievich that, however tired he was, he would never get to sleep unless he could keep this abomination away from him. The first thing before settling down for the night was to stop the ratholes. Fortunately, there were fewer of them in the bedroom than in the rest of the flat, where the floor boards and skirtings were in a worse state. But he had to hurry. It was getting dark. It was true that a lamp stood on the kitchen table—perhaps in expecta-tion of his coming it had been taken down from its bracket and half filled with kerosene, and a match box with a few matches in it had been left out. But it was better to save both the matches and the kerosene. In the bedroom he found a small oil lamp; the rats had been at the oil but a little was left.

In some places the skirting had come away from the floor. It took him a little over an hour to pack the cracks with broken glass. The door fitted well, and once it was closed the bedroom should be ratproof.

There was a Dutch stove in a corner of the room, with a tiled cornice not quite reaching the ceiling. In the kitchen there was a stack of logs. Yurii Andreievich decided to rob Lara of a couple of armfuls and, getting down on one knee, he gathered them up and balanced them on his left arm. Carrying them into the bedroom, he stacked them near the stove and had a look inside to see how it worked and in what condition it was. He had meant to lock the door but the latch was broken; he wedged it firmly with paper; then he laid the fire at his leisure and lit it.

As he put in more logs, he noticed that the cross section of one of them was marked with the letters "K.D." He recognized them with surprise. In the old Krueger days when timber rejected by the factories was sold for fuel, the boles were stamped before they were cut up into sections to show where they came from. "K.D." stood for Kulabish Division in Varykino.

The discovery upset him. These logs in Lara's house must mean that she was in touch with Samdeviatov and that he provided for her as he had once supplied the doctor and his household with all their needs. He had always found it irksome to accept his help. Now his embarrassment at being in his debt was complicated by other feelings.

It was hardly likely that Samdeviatov helped Lara out of sheer goodness of heart. He thought of Samdeviatov's free and easy ways and of Lara's rashness as a woman. There must surely be something between them.

The dry Kulabish logs crackled merrily and stormed into a blaze, and, as they caught, Yurii Andreievich's blind jealousy turned from the merest suppositions into certainty.

But so tormented was he on every side that one anxiety drove out another. He could not get rid of his suspicions, but his mind leapt from subject to subject, and the thought of his family, flooding it again, submerged for a time his jealous fantasies.

"So you are in Moscow, my dear ones?" It seemed to him now that the seamstress had given him an assurance of their safe arrival. "So you made all that long journey once again, and this time without me. How did you manage on the way? Why was Alexander Alexandrovich called back? Was it to return to his chair at the Academy? How did you find the house? How silly of me! I don't even know whether the house is still standing. Lord, how hard and painful it all is! If only I could stop thinking. I can't think straight. What's the matter with me, Tonia? I think I'm ill. What will become of us? What will become of you, Tonia, Tonia darling, Tonia? And Sashenka? And Alexander Alexandrovich? And myself? Why hast Thou cast me off? O Light everlasting! Why are we always separated, my dear ones? Why are you always being swept away from me? But we'll be together again, we'll be reunited, won't we, darling? I'll find you, even if I have to walk all the way to get to you. We'll see each other, we'll be together, we'll be all right again, won't we?"

"Why doesn't the earth swallow me up, why am I such a monster that I keep forgetting that Tonia was to have another child, and that she has surely had it? This isn't the first time I've forgotten it. How did she get through her confinement? To think that they all stopped in Yuriatin on their way to Moscow! It's true that Lara didn't know them, but here is a complete stranger, a seamstress, a hairdresser who has heard all about them, and Lara says nothing about them in her note. How could she be so careless, so indifferent? It's as strange as her saying nothing about knowing Samdeviatov."

Yurii Andreievich now looked around the room with a new discernment. All its furnishings belonged to the unknown tenants who had long been absent and in hiding. There was nothing of Lara's among them, and they could tell him nothing of her tastes. The photographs on the walls were of strangers. However that might be, he suddenly felt uncomfortable under the eyes of all these men and women. The clumsy furniture breathed hostility. He felt alien and unwanted in this bedroom.

What a fool he had been to keep remembering this house and missing it, what a fool to have come into this room not as into an ordinary room but as if into the heart of his longing for Lara!

How silly his way of feeling would seem to anyone outside! How different was the way strong, practical, efficient, handsome males, such as Samdeviatov, lived and spoke and acted! And why should Lara be expected to prefer his weakness and the dark, obscure, unrealistic language of his love? Did she need this confusion? Did she herself want to be what she was to him?

And what was she to him, as he had just put it? Oh, that question he could always answer.

A spring evening. The air punctuated with scattered sounds. The voices of children playing in the streets coming from varying distances as if to show that the whole expanse is alive. And this vast expanse is Russia, his incomparable mother; famed far and wide, martyred, stubborn, extravagant, crazy, irresponsible, adored, Russia with her eternally splendid, and disastrous, and unpredictable adventures. Oh, how sweet to be alive! How good to be alive and to love life! Oh, the ever-present longing to thank life, thank existence itself, to thank them as one being to another being.

This was exactly what Lara was. You could not communicate with life and existence, but she was their representative, their expression, in her the inarticulate principle of existence became sensitive and capable of speech.

And all that he had just reproached her with in a moment of doubt was untrue, a thousand times untrue! Everything about her was perfect, flawless.

Tears of admiration and repentance filled his eyes. Opening the stove door, he poked the fire; he pushed the logs that were ablaze and had turned into pure heat to the back and brought forward into the draft those that were less incandescent. Leaving the door open, he sat before the open flames, delighting in the play of light and the warmth on his face and hands. The warmth and light brought him completely to his senses. He missed Lara unbearably and he longed for something that could bring him into touch with her at that very moment.

He drew her crumpled letter from his pocket. It was folded so that the back of the page he had read earlier was outside, and now he saw that there was something written on it. Smoothing it out, he read it by the dancing firelight:

"You surely know what's happened to your family. They are in Moscow. Tonia has had a little girl." After that several lines were crossed out, then: "I've crossed it out because it's silly to write about it. We'll talk our fill when we meet. I'm rushing out, I must get hold of a horse. I don't know what I'll do if I can't. It's so difficult with Katenka. . . ." The rest of the sentence was smudged and illegible.

"She got the horse from Samdeviatov," Yurii Andreievich reflected calmly. "If she had anything to conceal, she wouldn't have mentioned it."

8

When the stove was hot Yurii Andreievich closed the flue and had something to eat. After that he felt so sleepy that he lay down on the sofa without undressing and at once fell fast asleep. The loud, insolent noise of the rats behind the walls and the door did not reach him. He had two bad dreams, one after the other.

He was in Moscow in a room with a glass door. The door was locked. For greater safety he was keeping hold of it by the handle and pulling it toward himself. From the other side, his little boy, Sashenka, dressed in a sailor suit and cap, was knocking, crying and begging to be let in. Behind the child, splashing him and the door with its spray, there was a waterfall. It was making a tremendous noise. Either the water was pouring from a burst pipe (a usual occurrence in those days) or else the door was a barrier against some wild countryside, a mountain gorge filled with the sound of its raging torrent and the millennial cold and darkness of its caves.

The noise of the tumbling water terrified the boy. It drowned his cries, but Yurii Andreievich could see him trying, over and over again, to form the word "Daddy" with his lips.

Heartbroken, Yurii Andreievich longed with all his being to take the boy in his arms, press him to his chest, and run away with him as fast as his feet would carry him.

Yet, with tears pouring down his face he kept hold of the handle of the locked door, shutting out the child, sacrificing him to a false notion of honor, in the name of his alleged duty to another woman, who was not the child's mother and who might at any moment come into the room from another door.

He woke up drenched in sweat and tears. "I've got a fever, I am sick," he thought. "This isn't typhus. This is some sort of exhaustion that is taking the form of a dangerous illness—an illness with a crisis, it will be just like any serious infection, and the only question is which is going to win, life or death. But I'm too sleepy to think." He dropped off to sleep again.

He dreamed of a dark winter morning in a bustling Moscow street. Judging by the early morning traffic, the trolleys ringing their bells, and the yellow pools of lamplight on the gray snow-covered street, it was before the revolution.

He dreamed of a big apartment with many windows, all on the same side of the house, probably no higher than the third story, with drawn curtains reaching to the floor.

Inside, people were lying about asleep in their clothes like travellers, and the rooms were untidy like a railway car, with half-eaten legs and wings of roast chicken and other remnants of food scattered about on greasy bits of newspaper. The shoes that the many friends, relatives, callers, and homeless people, all sheltering in the apartment, had removed for the night, were standing in pairs on the floor. The hostess, Lara, in a dressing gown tied hastily around her waist, moved swiftly and silently from room to room, hurrying about her chores, and he was following her step by step, muttering clumsy irrelevant explanations and generally making a nuisance of himself. But she no longer had a moment to give him and took no notice of his mutterings except for turning to him now and then with a tranquil, puzzled look or bursting into her inimitable, candid, silvery laughter. This was the only form of intimacy that remained between them. And how distant, cold, and compellingly attractive was this woman to whom he had sacrificed all he had, whom he had preferred to everything, and in comparison with whom everything seemed to him worthless!

9

It was not he but something greater than himself that wept and sobbed in him, and shone in the darkness with bright, phosphorescent words. And with weeping soul, he too wept. He felt pity for himself.

"I am ill," he realized in intervals of clarity between sleep, and delirium, and unconsciousness. "I must have some form of typhus that isn't described in textbooks, that we didn't study at school. I ought to get myself something to eat or I'll die of starvation."

But the moment he tried to raise himself on his elbow he found that he was incapable of moving, and fainted or fell asleep.

"How long have I been lying here?" he wondered during one such interval of clarity. "How many hours? How many days? When I lay down it was early spring. But now the windows are so thick with hoarfrost that the room is dark."

In the kitchen, rats were rattling the plates, scurrying up the walls, and heavily flopping down and squealing in their disgusting contralto voices.

And he again fell asleep, and on awakening discovered that the snowy windows had filled with a pink light, glowing like red wine in crystal glasses. And he wondered whether it was dawn or dusk.

Once he thought he heard voices near him and was terrified, imagining that he was going mad. Crying with self-pity, he complained in a soundless whisper that Heaven had abandoned him. "Why hast Thou cast me off, O Light everlasting, and cast me down into the darkness of hell?"

Suddenly he realized that he was not delirious, that he no longer had his clothes on, that he had been washed and was in a clean shirt, lying not on the sofa but in a freshly made bed, and that sitting beside him, leaning over him, her hair mingling with his and her tears falling with his own, was Lara. He fainted with joy.

10

He had complained that Heaven had cast him off, but now the whole breadth of heaven leaned low over his bed, holding out two strong, white, woman's arms to him. His head swimming with joy, he fell into a bottomless depth of bliss as one who drops unconscious.

All his life he had been active, doing things about the house, looking after patients, thinking, studying, writing. How good it was to stop doing, struggling, thinking, to leave it all for a time to nature, to become her thing, her concern, the work of her merciful, wonderful, beauty-lavishing hands.

His recovery was rapid. Lara fed him, nursed him, surrounded him with her care, and her dazzling loveliness, her questions and answers, whispered in a warm, gentle voice, were always present.

Their subdued conversations, however casual, were as full of meaning as the dialogues of Plato.

Even more than by what they had in common, they were united by what separated them from the rest of the world. They were both equally repelled by what was tragically typical of modern man, his textbook admirations, his shrill enthusiasms, and the deadly dullness conscientiously preached and practiced by countless workers in the field of art and science in order that genius should remain a great rarity.

Their love was great. Most people experience love without becoming aware of the extraordinary nature of this emotion. But to them—and this made them exceptional—the moments when passion visited their doomed human existence like a breath of eternity were moments of revelation, of continually new discoveries about themselves and life.

11

"Of course you must go back to your family. I won't keep you a day more than necessary. But just look at what is going on. As soon as we became part of Soviet Russia we were sucked into its ruin. To keep going, they take everything from us. You have no idea of how much Yuriatin has changed while you were ill. Our supplies are sent to Moscow—for them it's a drop in the ocean, all these shipments simply vanish down a bottomless pit —and in the meantime nothing is left to us. There are no mails, there is no passenger service, all the trains are used for bread. There's a lot of grumbling going on in town, as there was before the Haida uprising, and once again, the Cheka is savagely putting down the slightest sign of discontent.

"How could you travel, weak as you are, nothing but skin and bones? Do you really imagine you could go on foot? You would never get there. When you are stronger, it will be different.

"I won't presume to give you advice, but in your place I would take a job for the time being. Work at your own profession—they'd like that. You might get something in the regional health service.

"You'll have to do something. Your father was a Siberian millionaire who committed suicide, your wife is the daughter of a local landowner and industrialist, you were with the partisans and you ran away. You can't get around it—you left the ranks of the revolutionary army, you're a deserter. Under no circumstances must you remain idle. I am not in a much better position myself. I'll have to do something too. I'm living on a volcano as it is."

"How do you mean? What about Strelnikov?"

"It's precisely because of him. I told you before that he has many enemies. Now that the Red Army is victorious those non-Party soldiers who got too near the top and knew too much are done for. Lucky if they're only thrown out and not killed so as to leave no trace. Pasha is particularly vulnerable; he is in very great danger. You know he was out in the East. I've heard he's run away. He's in hiding. They're hunting for him. But don't let's talk about it. I hate crying, and if I say another word about him I know I'll howl."

"You were very much in love with him? You still are?"

"I married him, he's my husband, Yurochka. He has a wonderful, upright, shining personality. I am very much at fault. It isn't that I ever did him any harm, it wouldn't be true to say that. But he is so outstanding, so big, he has such immense integrity —and I'm no good at all, I'm nothing in comparison. That's where my fault lies. But please let's not talk about it now. I'll tell you more some other time, I promise you I will.

"How lovely your Tonia is. Just like a Botticelli. I was there when she had her baby. We got on terribly well. But let's not talk about that either just at the moment!

"As I was saying, let's both get jobs. We'll go out to work every morning, and at the end of the month we'll collect our salaries in billions of rubles. You know, until quite recently the old Siberian bank notes were still valid. Then they were declared invalid and for a long time, all the time you were ill, we had no currency at all! Just imagine! Well, we managed somehow. Now they say a whole trainload of new bank notes has arrived, at least forty carfuls! They are printed on big sheets in two colors, red and blue, and divided into little squares like postage stamps. The blue squares are worth five million rubles each and the red ones ten. They are badly printed, they fade and the colors are smudged."

"Yes, I've seen that kind of money. It was put into circulation in Moscow just before we left."

12

"Why were you so long in Varykino? Is there anybody there? I thought there wasn't a soul, it was deserted. What kept you so long?"

"I was cleaning your house with Katenka. I thought you'd go there first thing and I didn't want you to see it in the state it was in."

"Why, what kind of state is it in? Is it so bad?"

"It was untidy, dirty, and we put it straight."

"How evasively terse! I feel there's something you are not telling me. But just as you like, I won't try to get it out of you. Tell me about Tonia. What did they call the little girl?"

"Masha, in memory of your mother."

"Tell me all about them."

"Please, not now. I've told you, I still can't talk about it without crying."

"That Samdeviatov who lent you the horse, he's an interesting character, don't you think?"

"Very."

"I know him quite well, you know. He was in and out of the house when we lived there. It was all new to us and he helped us to settle in."

"I know, he told me."

"You must be great friends. Is he trying to help you, too?"

"He positively showers me with kindness! I don't know what I should do without him."

"I can imagine! I suppose you're on informal, comradely terms. Does he run after you much?"

"All the time! Naturally!"

"And you like him? Sorry. I shouldn't have asked you that. I've got no business to question you. That was going too far! I apologize."

"Oh, that's all right! I suppose what you really mean is, what kind of terms are we on? Is there anything more between us than friendship? Of course there isn't! He has done a tremendous amount for me, I am enormously in his debt, but if he gave me my weight in gold, if he gave his life for me, it wouldn't bring me a step nearer to him. I have always disliked men of that kind, I have nothing whatever in common with them. These resourceful, self-confident, masterful characters—in practical things they are invaluable, but in matters of feeling I can think of nothing more horrible than all this impertinent, male complacency! It certainly isn't my idea of life and love! More than that, morally Anfim reminds me of someone else, of someone infinitely more repulsive. It's his fault that I've become what I am."

"I don't understand. What do you think you are? What have you got in mind? Explain to me. You are the best person in the world."

"How can you, Yurochka! I am talking seriously, and you pay me compliments as though we were in a drawing room. What am I like? There's something broken in me, there's something broken in my whole life. I discovered life much too early, I was made to discover it, and I was made to see it from the very worst side—a cheap, distorted version of it—through the eyes of a self-assured, elderly parasite, who took advantage of everything and allowed himself whatever he fancied."

"I think I understand. I thought there was something. But wait a moment. I can imagine your suffering as a child, a suffering much beyond your years, the shock to your inexperience, a very young girl's sense of outrage. But all that is in the past. What I mean is that it isn't for you to make yourself unhappy about it now, it's for people who love you, people like myself. It's I who should be tearing my hair because I wasn't with you to prevent it, if it really makes you unhappy. It's a curious thing. I think I can be really jealous—deadly, passionately jealous—only of my inferiors, people with whom I have nothing in common. A rival whom I look up to arouses entirely different feelings in me. I think if a man whom I understood and liked were in love with the same woman as I am I wouldn't feel a grievance, or want to quarrel with him, I would feel a sort of tragic brotherhood with him. Naturally, I wouldn't dream of sharing the woman I loved. But I would give her up and my suffering would be something different from jealousy—less raw and angry. It would be the same if I came across an artist who was doing the same sort of thing as I do and doing it better. I would probably give up my own efforts, I wouldn't want to duplicate his, and there would be no point in going on if his were better.

"But that wasn't what we were talking about. I don't think I could love you so much if you had nothing to complain of and nothing to regret. I don't like people who have never fallen or stumbled. Their virtue is lifeless and of little value. Life hasn't revealed its beauty to them."

"It's this beauty I'm thinking of. I think that to see it your imagination has to be intact, your vision has to be childlike. That is what I was deprived of. I might have developed my own view of life if I hadn't, right from the beginning, seen it stamped in someone else's vulgar distortion. And that isn't all. It's because of the intrusion into my life, right at the start, of this immoral, selfish nonentity that when later on I married a man who was really big and remarkable, and who loved me and whom I loved, my marriage was destroyed."

"Wait a moment before you tell me about your husband. I am not jealous of him. I told you I can be jealous only of my inferiors, not of my equals. Tell me first about this other man."

"Which man?"

"This wrecker who spoiled your life. Who was he?"

"A fairly well-known Moscow lawyer. A friend of my father's. When Father died and we were very badly off he gave my mother financial help. He was unmarried, rich. I've probably made him sound a lot more interesting than he is by painting him so black. He couldn't be more ordinary. I'll tell you his name if you like."

"You needn't. I know it. I saw him once."

"Really?"

"In a hotel room, when your mother took poison. It was late at night. You and I were both still at school."

"Oh, I remember. You came with someone else. You stood in the shadow, in the hallway. I don't know if I would have remembered by myself, but I think you reminded me of it once, it must have been in Meliuzeievo."

"Komarovsky was there."

"Was he? Quite possible. It wasn't unusual for us to be in the same place. We often saw each other."

"Why are you blushing?"

"At the sound of Komarovsky's name coming from you. I'm no longer used to hearing it, I was taken by surprise."

"There was a school friend of mine who went with me that night, and this is what he told me there in the hotel. He recognized Komarovsky as a man he had happened to see once before. As a child, during a journey, this boy, Misha Gordon, witnessed the suicide of my father—the millionaire industrialist. They were in the same train. Father jumped deliberately from the moving train and was killed. He was accompanied on this journey by Komarovsky, who was his lawyer. He made Father drink, he got his business into a muddle, he brought him to the point of bankruptcy, and he drove him to suicide. It was his fault that my father killed himself and that I was left an orphan."

"It isn't possible! It's extraordinary! Can it really be true? So he was your evil genius, too! It brings us even closer! It must be predestination!"

"He is the man of whom I shall always be incurably, insanely jealous."

"How can you say such a thing? It isn't just that I don't love him—I despise him."

"Can you know yourself as well as that? Human nature, and particularly woman's, is so mysterious and so full of contradictions. Perhaps there is something in your loathing that keeps you in subjection to him more than to any man whom you love of your own free will, without compulsion."

"What a terrible thing to say! And as usual, the way you put it makes me feel that this thing, unnatural as it is, seems to be true. But how horrible if it is!"

"Don't be upset. Don't listen to me. I only meant that I am jealous of a dark, unconscious element, something irrational, unfathomable. I am jealous of your toilet articles, of the drops of sweat on your skin, of the germs in the air you breathe which could get into your blood and poison you. And I am jealous of Komarovsky, as if he were an infectious disease. Someday he will take you away, just as certainly as death will someday separate us. I know this must seem obscure and confused, but I can't say it more clearly. I love you madly, irrationally, infinitely."

13

"Tell me more about your husband—'One writ with me in sour misfortune's book,' as Shakespeare says."

"Where did he say that?"

"In *Romeo and Juliet*."

"I told you a lot in Meliuzeievo when I was looking for him, and then here, when I heard how his men arrested you and took you to his train. I may have told you—or perhaps I only thought I did—how I once saw him from a distance when he was getting into his car. But you can imagine how many guards there were around him! I found him almost unchanged. The same handsome, honest, resolute face, the most honest face I've ever seen in my life. The same manly, straightforward character, not a shadow of affectation or make-believe. And yet I did notice a difference, and it alarmed me.

"It was as if something abstract had crept into this face and made it colorless. As if a living human face had become an embodiment of a principle, the image of an idea. My heart sank when I noticed it. I realized that this had happened to him because he had handed himself over to a superior force, but a force that is deadening and pitiless and will not spare him in the end. It seemed to me that he was a marked man and that this was the seal of his doom. But perhaps I'm confused about it. Perhaps I'm influenced by what you said when you described your meeting with him. After all, in addition to what we feel for each other, I am influenced by you in so many ways!"

"Tell me about your life with him before the revolution."

"Very early, when I was still a child, purity became my ideal. He was the embodiment of it. You know we grew up almost in the same house. He, Galiullin, and I. As a little boy he was infatuated with me. He used almost to faint whenever he saw me. I probably shouldn't be talking this way. But it would be worse to pretend I didn't know. It was the kind of all-absorbing childish passion that a child conceals because his pride won't let him show it, but one look at his face is enough to tell you all about it. We saw a lot of each other. He and I were as different as you and I are alike. I chose him then and there in my heart. I decided that as soon as we were old enough I would marry this wonderful boy, and in my own mind I became engaged to him.

"You know it's extraordinary how gifted he is! His father was a signal man, or a crossing guard, I don't know which, and by sheer brains and hard work he reached, I was going to say the level, but it's more like the summit, of present academic knowledge in two fields—classics and mathematics! After all, that's something!"

"But then what spoiled your marriage, if you loved each other so much?"

"Ah, that's hard to answer. I'll try to tell you. But it's strange that I, an ordinary woman, should explain to you, who are so wise, what is happening to human life in general and to life in Russia and why families get broken up, including yours and mine. Ah, it isn't a matter of individuals, of being alike or different in temperament, of loving or not loving! All customs and traditions, all our way of life, everything to do with home and order, has crumbled into dust in the general upheaval and reorganization of society. The whole human way of life has been destroyed and ruined. All that's left is the naked human soul stripped to the last shred, for which nothing has changed because it was always cold and shivering and reaching out to its nearest neighbor, as cold and lonely as itself. You and I are like Adam and Eve, the first two people on earth who at the beginning of the world had nothing to cover themselves with—and now at the end of it we are just as naked and homeless. And you and I are the last remembrance of all that immeasurable greatness which has been created in the world in all the thousands of years between them and us, and it is in memory of all those vanished marvels that we live and love and weep and cling to one another."

14

She was silent for a while, then she went on more calmly:

"I'll tell you. If Strelnikov became Pashenka again, if he stopped his raging and rebelling; if time turned back; if by some miracle, somewhere, I could see the window of our house shining, the lamplight on Pasha's desk and his books, even if it were at the end of the earth—I would crawl to it on my knees. Everything in me would respond. I could never hold out against the call of the past, of loyalty. There is nothing I wouldn't sacrifice, however precious. Even you. Even our love, so carefree, so spontaneous, so natural. Oh, forgive me! I don't mean that. It isn't true!"

She threw herself into his arms, sobbing. But very soon she controlled herself and, wiping away her tears, said:

"Isn't it the same call of duty that drives you back to Tonia? Oh, God, how miserable we are! What will become of us? What are we to do?"

When she had recovered she went on:

"But I haven't answered your question about what it was that spoiled our happiness. I came to understand it very clearly afterward. I'll tell you. It isn't only our story. It has become the fate of many others."

"Tell me, my love, you who are so wise."

"We were married two years before the war. We were just beginning to make a life for ourselves, we had just set up our home, when the war broke out. I believe now that the war is to blame for everything, for all the misfortunes that followed and that hound our generation to this day. I remember my childhood well. I can still remember a time when we all accepted the peaceful outlook of the last century. It was taken for granted that you listened to reason, that it was right and natural to do what your conscience told you to do. For a man to die by the hand of another was a rare, an exceptional event, something quite out of the ordinary. Murders happened in plays, newspapers, and detective stories, not in everyday life.

"And then there was the jump from this peaceful, naïve moderation to blood and tears, to mass insanity, and to the savagery of daily, hourly, legalized, rewarded slaughter.

"I suppose one must always pay for such things. You must remember better than I do the beginning of disintegration, how everything began to break down all at once—trains and food supplies in towns, and the foundations of the family, and moral standards."

"Go on. I know what you'll say next. How well you see all these things. What a joy to listen to you!"

"It was then that untruth came down on our land of Russia. The main misfortune, the root of all the evil to come, was the loss of confidence in the value of one's own opinion. People imagined that it was out of date to follow their own moral sense, that they must all sing in chorus, and live by other people's notions, notions that were being crammed down everybody's throat. And then there arose the power of the glittering phrase, first the Tsarist, then the revolutionary.

"This social evil became an epidemic. It was catching. And it affected everything, nothing was left untouched by it. Our home, too, became infected. Something went wrong in it. Instead of being natural and spontaneous as we had always been, we began to be idiotically pompous with each other. Something showy, artificial, forced, crept into our conversation—you felt you had to be clever in a certain way about certain world-important themes. How could Pasha, who was so discriminating, so exacting with himself, who distinguished so unerringly between reality and appearance, how could he fail to notice the falsehood that had crept into our lives?

"And at this point he made his fatal, terrible mistake. He mistook the spirit of the times, the social, universal evil, for a private and domestic one. He listened to our clichés, to our unnatural official tone, and he thought it was because he was second-rate, a nonentity, that we talked like this. I suppose you find it incredible that such trivial things could matter so much in our married life. You can't imagine how important this was, what foolish things this childish nonsense made him do.

"Nobody asked him to go to the war, he went because he imagined himself a burden to us, so that we should be free of him. That was the beginning of all his madness. Out of a sort of misdirected, adolescent vanity he took offense at things at which one doesn't take offense. He sulked at the course of events. He quarrelled with history. To this day he is trying to get even with it. That's what makes him so insanely defiant. It's this stupid ambition that's driving him to his death. God, if I could only save him!"

"How immensely pure and strong is your love for him! Go on, go on loving him. I'm not jealous of him. I won't stand in your way."

15

Summer came and went almost unnoticed. The doctor recovered. While planning to go to Moscow he took not one but three temporary jobs. The rapid devaluation of money made it difficult to make ends meet.

Every morning he got up at daybreak, left the house, and walked down Merchant Street, past the "Giant" movie house as far as the former printing shop of the Urals Cossack Army, now renamed the Red Compositor. At the corner of City Street the door of the town hall bore the notice "Complaints." He crossed the square, turned into Buianovka Street, and coming to the hospital went in through the back door to the out-patient department of the Army Hospital, where he worked. This was his main job.

Most of his way from Lara's to the hospital lay in the shadow of spreading trees, past curious little frame houses with steep roofs, decorated doors, and carved and painted patterns around the windows. The house next to the hospital, standing in its own garden, had belonged to Goregliadova, a merchant's wife. It was faced with glazed, diamond-cut tiles, like the ancient boyar houses in Moscow.

Three or four times a week Yurii Andreievich attended the board meetings of the Yuriatin Health Service in Miassky Street.

At the other end of town stood the former Institute of Gynecology, founded by Samdeviatov's father in memory of his wife, who had died in childbirth, now renamed the Rosa Luxemburg Institute, where Yurii Andreievich lectured on general pathology and one or two optional subjects as part of the new, shortened course of medicine and surgery.

Coming home at night, hungry and tired, he found Lara busy at her domestic chores, cooking or washing. In this prosaic, weekday aspect of her being, dishevelled, with her sleeves rolled and her skirts tucked up, she almost frightened him by her regal attractiveness, more breath-taking than if he had found her on the point of going to a ball, taller in high-heeled shoes and in a long, low-cut gown with a sweeping, rustling skirt.

She cooked or washed and used the soapy water to scrub the floors, or more quietly, less flushed, pressed and mended linen for the three of them. Or when the cooking, washing, and cleaning had all been got out of the way, she gave lessons to Katenka; or with her nose in her textbooks worked at her own political re-education, in order to qualify as a teacher at the new, reorganized school.

The closer this woman and her daughter became to him, the less he dared to think of them as family and the stricter was the control imposed on his thoughts by his duty to his own family and the pain of his broken faith. There was nothing offensive to Lara or Katenka in this limitation. On the contrary, this attitude on his part contained a world of deference that excluded every trace of vulgarity.

But the division in him was a sorrow and a torment, and he became accustomed to it only as one gets used to an unhealed and frequently reopened wound.

16

Two or three months went by. One day in October Yurii Andreievich said to Larisa Feodorovna:

"You know, it looks as if I'll be forced to resign from my jobs. It's always the same thing—it happens again and again. At first everything is splendid. 'Come along. We welcome good, honest work, we welcome ideas, especially new ideas. What could please us better? Do your work, struggle, carry on.'

"Then you find in practice that what they mean by ideas is nothing but words—claptrap in praise of the revolution and the regime. I'm sick and tired of it. And it's not the kind of thing I'm good at.

"I suppose they are right, from their point of view. Of course, I'm not on their side. Only I find it hard to reconcile myself to the idea that they are radiant heroes and that I am a mean wretch who sides with tyranny and obscurantism. Have you ever heard of Nikolai Vedeniapin?"

"Well, of course! Both before I met you and from what you've told me yourself. Sima Tuntseva often speaks of him, she's a follower of his. To my shame, I haven't read his books. I don't like purely philosophical works. I think a little philosophy should be added to life and art by way of seasoning, but to make it one's specialty seems to me as strange as eating nothing but horseradish. But I'm sorry, I've distracted you with my nonsense."

"No, actually it's very much what I think myself. Well, about my uncle, I'm supposed to be corrupted by his influence. One of my sins is a belief in intuition. And yet see how ridiculous: they all shout that I'm a marvellous diagnostician, and as a matter of fact it's true that I don't often make mistakes in diagnosing a disease. Well, what is this immediate grasp of a situation as a whole supposed to be if not the intuition they find so detestable?

"Another thing is that I am obsessed by the problem of mimicry, the outward adaptation of an organism to the color of its environment. I think this biological phenomenon can cast light on the problem of the relationship between the inward and the outward world.

"I dared to touch on this problem in my lectures. Immediately there was a chorus: 'Idealism, mysticism, Goethe's *Naturphiloso-phie*, neo-Schellingism.'

"It's time I got out. I'll stay on at the hospital until they throw me out, but I'll resign from the Institute and the Health Service. I don't want to worry you, but occasionally I have the feeling that they might arrest me any day."

"God forbid, Yurochka. It hasn't come to that yet, fortunately. But you are right. It won't do any harm to be more careful. I've noticed that whenever this regime comes to power it goes through certain regular stages. In the first stage it's the triumph of reason, of the spirit of criticism, the fight against prejudice and so on.

"Then comes the second stage. The accent is all on the shady activities of the pretended sympathizers, the hangers-on. There is more and more suspicion—informers, intrigues, hatreds. And you are right—we are at the beginning of the second stage.

"We don't have to go far to find evidence of it. The local revolutionary court has had two new members transferred to it from Khodatskoie—two old political convicts from among the workers, Tiverzin and Antipov.

"They both know me perfectly well—in fact, one of them is my father-in-law. And yet it's only since their arrival, quite recently, that I've begun really to tremble for Katenka's and my life. They are capable of anything. Antipov doesn't like me. It would be quite like them to destroy me and even Pasha one of these days in the name of higher revolutionary justice."

The sequel to this conversation took place very soon. A search had been carried out by night at the widow Goregliadova's, at 48 Buianovka Street, next door to the hospital. A cache of arms had been found and a counterrevolutionary organization uncovered. Many people were arrested and the wave of searches and arrests continued. It was whispered that some of the suspects had escaped across the river. "Though what good will it do them?" people said. "There are rivers and rivers. Now the Amur, for instance, at Blagoveshchensk—you jump in and swim across and you are in China! That really is a river. That's quite a different matter."

"The air is full of threats," said Lara. "Our time of safety is over. They are sure to arrest us, you and me. And then what

will become of Katenka? I am a mother, I can't let this misfortune happen, I must think of something. I must have a plan.
It's driving me out of my mind."

"Let's try to think. Though what is there that we can do? Is it
in our power to avert this blow? Isn't it a matter of fate?"

"We certainly can't escape, there's nowhere to go. But we
could withdraw into the shadow, into the background. Go to
Varykino, for instance. I keep thinking of the house there. It's
very lonely and neglected, but we would be less in the way
than here, we wouldn't attract so much attention. Winter is
coming on. I wouldn't at all mind spending it there. By the
time they got around to us we'd have gained a year of life; that's
always something. Samdeviatov would be a link between us and
the town. Perhaps he'd help us to go into hiding. What do you
think? It's true, there isn't a soul, it's empty and desolate, at
least it was when I was there in March. And they say there are
wolves. It's rather frightening. But then people, anyway people like Tiverzin and Antipov, are more frightening than wolves."

"I don't know what to say. Haven't you been urging me to go
to Moscow all this time, telling me not to put it off? That's
easier now. I made inquiries at the station. Apparently they've
stopped worrying about black-marketeers. Not everyone whose
papers aren't in order gets taken off the train. They shoot less,
they've got tired.

"It worries me that I've had no reply to my letters to Moscow.
I ought to go there and see what's happening to them—you keep
telling me so yourself. But then how am I to take what you say
about Varykino? You surely wouldn't go to such an out-of-the-
way place by yourself?"

"No, of course, without you it would be impossible."

"And yet you tell me to go to Moscow?"

"Yes, you should go."

"Listen. I'll tell you what, I've got a wonderful idea—let's go
to Moscow, all three of us."

"To Moscow? You're mad! What should I do in Moscow? No,
I have to stay, I must be near here. It's here that Pasha's fate
will be decided. I must wait here and be within reach if he
needs me."

"Well then, let's think about Katenka."

"I was talking about her with Sima—Sima Tuntseva, she comes to see me sometimes."

"Yes, I know, I've often seen her."

"I'm surprised at you. In your place I'd have fallen in love with her at once. I don't know where you men keep your eyes! She's such a marvel! Pretty, graceful, intelligent, well read, kind, clear-headed."

"Her sister gave me a haircut the day I arrived—Glafira, the seamstress."

"I know. They both live with their oldest sister, Avdotia, the one who's a librarian. They are a good honest working family. I thought of asking them—if it comes to the worst, if you and I are arrested—if they would look after Katenka. I haven't made up my mind yet."

"Only if there really isn't any other way out. Pray God, it won't come to that."

"They say Sima is a bit odd—not quite right in the head. It's true she is not quite normal, but that's only because she's so profound and original. She's not an intellectual, but she's phenomenally educated. You and she are extraordinarily alike in your views. I think I should be quite happy about Katenka if she brought her up."

17

Once again he had been to the station and had again come back without having accomplished anything. Everything was still undecided. He and Lara were faced with the unknown. The weather was cold and dark as before the first snow. The sky, particularly where large patches of it could be seen, as at intersections, had a wintry look.

When Yurii Andreievich came home, he found that Lara had a visitor, Sima. They were having a conversation that was more like a lecture Sima was delivering to her hostess. Yurii Andreievich did not want to be in their way. He also wanted to be alone a little. The women were talking in the next room. The door between the two rooms was open; through the curtain that hung to the floor he could hear all they were saying.

"I'll go on with my sewing but don't take any notice of it, Sima dear. I'm listening. I attended lectures on history and philosophy. Your way of thinking interests me very much. Moreover, it's a great relief to listen to you. We haven't slept much the last few nights, worrying about Katenka. I know it's my duty as her mother to see to it that she is safe if anything happens to us. I ought to think it out calmly and sensibly, but I'm not very good at that. It makes me sad to realize it. I am depressed from exhaustion and sleeplessness. It steadies me to listen to you. And then, it's going to snow any minute. It's lovely when it's snowing to listen to long, intelligent talk. If you glance out of the corner of your eye at the window when it's snowing you always feel as if someone were coming to the door across the yard, have you noticed? Go on, Sima dear. I'm listening."

"Where did we leave off last time?"

Yurii Andreievich did not catch Lara's reply. He listened to what Sima was saying:

"It's possible to use words such as 'culture,' 'epochs.' But people understand them in so many different ways. Because their meaning is ambiguous, I won't use them. I'll replace them with other words.

"I would say that man is made up of two parts, of God and work. Each succeeding stage in the development of the human spirit is marked by the achievement over many generations of an enormously slow and lengthy work. Such a work was Egypt. Greece was another. The theology of the Old Testament prophets was a third. The last in time, not yet superseded by anything else and still being accomplished by all who are inspired, is Christianity.

"To show you the completely new thing it brought into the world in all its freshness—not as you know it and are used to it but more simply, more directly—I should like to go over a few extracts from the liturgy—only a very few, and abridged at that.

"Most liturgical texts bring together the concepts of the Old and the New Testament and put them side by side. For instance, the burning bush, the exodus from Egypt, the youths in the fiery furnace, Jonah and the whale are presented as parallels to the immaculate conception and the resurrection of Christ.

"Such comparisons bring out, very strikingly, I think, the way in which the Old Testament is old and the Gospel is new. In a number of texts Mary's motherhood is compared to the crossing of the Red Sea by the Jews. For instance there is one verse that begins: 'The Red Sea is the likeness of the virgin bride,' and goes on to say that 'as the sea was impenetrable after its crossing by the Israelites, the Immaculate One was incorrupt after the birth of Emmanuel.' That is to say, after the Jews crossed the Red Sea it became impassable, as before, and the Virgin after giving birth to our Lord was as immaculate as before. A parallel is drawn between the two events. What kind of events are they? Both are supernatural, both are recognized as miracles. What, then, was regarded as miraculous in each epoch—the ancient, primitive epoch and the later, post-Roman epoch which was far more advanced?

"In the first miracle you have a popular leader, the patriarch Moses, dividing the waters by a magic gesture, allowing a whole nation—countless numbers, hundreds of thousands of people—to go through, and when the last man is across the sea closes up again and submerges and drowns the pursuing Egyptians. The whole picture is in the spirit of antiquity—the elements obeying the magician, great jostling multitudes like Roman armies on the march, a people and a leader. Everything is visible, audible, overpowering.

"In the second miracle you have a girl—an everyday figure who would have gone unnoticed in the ancient world—quietly, secretly bringing forth a child, bringing forth life, bringing forth the miracle of life, the 'universal life,' as He was afterwards called. The birth of her child is not only a violation of human laws as interpreted by the scribes, since it was out of wedlock; it also contradicts the laws of nature. She gives birth not by virtue of a natural process but by a miracle, by an inspiration. And from now on, the basis of life is to be that inspiration which the Gospel strives to make the foundation of life, contrasting the commonplace with the unique, the weekday with the holiday, and repudiating all compulsion.

"What an enormously significant change! How did it come about that an individual human event, insignificant by ancient standards, was regarded as equal in significance to the migration of a whole people? Why should it have this value in the eyes of heaven?—For it is through the eyes of heaven that it must be judged, it is before the face of heaven and in the sacred light of its own uniqueness that it all takes place.

"Something in the world had changed. Rome was at an end. The reign of numbers was at an end. The duty, imposed by armed force, to live unanimously as a people, as a whole nation, was abolished. Leaders and nations were relegated to the past.

"They were replaced by the doctrine of individuality and freedom. Individual human life became the life story of God, and its contents filled the vast expanses of the universe. As it says in a liturgy for the Feast of the Annunciation, Adam tried to be like God and failed, but now God was made man so that Adam should be made God.

"I'll come back to this in a minute," said Sima. "But now I'd like to digress a little. With respect to the care of the workers, the protection of the mother, the struggle against the power of money, our revolutionary era is a wonderful, unforgettable era of new, permanent achievements. But as regards its interpretation of life and the philosophy of happiness that is being propagated, it's simply impossible to believe that it is meant to be taken seriously, it's such a comic survival of the past. If all this rhetoric about leaders and peoples had the power to reverse history, it would set us back thousands of years to the Biblical times of shepherd tribes and patriarchs. But fortunately this is impossible.

"Now a few words about Christ and Mary Magdalene—this isn't from the Gospel but from the prayers for one of the days in Holy Week, I think it's Tuesday or Wednesday. You know it all, Larisa Feodorovna, without me; I only want to remind you of something, I am not trying to teach you.

"As you know, the word 'passion' in Slavonic means in the first place suffering, the passion of Christ—'Christ entering upon His passion.' The liturgy also uses it in its later Russian connotation of 'lust' and 'vice.' 'My soul is enslaved by passions, I have become like the beasts of the field,' 'Being cast out of paradise, let us become worthy to be readmitted to it by mastering our passions,' and so on. It may be wrong of me, but I don't like the

Lenten texts on the curbing of the senses and the mortification of the flesh. They are curiously flat and clumsy and without the poetry of other spiritual writings. I always think they were composed by fat monks. Not that I care if they themselves broke the rules and deceived other people or if they lived according to their conscience—it's not they that I'm concerned with, but with the actual content of these passages. All these acts of contrition give too much importance to various infirmities of the flesh and to whether it is fat or famished—it's repulsive. It seems to me to raise something dirty, unimportant, inconsequential, to a dignity that does not belong to it. Forgive me for all these digressions.

"I have always wondered why Mary Magdalene is mentioned on the very eve of Easter, just before the death and resurrection of Christ. I don't know the reason for it, but this reminder of what life is seems so timely at the moment of His taking leave of it and shortly before He rises again. Now listen to how the reminder is made—what genuine passion there is in it and what an uncompromising directness.

"There is some doubt as to whether this does refer to the Magdalene or to one of the other Marys, but anyway, she begs our Lord:

"'Unbind my debt as I unbind my hair.' It means: 'As I loosen my hair, do Thou release me from my guilt.' Could any expression of repentance, of the thirst to be forgiven, be more concrete, more tangible?

"And later on in the liturgy for the same day there is another, more detailed passage, and this time it almost certainly refers to Mary Magdalene.

"Again she repents in a terribly tangible way over her past, saying that every night her flesh burns because of her old, inveterate habits. 'For the night is to me the flaring up of lust, the dark, moonless zeal of sin.' She begs Christ to accept her tears of repentance and be moved by the sincerity of her sighs, so that she may dry His most pure feet with her hair—reminding Him that in the rushing waves of her hair Eve took refuge when she was overcome with fear and shame in paradise. 'Let me kiss Thy most pure feet and water them with my tears and dry them with the hair of my head, which covered Eve and sheltered her in its rushing waves when she was afraid in the cool

of the day in paradise.' And immediately after all this about her
hair, she exclaims: 'Who can fathom the multitude of my sins or
the depths of Thy mercy?' What familiarity, what equality between God and life, God and the individual, God and a
woman!"

18

Yurii Andreievich had come home from the station tired. It was
his day off, and usually he slept enough that day to last him
the nine others of the ten-day week. He sat sprawling on the
sofa, occasionally half reclining or stretching full length. But although he listened to Sima through a mist of oncoming drowsiness, her reflections delighted him. "Of course, she's taken it all
from Uncle Nikolai," he thought. "But how intelligent she is,
how talented."

He got up and went to the window. It looked out on the yard,
like the window of the room next door from which only unintelligible whispers could now be heard.

The weather was getting worse, and it was growing dark in
the yard. Two magpies flew in from the street and fluttered
around looking for a place to settle, their feathers ruffled by the
wind. They perched on the lid of the trash bin, flew up onto the
fence, flew down to the ground, and walked about the yard.

"Magpies mean snow," thought the doctor. At the same moment Sima said aloud in the other room:

"Magpies mean news. You'll have guests, or else a letter."

A little later someone pulled the handle of the doorbell, which
Yurii Andreievich had mended a few days earlier. Lara came out
from behind the curtain and walked swiftly through to the hall
to open the door. Yurii Andreievich heard her talking with
Sima's sister Glafira.

"You've come for your sister? Yes, she's here."

"No, I didn't come for her, though we might as well go home
together if she is ready. I've brought a letter for your friend. It's
lucky for him that I once had a job at the post office. I don't
know how many hands it's been through, it's from Moscow and
it's been five months on the way. They couldn't find the ad-

dressee. At last they thought of asking me and I knew, of course—he once came to me for a haircut."

The long letter, written on many sheets of paper, crumpled and soiled in its tattered envelope, which had been opened at the post office, was from Tonia. The doctor found it in his hands without knowing how it had got there; he had not noticed Lara handing it to him. When he began reading it he was still conscious of being in Yuriatin, in Lara's house, but gradually, as he read on, he lost all realization of it. Sima came out, greeted him, and said goodbye; he said the right things automatically but paid no attention to her and never noticed when she left the house. Gradually he forgot more and more completely where he was or what surrounded him.

"Yura," Antonina Alexandrovna wrote, "do you know that we have a daughter? We have christened her Masha in memory of your mother, Maria Nikolaievna.

"Now something entirely different. Several prominent people, professors who belonged to the Cadet Party and Right-wing Socialists, Miliukov, Kizevetter, Kuskov, and several others including your Uncle Nikolai, my father, and the rest of us, are being deported abroad.

"This is a misfortune, especially in your absence, but we must accept it and thank God that our exile takes so mild a form when at this terrible time things could have been so much worse for us. If you were here, you would come with us. But where are you? I am sending this letter to Antipova's address, she'll give it to you if she finds you. I am tortured by not knowing if the exit permit we are getting as a family will be extended to you later on, when, if God is willing, you are found. I have not given up believing that you are alive and that you will be found. My loving heart tells me that this is so, and I trust it. Perhaps by then, by the time you reappear, conditions in Russia will be milder and you will manage to get a separate visa for yourself and we shall all be together once again in the same place. But as I write this, I don't believe in the possibility of such happiness.

"The whole trouble is that I love you and that you don't love me. I keep trying to discover the meaning of this judgment on me, to interpret it, to justify it. I look into myself, I go over our whole life together and everything I know about myself, and I can't find the beginning, and I can't remember what it is I did or how I brought this misfortune on myself. I have a feeling that you misjudge me, that you take an unkind view of me, that you see me as in a distorting mirror.

"As for me, I love you. If only you knew how much I love you! I love all that is unusual in you, the good with the bad, and all the ordinary traits of your character, whose extraordinary combination is so dear to me, your face ennobled by your thoughts, which otherwise might not seem handsome, your great gifts and intelligence which, as it were, have taken the place of the will that is lacking. All this is dear to me, and I know no man who is better than you.

"But listen, do you know what? Even if you were not so dear to me, even if I did not like you so much, even then the distressing truth of my coldness would not have been disclosed to me, even then I would have believed that I love you. Out of sheer terror before the humiliating, destructive punishment which failure to love is, I would unconsciously have shunned the realization that I do not love you. Neither I nor you would ever have learned it. My own heart would have concealed it from me, for failure to love is almost like murder and I would have been incapable of inflicting such a blow on anyone.

"Nothing is definitely settled yet, but we are probably going to Paris. I'll be in those distant lands where you were taken as a child and where Father and my uncle were brought up. Father sends you his greetings. Sasha has grown a lot, he is not particularly good-looking but he is a big, strong boy and whenever we speak of you he cries bitterly and won't be comforted. I can't go on. I can't stop crying. Well, goodbye. Let me make the sign of the cross over you and bless you for all the years ahead, for the endless parting, the trials, the uncertainties, for all your long, long, dark way. I am not blaming you for anything, I am not reproaching you, do as you please with your life, I'll be happy if all is well with you.

"Before we left the Urals—what a terrible and fateful place it turned out to be for us—I got to know Larisa Feodorovna fairly well. I am thankful to her for being constantly at my side at a difficult time and for helping me through my confinement. I must honestly admit that she is a good person, but I don't want to be a hypocrite—she is my exact opposite. I was born to make life simple and to look for sensible solutions; she, to complicate it and create confusion.

"Farewell, I must stop. They have come for the letter, and it's time I packed. Oh, Yura, Yura, my dear, my darling, my husband, the father of my children, what is happening to us? Do you realize that we'll never, never see each other again? Now I've written it down, do you realize what it means? Do you understand, do you understand? They are hurrying me and it's as if they had come to take me to my death. Yura! Yura!"

Yurii Andreievich looked up from the letter with absent, tearless eyes, dry with grief, ravaged by suffering. He could see nothing around him, he was not conscious of anything.

Outside it was snowing. The wind swept the snow aside, ever faster and thicker, as if it were trying to catch up with something, and Yurii Andreievich stared ahead of him out of the window, as if he were not looking at the snow but were still reading Tonia's letter and as if what flickered past him were not small dry snow crystals but the spaces between the small black letters, white, white, endless, endless.

Involuntarily he groaned and clutched his breast. He felt he was going to faint, hobbled the few steps to the sofa, and fell down on it unconscious.

CHAPTER FOURTEEN

RETURN TO VARYKINO

1

Winter had settled in. It was snowing hard as Yurii Andreievich walked back from the hospital. Lara met him in the hall.

"Komarovsky is here," she said in a low, hoarse voice. She stood looking bewildered as if she had been struck.

"Where? Here?"

"No, of course not. He came this morning and said he would come back tonight. He'll be here soon. He wants to have a word with you."

"Why has he come?"

"I didn't understand all he said. He said he was going to the Far East and that he had come out of his way to see us. Particularly to see you and Pasha. He talked a great deal about both of you. He insists that we are in mortal danger, all three of us, you and Pasha and I. And that he alone can save us, provided we do as he says."

"I will go out. I don't want to see him."

Lara burst into tears and tried to throw herself at his feet and clasp his knees, but he forced her to get up.

"Please don't go, for my sake," she implored him. "It isn't that I'm frightened of being alone with him, but it's so painful. Spare me from having to see him alone. Besides, he is practical, experienced—he might really have some advice to give us. Your aversion for him is natural, but please put your feelings aside. Don't go."

"What is the matter with you, darling? Don't be so upset. What are you trying to do? Don't fall on your knees. Get up now, and cheer up. You really must get rid of this obsession

419

—he's frightened you for life. You know I'm with you. I'll kill him if necessary, if you tell me to."

Night fell about half an hour later. It was completely dark. It was half a year now since all the ratholes had been stopped up. Yurii Andreievich watched for new ones, plugging them up in time. They also kept a big, fluffy tomcat who spent his time in immobile contemplation, looking enigmatic. The rats were still in the house, but they were now more cautious.

Waiting for Komarovsky, Larisa Feodorovna cut some slices of rationed black bread and put a plate with a few boiled potatoes on the table. They had decided to receive him in the old dining room, which they still used for their meals. The large, heavy, dark oak table and sideboard were part of its original furnishings. Standing on the table was a bottle of castor oil with a wick in it which they used as a portable lamp.

Komarovsky came in out of the dark December night covered with snow. Lumps of it fell from his hat, coat, and galoshes and melted into puddles on the floor. His mustache and beard, plastered with snow, made him look like a clown. (He had been clean-shaven in the old days.) He wore a well-preserved suit with striped, well-creased trousers. Before greeting his hosts he spent a long time combing his rumpled, glistening hair with a pocket comb and drying his mustache and eyebrows with a handkerchief. Then, silently and with a solemn expression, he stretched out both his hands—the left one to Larisa Feodorovna and the right one to Yurii Andreievich.

"We'll assume that we are old acquaintances," he said to Yurii Andreievich. "I was a great friend of your father's, as you probably know. He died in my arms. I keep looking at you to see if there is any likeness. But I don't think you take after him. He was an expansive man, spontaneous and impulsive. You must be more like your mother. She was gentle, a dreamer."

"Larisa Feodorovna asked me to see you. She said you had some business with me. I agreed, but our meeting is not of my choice, and I don't consider that we are acquainted. So shall we get on with it? What is it you want?"

"I am so happy to see you both, my dears. I understand everything, absolutely everything. Forgive my boldness, but you are wonderfully well suited to each other. A perfect match."

"I'll have to interrupt you. Kindly don't interfere in what doesn't concern you. We haven't asked for your sympathy. You forget yourself."

"Don't be so touchy, young man. Perhaps after all you do take after your father. He used to lose his temper just like that. Well, my children, with your permission I offer you my best wishes. Unfortunately, however, you really are children—not just in a manner of speaking—completely ignorant and thoughtless children. In two days here I've learned more about you than you know or suspect about yourselves. Without knowing it, you are walking on the brink of a precipice. Unless you do something about it, the days of your freedom and perhaps even of your lives are numbered.

"There exists a certain Communist style, Yurii Andreievich. Few people measure up to it. But no one flouts that way of life and thought as openly as you do. Why you have to flirt with danger, I can't imagine. You are a living mockery of that whole world, a walking insult to it. If at least your past were your own secret—but there are people from Moscow who know you inside out. Neither of you are at all to the liking of the local priests of Themis. Comrades Antipov and Tiverzin are busy sharpening their claws, ready to pounce on Larisa Feodorovna and you.

"However, you are a man, Yurii Andreievich, you are your own master, and you have a perfect right to gamble with your life if you feel like it. But Larisa Feodorovna is not a free agent. She is a mother, she has a child's life in her hands, and she can't go about with her head in the clouds.

"I wasted all my morning trying to get her to take the situation seriously. She wouldn't listen to me. Will you use your influence? She has no right to play with her daughter's safety. She must not disregard my arguments."

"I've never in my life forced my views on anyone. Certainly not on those who are close to me. Larisa Feodorovna is free to listen to you or not as she thinks fit. It's her business. Apart from that, I have no idea what you are talking about. I haven't heard what you call your arguments."

"Really, you remind me more and more of your father—just as intractable. Well, I'll tell you. But it's a fairly complicated business, so you'll have to be patient with me and not interrupt.

"Big changes are being planned at the top. Yes, really, I have it from a most reliable source and you can take it that it's true. What they have in mind is to take a more democratic line, make a concession to legality, and this will come about quite soon.

"But just because of it, the punitive organs that are to be abolished will be in all the greater hurry to settle their local accounts before the end, and they will be all the more savage. You are marked for destruction, Yurii Andreievich. Your name is on the list—I am telling you this in all seriousness, I've seen it myself. You must think of saving yourself before it is too late.

"But all this is by way of introduction. I am coming to the point.

"Those political forces that are still faithful to the Provisional Government and the disbanded Constituent Assembly are concentrating in the Maritime Province on the Pacific coast. Deputies to the Duma, the more prominent members of the old Zemstvos, and other public figures, businessmen and industrialists, are getting together. The remnants of the armies that fought against the Reds are being concentrated there.

"They intend to form a Far Eastern republic, and the Soviet Government winks at it, because at the moment it would suit it to have a buffer between Red Siberia and the outside world. The republic is to have a coalition government. More than half the seats, at the insistence of Moscow, will go to Communists. When it suits them, they will stage a *coup d'état* and bring the republic to heel. The plan is quite transparent, but it gives us a certain breathing space; and we must make the most of it.

"At one time before the revolution I used to look after the affairs of the Merkulovs, the Arkharov Brothers, and several other banks and trading firms in Vladivostok. They know me there, and an emissary came to see me on behalf of the shadow cabinet, to offer me the post of Minister of Justice in the future government. This was done secretly, but with unofficial Soviet approval. I accepted and I am on my way there now. All I've just told you is happening with the tacit consent of the Soviet Government, but not so openly that it would be wise to talk much about it.

"I can take you and Larisa Feodorovna with me. From there, you can easily get a boat and join your family overseas. You know, of course, that they have been deported. It made a lot of noise; the whole of Moscow is still talking about it.

"I have promised Larisa Feodorovna to save Strelnikov. As a member of an independent government recognized by Moscow, I can look for him in eastern Siberia and help him to cross over into our autonomous region. If he does not succeed in escaping, I'll suggest that he should be exchanged for someone who is in Allied custody and is valuable to the Moscow Government."

Larisa Feodorovna had followed Komarovsky's explanation with difficulty, but when he came to the arrangements for the safety of the doctor and of Strelnikov, she pricked up her ears. Blushing a little, she said:

"You see, Yurochka, how important all this is for you and for Pasha?"

"You are too trusting, my dear. You can't take a half-formed plan for an accomplished fact. I don't say Victor Ippolitovich is deliberately misleading us, but so far he has only told us about castles in the air. For my part," he said, turning to Komarovsky, "thank you for the interest you take in my affairs, but you surely don't imagine that I am going to let you run them? As for Strelnikov, Lara will have to think it over."

"All it comes down to," said Lara, "is whether we go with him or not. You know perfectly well I wouldn't go without you."

Komarovsky sipped the diluted alcohol that Yurii Andreievich had brought from the hospital, ate boiled potatoes, and became more and more tipsy.

2

It was getting late. Every time the wick was trimmed it spluttered and burned brightly, lighting up the room, then the flame died down and the shadows returned. The hosts were sleepy, they wanted to talk things over by themselves and go to bed, but Komarovsky stayed on. His presence was oppressive, as was the sight of the heavy oak sideboard and the December darkness outside the windows.

He was not looking at them but over their heads, his glazed eyes staring at some distant point and his drowsy, slurred voice grinding on and on, tedious and interminable. His latest hobbyhorse was the Far East. He was explaining the political importance of Mongolia. Yurii Andreievich and Larisa Feodorovna, who were not interested in the subject, had missed the point at which he had got onto it, and this made his explanations even more boring. He was saying:

"Siberia—truly a New America, as it is often called—has immense possibilities. It is the cradle of Russia's future greatness, the gauge of our progress toward democracy and political and economic health. Still more pregnant with future possibilities is our great Far Eastern neighbor—Outer Mongolia. What do you know about it? You yawn and blink shamelessly, and yet Mongolia has nearly a million square miles and untold mineral wealth; it is a virgin land that tempts the greed of China, of Japan, and of the United States. They are all ready to snatch at it to the detriment of our Russian interests—interests that have been recognized by all our rivals, whenever there has been a division of that remote quarter of the globe into spheres of influence.

"China exploits the feudal-theocratic backwardness of Mongolia through her influence over the lamas and other religious dignitaries. Japan backs the local princes—the *hoshuns*. Red Russia has found an ally in the Revolutionary Association of Insurgent Mongolian Herdsmen. I myself would like to see a really prosperous Mongolia with a freely elected government. What should interest you personally is that once you are across the Mongolian frontier, the world is at your feet—you are as free as a bird."

His wordy dissertation got on Larisa Feodorovna's nerves. Finally, bored to tears and utterly tired, she held out her hand to him and said abruptly and with undisguised hostility:

"It's late and it's time for you to go. I am sleepy."

"I hope you aren't going to be so inhospitable as to throw me out at this hour of the night! I don't believe I can find my way—I don't know the town and it's pitch dark."

"You should have thought of that earlier, instead of sitting on and on. No one asked you to stay so late."

"Why are you so sharp with me? You didn't even ask me if I have anywhere to stay."

"It doesn't interest me in the slightest. You are perfectly well able to look after yourself. If you are angling for an invitation to spend the night, I certainly won't put you in the room where we and Katenka sleep, and the other rooms are full of rats."

"I don't mind them."

"Well, have it your way."

3

"What is wrong, darling? You don't sleep for nights on end, you don't touch your food, you go about all day looking like a maniac. You are always brooding about something. What is bothering you? You mustn't let your worries get the better of you."

"Izot, the watchman from your hospital, has been around again—he is having an affair with the laundress downstairs. So he dropped in and gave me a cheerful piece of news! 'It's terribly secret,' he said. 'It's jail for your friend. Any day now. And then it'll be your turn, poor thing.' 'How do you know?' I asked him. 'Oh, it's quite certain, I heard it from a friend who works at the Comics.' Of course, what he means by that is the Executive Committee. That's what he calls the Comics." They both burst out laughing.

"He is quite right," said Yurii Andreievich. "The danger has caught up with us and it's time we vanished. The problem is where. There is no question of going to Moscow—we couldn't make the arrangements for the journey without attracting attention. We must slip away so that nobody sees us go. Do you know, my love, we'll do what you thought of in the first place, we'll go to Varykino and drop out of sight. Let's go there for a week or two or a month."

"Thank you, thank you, my dear. Oh, how glad I am! I understand how much you dislike the idea. But we wouldn't live in your house. You couldn't possibly face that—the sight of the empty rooms, the self-reproach, the comparisons with the past. How well I know what it means to build one's happiness on the sufferings of others, to trample on what is dear to one, and holy. I'd never accept such a sacrifice from you. But there is no question of that. Your house is in such a state that it would be difficult to make the rooms fit to live in, anyway. I was thinking of the house where the Mikulitsyns lived."

"All that is true enough, and I am grateful to you for being so considerate. But wait a minute. I keep meaning to ask you and forgetting. What has happened to Komarovsky? Is he still here or is he gone? Since I quarrelled with him and threw him out I've heard nothing more of him."

"I don't know anything either. But who cares! What do you want with him?"

"I have come to think that perhaps we shouldn't have rejected his proposal outright—I mean both of us. We are not in the same position. You have your daughter to think of. Even if you wanted to share my fate, you'd have no right to do it.

"But about Varykino. Of course, to go to that wilderness in winter, without food, without strength or hope—it's utter madness. But why not, my love! Let's be mad, if there is nothing except madness left to us. We'll forget our pride once more and beg Samdeviatov to lend us a horse. And we'll ask him, or not even him but the speculators who depend on him, to let us have flour and potatoes on credit, for what our credit is still worth. And we'll persuade him not to take advantage of the favor he's doing us by coming to see us at once, but to wait until later—not to come until he needs his horse. Let's be alone for a while. Let's go, my love. And we'll cut and use more logs in a week than a careful housewife would use in a year in peaceful times.

"And once again, forgive me for my confused way of speaking. How I wish I could talk with you without being so stupidly solemn! But after all, it's true that we haven't any choice. Call it what you like, death is really knocking at our door. Our days are really numbered. So at least let us take advantage of them in our own way. Let us use them up saying goodbye to life, being together for the last time before we are parted. We'll say goodbye to everything we hold dear, to the way we look at things, to the way we've dreamed of living and to what our conscience has taught us, and to our hopes and to each other. We'll speak to one another once again the secret words we speak at night, great and pacific like the name of the Asian ocean. It's not for nothing that you stand at the end of my life, my hidden, forbidden angel, under the skies of wars and turmoil, you who arose at its beginning under the peaceful skies of childhood.

"That night, as a girl in a dark brown school uniform, in the half shadow of the hotel room, you were exactly as you are now, and just as breath-takingly beautiful.

"Often since then I have tried to define and give a name to the enchantment that you communicated to me that night, that faint glow, that distant echo, which later permeated my whole being and gave me a key to the understanding of everything in the world.

"When you rose out of the darkness of that room, like a shadow in a schoolgirl's dress, I, a boy who knew nothing about you, understood who you were, with all the tormenting intensity which responded in me: I realized that this scraggy, thin little girl was charged, as with electricity, with all the femininity in the world. If I had touched you with so much as the tip of my finger, a spark would have lit up the room and either killed me on the spot or charged me for the whole of my life with magnetic waves of sorrow and longing. I was filled to the brim with tears, I cried and glowed inwardly. I was mortally sorry for myself, a boy, and still more sorry for you, a girl. My whole being was astonished and asked: If it is so painful to love and to be charged with this electric current, how much more painful must it be to a woman and to be the current, and to inspire love.

"There—at last I've said it. Such a thing can drive you mad. It expresses my very being."

Larisa Feodorovna lay dressed at the edge of her bed. She was not feeling well, and had curled up and covered herself with a shawl. Yurii Andreievich sat on a chair beside her, speaking quietly, with long pauses. Sometimes she raised herself on her elbow, propped her chin on her hand, and gazed at him, her lips parted. At other times she buried her head in his shoulder and cried silently with joy, without noticing her tears. At last she leaned out of bed, put her arms around him, and whispered happily:

"Yurochka! Yurochka! How wise you are! You know everything, you divine everything, Yurochka, you are my strength and my refuge, God forgive me the blasphemy. Oh, I am so happy. Let's go, my darling, let's go. Out there I'll tell you something I have on my mind."

He decided that she was referring to pregnancy, probably a false pregnancy, and he said: "I know."

4

They left town on the morning of a gray winter day. It was a weekday. People in the streets were going about their business; there were many familiar faces. At the squares, women who had no wells in their yards were queueing up for water at the old pumps, their yokes and buckets on the ground beside them. The doctor drove around them carefully, checking Samdeviatov's spirited, smoky-yellow horse. The sleigh kept gliding off the slope of the street, icy with splashed water, onto the sidewalks and hitting lampposts and curbstones.

Galloping at full tilt, they caught up with Samdeviatov, who was walking down the street, and swept past him without looking back to see if he had recognized them and his horse, or whether he had anything to say to them. A little farther on they passed Komarovsky, and again swept by without a greeting.

Glafira Tuntseva shouted to them from across the street: "What lies people tell! They said you had left yesterday. Going for potatoes?" and signalling that she could not hear what they replied waved them goodbye.

They slowed down for Sima, and this was on an awkward slope where it was impossible to stop; the horse kept pulling at the reins. Sima, muffled from head to foot in several shawls and looking as stiff as a log, hobbled out into the middle of the street to say goodbye and wish them a good journey.

"When you come back we must have a talk," she said to Yurii Andreievich.

At last they left the town behind. Although the doctor had been on this road in winter, he mostly remembered it in its summer aspect and hardly recognized it now.

They had pushed their sacks of food and other bundles deep into the hay in the front of the sleigh and had tied them down with rope. Yurii Andreievich drove either kneeling upright on the floor of the sleigh like the local peasants or sitting with his legs in Samdeviatov's felt boots hanging over the side.

In the afternoon when, as usual in winter, the day seemed on the point of ending long before sunset, Yurii Andreievich began to whip the horse mercilessly. It shot forward like an arrow. The sleigh pitched and tossed on the uneven road, like a ship in a storm. Lara and Katia were bundled up in their fur coats so that they could hardly move. Swinging around corners and bumping over ruts, they rolled from side to side and down into the hay like sacks, laughing themselves sick. Sometimes the doctor drove into the snowy banks on purpose, for a joke, and harmlessly tipped them all out into the snow. After being dragged for a few yards by the reins he stopped the horse, righted the sleigh, and was pummelled by Lara and Katia, who climbed back, scolding and laughing.

"I'll show you the place where I was stopped by the partisans," the doctor told them when they were at some distance from the town, but he was unable to keep his promise because the winter bareness of the woods, the dead quiet, and the emptiness all around changed the country beyond recognition. "Here it is," he soon shouted, mistaking the first of the Moreau & Vetchinkin signs, which stood in a field, for the one in the forest where he was captured. When they galloped past the second, still in its old place in the thicket at the Sakma crossroads, it was indistinguishable from the dazzling lacework of hoarfrost that made the forest look like black and silver filigree, so that they never saw it.

It was still daylight when they swept into Varykino, and as the Zhivagos' house came first they stopped in front of it. They burst in like robbers, hurrying because it would soon be dark. But inside it was dark already, so that Yurii Andreievich never saw half the destruction and abomination. Part of the furniture he remembered was still there; Varykino was deserted and there was no one to complete the damage. He could see no personal belongings; but as he had not been there when his family left he could not tell how much they had taken with them. In the meantime Lara was saying:

"We must hurry. It will be dark in a moment. We haven't time to stand about thinking. If we are to stay here, the horse must go into the barn, the food into the hallway, and we must fix this room for ourselves. But I'm against it. We talked it all out before. It will be painful for you and therefore also for me. What was this room, your bedroom? No, the nursery. There's your son's crib. It would be too small for Katia. On the other hand, the windows are whole, there are no cracks in the walls or ceiling, and the stove is marvellous—I admired it last time I came. So if you insist on our staying here—though I am against it—I'll get out of my coat and set to work at once. The first thing is to get the stove going, and to stoke and stoke and stoke, we'll have to keep it going all the time for at least twenty-four hours. But what is it, my darling? You haven't answered."

"In a moment. I'm all right. I'm sorry. . . . No, perhaps we'd better have a look at the Mikulitsyns' house."

They drove on.

5

The Mikulitsyns' door was padlocked. Yurii Andreievich wrenched off the lock together with its screws and splintered wood, and here again they rushed in hurriedly, going straight to the inner rooms without taking off their coats, hats, and felt boots.

They were immediately struck by the tidiness of certain parts of the house, particularly of Mikulitsyn's study. Someone must have been living here until recently, but who? Had it been any of the Mikulitsyns, where had they gone, and why had they put a padlock on the door instead of using their keys? Furthermore, if the Mikulitsyns had been here continuously for long stretches, wouldn't the whole house have been tidy and not just some of the rooms? Everything spoke of an intruder, but who could it have been? Neither the doctor nor Lara worried about the mystery. They did not try to solve it. There were plenty of half-looted houses now, and plenty of fugitives. "Some White officer on the run," they told each other. "If he comes we'll make some arrangement."

Once again, as so long before, Yurii Andreievich stood spellbound in the door of the study, so spacious and comfortable with its large, convenient table by the window. And once again he thought that such austere surroundings would be conducive to patient, fruitful work.

Among the outbuildings in the yard was the stable adjoining the barn, but it was locked and Yurii Andreievich did not bother to break in, since in any case it might not be fit to use. The horse could spend the night in the barn, which opened easily. He unharnessed the horse and when it had cooled down gave it water which he had got at the well. He had meant to give it the hay he had brought along, but it had been trampled to rubbish under their feet. Luckily, there was enough of it in the large loft over the barn.

They lay down without undressing, using their fur coats for blankets, and fell into a deep, sound, blissful sleep, like children after running about and playing all day.

6

From the moment they got up, Yurii Andreievich kept glancing at the table standing so temptingly by the window. His fingers itched for paper and pen. But he put off writing until the evening, until after Lara and Katia would have gone to bed. Until then he would have his hands full, even if no more than two of the rooms were to be made habitable.

In looking forward to the evening he had no important work in mind. It was merely that the passion to write possessed him.

He had to scribble something. For a beginning, he would put down old unwritten thoughts, just to get him into trim. Later, he hoped, if he and Lara managed to stay on, there would be time for undertaking something new, important.

"Are you busy? What are you doing?"

"Stoking and stoking. What is it?"

"I want a tub to wash the linen in."

"We'll run out of logs in three days if we go on using them at this rate. I must have a look in our old woodshed, there might be some left—who knows? If there are, I'll bring them over. I'll do that tomorrow. A tub, you said. I'm sure I've seen one somewhere, I can't think where."

"So have I, and I can't think where either. It must have been somewhere it had no business to be, that's why I forgot. Well, never mind. Remember, I'm heating a lot of water for cleaning up. What's left I'll use for laundering some of Katia's and my things. You might as well give me your laundry too. We'll have baths in the evening, when we've settled in, before we go to bed."

"Thank you. I'll get my things now. I've moved all the heavy furniture away from the walls, as you wanted it."

"Good. I'll use the dish-washing basin for the laundry, since we can't find the tub. But it's greasy, I'll have to scrub it."

"As soon as the stove is properly stoked I'll go through the rest of the drawers. I keep finding more things in the desk and the chest—soap, matches, paper, pencils, pens, ink. And the lamp on the table is full of kerosene. I am sure the Mikulitsyns didn't have any, it must come from somewhere else."

"What luck! It's our mysterious lodger. Just like something out of Jules Verne. But here we are gossiping again, and my water's boiling."

They bustled and dashed about from room to room, their hands never still or empty for a moment, running into one another and stumbling over Katenka, who was always under their feet. She drifted about, getting in the way of their work and sulking when they scolded her. She shivered and complained of the cold.

"These poor modern children," thought the doctor, "victims of our gypsy life, wretched little fellow wanderers." Aloud he said:

"Cheer up, girl. You can't be cold, that's nonsense, the stove is red hot."

"The stove may be feeling warm but I'm cold."

"Well then, you'll have to be patient till this evening. I'll get a huge blaze going and you heard Mama say she'll give you a hot bath. And now you play with these—catch." He got all Liberius's old toys out of the chilly storeroom and dumped them on the floor, some whole, some broken, blocks, trains, and locomotives, boards with squares and pictures or numbers on them for games with dice and counters.

"What can you be thinking of, Yurii Andreievich?" Katia protested like a grownup. "They aren't mine. And they are for a baby. I'm too big."

But the next moment she had made herself comfortable in the middle of the rug and all the toys had turned into bricks for a house for Ninka, the doll she had brought from town. It was a much more sensible and settled home than any of the temporary lodgings in other people's houses where she had spent most of her life.

Lara watched her from the kitchen. "Look at that instinct for domesticity. It just shows, nothing can destroy the longing for home and for order. Children are more honest, they aren't frightened of the truth, but we are so afraid of seeming to be behind the times that we are ready to betray what is most dear to us and praise what repels us and say yes to what we don't understand."

"Here's the tub," said Yurii Andreievich, coming in out of the dark hallway. "It certainly wasn't in its place. It was standing under the leak in the ceiling. I suppose it's been there since last autumn."

7

For dinner, Lara, who had started on the provisions they had brought and had cooked enough for three days, served an unprecedented feast of potato soup and roast mutton and potatoes. Katenka ate till she could eat no more, giggling and getting more and more naughty, and afterwards, warm and full, curled up in her mother's shawl on the sofa and went to sleep.

Larisa Feodorovna, hot and tired from the oven, almost as sleepy as her daughter, and pleased with the success of her cooking, was in no hurry to clear away the plates and sat down to have a rest. After making sure that Katenka was asleep, she said, leaning forward on the table, with her chin on her hand:

"I'd slave and be happy if only I knew it was getting us somewhere, if it wasn't all for nothing. You'll have to keep reminding me that we came here to be together. Keep cheering me up, don't let me think. Because strictly speaking, if you look at it honestly, what are we doing, what is all this? We've raided someone else's house, we've broken in and made ourselves at home, and now we bustle around like mad so as not to see that this isn't life, that it's a stage set, that it isn't real, that it's all 'pretend,' as children say, a child's game—just ridiculous."

"But, darling, isn't it you who insisted on our coming? Don't you remember how long I held out against it?"

"Certainly I did. I don't deny it. So now I am at fault! It's all right for you to think twice and hesitate, but I have to be logical and consistent all the time! You come in, you see your son's crib, and you nearly faint. That's your right, but I'm not allowed to be worried, to be afraid for Katenka, to think about the future, everything has to give way before my love for you."

"Larusha! Pull yourself together. Think. It's not too late to go back on your decision. I was the first to tell you to take Komarovsky's plan more seriously. We've got a horse. If you like we'll go straight back to Yuriatin tomorrow. Komarovsky is still there, we saw him—and incidentally I don't think he saw us. I'm sure we'll still find him."

"I've hardly said a word, and you sound annoyed. But tell me, am I so wrong? We might just as well have stayed in Yuriatin if we weren't going to hide better than this. If we really meant to save ourselves we should have had a sensible plan, properly thought out, and that after all is what Komarovsky offered us. Disgusting as he is, he is a well-informed and practical man. We are in greater danger here than anywhere else. Just think!—alone on a boundless, wind-swept plain! If we were snowed under in the night we couldn't dig ourselves out in the morning! Or suppose our mysterious benefactor, who visited this house, turns out to be a bandit and comes and slits our throats! Have you at least got a gun? I thought not! You see? What terrifies me is your thoughtlessness, and you've infected me with it as well. I simply can't think straight."

"But what do you want? What do you want me to do now?"

"I don't know myself what to say. Keep me under your thumb all the time. Keep reminding me that I'm your loving slave and that it's not my business to think or argue. Oh, I'll tell you what. Your Tonia and my Pasha are a thousand times better than we are, but that isn't the point. The point is that the gift of love is like any other gift. However great it is, it won't thrive without a blessing. You and I, it's as though we have been taught to kiss in heaven and sent down to earth together, to see if we know what we were taught. It's a sort of crowning harmony—no limits, no degrees, everything is of equal value, everything is a joy, everything has become spirit. But in this wild tenderness that lies in wait for us at every moment there is something childish, unrestrained, irresponsible. It's a willful, destructive element, hostile to domestic happiness, such a love. It's my duty to be afraid of it and to distrust it."

She threw her arms around his neck, struggling with tears.

"Don't you see, we are not in the same position. You were given wings to fly above the clouds, but I'm a woman, mine are given me to stay close to the ground and to shelter my young."

He was deeply moved by everything she said, but he didn't show it, lest he give way to his emotions.

"It's quite true that there is something false and strained about this camp life we lead. You are perfectly right. But it isn't we who invented it. This frantic dashing about from pillar to post is what is happening to everyone, it's in the spirit of the times.

"I've been thinking about it myself all day. I should like to do everything possible to stay here for some time. I can't tell you how I'm longing to get back to work. I don't mean farming. That's what we were doing here before, we took it on as a family and we succeeded. But I wouldn't have the strength to do it again. I've got something else in mind.

"Things are gradually settling down. Perhaps one day they'll start publishing books again.

"This is what I was thinking. Couldn't we come to an agreement with Samdeviatov—we'd have to give him profitable terms, of course—so that he should keep us here for six months at his expense, on condition that I spend this time writing a book, say a textbook on medicine, or something literary, perhaps a collection of poems. Or I might translate some famous classic. I'm good at languages. I saw an advertisement the other day, there's a big publisher in Petersburg who is doing nothing but translations. I'm pretty sure this sort of work will have a value in terms of money. I'd be very happy doing something of that kind."

"I am glad you reminded me, I was also thinking of something like that today. But I have no faith in our future here. On the contrary, I have a foreboding that we'll soon be swept away, somewhere even more distant. But so long as we still have this breathing space, I want to ask you a favor. Will you give up a few hours in the next few evenings and put down all the poems

I have heard from you at different times? Half of them you've lost and the rest you've never written down, and I'm afraid you'll forget them and they'll be lost altogether as you say has often happened before."

8

At the end of the day they washed in plenty of hot water, and Lara bathed Katenka. Feeling blissfully clean, Yurii Andreievich sat down at the table before the window, his back to the room where Lara, wrapped in a bath towel and fragrant with soap, her hair twisted in a turban with another towel, was putting Katenka to bed and tucking her up. Enjoying the foretaste of concentrated work, he took in what was going on around him with a happy, diffuse attentiveness.

It was one in the morning when Lara, who had been pretending, finally went to sleep. Her nightdress and Katenka's, like the freshly laundered linen on the beds, shone clean and lacy. Even in those days, Lara managed somehow to get starch.

The stillness that surrounded Yurii Andreievich breathed with happiness and life. The lamplight fell softly yellow on the white sheets of paper and gilded the surface of the ink inside the inkwell. Outside, the frosty winter night was pale blue. To see it better, Yurii Andreievich stepped into the next room, cold and dark, and looked out of the window. The light of the full moon on the snow-covered clearing was as viscid as white of egg or thick white paint. The splendor of the frosty night was inexpressible. His heart was at peace. He went back into the warm, well-lit room and began to write.

Careful to convey the living movement of his hand in his flowing writing, so that even outwardly it should not lose individuality and grow numb and soulless, he set down, gradually improving them and moving further and further away from the original as he made copy after copy, the poems that he remembered best and that had taken the most definite shape in his mind—"Christmas Star," "Winter Night," and a number of others of the same kind, which later were forgotten, mislaid, and never found again.

From these old, completed poems, he went on to others that he had begun and left unfinished, getting into their spirit and sketching the sequels, though without the slightest hope of finishing them now. Finally getting into his stride and carried away, he started on a new poem.

After two or three stanzas and several images by which he himself was struck, his work took possession of him and he felt the approach of what is called inspiration. At such moments the relation of the forces that determine artistic creation is, as it were, reversed. The dominant thing is no longer the state of mind the artist seeks to express but the language in which he wants to express it. Language, the home and receptacle of beauty and meaning, itself begins to think and speak for man and turns wholly into music, not in terms of sonority but in terms of the impetuousness and power of its inward flow. Then, like the current of a mighty river polishing stones and turning wheels by its very movement, the flow of speech creates in passing, by virtue of its own laws, meter and rhythm and countless other forms and formations, which are even more important, but which are as yet unexplored, insufficiently recognized, and unnamed.

At such moments Yurii Andreievich felt that the main part of the work was being done not by him but by a superior power which was above him and directed him, namely the movement of universal thought and poetry in its present historical stage and the one to come. And he felt himself to be only the occasion, the fulcrum, needed to make this movement possible.

This feeling relieved him for a time of self-reproach, of his dissatisfaction with himself, of the sense of his own insignificance. He looked up, he looked around him.

He saw the two sleeping heads on their snow-white pillows. The purity of their features, and of the clean linen and the clean rooms, and of the night, the snow, the stars, the moon, surged through his heart in a single wave of meaning, moving him to a joyful sense of the triumphant purity of being.

"Lord! Lord!" he whispered, "and all this is for me? Why hast Thou given me so much? Why hast Thou admitted me to Thy presence, allowed me to stray into Thy world, among Thy treasures, under Thy stars, and to the feet of my luckless, reckless, uncomplaining love, who fills my eyes with perpetual delight?"

At three in the morning Yurii Andreievich looked up from his papers. He came back from his remote, selfless concentration, home to reality and to himself, happy, strong, peaceful. Suddenly the stillness of the open country stretching into the distance outside the window was broken by a mournful, plaintive sound.

He went into the unlit adjoining room to look through the window, but while he had been working the glass had frosted over. He dragged away the roll of carpet that had been pushed against the front door to stop the draft, threw his coat over his shoulders, and went out.

He was dazzled by the white glow playing on the shadowless, moonlit snow and could at first see nothing. Then the long, whimpering, deep-bellied howl sounded again, muffled by the distance, and he noticed four long shadows, no thicker than pencil strokes, at the edge of the clearing just beyond the gully.

The wolves stood in a row, their heads raised and their muzzles pointing at the house, baying at the moon or at its silver reflection on the windows. But scarcely had Yurii Andreievich realized that they were wolves when they turned and trotted off like dogs, almost as if they could read his thoughts. He lost sight of them before he noticed the direction in which they had vanished.

"That's the last straw!" he thought. "Is their lair quite close? Perhaps in the gully? How terrible! And Samdeviatov's horse in the barn! They must have scented it."

He decided for the time being not to tell Lara, lest he upset her. Going back, he shut all the doors between the cold rooms and the heated part of the house, pushed rugs and clothes against the cracks to keep out the draft, and went back to his desk. The lamplight was bright and welcoming as before. But he was no longer in the mood to write. He couldn't settle down. He could think of nothing but wolves and of looming dangers and complications of every kind. Moreover, he was tired.

Lara woke up. "Are you still burning, my precious bright light?" she whispered in a husky voice heavy with sleep. "Come and sit beside me for a moment. I'll tell you my dream."

He put out the light.

9

Another day of quiet madness went by. They had found a child's sled in the house. Katenka, flushed bright red and bundled up in her coat, glided, shrieking with laughter, down the unswept paths from the snow-chute Yurii Andreievich had made for her by packing the snow hard with his spade and pouring water on it. Endlessly, she climbed back to the top of the mound, pulling the sled by a string, her smile never leaving her face.

It was freezing; the air was getting noticeably colder, but it was sunny. The snow was yellow at noon, with orange seeping into its honey color like an aftertaste at sunset.

The laundering and washing that Lara had done the day before had made the house damp. The steam had covered the windows with thick hoarfrost and left black streaks of damp on the wallpaper. The rooms were dark and cheerless. Yurii Andreievich carried logs and water and went on with his inspection of the house, making more and more discoveries, and he helped Lara with her endless chores.

In the rush of some task or other their hands would meet and join, and then they set down whatever they were carrying, weak and giddy with the irresistible onslaught of their tenderness, all thought driven from their heads. And the moments went by until it was late and they both remembered, horrified, that Katenka had been left alone much too long or that the horse was unwatered and unfed, and rushed off, conscience-stricken, to make up for their omissions.

Yurii Andreievich had not slept enough; there was a pleasant haze in his head, like tipsiness, and he ached all over with a nagging blissful weakness. He waited impatiently for the night, to go back to his interrupted writing.

The preliminary part of the work was being done outside his consciousness, during the drowsiness that filled him and veiled his surroundings and his thoughts. The diffuse mistiness in which everything was enveloped marked the stage preceding the distinctness of the final embodiment. Like the confusion of a first rough draft, the wearisome inactivity of the day was a necessary preparation for the night.

Although he felt exhausted, nothing was left untouched, unchanged. Everything was being altered and transformed.

Yurii Andreievich felt that his dream of remaining in Varykino would not come true, that the hour of his parting with Lara was at hand; he would inevitably lose her and with her the will to live and perhaps life itself. He was sick at heart, yet his greatest torment was his impatience for the night, his longing so to express his grief that everyone should be moved to tears.

The wolves he had been remembering all day long were no longer wolves on the snowy plain under the moon, they had become a theme, they had come to symbolize a hostile force bent upon destroying him and Lara and on driving them from Varykino.

The thought of this hostility developed in him and by evening it loomed like a prehistoric beast or some fabulous monster, a dragon whose tracks had been discovered in the ravine and who thirsted for his blood and lusted after Lara.

The night came and once again the doctor lit the lamp on the table. Lara and Katenka went to bed earlier than the night before.

What he had written that night fell into two parts. Clean copies—improved versions of earlier poems—were set out in his best penmanship. New work was written in an illegible scrawl full of gaps and abbreviations.

In deciphering these scribbles, he went through the usual disappointments. Last night these rough fragments had moved him to tears, and he himself had been surprised by some felicitous passages. Now these very passages seemed to him distressingly and conspicuously strained.

It had been the dream of his life to write with an originality so discreet, so well concealed, as to be unnoticeable in its disguise of current and customary forms; all his life he had struggled for a style so restrained, so unpretentious that the reader or the hearer would fully understand the meaning without realizing how he assimilated it. He had striven constantly for an unostentatious style, and he was dismayed to find how far he still remained from his ideal.

Last night he had tried to convey, by words so simple as to be almost childish and suggesting the directness of a lullaby, his feeling of mingled love and fear and longing and courage, in

such a way that it should speak for itself, almost apart from the
words.

Looking over these rough sketches now, he found that they
needed a connecting theme to give unity to the lines, which for
lack of it fell apart. He crossed out what he had written and began to write down the legend of St. George and the dragon in the
same lyrical manner. At first he used a broad, spacious pentam-
eter. The regularity of the rhythm, independent of the meaning and inherent in the meter itself, annoyed him by its dog-
gerel artificiality. He gave up the pompous meter and the
caesura and cut down the lines to four beats, as you cut out useless words in prose. The task was now more difficult but more
engaging. The result was livelier but still too verbose. He forced
himself to even shorter lines. Now the words were crammed in
their trimeters, and Yurii Andreievich felt wide awake, roused,
excited; the right words to fill the short lines came, prompted by
the measure. Things scarcely named in the lines evoked concrete
images. He heard the horse's hoofs ringing on the surface of the
poem, as you hear the ambling of a horse in one of Chopin's bal-
lades. St. George was galloping over the boundless expanse of
the steppe. He could watch him, as he grew smaller in the distance. He wrote in a feverish hurry, scarcely able to keep up with
the words as they poured out, always to the point and tumbling
into place of themselves.

He had not noticed Lara getting out of bed and coming across
to the table. She seemed very thin in her long nightdress and
taller than she really was. He started with surprise when she
appeared beside him, pale, frightened, stretching out her hand
and whispering:

"Do you hear? A dog howling. Even two of them, I think. Oh,
how terrible! It's a very bad omen. We'll bear it somehow till
the morning, and then we'll go, we'll go! I won't stay here any
longer."

An hour later, after much persuasion, she calmed down and
fell asleep. Yurii Andreievich went outside. The wolves were
nearer than the night before. They vanished even more swiftly
and again before he could make out in which direction they
went. They had stood in a bunch and he had not had time to
count them, but it seemed to him that there were more of them.

10

It was the thirteenth day of their stay at Varykino. There was nothing new or different about it. The wolves, after having disappeared for a few days, had again howled in the night. Once again, mistaking them for dogs, and frightened by the omen, Larisa Feodorovna, just as before, announced that she was leaving the next day. Her usual balance was disturbed by attacks of anxiety, natural in a woman unused to pouring out her feelings all day long or to the luxury of unrestrained affection.

The same scenes were repeated again and again, so that when that morning Lara, as she had done so many times before, began to pack for the return journey, it was as if the thirteen days since their arrival had not existed at all.

It was again damp and dark in the rooms, this time because the weather was overcast. It was less cold, and judging from the look of the dark, low clouds it would snow any moment. Yurii Andreievich was exhausted by the physical and mental strain of too many sleepless nights. His legs were weak and his thoughts were in a tangle; shivering with cold and rubbing his hands, he walked about from room to room, waiting to see what Lara would decide and what he would have to do in consequence.

She did not know herself. Just then she would have given anything to exchange their chaotic freedom for a daily round, however strenuous, but laid down once and for all, for work and obligations, so that they could live a decent, honest, sensible life.

She began her day as usual by making the beds, sweeping, dusting, and cooking breakfast. Then she began to pack and asked the doctor to harness the horse; she had firmly resolved to go.

Yurii Andreievich did not argue. It was mad to return to town, where the wave of arrests must have reached its peak, but it was equally mad to remain, alone and unarmed, in this winter desert with its own hazards.

Besides, there was hardly an armful of hay left in the barn or the sheds. Of course, had it been possible to settle down for a long stay, the doctor would have scouted around looking for new ways of getting food and fodder, but it wasn't worth it for a few uncertain days. He gave up the thought and went to harness the horse.

He wasn't good at it. Samdeviatov had taught him how to do it, but he kept forgetting. Still, he managed it, though clumsily. He strapped the yoke to the shafts, wound the slack and knotted the end of the metal-studded strap around one of them, then, one leg braced against the horse's flank, pulled the two ends of the stiff collar tight and fastened them. At last he led the horse to the porch, tied it, and went inside to call Lara.

She and Katenka had their coats on and everything was packed, but Lara was in great distress. Wringing her hands and on the verge of tears, she begged him to sit down a moment and, throwing herself into a chair and getting up again, spoke incoherently, in a high-pitched plaintive singsong, stumbling over her words and repeatedly interjecting: "What do you think?"

"I can't help it, I don't know how it's happened, but you can see for yourself, we can't possibly go now, so late, it will be dark soon, we'll be caught in the darkness in your terrible forest. What do you think? I'll do whatever you tell me to, but I simply can't make up my mind to go, something tells me not to, but do whatever you think best. What do you think? Why don't you say something? We've wasted half the day, goodness knows how. Tomorrow we'll be more sensible, more careful. What do you think? How would it be if we stayed one more night? And tomorrow we'll get up early and start at daybreak, at six or seven. What do you think? You'll light the stove and write one more evening and we'll have one more night here, wouldn't that be lovely, darling, wonderful? Oh, God, have I done something wrong again? Why don't you say something?"

"You're exaggerating. Dusk is a long way off, it's quite early. But have it your way. We'll stay. Only calm yourself, don't be so upset. Come now, let's take off our coats and unpack. And Katenka says she's hungry. We'll have something to eat. You are quite right, there would have been no point in going so suddenly, with so little preparation. But don't be so upset, and don't cry. I'll light the stove in a moment. But before I do that, I might as well take the sleigh, since it's at the door, and bring what's left of the logs in our old woodshed; we're entirely out. Don't cry now. I'll be back soon."

11

Several sets of sleigh tracks led up to the woodshed of the Zhivagos' house; Yurii Andreievich had made them on his earlier trips, and the snow over the threshold was trampled and littered from his last visit two days before.

The sky, which had been cloudy since morning, had cleared. It was cold again. The old park came right up to the shed, as if to peer at the doctor's face and remind him of something. The snow was deep that winter. It was piled high over the threshold so that the lintel seemed lower and the shed hunchbacked. Snow hung over the edge of the roof almost down to the doctor's head, like the rim of a gigantic mushroom. Just above it, as though plunging a point of its crescent into the snow, stood the new moon, glowing with a gray blaze along its edge.

Although it was early in the afternoon and full daylight, the doctor felt as if he were standing late at night in the dark forest of his life. Such was the darkness in his soul, such was his dejection. The new moon shining almost at eye level was an omen of separation and an image of solitude.

He was so tired that he could hardly stand. He threw the logs out of the shed onto the sleigh in smaller armfuls than usual; to handle the icy wood with snow clinging to it was painful even though he wore gloves. The work did not make him feel any warmer. Something within him had broken and come to a standstill. He cursed his luckless fate and prayed God to spare the life of the beautiful, sad, humble, and simple-hearted woman he loved. And the new moon stood over the barn blazing without warmth and shining without giving light.

The horse turned its head in the direction of the Mikulitsyns' house and whinnied, at first softly, timidly, then louder, with assurance.

"What's that for?" Yurii Andreievich wondered. "It can't be fright. A frightened horse wouldn't neigh, and it wouldn't be such a fool as to signal to the wolves if it had scented them, and so cheerfully, too. It must be looking forward to going home. Hold on a moment, we'll soon be off."

He added chips for kindling to the logs, and strips of bark that curled like shoe leather, covered the load with sacking, lashed it to the sleigh with a rope, and turned back, walking at the horse's head.

The horse neighed again, this time in answer to another horse neighing in the distance. "What can that be? Is it possible that Varykino is not as deserted as we thought?" It never occurred to him that they had guests or that the neighing came from the direction of Mikulitsyn's house. He took the sleigh around the farm buildings, and since the house was hidden from him by snowy folds of land he did not see its front entrance.

Taking his time—why should he hurry?—he stacked the wood and, unhitching the horse, left the sleigh in the barn. Then he took the horse to the stables, put it in the far stall where there was less draft, and stuffed the few remaining handfuls of hay into the rack of the manger.

He felt uneasy as he walked home. In front of the porch stood a roomy peasant sleigh with a sleek black foal harnessed to it, and walking up and down beside it was an equally sleek, plump stranger, who gave the horse an occasional slap and had a look at its fetlocks.

There were voices coming from the house. Neither wishing to eavesdrop nor close enough to hear more than an occasional word, Yurii Andreievich nevertheless involuntarily slowed down and suddenly stopped. He recognized the voice of Komarovsky talking to Lara and Katenka. They were apparently in the first room near the door. They were arguing, and, judging from the sound of her voice, Lara was upset and crying, now violently contradicting him and now agreeing with him.

Something made Yurii Andreievich feel that just then Komarovsky was speaking about him, saying something to the effect that he should not be trusted ("serving two masters," he thought he heard), that it was impossible to tell if he were more attached to Lara or to his family, that Lara must not rely on him, because if she did she would be "running with the hare and the hounds" and would "fall between two stools." Yurii Andreievich went in.

As he had thought, they were in the first room on the right, Komarovsky in a fur coat reaching to his heels, Lara holding Katenka by her coat collar, trying to fasten it but not finding the hooks and shouting at her not to wriggle, and Katenka protesting: "Easy, Mama, you'll choke me." All three were standing in their outdoor clothes, ready to leave. When Yurii Andreievich came in, Lara and Komarovsky rushed to meet him, speaking together:

"Where have you been all this time? We need you so badly!"

"Hello, Yurii Andreievich. As you see, in spite of the rude things we said to each other last time, I'm with you once again, though you didn't invite me."

"Hello, Victor Ippolitovich."

"Where on earth have you been?" Lara asked again. "Now listen to what he says and decide quickly for both of us. There isn't any time. We have to hurry."

"But why are we all standing? Sit down, Victor Ippolitovich. How do you mean, darling, where have I been? You know I went to get the wood, and afterwards I saw to the horse. Victor Ippolitovich, do sit down, please."

"Well, aren't you amazed to see him? How is it you don't look surprised? Here we were, regretting that he had gone away and that we hadn't jumped at his offer, and now here he is, right under your very eyes, and you don't even look surprised! But what is even more astonishing is what he has to tell us now. Tell him, Victor Ippolitovich."

"I don't know what Larisa Feodorovna has in mind. One thing I must explain is this: I deliberately spread the rumor that I had left, but I stayed on to give you and Larisa Feodorovna more time to think over what we had discussed, and perhaps come to a less rash decision."

"But we can't put it off any longer," broke in Lara. "Now is the perfect time to leave. And tomorrow morning . . . But let Victor Ippolitovich tell you himself."

"One moment, Lara dear. Forgive me, Victor Ippolitovich. Why should we all stand about in our coats? Let's take them off and sit down. After all, these are serious things we have to talk about, we can't settle them in a minute. I am afraid, Victor Ippolitovich, our discussion has touched on something personal; it would be ludicrous and embarrassing to go into it. But the fact is that while I have never considered going away with you, Lara's case is different. On the rare occasions when our concerns were not the same and we remembered that we were not one person but two, I have always told her that she ought to give your suggestion more consideration. And in fact she has never stopped thinking about it, she has come back to it again and again."

"But only on condition that you come with us," broke in Lara.

"It is as difficult for you as it is for me to think of our being separated, but perhaps we ought to put our feelings aside and make this sacrifice. Because there's no question of my going."

"But you haven't heard anything yet, you don't know . . . Listen to what Victor Ippolitovich says. . . . Tomorrow morning . . . Victor Ippolitovich."

"Larisa Feodorovna is evidently thinking of the news I brought and have already told her. In the sidings at Yuriatin, an official train of the Far Eastern Government is standing under steam. It arrived yesterday from Moscow and is leaving for the East tomorrow. It belongs to our Ministry of Communications. Half the carriages are *wagons-lits.*

"I have to go by this train. Several seats have been put at my disposal for my assistants. We could travel in great comfort. There won't ever be another chance like this again. I realize that you are not in the habit of speaking lightly, you are not the man to go back on your decisions, and you have made up your mind not to go with us. But even so, shouldn't you reconsider it for Larisa Feodorovna's sake? You heard her say that she won't go without you. Come with us, if not to Vladivostok, then at least as far as Yuriatin—and there we shall see. Only we must really hurry—there is not a moment to lose. I have a driver with me—I don't drive myself—and there isn't room for five of us in my sleigh. But I understand you have Samdeviatov's horse—didn't you say you had gone with it to get the wood? Is it still harnessed?"

"No, I have unharnessed it."

"Well then, harness it again as quickly as you possibly can. My driver will help you. . . . Though, come to think of it, why bother—let's forget about your sleigh, we'll manage with mine, we'll squeeze in somehow. Only let's hurry, for heaven's sake. You only need to pack the most essential things for the journey —whatever comes to hand first. There's no time to fuss with packing when it's a question of a child's life."

"I don't understand you, Victor Ippolitovich. You talk as if I had agreed to come. Go and good luck to you, and let Lara go with you if she wishes. You needn't worry about the house. I'll clean it up and lock it after you've gone."

"What are you talking about, Yura? What's all this nonsense you don't even believe yourself? 'Lara's wishes' indeed! As if you didn't know perfectly well that I won't go without you and I won't make any decision on my own. So what's all this talk about your locking up the house?"

"So you are quite adamant?" said Komarovsky. "In that case, with Larisa Feodorovna's permission I should like to have a couple of words with you, if possible alone."

"Certainly. We can go into the kitchen. You don't mind, darling?"

12

"Strelnikov has been captured, condemned to death, and shot."

"How horrible! Are you really sure?"

"It's what I've been told, and I am convinced it's true."

"Don't tell Lara. She would go out of her mind."

"Of course I won't. That's why I asked to speak to you alone. Now that this has happened, she and her daughter are in imminent danger. You must help me to save them. Are you quite sure you won't go with us?"

"Quite sure. I've told you already."

"But she won't go without you. I simply don't know what to do. You'll have to help me in a different way. You'll have to pretend, let her think that you might be willing to change your mind, look as if you might allow yourself to be persuaded. I can't see her saying goodbye and leaving you, either here or at the station at Yuriatin. We'll have to make her think that you are coming after all, if not now, then later, when I've arranged another opportunity for you to come. You'll have to pretend that you'll be willing to do that. You'll just have to convince her of this, even if you have to lie. Though this is no empty offer on my part—I swear to you on my honor that at the first sign you give me I'll get you out to the East and I'll arrange for you to go on from there anywhere you like. But Larisa Feodorovna must believe that you are at least coming to see us off. You'll simply have to make her believe that. For instance, you might pretend that you are going to get your sleigh ready and urge us to start at once, without waiting for you, not to waste any time—say you'll catch up with us as soon as you are ready."

"I am so shaken by the news about Strelnikov that I cannot collect my wits. I have hardly taken in all you've said. But you are right. Now that they've settled accounts with him, we must conclude, things being as they are, that Larisa Feodorovna and Katia's lives are also threatened. Either she or I will certainly be arrested, so we'll be parted anyway. It's better that it should be you who separate us and take them off, as far away as possible. I am saying this, but it doesn't make much difference—things are already going your way. Probably in the end I'll break down completely, and swallow my pride and my self-respect and crawl to you, and ask you for her, for my life, and for a sea passage to my family, and for my own salvation, and accept it all from your hands. But you must give me time to think about it. I am stunned by the news. I am so distressed that I can't think or reason properly. Perhaps, by putting myself in your hands, I am making a disastrous mistake and it will appall me all the rest of my life. But I am so dazed and overcome that all I can do at the moment is to agree with you blindly and obey you helplessly. . . . Very well, then, for her sake I'll go out now and tell her that I'll get the sleigh ready and catch up with you, but in fact I shall stay behind. . . . There's one thing, though. How can you go now, when it will soon be dark? The road runs through woods, and there are wolves. Watch out."

"I know. Don't worry. I've got a gun and a revolver. I've brought a bit of liquor too, by the way, to keep out the cold. Would you like some? I've got enough."

13

"What have I done? What have I done? I've given her up, renounced her, given her away. I must run after them. Lara! Lara!

"They can't hear. The wind is against me and they are probably shouting at each other. She has every reason to feel happy, reassured. She has no idea of the trick I've played on her.

"She is thinking: It's wonderful that things have gone so well, they couldn't be better. Her absurd, obstinate Yurochka has relented at last, thank heaven, we are going to a nice, safe place, where people are more sensible than we are, where you can be sure of law and order. Suppose even, just to be annoying, he doesn't come on tomorrow's train, Komarovsky will send another to bring him, and he'll join us in no time at all. And at the moment, of course, he's in the stable, hurrying, excited, fumbling with the harness, and he'll rush after us full tilt and catch up with us before we get into the forest.

"That's what she must be thinking. And we didn't even say goodbye properly, I just waved to her and turned back, trying to swallow my pain as if it were a piece of apple stuck in my throat, choking me."

He stood on the veranda, his coat over one shoulder. With his free hand he was clutching the slender wooden pillar just under the roof as if he meant to strangle it. His whole attention was concentrated on a point in the distance. There a short stretch of the road could be seen climbing uphill, bordered by a few sparse birches. The low rays of the setting sun fell on this open space, and there the sleigh now hidden by a shallow dip would appear at any moment.

"Farewell, farewell," he said over and over again in anticipation of that moment; his words were breathed almost soundlessly into the cold afternoon air. "Farewell, my only love, my love forever lost.

"They're coming, they're coming," he whispered through dry, blenched lips as the sleigh shot like an arrow out of the dip, swept past the birches one after another, gradually slowing down, and—oh, joy!—stopped before the last of them.

His heart thumped with such a wild excitement that his knees shook and he felt weak and faint, the whole of his body soft as cloth, like the coat slipping from his shoulder. "O God, is it Thy will to give her back to me? What can have happened? What is going on out there near the sunset? What can be the meaning of it? Why are they standing still? No. It's finished. They've moved. They're off. She must have stopped for a last look at the house. Or perhaps to make sure that I had left? That I was chasing after them? They've gone."

With luck, if the sun didn't go down first (he wouldn't see them in the dark) they would flash past once again, for the last time, on the other side of the ravine, across the field where the wolves had stood two nights before.

And now this moment also had come and gone. The dark red sun was still round as a ball above the blue snowdrifts along the horizon, flooding the plain with a juicy pineapple-colored light that the snow greedily sucked in, when the sleigh swept into sight and vanished. "Farewell, Lara, until we meet in the next world, farewell, my love, my inexhaustible, everlasting joy. I'll never see you again, I'll never, never see you again."

It was getting dark. Swiftly the bronze-red patches of sunset scattered on the snow died down and went out. The soft, ashy distance filled with a lilac dusk that turned to deep mauve, its smoky haze smudging the fine lacework of the roadside birches lightly traced on the pink sky, pale as though it had suddenly grown shallow.

Grief had sharpened Yurii Andreievich's senses and quickened his perception a hundredfold. The very air surrounding him was rare, unique. The winter evening was alive with sympathy, like a friendly witness. It was as if there had never been such a dusk before and night were falling now for the first time in order to console him in his loneliness and bereavement; as if the valley were not always girded by a panorama of wooded hills on the horizon but the trees had only taken up their places now, rising out of the ground in order to comfort him with their presence.

He almost waved away the tangible beauty of the hour, like a crowd of persistent friends, almost saying to the lingering after-glow: "Thank you, thank you, I'll be all right."

Still standing on the veranda, he turned his face to the shut door, his back to the world. "My bright sun has set," he kept repeating inwardly, as though trying to engrave these words in his memory. He did not have the strength to utter all these words aloud.

He went into the house. A double monologue was going on in his mind, two different kinds of monologue, the one dry and businesslike, the other addressed to Lara, like a river in flood.

"Now I'll go to Moscow," ran his thoughts. "The first job is to survive. I must not force myself to sleep. Instead, I must work all through the night till I drop with exhaustion. Yes, and another thing, light the stove in the bedroom at once, there is no reason why I should freeze tonight."

But there was also this other inward conversation: "I'll stay with you a little, my unforgettable delight, for as long as my arms and my hands and my lips remember you. I'll put my grief for you in a work that will endure and be worthy of you. I'll write your memory into an image of aching tenderness and sorrow. I'll stay here till this is done, then I too will go. This is how I will portray you, I'll trace your features on paper as the sea, after a fearful storm has churned it up, traces the form of the greatest, farthest-reaching wave on the sand. Seaweed, shells, cork, pebbles, the lightest, most imponderable things that it could lift from its bed, are cast up in a broken, sinuous line on the sand. This line endlessly stretching into the distance is the frontier of the highest tide. That was how life's storm cast you up on my shore, O my pride, that is how I'll portray you."

He went in, locked the door behind him, and took off his coat. When he went into the bedroom, which Lara had tidied up so well and so carefully that morning and which her hurried packing had again turned inside out, when he saw the disarranged bed and the things thrown about in disorder on the chairs and floor, he knelt down like a little boy, leaned his breast against the hard edge of the bedstead, buried his head in the bedclothes, and wept freely and bitterly as children do. But not for long. Soon he got up, hastily dried his face, looked around him with tired, absent-minded surprise, got out the bottle of vodka Komarovsky had left, drew the cork, poured half a glass, added water and snow, and with a relish almost equal in strength to the hopelessness of the tears he had shed drank long, greedy gulps.

14

Something unaccountable was going on in Yurii Andreievich. He was slowly losing his mind. Never before had he led such a strange existence. He neglected the house, he stopped taking proper care of himself, he turned night into day and had lost count of time since Lara had left.

He drank vodka and he wrote about Lara; but the more he

crossed out and rewrote what he had written the more the Lara
of his poems and notebooks grew away from her living prototype,
from the Lara who was Katia's mother off on a journey with her
daughter.

The reason for his revision and rewriting was his search for
strength and exactness of expression, but they also followed the
promptings of an inward reticence that forbade him to disclose
his personal experiences and the real events in his past with too
much freedom, lest he offend or wound those who had directly
taken part in them. As a result, his feeling, still pulsing and warm,
was gradually eliminated from his poems, and romantic morbid-
ity yielded to a broad and serene vision that lifted the particular
to the level of the universal and familiar. He was not deliberately
striving for such a goal, but this broad vision came of its own accord as a consolation, like a message sent to him by Lara from her
travels, like a distant greeting from her, like her appearance in a
dream or the touch of her hand on his forehead, and he loved this
ennobling imprint.

At the same time that he was working on his lament for Lara
he was also scribbling the end of the notes he had accumulated
over the years concerning nature, man, and various other things.
As had always happened to him whenever he was writing, a
host of ideas about the life of the individual and of society assailed him.

He reflected again that he conceived of history, of what is
called the course of history, not in the accepted way but by
analogy with the vegetable kingdom. In winter, under the
snow, the leafless branches of a wood are thin and poor, like the
hairs on an old man's wart. But in only a few days in spring
the forest is transformed, it reaches the clouds, and you can hide
or lose yourself in its leafy maze. This transformation is achieved
with a speed greater than in the case of animals, for animals do
not grow as fast as plants, and yet we cannot directly observe the
movement of growth even of plants. The forest does not change
its place, we cannot lie in wait for it and catch it in the act of
change. Whenever we look at it, it seems to be motionless. And
such also is the immobility to our eyes of the eternally growing,
ceaselessly changing history, the life of society moving invisibly
in its incessant transformations.

Tolstoy thought of it in just this way, but he did not spell it out so clearly. He denied that history was set in motion by Napoleon or any other ruler or general, but he did not develop his idea to its logical conclusion. No single man makes history. History cannot be seen, just as one cannot see grass growing. Wars and revolutions, kings and Robespierres, are history's organic agents, its yeast. But revolutions are made by fanatical men of action with one-track minds, geniuses in their ability to confine themselves to a limited field. They overturn the old order in a few hours or days, the whole upheaval takes a few weeks or at most years, but the fanatical spirit that inspired the upheavals is worshipped for decades thereafter, for centuries.

Mourning for Lara, he also mourned that distant summer in Meliuzeievo when the revolution had been a god come down to earth from heaven, the god of the summer when everyone had gone crazy in his own way, and when everyone's life had existed in its own right, and not as an illustration for a thesis in support of the rightness of a superior policy.

As he scribbled his odds and ends, he made a note reaffirming his belief that art always serves beauty, and beauty is delight in form, and form is the key to organic life, since no living thing can exist without it, so that every work of art, including tragedy, expresses the joy of existence. And his own ideas and notes also brought him joy, a tragic joy, a joy full of tears that exhausted him and made his head ache.

Samdeviatov came to see him. He brought him more vodka and told him of how Antipova and her daughter had left with Komarovsky. He came by the railway handcar. He scolded the doctor for not looking after the horse properly and took it back, unwilling to leave it for three or four more days as Yurii Andreievich wished, but promising to come back within the week, and personally take him away from Varykino for good.

Sometimes, after losing himself in his work, Yurii Andreievich suddenly remembered Lara as vividly as if she were before him, and broke down from tenderness and the sharpness of his loss. As in his childhood, when after his mother's death he thought he heard her voice in the bird calls, in the summer magnificence of Kologrivov's garden, so now his hearing, accustomed to Lara's voice and expecting it as part of his life, played tricks on him and he heard her calling, "Yurochka!" from the next room.

He also had other hallucinations that week. Toward the end of it, he woke up in the night from a nonsensical nightmare about a dragon that had its lair underneath the house. He opened his eyes. A light flashed from the gully and he heard the crack and echo of a rifle shot. Strangely, a few moments after so unusual an experience, he went back to sleep, and in the morning told himself that it had been a dream.

15

This is what happened a day or two later. The doctor had at last convinced himself that he must be sensible, that if he wished to kill himself he could find a quicker and less painful method. He promised himself to leave as soon as Samdeviatov came for him.

A little before dusk, while it was still light, he heard loud crunching footsteps on the snow. Someone was calmly approaching the house with a firm, easy step.

Strange! Who could it be? Samdeviatov had his horse, he would not have come on foot, and Varykino was deserted. "They've come for me," Yurii Andreievich decided. "A summons or an order to go back to town. Or they've come to arrest me. No, there would be two of them and they would have transportation to take me back. It's Mikulitsyn," he thought joyfully, imagining that he recognized the step. The stranger, still unidentified, fumbled at the door with its broken bolt, as if he had expected the padlock to be there; then he walked in confidently, certain of his way, opening the connecting doors and closing them carefully behind him.

Yurii Andreievich had been sitting at his desk with his back to the door. As he rose and turned to face it he found the stranger already in the doorway, where he had stopped dead.

"Whom do you want to see?" The doctor mechanically blurted out these conventional words without thinking, and was not surprised when there was no reply.

The stranger was a powerful, well-built man with a handsome
face. He was dressed in a fur jacket and trousers, and warm,
goatskin boots, and he had a rifle slung over his shoulder on a
strap.

Only the moment of his appearance took the doctor by surprise, not his arrival in itself. The traces of occupation in the
house had prepared him for it. This, evidently, was the owner of
the supplies he had found, which, as he knew, could not have
been left by the Mikulitsyns. Something about him struck Yurii
Andreievich as familiar, he felt he had seen him before. Neither
did the caller look as astonished as might have been expected
at the sight of Yurii Andreievich. Perhaps he had been told that
the house was lived in, and even who was living in it. Perhaps
he even recognized the doctor.

"Who is he? Who is he?" The doctor racked his brains.
"Where have I seen him, for heaven's sake? Surely not . . . A
hot morning in May, God knows in what year. The station at
Razvilie. The Commissar's coach, promising nothing good. Cut-
and-dried ideas, a one-track mind, harsh principles, and integrity,
absolute integrity . . . Strelnikov!"

16

They had been talking for hours. They talked as only Russians
in Russia can talk, particularly as they talked then, desperate
and frenzied as they were in those anxious, frightened days.
Night was falling, and it was getting dark.

Apart from the nervous garrulousness that was common in
those days, Strelnikov had some personal reason for talking
ceaselessly.

He went on and on, doing everything possible to keep the conversation going, in order to avoid being alone. Was it his conscience he was afraid of, or the sad memories that haunted him,
or was he tormented by that self-dissatisfaction which makes a
man so hateful and intolerable to himself that he is ready to die
of shame? Or had he made some dreadful, irrevocable decision
and was he unwilling to remain alone with it and anxious to

delay its execution by chatting with the doctor and staying in his company?

Whatever it was, he was evidently keeping to himself some important secret that burdened him, while pouring out his heart all the more effusively on every other subject.

It was the disease, the revolutionary madness of the age, that at heart everyone was different from his outward appearance and his words. No one had a clear conscience. Everyone could justifiably feel that he was guilty, that he was a secret criminal, an undetected impostor. The slightest pretext was enough to launch the imagination on an orgy of self-torture. Carried away by their fantasy, people accused themselves falsely not only out of terror but out of a morbidly destructive impulse, of their own will, in a state of metaphysical trance, in a passion for self-condemnation which cannot be checked once you give it its head.

As an important military leader who had often presided at military courts, Strelnikov must have heard and read any number of confessions and depositions by condemned men. Now he was himself swayed by the impulse to unmask himself, to reappraise his whole life, to draw up a balance sheet, while monstrously distorting everything in his feverish excitement.

He spoke incoherently, jumping from confession to confession. "This all happened near Chita. . . . Were you surprised at all the outlandish things you found in the drawers and cupboards? All that comes from the requisitioning we did when the Red Army occupied eastern Siberia. Naturally, I didn't bring it here all by myself. I've always had trustworthy, devoted people around me; life has been very good to me that way. These candles, matches, coffee, tea, writing materials, and so on all come from requisitioned military stores, partly Czech, partly English and Japanese. Odd, don't you think? . . . 'What do you think?' was my wife's favorite expression, I suppose you noticed. I couldn't make up my mind whether to tell you when I arrived, but I might as well admit it now—I came to see her and my daughter. The message saying that they were here didn't reach me till too late. That's how I missed them. When rumors and reports reached me of your intimacy with her and the name Dr. Zhivago was mentioned to me, for some inexplicable reason, out of the thousands of faces I'd seen in these years, I remembered a doctor of that name who had once been brought to me for questioning."

"And were you sorry you hadn't had me shot?"

Strelnikov ignored the question. Perhaps he had not even heard the interruption. Lost in his thoughts, he went on with his monologue.

"Naturally, I was jealous—I'm jealous now, for that matter. What could you expect? . . . I came to this district only a few months ago, after my other hide-outs farther east were uncovered. I was to be court-martialled on a trumped-up charge. It wasn't difficult to guess the outcome. I wasn't guilty. I thought there might be a hope of defending myself and clearing my good name at some time in the future, in more propitious circumstances. So I decided to disappear while I still could, before they arrested me, and hide for the present, lead a hermit's life, keep moving. Perhaps I would have succeeded if it hadn't been for a young scoundrel who wheedled himself into my confidence.

"It was while I was making my way westward across Siberia, on foot, keeping out of people's way and starving. I used to sleep in snowdrifts, or in trains—there were endless rows of them standing buried in the snow all along the line.

"Well, I came across this boy, a tramp, who said he had got away from a partisan shooting squad—they had lined him up with a lot of other condemned men, but he was only wounded, and he crawled out from under a pile of dead bodies and hid in the forest and recovered, and now he was moving from one hide-out to another, like me. That was his story, anyway. He was a good-for-nothing, vicious and backward; he had been kicked out of school because he was dull-witted."

The more details Strelnikov added to his description, the more certain the doctor felt that he knew the boy.

"Was his name Terentii Galuzin?"

"Yes."

"Then everything he said about the partisans and the shooting was true. He didn't invent a word."

"The only good thing about him was that he was devoted to

his mother. His father had been shot as a hostage, and his mother was in prison, and the same thing was likely to happen to her. When he heard that, he made up his mind to do all he could to get her out. He went to the local Cheka, gave himself up, and offered to work for them. They agreed to give him a chance on condition he made some important betrayal. He told them where I was hiding. But fortunately I got away in time.

"By a fantastic effort and after endless adventures, I got across Siberia and reached this part of the country. I am so well known here, I thought it was the last place they'd expect to find me; they wouldn't suppose I'd have the nerve. And in fact, they went on for a long time looking for me around Chita, while I was hiding either in this house or in one or two others I knew were safe in the neighborhood. But now that's out, they're on my trail. Listen. It's getting dark and I don't like it because I haven't been able to sleep for ages. You know what a torment that is. If any of my candles are still left—good, aren't they, real tallow!—then let's go on talking for a bit. Let's go on talking for as long as you can stand it, right through the night, in luxury, by candlelight."

"The candles are all there. I've opened only one box. I've been using the kerosene, which probably you also left."

"Have you any bread?"

"No."

"Then what have you been living on? But what a silly question! Potatoes, of course."

"That's right. Any amount of those. The people who used to live here were good housekeepers, they knew how to store them, they're all safe and sound in the cellar, neither rotten nor frozen." Strelnikov suddenly switched to the revolution.

17

"None of this can mean anything to you. You couldn't understand it. You grew up quite differently. There was the world of the suburbs, of the railways, of the slums and tenements. Dirt, hunger, overcrowding, the degradation of the worker as a human being, the degradation of women. And there was the world of the mother's darlings, of smart students and rich merchants' sons; the world of impunity, of brazen, insolent vice; of rich men laughing or shrugging off the tears of the poor, the robbed, the insulted, the seduced; the reign of parasites, whose only distinction was that they never troubled themselves about anything, never gave anything to the world, and left nothing behind them.

"But for us life was a campaign. We moved mountains for those we loved, and if we brought them nothing but sorrow, they did not hold it against us because in the end we suffered more than they did.

"But before I go on, I ought to tell you something. This is the point. You've got to leave Varykino, don't put it off if you value your life. They are closing in on me, and whatever happens to me will involve you. You are implicated already by the very fact of talking to me now. And apart from everything else, there are a lot of wolves around here; I had to shoot my way out of the Shutma the other night."

"So it was you shooting."

"Yes. Of course, you heard me. I was on my way to another hide-out, but before I got there I saw by various signs that it had been discovered. The people who were there have probably been shot. I won't stay long with you. I'll spend the night and leave in the morning. . . . Well, I'll go on if I may.

"Of course, it wasn't only in Moscow or in Russia that there existed these elegant Tverskaia Yamskaia Streets with young rakes in fancy hats and spats rushing about with their girls in cabs. That street, the night life of the street, the night life of the past century, and the race horses and the rakes, existed in every city in the world. But what gave unity to the nineteenth century, what set it apart as one historical period? It was the birth of socialist thought. Revolutions, young men dying on the barricades, writers racking their brains in an effort to curb the brute insolence of money, to save the human dignity of the poor. Marxism arose, it uncovered the root of the evil and it offered the remedy, it became the great force of the century. And the elegant streets of the age were all that, as well as the dirt and the heroism, the vice and the slums, and the proclamations and the barricades.

"You can't think how lovely she was as a child, a schoolgirl.

You have no idea. She had a school friend who lived in a tenement next door to us; most of the tenants were railway workers on the Brest line. It was called the Brest line in those days, it's been renamed several times since. My father—he's a member of the Yuriatin revolutionary court now—he was a track overseer. I used to go to that house and see her there. She was still a child, but even then, the alertness, the watchfulness, the restlessness of those days—it was all there, you could read it all in her face, her eyes. All the themes of the century—all the tears and the insults and the hopes, the whole accumulation of resentment and pride were written in her face and bearing, which expressed both girlish shyness and self-assured grace. She was a living indictment of the age. This is something, isn't it? It's predestination. Something nature endowed her with, something to which she had a birthright."

"How well you speak of her. I too saw her in those days, just as you have described her. A schoolgirl, and yet at the same time the secret heroine of an unchildish drama. Her shadow on the wall was the shadow of helpless, watchful self-defense. That was how I saw her, and so I still remember her. You put it perfectly."

"You saw and you remembered? And what did you do?"

"That's another story altogether."

"Yes. Well. So you see, the whole of this nineteenth century —its revolutions in Paris, its generations of Russian exiles starting with Herzen, its assassinations of Tsars, some only plotted, others carried out, the whole of the workers' movement of the world, the whole of Marxism in the parliaments and universities of Europe, the whole of this new system of ideas with its newness, the swiftness of its conclusion, its irony, and its pitiless remedies elaborated in the name of pity—all of this was absorbed and expressed in Lenin, who fell upon the old world as the personified retribution for its misdeeds.

"And side by side with him there arose before the eyes of the world the vast figure of Russia bursting into flames like a light of redemption for all the sorrows and misfortunes of mankind. But why on earth am I telling you all this? To you it must be the tinkling of a cymbal—just words.

"For the sake of this girl I studied and became a teacher,

and went to Yuriatin, which I did not know at that time. For her sake I devoured piles of books and absorbed a great mass of knowledge, to be available to her if she asked for my help. To win her back after three years of marriage, I went to war, and when the war was over and I returned from captivity, I took advantage of having been listed as dead, and under an assumed name plunged headlong into the revolution, to pay back in full all the wrongs that she had suffered, to wash her mind clean of those memories, so that it should not be possible to return to the past, so that there should be no more Tverskaia-Yamskaias. And all the time they, she and my daughter, were next door, they were here! What an effort it cost me to resist the longing to rush to them, to see them! But I wanted to finish my life's work first. Oh, what wouldn't I give now for one look at them! When she came in it was as if the window flew open and the room filled with air and light."

"I know how much you loved her. But forgive me, have you any idea of her love for you?"

"Sorry. What was that you said?"

"I asked you, had you any idea of how much she loved you— more than anyone in the world?"

"What makes you say that?"

"Because she told me so herself."

"She said that? To you?"

"Yes."

"Forgive me, I realize it's an impossible thing to ask, but if it isn't hopelessly indiscreet, if you can, will you tell me exactly what it was she said to you?"

"Gladly. She said that you were the embodiment of what a human being should be, a man whose equal she had never met, that you were unique in your genuineness, and that if she could go back to the home she had shared with you she would crawl to it on her knees from the end of the earth."

"Forgive me, but if it isn't intruding on something too intimate, can you remember the circumstances in which she said this?"

"She had been doing this room and she went outside to shake the carpet."

"Sorry, which carpet? There are two."

"That one, the larger one."

"It would have been too heavy for her. Did you help her?"
"Yes."

"Each of you held one end, and she leaned far back throwing
up her arms high as on a swing and turning away her face
from the blowing dust and squinted her eyes and laughed? Isn't
that how it was? How well I know her ways! And then you
walked toward each other folding up the heavy carpet first in
two and then in four, and she joked and made faces, didn't she?
Didn't she?"

They stood up and went to different windows and looked out
in different directions. After a time Strelnikov walked up to
Yurii Andreievich, caught hold of his hands, pressed them to
his breast, and went on as hurriedly as before:

"Forgive me. I realize that I am touching on things that are
dear and holy to you. But I should like to ask you more questions, if you'll let me. Only please don't go away. Don't leave
me alone. I'll be going soon myself. Just think—six years of
separation, six years of inconceivable self-restraint. But I kept
thinking that freedom was not yet wholly won. When I'd won
it, I thought, my hands would be untied and I could belong to
my family. And now, all my calculations have come to nothing.
They'll arrest me tomorrow. You are near and dear to her. Perhaps you'll see her one day and . . . But what am I saying!
I'm mad. They'll arrest me, and they won't let me say a word
in my own defense. They'll come at me with shouts and curses
and gag me. Don't I know how it's done!"

18

At long last, Yurii Andreievich had a good sleep. For the first
time in many nights he fell asleep the moment he lay down.
Strelnikov spent the night; the doctor put him in the next
room. The few times the doctor woke up and turned over or
pulled the blankets up to his chin, he was conscious of the strong
refreshment of sleep and he dropped off happily again at once.
Toward morning he had several short, kaleidoscopic dreams of
his childhood, so detailed and logical that he took them for
reality.

He dreamed, for instance, that his mother's watercolor showing a place on the Italian Riviera suddenly dropped from the wall, and he was aroused by a sound of breaking glass. He opened his eyes. "No, it can't be that," he thought. "It's Antipov, Lara's husband Strelnikov, scaring the wolves in the Shutma as Bacchus would say." But no, what nonsense! It was the picture. There it was, lying in pieces on the floor, he assured himself, back in his dream.

He woke up late, with a headache from having slept too long. For a time he couldn't think who or where he was.

Then he remembered: "Strelnikov is in here. It's late. I must get dressed. He must be up by now. If not, I'll wake him and make some coffee, and we'll have it together."

"Pavel Pavlovich!" he called out.

There was no answer. "He's still asleep. He's a sound sleeper, I must say." He dressed unhurriedly and went into the next room. Strelnikov's fur hat was on the table, but he was nowhere in the house. "Must have gone for a walk. And without his hat. Toughening himself up. I ought to be getting out of Varykino today, but it's too late now. Again I've overslept, it's the same thing every day."

He lit the kitchen range, picked up a bucket, and started toward the well. A few yards from the door, Strelnikov lay across the path with his head in a snowdrift. He had shot himself. The snow was a red lump under his left temple where he had bled. Drops of spurting blood that had mixed with the snow formed red beads that looked like rowanberries.

CHAPTER FIFTEEN

CONCLUSION

1

It remains to tell the brief story of the last eight or ten years of Zhivago's life, during which he went more and more to seed, gradually losing his knowledge and skill as a doctor and a writer, emerging from his state of depression and resuming his work only to fall back, after a short flare-up of activity, into long periods of indifference to himself and to everything in the world. During these years the heart disease which he had himself diagnosed earlier but without realizing its gravity developed to an advanced stage.

He went to Moscow at the beginning of the NEP, the most ambiguous and hypocritical of all Soviet periods. He was even thinner, more neglected, and more unkempt than when he went to Yuriatin after escaping from the partisans. In the course of his journey he had again gradually discarded those of his clothes that had some value, exchanging them for bread and a few worn old rags to cover his nakedness. So he had lived off his second fur coat and suit, and arrived in the streets of Moscow dressed in a gray sheepskin hat, puttees, and a worn-out army overcoat stripped of all its buttons like a convict's uniform. In this getup he was indistinguishable from the countless Red Army men who thronged the stations and the streets and squares of the capital.

He had not arrived alone. Following him wherever he went was a good-looking young peasant boy who was also dressed in old army clothes. They both turned up in the few surviving Moscow drawing rooms like those in which Yurii Andreievich had spent his childhood, where he was remembered and welcomed with his companion (after tactful inquiries as to whether they had been to the baths—typhus was still raging) and in which he was soon told of the circumstances of his family's departure from Russia.

Both of them shied away from people, and their unsociability made them avoid going among people separately, for fear of becoming the center of attention and having to talk. Usually, when these two lanky figures made their appearance at any gathering of friends, they retired to some corner, where they could spend the evening in silence, without having to take part in the general conversation.

Dressed in his rags and accompanied everywhere by the boy, the tall, gaunt doctor looked like a peasant Seeker after Truth, and his companion like a patient, blindly devoted, and obedient disciple. Who was his young companion?

2

Yurii Andreievich had made the last stage of his journey by train but had covered the earlier and much longer part on foot.

The villages he went through looked no better than those he had seen in Siberia and the Urals, after running away from his captivity in the woods. Only then it had been winter, while now, at the end of the summer and the beginning of a warm, dry autumn, the weather made things easier.

Half the villages he passed were deserted, the fields abandoned and unharvested as after an enemy raid. Such were the effects of war—the civil war.

For two or three days at the end of September his road followed the steep bank of a river. The river flowing toward him was on his right. On his left the wide, unharvested fields stretched from the road to the cloudbanks on the horizon. At long intervals they were interrupted by woods, for the most part oak, maple, and elm. The woods ran to the river in deep gullies, which dropped precipitously and cut across the road.

In the unharvested fields the ripe grain spilled and trickled on the ground. Yurii Andreievich gathered it in handfuls, and at the worst, if he had no means of boiling it and making gruel, he stuffed it into his mouth and chewed it with great difficulty. The raw, half-chewed grain was almost indigestible.

Never in his life had he seen such dark-looking rye, rusty, brown, the color of old gold. Usually, when it is harvested in time, its color is much lighter.

These flame-colored fields blazing without fire, these fields silently proclaiming their distress, were coldly bordered by the vast, quiet sky, its face already wintry and shadowed by ceaselessly moving, long, flaky snow-clouds with black centers and white flanks.

Everything was moving slowly, regularly—the flowing river, the road running by it, and the doctor walking along the road in the same direction as the drifting clouds. Nor were the rye fields motionless. Their surface was alive, they were astir with an incessant crawling that suggested something foul and repellent.

Never had there been such a plague of mice. They had bred in unprecedented quantities. They scurried over the doctor's face and hands and inside his sleeves and trousers at night, when he was caught by darkness and forced to sleep in the open, they raced across the road by day, gorged and teeming, and turned into squeaking, pulsing slush when they were trodden underfoot.

Shaggy village curs, turned wild, followed him at a respectful distance, exchanging glances as if to decide on the best moment to fall on him and tear him to pieces. They fed on carrion, did not disdain mice, and eyed Yurii Andreievich from afar, moving after him confidently as though waiting for something. For some reason they never ventured into the wood and, whenever he came near one, gradually fell back, turned tail, and vanished.

The woods and the fields offered a complete contrast in those days. Deserted by man, the fields looked orphaned as if his absence had put them under a curse. The forest, however, well rid of him, flourished proudly in freedom as though released from captivity.

Usually the nuts are not allowed to ripen, as people, and particularly village children, pick them green, breaking off whole branches. But now the wooded sides of hills and gullies were thick with rough, golden foliage dusted and coarsened by the sun. Festive among it were bulging clusters of nuts, three or four, as if tied together, ripe and ready to fall from the branches. Yurii Andreievich cracked and crunched them in quantity. He stuffed his pockets and his bag full of them; for a whole week he fed on hazelnuts.

The fields appeared to him as something seen in the fever of a dangerous illness, and the woods, by contrast, in the lucidity of health regained. God, so it seemed to him, dwelled in the woods, while the fields echoed with the sardonic laughter of the devil.

3

At this point of his journey, Yurii Andreievich came to a deserted, burned-out village. All the houses had stood in one row on the side of the road opposite the river. The strip of land between the road and the edge of the steep riverbank had not been built on.

Only a few houses, blackened by the fire, were still standing, but they too were empty, uninhabited. Nothing was left of the others but piles of charred rubble with black chimneys rising out of them.

The cliffs facing the river were honeycombed with pits where the villagers had quarried rock for millstones; this had been their means of livelihood. Three such unfinished stones were lying on the ground in front of the last house in the row, one of the few that had remained standing. Like the others, this house was uninhabited.

Yurii Andreievich went inside. It was a still afternoon, but the moment he entered it was as if a gust of wind burst into the house. Tufts of straw and hay slithered across the floors, remnants of paper flapped on the walls, and the whole place stirred and rustled. Like the countryside, it swarmed with mice which scampered off, squeaking, in all directions.

He came out. The sun was setting behind the fields in back of the village. A warm, golden glow flooded the opposite bank, and its fading brilliance was reflected by pools and on bushes, some of which reached out into the middle of the stream. Yurii

Andreievich crossed the road and sat down on one of the mill-stones that lay on the grass.

A fair, shaggy head came up over the edge of the bank, then shoulders, then arms. Someone was climbing up the cliff path with a bucket of water. Seeing the doctor, he stopped, still visible only from the waist up.

"Would you like a drink of water? If you won't hurt me, I won't hurt you."

"Thank you. Yes, I'd like a drink. But come over here, don't be frightened. Why should I hurt you?"

The water carrier was a boy in his teens, barefoot, ragged, and dishevelled.

In spite of his friendly words, he pierced the doctor with a worried, suspicious stare. For some reason the boy was strangely agitated. Finally, putting down his bucket, he rushed toward the doctor but stopped halfway, muttering:

"It isn't . . . It can't be . . . I must be dreaming. Pardon me, comrade, if I ask you, but haven't I seen you before? Yes! Yes! Surely! You're the doctor, aren't you?"

"And who are you?"

"Don't you recognize me?"

"No."

"We were in the same train from Moscow, in the same car. They'd conscripted me for labor. I was in the convoy."

It was Vasia Brykin. He threw himself on the ground before the doctor, kissed his hands, and wept.

The burned ruins were those of his native village, Vereten-niki. His mother was dead. When the village was destroyed, Vasia hid in a cave in the quarries, but his mother, thinking he had been taken off to town, went mad with grief and drowned herself in the river—that very river Pelga which flowed at the foot of the cliff where they were sitting and talking. His sisters Alia and Aria were said to be in an orphanage in another district, but he knew nothing certain about them. He went on to Moscow with the doctor, and on the way told him of many terrible happenings.

4

"That's last winter's corn going to waste in the fields. We'd just finished sowing it when our troubles began. It was after Aunt Polia went away. Do you remember Aunt Polia?"

"No. I never even knew her. Who is she?"

"You never knew Aunt Polia? She was with us in the train! Tiagunova. The one who was plump and fair, and looked you straight in the eye."

"That's the one who was always braiding and undoing her hair?"

"That's it! The one with the pigtail, that's the one!"

"Yes, I remember her. Wait a moment, now I come to think of it, I met her later in a town in Siberia, we met in the street."

"You don't mean it! You met Aunt Polia!"

"What's the matter with you, Vasia? Why are you shaking my hands like a madman? If you're not careful you'll pull them off. And what are you blushing for, like a girl?"

"Well, tell me quickly, how is she? Tell me."

"She was all right when I saw her. She spoke about you and your people. Didn't she say she'd been staying with you, or have I got it wrong?"

"Of course she did, of course she did. She stayed with us. My mother loved her like her own sister. She's quiet and a good worker, very clever with her hands. We had plenty of everything in the house as long as she was living with us. But they made her life a misery in Veretenniki with all their talk.

"There was a man in the village called Rotten Kharlam. He was making up to Polia. He's a slanderer, and he had no nose. She wouldn't even look at him. He had a grudge against me for that. He spoke evil about me and Polia. In the end she left, she couldn't stand it any more. And that was the beginning of all our troubles.

"There was a terrible murder near here. A widow who lived all by herself on a farm, up toward Buiskoie. Used to walk about in a man's shoes with elastic straps. She kept a fierce dog chained to a long wire, which ran all around the house. Gorlan, she called it. She did all the work around the house and on the farm by herself, without any help. Well, last year the winter came before anyone expected it. The snow was early, and the old woman hadn't dug up her potatoes. So she comes to Vereten-niki and says, 'Help me,' she says, 'I'll pay you either in money or a share of the potatoes.'

"I said I'd do it, but when I got to the farm Kharlam was there, he'd taken the job on before me and she hadn't bothered to tell me. Well, I wasn't going to fight him about it, so we did the work together. It was wicked weather—rain and snow and mud and slush. We dug and we dug, and we burned the tops to dry the potatoes in the smoke. When we'd finished she set-tled with us, fair and square, and she let Kharlam go, but she gave me a wink as much as to say, I should stay on or come back later.

"So I went back again and she said: 'I don't want to give up my surplus to the state. You're a good boy,' she says, 'I know you won't give me away. You see, I'm not hiding anything from you. I would dig a pit myself, but you see what it's like outside. I've left it too late, it's winter, I can't manage by my-self. If you dig it for me, you won't be sorry.'

"So I made the pit in the proper way for a hiding place, wide at the bottom and narrow at the top, like a jug, and we started a fire again and warmed and dried the pit with the smoke—all in a howling blizzard. Then we put the potatoes into the pit and the earth back on top. A very neat job it was. Of course, I didn't say a word to a living soul, not even to my mother or my sisters. God forbid!

"Well, hardly a month went by before the farm was robbed. People coming past from Buiskoie said the door was wide open, and the whole place was cleaned out. No sign of the widow, and Gorlan had broken his chain and bolted.

"A bit later still, there was a thaw just before the New Year. On St. Basil's Eve it rained, so the snow got washed off the high ground, you could see the bare soil. Then Gorlan came back to the farm and found the place where the potatoes were buried, and started rooting up the earth. He dug and dug and threw the earth back, and there were the old woman's feet sticking up out of the hole, in those shoes with elastic straps she used to wear—horrible!

"Everyone in Veretenniki was sorry for the old woman. No

one suspected Kharlam, and can you blame them? It was unthinkable. He wouldn't have had the nerve. If he had done it,
he would have run away, far from here.

"The kulaks, in the village, were very pleased about the murder. Here's a chance to stir up trouble, they thought. 'See what
those town people are doing to you,' they said. 'They did it on
purpose to frighten you, so you wouldn't hide your grain and
bury your potatoes. And you think it's bandits from the woods
that killed her, fools that you are! Just you go on doing what
the town people tell you. They've got a lot more up their sleeves,
they'll take everything, they'll starve you out. If you want to
know what's good for you, then listen to us, we'll teach you some
sense. When they come to take away what you've earned by the
sweat of your brow, tell them, We haven't so much as a grain
of rye, let alone surpluses. And in case of trouble, use your pitchforks. And anyone who's against the village had better look
out!' Well, the old fellows talked and held village meetings, and
that was just what Kharlam wanted. Off he went to the town
with his tale. 'Fine goings on in the village,' he says, 'and what
are you doing about it? A Poor Peasants' Committee, that's what
we need. Give the word and I'll have them all at each other's
throats in no time.' Then he made off somewhere, and never
showed up in our parts again.

"What came after happened of itself. Nobody informed. Nobody's to blame. They sent Red Army men from the town, and
they set up a court. And they started on me. That was because
of what Kharlam had told them. I'd dodged the labor service.
I'd run away. And I'd killed the old woman and stirred up the
village, they said. They locked me up, but luckily I thought to
pull up one of the floor boards and get away. I hid in a cave
in the old quarry. The village was burned over my head—I never
saw it, and my own mother drowned herself in a hole in the ice
and I never knew. It all happened by itself. They'd put the Red
Army men in a house by themselves and given them liquor,
and they all got dead drunk. In the night the house happened
to catch fire, and the fire spread to the other houses, from one
to the next. Our village people, when it started, jumped out
of their houses and ran away. But the people from town—mind
you, nobody set fire to them—naturally, they were all burned to

death. Nobody told our people to run away or to stay away from their burned-out homes, but they were afraid that something else would happen. The kulaks spread a rumor that every tenth man would be shot. When I came out of the cave, they'd all gone, I didn't find a soul, they're wandering around somewhere."

5

The doctor and Vasia arrived in Moscow in the spring of 1922 at the beginning of the NEP. The weather was fine and warm. Sunshine glancing off the golden domes of the Church of the Saviour played on the square below where grass was growing in the cracks between the paving stones.

The ban on private enterprise had been lifted and trade within certain narrow limits was allowed. Deals were made on the scale of the turnover of a rag-and-bone merchant in a flea market; their pettiness led to speculation and abuses. No new wealth was created by these transactions and they did nothing to relieve the squalor of the town, but fortunes were made out of the futile reselling of goods already sold a dozen times over.

The owners of several modest private libraries got down their books from their shelves and collected them all in one place. They notified the Town Soviet of their wish to start a co-operative bookshop. They applied for premises and obtained the use of some shoestore or florist's, which had been empty and closed down since the first days of the revolution, and there, under its spacious vaults, they sold out their small haphazard collections.

Professors' wives who, when times had been hard before, had secretly baked white rolls and sold them in defiance of the regulations, now sold them openly at some bicycle repair shop or other which had been requisitioned and left unused all these years. They changed sides, accepted the revolution, and no longer used their genteel language.

In Moscow Yurii Andreievich said:

"You'll have to work at something, Vasia."

"I'd like to study."

"That goes without saying."

"Another thing I want to do is draw my mother's picture from memory."

"That's a good idea too. But for that you'd have to know how to draw. Have you ever tried?"

"When I was apprenticed to my uncle I used to play around with charcoal when he wasn't looking."

"Well, why not? We'll see what can be done."

Vasia did not show any great talent for drawing but he had enough aptitude to enter a school of industrial design. With the help of his friends, Yurii Andreievich got him into what had been the Stroganov Institute, where he first took a course in general subjects and then specialized in printing, binding, and book design.

The doctor and Vasia combined their efforts. The doctor wrote booklets on various subjects and Vasia set them up and printed them in small editions, as part of his training at the Institute. They were then distributed through the secondhand bookshops that had been recently opened by their friends.

These booklets contained Yurii Andreievich's philosophy, his views on medicine, his definitions of health and sickness, reflections on the doctrine of evolution, his theory of individuality as the biological basis of the organism, and thoughts about religion and history (which had much in common with those of his uncle and Sima), as well as his poems, short stories, and sketches of the Pugachev country he had visited.

They were written in an easy conversational style but were anything but works of popularization, since they advanced opinions that were controversial, hypothetical, and untested, though always lively and original. The booklets found an easy sale among collectors.

In those days everything became a specialty, including versification and the art of translation; theoretical studies were written on all possible subjects, and institutes were founded right and left. There arose all sorts of Palaces of Thought, Academies of Artistic Ideas. Yurii Andreievich acted as medical consultant to half of these pseudo-cultural institutions.

For a long time he and Vasia remained friends and lived together. During that period they moved from one dilapidated place to another, each uninhabitable and uncomfortable in a different way.

Immediately on arriving in Moscow, Yurii Andreievich had revisited his old home in Sivtsev Vrazhok. He was told that his family had not stayed there when they returned to Moscow. After their deportation, the rooms registered in their name had been given to new tenants and there was not a sign of their belongings. Yurii Andreievich himself was avoided by his former neighbors, who regarded him as dangerous to know.

Markel was no longer there. He had gone up in the world and had been appointed house manager at Flour Town. The manager's flat had been put at his disposal, but he preferred the old porter's lodge, which had floors of beaten earth but which also had running water and an enormous Russian stove. All the pipes and radiators in the buildings burst in the cold weather, but the porter's lodge was always warm and dry, and the water did not freeze.

There came a time when the friendship between Yurii Andreievich and Vasia cooled. Vasia had developed remarkably. He no longer thought or spoke like the ragged, barefoot, dishevelled boy from Veretenniki. The obviousness, the self-evidence of the truths proclaimed by the revolution attracted him increasingly, and the doctor's language, with its obscurities and its imagery, now struck him as the voice of error, doomed, conscious of its weakness and therefore evasive.

The doctor was making calls on various government departments. He was trying to obtain the political rehabilitation of his family and permission for them to return to Russia. At the same time he applied for a foreign passport for himself and permission to bring his family back from Paris.

Vasia was astonished at how lukewarm and half-hearted his efforts were. Yurii Andreievich seemed always to be in a hurry to decide that he was not getting anywhere, and he spoke with too much conviction and almost with satisfaction of the futility of undertaking anything further.

Vasia found fault with him more and more often, and although Yurii Andreievich did not take offense at being justly criticized, his relationship with Vasia gradually deteriorated. Finally their friendship broke up, and they parted company.

The doctor left the room that they had shared to Vasia and moved to Flour Town, where Markel was all-powerful and had set aside for him a corner at the back of what had been the Sventitskys'. It consisted of a derelict bathroom, a room with a single window adjoining it, and the dilapidated, crumbling kitchen and back entrance. After he had moved in, Yurii Andreievich gave up medicine, neglected himself, stopped seeing his friends, and lived in great poverty.

6

It was a gray Sunday in winter. Smoke was rising in columns from the roofs and in thin black streams from the windows, which, in spite of the regulations, were still used as outlets for the metal pipes of stoves. The amenities of town life had still not been restored. The tenants of Flour Town went about unwashed and suffered from boils and colds.

As on every Sunday, Markel Shchapov and his family were all at home.

They were having dinner at a large kitchen table. At this same table in days gone by, at the time of the bread rationing, all the tenants' coupons were collected and cut, snipped, counted, sorted, and wrapped in pieces of paper or tied into bundles according to their category before being taken to the baker's at dawn; and here too, later on in the morning, the loaves were cut and broken and crumbled to make up each tenant's apportioned weight. But all this was now only a memory. Food rationing had been replaced by other forms of control, and the Shchapovs at their midday meal ate their fill and champed and chewed with relish.

Half the room was taken up by the broad Russian stove, which stood in the middle and had bedding on its flat top and quilts hanging down over the sides.

Near the entrance was a faucet, and here the pipes were not frozen. Benches ran down two sides of the room; under them were kept the family belongings in trunks and bundles. The table was on the left and had a plate rack fixed above it.

The room was very hot. The stove was going full blast. In

front of it stood Markel's wife Agafia; her sleeves were rolled
up above her elbows and she was using a long pair of tongs to
move the pots inside the oven, crowding them together or spacing them out according to need. Her sweating face was in turn
lit by the blaze in the oven and misted over by steam. Pushing
the pots to one side, she pulled out from behind them a pastry
on an iron sheet, flipped it over, and put it back to brown. Yurii
Andreievich came in with two buckets.

"Good appetite."

"Make yourself at home. Sit down and have dinner with us."

"Thank you, I've had mine."

"We know what you call dinner. Why don't you sit down
and have something hot? You needn't turn up your nose at it—
it's good stuff, baked potatoes, pie with kasha."

"No thanks, really. . . . I'm sorry to keep on opening the door
and letting in the cold. I want to take up as much water as I
can. I've cleaned the bathtub, now I'm filling that and the wash
tubs. I'll come in half a dozen times and then I won't trouble
you again for a long time. Forgive me for bothering you
like this, but I can't get water anywhere else."

"Help yourself. If you asked for syrup, we haven't got any,
but there's plenty of water. Take as much as you like, we won't
even charge you for it!"

They all laughed.

When Yurii Andreievich came for the third time to fill his
fifth and sixth buckets, the tone had changed.

"My sons-in-law have been asking me who you are. I told
them but they don't believe me. You go on running the water,
don't mind me. Only don't slop it on the floor, clumsy! Don't
you see, you've splashed some in the doorway. If it freezes over
I can't see you coming to hack it up with a crowbar. And
shut the door properly, you oaf, there's a draft coming in. Yes,
so I was telling them who you are but they won't believe it. The
money that was spent on you! All that learning, and where has
it got you, I'd like to know?"

When Yurii Andreievich came in for the fifth or sixth time,
Markel frowned.

"Just once more and that's that. There's a limit to everything,
old man. If our little Marina didn't keep sticking up for you,

I'd lock the door, no matter how high-born you are. You remember our Marina, don't you? There she is, the dark one at the end of the table. She's gone all red, look. 'Don't hurt his feelings, Dad,' she keeps telling me. As if anybody wants to hurt your feelings. She's a telegrapher at the Central Post Office—she knows foreign languages. 'He's unfortunate,' she says. She's so sorry for you, she'd go through fire and water for you! As if I'm to blame that you're a poor fish! You shouldn't have run away to Siberia, leaving your house at a bad time. It's your own fault. Look at us here—we sat it out through the famine and the White blockade, we didn't flinch—so here we are, safe and sound. Blame yourself. If you'd taken proper care of Tonia, she wouldn't be traipsing abroad now. Well, it's your business, what do I care. Only what I'd like to know, begging your pardon, is what do you want with all this water? Hired yourself out to make a skating rink or something? You and your water! I can't even get mad at you, you're such a wet rag!"

Again they all laughed. Marina, however, looked around angrily, flared up, and began to chide them. Yurii Andreievich was astonished by the sound of her voice, though he could not as yet have said why.

"There's a lot of cleaning to be done in the house, Markel. I've got to scrub the floors and wash some of my things as well."

The Shchapovs were amazed.

"Aren't you ashamed of yourself, saying such things, let alone doing them? You'll be starting a Chinese laundry next."

"Let me send my daughter up," said Agafia. "She'll do your washing and scrubbing, and your mending, if there is any. You don't need to be afraid of him, my dear. You can see how well brought up he is, he wouldn't hurt a fly."

"What an idea, Agafia Tikhonovna! I wouldn't dream of letting Marina do my scrubbing. Why on earth should she dirty her hands for me? I'll manage all right."

"You can dirty your hands and I can't, is that it?" Marina broke in. "Why are you so difficult, Yurii Andreievich? Would you really drive me out if I came up to see you?"

Marina could have been a singer. She had a pure, well-modulated voice of great range and strength. She did not speak loudly, but her voice gave the impression of being stronger than was needed for ordinary conversation; it seemed to have a life of its own, as though it did not belong to her. It seemed to come from behind her back or from the next room. This voice was her protection, her guardian angel; no one could wish to hurt or distress a woman with such a voice.

It was from this water-carrying on a Sunday that a friendship sprang up between the doctor and Marina. She would often come and help him with his housework. One day she stayed with him and did not again go back to the lodge. Thus she became Yurii Andreievich's third wife, though he was not divorced from the first, and they did not register their marriage. They had children. Markel and Agafia spoke of their daughter, not without pride, as the doctor's wife. Her father grumbled that there had never been a proper wedding either in church or at the registry, but his wife said: "Are you out of your mind? With Tonia still alive, that would be bigamy."—"It's you that's stupid," said Markel. "What's Tonia got to do with it? It's just the same as if she were dead. There's no law to protect her."

Yurii Andreievich sometimes said jokingly that theirs was a romance in twenty buckets, as you might have a novel in twenty chapters.

Marina forgave the doctor his eccentricities, the dirt and disorder he made in the house, his moods and his fancies; they were those of a man who was letting himself go and knew it. She bore with his grumbling, his tempers, and his nerves.

Her devotion went even further. At times they were destitute through his fault, and in order not to leave him alone at such moments she would give up her own job at the post office, where her work was so highly thought of that she was always taken back after her enforced absence. In obedience to Yurii Andreievich's whim, she would go out with him, doing odd jobs from house to house. They chopped wood for a good many of the tenants on the different floors. Some of them, particularly speculators who had made fortunes at the beginning of the NEP and artists and scholars who were close to the government, were setting up house on a comfortable scale. One day Yurii Andreievich and Marina, stepping carefully in their felt boots so as not to dirty the carpet with sawdust, were carrying wood into the study of a tenant who remained insultingly engrossed in something he was reading and did not honor them with so much as a glance. It was his wife who gave the orders and who paid them.

"What has the pig got his nose in?" the doctor wondered. The scholar was scribbling furiously in the margins of his book. As he passed him with a bundle of logs, Yurii Andreievich glanced over his shoulder. On the desk lay a pile of the early editions of the booklets that he had written and Vasia had printed.

7

Yurii Andreievich and Marina were now living in Spiridonovka Street, and Gordon had a room in Malaia Bronnaia Street near by. Marina and the doctor had two daughters, Kapka (Capitolina), who was five years old, and the baby Klazhka (Claudia), who was only six months.

The early summer of 1929 was very hot. People who lived in the same neighborhood would go to see each other, hatless and in their shirtsleeves.

Gordon's room was part of a curious structure, which had once been the premises of a fashionable tailor. The shop had been on two floors, connected by a spiral staircase, and both looking out onto the street through one large plate-glass window, on which the tailor's name and occupation were traced in gold letters.

The premises were now divided into three. By means of floor boards an extra room had been fitted into the space between the lower and the upper levels. It had what was, for a living room, a curious window, about three feet high, starting at floor level and with part of the gold letters remaining. From outside through the gaps in the lettering, anyone in the room could be seen up to the knees. This was Gordon's room. With him at the moment were Zhivago, Dudorov, Marina, and the children, who, unlike the grownups, were entirely visible through the glass. Marina soon left with the little girls, and the three men remained alone.

They were having one of those unhurried, lazy summer conversations that go on between men who were at school together and have many years of friendship behind them.

To carry on a conversation naturally and intelligently, a man must have an adequate supply of words. Of the three, only Yurii Andreievich answered this requirement.

The other two were always at a loss for an expression. They did not possess the gift of eloquence. At a loss for words, they paced up and down, puffed at their cigarettes, gesticulated, and repeated themselves. ("That, plainly, is dishonest, old man! Dishonest, yes, yes, that's what it is, dishonest.")

They were unaware that such dramatic excesses, far from showing their warmth and breadth of character, expressed intellectual poverty.

Both Gordon and Dudorov moved among cultured academicians, they spent their lives among good books, good thinkers, good composers and good music, which was as good yesterday as today (but always good!), and they did not know that the misfortune of having average taste is a great deal worse than the misfortune of having no taste at all.

Neither Dudorov nor Gordon realized that even their admonitions to Zhivago were prompted less by a friendly wish to influence his conduct than by their inability to think with freedom and to guide the conversation at will. Like a runaway cart, the conversation took them where they did not want to go. Unable to steer it, they were bound, sooner or later, to bump into something, and to be hit. And so, in their sermonizing, time and again they got off their tracks.

To Zhivago, their unconscious motives, their artificial emotionalism, and their strained reasoning were transparent. But he could hardly say to them: "Dear friends, how desperately commonplace you are—you and your circle, the names and the authorities you always quote, their glamour and art which you so much admire! The only bright and vital thing about you is that you are my contemporaries and friends!" How could anyone confess to such a thought? So, in order to spare their feelings, he listened meekly.

Dudorov had recently come back from his first deportation. His civil rights had been restored, and he had been allowed to resume his regular work at the university.

Now he was telling his friends about his experiences as a deportee. He spoke sincerely and without hypocrisy. He was not motivated by fear; he really believed in what he was saying.

He said that the arguments of the prosecution, his treatment in prison and after he came out, and particularly his private talks with the examining judge had "aired" his brains, re-educated him politically, opened his eyes to many things he had not seen before, and made him more mature as a person.

These reflections appealed to Gordon just because they were so hackneyed. He nodded his head with sympathy and agreed with Dudorov in everything. It was the very triteness of the feelings and expressions that moved him most; he mistook Dudorov's reflection of prescribed feeling for a genuine expression of humanity.

Dudorov's pious platitudes were in the spirit of the times. But it was precisely their conformism, their transparent sanctimoniousness, that exasperated Yurii Andreievich. Men who are not free, he thought, always idealize their bondage. So it was in the Middle Ages, and later the Jesuits always exploited this human trait. Zhivago could not bear the political mysticism of the Soviet intelligentsia, though it was the very thing they regarded as their highest achievement, or as it would have been called in those days, "the spiritual ceiling of the age." But this he also kept to himself in order not to hurt the feelings of his friends.

What did interest him in Dudorov's story was his account of a cellmate of his, Bonifatii Orletsov, a follower of Tikhon, the Patriarch of Moscow. Orletsov had a six-year-old daughter, Christina. The arrest and subsequent fate of her beloved father had been a terrible blow to her. Terms such as "obscurantist priest" and "disenfranchised" seemed to her the stigma of dishonor. Dudorov felt that in her childish ardor she had vowed someday to remove that stigma from her family name. This goal, conceived at such an early age and nursed with burning resolution, made of her even now an enthusiastic champion of Communist ideals.

"I must go," said Yurii Andreievich. "Don't be cross with me, Misha. It's hot and stuffy in here. I need to get some air."

"But the window is open, look, down there on the floor. . . . I'm sorry, we've been smoking too much. We keep forgetting that we shouldn't smoke with you here. It isn't my fault that it gets so stuffy, it's the idiotic way the window is made. You should find me another room."

"I must be off, Misha. We've talked enough. Thank you both for your concern. . . . I'm not pretending, you know. It's an illness I've got, sclerosis of the heart. The walls of the heart muscle wear out and get thin, and one fine day they may burst. I'm not yet forty, you know, and it isn't as if I were a drunkard, or burned the candle at both ends!"

"Nonsense! We aren't playing your funeral march yet. You'll last us out."

"Microscopic forms of cardiac hemorrhages have become very frequent in recent years. They are not always fatal. Some people get over them. It's a typical modern disease. I think its causes are of a moral order. The great majority of us are required to live a life of constant, systematic duplicity. Your health is bound to be affected if, day after day, you say the opposite of what you feel, if you grovel before what you dislike and rejoice at what brings you nothing but misfortune. Our nervous system isn't just a fiction, it's a part of our physical body, and our soul exists in space and is inside us, like the teeth in our mouth. It can't be forever violated with impunity. I found it painful to listen to you, Innokentii, when you told us how you were re-educated and became mature in jail. It was like listening to a circus horse describing how it broke itself in."

"I must stand up for Dudorov," said Gordon. "You've got unused to simple human words, they don't reach you any more."

"It may very well be, Misha. But in any case, you must let me go now. I can hardly breathe. I swear, I'm not exaggerating."

"Wait a moment, you're just looking for excuses. We won't let you go until you've given us an honest, straightforward answer. Do you or don't you agree that it's time you changed your ways and reformed? What are you going to do about it? To start with, you must clarify your situation with Tonia and Marina. They are human beings, women who feel and suffer, not disembodied ideas existing only in your head. And second, it's a scandal that a man like you should go to waste. You've got to wake up and shake off your inertia, pull yourself together and look at things without this impermissible arrogance, yes, yes, without this inexcusable haughtiness in regard to everyone, you must go back to work and take up your practice."

"All right, I'll give you my answer. I've been thinking something of this sort myself recently, so I can really promise you that there's going to be a change. I think everything will come out all right. And quite soon, at that. You'll see. I really mean it. It's already begun. I have an incredible, passionate desire to live, and to live always means to strive to move higher, toward perfection, and to achieve it.

"I am glad that you stand up for Marina, Misha, just as you always stood up for Tonia. But after all, I have no quarrel with either of them, I am not at war with them, or with anyone else for that matter. You used to reproach me at first because Marina said 'you' to me and called me Yurii Andreievich, while I said 'thou' and 'Marina' to her—as though it didn't distress me too! But you know that the deeper causes of this unnatural behavior were removed long ago, and now we treat each other as equals.

"Now I can tell you another piece of good news. I've been getting letters again from Paris. The children are growing up, they have a lot of French friends of their own age. Sasha is about to graduate from the *école primaire* and Masha is soon going to it. I've never seen her, you know. I have a feeling in spite of everything that although they've become French citizens, they'll soon be back and that everything will be straightened out in some way or other.

"It seems that Tonia and my father-in-law know about Marina and our children. I didn't tell them in my letters, but they must have heard about it from others. Naturally, Alexander Alexandrovich, as a father, feels outraged and hurt. That would explain why our correspondence was interrupted for almost five years. I used to correspond with them, you know, after I got back to Moscow, and then they suddenly stopped writing.

"Now, quite recently, they've begun writing again, all of them, even the children. They write very warmly and affectionately. For some reason they've relented. Perhaps Tonia has found someone else; I hope with all my heart she has. I don't know. I too write from time to time. . . . But I really can't stay any longer. I must go or I'll get an attack. Goodbye."

Next morning Marina came running in to Gordon, greatly distressed. There was no one she could leave the children with, so in one arm she carried the baby wrapped in a blanket and with her free hand she was pulling Kapka, who trailed behind and dragged her feet.

"Is Yura here, Misha?" she asked in a frightened voice.

"Didn't he go home last night?"

"No."

"Then he must have spent the night at Innokentii's."

"I've come from there. Innokentii is at the university, but the neighbors know Yura and they say he hasn't been there."

"Where can he be, then?"

Marina put Klazhka down on the sofa, and then she began to sob hysterically.

8

For two days Gordon and Dudorov did not dare to leave Marina alone and took turns watching her and hunting for the doctor. They called at all the places he might conceivably have gone to —Flour Town, Sivtsev Vrazhok, all the Palaces of Thought and Academies of Ideas he had ever been employed in; they looked up every friend of his they had ever heard him talk about and whose address they could discover—but with no success.

They did not report him as missing to the police. Although he was registered and had no police record, it was better not to draw the attention of the authorities to a man who, by the standards of the day, lived anything but an exemplary life. They decided not to put them on his track except as a last resort.

On the third day, letters from Yurii Andreievich came by different mails for all three of them—Gordon, Dudorov, and Marina. He was full of regret for the trouble and anxiety he had caused them, he begged them not to worry about him, and he implored them by everything that was holy to give up their search for him, saying that it would in any case be fruitless.

He told them that in order to rebuild his life as completely and rapidly as possible, he wished to spend some time by himself, concentrating on his affairs, and that as soon as he was settled in a job and reasonably certain of not falling back into his old ways he would leave his hiding place and return to Marina and the children.

He told Gordon that he was sending him a money order for Marina and asked him to get a nurse for the children, so that Marina could go back to work. He explained that he was not sending the money to her address for fear of someone seeing the receipt and her thus being exposed to the risk of robbery.

The money soon came, and the amount far exceeded the standards of Yurii and his friends. The nurse was hired. Marina went back to work at the post office. She was still greatly upset but, accustomed as she was to Yurii Andreievich's oddities, she eventually resigned herself to his latest whim. All three of them went on looking for him, but gradually they came to the conclusion that it was as futile as he had warned them it would be. They could find no trace of him.

9

Yet all the time he was living within a stone's throw, right under their eyes and noses, in the very middle of the district they were combing for him.

On the day of his disappearance he left Gordon and went out into Bronnaia Street a little before dusk. He turned straight toward home, but almost immediately, within less than a hundred yards, he ran into his half brother Evgraf, who was coming down the street toward him. He had neither seen him nor heard of him for more than three years. It turned out that Evgraf had just arrived in Moscow; as usual, he came quite unexpectedly, and he shrugged off all questions with a smile or a joke. On the other hand, from the few questions he asked Yurii Andreievich, he gathered the gist of his troubles at once, and then and there, between one corner and another as they walked along the narrow, twisting, crowded street, he worked out a practical plan to rescue him. It was his idea that Yurii Andreievich should disappear and remain in hiding for some time.

He took a room for him in Kamerger Street, as it was still called, near the Arts Theater. He provided him with money. He took steps to get him a good position in a hospital, with plenty of opportunity for going on with his research, and assisted him by his patronage. Finally, he gave him his word that the ambiguity of his family's situation in Paris would be resolved. Either Yurii Andreievich would go to them or they would come to him. All these things Evgraf undertook to see to himself. As usual, his brother's help put new heart into Yurii Andreievich. As always before, the riddle of his power remained unsolved. Yurii Andreievich did not even try to penetrate the secret.

10

His room faced south. It almost adjoined the theater and looked out over the rooftops opposite; beyond them, the summer sun stood over Okhotny Ryad, and the street below was in shadow.

To Yurii Andreievich the room was more than a place for work, more than his study. At this time of devouring activity, when the pile of notebooks on his desk was too small to hold all his plans and ideas and the surplus floated in the air like apparitions—as unfinished pictures stand with their faces to the walls in a painter's studio—his living room was to him a banqueting room of the spirit, a cupboard of mad dreams, a storeroom of revelations.

Fortunately, Evgraf's negotiations with the hospital dragged on, and the start of Yurii Andreievich's new job was indefinitely postponed. The delay gave him time to write.

He began by trying to sort out those of his earlier poems of which he could remember snatches or of which Evgraf somehow got him the texts. (These were manuscripts, some in his own hand, some copies made by others.) But the disorderliness of the material made him squander his energy even more than he was inclined to do by nature. He soon gave it up and turned to new work.

He would make the rough draft of an article, like the notes he had kept when he first went to Varykino, or put down the middle, or the end, or the beginning of a poem as it came into his mind. There were times when he could hardly keep pace with his thoughts, even in his shorthand made up of initials and abbreviations.

He was in a hurry. Whenever his imagination flagged he whipped it up by making drawings in the margins of his notebooks. The drawings were always of forest cuttings or of street intersections marked by the sign: *"Moreau & Vetchinkin. Mechanical seeders. Threshing machines."*

The articles and poems were all on the same theme, the city.

11

These notes were found later among his papers:

"When I came back to Moscow in 1922 I found it deserted and half destroyed. So it had come out of the ordeals of the first years after the revolution; so it remains to this day. Its population has decreased, no new houses are being built, and the old ones are left in disrepair.

"But even in this condition it is still a big modern city, and cities are the only source of inspiration for a new, truly modern art.

"The seemingly incongruous and arbitrary jumble of things and ideas in the work of the Symbolists (Blok, Verhaeren, Whitman) is not a stylistic caprice. This is a new order of impressions, taken directly from life.

"Just as they hurry their succession of images through the lines of their poems, so the street in a busy town hurries past us, with its crowds and its broughams and carriages at the end of the last century, or its streetcars and subways at the beginning of ours.

"Pastoral simplicity doesn't exist in these conditions. When it is attempted, its pseudo-artlessness is a literary fraud, not inspired by the countryside but taken from the shelves of academic archives. The living language of our time, born spontaneously and naturally in accord with its spirit, is the language of urbanism.

"I live at a busy intersection. Moscow, blinded by the sun and the white heat of its asphalt-paved yards, scattering reflections of the sun from its upper windows, breathing in the flowering of clouds and streets, is whirling around me, turning my head and telling me to turn the heads of others by writing poems in its praise. For this purpose, Moscow has brought me up and made me an artist.

"The incessant rumbling by day and night in the street outside our walls is as inseparable from the modern soul as the opening bars of an overture are inseparable from the curtain, as yet secret and dark, but already beginning to crimson in the glow of the footlights. The city, incessantly moving and roaring outside our doors and windows, is an immense introduction to the life of each of us. It is in these terms that I should like to write about the city."

There are no such poems in what has been preserved of Zhivago's work. Or does the one entitled "Hamlet" belong to this category?

12

One morning at the end of August, Yurii Andreievich took the trolley at a stop at a corner of Gazetny Street which went up along Nikita Street to the Kudrinskaia terminal. He was going for the first time to his job at the Botkin Hospital, which was then known as the Soldatenko Hospital. He had been there before only once or twice for reasons connected with his job.

He had no luck with his trolley; it had a defective motor and kept getting into trouble of every sort. Either its way was blocked by a cart in front of it with its wheels caught in the grooves of the rails, or the insulation went wrong on the roof or under the floor and the current short-circuited with a flash and a crackle.

The driver would step off the front platform, walk around the trolley with a wrench, and squat down and tinker with the machinery between the rear platform and the wheels.

The ill-fated trolley blocked the traffic all along the line. The whole street was dammed up with other trolleys that had already been stopped, and still others kept joining. The end of the line now reached as far back as the riding school and beyond. Passengers from cars in the rear moved to the front car, hoping to gain time, and got into the very car that was the cause of all the trouble. It was a hot morning, and the car was crowded and stuffy. Above the crowds running about in the street from one trolley to another, a dark lilac thundercloud was creeping higher and higher up the sky. A storm was gathering.

Yurii Andreievich sat on a single seat on the left, pressed against the window. He could see the left side of Nikita Street, where the Conservatory was situated. With the vague attention of a man thinking of something else, he watched the people walking and driving past on that side, missing no one.

A gray-haired old lady, in a light straw hat with linen daisies and cornflowers and a tight old-fashioned lilac dress, was trudging along the pavement, panting and fanning herself with a flat parcel that she was carrying in her hand. Tightly corseted, exhausted by the heat, and streaming with sweat, she kept mopping her damp lips and eyebrows with a small lace handkerchief.

Her course was parallel to that of the trolley. Yurii Andreievich had already lost sight of her several times, whenever the trolley had started up after a stop for repairs and passed her. She had again come back into his field of vision when it broke down once more and she overtook it.

Yurii Andreievich thought of the problems in school arithmetic in which you are asked how soon and in what order trains, starting at different times and going at different speeds, get to their destinations; he tried to remember the general method of solving them, but it escaped him and he went on from these school memories to others and to still more complicated speculations.

He tried to imagine several people whose lives run parallel and close together but move at different speeds, and he wondered in what circumstances some of them would overtake and survive others. Something like a theory of relativity governing the hippodrome of life occurred to him, but he became confused and gave up his analogies.

There was a flash of lightning and a roll of thunder. The ill-starred trolley was stuck for the nth time; it had stopped halfway down the hill from Kudrinskaia to the Zoo. The lady in lilac appeared in the frame of the window, passed beyond it, and moved on. The first heavy drops of rain fell on the street, the sidewalk, and the lady. A gusty wind whipped past the trees, flapped the leaves, tugged at the lady's hat, ballooned her skirt, and suddenly died down.

The doctor felt an attack of nausea coming on. Surmounting his weakness, he got up from his seat and jerked the window straps up and down trying to open the window. But he could not budge it.

People shouted to him that the window was fastened with screws, but the doctor, fighting against his attack and seized by a sort of panic, was not aware that the people were addressing him, or of the meaning of their words. He continued his attempts to open the window and again gave three sharp tugs at the strap—up, down, and toward himself. Suddenly he felt a sharp pain, greater than any he had ever experienced before; he realized that something had broken in him, he had done something irreparable, fatal, that this was the end. At this moment the trolley started, but after going only a short way down the Presnia it stopped again.

By a superhuman effort of the will, Yurii Andreievich pushed through the solid crowd down the center passage, swaying and stumbling, and came out on the rear platform; people blocked his way and snapped at him. The fresh air seemed to revive him and he thought that perhaps everything was not lost, that he was better.

He began to squeeze his way through the crush on the rear platform, provoking kicks and more abuse. Ignoring the resentful cries, he broke through the crowd, got down from the standing trolley into the street, took a step, another, a third, collapsed on the stone paving, and did not get up again.

There arose a hubbub of talk, arguments, suggestions. Several people got off the trolley and surrounded him. They soon found that he was not breathing and his heart had stopped. The group around the body was joined by others who stepped off the sidewalks, some relieved and others disappointed that the dead man had not been run over and his death had nothing to do with the trolley. The crowd grew larger. The lady in lilac came up too, stood a moment, looked at the body, listened to the talk, and went on. She was a foreigner, but she understood that some people were in favor of putting the body on the trolley and taking it to the hospital, while others said that the police should be called. She did not wait to learn the outcome.

The lady in lilac was a Swiss national; she was Mademoiselle Fleury, from Meliuzeievo, and she was now very, very old. For twelve years she had been writing to the authorities in Moscow for permission to return to her native country, and quite recently her application had been granted. She had come to Moscow for her exit visa and was now on her way to her embassy to collect it, fanning herself as she went along with her documents, which were done up in a bundle and tied with a ribbon. So she walked on, overtaking the trolley for the tenth time and quite unaware that she had overtaken Zhivago and survived him.

13

Through the open door of the passage could be seen one end of the room with the table placed at an angle in the corner. On the table the coffin, like a roughly carved canoe, pointed at the door with its lower, narrow end, which bore the feet of the corpse. It was the same table at which Yurii Andreievich had done his writing; the room had no other. The manuscripts had been put away in a drawer, and the coffin stood on the top. His head was raised on a mound of pillows, and his body lay in the coffin as on a hillside.

He was surrounded by a great many flowers, whole bushes of white lilac, hard to find at this season, cyclamen and cineraria in pots and baskets. The flowers screened the light from the windows. The light filtered thinly through the banked flowers to the waxen face and hands of the corpse and the wood and lining of the coffin. Shadows lay on the table in a pattern of leaves and branches as if they had just stopped swaying.

The custom of cremating the dead had by this time become widespread. In the hope of a pension for the children, and to ensure their education and Marina's position at the post office, it had been decided to dispense with a church service and simply have a civil cremation. The proper authorities had been notified and their representatives were expected.

In the interval the room seemed empty, like premises vacant between the going of one set of tenants and the coming of another. The stillness was broken only by the unwitting shuffling of the mourners, as they tiptoed in to take their leave of the dead. There were not many of them, but nevertheless a good many more than might have been expected. The news of the death of this almost unknown man had spread with amazing speed. Among the people were many who had known him at different times in his life, though he had afterwards lost touch with them and forgotten them. His poetry and scientific work attracted an even greater number of unknown friends who had never met the man but had been drawn to him and had now come to see him for the first and last time.

In these hours when the silence, unaccompanied by any ceremony, became oppressive as if it were an almost tangible privation, only the flowers compensated for the absence of the ritual and the chant.

They did more than blossom and smell sweet. Perhaps hastening the return to dust, they poured forth their scent as in a choir and, steeping everything in their exhalation, seemed to take over the function of the Office of the Dead.

The vegetable kingdom can easily be thought of as the nearest neighbor of the kingdom of death. Perhaps the mysteries of evolution and the riddles of life that so puzzle us are contained in the green of the earth, among the trees and the flowers of graveyards. Mary Magdalene did not recognize Jesus risen from the grave, "supposing Him to be the gardener. . . ."

14

When Yurii Andreievich's body was taken to the flat in Kamerger Street (this had been his last registered address), his friends, notified of his death and shaken by it, came in, straight from the landing through the wide-open door, bringing Marina with them. Half out of her mind with shock and grief, she threw herself down on the floor, beating her head against the edge of the long wooden chest in the hallway. The body had been left there until the coffin (which had already been ordered) was delivered and the living room was put in order. She was in a flood of tears, now whispering, now crying out, choking over her words and breaking into loud lamentations. She grieved with an abundance of speech, as peasants do, neither distracted nor embarrassed by strangers. She clung to the body and could scarcely be torn away when the time came for it to be carried into the room, washed, and placed in the coffin. All this had been the day before. Today the frenzy of her grief had abated, giving way to a weary numbness; she sat in silence, though still only half conscious of herself or her surroundings.

Here she had stayed the rest of the preceding day and all through the night, never leaving the room. Here the baby had been brought for her to feed, and Kapka and her young nurse had come and gone.

She was accompanied by her friends Gordon and Dudorov, who also were numb with grief. Markel, her father, would sit down on the bench by her side and sob and blow his nose into his handkerchief loudly. Her weeping mother and sisters came and went.

But there were two people in the gathering, a man and a woman, who stood out from all the rest. They did not claim any closer tie with the deceased than the others. They did not compete in sorrow with Marina, her daughters, or his friends. But although they made no claims, they evidently had their own special rights over the dead man, and no one questioned or disputed the undeclared authority that they had unaccountably assumed. These were the people who had apparently taken it upon themselves to arrange the funeral, and they had seen to everything from the first with unruffled calm, as if it gave them satisfaction. Their composure was remarkable and it produced a strange impression, as if they were involved not only in the funeral but also in the death, not in the sense of having directly or indirectly caused it but as people who, once it had occurred, had given their consent to it, were reconciled, and did not see it as the most important event in the story of Zhivago. Few of the mourners knew them, a few others surmised who they were, but most had no idea.

Yet whenever this man, whose narrow Kirghiz eyes both expressed and aroused curiosity, came into the room with the casually beautiful woman by his side, they all, including even Marina, at once, without protest, as if by agreement, got up from where they had been sitting on the chairs and stools placed in a row against the wall, and went out, crowding uncomfortably into the corridor and the hallway and leaving the couple alone, behind half-closed doors, like two experts who needed, quietly, unhindered, to accomplish something directly concerned with the funeral, and vitally important.

So it was now. They remained alone, sat down on two chairs near the wall, and at once began to talk.

"What have you found out, Evgraf Andreievich?"

"The cremation is to be tonight. In half an hour they'll come from the Medical Workers' Union to get the body and take it to their club. The civil ceremony is at four. Not one of his papers was in order; his workbook was out of date, he had an old union card, which he hadn't changed for the new one, and his dues hadn't been paid up for years. All that had to be put in order, that was why I took so long. Before they take him away—that's quite soon, we ought to get ready—I'll leave you here alone as you asked. . . . Sorry. That's the telephone. I'll just be a moment."

Evgraf went out into the corridor crowded with the doctor's colleagues, his school friends, junior members of the hospital staff, and people from the publishing world. Marina, her arms around both her children, sheltered them in the folds of the coat she had thrown over her shoulders (it was a cold day), and sat on the edge of the wooden bench waiting to go back into the living room, as a visitor who has gone to see a prisoner in jail waits for the guard to admit her. The corridor and hall were overcrowded. The front door was open and a great many people were standing or strolling about smoking on the landing. Others stood talking on the flight of stairs leading down to the ground floor, the louder and more freely the lower down and closer to the street they were.

Straining to hear above the sustained murmur and speaking in a decorously muffled voice, his hand over the receiver, Evgraf answered questions over the telephone about the funeral arrangements and the circumstances of the doctor's death. Then he went back into the living room and the conversation was resumed.

"Please don't vanish after the cremation, Larisa Feodorovna. I don't know where you are staying, don't disappear without letting me know. I have a great favor to ask you. I'd like as soon as possible—tomorrow or the day after—to begin sorting my brother's papers. I'll need your help. You know so much about him, probably more than anyone else. You mentioned that you had come from Irkutsk only a couple of days ago and not for long, and that you came up here for some other reason, not knowing it had been my brother's flat in recent months or what had happened to him. I didn't understand all you said and I am not asking you to explain, but please don't go away without leaving me your address. It would be best if we could spend the few days that we still need to go through these manuscripts in the same room, or at least quite near, perhaps in two other rooms in this house. It could be arranged. I know the manager."

"You say you didn't understand what I said. What is there to understand? I arrived in Moscow, checked my things at the station, and went for a walk through some old Moscow streets. Half of it I couldn't recognize, I've been away so long I'd forgotten. Well, I walked and walked, down Kuznetsky Most and up Kuznetsky Pereulok, and suddenly I saw something terribly, extraordinarily familiar—Kamerger Street. That was where my husband, Antipov, who was shot, used to live as a student—in this house and in this very room where you and I are sitting now. I'll go in, I thought; who knows, the old tenants might still be there, I'll look them up. You see, I didn't know it had all changed —no one so much as remembers their name—I didn't find that out till later, the day after and today, gradually, by asking people. But you were there, I don't know why I'm telling you. I was thunderstruck—the door wide open, people all over the place, a coffin in the room, a dead man. Who is it? I come in, I come up and look. I thought I had lost my mind. But you were there, you saw me, didn't you? Why on earth am I telling you?"

"Wait a moment, Larisa Feodorovna, I must interrupt you. I've already told you, neither my brother nor I ever suspected that there was anything extraordinary about this room—for instance, that Antipov once lived here. But even more amazing is something you said just now. I'll tell you in a moment. About Antipov, Strelnikov, at one time at the beginning of the civil war I used to hear of him very often, almost every day, and I met him two or three times, never realizing, of course, that his name would come to mean so much to me for family reasons. But forgive me, I may have misheard you, I thought you said—it could only have been a slip of the tongue—that he'd been shot. You must surely know that he shot himself?"

"Yes, I've heard that version, but I don't believe it. Pavel Pavlovich wasn't a man to commit suicide."

"But it's quite certain. Antipov shot himself in that house where, my brother said, you were living before you went to Vladivostok. It happened very soon after you left. My brother found his body. He buried him. How is it you weren't told?"

"I was told something different. . . . So it's really true, he shot himself? People said so but I didn't believe it. And in that very house? It doesn't seem possible. It's very important to me, that detail. You don't know, I suppose, whether he and Zhivago ever met, whether they got to know each other?"

"From what Yurii told me, they had a long conversation."

"Is it possible! Well, thank God, thank God, that's better." Antipova slowly crossed herself. "What an extraordinary, pre-ordained coincidence! Will you let me come back to this and ask you more about it later? Every detail is so dear to me. But this isn't the moment, don't you think? I couldn't, I'm too upset. I'll keep quiet a little, I'll rest and collect my thoughts. What do you think?"

"Of course! Of course!"

"Don't you really think so?"

"Yes, naturally."

"Oh, yes. I nearly forgot. You asked me not to go away after the cremation. All right. I promise. I won't disappear. I'll come back here with you and stay wherever you tell me and for as long as necessary. We'll go through Yurochka's manuscripts. I'll help you. It's true, I might be useful to you. It will comfort me a great deal. I know his writing so well, every twist of it. I know it with my heart, with my life's blood. And then, you know, there's something I want to ask you, too. I'll need your help. Didn't I hear you were a lawyer? Or anyway, you know all the present customs and regulations. And another thing, I need to know what government department to apply to for information. So few people can tell one things like that. What do you think? I'll need your advice about something terrible, something really terrible. It's about a child. But we'll talk about it later, when we come back from the crematorium. All my life I've had to keep looking for people. Tell me, suppose in some quite imaginary case it was necessary to trace a child, a child who had been turned over to strangers to be brought up by them, is there any centralized source of information about all the children's homes throughout the country? And is there any record of all the waifs and strays, has anything like that ever been done or attempted? No, don't tell me now, please don't. We'll talk about it later. I'm so frightened. Life is so terrifying—what do you think? I don't know about later on, when my daughter comes and joins me, but for the moment I don't see why I shouldn't stay in this flat. Katia has a remarkable talent for music and for acting, she's marvellous at imitating people and she acts out entire scenes that she makes up herself, and she sings whole operatic arias, all by ear. She's a remarkable child. What do you think? I want her to go to the junior classes either at the drama school or the Conservatory, whichever will take her, and I must apply for a scholarship, that's really why I've come without her at the moment, to make the arrangements; when I've fixed it all I'll go back. Things are so complicated, don't you think, you can't explain everything. But we'll talk about it later. Now I'll wait a bit, I'll pull myself together, I'll keep quiet and collect my thoughts and try to forget my anxieties. Besides, we've kept Yurii's friends out of the room much too long. Twice I thought I heard someone knocking. And there's something going on outside, they've probably come from the undertaker's. I'll stay here quietly for a bit, but you'd better open the door and let them come in. It's time, don't you think? Wait, wait. There ought to be a footstool near the coffin, otherwise people can't reach up to Yurochka. I tried to on tiptoe, but it's very difficult. And Marina Markelovna and the children, they'll need it. Besides, it's prescribed in the ritual: 'And you shall kiss me with a last kiss.' Oh, I can't bear it. It's all so terrible. What do you think?"

"I'll let them in. But just one thing before I do that. You have said so many baffling things and raised so many questions that are evidently painful to you that I don't know what to tell you. But there's one thing I want you to know. Please count on my help in everything. I offer it to you willingly, with all my heart. And remember: you must never, under any circumstances, despair. To hope and to act, these are our duties in misfortune. To do nothing and to despair is to neglect our duty. Now I'm going to let the mourners in. You're right about the footstool, I'll get one."

But Antipova was no longer listening. She never heard him opening the door nor the people pouring in from the corridor, nor the directions he gave to the undertaker's men and the chief mourners; she heard neither the shuffling of the crowd nor Marina's sobs, neither the coughing of the men nor the tears and cries of the women.

The ceaseless, monotonous noise made her feel sick and giddy. It took all her strength not to faint. Her heart was bursting and her head ached. Lowering her head, she withdrew into memories, reflections, conjectures. She escaped into them, sank into them, as though carried forward for a time, for a few hours, into some future that she might not live to see, a future that aged her by several decades, a future where she was an old woman. In her thoughts she seemed to touch the very bottom of her unhappiness.

"No one is left. One has died. The other has killed himself. And only that one is left alive who should have been killed, whom I tried to kill and missed, that stranger who had nothing in common with me, that complete cipher who turned my life into a chain of crimes beyond my knowing. And that monster of mediocrity is busy dashing about in the mythical byways of Asia known only to stamp collectors, and not one of those who are near to me and whom I need is left.

"Ah, it was at Christmastime, and I had set out to shoot that caricature of vulgarity when I had that talk in this very room, lit only by a candle, with Pasha, who was still a boy, and Yura, whose body they are taking leave of now, had not yet come into my life."

She strained her memory to reconstruct that Christmas conversation with Pasha, but she could remember nothing except the candle burning on the window sill and melting a round patch in the icy crust on the glass.

Did she divine that Yurii, whose dead body was lying on the table, had seen the candle as he was driving past, and noticed it, and that from the moment of his seeing its light from the street ("A candle burned on the table, a candle burned . . .") his life took its fatal course?

Her thoughts scattered. She thought: "But what a pity he isn't having a church funeral. The burial service is so grand and solemn! It's more than most people deserve when they die, but it would have been so appropriate for Yurochka! He would have deserved all that, he would have justified and given meaning to 'the lament over the grave which is the hymn of Alleluiah.'"

Now she felt a wave of pride and relief, as always at the thought of Yurii and as in the short intervals of her life that she had spent beside him. Now, too, she was enveloped in the air of that freedom and unconcern that he had always emanated. She got up impatiently from her chair. Something incomprehensible was happening to her. She wanted, if only for a few moments, to break free with Yurii's help into the open, out of the sorrows that imprisoned her, to feel again the joy of liberation. Such a joy, it seemed to her, would be the joy of taking leave of him, of using the right and the occasion to weep her fill over him unhindered. With a passionate haste, she looked around her at the crowd, with eyes as smarting, unseeing, and tearful as if an oculist had put caustic eye-drops into them, and all the people began to move, shuffle, and walk out of the room, leaving her at last alone, behind half-closed doors. She went up to the table with the coffin on it, quickly crossing herself, got up on the footstool Evgraf had brought, made three sweeping signs of the cross over the body, and pressed her lips to the cold forehead and hands. She brushed aside the impression that the cold forehead was somehow smaller, like a hand clenched into a fist, she managed not to notice it. For a moment she stood still and silent, neither thinking nor crying, bowed over the coffin, the flowers, and the body, shielding them with her whole being, her head, her breast, her heart, and her arms, as big as her heart.

15

She was shaken by her repressed sobs. She fought her tears as long as she could, but at times it was beyond her strength and they burst from her, pouring down her cheeks and onto her dress, her hands, and the coffin, to which she clung.

She neither spoke nor thought. Sequences of ideas, notions, insights, truths drifted and sailed freely through her mind, like clouds in the sky, as happened so often before during their nighttime conversations. It was such things that had brought them happiness and liberation in those days. A spontaneous mutual understanding, warm, instinctive, immediate.

Such an understanding filled her now, a dark, indistinct knowledge of death, preparedness for death, a preparedness that removed all feeling of helplessness in its presence. It was as if she had lived twenty lives, and had lost Yurii countless times, and had accumulated such experience of the heart in this domain that everything she felt and did beside this coffin was exactly right and to the point.

Oh, what a love it was, utterly free, unique, like nothing else on earth! Their thoughts were like other people's songs.

They loved each other, not driven by necessity, by the "blaze of passion" often falsely ascribed to love. They loved each other because everything around them willed it, the trees and the clouds and the sky over their heads and the earth under their feet. Perhaps their surrounding world, the strangers they met in the street, the wide expanses they saw on their walks, the rooms in which they lived or met, took more delight in their love than they themselves did.

Ah, that was just what had united them and had made them so akin! Never, never, even in their moments of richest and wildest happiness, were they unaware of a sublime joy in the total design of the universe, a feeling that they themselves were a part of that whole, an element in the beauty of the cosmos.

This unity with the whole was the breath of life to them. And the elevation of man above the rest of nature, the modern coddling and worshipping of man, never appealed to them. A social system based on such a false premise, as well as its political application, struck them as pathetically amateurish and made no sense to them.

16

And now she took her leave of him, addressing him in the direct language of everyday life. Her speech, though lively and informal, was not down-to-earth. Like the choruses and monologues of ancient tragedies, like the language of poetry or music, or any other conventional mode of expression, its logic was not rational but emotional. The rhetorical strain in her effortless, spontaneous talk came from her grief. Her simple, unsolemn words were drenched in tears.

It was these tears that seemed to hold her words together in a tender, quick whispering like the rustling of silky leaves in a warm, windy rain.

"At last we are together again, Yurochka. And in what a terrible way God has willed our reunion. Can you conceive of such misfortune! I cannot, cannot. Oh, God! I can't stop crying. Think of it! It's again so much in our style, made to our measure. Your going—my end. Again something big, irreparable. The riddle of life, the riddle of death, the enchantment of genius, the enchantment of unadorned beauty—yes, yes, these things were ours. But the small problems of practical life—things like the reshaping of the planet—these things, no thank you, they are not for us.

"Farewell, my great one, my own, farewell, my pride, farewell, my swift, deep, dear river, how I loved your day-long splashing, how I loved to plunge into your cold waves.

"Remember how we said goodbye that day out there in the snow? How you deceived me! Would I ever have gone without you? Oh, I know, I know, you forced yourself to do it, you thought it was for my good. And after that everything was ruined. Oh, God, what I suffered there, what I went through! But of course you don't know any of that. Oh, what have I done, Yura, what have I done? I am such a criminal, you have no idea. But it wasn't my fault. I was in the hospital for three months, a whole month I was unconscious. And since then my life has been nothing but torment, Yura. My soul has no peace, I am torn by remorse and pain. But I'm not telling you the most important thing. I can't say it, I haven't the strength. Every time I come to that part of my life my hair stands on end with horror. And you know, I'm not even sure I'm in my right mind. But you see, I haven't taken to drink as so many people do, I'm staying away from that, because a drunken woman, that really is the end, it's impossible, don't you think?"

She went on speaking and sobbing in her agony. Suddenly she looked up in surprise and glanced around her. People had come into the room and were going about their business. She got down from the footstool and moved away from the coffin, swaying, pressing her hand to her eyes as if to wipe away the last of her tears.

Men came up to the coffin and lifted it on three cloths. The funeral procession began.

17

Larisa Feodorovna stayed several days in Kamerger Street. The sorting of Zhivago's papers was begun with her help but finished without her. She also had her talk with Evgraf Andreievich and told him an important fact.

One day Larisa Feodorovna went out and did not come back. She must have been arrested in the street at that time. She vanished without a trace and probably died somewhere, forgotten as a nameless number on a list that afterwards got mislaid, in one of the innumerable mixed or women's concentration camps in the north.

CHAPTER SIXTEEN

EPILOGUE

1

In the summer of 1943, after the breakthrough on the Kursk bulge and the liberation of Orel, Gordon, recently promoted to Second Lieutenant, and Major Dudorov were returning to their unit, the one from a service assignment in Moscow, the other from three days' furlough.

They met on their way back and spent the night at Chern, a small town which, although in ruins, was not completely destroyed, as were most of the settlements in this "desert zone" left in the wake of the retreating invader.

Among the heaps of broken bricks and stone ground into fine dust they found an undamaged barn and settled down in it for the night.

They could not sleep, and talked for hours on end. When Dudorov finally dozed off at about three in the morning, a little before dawn, he was soon waked up again by Gordon. Awkwardly diving into the soft hay and rolling about in it as in water, he collected a few clothes into a bundle and then just as awkwardly crawled off the top of the mountain of hay, down to the door.

"Where are you going? It's early."

"I'm going down to the river. I want to wash my things."

"That's mad. We'll be back with the unit by evening. Tania, the laundry girl, will give you a change of clothes. What's the hurry?"

"I don't want to wait till then. They're sweaty, filthy. I'll rinse them quickly and wring them out well, in this heat they'll be dry in no time. I'll have a bath and change."

"Still, it won't look good. After all, you're an officer."

"It's early, there's no one about, they're all asleep. Anyway, I'll get behind a bush or something, nobody will see me. Stop talking and go back to sleep, or you'll wake yourself up for good."

"I won't sleep any more anyway. I'll go with you."

So they went down to the river, past the white stone ruins, already hot though it was only a little after sunrise. In what had once been streets, people were sleeping on the ground in the sun, snoring, their faces red and sweaty. They were mostly natives who had lost their homes, old men, women, and children, with a sprinkling of Red Army men who had lost touch with their units and were trying to catch up with them. Gordon and Dudorov made their way carefully through them so as not to disturb their sleep.

"Keep your voice down or you'll wake up the town and then it'll be goodbye to my washing."

They continued their last night's conversation quietly.

2

"What's this river?"

"I don't know. The Zusha, probably."

"No, that isn't the Zusha."

"Then I don't know what it is."

"It's on the Zusha, you know, that it all happened—Christina, I mean."

"Yes, but that would be lower down the river. They say the Church has canonized her."

"There was an old stone building, which they called Stables. Once it actually was used as the stables of a sovkhoz stud-farm —now the name will go down in history—a very old place with huge thick walls. The Germans fortified it and made it impregnable. It was on a hill and they had the whole district under fire and were holding up our advance. It had to be captured. Christina, by a miracle of courage and ingenuity, got inside the German lines and blew it up, and was taken alive and hanged."

"Why do they call her Christina Orletsova and not Dudorova?"

"We were only engaged, you know. We decided in the summer of forty-one that we'd be married at the end of the war. After that I moved about a great deal, like everybody in the army. My unit was sent from one place to another. Because of all those endless transfers I lost touch with her. I never saw her again. I heard of her extraordinary exploit and heroic death like everyone else—from the newspapers and the regimental orders. They say they're going to put up a monument to her somewhere near here. I hear Zhivago—the General, Yurii's brother—is going around the district collecting data about her."

"I'm sorry—I shouldn't have made you talk about her. It must all be very painful to you."

"Well . . . But we've lost track of time, and I don't want to hold you up. You get undressed and into the water, and get going. I'll lie on the bank and chew a blade of grass and think. I may even sleep a bit."

A few moments later they began to talk again.

"Where did you learn to wash clothes like that?"

"From necessity. We were unlucky. We got sent to just about the worst of the penal camps. There were very few survivors. Our arrival, to begin with. We got off the train. A wilderness of snow. Forest in the distance. Guards with rifles, muzzles pointing at us, wolfhounds. About the same time, other groups were brought up. We were spread out and formed into a big polygon all over the field, facing outward, so that we wouldn't see each other. Then we were ordered down on our knees, and told to keep looking straight ahead on pain of death. Then the roll call, an endless, humiliating business going on for hours and hours. And all the time we were on our knees. Then we got up and the other groups were marched off and ours was told: 'This is your camp. Make the best of it!' An open snow field with a post in the middle and a notice on it saying: 'GULAG 92 Y.N. 90'—that's all there was."

"It wasn't nearly so bad with us; we were lucky. Of course I was doing my second stretch, which followed automatically from the first. Moreover, I was sentenced under a different article, so the conditions were quite different. When I came out, I was reinstated again as I'd been the first time and allowed to go on lecturing. And when I was mobilized I was given my full rank of Major, not put into a disciplinary battalion, like you."

"Yes, well . . . That was all there was, the post and the notice board, 'GULAG 92 Y.N. 90.' First we broke saplings with our bare hands in the bitter cold, to get wood to build huts. And in the end, believe it or not, we gradually built our whole camp. We put up our prison and our stockade and our cells and our watch-towers, all with our own hands. And then we began our job as lumberjacks. We cut trees. We harnessed ourselves, eight to a sledge, and we hauled timber and sank into the snow up to our necks. For a long time we didn't know the war had started. They kept it from us. And then suddenly there came the offer. You could volunteer for front-line service in a disciplinary battalion, and if you came out alive you were free. After that, attack after attack, mile after mile of electrified barbed wire, mines, mortars, month after month of artillery barrage. They called our company the death squad. It was practically wiped out. How and why I survived, I don't know. And yet—would you believe it—all that utter hell was nothing, it was bliss compared to the horrors of the concentration camp, and not because of the material conditions but for an entirely different reason."

"Yes, poor fellow. You've taken a lot."

"It wasn't just washing clothes you learned out there, you learned everything there is to learn."

"It's an extraordinary thing, you know. It isn't only in comparison with your life as a convict, but compared to everything in the thirties, even to my easy situation at the university in the midst of books and money and comfort, the war came as a breath of fresh air, a purifying storm, a breath of deliverance.

"I think that collectivization was an erroneous and unsuccessful measure and it was impossible to admit the error. To conceal the failure people had to be cured, by every means of terrorism, of the habit of thinking and judging for themselves, and forced to see what didn't exist, to assert the very opposite of what their eyes told them. This accounts for the unexampled cruelty of the Yezhov[1] period, the promulgation of a constitution that was never meant to be applied, and the introduction of elections that violated the very principle of free choice.

"And when the war broke out, its real horrors, its real dangers, its menace of real death were a blessing compared with the inhuman reign of the lie, and they brought relief because they broke the spell of the dead letter.

[1] Nikolai Ivanovich Yezhov, head of the Secret Police, 1936-38.

"It was felt not only by men in your position, in concentration camps, but by absolutely everyone, at home and at the front, and they all took a deep breath and flung themselves into the furnace of this mortal, liberating struggle with real joy, with rapture.

"The war has its special character as a link in the chain of revolutionary decades. The forces directly unleashed by the revolution no longer operated. The indirect effects of the revolution, the fruit of its fruit, the consequences of the consequences, began to manifest themselves. Misfortune and ordeals had tempered characters, prepared them for great, desperate, heroic exploits. These fabulous, astounding qualities characterize the moral elite of this generation.

"And when I see such things I am filled with happiness, in spite of Christina's martyrdom and our losses and my wounds, in spite of the high cost in blood of the war. The light of self-sacrifice that illuminates Orletsova's death and the lives of all of us helps me to bear her loss.

"I was released just when you, poor fellow, were going through your endless torture. Soon after that, Christina came to the university as a history student. I taught her. I had noticed her before, after my first term in concentration camp, as a remarkable girl, when she was still a child. You remember, Yurii was still alive, I told you both. Well, now she was one of my students.

"That was the time when the custom of political re-education of teachers by students had come in. Orletsova flung herself into that work with passion. I had no idea why she went at me so fiercely. She was so aggressive and unjust that sometimes the other students protested and stood up for me. She had a great sense of humor and she made fun of me to her heart's content in the wall newspaper, referring to me by some invented name that everyone could see through. And then suddenly, completely by chance, I realized that this inveterate hostility was a camouflage of her love for me—a strong, enduring love she had felt for a long time, and which I had always returned.

"We spent a wonderful summer in forty-one, just before and after the beginning of the war. Christina was in a group of undergraduates, men and women, who were billeted in a Moscow suburb where my unit was also stationed. Our friendship began and ran its course against this background. At that time civilian units were being formed, Christina was being trained as a parachutist, the first German bombers were spotted from the rooftops of Moscow and driven back. That was when we became engaged, as I told you, but we were separated almost at once because my regiment was moved. I never saw her again.

"Later on, when the war took a turn for the better and the Germans were surrendering by the thousands, I was transferred after I had been wounded twice, from Anti-Aircraft to the Seventh Staff Division, where they needed people who knew languages. Then, after I fished you out of the depths, I got you assigned to my unit."

"Tania, the laundry girl, was a friend of Christina's. They got to know each other at the front. She talks a lot about her. Have you noticed the way Tania smiles, all over her face, like Yurii? You forget the snub nose and the high cheekbones, and you think she's quite pretty and attractive. It's the same type, you see it all over Russia."

"I know what you mean. No, I hadn't noticed."

"What a hideous, barbarous nickname, Tania Bezocheredeva, 'Tania Out-of-Turn.' It can't possibly be her surname. I wonder how she got it."

"She told us, you know. She was a bezprizornaia of unknown parents. Probably somewhere in the depths of Russia where the language is still pure she was called Bezotchcheia, 'Fatherless.' Then her name was distorted by city people who introduced a connotation closer to their recent experiences."

3

Shortly after this, Gordon and Dudorov were in the town of Karachev, which had been razed to the ground. There they caught up with some rear units of their army.

It was a hot autumn; the weather had been fine and still for more than a month. The black soil of Bryanshchina, the blessedly fertile region between Orel and Bryansk, shimmered a chocolate or coffee brown under the blue, cloudless sky.

The main street, which was part of the highway, cut straight across the town. On one side of it had been houses that were blown up and turned into piles of rubble by mines, and up-rooted, splintered, and charred fruit trees from the blasted gardens. Nor were there any houses on the other side, but it was less ravaged by fire and explosions, probably because it had con-sisted largely of vacant lots and thus offered no targets for de-struction.

On the side where there had once been houses, the homeless inhabitants were poking about in the still smoldering ashes, picking up odds and ends in different corners of the ruins and putting them all together in one place. Others were busy making dugouts and cutting strips of turf with which to roof them.

The vacant lots across the road were white with tents and crowded with auxiliary-service trucks and horse-drawn wagons of all kinds—field ambulances, cut off from their divisional staffs, and units of every sort of commissariat and depot, lost and mixed up and trying to sort themselves out. And here, too, weedy boys from the replacement companies, in gray caps, with heavy, rolled-up overcoats on their backs, their faces earthy, drawn, and wasted from dysentery, rested their packs and had a sleep and a snack before trudging on farther west.

Half the gutted, blown-up town was still burning and in the distance delayed-action mines kept exploding. Every now and then, people digging in their yards straightened their bent backs, leaned on their picks, and rested, turning and gazing in the di-rection of a blast.

There, the gray, black, brick-red clouds of smoke, flame, and rubble rose into the sky, first in jets and fountains, then more lazily, like heavily rising scum, then fanning and spreading into plumes; finally they scattered and sank back to earth. Then the diggers went on with their work.

Across the road from the ruins there was an open space bor-dered by a hedge and shaded by tall old trees. The trees and the hedge isolated it from the rest of the world, like a private courtyard, shaded and cool.

Here Tania, the laundry girl, together with several people from her unit, as well as others who had joined them, including Dudorov and Gordon, had been waiting since morning for the truck that had been sent for her. The regimental laundry entrusted to her care was packed in several crates that stood piled one on top of the other on the ground. Tania kept a close eye on it, and the rest of the group remained in sight for fear of missing the chance of a lift.

They had been waiting a long time—more than five hours. With nothing to do, they listened to the incessant chatter of the garrulous girl, who had seen a great deal in her life. At the moment she was telling them of how she had met Major-General Zhivago.

"Of course. Yesterday. They took me to the General himself. Major-General Zhivago. He was passing through here, and asking everyone about Christina. He was looking for eye-witnesses, people who had known her personally. They pointed me out to him. They said we'd been friends. He told them to bring me along. So they came and got me. He didn't scare me a bit. Nothing special about him, just like everybody else. He's got slit eyes and black hair. Well, I told him what I knew. He heard me out and said thank you. And who are you? he said to me. Where do you come from? Well, naturally, I was shy. What have I got to boast about? I'm a bezprizornaia. One of the homeless children. And all that. I don't have to tell you. Reformatories, always on the move. But he kept at me. Let's have it, he said. Don't be embarrassed. There's nothing to be ashamed of. Well, at first I couldn't say much, then I told him a bit more, and he kept nodding his head, then as he went on nodding, I wasn't afraid any longer. And it's true I've got a lot to tell. You wouldn't believe it if I told you; you'd say, She's making it up. Well, it was the same with him. When I finished he got up and started walking up and down the room. That's extraordinary, he said. Really extraordinary. I'll tell you what, he said. I haven't got time now. But I'll find you again, you can be sure of that. I'll find you and send for you again. I never thought I'd hear a thing like that. I won't leave you this way, he said, I've just got to take care of a few things. And then, who can tell, I might put myself down as your uncle, you'll be promoted to being General's niece. And I'll send you to a university, he said. Anywhere you like. I swear to God, that's what he said. Probably a joke, just to tease me."

At this moment a long, empty cart with high sides, of the kind used for carting hay in Poland and West Russia, drove up. The two horses in their shaft harness were driven by a soldier from the horse transport corps who in the old days would have been called a wagoner. He pulled up, jumped down from his seat, and began to unhitch the cart. Everyone except Tania and one or two soldiers crowded around him begging him to take them wherever they were going, telling him, of course, that they would make it worth his while. But the driver refused, saying he had no right to use the cart or the horses except as he was ordered. He led the horses away and was not seen again.

Tania and the others, who until then had beeen sitting on the ground, all climbed into the empty cart, which had been left standing in the field. The conversation, interrupted by its arrival and by the argument with the driver, was resumed.

"What did you tell the General?" asked Gordon. "Tell us, if you can."

"Why not? I'll tell you."

And so she told them her terrible story.

4

"Yes, it's true that I've got a lot to tell. They say I don't come from poor people. Whether strangers told me or I somehow remembered it, I don't know, but I've heard it said that my mother, Raïsa Komarova, was the wife of a Russian cabinet minister, Comrade Komarov, who was in hiding in White Mongolia. But I guess Komarov was not my real father. Well, of course, I'm not an educated girl, I grew up an orphan without a father and mother. Perhaps what I say seems funny to you, but I'm only saying what I know, you have to put yourselves in my place.

"Yes. Well now, what I'm going to tell you. It all happened beyond Krushitsy, the other end of Siberia, beyond the Cossack country, near the Chinese border. When we—the Reds, that is —moved up to the chief town of the Whites, that same Komarov, the minister, he put my mother and all those families on a special train and ordered it to take them away. My mother was frightened, you see, she didn't dare to move a step without him.

"This Komarov didn't know about me. He didn't know that I

even existed. My mother had me when she had been parted from him for a long time, and she was frightened to death that somebody might tell him. He hated children terribly, and he yelled and stamped his feet. They only bring filth and worry into the house, I can't stand it, he used to yell.

"Well now, as I was saying, when the Reds began to come up to the town, my mother sent to Nagornaia Station for Marfa, the signal woman. That was three stations away from the town. I'll tell you how it was. First there was Nizovaia, and then there was Nagornaia, and then there was the Samsonov Pass. Now I think I understand it, why Mother knew this signal woman. I think this signal woman, Marfa, used to come and sell milk and vegetables in the town. That's it.

"And here is something I don't know. I think they cheated Mother, they didn't tell her the truth. The Lord only knows what sort of story they told her, I suppose they said it was just for a time, for a day or two, till things settled down. She didn't mean to give me to strangers forever. To be brought up by strangers —Mother could not have given up her own child like that.

"Well, you know how it is with a child. 'Go and talk to Auntie, she'll give you a piece of gingerbread, nice Auntie, don't be frightened of Auntie.' How I cried afterwards, how heartbroken I was, how I missed my mother—it's better not to remember that. I wanted to hang myself, I nearly went out of my mind as a small child. That was all I was at that time. I suppose Aunt Marfa got money for my keep, a lot of money.

"There was a rich farm that went with the signal job, a cow and a horse and of course all kinds of fowl, and a big place for vegetables—out there you could get as much land as you liked—and of course no rent because the house belonged to the government; it was right next to the tracks. When the train was coming from home, it could hardly get up the hill, it was so steep, but coming from your parts, from Russia, down it came so fast they had to use the brakes. Down below, in the autumn, when the woods thinned out, you could see Nagornaia as if it were set on a saucer.

"The signal man, Uncle Vasilii, I used to call just Daddy. He was a kind and cheerful man, only terribly trusting, especially when he was drunk. Everybody knew all there was to know about him all over the countryside. He'd turn his heart inside out to every stranger he met.

"But the signal woman I never could call Mother. Whether it was because I couldn't forget my own mother or for some other reason, the fact is Aunt Marfa really was terrible. Yes. And so I called the signal woman Aunt Marfa.

"Well, time went on, years went by, how many I don't know. I was beginning to go out to the trains to wave the flag, and I could bring the cow in or unhitch the horse. Aunt Marfa taught me to spin, and as for the housework, it goes without saying I did that. Anything like sweeping or tidying or doing a bit of cooking, that was nothing to me, I did all that. Oh, yes, and I forgot to tell you, I looked after Petia. Our Petia had withered legs, he was three but he couldn't walk at all, so I carried him around. And now, after all those years, I still get shivers down my back when I think of how Auntie Marfa used to squint at my strong legs as much as to say why weren't my legs withered, it would be better if I had withered legs instead of her Petia, as if I'd put the evil eye on him. You wouldn't believe what spite and superstition there is in the world.

"But now listen to what I'm going to tell you. All that was nothing to what happened later. It'll make your hair stand on end.

"It was the time of NEP, a thousand rubles was worth a kopeck. Uncle Vasia sold a cow down below and got two sacks full of money. Kerenki it was called—no, sorry, they were called lemons then, that's what they were called. He had a drink and told everyone in Nagornaia how rich he was.

"I remember it was a windy day in autumn. The wind was tearing at the roof, it nearly knocked you off your feet, and the engines couldn't get uphill because the wind was head on. Suddenly I saw an old beggar woman coming down from the top of the hill, the wind tugging at her skirt and blowing off her kerchief.

"She was walking along and moaning and clutching her belly. She asked us to take her in, and we put her on the bench. Oh, she yelled, I can't stand it, I can't stand it, my belly is on fire, this is my end. In Christ's name, she begged, take me to the hospital, I'll pay you whatever you like. Well, Daddy hitched

Udaloy, the horse, to the cart, put the old woman in the cart, and took her to the county hospital, which was eleven miles away.

"After a time we went to bed, Aunt Marfa and I, then we heard Udaloy neighing outside and the cart driving into the yard. It seemed a bit too soon for them to be back. But anyway Aunt Marfa lit a light, put on her jacket, and undid the bolt without waiting for Daddy to knock.

"She opened the door, but it wasn't Daddy, it was a stranger, dark and frightening, and he said, Show me where the money is that you got for the cow. I've killed your old man in the wood, he said, but you being a woman I'll let you alone if you tell me where the money is. If you don't tell me you know what will happen, you'll only have yourself to blame, and better not keep me waiting, I don't have any time to hang around.

"Oh, God in heaven, need I tell you the state we were in, you can imagine, yourselves. We were shaking all over, half dead with fright and speechless with terror! First Uncle Vasia was killed, he'd said so himself, he'd killed him with an ax, and now we were alone with him, a murderer right in our house, we could see he was a murderer.

"I suppose it was just then that Aunt Marfa went out of her mind. The moment she heard her husband was dead, something snapped inside her. And she knew she mustn't show how she felt.

"First she threw herself at his feet. Have mercy on me, she said, don't kill me, I don't know a thing, I've never heard about any money, I don't know what money you are talking about. But he wasn't going to be put off with that, he wasn't such a fool, the devil. All right, then, she told him. The money is in the cellar. I'll open the trap door for you. But the devil saw right through that. No, he said, you go down, you know the way, you get it. I don't care if you go down to the cellar or up on the roof, all I want is the money. But remember—don't try to pull any tricks, he said, it doesn't pay to fool with me.

"Then she said to him: God be with you, why are you so suspicious? I'd gladly go down and get it for you myself, but my legs are bad, I can't manage the ladder. I'll stand on the top step and hold the light for you. Don't worry, I'll send my daughter down with you, she said. That was me she meant.

"Oh, God in heaven, need I tell you how I felt when I heard that? Well, that's the end of me, I thought, and everything went black in front of my eyes and my legs wouldn't hold me up, I thought I'd fall down.

"But that devil, he was no fool, he took one look at both of us and screwed up his eyes and grinned at her, showing all his teeth, as much as to say: I know your tricks, you can't fool me. He could see that I meant nothing to her, I wasn't her own flesh and blood, so he made a grab at Petia and picked him up in one hand and pulled up the trap door with the other. Let's have a light, he said to her, and down he went—down the ladder into the cellar with Petia.

"I think she was already cracked and couldn't understand anything; her mind was gone. As soon as he had gone down with little Petia, bang, she slammed the trap door and locked it and began to drag a heavy trunk on top of it, nodding and beckoning to me to help her, because it was too heavy for her. She got it in place and sat on it, pleased with herself, the crazy woman. No sooner had she sat down than the robber started yelling and banging on the floor. You couldn't make out what he was saying, the floor boards were too thick, but you could tell from his voice what he meant: let him out or he'd murder Petia. He roared worse than a wild beast to frighten us. Now your Petia's in for it, he yelled, but she couldn't understand a thing. She just sat there winking at me and laughing, as much as to say: No matter what you do, I won't budge from the trunk and I'll keep the keys. I did everything I could with her, I screamed right into her ears saying she must open up the cellar and save Petia, and I tried to push her off the trunk, but I couldn't, she was too strong for me and she wouldn't listen.

"Well, he was banging, banging on the floor, and the time was going by, and she just sat there rolling her eyes, not listening to anything.

"Well, after a time—Oh, God in heaven, I've been through many things in my life, but this I'll never forget. As long as I live I'll hear Petia's thin little voice—little Petia cried and groaned down below, the little angel, that devil choked him to death.

"Now what shall I do, what shall I do with this mad old woman and this murderer, I thought. And I had to do something. The moment I thought this I heard Udaloy neighing outside. He'd been standing out there in the yard and he hadn't been unharnessed. Yes. Udaloy was neighing as much as to say: Let's fly quickly, Tania, and find some good people and get help. I looked out of the window and I saw that it was near dawn. You're right, Udaloy, it's a good idea, I thought. Let's go. But hardly had I thought this when again I heard, like a voice calling from the wood, Wait, don't hurry, Tania, we'll do it another way. And again I knew I wasn't alone in the wood. It was like our own cock crowing. An engine hooted down below. I recognized its whistle; it was from the engine that they always kept ready at Nagornaia—a pusher, they called it—to help freight trains up the hill. This was a mixed train going by, it always went by at that time every night. Well, I heard this engine I knew, calling me from below. I listened and my heart leapt. Am I off my head, I wondered, like Auntie Marfa, that every living beast and every dumb engine speaks to me in plain Russian?

"Well, it was no good thinking, the train was getting near, there was no time to think. I grabbed the lantern—there wasn't much light yet—and I raced to the track and stood right in the middle, between the rails, waving the light up and down.

"Well, what more is there to say? I stopped the train. Because of the wind it was going slowly, very slowly, almost at a crawl. I stopped it and the driver, who knew me, leaned out of the window of the cab and called out something, I couldn't hear what it was because of the wind. I shouted to him, the signal house had been raided, murder and robbery, a killer in the house, help us, Comrade Uncle, we need help right away. And while I was saying this, Red Army men came jumping out of the train, one after the other, it was an army train, they jumped out on the track. What's up? they asked, they couldn't make out why on earth the train had stopped in the wood, on a steep hill at night, and was standing still.

"I told them everything. They dragged the murderer out of the cellar. He was squealing in a voice thinner than Petia's, Have mercy on me, good people, he said, don't kill me, I'll never do it again. They took the law into their own hands. They dragged him out onto the tracks, tied his hands and feet to the rails, and drove the train over him.

"I never even went back for my clothes, I was so frightened. I asked them to take me along in the train, and they put me on the train and off I went. After this, I wandered over half our own country and others with the bezprizornys, I don't know where I haven't been. I'm not exaggerating. What happiness, what freedom now, after all I suffered as a child! Though it must be said that there was also much sin and misery. But all this came later, I'll tell you about it some other time. . . . That night I was telling you about, a railway official came off the train and went to the house to take charge of the government property, and to decide what to do about Auntie Marfa. Some say she never recovered and died in a madhouse, but others say she got better and came out."

For a long time after hearing Tania's story Gordon and Dudorov strolled about under the trees in silence. Then the truck came; it turned clumsily off the road into the clearing, and the crates were loaded onto it. Gordon said:

"You realize who this Tania is?"

"Yes, of course."

"Evgraf will look after her." Gordon added after a pause: "It has often happened in history that a lofty ideal has degenerated into crude materialism. Thus Greece gave way to Rome, and the Russian Enlightenment has become the Russian Revolution. There is a great difference between the two periods. Blok says somewhere: 'We, the children of Russia's terrible years.' Blok meant this in a metaphorical, figurative sense. The children were not children, but the sons, the heirs, the intelligentsia, and the terrors were not terrible but sent from above, apocalyptic; that's quite different. Now the metaphorical has become literal, children are children and the terrors are terrible, there you have the difference."

5

Five or ten years later, one quiet summer evening, Dudorov and Gordon were again together, sitting at an open window above Moscow, which extended into the dusk as far as the eye could reach. They were looking through an album of Yurii's writings that

Evgraf had put together, a book they had read more than once and almost knew by heart. They read and talked and thought. By the time they came to the middle of the book it was dark and they turned on the light.

And Moscow, right below them and stretching into the distance, the author's native city, in which he had spent half his life—Moscow now struck them not as the stage of the events connected with him but as the main protagonist of a long story, the end of which they had reached that evening, book in hand.

Although victory had not brought the relief and freedom that were expected at the end of the war, nevertheless the portents of freedom filled the air throughout the postwar period, and they alone defined its historical significance.

To the two old friends, as they sat by the window, it seemed that this freedom of the soul was already there, as if that very evening the future had tangibly moved into the streets below them, that they themselves had entered it and were now part of it. Thinking of this holy city and of the entire earth, of the still-living protagonists of this story, and their children, they were filled with tenderness and peace, and they were enveloped by the unheard music of happiness that flowed all about them and into the distance. And the book they held seemed to confirm and encourage their feeling.

THE POEMS
OF YURII ZHIVAGO

HAMLET

The stir is over. I step forth on the boards.
Leaning against an upright at the entrance,
I strain to make the far-off echo yield
A cue to the events that may come in my day.

Night and its murk transfix and pin me,
Staring through thousands of binoculars.
If Thou be willing, Abba, Father,
Remove this cup from me.

I cherish this, Thy rigorous conception,
And I consent to play this part therein;
But another play is running at this moment,
So, for the present, release me from the cast.

And yet, the order of the acts has been schemed and plotted,
And nothing can avert the final curtain's fall.
I stand alone. All else is swamped by Pharisaism.
To live life to the end is not a childish task.

MARCH

The sun is hotter than the top ledge in a steam bath;
The ravine, crazed, is rampaging below.
Spring—that corn-fed, husky milkmaid—
Is busy at her chores with never a letup.

The snow is wasting (pernicious anemia—
See those branching veinlets of impotent blue?)
Yet in the cowbarn life is burbling, steaming,
And the tines of pitchforks simply glow with health.

523

These days—these days, and these nights also!
With eavesdrop thrumming its tattoos at noon,
With icicles (cachectic!) hanging on to gables,
And with the chattering of rills that never sleep!

All doors are flung open—in stable and in cowbarn;
Pigeons peck at oats fallen in the snow;
And the culprit of all this and its life-begetter—
The pile of manure—is pungent with ozone.

HOLY WEEK

The murk of night still prevails.
It is yet so early in this world
That the sky even now flaunts its countless stars,
And each star is radiant as the day.
And if the earth could really have its way
It would sleep through all of Eastertide
To the droning of the Psalms as a lullaby.

The murk of night still prevails.
The Creation's hour is yet so early
That the square extends like eternity
From one corner to the other,
And there is still a millennium
Until the dawn and warmth come.

The earth is stark-naked yet:
It hasn't got a stitch to wear of nights
To ring the bells, or to chime in
Of its own accord, with choirs singing.

From Maundy Thursday right up to
The very eve of Easter the waters gnaw
At riverbanks, and are busy weaving
Their currents, whirlpools, and eddies.

The forest, too, is stripped, exposed,
And all through Passiontide
The trunks of pines stand in a throng
Like worshippers aligned in prayer.

While in the town, not too far off,
The trees stand mother-naked too,
As if about to enter church
And peering within its gratings.

Their gaze is overcome with awe,
Nor is their panic hard to fathom:
The gardens leave their boundary walls,
The laws that govern the earth are shaken—
A god is being interred.

They see a glow about the altar screen,
And the black pall, and tapers in a row,
And faces all in tears. . . .
And a procession suddenly emerges
Bearing the Cross and Shroud,
And comes toward them. Two birches
Guarding the portals have to step aside
And yield the right of way.

The procession makes a circuit of the church grounds,
Walking along the very curb of the pavement,
And brings in from the street within the portals
The spring, and all the murmurings of spring,
And air that has about it the tang of consecrated wafers
And of the heady fumes of spring.

And March scoops up the snow on the porch
And scatters it like alms among the halt and lame—
As though a man had carried out the Ark,
And opened it, and distributed all it held.

The singing lasts until the glow of dawn.
The voices, having sobbed their fill,
Are more subdued. Their chanting of the Psalms and Gospels
Floats out more and more faintly
Until it reaches wastelands under lonely lamps.

And when the midnight comes
All creatures and all flesh will fall silent
On hearing spring put forth its rumor
That just as soon as there is better weather
Death itself can be overcome
Through the power of the Resurrection.

WHITE NIGHT

I have visions of a remote time:
A house on the Petersburg side of the Neva;
You, the daughter of a none-too-well-off landed proprietress
(The land being out in the steppes),
Are taking courses—and were born in Kursk.

You are a darling; you have admirers.
This night you and I
Have made ourselves cozy on your window sill;
We are looking down from this skyscraper of yours.

The street lamps are just like butterflies of gas.
The morning has flicked us with its first chill.
That which I am telling you is so much like
The far-off vistas now plunged in sleep.

You and I are in the grasp
Of precisely that timid devotion to a mystery
Which holds St. Petersburg, spread like a panorama
Beyond the unencompassable Neva.

There, far, far among thick-wooded landmarks,
On this night, so vernal and so white,
The nightingales roll and trill their paeans,
Filling with rumbling the city's wooded limits.

Their frenzied trilling surges.
The song of each tiny, dull-hued singer
Stirs rapture and awakens unrest
Deep within each ensorcelled grove.

Night, like a barefooted pilgrim woman,
Is creeping close to the fences as she makes her way there,
And the tracks of our murmurs, which she has eavesdropped,
Trail after her from our window sill.

Amid echoes of these overheard murmurs
The boughs of the apple and cherry trees
Bedeck themselves in whitish blossoms
In the gardens with their rough-hewn palings.

And the trees, themselves white as specters,
Come out on the road jostling and thronging,
Just as if they were waving their farewells
To the white night which has witnessed so very many things.

BAD ROADS IN SPRING

The flames of sunset were smoldering out.
A horseman headed for a remote farmstead in the Urals
Was plodding over a spring-mired trail
In a thick pine forest.

The horse's inwards heaved. In answer
To the swish and clink of its shod hoofs
The swirling whirlpools loosed their echoes
Over the road, in pursuit.

But when the horseman, dropping reins,
Would slow his mount down to a walk,
The spring freshets would roll very close to him
All of their roaring, all their din.

Someone was laughing, someone wept;
Stones ground to dust against the flints,
And loosened and uprooted tree-stumps
Went tumbling into churning pools.

A nightingale raged in frantic song
Like a church bell pealing forth a tocsin;
He sang among branches interlaced and darkling
Against the sunset's conflagration.

Where a willow leant over a hollow
Like a widow burying her mate
The bird was whistling on seven oaks,
As Robber Nightingale did in days of old.

Against what evil, against what forlorn love
Was this predestined fervor meant?
Against whom had the singer fired
This charge of small shot in the woods?

It seemed that he would emerge like a wood demon
From the camp of the escaping convicts
To meet the outposts of the partisans,
Whether on foot or horse.

The earth and sky, the field and forest
Hearkened to catch each unique note,
These measured doles of sheerest madness,
Of pain, of happiness, of anguish.

EXPLANATION

Life has returned with just as little reason
As on a time it so oddly snapped.
I am on the same ancient thoroughfare
That I was on that summer, on that day and hour.

The same people, and their cares are the same,
And the sunset's red fire has not yet grown cold:
It was just the same when that deathly evening
Quickly nailed it against a white wall.

Women in worn and sleazy cottons
Go tap-tapping along (just as they did then)
And night (just as it did then) will crucify them
Under the tin roofs of their garret rooms.

There, one of them, with her feet dragging,
Slowly emerges upon her threshold
And, climbing out of her semibasement,
Goes cater-corner across the yard.

I am again brushing up on excuses
And (once again) nothing means much to me.
Now my fair neighbor, having skirted the back yard,
Leaves us alone, all alone by ourselves.

Keep back your tears. And do not twist
Your swollen lips. And don't pucker them,
For that would merely break the scab
That was formed by the enfevered spring.

Remove your hand—don't keep it on my breast:
We are merely wires—and the current's on.
Once more—watch out!—we will be thrown together,
And this time not by chance.

The years will pass and you will marry.
You will forget the hardships you endured.
To be a woman is a great adventure;
To drive men mad is a heroic thing.

For my part, all my life long
I have stood like a devoted slave
In reverence and awe before the miracle
Of woman's hands, her back, her shoulders, and her sculptured throat.

And yet, no matter how the night
May chain me within its ring of longing,
The pull of separation is still stronger
And I have a beckoning passion for the clean break.

SUMMER IN TOWN

Conversation in murmured tones.
With an impatient gesture
She upsweeps her hair—the whole sheaf of it—
From the nape of her neck.

As she peers out from under her heavy comb
She is a woman in a helmet.
Her head, braids and all,
Is thrown back.

Outside, the sultry night
Threatens to turn inclement.
Pedestrians, shuffling their feet,
Hasten homeward.

You can hear abrupt thunderings
And their grating echoes,
While the gusts of wind
Are making the curtains sway.

Not a word breaks the silence.
The air is as sticky as it was before
And, as before, lightnings go rummaging,
Rummaging, rummaging all over the sky.

And when the morning comes
Sunshot and sultry
And once more starts drying the puddles
Left on the street by last night's downpour,

The fragrant lindens,
Ages old but still in full blossom,
Have a glum look about them
Because they haven't slept themselves out.

WIND

I have died, but you are still among the living.
And the wind, keening and complaining,
Makes the country house and the forest rock—
Not each pine by itself
But all the trees as one,
Together with the illimitable distance;
It makes them rock as the hulls of sailboats
Rock on the mirrorous waters of a boat-basin.
And this the wind does not out of bravado
Or in a senseless rage,
But so that in its desolation
It may find words to fashion a lullaby for you.

HOPBINES

We seek shelter from inclement weather
Under a willow entwined with ivy.
A raincape is thrown over our shoulders.
My arms are tightly encircled about you.

Sorry—I erred. The shrubs in these thickets
Are not ivy-grown but covered with hopbines.
Well, we'll do better if we take this raincape
And spread it out wide for a rug beneath us.

FALSE SUMMER

The leaves of the currants are coarse and woolly.
The house shakes with laughter, the windowpanes ring.
There's great chopping within it, and pickling, while pepper
And cloves are put in to lend tang to the brine.

The grove, like a cavorting clown, casts this hubbub
As far as that field with its rather steep slope
Where the sun-scorched hazels are blazing with color
As if they'd been seared by the heat of a fire.

Here the road dips to a gravelly gully;
Here among the ancient and gnarled river-snags
One can feel sorry for even that rag-picking crone Autumn
Who has swept all of her queer treasure-trove down here.

And also because all Creation is simpler
Than some of our crafty philosophers think.
And because the grove seems to be plunged under water,
And because for all things there's a predestined end.

And because there's no sense for one's eyes to be blinking
When all they behold has been scorched by the sun,
And the fine ashes of Autumn (its white gossamer)
Float in at the windows with each vagrant breeze.

There's a hole in the fence; it leads from the garden
To a path that gets lost where the birches grow thick.
The house hums with laughter and housewifely bustling—
That bustling and laughter also come from afar.

WEDDING

Guests came until dawn
To the bride's house for the celebration,
Cutting right across the yard,
Bringing their own music.

After midnight until seven
Not a murmur came
From behind the felt-lined door
Of the master's bedroom.

But at dawn (the sleepiest time
When one could sleep forever)
The accordion struck up,
Once again, at leaving.

The harmonica played too
Like a hurdy-gurdy;
Clapping hands and clicking beads
Helped the charivari.

And again, again, again
Sped by guests carousing
All the ribald catches burst
Right into the bedroom,

While one wench, as white as snow,
To the calls and whistles
Once more did her peahen dance
Gliding, with hips swinging,

Head tossed high
And right hand waving,
Dancing fast on cobbles—
Just a peahen, peahen!

Suddenly the din and doings
And rings-around-a-rosy
Vanished as if hell had yawned
Or water had engulfed them.

Noisily the barnyard woke
And sounds of daily chores
Mingled with the noisy talk
And the peals of laughter.

Up into the boundless skies
Rose whirlwinds of gray patches:
Flocks of pigeons taking off
In fast flight from dovecotes.

Just as if some drowsy soul
Bestirred himself to set loose
Birds with wishes for long life
To overtake the wedding.

For life, too, is only an instant,
Only the dissolving of ourselves
In the selves of all others
As if bestowing a gift—

Only wedding noises
Soaring in through a window;
Only a song, only a dream,
Only a gray pigeon.

AUTUMN

I have let all the members of my household go their ways;
All those close to me have long since scattered.
And everything—within the heart and throughout nature—
Is filled with the loneliness of always.

And now I am here with you in the forester's hut.
The forest is unpeopled and deserted.
Its trails and paths are (as the old song has it)
Half overgrown with grass and weeds.

We are the only ones now
For the walls of logs to regard in melancholy.
We made no promises to storm barricades;
We shall go down to perdition openly.

We will take our seats at one; at three we will leave our seats—
I with a book, you with your needlework.
And when day breaks we shall not notice
At what time we had done with our kissing.

Be noisy, leaves, as you flutter down—
Still more flamboyantly, with more abandon!
And raise the level of the gall of yesterday
Within the cup, by adding to it today's yearning.

Attachment, craving, splendor of beauty. . . .
Let us scatter like smoke in this September soughing.
Bury all of yourself, my dearest, in this autumnal rustling;
Swoon, or go half insane!

You shed your coverings in much the same fashion
As this grove sheds its leaves,
Whenever you fall into my embraces
In your dressing gown with its silken tassels.

You are the blessing in a stride toward perdition,
When living sickens more than sickness does itself;
The root of beauty is audacity,
And that is what draws us to each other.

FAIRY TALES

Once upon a time
In a faery realm
A knight was urging his steed
Over a steppe of burdocks.

He was most eager
To take part in battle,
Yet he could see through the dust
A forest looming ahead.

A nagging foreboding
Gnawed at his doughty heart.
(Shun the water hole—
Tighten saddle-girth!)

But the knight, unheeding,
Put spurs to his steed
And at full tilt rode
Up the wooded knoll.

Then, from this burial mound,
He rode into a dry river bed.
Next, skirting a meadow,
He crossed over a mountain.

He veered into a hollow
And, by a forest trail,
Came upon a spoor,
Found a water hole.

Deaf to any warning,
Unheeding his inner call,
He led his steed down from *a rise*
To drench him at the stream.

By the stream a cave yawned,
Before the cave was a ford;
Flaming brimstone seemed
To light the cavern's mouth.

From behind the crimson smoke
That screened everything from sight
A far-off cry came echoing
Through the towering pines.

The knight, startled,
Dashed off straight ahead,
Racing through the ravine
In answer to this cry for help.

And the knight beheld
A dread dragon's head,
And its scales and tail—
And gripped his lance hard.

Flaming at its maw,
The dragon scattered light like seed.
Its spine was wound in a triple coil
Around a maid.

The great serpent's neck
Flicked like the tip of a whip
Over the white shoulders
Of his fair captive.

For that country's custom
Gave up to this forest monster
A beautiful young creature
As its prey.

The people of that region
Paid this tribute to save
Their wretched huts and hovels
From the great worm's wrath.

Its body bound her arms
And was wound about her throat:
It had accepted this sacrifice
To torture as it willed.

With his eyes turned up to heaven
The knight implored its aid
And ready to give battle
Aimed his lance at full tilt.

Tightly closed eyelids.
Towering heights. And clouds.
Waters. Fords. And rivers.
Years. And countless ages.

The knight in dented helmet
Lies unhorsed in the battle.
His faithful steed's hoofs trample
The life out of the serpent.

Steed and dragon carcass
Lie together on the sand.
The knight lies there unconscious.
The maid is in a swoon.

The noontide vault of heaven
Is radiant and blue.
Who is this maid? A princess?
Bred to the land? Or to the purple born?

Tears from excess of joy
Course down her cheeks in streams.
Then her soul is overcome
By sleep and oblivion.

He feels he is recovering,
Then cannot stir a limb—
So great his loss of blood,
So much his strength is spent.

Yet both their hearts are beating.
By turns he and she
Strain to come to,
Only to sleep again.

Tightly closed eyelids.
Towering heights. And clouds.
Waters. Fords. And rivers.
Years. And countless ages.

AUGUST

The sun, keeping its promise without deception,
Had penetrated early in the morning,
Tracing a saffron streak obliquely
From the window curtains to the divan.

The same sun splashed with sultry ocher
The woods near by, the hamlet's houses,
My bed, my dampened pillow
And the wall's angle near the bookshelf.

I have recalled the very reason
For the slight dampness of my pillow.
I had dreamt that all of you were trailing
Through the woods, coming to see me off.

There was a crowd of you, yet you were straggling. **Suddenly**
Someone recalled: according to the Old Style
It was the sixth of August—
The Lord's Transfiguration.

On this day, usually, a light without a flame
Issues from Mount Tabor, and Autumn,
Refulgent as an oriflamme,
Draws all eyes by its many glories.

And you traversed the stunted, beggared,
Denuded, quaking scrubwood of the alders
And entered the cemetery coppice
Of flaring red and ornate as a ginger bunny.

The sky was pompously playing neighbor
To the unstirring treetops, while the distance
Was clamorous with the exchange
Of long-drawn clarion calls of roosters.

Death stood like a state surveyor
Within God's acre in this forest, scanning
My lifeless face, as if in thought
How best to dig my grave to proper measure.

All of you heard (not inwardly but with your sense of hearing)
The calm voice of someone close beside you.
That voice had been mine once, a fatidic voice.
It sounded now, untouched by death's corruption:

"Farewell to Transfiguration's azure
And to the Second Coming's gold!
Abate, with a last womanly caress,
The bitterness to me of this predestined hour.

Farewell to years of timelessness.
Let us part now, you who threw
Your woman's gauntlet to an abyss of degradations:
I am the arena of your ordeal.

Farewell, broad sweep of outspread wings,
Farewell to willfulness of soaring,
And to the image of the world through words made manifest,
And to creativity, and to working wonders."

541

WINTER NIGHT

It snowed and snowed, the whole world **over,**
Snow swept the world from end to end.
A candle burned on the table;
A candle burned.

As during summer midges swarm
To beat their wings against a flame,
Out in the yard the snowflakes swarmed
To beat against the windowpane.

The blizzard sculptured on the glass
Designs of arrows and of whorls.
A candle burned on the table;
A candle burned.

Distorted shadows fell
Upon the lighted ceiling:
Shadows of crossed arms, of crossed legs—
Of crossed destiny.

Two tiny shoes fell to the floor
And thudded.
A candle on a nightstand shed wax tears
Upon a dress.

All things vanished within
The snowy murk—white, hoary.
A candle burned on the table;
A candle burned.

A corner draft fluttered the flame
And the white fever of temptation
Upswept its angel wings that cast
A cruciform shadow.

It snowed hard throughout the month
Of February, and almost constantly
A candle burned on the table;
A candle burned.

PARTING

The man is staring across the threshold
And cannot recognize his home.
Her going had been like a flight.
Havoc has left its traces everywhere.

Chaos prevails in all the rooms.
He cannot judge the devastation
Because his eyes are blurred with tears,
Because his head is pounding.

Ever since morning his ears have been ringing.
Is he awake or having a bad dream?
And why do thoughts about the sea
Persist in coming to his mind?

When one no longer sees the day
Because of hoarfrost on the panes
The hopelessness of grief redoubles
Its likeness to the sea's vast desert.

He drew her every trait to him
Even as the sea draws near it
Each of the many littorals
Throughout the stretch of its incoming tide.

Even as reeds go down beneath
The rough seas following a storm
So every line of her had gone
To the bottom of his soul.

543

In years of hardships, in the days
Of an unthinkable existence
She had been cast up from the depths
By a high wave of destiny.

Amid innumerable perils,
Avoiding every reef and shoal
The wave had borne her on and on
And brought her close.

And now, this flight of hers. Perhaps
It had been forced upon her.
This parting will consume them both
And grief gnaw clean their bones.

His eyes take in the whole scene.
At the moment of her going
She had upset the contents of
Every compartment in her dresser.

He paces aimlessly and till dark comes
Keeps putting back inside a drawer
The scattered scraps of cloth,
The crumpled sample patterns.

And having run into his hand
A needle left in some unfinished sewing
He suddenly sees all of her.
And falls to sobbing. Softly.

ENCOUNTER

The snow will bury roads,
Will cover the roofs deeply.
If I step out to stretch my legs
I will see you from the door.

Alone, in a fall coat,
No hat and no snow boots;
You are trying to be calm,
Nibbling your snow-wet lips.

The distant trees and fences
Recede into the murk.
You stand at the corner
Alone in the midst of the falling snow.

Water runs down your scarf,
Inside your sleeves, your collar,
And melted snow sparkles
In dewdrops on your hair.

And a flaxen strand of it
Lights up your face, your scarf,
Your bravely erect figure,
That wretched coat of yours.

Snow melts upon your lashes.
Sadness is in your eyes.
And all of you seems fashioned
Out of a single piece.

It is as if your image
Were being etched forever
With burin and strong acid
Upon my very heart.

Nor can your submissive features
Ever be burnished off.
And so, what does it matter
If the world is stonyhearted?

And so, this night is doubling itself
With all its murk and snow
And I cannot draw a line
Dividing you and me.

For who are we, and where from,
If after all these years
Gossip alone still lives on
While we no longer live?

STAR OF THE NATIVITY

It was wintertime.
The wind blew from the plain
And the infant was cold
In the cave on the slope of a knoll.

The breath of an ox served to warm Him.
The cattle were huddling
Within the cave.
Warmth hovered in a mist over the manger.

Up on a cliff shepherds shook from their sheepskins
The straws from their pallets
And stray grains of millet
And sleepily stared into the midnight distance.

Far off were fields covered over with snow,
And a graveyard, and gravestones and fences,
A cart with its shafts deep in a snowdrift
And, over the graveyard, a star-studded sky.

546

And seemingly near yet unseen until then,
Its light more timorous than that of a tallow-dip
Set in the window of some watchman's hut,
A star glimmered over the road to Bethlehem.

Now it looked like a hayrick blazing
Off to one side from heaven and God;
Like the reflection of an arsonous fire,
Like a farmstead in flames or a threshing floor burning.

It reared in the sky like a fiery stack
Of straw, of hay,
In the midst of a Creation startled, astounded
By this new Star.

An increasing redness that was like a portent
Was glowing above it.
And three stargazers heeded, and hasted
To answer the call of these unwonted lights.

Gift-laden camels plodded behind them,
And caparisoned asses, each one smaller and smaller,
Were daintily, cautiously descending a hill.

And all of the things that were to come after
Sprang up in the distance as a strange prevision:
All the thoughts of the ages, all the dreams, all the worlds,
All the future of galleries and of museums,
All the pranks of goblins, all the works of the workers of miracles,
All the yule trees on earth, all the dreams of small children,
All the warm glow of tremulous candles, all chains,
All the magnificence of brightly hued tinsel. . . .
(Ever more cruel, more raging, the wind blew from the plain.)
. . . All rosy-cheeked apples, all the blown-glass gold globes.

Part of the pond was screened by alders
But, beyond rook nests among the treetops,
Part could be seen clearly from the brink of the cliff.
The shepherds could mark well the camels and asses

Threading their way at the edge of the milldam.
"Let us go with all others and worship the miracle,"
Said they, and muffled their sheepskins about them.

Plowing through snow made their bodies feel warm.
Tracks of bare feet, glinting like mica,
Led over the bright plain and beyond the inn's hut,
And the dogs sighting these tracks by the Star's light
Growled at them as if at a candle-end's flame.

The frosty night was like a fairy tale,
And some beings from the snow-crushed mountain ridge
Were mingling constantly, unseen, with all the others.
The dogs were wavering, looking back in terror,
And, in dire foreboding, cringed close to a young shepherd.

Through the same countryside, over the same highway
Some angels walked among the throng of mortals.
Their incorporeality made them invisible
Yet each step they took left the print of a foot.

Day was breaking. The trunks of the cedars stood out.
A horde of men milled by the stone at the cave's mouth.
"Who are you?" Mary asked them.
"We are from a shepherd tribe, and envoys of heaven.
We have come to sing praises to both of you."
"You cannot all enter. Bide a while here."

In the gloom before dawn, gray as cold ashes,
The drovers and shepherds stamped to keep warm.
Those come on foot bickered with those who came mounted.
Near the hollowed-out log that served as a water trough
The camels bellowed, the gray asses kicked out.

Day was breaking. Dawn swept the last of the stars
Off heaven's vault as if they were ash motes.
And Mary, out of all the countless multitude, allowed
Only the Magi to enter the cleft in the crag.

He slept, all refulgent, in the manger of oakwood,
Like a moonbeam within a deep-hollowed tree.
In lieu of sheepskins His body was warmed
By the lips of an ass and the nostrils of an ox.

The Magi stood in shadow (the byre seemed in twilight);
They spoke in whispers, groping for words.
Suddenly one, in deeper shadow, touched another
To move him aside from the manger, a little to the left.
The other turned: like a guest about to enter,
The Star of the Nativity was gazing upon the Maid.

DAWN

You were the be-all in my destiny.
Then came the war, the devastation,
And for a long, long time there was
No word from you, not even a sign.

And after many, many years
I find again your voice disturbs me.
All night I read your testament—
And found my consciousness returning.

I'm drawn to people, to be one of a crowd,
To share their morning animation.
I'm ready to smash everything to smithereens
And make all kneel in schoolboy penance.

And so I dash down all the stairs
As if this were my first sortie
Into these streets and their deep snow
And pavements that long since died out.

Each way I turn I see awakenings, lights, comfort.
Men gulp their tea, they hurry to catch trolleys.
Within the space of a few minutes
You'd never recognize the town.

The blizzard weaves its nets in gateways
Out of the thickly falling flakes.
And all, to get to work in time,
Dash madly, hardly taking breakfast.

I feel for all these people
As if I'd been within their hides;
I feel I'm melting, even as the snow melts,
I feel I glower, even as the morning glowers.

The nameless ones are part of me.
Children also, the trees, and stay-at-homes.
All these are victors over me—
And therein lies my sole victory.

MIRACLE

He was on His way from Bethany to Jerusalem,
Languishing under the sadness of premonitions.

The slope's prickly scrubwood had been scorched by the sun;
No smoke rose from a near-by hut.
The air was hot; the reeds did not stir
And the calm of the Dead Sea was unbroken.

And, knowing a bitterness that rivalled the bitterness of the sea,
Accompanied only by a small band of clouds,
He went on along the dusty road
Intent on reaching a certain religious school.
He was on His way to attend a gathering of disciples.

550

And so deeply was He plunged in His thoughts
That the countryside sent forth an odor of wormwood.
A stillness fell over all things. He stood alone
In the midst of it all. And all the region lay prostrate
As if in a swoon. All things became confused:
The sultriness and the desert,
And lizards, and wellsprings and streams.

A fig tree rose up a short distance ahead—
Utterly fruitless, putting forth only branches and leaves.
And He said unto it: "Of what use art thou?
What joy have I from thee, standing there petrified?
I am enhungered and athirst, yet thou art all barren
And coming upon thee is of less joy than stumbling on granite.
Oh, how thou dost offend, how void of any gift!
Remain, then, even as thou art until the end of time."

A shudder at the condemnation ran through the tree
Even as a spark of lightning runs down a rod.
The fig tree was instantly consumed to ashes.

If at that point but a moment of free choice had been granted
To the leaves, the branches, to the trunk and roots
The laws of nature might have contrived to intervene.

But a miracle is a miracle—and miracle is God.
When we are in confusion, then in the midst of our straggling
It overtakes us and, on the instant, confounds us.

EARTH

High-handed spring barges right into
The stateliest Moscow houses.
Moths flutter out when one opens closets
And start crawling over summer headgear.
Furs are put away in trunks.

The ledges of high wooden garrets
Put forth their vernal flowerpots
Of gillyflowers and wallflowers;
Rooms flaunt a free-and-easy air
And attics smell of dust.

Streets are on hail-fellow-well-met terms
With each and every purblind window.
White night and sunset, by the river,
Just can't, somehow, pass each other.

And you can hear inside the hallway
What's going on out in the open,
Or overhear the eavesdrop talking
By chance with April (which month has
Thousands and thousands of true stories
That have to do with mankind's woes).
Dawnglows and evenglows congeal on fences,
Dawdling and shirking at their tasks.

The selfsame blend of fire and eeriness
Prevails outside and in snug dwelling.
Everywhere the air is not its own self.
The selfsame pussywillow twigs interlace,
The selfsame white buds beget their swellings,
Whether on window sill or at crossroads,
Whether in the street or in a workshop.

Why, then, does the distance weep in a mist
And humus have so sharp an odor?
For that's just what my calling's for—
To keep the vistas from being bored,
To keep the land beyond the city
From pining by its lonely self.

That is the reason my friends gather
To be with me in early spring
And why our evenings serve as farewells
And our little feasts as testaments,
So that the secret stream of sorrow
May impart some warmth to the chill of being.

EVIL DAYS

When He was entering Jerusalem
During that last week
He was hailed with thunderous hosannas;
The people ran in His wake, waving palm branches.

Yet the days were becoming ever more ominous, more grim.
There was no stirring the hearts of men through love:
Their eyebrows knit in disdain.
And now, the epilogue. Finis.

The heavens lay heavy over the houses,
Crushing with all of their leaden weight.
The Pharisees were seeking evidence against Him,
Yet cringed before Him like foxes.

Then the dark forces of the Temple
Gave Him up to be judged by the offscourings.
And, with the same fervor with which they once sang His praises,
Men now reviled Him.

The rabble from the vicinity
Was peering in at the gateway.
They kept jostling as they bided the outcome,
Surging, receding.

The neighborhood crawled with sly whispers
And rumors crept in from all sides.
He recalled the flight into Egypt and His childhood
But recalled them now as if in a dream.

He remembered the majestic cliffside in the wilderness
And that exceeding high mountain
Whereon Satan had tempted Him,
Offering Him all the kingdoms of the world.

And the marriage feast at Cana
And the guests in great admiration over the miracle.
And the sea on which, in a mist,
He had walked to the boat as if over dry land.

And the gathering of the poor in a hovel
And His going down into a cellar by the light of a taper
Which had suddenly gone out in affright
When the man risen from the dead was trying to get to his feet.

MAGDALENE

I

As soon as night comes my demon springs up out of the ground.
That is the price I pay for my past.
They come, those memories of vice,
And fall to gnawing at my heart.
Those memories of days when I, a slave
To the whims and quirks of males,
Was but a demoniac fool and the street was all my shelter.

A few scant moments still remain
And then a silence as of the grave will fall.
But before they pass I, having reached
The very limit of my life,
Am shattering that life at Thy feet
As if it were an alabaster vessel.

Oh, where would I now be,
My Master and my Saviour,
If eternity were not awaiting me
Of nights, standing by my bed
Like a new visitor enticed
Into the net of my profession?

But still, I would have Thee expound for me the meaning
Of sin, and death, and hell and brimstone fire—
When I, before the eyes of all, have grown into one
With Thee, even as scion and tree,
Because my yearning is beyond all measure.

When, Jesus, I embrace Thy feet
As I support them on my knees
It may be that I am learning to embrace
The squared beam of the Cross
And, bereft of my senses, am straining for Thy body
As I prepare Thee for Thy interment.

People are tidying up before the holiday.
Aloof from all this bustle,
I am anointing Thy most immaculate feet
With myrrh from a small bowl.

I grope for and cannot find Thy sandals.
I can see naught because of my tears.
Strands of my loosened hair have fallen
Like a pall over my eyes.

I have set Thy feet upon my lap,
I have poured my tears over them, Jesus;
I have entwined them with the string of beads from around my neck,
I have buried them in my hair, as in the folds of a burnous.

I see the future in such detail
As if Thou hast made it stand still.
At this moment I can foretell events
With the fatidical clairvoyance of the Sybils.

The veil will fall on the morrow within the Temple.
We will be huddled in a knot off to one side.
And the earth will rock underfoot—
Out of pity for me, perhaps.

The ranks of the guard will realign
And the mounted soldiers will start dispersing.
Just as a waterspout in a storm strains upward
So will that Cross be straining to reach the sky.

I shall prostrate myself on the earth at the foot of the crucifix.
I shall make my heart stop its beating, I shall bite my lips.
Thou hast spread Thy arms to embrace far too many,
Flinging Thy hands out till they reach the ends of the crossbeam.

For whom in this world is all this breadth,
So much agony and such power?
Are there so many souls and lives in this universe—
So many settlements, and rivers and groves?

Yet three days such as this shall pass
And they shall thrust me into such a void
That during this brief interval of time
I shall, even before the Resurrection, attain my full stature.

GARDEN OF GETHSEMANE

The turn in the road was illumined
By the indifferent glimmer of the remote stars.
The road led around the Mount of Olives;
Below, in its valley, the Brook Kedron ran.

Halfway, the small meadow dipped in a sharp break;
Beyond it began the great Milky Way,
While the silver-gray olives still strained forward
As if to stride onward upon empty air.

Furthest away was someone's garden plot.
He left His disciples outside the stone fence
Saying, "My soul is exceeding sorrowful, even unto death;
Tarry ye here, and watch with me."

He had rejected without resistance
Dominion over all things and the power to work miracles,
As though these had been His only on loan
And now was as all mortals are, even as we.

Night's distance seemed the very brink
Of annihilation, of nonexistence.
The universe's span was void of any life;
The garden only was a coign of being.

And peering into these black abysses—
Void, without end and without beginning—
His brow sweating blood, He pleaded with His **Father**
That this cup of death might pass from Him.

Having eased His mortal anguish through prayer,
He left the garden. Beyond its wall His disciples,
Overcome with sleep, sprawled on the ground
In the wayside feathergrass.

He awakened them: "God hath granted you to live
During my days on earth, and yet you lie there sprawling.
Behold, the hour is at hand, and the Son of Man
Shall betray Himself into the hands of sinners."

He had scarcely spoken when, coming from none knew **where,**
A throng of slaves sprang up, a host of vagrant men
With swords and torches, and at their head stood **Judas**
With the perfidious kiss writhing on his lips.

Peter drew sword and thrust the cutthroats back
And struck a man and smote off his ear.
Whereon he heard, "No metal can resolve dissension.
Put up thy sword again into his place.

Thinkest thou my Father would not send
Sky-darkening hosts of winged legions to my **succor?**
And without harming even a hair of mine
My enemies would scatter, leaving no trace behind.

But now the book of life has reached a page
Which is more precious than are all the holies.
That which was written now must be fulfilled.
Fulfillèd be it, then. Amen.

Seest thou, the passing of the ages is like a **parable**
And in its passing it may burst to flame.
In the name, then, of its awesome majesty
I shall, in voluntary torments, descend into my grave.

I shall descend into my grave. And on the third day rise again.
And, even as rafts float down a river,
So shall the centuries drift, trailing like a caravan,
Coming for judgment, out of the dark, to me."

Service Etiquette

FOURTH EDITION

Service Etiquette

Oretha D. Swartz

NAVAL INSTITUTE PRESS
ANNAPOLIS, MARYLAND

Library of Congress Cataloging-in-Publication Data
Swartz, Oretha D.
Service etiquette / Oretha D. Swartz. — 4th ed.
p.   cm.
Includes index.
ISBN 0-87021-620-1
1. United States—Armed Forces—Military life.   2. Etiquette—
United States.   I. Title.
U766.S88   1988
355.1'336'0973—dc19   88-10063

Printed in the United States of America
on acid-free paper ∞

8   10   9   7

Contents

Preface to the Fourth Edition

AXIOMS HAVE A WAY of coming true. And it is a fact that times have changed. In the past there have been definite times of social change—for example, the Victorian Age and the Jazz Age. Perhaps one could say that today is the age of informality. As with any great change in social customs, there are fads that come and go. But good behavior never goes out of style.

Informality does not imply a barrier to gracious living. Many of the old, established customs are blended with today's less restricted ways of life—in entertaining with little or no help, in communicating with others, and in coping with everyday problems that once were handled by a staff. The full integration of sexes and races in the services brought more changes. Service people now live more informed lives. Still, as in bygone years, there are certain rules to follow in order to reach the goal of easier, gracious living.

A charted course will get you to a specific place at a given time for a certain occasion. Should you plan to drive from the East to the West Coast you would get a comprehensive map for the entire distance. The best highways, the mileage between points of interest, the exits, and posted speed limits would all be of concern to you.

Should you decide to drive on uncharted highways and go as fast as you please, you can expect to run into trouble: your way will be longer, with penalties and roadblocks. There is little difference between life's highways and those for the military: both are time-tested, and both are constantly upgraded. The latter are charted in *Service Etiquette* for the single purpose of bettering your daily living.

Many persons have given of their knowledge in order to make this book of equal value to men and women officers in all branches of the armed forces, and to their families. This revised fourth edition not only is updated but includes more about women in the services, the Reserves, the retired, the military family, and the Maritime Service—an important force though not an armed one.

First, my thanks to the Department of Defense for its *Defense Almanac*, which gives capsule information for all services. In particular I appreciate the help of Mr. Robert B. Sims, Assistant Secretary for Public Affairs, DoD, who put me in touch with Ms. Bettie Sprigg, Directorate for Defense Information. To her I am indebted for contacts with personnel in each service who helped me obtain information pertinent to their service.

In the Washington area I wish to thank Chaplain John Whitley, Ecclesiastical Publications Officer, Office of the Air Force Chief of Chaplains. Also General Larry D. Welch, USAF, Chief of Staff, Department of the Air Force; he steered me to Senior Master Sergeant Stanley W. Gaas, Assistant Chief, Air Force Uniform Board Secretariat, who was helpful in updating the uniform charts in the book. Major Bruce Bell, USA, Chief Warrant Officer Paul K. Wood, USA, Major Anthony P. Rothfork of the Marine Corps, Lieutenant Commander Scott E. Wilson, USN, Ensign George Eldredge, USCG, and Mr. Nicholas Sandifer of Coast Guard Headquarters all aided in updating the uniform charts. Mrs. Jacqueline E. Neyhart, Protocol Office, U.S. Army Engineer Center, Belvoir, Virginia, was also helpful.

My sincere thanks go to Mrs. William P. Lawrence, the wife of Vice Admiral Lawrence, USN, Ret., of Annapolis, who took time from her work as director of Rehab, Inc., Clinic in Alexandria, Virginia, to read through *Service Etiquette* and make important suggestions. Also giving of their time to review the book were Chaplain [Major] Charles H. Morrison III, USA, and Susan Morrison, artist, at Fort Clayton, Republic of Panama.

My appreciation extends to Captain A. B. Holderby, CHC, USN, Command Chaplain at the Naval Academy, who painstakingly updated chapters on religion and military weddings and funerals. Also to Captain Elizabeth G. Wylie, USN, Deputy Director, Politico-Military Policy and Current Plans Division, Navy Department, for her insight into military affairs.

In visits to all four service academies, meetings with men and women officers, both staff and faculty, produced up-to-date information on the changing times not only at the academies but at ROTC units throughout the country.

At the U.S. Air Force Academy, Colorado Springs, Colorado, Colonel Joseph L. Coates, USAF, Vice Commandant of Cadets, and Colonel Wayland L. Krick, USAF, Director of Cadet Personnel Services, were very helpful. And my thanks to the following Air Force women officers: Major Hedy C. Pinkerton, Major Kelly S. C. Hamilton, Major Foreaser Steele, Captain Wendy J. Rogers, Captain Barbara E. Chine, and Captain Neville DeArmond. Also thanks to Cadets Vicki Rojas and Steve Mauro.

At the U.S. Military Academy, West Point, New York, Colonel Seth Hudgins, Jr., USA, Chief of Staff, Office of the Commandant of Cadets, and his aide gave considerable time in discussing the fourth edition. In a round-table discussion, the following women officers gave important suggestions: Lieutenant Colonel Cathy Kelly, Lieutenant Colonel Teresa Netherton, Major Janet E. Drummond (Office of the Special Assistant to the Superintendent), Captain Jeanne Charbonneau, and Captain Sue Anne Sandusky, all USA. Also Cadets Charles Holton, Christopher Rigoni, William Riggins, Kenneth Bergeron, and Cori Lowe.

At the U.S. Coast Guard Academy, New London, Connecticut, a meeting was held with several women officers, including Lieutenant Linda Johansen, USCG, aide to the superintendent. Also attending were Lieutenants Christine J. Quedens, Anne Flammang, and Joanne McCaffrey, all USCG.

At the U.S. Naval Academy, Annapolis, Maryland, I especially want to say thanks to Lieutenant Commander Thomas J. Cutler, USN, of the History Department, who acted as consultant on military matters. Also to Captain Stephen R. Woodall, Director, Division of Professional Development, who is in charge of classes in protocol and good manners for all classes of midshipmen; and Lieutenant Commander Brian A. Beckman, formerly assigned to the department.

At Quantico, Virginia, Colonel William V. H. White, USMC, Ret., editor of *The Leatherneck,* was helpful in discussing Marine activities. And I appreciate the assistance of Captain and Mrs. James W. Foust, owners of Pris' Paper Parlor in West Annapolis, Maryland, who furnish cards for the military.

The social directors at the four service academies receive worlds of thanks for their help in discussing changes in the social life of the cadets and midshipmen. To Mrs. Cinda Sue Thorhauer, Cadet Wing

Hostess at the Air Force Academy, I again want to say thanks not only for the time given in meeting with Air Force officials but for driving me around the extensive academy grounds.

At West Point, Mrs. Carolyn Gaspard, Cadet Wing Hostess, gave fully of her busy time to make suggestions for the revision. And my many thanks to Mrs. Brenda Fullmer at the Coast Guard Academy, Mrs. Carol R. Baysinger at the Naval Academy, and Mrs. Mary Cunningham of the Merchant Marine Academy. And last but far from least, my sincere appreciation for the sharp eye of my editor, Mrs. Jackie Eckhart Wehmueller.

Space does not permit me to acknowledge each person individually who helped with this edition of *Service Etiquette*, so I'll simply thank all of you, collectively, for your time and knowledge.

I do, however, want to extend special thanks to Ms. Patricia Jett Toombs, visual information specialist for the Information Support Services Division of the Department of Defense, and Ms. Martha Rudd of the Pentagon's Office of the Chief of Public Affairs.

As always, I rely on and appreciate the social/activity directors at the four service academies for changes in cadet and midshipmen affairs. Likewise, I extend thanks to Ms. Tina McGuire, the protocol officer at the U.S. Army's 100th Area Support Group based at Grafenwohr, Germany.

For section XII—Strictly Service—I gleaned up-to-date information from the editors at Uniformed Services Almanac, Inc., of Falls Church, Virginia.

My appreciation also goes to Ms. Linda W. O'Doughda, production editor at the Naval Institute Press.

ORETHA D. SWARTZ

Annapolis, Maryland

Introduction

WHAT IS ETIQUETTE? According to Webster, the word *etiquette* means: "The forms required by good breeding, social conventions, or prescribed by authority, to be observed in social or official life; the rules of decorum." Good manners are the rules of the game of life—the rules you observe in your daily living with others. Good manners are more than a way of holding your fork, the proper words spoken in an introduction, or the correct form for going through a receiving line. These tools of etiquette are important, but there is more to being a well-bred person than the mechanics of good manners.

Good manners also mean kindness to others, respect for the other person's feelings, an acknowledgment of right and wrong, an awareness of someone—*anyone*—whom you meet in a hallway, on the street, or at a party. Good manners mean the consideration you grant someone as a person, not because he is important or of high rank, but because he is a human being. George Bernard Shaw expressed it this way: "The great secret . . . is not having bad manners or good manners or any other particular sort of manners, but having the same manner for all human souls."

And what is service etiquette? It is all these aspects of everyday good manners combined with the traditions and customs of the various branches of the armed forces. Servicemen and servicewomen are considered as representatives not only of their service, but of the

United States government. They are judged not only by their professional ability but by their manners in social and official life, at home and abroad.

This book was written for all officers in the armed forces, men and women, and for retired officers and members of service families. But it was written especially for the young officers. As cadets and midshipmen, they must undergo the transition from civilian to military life; upon graduation, they must adjust to a second transition, blending both military and civilian social customs, since they will be a part of both worlds.

To you, the prospective new officers—cadets and midshipmen of the service and maritime academies, students in the Reserve Officer Training Corps units, the Officer Candidate and Officer Training Schools, and the military schools—this book is dedicated.

SECTION I

Manners & Dress

CHAPTER 1

Everyday Good Manners— In Uniform & Out

GOOD GROOMING

A good first appearance depends to a great extent upon your personal grooming. As a midshipman or cadet you are trained during your years at the academies, in the ROTC units, or in any military school to take care of your gear and your person—and this training should be observed for the rest of your life.

A first appearance may be crucial to one of the most important events of your life. It is impossible to foresee on which day, at which hour, that most important event will take place, or what casual meeting may lead to your being accepted—or refused—by a person of value to your career.

It is important that you keep your uniform, cap cover, and gloves neat and clean; your shoes must be shined, and your hair well cut and shampooed.

For military women in uniform, extremes in hair styling, nail polish, and makeup are not acceptable. Back hair may touch but not fall below the lower edge of the collar.

Out of uniform, you dress pretty much as you please—but always using good taste.

ON TIME!

One of the most valuable habits that you can acquire is that of being on time. All officers are trained to be punctual in their official duties—and this habit should not be laid aside in your daily or social life. It is said that promptness and responsibility go hand in hand—therefore, a habitual lack of punctuality must be considered irresponsible.

At official or state occasions, you are expected to be on time. When royalty, very high-ranking officers, or dignitaries of state are guests at a luncheon or dinner, you arrive before they do, but do not leave before they do.

While you are not expected to be late at a dinner party, neither should you arrive before the hour named in the invitation and catch your hosts unprepared. It is permissible to arrive up to 15 minutes after the stated time.

There may be times when you are late through no fault of your own—when the plane is late, when the car has a flat tire, or when fog closes in and your boat cannot leave the ship.

When a man is unavoidably late at a dinner and the guests have already gone into the dining room, he should go directly to the hostess and briefly apologize, then take his seat at the table. For reasons of her own, the hostess may not be able to wait more than 15 minutes after the time set for serving dinner.

When a woman is late, she also briefly apologizes to the hostess, then takes her place at the table. Her dinner partner should rise and assist with her chair. The hostess does not rise; thus, other men at the table do not rise—which would inconvenience the other seated guests.

You should never deliberately be late at a party in order not to be the first guest to arrive. This is inconsiderate to the hosts and does *not* show sophistication on your part.

At an afternoon reception, at-home, or cocktail party, you may arrive at any time after the first hour named in the invitation, but not later than about a half-hour before the last hour indicated.

When you are a guest at a family dinner, be on time. Older children may join the family group at the table, and they are invariably hungry and impatient to be fed. Most hosts feed small children early and have them squared away before guests arrive. In this case, the dinner hour may be a little later than usual.

Of course, a host and hostess are *never* late.

TIME TO GO?

There are no set regulations that will tell you exactly when it is time to leave after a party, but many a weary host and hostess wish there were. The aim of any host is to ensure that guests enjoy the occasion—but sometimes a guest exceeds the limits of his host's hospitality.

In the services, officers of high rank are frequently the busiest persons on the base or station. Other than their official responsibilities, senior officers have many social, community, and station obligations. Sometimes, such an officer makes only a token appearance at a reception or cocktail party.

If you are a junior officer at an official or very important social function, you should not leave until after the guest of honor or the high-ranking guest departs. This person may leave within 30 minutes after a dinner, and then you may also leave. The ranking person makes the first move to leave.

However, a junior officer (or anyone) may have reason to leave before the guest of honor, and this should have been explained to the hosts beforehand. When it is time for you to leave, briefly tell the ranking guest why you are leaving early, then say goodnight and quietly go.

Customarily, the ranking guest stays from 30 to 45 minutes after dinner when nothing has been planned such as dancing or the theater. If you are the high-ranking guest, always remember that no one can properly leave until you do—and another guest may have a real reason to leave. When nothing has been planned afterwards, the time involved at a formal dinner is between three and three and a half hours.

When to leave after an official luncheon is determined by the station duty of the host and the guests, as well as by the time schedule and what is planned for the visiting dignitary. Usually guests stay about half an hour after luncheon. All together, such luncheons last about an hour and a half.

At an afternoon reception, at-home, or cocktail party, you should stay no less than 20 or 30 minutes, but do not remain uncomfortably close to the probable dinner hour of your hosts.

At an evening reception, you will probably stay about 45 minutes, possibly a little longer at a smaller reception or cocktail party—say an hour or an hour and a half.

A young couple making a call on a senior couple usually stay about 20 minutes. Although the husband or wife—or single officer—must not be obvious in watching the time, watch it one must. Senior officers have many demands on their time.

Should you, a junior officer, make a call and should a senior officer and his or her spouse also call, you leave at the proper time. There is no discourtesy in your leaving before the senior.

A midshipman or cadet should not form the habit of calling at all hours and staying for hours. If the hosts invite you to their quarters and insist that you stay on for TV or tennis, feel free to do so. When you call unannounced and stay too long, you may be upsetting plans made by your hosts. Half an hour is usually long enough to stay. Plans will have been made in advance for a visit to your sponsor.

RANK TERMINOLOGY

In the Navy and Coast Guard, *junior officers* are those of the grades of ensign, lieutenant junior grade (j.g.), lieutenant, and lieutenant commander; *senior officers* are of the grades of commander and captain; *flag officers* are of the grades of rear admiral, upper and lower half, vice admiral, and admiral.

In the Army, Air Force, and Marine Corps, *company grade officers* are those of the grades of second lieutenant, first lieutenant, and captain; *field grade officers* are those of the grades of major, lieutenant colonel, and colonel; *general officers* are of the grades of brigadier general, major general, lieutenant general, and general.

All officers in the armed forces are introduced and addressed by rank (see chapter 8).

FORMS OF ADDRESS

When you, a junior officer, report to the office of a senior, you announce yourself either through the orderly or by knocking. You wait until told to enter, then say, "Lieutenant John (or Jane) Doe, Sir." When the business has been terminated, you leave promptly.

You address seniors by their title and name, "Colonel Jones," rather than by the impersonal "Sir" or "Ma'am." On board ship or in any naval organization, there is only one "Captain" (the regularly assigned commanding officer), who is addressed as "Captain" regardless of his or her actual rank, without adding the surname.

Juniors reporting to senior female officers announce themselves in the same way as they would to senior male officers.

Even though you, the junior, are on a first-name basis with senior officers, do not call them by their first name during official occasions.

Always remember that a senior sends his or her *compliments* to a junior; the junior sends his or her *respects*. In written correspondence the senior may "call" attention to a problem or other matter, but the junior may only "invite" it.

Service academy women are addressed in the same way as their male counterparts: "Midshipman" or "Cadet." The terminology is of military rank, not title. At unofficial occasions she may be addressed as "Miss Doe."

COURTESIES OF JUNIORS TO SENIORS

By the time you have been a cadet or midshipman or ROTC, OTS, or OCS student for a few weeks, showing respect to military seniors will be automatic. Such things as saying "Sir" or "Ma'am," rising when spoken to, writing or saying "thank you" for a gift or favor— all these and many more fine points become instinctive.

But what about your courtesy to nonmilitary seniors and to your contemporaries? Courtesy and consideration are not to be turned on and off because of rank. Generally speaking, the older the person, the more respect you show. Therefore, age is an acceptable yardstick, since civilians do not wear such convenient things as insignia of rank.

Undue familiarity from you, a junior, will not be appreciated by a doctor, lawyer, or college president any more than it will be tolerated by an officer of rank considerably higher than your own.

When a male cadet or midshipman—or anyone in military training or on duty—fails to address a woman officer correctly, he is out of order. At the service academies, all cadets and mids are required to attend classes in everyday good manners as well as protocol. Therefore, it is not enough to say "Oh, I forgot" after addressing a woman officer as "Sir" or drawling out the "Ma'am."

COURTESIES OF SENIORS TO JUNIORS

Are you, the senior, mindful of the feelings of those younger in years or of persons older but subordinate in rank to yourself? Do you remember when you were the junior, fearful of social or career error?

Juniors are expected to show courtesy to their seniors in civilian life and are required to in the military. The senior should never forget that he or she is the example to subordinates. Seniors set a leadership example by treating respectfully everyone they come into contact with—something never to be forgotten.

When you, the senior—civilian or military—enter your office, do you return the greetings of those who carry out the humdrum but invaluable affairs of your working day? Or do you nod or half-grunt some sort of greeting that is no greeting at all? Perhaps some weighty problem is on your mind. Regardless, you are discourteous. That subordinate may have a weighty problem of his or her own and needs to feel of more value than the desk or typewriter. This is not fraternization—just common courtesy.

DISCOURTESY

Do you, the senior male officer, always address a woman officer by rank as you do a male officer of the same rank? Or do you at times say "Miss Jones" (or worse, "Jane") while calling him "Lieutenant Smith"? If so, you are in error.

By law, officers in the armed forces, male and female, are of equal rank, and are so addressed. This is important to the woman officer who considers it a slight when she is not correctly addressed. Women have not been in the services in strength until fairly recently—since World War II. Until then, the armed forces were a male domain. but women are in the military to stay, and their presence should be respected.

Courtesy is something that comes from within and requires no prompting. It is the consideration one shows another. As a West Point officer* said, "I cannot forgive or forget anyone who is deliberately discourteous or rude to another human being."

HATS ON—AND OFF

THE MALE OFFICER

In uniform, it is a custom of the services that you do not raise your headcover when greeting a man or woman in passing out-of-doors.

---

*Colonel Seth S. Hudgins, USA, Chief of Staff, Office of the Commandant of Cadets, U.S. Military Academy.

Instead, you give a hand salute. When greeting and passing a woman, a man may accompany the hand salute with a slight bow, but the bow is not customary. You do not uncover when you are introduced to a woman out-of-doors, and you may salute again when leaving.

You always wear your hat or cap when reporting outdoors under arms. Indoors, reports are rarely made under arms, but when necessary, headgear is kept on.

Aboard ship, junior officers uncover when passing through captain's or admiral's country, except when in evening dress uniform or wearing sword.

Male officers remove their caps on entering sick bay and when passing through messing compartments while meals are in progress.

At home or in your office—or anyplace—form the good habit of not tossing your headcover on the dining table or nearest chair.

In civilian dress, it is easy for a male officer to forget to take off his hat as custom demands in civilian life. Take it off when you stop to talk, or are introduced, to a woman out-of-doors, and leave it off unless the weather is bad.

You take off your hat in a place of worship, except in Orthodox Jewish synagogues and in some conservative synagogues; you leave it off at a burial, an outdoor wedding, or a dedication.

You remove your hat indoors except in stores, lobbies, corridors, and in such public buildings as an airport terminal, post office, and bank. Your hat is safer on your head in a crowded elevator than when held in front of you.

Inside an office building leave your hat on—but take it off when entering an office. If you stop to ask directions of the receptionist, you may touch your hat, an old custom. Touching your hat means touching the crown of a soft hat or the brim of a stiff one.

Your hat may be lifted momentarily when saying "Hello," "Good-bye," "Thank you," "Excuse me." Grasp the front crown of a soft hat or the brim of a stiff one, then lift it slightly up and forward, or just smile.

A young man lifts his hat to an older man, and a man of any age lifts his hat in respect to a dignitary or an elderly gentleman. An abbreviated hat tip, something of an informal salute, is a friendly gesture from one man to another.

You may check your hat before entering a public or club dining room, and it may be checked in a theater or placed in the rack under your seat. (A smart man leaves it at home.)

THE FEMALE OFFICER

In uniform you wear a hat or cap out-of-doors, as a passenger in an automobile, taxi, bus, train, or aircraft, and in naval ships.

Indoors, caps/hats are generally worn at restaurant luncheons and in church. Remain covered in such public areas as hotels and department stores, and never carry headgear in your hand.

At official ceremonies, you cover indoors if military men remain covered, and uncover if they uncover. However, at some formal official ceremonies, such as a military graduation, memorial service, or invocation, at which military men uncover during the ceremony, you remain covered.

You uncover in the dining room and cocktail lounge of an officers' club. It is optional to uncover when making social calls, and on a long trip by bus, train, or plane. Hats are worn or removed in conformance with local custom when meeting the commanding officer in his office and when visiting in hospitals and other military buildings.

In civilian dress, you comply with customs established by civilian women; at most functions you don't wear a hat or gloves.

BOWING

A bow is an old custom, somewhat out of date, but a man returns any bow directed to him—on the street, in a bus, or across the room. When introduced to a woman, an older man sometimes bows slightly while shaking hands.

A bow is a slight inclination of the body from the waist up, feet together. A deep bow expresses great respect. A very deep bow is strictly Continental, not customary in the United States.

When seated at a restaurant table and it is awkward or impossible to rise without disturbing others, a man may half-rise and give a slight bow. But do not remain seated and bow, unless to someone junior to you. Whenever you bow, don't give the effect of bobbing your head.

SALUTING IN CIVILIAN DRESS

As all servicemen and servicewomen know, in uniform you salute whenever the national anthem is played, when the flag is passing in parade or in review, or when the flag is hoisted or lowered.

Out of uniform, you stand at attention, remove your hat with your right hand, and place the hat over your heart—but no higher than shoulder level. Uncovered, you place your hand over your heart. A civilian man does the same.

A civilian woman stands at attention as she faces the flag or the direction of the music.

In the Navy, when you are wearing a hat or a cap as you step on the quarterdeck of a ship, you face aft and salute the national ensign, then the officer of the deck. When not wearing headgear you face aft at attention briefly, then carry on.

Military members exchange salutes whenever they recognize one another, in civvies or in uniform.

GLOVES

In uniform, you wear or carry gloves as prescribed. If you should be introduced outdoors, you may remove your right glove—if you have time. It is better to shake hands with your gloves on than to keep a person waiting—and you need not apologize for leaving them on.

Remove your gloves indoors except when ushering at a wedding or funeral, or when you have official guard duty. When introduced to someone during any of these occasions do not take off your glove.

At an academy formal, midshipmen and cadets are not required to wear white gloves. It is optional for ladies in the receiving line to wear gloves, but they rarely do.

Men wear white gloves at a very formal ball, such as a debutante cotillion, and leave them on throughout the receiving line and dance, removing them when eating or smoking. At less formal occasions gloves, when worn, are removed.

Women may wear gloves but remove the right glove when going through the line at a formal reception. When shaking hands with a head of state or a church dignitary, the right glove is always removed. After going through the line, she may take the gloves off.

YOUR HANDS AND HANDSHAKE

Most people shake hands upon being introduced or taking their leave, with the senior making the first move. It is unforgivable not to accept a proffered hand. A man usually waits until a woman offers her hand before extending his, but in either case she shakes it. If seated, he rises when introduced to anyone and upon the departure of anyone.

A good handshake is at elbow level. Avoid a handclasp that crushes or is too limp. Do not hold another's hand too long, or pump it up and down.

As mentioned before, you remove your right glove before shaking hands with anyone—if you have time. And when shaking hands, look at the person you are greeting.

Kissing a woman's hand is not customary in the United States. However, if a Continental woman should extend her hand to be kissed, here is the correct technique. Take her hand lightly in yours, then with a slight bow over her hand, merely touch your lips to the back of her hand. It is improper to kiss the hand of an unmarried woman unless she is an older woman.

When women shake hands, the younger waits for the older or higher-ranking woman to extend her hand in greeting first. When seated, the younger woman rises when introduced to the wife of a senior officer or an older woman, and remains standing until that woman is seated. You do not rise for an introduction to a contemporary, although a military woman rises when the contemporary is her senior.

Your hands should be in your lap when you are not eating at the dinner table. Avoid awkward positions with your hands at all times—such as locking them behind your head, thrusting them in your suit pockets in unattractive bulges, or standing with hands clasped behind your back or pressed together steeplelike in front.

To stroke your chin, pick at your ears or head, or drum on a table shows a lack of poise. When you are walking or standing, your hands should be in a relaxed position at your sides. When talking, *don't* wave them around like flags.

Midshipmen and cadets do not hold hands or link arms with others in public; any ostentatious show of affection indicates a lack of training.

Traditionally, when a man is dancing, his left or leading hand holds the woman's right hand lightly and naturally. His right or holding hand should be placed firmly yet easily just above her waist.

When a man wishes to help a woman down from a bus or train, he extends his hand to her, palm up. He does not put his hand under her arm.

Women in uniform conform with military etiquette; in civilian dress, they conform with civilian etiquette on social occasions.

OFFERING YOUR ARM

A man offers a woman his arm only to give assistance when needed or as an escort at a formal dinner or as an usher at a wedding.

Never grasp or take hold of the woman's arm—unless an accident is to be avoided. She will take your arm—you do not take hers.

You don't offer your arm in the daytime unless a woman needs help over rough ground or in a crowd, or when you assist an elderly or invalid man or woman. Do *not* offer your arm to a woman at a luncheon.

When a man offers his right arm at a formal dinner, he bends his arm slightly at the elbow, with his forearm parallel to the floor. His partner should hold his arm lightly, but not hang on to it. When a guest at a wedding, a woman takes the usher's right arm. A man does not take the usher's arm unless he is elderly or an invalid.

Military women, either in uniform or in civilian dress, do not hang on a man's proffered arm.

ON YOUR FEET

At a social occasion, such as a dinner party, men should stand when a woman enters the room, remain standing until she sits down, and rise again upon her departure from the room.

However, common sense will dictate how long you remain standing when a woman continues to stand and keeps all the men on their feet. When she remains standing with a group, you sit down.

A man is not expected to rise to his feet every time a hostess reenters or leaves a room. And he need not rise to his feet at a business or organization meeting when a woman arrives late. He stands when an elderly or high-ranking man enters the room.

You stand up—not jump up—for introductions, greetings, farewells, and whenever a person wants to pass in front of you at the movies, a football game, or any place where someone must pass in front of you and you do not want your feet stepped on.

When a woman, senior officer, dignitary, or elderly person comes to his table in a restaurant, a man may rise to his feet. When it is difficult to stand at a crowded table, a half-standing gesture is better than upsetting something on the table or annoying others. The person stopping by should stay only a few moments, not linger in conversation.

A junior stands when introduced to a senior officer—male or female—or when the senior enters the room. When in civilian dress at social functions, you conform to civilian etiquette: the junior stands when introduced to an elderly or a prominent personage, or to the spouse of his or her commanding officer, regardless of age.

It is not necessary in this age of equality among the sexes for a man to offer his seat in a bus or subway to a strange woman, but he may if he chooses to do so, particularly if the person is elderly, disabled, burdened, or obviously tired—though he may be very tired himself. For that matter, a woman may offer her seat to a burdened person of either sex.

When it is time to leave a party, thank your hosts, then say good-bye. Don't continue in conversation or otherwise dawdle and delay. Just—go.

WALKING OUTDOORS

Traditionally, when a man is walking with a woman outdoors, he is on the curb side or, if there is no curb, on her left. When walking with two women, he may walk between them when crossing the street or if both ladies are elderly or are in poor health and need assistance. Although the old rule of a man never walking between two women is outmoded, most American men still prefer to walk to their left or curbside. When abroad, learn the local custom and follow it.

When two service members are walking together, the junior walks on the left of the senior. You keep in step, with the senior setting the pace.

When passing a senior approaching from the opposite direction, salute well in advance. When overtaking a senior, pass to the left if possible (otherwise to the right), salute and say, "By your leave, Sir (or Ma'am)." Do not proceed until the senior says "Carry on."

OPENING DOORS

Traditionally, when a man is escorting a woman, he holds any door open, then follows her through and closes it. If she gets to the door first and opens it, he should not make an issue of it, but hold the door for her to pass through.

A man may start a revolving door for a woman or a male senior to pass through. He should precede a woman through any door that opens onto a dark street or leads down steep stairs.

In the services a junior officer opens a door for his or her senior, stands aside for the senior to pass through, then follows.

To be militarily proper, upon official occasions or in his office, the senior male officer does not hold the door open for the junior woman officer; nor would he follow her through the door.

Unofficially, common courtesy prevails.

WHO GOES FIRST?

When a man is with a woman, she does—except:

When assistance is needed, such as when she is stepping down from a bus or train.
When there is no waiter to precede her to a table in a restaurant, or no usher at the theater or movies.
In a crowd, when the man will clear the way.
When going down the White House or an official/formal receiving line. It is the title that takes precedence.
At official military occasions the senior male officer precedes a junior woman officer.

MILITARY COURTESY IN BOATS, AIRCRAFT, AND CARS

The procedure for getting into a boat, car, or aircraft is: the senior officer enters last, and the junior enters first. This procedure may be reversed in entering at a left-hand curb. Then the senior may enter first, in order that he may sit to the right without stumbling over juniors who are seated to the left. Seniors are always accorded the most desirable seats. When three persons are in the back seat, the junior is in the middle.

In a boat, the junior officer sits forward, with the senior sitting aft. In a car, the junior sits on the left, the senior on the right. In cases of full cars, the senior officers sit in the back seat, the juniors in front.

In getting out of the boat, car, or aircraft, the order is reversed: the senior officer disembarks first, and the junior last. However, if a car draws up to a left-hand curb, it may be more appropriate for the junior to step out first. In an aircraft, if the senior officer is engaged in flying the plane, the disembarkation procedure applies only among the passengers.

When you travel aboard the personal aircraft of a high-ranking senior—for example, the aircraft of a flag or general officer—unless instructed otherwise, you should be aboard in a designated seat before the senior arrives at the aircraft. You remain in your seat until the VIP leaves the plane at its destination.

CUSTOMS IN AIRCRAFT

Air Force customs while traveling in military aircraft include:

1. Passengers are subject to the orders of the first pilot or airplane commander, regardless of rank, seniority, or service.

2. Dependents are loaded and unloaded after dignitaries, but before officers, regardless of rank.

3. An aircraft with general and/or flag officers aboard is marked with a detachable plate carrying stars appropriate to the highest rank aboard.

4. Passengers do not enter the flight deck or pilot's compartment unless invited to do so.

5. All safety regulations must be observed, including no smoking on takeoff and landing, and during flight, if so announced. Parachute rules must always be observed.

6. Flights are decided by weather conditions; thus, the pilot's decision to fly or not to fly is never questioned.

MANNERS AT THE WHEEL

When driving a car, be considerate of others on the road. It is inconsiderate—and dangerous—to stop suddenly to pick up a friend or to talk with someone. It is far better to pull over to the curb.

On dates, a man of high school or college age goes to the door of his date's house and properly calls for her rather than just blowing the horn and waiting for her to come out. In a crowded area where you cannot park, ask her beforehand to meet you at a given time; when she appears, reach across the seat and open the door.

When a man is the driver and a doorman opens the car door, the woman gets out first. When a man and a woman are passengers in a car or taxi and not in city traffic, he gets out first—even if she is closer to the door—walks around the car, and opens the door for her. In traffic, whoever is closer to the door on the safe side gets out first.

RIDING IN TAXIS

When escorting a woman, a man gives the directions to the driver and pays the taxi fare. If he is not accompanying her to her destination, he should ask the driver what the amount will be and pay it along with the tip.

When a man shares a taxi with a woman member of the armed forces or a business woman, she will want to pay for her share of the fare. If she gets out first, she pays her share to that point, plus her share of the tip.

A man should not ask an unknown woman to share a taxi, but if she is going his way, he may offer to do so in case of bad weather or at a rush hour. When he has an important appointment to keep, he is driven there first.

Two or more acquaintances may share a taxi fare. If one

person insists upon paying, you may agree and say, "Next time it's mine." Then be sure there is a next time.

Taxi tips vary, but usually they are 15 percent of the bill. Do not tip less than twenty-five cents, which is adequate for a fare of one dollar.

SEATING A WOMAN

A man assists the woman to his right with her chair when she sits down at the dining table, and when she rises. The chair is pulled back as she steps into place from the left, then he slides the chair under her as she bends to sit down. When she rises from the table, he draws the chair back without jerking it.

Although it seems easier for a woman to sit down from the left, there is no established rule to this effect. A man should be alert to note from which side the ladies nearest him are being seated by their dinner partners, and then, to avoid confusion, seat his own dinner partner accordingly. If he is the host, he should assist the lady at his right; if he is seated at the right of the hostess, he assists with her chair.

HOLDING COATS

When a man helps a woman with her coat, he holds the coat with the armholes at a comfortable height for her to slip her arms into them, and is careful not to muss her hair.

A woman may prefer to wear her coat into a restaurant or the theater. The coat may be laid across a vacant chair at the table, or across the back of her chair at the table or in the theater. He should see that the coat does not trail on the floor.

A man checks his own coat and hat before going into the dining room. These articles may also be checked at the theater.

SENDING FLOWERS

When sending flowers to a woman, choose them to fit her type as well as the occasion at which they will be worn. Try to find out what she is wearing, and send flowers that are appropriate—chrysanthemums for attending a football game, gardenias or an orchid for a dance. A short woman will not care for a large corsage but would like a small corsage or nosegay. Flowers are pinned on a costume heads up—just as they grow.

Flowers may be sent to a hostess by a guest of honor, or as

thanks for a favor received or a special party attended. It is not advisable to send a potted plant to a hostess whose husband has orders, as she may be moving and the plant and your money would be wasted.

At the service academies, college ROTC units, and most colleges, corsages are not sent to dates before dances, except on special occasions, such as the "flower formal" at the Coast Guard Academy, and ring and graduation dances. Then, the midshipmen and cadets reduce expenses by placing group orders for flowers.

CHANCE ENCOUNTERS

You should not feel obligated to pay for the lunch or dinner at a chance encounter with a senior or ranking person.

If a man must speak to a woman who is a stranger or hand her something—such as an object she dropped on the sidewalk—he may touch her arm lightly when he catches up with her, to get her attention; then he should turn away as soon as he has accomplished his mission.

When a man gives his seat to a woman in a bus, subway, or train, he need not say anything. When a stranger gives his seat to the woman you are escorting, thank him. An older man probably will touch his hat when acknowledging the courtesy.

A man should avoid calling out a woman's name in public in loud tones, even when he is surprised and pleased at the encounter.

TELEPHONE COURTESY

You should be courteous when talking on the telephone. When answering or placing a call, identify yourself. "Hello" may be used in answering when at home, but in an office or upon an official occasion it is discourteous, for the other person must then ask to whom he is speaking. Say "L Two Company orderly room, Cadet Abbott speaking."

When telephoning a stranger or someone you do not know well, say "This is Lieutenant Jones," then state your business. When you know the person, simply say "This is John (or Jane) Jones," and so on.

In an office a secretary would say, "Captain Smith's office, Mr. (or Miss) Jones speaking." An individual calling his or her spouse at the office would inform the secretary, "This is Mr. (or Mrs.) Smith. Is Captain Smith in?"

Always be careful of the time you phone. Unless necessary, do not call a private residence before nine in the morning or after ten o'clock at night. Avoid calling at meal hours.

When you are placing a call and get a wrong number, apologize, then make certain that you have the right number before placing the call again. And remember the difference in time zones, particularly overseas.

After making a long-distance call in another person's home, ask the operator how much the call cost, then pay for it.

It is inconsiderate to engage in lengthy chitchat when others may urgently need to use the phone or may be trying to call in. Therefore, conduct your business and allow others to do the same.

OBSCENE CALLS

Hang up immediately when you receive an obscene call. Take the receiver off the hook for a short time. The caller wants to shock you, to receive attention, so do not give the person the satisfaction of upsetting you. Be prepared for such calls if they continue. Have a shrill whistle at hand and blow it full force into the speaker.

If such calls continue, notify the telephone company. The calls can be traced or an instrument installed in your home that identifies the caller.

SMOKERS

Today, all services have posted areas for smoking on land, sea, or plane. Almost all states and the District of Columbia have enacted some form of legislation in restricting smoking in public areas, in offices, buildings, and airplanes.

The surgeon general's annual report,* required by Congress, states that smoke from other people's cigarettes can cause disease in healthy nonsmokers. It also says that separating smokers from non-smokers does not eliminate the risk of lung cancer or other diseases, because the suspended particles spread through the area and remain for hours in closed rooms in a home, office, or building.

According to the report, the inhalation of tobacco smoke is not limited to the smoker, as formerly thought, but extends to all who breathe the smoke. Furthermore, children of parents who smoke have an increased chance of respiratory infection.

Smoking is responsible for more than 300,000 deaths annually in this country, or about 15 percent of all mortality. Like drugs or alcohol, smoking can become compulsive, a habit difficult to stop. It is easy to say, "Oh, I'll quit tomorrow"—easier said than done.

*U.S. Public Health Service, *Annual Report,* Washington, D.C.

SMOKING RULES

Do not blow smoke or allow it to drift from a cigarette in your hand or ashtray into another person's face.

Never smoke at a formal or official occasion such as a wedding, a reception, or a parade.

Never use a saucer, dish, or plate for an ashtray—ask for one, when needed.

When there are no ashtrays in a home, or on the dining table, the hosts do not want any smoking.

When a person asks if you mind smoking—say so if you do. But be courteous. Few persons realize that a smoke-allergic individual can become ill quickly.

Do not spill ashes on the floor, flip ashes into a wastepaper basket, or put a lighted cigarette on a table.

Never toss a lighted cigarette out of a car window—particularly in a wooded area.

Some people find the smoke from pipes and cigars stronger and more offensive than cigarette smoke; be especially careful in a car or closed area.

SOUNDING OFF

There is an old rule: "Never volunteer information." If you don't give free information about someone or something, you can't be quoted. Gossip is not confined to the feminine sex—a study of military history through the ages forces one to the conclusion that there would be no Mata Haris if servicemen didn't talk.

A young officer should learn early in his or her career not to discuss carelessly military subjects of a classified nature. You should never speak critically of your seniors.

A lady or gentleman does not discuss such subjects as personal business or sex in the officers' mess or in the wardroom. If you must discuss anything personal, do so elsewhere—and discreetly. Always remember that your business ceases to be personal if made public.

Everyone has been bored to distraction by the conversationalist who drones on and on. But—are *you* sometimes guilty of being a bore by going overboard on a subject that interests you greatly? When you suspect that you are becoming long-winded—and you detect this by observing the reactions of those around you—then change the subject and let someone else talk while you listen. Don't be a know-it-all.

In reverse, there are times when you are exhausted beyond endurance by a monologue, and the only way to break the spell is to interject a remark at the end of a sentence or when the bore needs a fresh breath. A favorite phrase is, "Oh, that reminds me—!"

When you unintentionally interrupt a speaker, say "I'm sorry" or "I'm sorry, but I thought you had finished." Try not to interrupt a speaker, and pay him the attention that you hope he pays you.

EXHIBITIONISM

Exhibitionism means drawing attention to yourself in a public place. This is accomplished by shouting, whistling, clowning, loud laughter, booing, or doing something foolish or unusual. A person of refinement does not care to be conspicuous.

Do not make a public display of your emotions or affections. Kissing in public is frowned upon except in cases of farewell when the separation is expected to be a long one, or upon a person's return. Generally, men shake hands in greeting and farewell with women as well as with men, although some women insist upon kissing when meeting—other women as well as men. Kissing and holding hands should be considered a private rather than a public demonstration.

One example of exhibitionism is the couple on the dance floor who execute too-intricate steps or who hold each other in exaggerated positions. No couple should monopolize the dance floor.

Although everyone enjoys talking about friends and acquaintances of high rank or position, and hearing interesting or amusing anecdotes about them, you can overdo it. A name-dropper can be a bore.

Another form of showing self-importance is the overuse of foreign words and phrases. An occasional foreign expression can be appropriate in good English conversation, but too many such expressions are tiresome to the person who may not speak that particular language.

When you use foreign phrases, be sure that you are proficient in their usage and pronunciation—you may be in the company of linguists who are really adept!

APOLOGIES

No one likes to apologize, but you do when in the wrong. A hard-headed person may not admit a wrong—and he will lose friends.

Be direct when you apologize. Look at the person, and don't fiddle with a pen or book; then he or she will know you mean it.

In turn, the recipient should not make it difficult for the person who is apologizing. A generous person could say "I really appreciate what you are saying," which may make all the difference in a future relationship. When it is desirable to renew the broken friendship, invite that person to lunch or to some occasion that is easy for both to enjoy.

Apologies are in order when:

You have caused harm, or have hurt someone needlessly or through carelessness. In this case you must do more than apologize—you must ask the other person's forgiveness.

You fail to keep an appointment. You telephone or write a brief note, explaining your failure to do so—and the reason must be a good one.

You cannot grant a request. In this case you must not only give your regrets, but if possible add some explanation, such as "I'm sorry, but owing to the great sentimental value attached to the object, I can't lend it for the exhibition."

You break or damage something. Try to replace the article exactly, but if you cannot, then send flowers or a book of interest to the family with a note saying you are sorry for the mishap.

You step or pass in front of someone, or bump into them. In such cases you say "Please excuse me" or "I beg your pardon" or "I'm sorry."

You are late at a luncheon or dinner party—or any social occasion such as a reception where the receiving line has already been dispersed. Then you go directly to the hostess and briefly apologize without giving long details. Do that later.

The host and hostess have waited for your arrival at a luncheon or dinner party and have not gone into the dining room. Tell them why you were late—and the reason must be valid.

SOCIAL OBLIGATIONS

A young single officer or married couple cannot be expected to repay in the same fashion the hospitality of an established person or older married couple. You repay your hosts' hospitality in your own way—at a small cocktail party or an informal lunch or dinner, or by performing some act or favor that is without ostentation.

As a general rule, when you accept someone's hospitality, you reciprocate in some fashion. The perennial guest will eventually wear out his or her welcome by always being a guest, never a host or hostess. No one wants the young couple to repay an expensive dinner party with the same kind of party, dollar for dollar. But the genuineness of the juniors' desire to repay is important. As the younger couple advances in seniority and rank through the years, they in turn will extend hospitality to junior officers and young couples.

Single officers, widows, and widowers often repay their hosts by inviting them to the theater, or to lunch or dinner in an officers' club or restaurant.

There is no requirement for repaying official social occasions. Junior officers frequently combine their efforts and finances in repaying unofficial social obligations by giving a dinner, cook-out, or cocktail party.

Do not fail to reply to an R.S.V.P.

YOUR THANKS

You do not write or telephone a host or hostess after all social occasions. A sincere expression of thanks at the time of leaving the party is generally sufficient. If many guests phoned after a very large party, the hosts would be on the line for hours.

But after any pleasant or special occasion (especially a small one), the hosts would be pleased to hear that you enjoyed their hospitality, and a note or phone call is in order.

If the occasion was a very special one, or whenever an occasion was very much enjoyed, express your appreciation in a note or by phone. The guest of honor at a party or dinner, and the cadet or midshipman who was a Christmas or Easter guest, should always do so.

Occasionally, when you have been an honored dinner guest or when a cadet or mid has visited a classmate's parents over the weekend, flowers or a small gift may be sent to the hostess. This is not expected, but a note is. When you are a frequent guest, you need not write after every visit—but do thank your host with simple sincerity before or upon departure.

All social invitations are answered promptly, preferably within a day or two. Thank-you notes should be written within 48 hours after the occasion. A note takes only a few minutes of your time, but this small courtesy is invaluable in matters of manners and good will.

Anyone who has many social engagements should keep a record of them in order not to overlook an obligation. Such a record includes the names of the hosts, their rank, address, and type of occasion—dinner, lunch, cocktails, etc.—as well as the date.

MORAL OBLIGATIONS

Always remember that your word—or signature—is your bond. Therefore, think twice before you make promises. Signed to a check, your signature means that you are good for the amount indicated. Signed to the endorsement at the end of an examination, it means that you subscribe to the work submitted and that it is your work. Signed to a letter, it means that the ideas expressed are your own.

It is of the utmost importance that men and women in the services be honest and direct in all their dealings. Juniors can avoid a great deal of embarrassment by giving a to-the-point answer in replies to questions put by their seniors.

If you are the junior and do not know or cannot give a complete or correct answer, then answer *only as much of the question as you can without being evasive or misleading*. An honest "I don't know, Sir (or Ma'am), but I will find out and let you know" is a better answer than an indirect one that gives misinformation on which your senior may be basing an important decision. An evasive reply can seriously affect your service reputation.

FINANCIAL OBLIGATIONS

It is a matter of honor that service personnel discharge their acknowledged and just financial obligations. As a member of a service you remain a citizen and, as such, you have a continuing obligation to obey certain civil statutes and to carry out any civil court orders, decrees, or judgments to which you are a party. You cannot use your service status as a pretext for evading your financial obligations.

This doesn't mean that you pay unjust claims to avoid unpleasant publicity. You are protected by the fact that your commanding officer must make a careful investigation into the justness of any claim you disavow. But be sure you are in the right before you put your CO to that trouble.

However, commanding officers do not act as agents for claimants in business transactions or claim collections; they only make sure that the claimant's communication reaches the person concerned and that a prompt reply is made. A commanding officer cannot tolerate actions of irresponsibility, gross carelessness, neglect, or dishonesty in the financial dealings of service personnel. If it is determined that the officer in question is negligent or careless in regard to personal finances, an entry will be made on that officer's fitness report and, if the circumstances warrant such action, a trial by court-martial will be recommended.

If you are assigned to a job involving the custody of funds—such as mess treasurer—make a careful check to ensure that you have everything you sign for when you take over. As a member of an auditing board, be sure that what you certify to be on hand is actually present. Never be careless in making audits and taking inventories. The fact that someone else may have signed does not mean that you can take for granted that all is well. Usually the junior signs first, at the bottom of the page.

Officers should never lend money to, or have financial dealings with, enlisted personnel. Service regulations are definite in directing you not to make such loans. When asked, you must decline and say that regulations prohibit your making the loan. If the case is a deserving one, the enlisted should have no trouble getting a loan from the ship's Welfare Fund or the Navy Relief Society, the Air Force Aid Society, the Army Emergency Relief, or other established welfare societies. The Family Support Program in each service will help the family in need.

YOUR SERVICE COMMUNITY

The armed services are friendly services. No matter where you go on active duty, there will be service people nearby in your own age group and financial circumstances. It's difficult to be lonely in the services, at home or abroad.

Most service communities are also friendly—however, a few service people make themselves undesirable in a town or community because of their lack of consideration for other people's feelings and possessions. Perhaps this lack of responsibility stems from the fact that service people are not in one place very long and thus grow careless in looking after someone else's property.

Take care of another person's property with at least as much respect as you would your own—and this is taking for granted that you *do* take care of your own things. When you are in quarters, or rent a house or apartment, do not abuse it. Don't leave dirt and trash lying around, or generally wreck the place—you will not be welcome again, nor will you leave a favorable impression of the service you represent.

It is thoughtless to borrow another person's property and not return it—whether this be a book, a golf club, or a pound of coffee. You must always return what you borrow—and develop the habit of not borrowing.

A wise person will try to fit into a new community rather than attempt to change it. Always be thoughtful of your neighbors. It is extremely unwise to walk into a store and say, "That can be bought at the Exchange for one-third your price!"

THE SEA OF MATRIMONY

Good manners in marriage mean loyalty to and respect for your partner—but loyalty and respect are earned, not demanded. A couple should share the responsibility in the management of the family finances, with each spouse fully understanding the limitations of a paycheck and the obligations that must be met each month. Since many officers are away from home during much of their career, it is necessary that someone carry on the family's financial obligations and keep an accurate account of expenditures during their absence.

A young couple may have had little experience in financial matters before marriage, so it is important that they work together as a team in sharing the household responsibilities.

A partnership in marriage includes a sound evaluation of each other's responsibilities: they may both have busy careers with the problems and worries that accompany careers, as well as a house to clean, food to cook, and children to care for. Today many women combine household activities with a career, or a part-time career, with little or no household help.

A husband often lends a hand—and the wife will do the same— in jobs formerly considered the chore of the other.

A partnership in marriage means that both partners say "we" instead of "I" and "our" instead of "my"—with the exception that official service business is the service person's concern only. Unless the wife is a servicewoman with her own rank, it is *his* orders, *his* crest, *his* rank—even though she may have contributed greatly to the success of the marriage and her partner's career. And the same is true when the wife is the serviceperson—it is *her* orders, etc.

A partnership, however, does not mean that one or the other cannot have any liberty of thought or action. Partnership and domination do not go hand-in-hand.

A happy household is one where both the man and the woman have a certain monetary allowance for their own personal use—with no strings attached.

As partners, a husband and a wife should never belittle each other. Any family dissension should be discussed in private—*not* before the children or anyone else. It should be a matter of personal pride for both to be as neat and attractive and as mentally stimulating after marriage as before.

HOSPITAL MANNERS

THE VISITOR

Nothing is more exhausting to a hospital patient than to have a visitor who comes too soon after surgery or a serious illness, or who stays too long, or who talks too loudly. If patients were in good health and feeling fine, they would not be in the hospital. Some visitors, however, seem to regard a hospital room as a fine place for a chat.

Any visitor in a hospital should observe these rules:

Walk and talk quietly in hospital corridors, and in patients' rooms. Guard against heels clacking on tiled floors.

The length of your visit depends upon the patient's condition and how he or she is momentarily feeling. Five minutes may be too long. Fifteen minutes is generally long enough, unless you are a relative.

There are definite visiting hours in most hospitals, and visitors should check them before going. Make sure in advance that a patient wants visitors, by telephoning the hospital or the patient's home. The patient may not care to see anyone.

Do not visit anyone in the hospital when you have a cold. Sick people are more susceptible to contagious diseases.

Do not sit on the patient's bed, and avoid jostling it.

If there are other visitors ahead of you, wait outside until some leave. The patient may be weary, so cut short your own stay—unless you are urged to stay. Better still, leave and go back another day.

Smoking in a hospital room is not permissible. Some hospitals have smoking areas.

Do not visit a new mother immediately after the event—unless it is your wife! You may always see the new baby by looking through the glass door of the nursery.

When you want to take the patient a small gift, flowers are always nice. But don't overdo it; too many flowers remind some people of funerals. If a patient is to be hospitalized for some time, he or she might appreciate a small potted plant to decorate the room. A good book is another thoughtful gift, but choose one that's not heavy to hold or too serious. Don't bring candy or rich food that the patient cannot eat.

Don't send a get well card to a person who is terminally ill. Instead, send a cheerful card or a note about something pleasant you enjoyed together—a trip, a party, a football game.

Avoid mentioning any problem that is worrying you; you don't want to add to the patient's woes by harping on your own.

THE PATIENT

When you are the patient, there are some do's and don'ts for you:

Do be considerate of the nurses and corpsmen—they are there to help you, not to wait on you. A nurse or corpsman is a professional, not a servant.

Do cooperate with hospital rules, and don't make too much fuss about pills, needles, etc.

In a private room, you can suit yourself (within reason) concerning the volume of your radio, TV, or air conditioner, but in a semiprivate room or ward, you must be considerate of your fellow patients, who may feel worse than you do. Your TV may disturb them.

Do not give orders to your nurse or supervisor. Call them by name: "Miss Smith" or "Lieutenant Jones." If the corpsman or nurse doesn't tell you his or her name, you may properly ask what it is. Do not ask for details of your illness—ask your doctor.

When you are not receiving adequate care, say so—to your doctor.

Patients do not tip a trained nurse or a corpsman. You may give them a gift when you leave, perhaps a large box of candy or cookies for the staff on your floor.

If you do not want to see a visitor—*don't*. A "no visitors" sign can be placed on your closed door and the desk notified that no one is to be admitted to your room. No explanation need be made.

CHAPTER 2

Service & Civilian Dress

THE BRIEF UNIFORM CHARTS which appear at the end of this chapter have been compiled for the convenience of men and women officers. These charts show the type of uniforms, with prescribed medals or ribbons, which are worn to informal, semiformal, and formal occasions.

The uniforms in the charts are the equivalent of the civilian formal afternoon dress and of the evening "black tie" and "white tie." However, the distinctions between black tie and white tie, and when each is worn, have necessitated further description of civilian dress. There is also a more general description of the civilian clothes needed by officers for everyday living out of uniform.

Decorations, medals, and ribbon bars are worn on the left breast pocket of the uniform coat or jacket, and are pinned or sewed from the wearer's right to the left in the order of official military precedence. Insignia, such as aviator's wings, are worn above the pocket.

NOTE: The local uniform regulations differ in various parts of the country, according to climate and locale. The change from one uniform to another differs in various sections, according to the season. Details of all uniforms will be found in the *Uniform Regulations* of each service.

In general, *regular size medals* are worn with semiformal dress; *miniature medals* are worn with mess dress, formal evening dress, and dress white uniforms; *unit award emblems* are worn with service dress, semiformal dress, and dress whites; *ribbons* are worn with service dress, semiformal dress, mess dress, evening dress, and dress whites. Decorations and service medals, regular size, are worn with semiformal dress uniforms in lieu of ribbons.

Insignia of specialty, grade, and branch of service are worn according to regulations, and aiguillettes are worn when authorized.

AWARDS

Awards is an all-inclusive term covering any decoration, medal, ribbon, badge, or an attachment thereto which is bestowed on an individual.

A *decoration* is an award conferred on a person for an act of gallantry or for meritorious service or achievement, or given to units distinguished for gallantry in action against the enemy. Certain decorations carry the word *medal,* for example the Medal of Honor and the Distinguished Service Medal. The Medal of Honor is worn from the neckband ribbon.

A *miniature medal* is one-half the size of the original large medal, with the exception of the Medal of Honor, which is not in miniature. A *ribbon* is a part of the suspension ribbon of a medal which is worn in lieu of the medal. The dimensions of all ribbons are $1^3/_8$ inches by $^3/_8$ inch. A *badge* is an award to an individual for a special proficiency and consists of a medallion.

Miniature medals are worn by men and women officers with formal and semiformal winter and summer uniforms. The holding bar is no longer than $2^3/_4$ inches in length. When 4 or fewer medals are worn, they are attached in a single row, fully exposed. When the number exceeds 4, each medal may overlap the medal to its left, but not more than 50 percent. Thus, the maximum number worn in a single row is 7. If more than this number are worn, they are arranged in two rows; if more than 14, in three rows evenly divided. If this cannot be done, the top row will contain the lesser number of medals, with the center of the row placed over the center of the row below it.

When ribbons are worn, badges, such as the Navy command insignia, are worn immediately below the bottom row of ribbons. When large medals are worn, badges are placed directly below the bottom row of medals.

MEDALS ON CIVILIAN DRESS

The Medal of Honor may be worn with civilian dress. Likewise, miniature medals may be worn with black or white tie in the same manner as prescribed for service evening dress uniforms.

Miniature replicas of ribbons made in the form of lapel buttons, or rosettes, may also be worn on the left lapel of civilian clothes, with the exception of civilian evening dress. Honorable discharge and service buttons may be worn on the left lapel of civilian clothes, except on evening dress.

RETIRED OFFICERS' DRESS

Although retired officers wear civilian dress at most official and social occasions, there are occasions when the uniform may be worn.

The number of years of retirement has nothing to do with the retired officer's decision to wear—or not to wear—his or her uniform; the elements of good taste and propriety are the key to the decision.

Retired officers on active duty wear the same uniforms prescribed for officers on active duty.

When not on active duty, a retired officer may wear the uniform corresponding to the grade at the time of retirement, or as authorized, upon the following occasions:

Military ceremonies.
Military weddings or funerals.
Memorial services, inaugurals, patriotic parades on national holidays.
Other military parades or ceremonies in which any active or Reserve United States military unit is taking part.
When giving military instruction or when responsible for military discipline at an educational institution.

Retired officers wear civilian clothing when riding in military aircraft unless engaged in a military activity, when they wear the uniform.

The uniform is *not* worn when you are visiting or living in a foreign country, except when attending by formal invitation a ceremony or social function at which the wearing of the uniform is required. Under these circumstances, authority to wear the uniform may be granted by the service secretary and/or the nearest military attaché.

RESERVE OFFICERS' DRESS

Reserve officers on active duty have the same minimum outfit of uniforms and insignia, as well as accessories, prescribed for the regular service, except if ordered to duty for less than six months, when the sword, sword accessories, and formal evening dress uniform are not required.

When not on active duty, Reserve officers wear the uniform on the same occasions that retired officers do.

DRESS OF SEPARATED PERSONNEL

Any person who has served in the Army (including personnel assigned to the air components prior to the establishment of the Department of the Air Force), Navy, Air Force, Marine Corps, or Coast Guard during wartime, and whose most recent service was terminated honorably, is entitled to wear the uniform of the highest grade held during his or her war service upon the following ceremonial occasions:

Military weddings or funerals, memorial services, inaugurals.
Patriotric parades on national holidays, or other military parades or ceremonies in which any active or reserve United States military unit is taking part.

The uniform worn may be the one authorized at the time of separation, or it may be that prescribed by authorization at the time of the ceremony.

CIVILIAN DRESS FOR MEN: FORMAL

BLACK TIE (AFTER 6:00 P.M. WHEN INDICATED IN INVITATION)

"Black tie" means your dinner jacket or tuxedo. The term *tuxedo* came about in the 1890s when the dinner jacket was introduced into the United States from England and was first worn at the Tuxedo Club.

This is the favorite form of men's evening dress and is worn at almost any formal occasion: receptions, weddings, theater or opera, dances, dinners, etc. Guests may wear dinner jackets at a formal evening church wedding, although members of the wedding party wear full dress. Black tie is not worn before six o'clock in the evening.

Jacket—Of black or dark blue tropical worsted or one of the new blended materials of good quality. The lapels may be faced with satin. For summertime, the jacket is of white linen, dacron, etc. The dark jacket may be worn in the summertime—but it is hot. Nowadays, a more colorful dinner jacket is worn for cruises and less formal occasions.

Trousers—Material matches the jacket with single stripe of matching colored braid or satin. Trousers are without cuffs. (Black trousers are also worn with white or colored jackets.)

Waistcoat—Not worn with a double-breasted jacket; with a single-breasted, the waistcoat will be of white piqué or black plain, ribbed, or self-figured silk. Instead of a waistcoat, a *cummerbund* is worn, of black, maroon, or midnight blue silk; in the summertime, plaid or figured.

Shirt—Attached fold collar with pleated or piqué bosom. White traditionally.

Tie—Black bow, or color to match cummerbund.

Socks—Black or dark blue to match trousers.

Shoes—Black leather or patent leather.

Hat—Rarely worn. A gray fedora goes with everything but white tie. A straw in the summer.

Gloves—Gray or white evening.

Topcoat—Black, charcoal gray, or dark blue.

Accessories—White handkerchief; white silk scarf; studs and cuff links.

Boutonniere—Red or white carnation. (See section on "white tie.")

WHITE TIE (AFTER 6:00 P.M.)

"White tie" means full-dress evening wear, or "tailcoat." Tails are not worn often except by men in the diplomatic service, senior officers, or at a very formal wedding or ceremonial occasion. When you need tails, a good rental service will furnish all the items necessary.

Like dinner jackets, tails should never be worn before six o'clock. Also, tails are not worn in the summer.

The boutonniere may be a white carnation for the left buttonhole, or a small white gardenia, lily of the valley, rosebud, or miniature rose. At a wedding, the bridegroom may wear a white carnation, the ushers a white flower that differs from those of the best man and groom. Do not wear a boutonniere when wearing decorations or uniform.

DAYTIME CLOTHES (BEFORE 6:00 P.M.)

Formal daytime clothes—the *cutaway* or *sack coat*—are mainly worn at diplomatic or governmental affairs. A man taking part in a formal daytime wedding party, or a pallbearer at a state funeral, may wear such dress. For a formal wedding, the cutaway is worn; for the semiformal wedding, the sack coat. A black four-in-hand tie with a fold-down collar is worn instead of an ascot. There are few occasions for the average man to wear a cutaway or sack coat, and therefore they should be rented.

Boutonnieres other than white or red carnations may be worn at various occasions. Cornflowers and small white gardenias are sometimes used, and a groom at a wedding occasionally wears an orange blossom or a small sprig of lily of the valley. Such flowers are always worn in the left buttonhole of a sack coat or tux, but *never* with uniform.

A handkerchief placed in the breast pocket is for show. It is folded, with an inch or two showing. A colored handkerchief blends with the colors in your tie.

A dress handkerchief is white and can be initialed with a single letter or with all your initials. For evening use, the initials are white, gray, or black, but other colors are acceptable for daytime use.

CIVILIAN DRESS FOR MEN: INFORMAL

Any serviceman faces a distinct problem in the matter of his clothes: he must possess two wardrobes—service and civilian. Since uniforms are a necessity, they are purchased first.

When an officer of average financial circumstances purchases his uniform wardrobe and maintains it in the high state of excellence in which it should be kept, usually there is only a modest amount left over in the clothes budget. It is wise to start off with a conservative civilian wardrobe which can be worn for many occasions and seasons.

The best clothes are those of good quality and tailoring, in such colors as gray, blue-gray, dark blue, tan, and brown. Sports jackets and slacks are always needed.

If you want more color in your wardrobe, it could be in such items as sports shirts, swimming trunks, and pajamas. Although there is more color in men's clothing today than ever before, do purchase shirts and ties, particularly, with care; don't succumb to extremes in color and style that quickly become outdated.

In the long run, cheap clothes are the most expensive, because they don't last as long as clothes of better quality.

It is well to remember that what is good taste in one part of the country may not be in another. The bright and unusual sports shirts and brief shorts so familiar in Hawaii and on the West Coast, for example, may not be acceptable in a more conservative—and cooler—New England area.

It is difficult to state any rule for wearing or buying clothes— particularly when you are transferred from one coast to another or abroad. Dress in some foreign countries is ultraconservative, and a "loudly" dressed American could be considered a poor representative of service or country.

The question often arises as to the clothes needed for a young officer's civilian wardrobe. The following suggestions are based on the consensus of a cross-section of officers who have learned through experience.

MINIMUM CLOTHING LIST FOR MEN

1. *Conservative suit.* One will be adequate at first, but plan on getting another as soon as the financial situation permits. One should be suitable for wearing after six o'clock when informal conditions are to be met. The dark blue business suit is traditional and is worn at daytime and less formal evening weddings and receptions. A gray suit is frequently worn during daytime activities.

2. *Sports jacket.* This will probably be the most useful and the most frequently worn item in your wardrobe. Be sure to get a good one that will stand many cleanings and can be worn with almost any color slacks.

3. *Slacks.* At least two pairs. Gray and tan are standard colors.

4. *Topcoat.* If you find that you cannot afford a topcoat in the early stages, wear your officer's raincoat without the insignia. But making the raincoat "double in brass" reduces its longevity.

5. *Dinner jacket.* Optional. When the need arises at a nonmilitary affair, there are rental services available almost everywhere. (See earlier section on "black tie.")

6. *Shirts.* Sports and dress shirts.

7. *Ties.* For all occasions. Styles in tie widths change frequently, so don't over-buy.

8. *Shoes.* Dress and casual. Black for formal wear.

9. *Socks.* Dress and casual. Black for formal wear; subdued shades with business suits; almost any color for casual wear. Avoid

the short sock that shows your skin below trousers when you sit down.

10. *Sweaters, pullovers.* A good washable sweater and several pullovers are needed for everyday.

11. *Swimming trunks.*

12. *Robe.* Packable but not bulky. Washable.

13. *Hat.* Rarely worn nowadays.

CIVILIAN DRESS FOR SERVICEWOMEN

The types of civilian clothes which are needed by women in the services must be determined by the climate and season, the size and location of your base, post, or station, and your specific needs.

The woman officer should select her wardrobe with care. She dresses like her civilian counterpart—the executive woman. Appropriate clothes—suits, tailored dresses, and street dresses—in becoming colors and of excellent quality are always in good taste for daytime wear.

Since the junior officer may be able to acquire only a limited civilian wardrobe, she should be careful to select fashions of such quality that they can be worn frequently and will remain in style for more than a season or so. Large and/or bright designs soon become tiresome, and such a dress may seem old after being worn only once or twice. On the other hand, an older dress of subdued shade and design may seem new when worn with different accessories.

Appropriate outfits and accessories for "after five" should be included in your wardrobe; at many such functions, uniforms will be required. The number and kind of social affairs you attend will dictate your needs. In such locations as Hawaii or Camp Pendleton, you may need more sports or casual clothes; in Washington, D.C., cocktail and evening dresses.

CIVILIAN WARDROBE FOR SERVICEWOMEN

The rapid changes in women's fashions make it impractical to give a detailed list of clothing for a civilian wardrobe. However, in general your civilian wardrobe should include:

1. *Raincoat or all-purpose coat.*

2. *Coat.* A cold-weather coat of basic color to go with almost anything.

3. *Casual suit.* Weight in accordance with the climate; preferably of easy-care material.

4. *Slacks.* Washable and machine or drip-dry.

5. *Jacket and/or sweater.* For sports or casual wear.

6. *Blouses/shirts.* Plain or print, washable, to wear with suit, slacks, shorts, skirts.

7. *Skirt.* Short and/or long.

8. *Afternoon dress.* "Lunch" or "church" type.

9. *Cocktail dress.* Dressy.

10. *Evening dress.* For formal occasions. Long skirt.

11. *Shoes.* Dress and casual. Comfortable walking shoes a must.

12. *Hats and gloves.* Optional. Rarely worn except in cold weather.

13. *Handbags.* For casual and dress.

14. *Robe.* Packable and washable. And house slippers.

WHAT TO WEAR AT WEDDINGS

Servicemen and servicewomen may wear the uniforms prescribed for formal, semiformal, and informal occasions such as weddings and receptions, as described in the uniform charts in this chapter. (For civilian dress at weddings, see chapter 25.)

GENERAL WEAR—INFORMAL VS. CASUAL

Although there is a great deal more informality (and color) in men's dress today, there are occasions where sports jackets are not worn. Before 6:00 P.M. almost anything goes. A rule of thumb is: after 6:00 P.M. when his wife or date wears a cocktail dress, a man wears a business suit appropriate for dinner and the theater.

Sports jackets and slacks are often seen at informal suppers and at late-afternoon cocktail parties, but there is a difference in the meaning of *casual* and *informal*. Very casual dress is not worn at informal occasions—unless the hosts say so. It's important that the hosts know the difference themselves.

Casual means sports or easy attire for cookouts, a poolside supper party, and the like. *Informal,* as stated, means coat and tie for men and afternoon dress for women.

There is no question about what to wear at a formal reception, dinner, or ball; it is spelled out on the invitation, either by the hour stated or by the "White tie" or "Black tie" written in the lower corner of the card. When a ball starts after nine or ten at night, it means white tie. An officer, cadet, or midshipman may wear evening dress uniform.

Servicewomen at official or formal civilian occasions wear uniforms in accordance with male officers, or civilian dress in accordance with local custom. When you are in doubt about what to wear at a dinner or luncheon—or any occasion—ask the hostess. It is better to phone and find out than to be sorry when you get there.

SPORTSWEAR

Sports and physical fitness enthusiasts need clothing in keeping with the sport. Shoes are most important for comfort and security. The skier will need ski boots; the angler, hip-high waders; the golfer, cleated shoes; the mountain climber, rugged boots or shoes with a grip. Golf shoes, tennis shoes, soft-soled deck shoes for boating—for your protection as well as that of the boat's deck—are some of the types worn.

The skier must have a warm jacket or parka and pants; the mountain climber's gear must be rugged but not heavy. Slacks are generally worn for bowling. Women golfers like shorts or slacks; men wear slacks and a wide variety of sports shirts or pullovers. Women tennis players wear brief dresses or skirts. Men prefer shorts to slacks when playing tennis. Jeans are worn by western riders—and everyone else; bathing suits and trunks in a rainbow of colors are at the beach or pool.

UNIFORM CHARTS

ARMY (Men)

Uniform	Coat/Jacket	Trousers	Cap	Shirt	Necktie	Shoes	Socks	Gloves
ARMY BLUE AND ARMY WHITE UNIFORMS: For general official/social occasions.								
Blue Mess	Army blue	Army blue	Blue	White	Black bow[1] or four-in-hand[2]	Black	Black	White
White Mess	Army white	Army white	White	White	Black bow[1] or four-in-hand	Black	Black	White

NOTE: Wear ribbons, miniature or regular medals.
[1]Constitutes black tie.
[2]Constitutes semidress.

Uniform	Coat/Jacket	Trousers	Cap	Shirt	Necktie	Shoes	Socks	Gloves
ARMY GREEN UNIFORM: For ceremonial and informal occasions.								
Army Green/ Army Blue	Army green	Army green/ Army blue	Green	Green/ White	Black four-in-hand	Black	Black	Black
Army White[1]								

NOTE: Wear full size medals or ribbons.
[1]For tropical wear. Accouterments the same as for Army White Mess.

Uniform	Coat/Jacket	Trousers	Cap	Shirt	Necktie	Shoes	Socks	Gloves
ARMY BLUE MESS AND WHITE MESS UNIFORMS: Equivalent to black tie.								
Blue Mess[1]	Army blue	Army blue mess	Blue	White evening dress	Black bow	Black	Black	White
White Mess[2]	Army white	Black dress	White	White evening dress	Black bow	Black	Black	White

NOTE: Wear miniature medals.
[1]Wear black cummerbund. With white vest constitutes evening dress uniform.
[2]Wear white vest. Optional, black cummerbund. Gold studs.

ARMY EVENING DRESS UNIFORM: Equivalent to white tie.

Blue Mess/ Evening Dress	Army blue	Army blue	Blue	White full dress, wing collar	Wing bow	Black	Black	White

NOTE: Wear miniature medals. Wear blue cape. White studs.

ARMY (Women)

Uniform	Coat/Jacket	Skirt	Shirt	Necktab	Shoes	Gloves
ARMY BLUE AND ARMY WHITE UNIFORMS: For general official/social occasions.						
Blue Mess[1]	Army blue	Army blue	White		Black pumps	White
White Mess[2]	Army white	Army white	White		White pumps	White

[1]Wear ribbons, miniature or full size medals. Black handbag; Army blue hat.
[2]Wear miniature medals. White handbag; Army white hat.

Uniform	Coat/Jacket	Skirt	Shirt	Necktab	Shoes	Gloves
ARMY MESS UNIFORMS: Equivalent to black tie.						
Blue Mess[1]	Army blue	Army blue street length	White blouse	Black	Black pumps	White
White Mess[2]	Army white	Army white street length	White blouse	Black	Black pumps	White
Army All-White Mess	Army white	Army white street length	White blouse	Black	White pumps	White

NOTE: Wear miniature medals.
[1]Wear black cummerbund. Black handbag.
[2]Wear white cummerbund. White handbag.

Uniform	Coat/Jacket	Skirt	Shirt	Necktab	Shoes	Gloves
ARMY EVENING DRESS UNIFORMS: Equivalent to white tie.						
Blue Mess/ Evening Dress	Army blue	Army blue long	White blouse	Black	Black pumps	White

| Army White/Evening Dress | Army white | Army white long | White blouse | Black | Black pumps | White |

NOTE: Wear miniature medals. Wear black cummerbund. Black dress handbag.

NOTE: The Army green uniform is for general year-round wear. The Army green cord uniform is for summer wear. Wear stockings complementary to uniform.

NAVY (Men)

Uniform	Coat/Jacket	Trousers	Cap, Combination	Shirt	Necktie	Shoes	Socks	Gloves
SERVICE DRESS UNIFORMS: For general wear.								
Service Dress Blue¹	Blue	Blue	White	White	Black four-in-hand	Black	Black	Black (optional)
Summer White²	White	White	White	White		White	White	

NOTE: Wear ribbons.
¹For Service Dress Blue (Yankee), substitute white trousers, white socks, and shoes for the dark.
²Service Dress White is the same as Full Dress White except that ribbons are worn and gloves are optional.

Uniform	Coat/Jacket	Trousers	Cap, Combination	Shirt	Necktie	Shoes	Socks	Gloves
FULL DRESS UNIFORMS: For general official/social occasions.								
Full Dress Blue	Blue	Blue	White	White	Black four-in-hand	Black	Black	White
Full Dress White	White	White	White	White		White	White	White

NOTE: Wear large medals.

Uniform	Coat/Jacket	Trousers	Cap, Combination	Shirt	Necktie	Shoes	Socks	Gloves
DINNER DRESS UNIFORMS: Equivalent to black tie.								
Dinner Dress Blue	Blue	Blue	White	White¹	Black bow	Black	Black	White
Dinner Dress White	White	White	White	White		White	White	White

NAVY (Men) (Continued)

Dinner Dress Blue Jacket[2]	Blue jacket	Blue evening	White	White[1,3]	Black bow	Black	Black	White
Dinner Dress White Jacket[2]	White jacket	Blue evening	White	White[1,3]	Black bow	Black	Black	White

NOTE: Wear miniature medals.
[1] Stiff-bosomed shirt or pleated soft-front shirt.
[2] Wear gold cummerbund.
[3] Turndown collar.

FORMAL DRESS UNIFORM: Equivalent to white tie.

Formal Dress	Blue dress jacket	Blue evening	White	White stiff bosomed	White bow	Black evening dress	Black	White

NOTE: Wear white waistcoat. Miniature medals.

NAVY (Women)

Uniform	*Coat/Jacket*	*Skirt*	*Shirt*	*Necktie*	*Hat, Combination*	*Shoes*	*Gloves*
SERVICE DRESS UNIFORMS: For general official/social occasions.							
Service Dress Blue A	Blue	Blue	White	Black	Complete	Black	White

NOTE: Wear with ribbons. Black handbag.
Service Dress White is the same as the Blue except for color.
Service Dress Blue and White uniforms, worn with large medals and white gloves, are referred to as *Full Dress Blue* and *White Uniforms*.

DINNER DRESS UNIFORMS: For general official/social functions, or black tie.							
Dinner Dress Blue[1]	Blue	Blue	White	Black	Complete	Black dress	White

	White	White	White	Black	Complete[2]	White dress	White
Dinner Dress White	White	White	White	Black	Complete[2]	White dress	White
Dinner Dress[3] Blue Jacket	Blue	Blue	White	Black	White[2]	Black formal dress	White
Dinner Dress[3] White Jacket	White	Blue	White	Black	White[2]	Black formal dress	White

NOTE: Wear miniature medals.
[1]Black handbag.
[2]Combination cap required, tiara optional.
[3]Wear black cummerbund. Black dress handbag.

FORMAL DRESS UNIFORM: For official formal evening functions, or white tie.

Formal Dress Blue	Blue	Blue long	White dress	Black dress	Tiara optional	Black formal dress	White

NOTE: Wear miniature medals. Wear black cummerbund. Black dress handbag.

NOTE: The long Formal Dress Blue Skirt is optional with the Dinner Dress Jacket Uniforms, when prescribed. Wear stockings complementary to uniform.

AIR FORCE (Men)

Uniform	Coat	Trousers	Hat	Shirt	Necktie	Shoes	Socks	Gloves
SERVICE UNIFORM: For general occasions.								
Service Dress	Blue[1]	Blue	Blue[2]	Light blue[3]	Blue	Black	Black	Black or gray

NOTE: Light blue shirts may be worn outdoors. When worn without a coat, the light blue short-sleeve shirt may be worn with or without necktie.
[1]Wear ribbons.
[2]Wear service hat or flight cap.
[3]Wear long- or short-sleeve shirt. Ribbons optional.

CEREMONIAL UNIFORMS: For informal daytime and evening occasions.

Ceremonial Blue	Blue[1]	Blue	Blue[2]	White	Blue	Black	Black	Black, gray, or white
Ceremonial White	White[3]	White	White[4]	White	White	White	White	White

[1]Wear ribbons. Company grade officers have blue sleeve braid; field grade officers have 1/2-inch silver sleeve braid; general officers have 3/4-inch silver sleeve braid.
[2]Wear service hat with silver chin strap.
[3]Wear ribbons. Company grade and field grade officers wear 1/2-inch silver sleeve braid with dark blue trim. General officers wear 3/4-inch silver sleeve braid with dark blue trim.
[4]Wear service hat with white cover and silver chin strap.

DRESS UNIFORM: Equivalent to black tie.

Mess Dress	Midnight blue[1]	Midnight blue[2]	Midnight blue service hat[3]	White[4]	Midnight blue satin bow	Black	Black	Black, gray, or white

[1]Wear miniature medals.
[2]Wear midnight blue satin cummerbund.
[3]Wearing of hat is optional.
[4]Turn-down collar, pleated front, and French cuffs.

FORMAL EVENING DRESS UNIFORM: Equivalent to white tie.

Formal Dress	Midnight blue[1]	Midnight blue[2]	Midnight blue service hat[3]	White wing collar	White bow	Black	Black	Black, gray, or white

[1]Wear miniature medals.
[2]Wear white vest, pearl studs.
[3]Wearing of hat is optional.

AIR FORCE (Women)

Uniform	Coat	Skirt	Hat	Shirt	Tab	Shoes	Gloves
SERVICE UNIFORM: For general occasions.							
Service Dress	Blue[1]	Blue[2]	Blue[3]	Light blue[4]	Blue	Black pumps	Black, gray, or white

NOTE: Light blue blouses may be worn without a coat. When worn without a coat, the light blue short-sleeve blouse with convertible collar may be worn with or without a tab.
[1]Wear ribbons
[2]Skirt or slacks permissible.
[3]Wear service hat, flight cap, or blue beret.
[4]Wear long- or short-sleeve blouse. Ribbons optional.

Uniform	Coat	Skirt	Hat	Shirt	Tab	Shoes	Gloves
CEREMONIAL UNIFORMS: For informal daytime and evening occasions.							
Ceremonial Blue	Blue[1]	Blue	Blue[2]	White	Blue	Black pumps	White
Ceremonial White	White[3]	White	White[4]	White	Blue	Black pumps	White

[1]Wear ribbons. Company grade officers have blue sleeve braid; field grade officers have 1/2-inch silver sleeve braid; general officers have 3/4-inch silver sleeve braid. Black clutch purse.
[2]Wear silver hat or blue beret.
[3]Wear ribbons. Company grade and field grade officers wear 1/2-inch silver sleeve braid with dark blue trim. General officers wear 3/4-inch silver sleeve braid with dark blue trim. White clutch purse.
[4]Wear service hat.

Uniform	Coat	Skirt	Hat	Shirt	Tab	Shoes	Gloves
DRESS UNIFORM: Equivalent to black tie.							
Mess Dress	Midnight blue	Midnight blue (long)	None	White mess	Midnight blue satin	Black pumps	White

NOTE: Wear miniature medals on coat. Wear midnight blue satin cummerbund. Black clutch purse.

FORMAL EVENING DRESS UNIFORM: Equivalent to white tie.

	Coat/Jacket and Belt	Trousers	Cap	Shirt	Necktie	Shoes	Socks	Gloves
Formal Dress	Midnight blue	Midnight blue (long)	None	White mess	Silver	Black pumps		White

NOTE: Wear miniature medals on coat. Wear silver cummerbund. Black clutch purse.

NOTE: Wear stockings complementary to uniform.

MARINE CORPS (Men)

BLUE DRESS A, B, C, AND WHITE DRESS UNIFORMS: For general official/social occasions.

Uniform	Coat/Jacket and Belt	Trousers	Cap	Shirt	Necktie	Shoes	Socks	Gloves
Blue Dress A[1]	Blue	Blue	Dress	White		Black	Black	White
Blue Dress B[2]	Same as "A"—except with ribbons.							
Blue Dress C[2]	Blue	Blue	Dress	Khaki		Black	Black	Black
White Dress A[1]	White	White	Dress			White	White	White
White Dress B[2]	Same as "A"—except with ribbons.							
Blue/White Dress A[1]	Blue	White	Dress	White		White	White	White
Blue/White Dress B[2]	Same as "A"—except with ribbons.							

NOTE: Wear badges; sword. Wear black leather gloves with outercoat.
[1]Wear large medals.
[2]Wear ribbons.

MESS DRESS UNIFORM: Equivalent to black tie.

Mess Dress							
White mess, scarlet cummerbund	Black mess	Dress	White pleated bosom	Black bow square ends	Black	Black	White

NOTE: Wear miniature medals.

EVENING DRESS A AND B UNIFORMS: Equivalent to white tie.

Evening Dress A	Black evening, waistcoat	Black evening	Dress	White stiff bosom		Black	Black	White
Evening Dress B	Same as "A"—except with cummerbund.							

NOTE: Wear miniature medals.

MARINE CORPS (Women)

Uniform	Coat/Jacket	Skirt	Shirtwaist	Scarf	Cap and Necktie	Shoes	Gloves

BLUE DRESS A AND B AND WHITE DRESS UNIFORMS: For general official/social occasions.

Uniform	Coat/Jacket	Skirt	Shirtwaist	Scarf	Cap and Necktie	Shoes	Gloves
Blue Dress A[1,2]	Blue	Blue	White	Red	Blue	Black pumps	White
Blue Dress B[3]	Same as "A"—except with ribbons.						
White Dress A[1,4]	White	White	White	White	Dress green	White pumps	White
White Dress B[3]	Same as "A"—except with ribbons.						

[1] Wear large medals.
[2] Black or clutch purse with black cover.
[3] Wear ribbons.
[4] Clutch purse with green cover.

MESS DRESS UNIFORM: Equivalent to black tie.

Uniform	Coat	Trousers	Cap Cover	Shirt	Necktie	Shoes	Socks	Gloves
Mess Dress	Mess, cummerbund	Black short	White	White		Black pumps	White	

NOTE: Wear miniature medals. Clutch purse with black cover.

EVENING DRESS A AND B UNIFORMS: Equivalent to white tie.

Uniform	Coat	Trousers	Cap Cover	Shirt	Necktie	Shoes	Socks	Gloves
Evening Dress A	Evening, cummerbund	Black long	White	White	Tiara	Black pumps	White	
Evening Dress B	Same as "A"—except short black evening skirt. Clutch purse with black cover. Cape.							

NOTE: Wear miniature medals. Clutch purse with black cover. Cape.

NOTE: Wear stockings complementary to uniform.

COAST GUARD (Men)

Uniform	Coat	Trousers	Cap Cover	Shirt	Necktie	Shoes	Socks	Gloves

SERVICE DRESS UNIFORMS: General wear.

Uniform	Coat	Trousers	Cap Cover	Shirt	Necktie	Shoes	Socks	Gloves
Service Dress Coast Guard Blue	Blue	Blue	White	Light blue	Blue	Black	Black	Black
Service Dress White	White	White	White			White	White	

NOTE: Wear ribbons.

FULL DRESS UNIFORMS: For official/social functions.

Uniform	Coat	Trousers	Cap Cover	Shirt	Necktie	Shoes	Socks	Gloves
Full Dress Blue	Blue	Blue	White	White	Blue	Black	Black	White
Full Dress White	White	White	White	White		White	White	White

NOTE: Wear large medals; sword.

DINNER DRESS UNIFORMS: Equivalent to black tie.

Uniform								
Dinner Dress Blue[1,2]	Blue	Blue	White	White dress[5]	Black bow	Black	Black	White
Dinner Dress Blue Jacket[1,3]	Blue dinner	Blue evening[4]	White	Formal soft front	Black bow	Black	Black	White
Dinner Dress White[1]	White	White	White			White	White	White
Dinner Dress White Jacket[1,3]	White dinner	Blue evening[4]	White	Formal soft front	Black bow	Black	Black	White

[1] Wear miniature medals.
[2] Primarily for lieutenants and below not possessing the jacket uniforms.
[3] Optional for lieutenants and below.
[4] With gold cummerbund.
[5] Stiff turn-down collar.

EVENING DRESS UNIFORMS: Equivalent to white tie.

Uniform								
Evening Dress Blue[1,2]	Blue dinner	Blue evening	White	Formal stiff bosomed[3]	White bow	Black	Black	White
Evening Dress White[1]	White	White	White			White	White	White

[1] Wear miniature medals.
[2] Wear white waistcoat.
[3] Wear winged collar.

COAST GUARD (Women)

Uniform	Coat	Skirt	Shirt	Necktie	Hat Cover	Shoes	Gloves
SERVICE DRESS UNIFORMS: For general official/social functions.							
Service Dress Coast Guard Blue[1]	Blue	Blue[3]	Light blue	Lt blue w/stripe	White	Black dress	White

COAST GUARD (Women) (*Continued*)

Service Dress White[2]		White[3]	White	Black	White	White	White

NOTE: Wear ribbons.
[1]Black handbag.
[2]White handbag.
[3]Skirt or slacks permissible.

FULL DRESS UNIFORMS: For official/social functions.

Full Dress Blue[1]		Blue	White	Black	White	Black dress	White
Full Dress White[2]		White[3]	White	Black	White	White dress	White

NOTE: Wear large medals.
[1]Black handbag.
[2]White handbag.
[3]Skirt or slacks permissible.

DINNER DRESS UNIFORMS: (Worn in lieu of evening dress uniforms.) Equivalent to black tie.

Dinner Dress Blue[1]	Blue	Blue	White	Black	White	Black dress	White
Dinner Dress Blue Jacket[2,3]	Blue dinner	Blue dinner[4]	White dress	Black dress	Tiara[5]	Black formal	White
Dinner Dress White[6]	White	White	White	Black	White	White dress	White
Dinner Dress White Jacket[2,3]	White dinner	Blue dinner[4]	White dress	Black dress	Tiara[5]	Black formal	White

NOTE: Wear miniature medals.
[1]Black handbag.
[2]Black dress handbag.

[3]Required for all lieutenant commanders and above; optional for others.
[4]Formal dress blue skirt optional.
[5]Optional.
[6]White dress handbag.

EVENING DRESS UNIFORMS: Equivalent to white tie.

	Blue dinner	Formal blue (long)	White dress	Black dress	Tiara[3]	Black formal	White
Evening Dress Blue[1,2]	White	White	White	Black	Tiara[3]	Black formal	White
Evening Dress White[4]	White	White	White	Black	White	White dress	White

NOTE: Wear miniature medals.
[1]Black dress handbag.
[2]Required for all officers captain and above.
[3]Optional.
[4]White dress handbag.

NOTE: Wear stockings complementary to uniform.

MERCHANT MARINE

UNIFORMS: Officers of the Merchant Marine who are officers of the U.S. Naval Reserve wear the Naval Reserve Merchant Marine insignia on their Merchant Marine uniforms. Members of the Naval Reserve who are serving as officers under licenses issued by the U.S. Coast Guard in ships under contract with the Federal Maritime Administration, or those serving as staff officers on certificates of registry issued by the Coast Guard, wear the USNR Merchant Marine insignia. Other members of the Naval Reserve serving in merchant ships in positions which require them to wear a uniform appropriate to an officer, wear the insignia on their uniforms.

Service Insignia

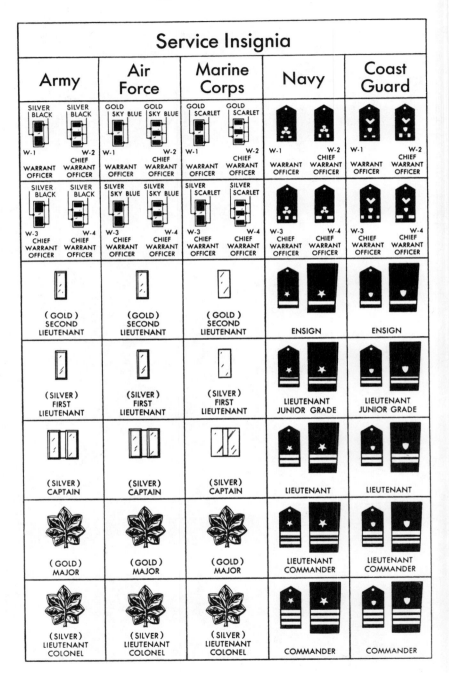

Army	Air Force	Marine Corps	Navy	Coast Guard
SILVER BLACK — W-1 WARRANT OFFICER / SILVER BLACK — W-2 CHIEF WARRANT OFFICER	GOLD SKY BLUE — W-1 WARRANT OFFICER / GOLD SKY BLUE — W-2 CHIEF WARRANT OFFICER	GOLD SCARLET — W-1 WARRANT OFFICER / GOLD SCARLET — W-2 CHIEF WARRANT OFFICER	W-1 WARRANT OFFICER / W-2 CHIEF WARRANT OFFICER	W-1 WARRANT OFFICER / W-2 CHIEF WARRANT OFFICER
SILVER BLACK — W-3 CHIEF WARRANT OFFICER / SILVER BLACK — W-4 CHIEF WARRANT OFFICER	SILVER SKY BLUE — W-3 CHIEF WARRANT OFFICER / SILVER SKY BLUE — W-4 CHIEF WARRANT OFFICER	SILVER SCARLET — W-3 CHIEF WARRANT OFFICER / SILVER SCARLET — W-4 CHIEF WARRANT OFFICER	W-3 CHIEF WARRANT OFFICER / W-4 CHIEF WARRANT OFFICER	W-3 CHIEF WARRANT OFFICER / W-4 CHIEF WARRANT OFFICER
(GOLD) SECOND LIEUTENANT	(GOLD) SECOND LIEUTENANT	(GOLD) SECOND LIEUTENANT	ENSIGN	ENSIGN
(SILVER) FIRST LIEUTENANT	(SILVER) FIRST LIEUTENANT	(SILVER) FIRST LIEUTENANT	LIEUTENANT JUNIOR GRADE	LIEUTENANT JUNIOR GRADE
(SILVER) CAPTAIN	(SILVER) CAPTAIN	(SILVER) CAPTAIN	LIEUTENANT	LIEUTENANT
(GOLD) MAJOR	(GOLD) MAJOR	(GOLD) MAJOR	LIEUTENANT COMMANDER	LIEUTENANT COMMANDER
(SILVER) LIEUTENANT COLONEL	(SILVER) LIEUTENANT COLONEL	(SILVER) LIEUTENANT COLONEL	COMMANDER	COMMANDER

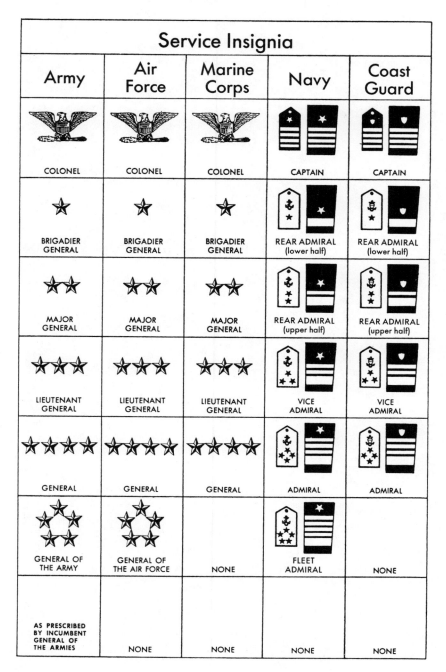

Service Insignia

Army	Air Force	Marine Corps	Navy	Coast Guard
COLONEL	COLONEL	COLONEL	CAPTAIN	CAPTAIN
BRIGADIER GENERAL	BRIGADIER GENERAL	BRIGADIER GENERAL	REAR ADMIRAL (lower half)	REAR ADMIRAL (lower half)
MAJOR GENERAL	MAJOR GENERAL	MAJOR GENERAL	REAR ADMIRAL (upper half)	REAR ADMIRAL (upper half)
LIEUTENANT GENERAL	LIEUTENANT GENERAL	LIEUTENANT GENERAL	VICE ADMIRAL	VICE ADMIRAL
GENERAL	GENERAL	GENERAL	ADMIRAL	ADMIRAL
GENERAL OF THE ARMY	GENERAL OF THE AIR FORCE	NONE	FLEET ADMIRAL	NONE
AS PRESCRIBED BY INCUMBENT GENERAL OF THE ARMIES	NONE	NONE	NONE	NONE

SECTION II

The Social Side of Life

CHAPTER 3

Formals & Informals

YOUNG MEN AND WOMEN in training at the service academies, ROTC units, or Officer Candidate Schools—or, for that matter, any young officer anywhere—will find that the etiquette observed at academy and college dances will generally be observed at any other dance or ball. The earlier the correct etiquette is learned, the easier it will be for you to attend with complete poise an academy hop, a debutante ball, or an embassy dance.

The fourth classmen at the academies each year are young people from all walks of life. Many have had previous college or preparatory school training and know how to escort or be escorted to fraternity or class dances. Others, directly out of high school, may not have had the opportunity to learn what to do at formal dances, or how to greet those in the receiving line.

Midshipmen, cadets, and other students should be well versed in such courtesies before receiving an assignment in a service that may take them all over the world and certainly will take them into various social situations.

THE ACADEMY DANCES

There are two kinds of dances: informal and formal. The distinction between them is mainly in dress. Informal dances are called *informals* and may be a hop, a mixer, or a dance to records. Midshipmen wear winter service dress blues or summer whites, according to the season, and cadets wear the equivalent uniform to an informal.

At mixers, a civilian male date wears a sports shirt and slacks, and a civilian woman wears a dress, or a skirt or slacks and a blouse.

Evening dress uniform is prescribed for all *formals*. Civilian dates wear long, short, or cocktail-style dresses and male civilians wear black tie. But at any dance the important thing for a date to remember is to dress in accordance with the formality or informality of the occasion.

An academy hostess is always on hand to receive or assist in receiving guests.

DANCE TIME

Formal dances, called *formals*, are held from 9:00 P.M. until midnight, or later, upon special occasions. At some of the service academies the cadets and midshipmen attend on a voluntary basis but must return to their quarters by a designated time after the dance. At other academies attendance is prescribed by the commandant of cadets or midshipmen.

After arriving at the dance, the man waits while his date takes her coat to the coatroom. There will be needles, thread, etc., for any emergency. Plebes at all academies attend a limited but mandatory number of formals during the academic year.

RECEIVING LINES AT FORMALS

It is a courtesy—and therefore mandatory—that you go through the receiving line at a formal. This is good training for the future, as the receiving line at a formal is similar to receiving lines at balls and receptions anywhere.

The receiving line forms near the entrance to the ballroom and is kept as short as possible. At a very large function there may be two lines. Standing first in line is the dance manager or chairman, with the person who is receiving standing next. The commanding officer, or spouse of an officer on active duty on the base or station, will be invited to receive the guests with his or her spouse.

The dance manager or chairman always keeps his (or her) hands at his sides, or at his back, so that guests will not shake hands with him. It is his duty to announce the names of guests to the receiving person at his side, who will shake hands with each guest and greet everyone in a friendly manner. When the commanding officer of the station, such as the superintendent of the academy, receives, he or she can stand next to either the manager (or chairman) or his or her own spouse.

Receiving lines are not held at informals and mixers. Academy hostesses mix with the guests.

At a West Point formal, the officer stands to the right of the dance manager, with the officer's wife to his right, then the cadet hostess.

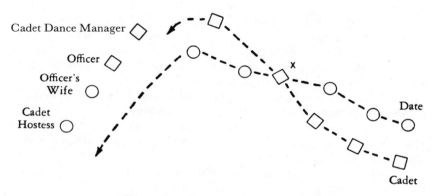

The receiving line at a West Point formal

The young lady is to the right of the cadet as they enter the ballroom. At point *x*, the cadet has passed behind the young lady and is now on her right.

PROCEDURE

The steps in going through the receiving line at West Point when the dance manager is a male cadet are:

1. The dance manager (chairman) stands first in line, in order to present the guests to the receiving officer at his side. He does *not* shake hands with the guests, but the officer does.

2. As the cadet and his date approach the line, she will be on his right. She does *not* hold his arm.

3. Nearing the line, she steps ahead and the cadet is now behind and to her right, in position to give their names to the dance manager.

4. The cadet gives her *last* name only: "Miss Smith," when she is a non-military guest.

5. When she steps ahead of the cadet, the dance manager turns to the receiving officer and says the *receiving officer's name first:* "General Brown, Miss Smith."

6. The receiving person shakes hands with the young lady and says something similar to, "Good evening, Miss Smith. It's nice to see you." She may answer, "Good evening, General Brown," or "Good evening. It's nice to be here."

7. After the dance manager presents her to the receiving person, he turns to you, the cadet, and you give your last name: "Cadet Jones." Do not fail to give your name, regardless of how well you know him. If a guest does not state his or her name, the dance manager may say, "Your name, please?" The civilian date of a woman cadet (or midshipman) would say "Mr. Jones."

8. The dance manager then presents you to the person who is receiving: "General Brown, Cadet Jones." You respond in this manner: "Good evening, Sir," or "Good evening, General Brown." It is always correct to say, "How do you do, Sir?"

9. You should look at the person addressed—escort, receiving person, etc.—but do not attempt a conversation.

10. The line does not form again at the end of the dance. It is always courteous, however, to thank those receiving, and the hostess, and to say good-bye.

At any social function where the person receiving is a lady, her name is given first.

INTERMISSIONS AT FORMALS

Fruit punch and cakes are served during intermission at formals. You may have the minor problem at very large dances of finding your date if she or he was dancing with someone else when intermission was called.

If a man should pass his date, he may extend his arm and tell her partner that he will take over, which will release the partner to find his own young lady. If something unexpected happens to the escort of the young lady with whom you have had that dance and he has not reclaimed her, *then it is your duty*—and your date's—to stand by until he appears.

CONDUCT AT DANCES

Midshipmen and cadets are expected to conduct themselves with decorum at all times—on or off the dance floor. Displays of affection are not tolerated, and Dance Committee Members will ask those who violate courtesies to leave. Members of the Committee at the Coast Guard and Naval Academies are distinguished by their gold aiguillettes; at the Air Force Academy by silver aiguillettes; at West Point by red sashes. They have the authority to enforce regulations.

A man never leaves his date sitting alone, or embarrasses her with boisterous conduct. Never leave her in mid-floor. If an occasion arises when you must leave, you should leave her with a group before excusing yourself. If you are not adept at certain dance steps, you may suggest "waiting this one out." Or she might say, "Shall we rest a moment?" or "Please, let's have some punch."

When you complete a dance with someone who is not your guest, take her back to her escort or party, and thank her.

Since the general tone of a ball is formal, rather formal dancing is expected. Contemporary dancing is enjoyed, but not so strenuously as to demand a wide area.

It is inconsiderate to remain talking in groups on the dance floor. If you want to talk rather than dance, you should move to the side of the floor.

OBLIGATIONS

The *first* obligation of a midshipman or cadet—or anyone—is to the person you are with. That person should be shown every consideration, and in turn, it is your date's duty to make this a pleasant occasion.

You dance with your date frequently, but not exclusively. You should introduce him or her to other couples. A man must see to it that his date is never neglected, even though this might be a blind date and she is not Miss America.

Your *second* obligation is to the others in your party or at your table. You must join in the general conversation, bring your date or others into the light talk, suggest refreshments during intermission, and dance with others in the group.

Your *third* obligation is to the midshipman or cadet hostess, to those in the receiving line, and to other seniors present.

Each cadet or midshipman in the host company for that evening has this particular obligation: to talk briefly with the receiving officer and any senior guests. Do not neglect your academy hostess. Seniors are well aware of your desire to dance with others of your own age, so don't be afraid of being stuck.

In asking an officer's wife for a dance, a male cadet or midshipman would first approach Colonel and Mrs. Rank, greet them, and introduce his date, although they have already met in the receiving line. After a brief exchange of small talk, he asks Mrs. Rank if she would care to dance. Colonel Rank then talks or dances with the cadet or midshipman's date.

At the end of the number—or earlier, if indicated by Mrs.

Rank—you both return to the place where you started. Thank her for the dance, as you would any partner, before you and your young lady move away.

GRADUATION WEEK AND RING DANCES

The dances and balls held during Graduation (or Commissioning) Week are considered the most important of all. They are the final dances for the first class. Informals and formals for all classes are held throughout the week, with the graduation dinner and ball held after the final parade and Color Girl presentation on graduation eve.

The ring dance is the highlight for the second class at the Naval and Air Force Academies, held during the week of graduation, with West Pointers and Coast Guard cadets receiving their rings a month earlier. Customs vary at the different academies, but at Annapolis couples pass through a replica of the class ring and each young lady receives a kiss. At the Air Force Academy the ring presentation and dining-in are for cadets only, followed by a formal dance in Arnold Hall.

During the ring banquet weekend at West Point, second class cadets receive their rings at a dining-in, and the formal dinner-dance is held the following night in Eisenhower Hall. At the Coast Guard Academy the ring dance is in Leamy Hall. At the Citadel the ring dance has a Junior Sword Drill composed of sergeants from the second class who form an arch of sabers through which pass the first classmen and their dates.

The ring dance is a tradition at the State Maritime Academies and the Merchant Marine Academy, with each academy observing a special custom. At the Massachusetts State Maritime Academy, for example, a feature is a precision drill by the Honor Guard. The ring dance at Kings Point is held in August.

The occasion of the ring dance and dinner is a prime time for cadets and midshipmen to give their One and Only a miniature of their class rings.

INFORMALS

An informal is held almost weekly at the academies. A hop,* an informal, a mixer, are about the same thing. For an informal, the

---

Hop is a military word for *dance* familiar at the older service and maritime academies but less frequently used today.

midshipmen and cadets invite their own dates. For a mixer, with a disc jockey (d.j.), the social director may send out invitations to young ladies at least sixteen years of age from nearby colleges and communities. Dress is casual for both, with skirts, slacks, and dresses worn, but not cut-off jeans or shorts. Nearby women's colleges often invite the midshipmen and cadets to their mixers.

The informals serve as opportunities to get acquainted with other young people as well as a means of improving dance steps and learning social mores. Dance instruction, including popular line dancing, is available for those who want it.

At times when dancing is not scheduled, country, pop, and rock concerts are enjoyed.

SPECIAL DANCES

Each academy and each military school and college in the country has a special dance all its own. Each class has its own, also, such as the plebe parents' formal held during Parents Weekend after spring break at West Point, with parents, plebes, and dates dancing in Eisenhower Hall. There is a homecoming dance, a Christmas ball, a spring formal, and a Valentine's Day dance.

At Annapolis, the International Ball is an annual formal with young ladies and men invited from nearby embassies. At the Air Force Academy, there are the all-class Dean's Ball and the Commandant's Ball, and the Recognition Ball held for all classes during Graduation Week; at West Point the Camp Illumination formal highlights the end of summer training for the third class at nearby Camp Buckner.

The formal held during Kings Point Weekend in early June at the Merchant Marine Academy is held on an outside dance floor overlooking Long Island Sound.

SERVICE BALLS

Each service has its own special ball, usually a charity fete with proceeds providing financial or educational assistance. The Navy Relief Ball Committee in Washington, D.C., issues some two thousand invitations for Navy Relief's annual formal dinner-dance. The Air Force has two main balls: the Iron Gate Ball, held annually on the East and West coasts, with guests other than Air Force officers including industrial personages; and the Air Force Charity Ball in Washington, D.C., with senior officers in the area attending as well as government officials and civic leaders. Both are black-tie affairs, with dinner preceding dancing.

The occasion of the birthday of the Marine Corps on 10 November 1775 is observed throughout the world—aboard ship and at all posts and stations. Distinguished guests from other services and from civilian life attend the formal ball in Washington, D.C. The cake-cutting ceremony follows a time-honored procedure including the playing of "The Marines' Hymn" while the cake escorts bring in a Mameluke sword on a serving cart with the cake.

Army Branch Balls (infantry, artillery, etc.) celebrate the founding of the particular branch at formal balls held throughout this country and abroad.

On Founders Day a dinner-dance is held at all Army posts, attended by graduates of West Point. Graduates of the other service academies are invited as courtesy guests.

SERVICE JUNIOR DANCES

Among the service dances held throughout the country is the Army-Navy-Air Force Cotillion in Washington, D.C., which is open to service juniors who are sons or daughters of active, retired, or deceased officers of the Army, Navy, Air Force, Marine Corps, and Coast Guard. Members must be at least sixteen years old.

A representative from one of the services and his or her spouse act as official hosts. There usually are three informals held during the year. The one formal—the Christmas cotillion—is attended by midshipmen and cadets on Christmas leave.

Informals are held for cadets and midshipmen following the interservice football games. When time permits, dances may be planned at universities where games with service academies are scheduled.

Commanders of various posts, bases, and stations, and service organizations such as Alumni Association chapters or ROTC units, often invite cadets and midshipmen to attend dances held during leave.

COLLEGE DANCES

A college man wears black tie—his tuxedo, or a white dinner jacket in the summer—to a formal college dance.

Midshipmen and cadets, ROTC students, OCS, OTS—or any officer—may wear the uniform that is the equivalent of black tie, or he or she may wear civilian dress.

When a dinner precedes a dance at a women's college, the man's date usually pays for the dinner in advance. But if he invites her out for dinner, he pays for the meal.

DEBUTANTE BALLS

In metropolitan cities throughout the country, debutantes (young ladies about eighteen years old) are introduced to society in large groups at cotillions and assemblies, more often called a coming-out. Such balls are usually held for benefit of various charity organizations, with the young ladies' parents making contributions to charities in lieu of the greater expense of private debuts.

Daughters, or daughters of close friends and relatives, are frequently honored by their parents or sponsors at afternoon tea dances held in private clubs or hotel ballrooms; these occasions are less elaborate.

Each young lady attending a formal ball subscribes for two or three partners—or more. Midshipmen, cadets, and young bachelor officers are often invited to attend "stag," and wear evening dress uniform. Civilian gentlemen wear white tie.

Partners of the debutante, as well as her close relatives and friends, send flowers to her before the ball, with one corsage or bouquet selected for the event. The other flowers are used as a background at the place she is presented.

A buffet supper is served after midnight, and the ball is over in the early morning hours. No line is formed at the conclusion of the affair, but guests are expected to thank the debutante's parents or sponsors. If you were a guest at a dinner held before the ball, then you thank the host and hostess of that dinner, also.

THE FORMAL DANCE

A formal dance may be held in a large room or club, usually starting about ten o'clock, with dancing getting underway an hour later. For a very formal affair, a carpet may run from the curb to the front entrance, with an awning overhead, and guests are announced.

The hostess and the guest of honor—say, a debutante—stand near the entrance to the ballroom, where they greet guests. Should the host stand in the receiving line during the early part of the evening, he will leave the line before the hostess and guest of honor, to mix with the guests. The receiving line usually breaks up after three-quarters of an hour; then the young lady is free to join the dancers. Her first dance is with her father, who has been circulating among the guests, then with the young man who is her escort for the evening and who will take her in to supper.

There is a stag line, with an extra man for each nine or ten honorees. If you are invited as a stag, your duty is to see that they never lack for dancing partners.

A buffet supper is served after midnight. The hostess initiates the movement of a few guests toward the buffet table, and other guests follow.

When you attend as a stag, you may ask any unattached woman to have supper with you. You fill your plates and sit wherever you like. At a large dance, the food may be served directly to guests seated at small tables.

DUTY DANCES

"Duty" dances are those that good manners require a man to have with certain ladies at a private dance or dinner dance. Such dances are those with your hostess, the guest of honor, and any female member of the hostess's family.

If you attended a dinner before the dance or ball, then you should also dance with the hostess and the guest of honor at that occasion. If the woman at your right was your assigned dinner partner, then you should dance with her.

When you are the guest of a particular woman at a party, or are the guest of a subscription party member, you should dance several times with her, and perhaps ask her to have supper with you.

At a service dance, you dance—or sit and talk for a few minutes—with the wife of the senior male officer present, whether she is the hostess or not.

CHAPTER 4

The Academy Weekend

WHEN YOU INVITE a date for the first time to your service academy, your military college, or a college having an ROTC unit, include in your letter or phone call a brief but general idea of the plans for the weekend. Write three or four weeks in advance of a special dance; if the invitation is for Graduation Week, then many more details must be included.

A weekend is for one or two nights. Usually, Graduation Week (Commissioning Week at the Naval Academy) starts the Friday before graduation, which takes place at most academies near the end of May.

After your date accepts your invitation, then write a more specific letter in return. Dates do not want to arrive either unprepared or overloaded with luggage, and should be told the best way to come—by bus, train, plane, or car. And they should also be told whether you can meet them or not, owing to drills or classes. If you know that others from the same area or college will be arriving that weekend, you might mention their names so that your date can have company on the trip.

For a regular weekend, you should inform your date about any formal or informal dances, and advise him or her about such activities as a football game or a play. At all academies, a full schedule is planned during Graduation Week, including parades, formals and informals, dinners, sailing, picnics, baseball, tennis, and for first classmen, the graduation reception, which parents and dates attend.

Your date will want to know about the accommodations you have arranged, and reservations should be made as early as possible—frequently a year ahead—for the week of graduation.

ARRIVAL BY BUS OR PLANE

When a person is not arriving by private car, a bus may be the most convenient method for a fairly short trip. For the person coming from a distance, a plane to the nearest large city will save time. A bus or taxi may be taken to the academy. When several people are traveling together, the expense of taxi and limousine travel is shared and thus becomes reasonable.

There are regular bus schedules out of New York City for West Point, New York (or Highland Falls), some 45 miles north, and much farther eastward, to New London, Connecticut. There are regular schedules out of Washington, D.C., for Annapolis, Maryland (about 35 miles), and from Baltimore (25 miles). The Air Force Academy is located about 10 miles north of Colorado Springs, and 60 miles south of Denver. On weekends, buses leave Colorado Springs on a regular schedule and take visitors to the academy complex 6 miles from the entrance to the main buildings. It is advisable to drive your own car, or to rent one, when visiting the USAFA.

The New York State Maritime College at Fort Schuyler, and the Merchant Marine Academy at Kings Point, both on Long Island Sound, are easily reached by car or bus, with parkways leading to them from almost any direction. The sites of all maritime academies are accessible by plane or car.

Airlines have daily schedules—subject to change—for flights to all large cities close to the academies. Arrival and departure information is ascertained at the time the plane tickets are reserved.

PLEBE DATES

Plebes at the service academies may date other plebes or civilians, but regulations do not permit them to date upper classmen.

A civilian man who is dating a woman cadet or midshipman wears black tie to a formal dance in accordance with the dress uniform worn by his counterpart. Civilian dress may be worn on base at some informal and recreational occasions by the midshipmen and cadets, and similar dress is worn by civilian men.

DRESS FOR DATES

Your date will want to know what clothes to bring for a weekend or for Graduation Week, and what type of events will be attended. For a young lady, a formal means your prettiest short or long dress. The informal means a short dress or skirt and blouse, perhaps a pantsuit. Slacks are worn at mixers, but cut-offs are not.

Sunday morning chapel services require women to wear day-time dress, but hats and gloves are not necessary. A man wears a coat and tie.

Shoes are probably the most important item of dress—there is considerable walking at all academies. Nowadays most women wear shoes with moderate heels for any occasion, but higher heels are worn for the more formal occasion when desired. Soft-soled shoes are mandatory when sailing (this protects the deck) and on the tennis court. Durable shoes are needed for hiking or a mountain climb.

For a sports weekend, the slacks worn on the trip may double for any contest. For an outside activity in cold weather, such as a late-season football game, a warm coat or jacket, a warm skirt or slacks, and sweater, boots, and scarf—these are essential. A wise date may bring along a blanket to help keep warm. A lightweight raincoat or an all-purpose coat is indispensable for the sudden storm.

In warm weather shorts may be worn for sailing, tennis, and other sports, but overly brief shorts and bare midriffs are frowned upon; bathing suits are not worn away from the beach or swimming pool.

And don't forget to bring dark glasses!

EXPENSES OF DATES

When dates come for a weekend, or for graduation, they usually pay for their own transportation. They also pay for their own meals en route and for any during the visit that have not been arranged for them by their cadet or midshipman host.

Dates may pay for their own room during the stay in a motel, hotel, or guest house—the popular B & B (bed and breakfast)—even though the reservation was made for them. Frequently, officers' quarters are open to young friends, who are invited as nonpaying guests.

A Squadron Sponsor Program at the Air Force Academy is backed by staff officers and airmen who "adopt" the cadets in the forty squadrons, and may invite members of their families and dates as guests in their quarters. The Rampart Lodge or VOQ (visiting officers' quarters) on the Air Force Academy grounds is available to Air Force personnel and their guests. There are a number of motels in the area, but none within walking distance.

At the Hotel Thayer on the grounds of the Military Academy, dormitory rooms are available for dates at reasonable rates. There are motels in the vicinity of all service and maritime academies. A list of rooms in accredited homes, and of hotels and motels in the area, is available in the office of each service academy social director. Upon request, the list will be sent to the date.

When you, a cadet or midshipman, ROTC, or college student, invite a guest for a meal, movie, or other activity, you pay for it. A man pays for flowers for his date. However, sending a corsage is an exception rather than the rule of former years, and is for very special occasions. Giving flowers is determined by class decision, with considerable savings gained by group purchase.

Although cadets and midshipmen receive a larger monthly allowance than in former years, they are not affluent. For those who have little or no financial assistance from home, the allowance does not go far.

CAR AND BICYCLE REGULATIONS

A date should be aware of the regulations regarding the driving of cars and riding in them by midshipmen and cadets. The regulations vary at each academy, but in general first classmen may own cars and leave them in a posted area on the academy grounds during the final academic year. They may drive them during weekend leave— when their grades are up—and return them by a specified time.

At all academies, all classes may ride in cars, and second classmen may drive them. Fourth classmen do not drive.

Regulations also vary at the academies concerning bicycles, with some midshipmen and cadets permitted to own and ride them at specified times, and others riding them as members of bicycle clubs.

DRINKING

A midshipman or cadet, or any college student, is considered a mature young man or woman. Usually voting age is considered the age of maturity, but the laws of each state determine the age when men and women may drink hard liquor—currently 21 in every state. Beer cannot be served to anyone under 18.

A beer-call may be held in a specified area at the academies at times designated by the commandant; wine may occasionally be served at a dining-in or a formal occasion. Hard liquor is permitted at the academies under limited conditions, to persons 21 years of age or older. The Twenty-One Club at the Air Force Academy is for cadets of at least 21 years, and serves limited amounts of liquor at stated times. Identification cards are required. Midshipmen and cadets during liberty may accept a cocktail when in the quarters of officers or in the homes of professors or sponsors, but at all times a date—or anyone—should remember not to offer drinks except at prescribed times and *when their guests are of legal age.*

FOURTH CLASS SPONSOR PROGRAMS

In order to provide cadets and midshipmen with support and friendship beyond the academy environment, families living near an academy may act as sponsors for a few or as many cadets or mids as they choose, throughout the academic year—or years.

Cadets and mids may ask someone—the head of a family, a retired officer or faculty member, a townsman—to become their sponsor. Or the adult may contact personnel services at any of the academies and offer his or her sponsorship.

The young people do not want to be "entertained." What they want most is a place to relax away from the pressures of the academy—to watch TV, make a sandwich, rake leaves, or take a nap. When they leave, however, the house should be in as good order as when they arrived.

There are responsibilities the sponsor must accept: not to serve beer to anyone under 18 years of age, and to serve alcoholic drinks only to those 21 and over—in limited amounts.

The sponsor probably will have to pick up the underclassmen, since they do not have cars and plebes cannot drive. And the sponsor must return the young people to the academy by the time set to report in. If sponsors or their charges break the rules, sponsorship privileges are revoked.

CHAPTER 5

Receptions & Cocktail Parties

RECEPTIONS

A reception is a "ceremony of receiving guests." There are many kinds of receptions: afternoon and evening, formal and informal. They are of a limited duration of time, and a few or many people may be invited.

Receptions are usually held in honor of someone: a dignitary, a bride and groom, a newcomer. They are also held to mark a special occasion, such as an officer's retirement, a parade, the christening or commissioning of a ship, a golden wedding anniversary, or the baptism of an infant. But regardless of the occasion, the routine of every reception is basically the same.

The purpose of a reception given in honor of someone is to have as many friends and acquaintances of the hosts as possible meet the guest (or guests) of honor.

In the services, the senior officer of a large command may designate a certain day for "calls made and paid" (see chapter 6) and/or host a "hail and farewell" party for newcomers and those detached from the station. Such receptions are in lieu of individual social calls that a busy CO does not have time to make or receive. At most stations it is no longer required for guests at these receptions to leave cards, and their "call" is considered repaid.

TIME

The hours of the reception are indicated on the invitation and usually span a two-hour interval. Receptions are held at various hours, according to their nature, frequently from six to eight in the evening. Afternoon receptions and at-homes may be held from five to seven. An informal reception may be in the midafternoon or early evening, a formal debutante reception at five o'clock, or at half past ten at night.

An official or formal reception usually starts at nine in the evening, and a very formal reception and dance at ten or half past ten.

DRESS

At *informal daytime receptions,* men wear the uniform of the day or dark business suits. Women wear afternoon dresses or suits. Ladies in the receiving line do not wear gloves. Such words as *informal, service dress white,* and *civilian informal* are written or printed in the lower right-hand corner of the invitation.

At *formal daytime receptions,* a man wears the uniform of the day or the prescribed civilian dress for the very formal occasion—the cutaway—which is worn at an inaugural reception or any formal state or public function. Such dress is also worn at a very formal wedding when he is a member of the bridal party. Women wear afternoon dresses and white gloves. The right glove is removed when going through the receiving line, and when shaking hands with a head of state or a dignitary of the church.

At *formal evening receptions,* the formality of the occasion is indicated by the words *black tie* written, engraved, or printed on the invitation. *White tie* indicates a very formal occasion. *Decorations* always indicates full evening dress.

A reception is usually black tie unless specified otherwise. Women wear evening dress, and men wear mess or dinner dress uniforms, or the prescribed uniform according to the season (see chapter 2).

At *semiformal receptions, black tie* or *civilian informal* (a man's best dark business suit) indicates the type of dress to be worn.

At large official receptions, or at a large reception of a somewhat public nature, *dress optional* is indicated in the lower right-hand corner of the invitation.

Small cards stating the type of uniform to be worn are usually enclosed with official invitations.

ARRIVAL

There are no rules about how long to stay at a reception. You may arrive at any time between the hours indicated on the invitation, but guests are expected to arrive before the receiving line disbands. It is imperative that you first pay your respects to your host and hostess. You probably will stay a little longer at a small reception.

You stay about 30 minutes—no longer than 45 minutes—but you may stay until the closing hours at a formal reception and dance. You should not arrive uncomfortably near the closing hour of the afternoon reception—unless you have been asked to stay on for supper by the hosts. A guest who arrives late at an afternoon reception and lingers on through the dinner hour can be a problem to the hosts, who may have other social obligations.

THE RECEIVING LINE

There are differences in the way receiving lines are formed at various official, formal, and informal receptions. The host stands first in line at *official* receptions, with his wife at his side. The hostess stands first in line at social, *nonofficial* functions, with her husband at her side.

At *official* receptions, an aide stands either at the head of the line or facing the host and announces the names of guests as they arrive. You do *not* shake hands with the aide. The protocol established by the State Department (not including the aide) is:

1. The official host
2. The guest of honor
3. The guest of honor's wife or husband
4. The official host's wife
5. Extra man, if possible, to avoid leaving a woman at the end of the line

When the guest of honor is the president of any country, a reigning king or queen, or a dignitary of the church, the host and hostess relinquish their positions in favor of their guest. The line would be:

1. President, King (or reigning Queen)
2. The honored guest's wife (or husband of Queen)
3. The official host
4. The official host's wife

At many Washington receptions, when the honor guests are of high rank or position (for example, when the Secretary of Defense gives a reception in honor of a service secretary), the receiving line is frequently arranged in the following manner:

1. The host
2. The hostess
3. The guest of honor
4. The guest of honor's wife

Some hosts invite a man appropriately connected to the occasion to stand at the end of the line, in order that a woman not be in this position. Other hosts feel that this is incorrect, since a reception is to honor certain individuals only.

At very formal *nonmilitary receptions,* a butler may announce the names of guests as they arrive. At most formal—and at some less formal—receptions, guests are received in the same way as at a formal dinner. The hostess greets each guest and presents him or her to the guests of honor; then the guest is greeted by the host, who is near the hostess but is mixing among the guests and introducing newcomers into groups.

The receiving line at receptions should be kept as small as possible. Usually, those in the line are the host, hostess, and guest or guests of honor. No one likes to go down a long line, in which generally a guest's name is mixed up midway. Names are not announced at small and informal receptions. (The receiving lines at wedding receptions, at-homes, and formal dances are discussed in chapters pertaining to those subjects.)

When a president, king, queen, or dignitary of the church, or a person of very high rank, attends a reception, all other guests should arrive before that person does. In the case of a king, president, or dignitary of the church, women are presented to that person, disregarding the customary rule of presenting men to women.

GARDEN PARTY RECEIVING LINE

The procedure for guests going through the receiving line at a large reception may be illustrated by the superintendent's garden party, which is held at the Naval Academy each spring during Commissioning Week for the parents and guests of members of the first class. In recent years two late afternoon parties have been held, because of the size of the graduating class.

The superintendent and his wife receive guests inside the superintendent's house. The guests greet their hosts and then go into the garden, where punch and small cakes are served. Staff officers and their spouses assist in hospitalities throughout the evening.

Customarily, owing to his official position, the superintendent is first in the line, with his wife at his side. The aide announcing the names of guests as they arrive stands nearer the entrance to the reception room, either at the head of the line or facing the host—whichever way names are more clearly heard. As the guests approach the line, the aide turns and faces them. Guests do not shake hands with the aide, and last names only are given.

If you are a graduate, you step forward and clearly state the name of each person in your party, starting with your parents: "Mrs. Jones," "Dr. Jones," and then your date, "Miss Smith" or "Mr. Smith." Members of a larger party would be presented in this order: mother, father, grandmother, grandfather, aunt, uncle, sister, brother, and last, your date.

After each person in your party has been presented, the aide turns to you and you give your name: "Midshipman Jones." The aide turns to the superintendent and says, "Admiral Blank, Midshipman Jones." The superintendent and his wife shake hands with each guest.

You will probably say "Good evening, Sir," or "Good evening, Admiral Blank," and "How do you do, Mrs. Blank?"

Remember to shake hands lightly—but with a degree of firmness. Your hosts have many hands to shake during the evening, and a pressure grip is to be avoided. Guests may arrive at any time between the hours stated in the invitation, but it is customary at this type of academy reception that the midshipmen attend by battalions at designated hours.

Upon leaving, do not look up your hosts and say good-bye. This is a very large reception, and it is not expected or desired that guests again shake hands.

FOOD

The type of food served at any reception is as simple or as elaborate as the hosts desire and the occasion requires. Fruit punch may be served for guests who do not drink alcoholic beverages, but cocktails, highballs, fruit punch, and coffee are offered at most receptions, with waiters to serve them.

One room is usually set aside for food, but more rooms may be needed at large receptions. After being received by their hosts, guests go into the room where the table is set with a cloth and centerpiece of flowers, and serve themselves. Food ranges from various kinds of roasts, breads and biscuits, shrimp, and lobster, to finger-foods frequently served at cocktail parties or formal teas.

WHITE HOUSE RECEPTIONS

Dress for a reception at the White House is the same as at any reception. A woman wears her most becoming dress, and gloves, and military personnel are in uniform.

As a guest, you must be on time. You should arrive at the White House gate no later than ten minutes before the hour of invitation, which will give you time to be checked at the gate where names of all guests are posted and to leave your hat and coat in the designated room.

You will be directed to the place of reception. Guests are expected to be in the room before the President, followed by his wife, enters. A military aide announces the guests' names. Before shaking hands with the President, a woman should remove her right glove. You say, "Good evening, Mr. President," and "Good evening, Mrs.————," and move on—unless they stop you briefly to say a few words. Otherwise, do not open a conversation with either the President or the First Lady while going through the line. You do not leave cards, and you do not leave the reception until after the President and his wife have left the room.

RECEPTIONS FOR GRADUATES

Before the day of graduation, the superintendents and presidents of the various service and maritime academies and their spouses entertain at an afternoon or evening reception in honor of the graduates, their parents and other members of their families, and guests.

This custom prevails not only at the academies, but also at the Officer Candidate and Officer Training Schools, Marine Corps schools, and ROTC units in universities and colleges. Nonmilitary women wear their most attractive afternoon dress or suit, and men wear a conservative business suit, with white shirt, to afternoon receptions.

When the reception is held after 6:00 P.M. and is followed by a dance (ball), officers wear evening dress uniform, civilian women wear long or short formal dress, and civilian men wear evening attire. After the reception, dancing will be held until midnight.

DEPARTURE

At some receptions the receiving line may form again at the end of the evening, and once again you go down the line. You thank your hosts as you shake hands, express pleasure for the evening, and say good-bye.

At a reception to meet a newcomer, the line is usually broken up after the first hour, but the hosts and guests of honor usually stay near the door, mingling with other guests. At a large affair, you do not look them up; at a small reception, you do. In the latter case, you thank them—and leave.

COCKTAIL PARTIES

Cocktail parties vary in size from a handful to many people. They are perhaps the easiest means of entertaining a large number of guests—who may arrive at any time within the customary two hours stated in the invitation.

The main difference between cocktail parties and receptions is that cocktail parties are informal, with no receiving line, and alcoholic drinks are always served. They are held during or near the close of daylight hours.

Cocktail parties are often given for a special guest or guests, or to introduce newcomers to the station or neighborhood. The guest (or guests) of honor stands near the hosts, in order to be introduced to other guests as they arrive.

The hosts stand near the door and greet their guests in an easy manner. If you are new to the area, your host or hostess should introduce you to someone nearby—but after this, you are on your own. You may talk with a stranger or friend, and stay as long as the invitation specifies.

A choice of drinks is offered at cocktail parties, with soft drinks available for nondrinkers. A host should never insist that a guest take a drink when it isn't wanted. The guest simply says "No, thank you," without explaining why the alcoholic drink is not wanted.

ARRIVAL AND DEPARTURE

Although cocktail parties never start or end at the time stated in the invitation, the guest who arrives toward the end of the closing hour cannot expect the party to go on and on. The hosts may have made other plans for the evening.

No party should be expected to last for more than 40 minutes after the closing time—unless the hosts want it to. The hosts may invite several guests to stay on for a late supper, but without such an invitation in advance, no guest should linger so long that he forces the hosts to invite him.

The best way to move the slow guest on his or her way is to close the bar. For the diehard, the host might say, "Sorry, but Jane and I are meeting the Dows in a few minutes"—or state whatever plans you have made.

The knotty problem of the guest who has had too much to drink but wants another may be handled by forgetting to bring him or her the drink. The barmen will be aware of a problem guest and will do what they can.

If this doesn't work, call on a friend to maneuver the unwise drinker into another room—or better, on his or her way—but not in the driver's seat of a car.

GENERAL WEAR—INFORMAL VS. CASUAL

There is many a mixup in what people wear to informal or casual social occasions. The *informal* afternoon reception, cocktail party, or dinner means coat and tie for men and afternoon dress for women—nothing fussy.

Casual on an invitation should mean simple but attractive sports attire. Cocktails on the patio, supper around the swimming pool (bring bathing trunks and suit), or a cookout in the backyard—this is when you hang up your uniform and don your comfortable civvies, probably slacks and sports shirt, skirt and blouse.

As host and hostess you must be careful how you extend your invitations. When you write or say *informal* when you mean casual, you will be at fault when your guests show up in coat and tie and find you dressed in jeans and sandals. Remember: *informal* means coat and tie, *casual* means sports attire.

FOOD

Cocktail food should be delicious, but a guest invited to a cocktail party other than cocktails-buffet should eventually move away from the table or tray of food. Roast ham, turkey, or beef, with hot and cold breads, seafood, elaborate dips, broiled olives wrapped in bacon, bite-size biscuits filled with hot mixtures, miniature meat balls on toothpicks—many of these may be served at a large party, and several are often served at small affairs.

Appetizers—called canapés, hors d'oeuvres, or finger-food—may be the only food at a small party. This could be toast or bread rounds topped with caviar or cream cheese, or any tasty food you can hold in your fingers.

Most cocktail food is eaten with the fingers, except that some food, such as shrimp or meatballs, is served on or with toothpicks. Food is not offered until after a guest has been served a drink. Napkins either are handed to guests or are on the buffet table.

SMALL PARTIES

Cocktail parties may be small affairs, for perhaps a dozen friends, with the host mixing and serving drinks from a tray placed at a convenient spot in the room. Cocktail food may be simple or lavish, with guests serving themselves or with waiters passing the food around the room. But at any party, be sure there are plenty of glasses of various sizes.

At the average party, a host should figure on two cocktails per person. Drinks are frequently served from a bar set up in a designated room, with a waiter in attendance. Guests are expected to order their choice. When you arrive, the host may say, "Won't you go over to the bar and have a drink?" A man will ask his date—or anyone he has brought—what she would like, then get both drinks. Do not set a damp or cold glass on a table without something underneath it.

Drinks may also be served on a tray by a waiter. If your host, or the waiter, should ask if you prefer a drink not offered, you may state your preference; otherwise do not request a drink not offered, other than nonalcoholic beverages. If you must request anything at a party—such as a glass of ginger ale or water—make your request to the waiter when there is one.

At small cocktail parties, the host usually acts as bartender. If he does not limit or state what he has to drink, you may ask, "What are you serving?" However, a host should first state what is on hand, and then ask each guest which he prefers. Some drinks, such as martinis and old-fashioneds, are mixed beforehand.

PAY-BACK PARTIES

The very large cocktail party is the way some people return a large number of social obligations. It is often necessary for those who have many cocktail obligations to return them at one big party. However, other than a cocktails-buffet party, where elaborate and substantial food is served, a cocktail party should not be a substitute for a formal dinner.

The pay-back cocktail party can be a way either to pay back numerous invitations or to ensure the hosts that they will remain on a continuous cocktail circuit—so almost anyone is invited. Such a party is usually crowded, and too often gives little more than was intended: a pay-back. A discriminating host may prefer to give several smaller parties rather than one blockbuster—even though doing so will cost more. Then, there will be a chance to talk with the guests and enjoy the evening.

ORGANIZED PARTIES

The organized group party for officers in a unit, division, wing, group, squadron, or department and their spouses or dates is a popular type of party.

A committee is appointed to make arrangements for the party, which is frequently held in the officers' club at a designated time.

Notices stating the proper dress and the estimated cost for each couple may be telephoned or posted.

Such parties are usually informal (with men in coat and tie), to allow those attending to become better acquainted. They may be of a more formal nature—say, an evening of cocktails, dinner, and dancing.

PROMOTION PARTIES

The promotion of an active duty officer to a higher rank calls for a celebration: a dinner or cocktail party, with toasts—or roasts.

The party may be large or small, formal or informal. It may be hosted by a member of the family, a friend, department coworkers or classmates, or the honoree. Guest include the CO.

In the naval service the occasion is called a "wetting down." But in any service or career the acme is the same: sharing one's success with family and friends.

COCKTAILS-BUFFET

A popular type of cocktail party is called *cocktails-buffet*. The time is usually 6:30 P.M.

The main purpose of the hosts in indicating *cocktails-buffet* on their invitation is to inform the guests that they need not make other plans for supper. As a guest, you are expected to partake of the buffet-style food, which is more elaborate than the usual cocktail fare. The table is covered with a cloth, and there will be a centerpiece of fruit or flowers. You can expect such food as roast beef, ham, seafood, and a number of hot dishes.

CHAPTER 6

Official Calls, Visits, & Personal Cards

IN TIMES OF WAR or national emergency, the social life in the services is relatively informal. Many social customs were held in abeyance during World War II and the later conflicts; some have been slow to come back, and others, owing to the changing times, may never return.

One of the customs that has changed is that of making social calls. Formerly, there was a rigid system of etiquette observed in making official and social calls. The system of official calls has been modified, but that of making and returning social calls is at the point of extinction.

There are problems involved in today's living that did not affect the services of the past. With little help in the modern household, there is far less time for social calls. There are many more officers serving at larger bases than ever before—thus more officers' families on whom to call. Mainly, there is the ever-growing number of women in the work force, and perhaps no one at home to receive guests.

The commanding officer of a large station cannot possibly take the time to receive and return all the calls that once were required. In order to extend hospitality to the officers in the command and members of their families, and to become better acquainted with them, the commanding officer will hold one or more receptions which are considered "calls made and paid." Usually, cards are not left.

OFFICIAL CALLS

A long-time custom that is modified but still carried out at many stations is that of the official call made by newly assigned officers on their commanding officer in his or her office ashore or aboard ship. The call lasts about ten minutes, unless the caller is requested to stay longer.

However, in the past few years such calls have become less common, especially in large stations or areas such as Washington, D.C., where great numbers of military personnel are stationed. Therefore, the newly assigned officer must find out what is expected of him upon arrival. Usually, an officer attached to the station will take the newcomer to the various offices and introduce him to fellow co-workers; later the newcomer will be introduced to the commanding officer at a staff meeting.

CALLS MADE AND PAID

It is a widespread custom for the senior officer (and his wife or her husband) to entertain at one or a series of receptions or at-homes, to which the officers in the activity and their spouses are invited. It is announced in advance that attendance serves as "All calls made and paid." The hours are usually 5:00 to 7:00 P.M.

At a large command, an aide stands near the entrance to the reception room and announces the name of each guest to the commanding officer, whose spouse stands at his or her side. A man gives the name of his lady to the aide, the last name only, "Mrs. Jones," or "Lieutenant Jones," if she is a servicewoman. The aide announces her, then he turns to the man, who says, "Captain Jones," or "Mr. Jones," if he is a civilian. The commanding officer and spouse greet and shake hands with each guest.

Staff officers and their spouses assist in greeting guests and in directing them to the punch bowls and food placed in the various rooms, or in a single room. Guests stay about 45 minutes. The line does not form again at the end of the reception, but if your host and hostess are nearby and are not busy with other guests, thank them and say good-bye.

VISITS

A brief visit at the quarters of a newly married couple or newcomers to the station means a welcome into the service community. It is the accepted custom all over the country to phone first and find out when it is convenient for you to stop by. When you stop in to see a new baby in the family, this shows a sincere interest in the family of a fellow officer.

Whenever time permits, it is desirable for midshipmen, cadets, ROTC students, and other young persons to pay a short visit to their senior officers and professors in the area. This gives them the opportunity to become better acquainted and more at ease with seniors.

Ask beforehand when it is convenient to call on a certain day, and stay only about 30 minutes, unless asked to stay on for a game of tennis or for supper.

CALLING PROCEDURES

Social calls are no longer a part of your everyday life. At any base or station where calls are still being made, you leave cards. At no time does any individual leave more than three cards.

CALLS ON FOREIGN STATIONS

The prevailing custom of official calls must be determined upon your arrival in a foreign country. The protocol officer of the American Embassy will provide guidance on the local requirements.

Officers on military and diplomatic assignment may be expected to call on officials within their own embassy and military activity, on officials of the host government, and on diplomatic representatives of other governments. In many countries, calls are greatly simplified.

When calls are expected, the following procedures may be helpful:

Upon the arrival of a new member of an embassy, such as a service attaché at a foreign capital, introductory calls are arranged by his predecessor and made promptly upon the civilian heads of foreign military establishments which correspond to the Secretary of Defense and/or the Secretaries of the Army, Navy, and Air Force. Calls are also made upon the military chiefs of these activities, and any other person, if according to local custom. These office calls are made in uniform, and usually cards are left.

The Chief of Mission (Ambassador or Minister) is the highest-ranking American on the diplomatic staff in a foreign embassy or legation. The attaché and his wife should call on the wife of the Chief of Mission at the Residence within 24 hours after their arrival. You should inquire of the protocol officer or his or her secretary whether the Chief of Mission's wife would like to receive you in person, or if you should leave cards instead. When received, you stay about 15 minutes.

Then you should call on the wife of the Counselor of Embassy, who will advise you concerning any necessary additional calls. Some foreign officers do not wish to be called upon at home, and this information can be determined in advance by asking the Secretary of Embassy.

It is customary in diplomatic circles for the new arrival to call first on those of equal rank and above; those of junior rank call first on the newcomer. Such calls should be made within one week of your arrival. All calls must be returned, first calls within a week.

In addressing high officials, you say "Mr. (or Madam) Ambassador" or "Mr. (or Madam) Minister," but his wife is "Mrs. Doe" and her husband is "Mr. Doe." If married, you refer to your spouse as "my wife" or "my husband," *not* as "Mrs. (or Mr.) Jones." And she or he refers to you as "my husband" or "my wife," or by your first name.

LEAVE-TAKING

When leaving a country, you may need to leave cards on the Ambassador or the Minister and the Economic Minister and their spouses. Then, "p.p.c." (*to take leave*) is written in pencil in the lower left-hand corner of the top card. Cards for Counselors, Army, Navy, and Air Attachés (and any others whom you wish to inform that you are leaving) may be mailed. Mailed cards also have "p.p.c." written on them.

When an officer and the officer's family are going on home leave, no cards need be left. When returning from home leave, single officers and spouses of officers should again leave cards and sign the book at the Residence. You write in pencil "returned from home leave" in the lower left-hand corner of the top card.

Should a Minister, Counselor, Army, Navy, or Air Attaché, or the officer's Section Chief, have arrived during your home leave, you leave cards on that person and his or her family.

Upon detachment, courtesy calls in the chain of command may be expected. When detached on short notice, cards marked "p.p.c." may be mailed when you do not have time to leave them.

However, customs have changed abroad as well as in the States. Your service or embassy protocol officer can advise you.

ATTACHÉ CARDS

On the cards of all officers attached to a diplomatic office, two sizes of lettering are used, with the larger for the name and the smaller for the title. Such officers sometimes have two sets of calling cards, one engraved in the language of their own country, the other engraved in the language of the country to which they are assigned. It is customary for such an officer serving in the Orient to have his name and title in the characters of the Oriental language on the back of his cards.

The cards illustrated here are for senior officers, junior officers, and staff corps attachés.

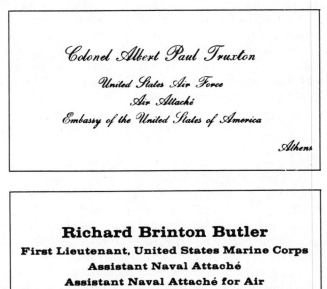

DESCRIPTION OF CARDS

Your name, rank, and service are engraved or printed in full on your personal cards, without abbreviations or initials, unless the

Commander Dan Murray Hill
Supply Corps, United States Navy
Assistant Naval Attaché
Embassy of the United States of America

Paris

initial is a part of your name—such as J. Paul Doe. Clear lettering is better than a heavy or unusual type, with shaded Roman and script widely used. Go to the best engraver and take his advice in the matter. Your service Exchange also will advise you.

Cards are white or a very light cream color. The lettering is always black. If cards are engraved the engraver will give you the engraving plate, and you can have additional cards made up at any time thereafter. However, you should order only the number that you anticipate using; when you advance in rank the old cards are not used.

Cards are printed or engraved on glazed or unglazed bristol board of medium weight. In the business world cards may be of thinner paper so as not to be bulky and to be more easily carried. Thermography, a form of raised printing, is extensively used in the military and in business, as it is much less expensive than engraving.

ENVELOPES

Matching envelopes should be ordered with the cards, since they have many uses. When the cards are for informal invitations, remember that postal regulations require the mailing envelopes to be at least 3½ by 5 inches. You may write only the name, "Miss Smith," on the envelope of the card and enclose it in a larger envelope for mailing.

"JUNIOR" AND OTHER DESIGNATIONS

When a man's name is the same as that of his living father he adds *Junior* written out in full—unless the line is too long, and *Junior* may then be written *Jr.* The Roman numeral II is used to identify a younger man who has the same name as the older living relative, such as a grandfather or uncle. Other numerals, III, IV, and so on, would be used accordingly.

It is correct to continue using such cards following the death of the senior. Later, it is optional to use the title at all.

MILITARY BUSINESS/PERSONAL CARDS

Today, men and women officers' military business cards, including an attaché's card, are the same size: 3¹/₂ by 2 inches. The necessary information may be placed on the card in one of several ways: your name and rank in the center of the card, the service designation underneath or in the lower right corner, phone number/address in the lower left corner.

[logo]

THOMAS P. MURPHY
Captain, USMC
Admissions Officer

Phone: 410-267-4361
Autovon: 281-4361   Candidate Guidance
Washington, D.C.: 261-2714   U.S. Naval Academy
Toll Free: 1-800-638-9156   Annapolis, Maryland 21402-5018

When more information is needed:

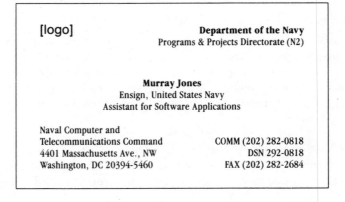

[logo]   **Department of the Navy**
Programs & Projects Directorate (N2)

Murray Jones
Ensign, United States Navy
Assistant for Software Applications

Naval Computer and
Telecommunications Command   COMM (202) 282-0818
4401 Massachusetts Ave., NW   DSN 292-0818
Washington, DC 20394-5460   FAX (202) 282-2684

FLAG AND GENERAL OFFICERS

A very senior officer or department head is entitled to place his or her rank and surname only in the center of the card, with the service designation in the lower right-hand corner. Ranks are inclusive of rear admiral through admiral in the Navy and Coast Guard, and brigadier general through general in the Army, Air Force, and Marines.

The officer may prefer to use his or her full name for complete identification:

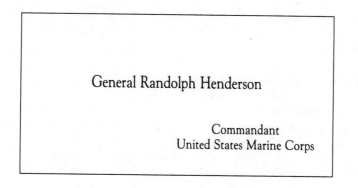

SENIOR AND FIELD GRADE OFFICERS

The titles of senior officers from commander through captain in the Navy and Coast Guard, and major through colonel in the Army, Air Force, and Marines, precede their full name in the center of the card. The service designation is usually in the lower right corner of the card but occasionally is placed under the name.

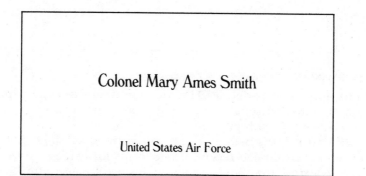

When providing more information, the card is a little larger.

Mary Ames Smith, Ph.D.

Professor	Colonel
Department of Computer Science	United States Military Academy
	West Point, New York 10996

JUNIOR AND COMPANY GRADE OFFICERS

Full names of junior and company grade officers, and of personnel below the rank of warrant officer, are placed in the center of the card, with rank and service in the lower right-hand corner. In the Coast Guard and Navy, junior rank includes lieutenant commander; in the Army, Air Force, and Marine Corps, company grade is inclusive of captain.

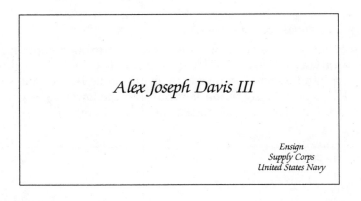

MIDSHIPMEN AND CADETS

A midshipman or cadet, ROTC or any other student, is not required to have personal cards, but may want them for various occasions, for use with gifts, and for brief notes.

Several months before graduation at the academies, first class cadets and midshipmen receive order forms for cards to fill in with their prospective rank and branch of service for use after graduation. As with junior officers' cards, the name is centered on the card, with title and service in the lower right corner.

William Paul Orr III

Cadet
United States Military Academy

RETIRED OFFICERS

A retired officer's card is the same as that for an officer of comparable grade on active duty, except that the word *Retired* is added on a line below the service affiliation. The word *Retired* is not abbreviated or placed within brackets or parentheses.

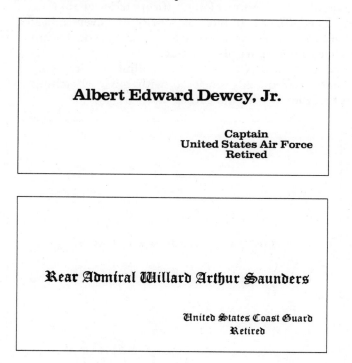

Albert Edward Dewey, Jr.

Captain
United States Air Force
Retired

Rear Admiral Willard Arthur Saunders

United States Coast Guard
Retired

RESERVE OFFICERS

The card of an active duty reserve officer is the same as that for the active duty officer, except that the word *Reserve* is placed at the end of the service affiliation.

JOINT CARDS

A senior flag or general officer's joint card for married couples may have only the rank and surname in the center of the card; a brigadier general or rear admiral and officers of lower rank use their full names. The officer's branch of service is never indicated on the card, and the retired or active status is not used. An initial is used when a customary part of the name.

The joint card is useful for extending and replying to invitations, and is frequently enclosed with gifts. Matching envelopes should be ordered with the cards.

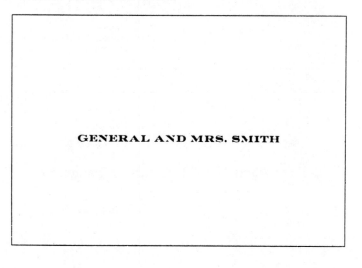

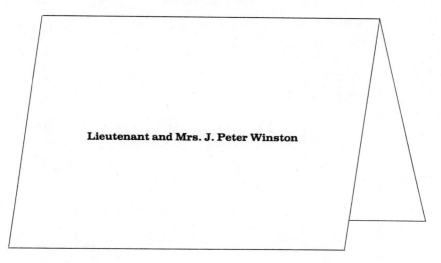

Lieutenant and Mrs. J. Peter Winston

VARIATIONS

On a joint card, a military woman or businesswoman may forgo her title: "Major and Mrs. John Doe" or "Senator and Mrs. John Doe" or "Mr. and Mrs. John Doe." (Her military or professional card could read: "Major Jane Doe" or "Jane Doe, R.N.")

When husband and wife are in the same service, both titles are used: "Major John and Lieutenant Jane Doe." When their rank is the same in the same service they are: "Majors John and Jane Doe."

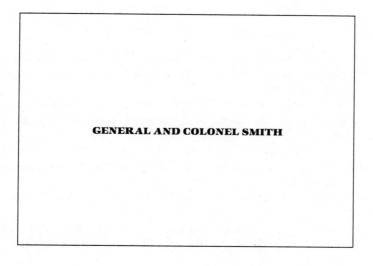

GENERAL AND COLONEL SMITH

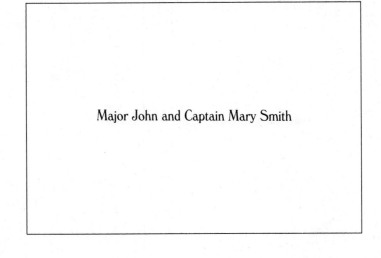

Major John and Captain Mary Smith

But when each is in a different service, or when one is a noncom, a commissioned officer, or a civilian, one may forgo his or her title and accept that of the spouse: "Sergeant and Mrs. John Doe" or "Doctor and Mrs. John Doe" or "Doctor John and Major Jane Doe."

When the military wife has retained her maiden name upon marriage, or when one or the other is noncommissioned and there is no compromise in forgoing one's title, it is recommended that personal/official, rather than joint, cards be used.

NONMILITARY CARDS

The personal/business cards for professional men and women are the same size as those for the military officer: the purpose is to give necessary information.

The title, administrative position, address, and telephone number (optional) are on the cards, and whenever possible titles are not abbreviated.

In the past, social calls dictated the sizes of calling cards for men and women. The *woman's* card is 3 to 3½ inches long and 2¼ to 2½ inches high.

A *man's* card is narrower: 3 to 3¼ inches long and 1¼ to 1⅝ inches high.

A *widow* does not change her card after her husband's death. A wife takes her husband's name for life—or until a divorce or

A married woman's or widow's card

remarriage. She is "Mrs. James Doe," *not* "Mrs. Jane Doe"—unless she prefers to use her first name.

A *divorcee's* card customarily has her maiden name before her former husband's last name: "Mrs. Smith Doe." When she legally takes back her maiden name she is "Miss Jane Smith." When she has children she usually retains her status: "Mrs. Jane Doe," "Mrs. Smith Doe," or "Mrs. Jane Smith Doe."

INFORMALS

The fold-over cards, known as *informals,* are widely used for informal invitations and brief notes, but they are *not* used for personal cards. The name is engraved, thermographed, or printed on the outside, or a monogram may be placed in the upper left-hand corner of the card. The message or invitation is written on the inside. Cards are about 3 by 4¼ inches in size.

Another style of informal is a single flat card about 3½ by 4½ inches in size. The address is engraved above and to the right of the name, with the name engraved in the center or near the top center of the card. Matching envelopes come with the cards.

ABBREVIATIONS ON CARDS

There are a number of conventional abbreviations on calling cards. Although they are rarely used in this country, you should be aware of their meaning. Such abbreviations are penciled in the lower left corner of the card.

p.p.c. (*Pour prendre congé*)—*To take leave.* This indicates that one is leaving the station or country.

p.c. (*Pour condoléance*)—*To extend sympathy.*

p.f. (*Pour féliciter*)—*To congratulate.*

p.p. (*Pour presenter*)—*To introduce.* This means that the friend who left the card is introducing a stranger to whom the receiver should send cards, phone, or call on. The stranger's name is written on the card.

p.r. (*Pour remercier*)—*To thank;* to reply to a "p.f." card.

n.b. (*Nota bene*)—*"Note well."* This calls attention to any words or messages written on the card.

R.s.v.p. or R.S.V.P. (*Répondez s'il vous plaît*)—*Please reply.* These initials are customarily written on invitations when an answer is requested.

SECTION III

Easy Conversation

CHAPTER 7

Introductions & Farewells

IT IS FORTUNATE that the mechanics of making introductions are simple and natural, because you probably will be introducing people to each other for the rest of your life. The simplest form of introduction is illustrated by a young child who introduces a hero-worshiped older child by announcing, "Mommy, this is Johnny!"

Brevity and accuracy are the two requirements that must be kept in mind when introducing people. Be sure of not only what you are going to say but how you say it.

INTRODUCTIONS

When making introductions, state all names clearly and correctly. You must know instantly whose name is given first. There are a few rules to remember:

A man is always presented *to* a woman—with the exception of the president of any country, a king, or a dignitary of the church, or when a junior woman officer is officially presented to a senior male officer.

The honored or higher-ranking person's name, or the woman's name, is stated first, then the name of the person being presented.

Young people are presented *to* older people of the same sex.
A single person is introduced *to* a group.

Consider the following examples:

"Mr. President, may I present Mrs. Jones?" or "Mrs. Jones, may I
  present Admiral Smith?" or "May I present Admiral Smith
  . . . Mrs. Jones."
"General Smith, may I present Lieutenant White . . . she is an
  Army nurse."
"General Smith, may I present Colonel Jones?"
"Mrs. Jones, this is my daughter Ann," or "Mrs. Jones, Miss
  White."
"Miss White (or This is Miss White)—Ensign Fields, Miss Lewis,
  Midshipman Brown, Miss Smith, Cadet Long," and so on. In
  this case, when you wish to indicate individuals in the services,
  junior rank is stated.

SERVICE INTRODUCTIONS

Commissioned and noncommissioned officers in all services, male
and female, are introduced and addressed by rank or rating.

Cadets and midshipmen at the service and maritime academies
and ROTC units are introduced and addressed as "Cadet John Doe"
or "Midshipman Mary Smith." Upon occasion they may be addressed thereafter as "Mr." or "Miss."

A sergeant in the Marines, Air Force, or Army is introduced
and addressed as "Sergeant Doe," or if he or she has the rating
"Master Sergeant," then with that rating.

A chaplain is introduced by rank in the Navy, and as "Chaplain" in the Army and Air Force. Doctors and nurses are introduced
by rank in all services, with the words *doctor* and *nurse* used in relation
to patient care situations.

When necessary, such as when introducing a speaker, you say,
for example: "Chaplain John Doe, a colonel in the Air Force, is
command chaplain at the Air Force Academy," or "Colonel John
Doe is a surgeon at Walter Reed Medical Center."

However, since their titles are distinguished, it is not improper
to call them Doctor Doe or Chaplain Doe.

WHAT TO SAY

The easiest way to make introductions is simply to state the names of the two persons concerned: "Miss White, Mr. Jones," or "Commander Brown, Mr. Smith." The phrase, "May I present" is more formal, but it is always correct to say "Miss White, may I present Mr. Jones?" You may then add, "Jack will be a plebe next year."

Midshipmen and cadets may introduce fellow classmates in this manner: "Mary, this is my roommate, John Jones—Miss White." If the friendships are less intimate, the introduction may be "Miss White, Mr. Jones." When you introduce your sister or your best girlfriend (or your fiancée) to your roommate who knows her name well, you may say, "Mary, this is John Jones." However, this form is reserved for close friends.

Although it is proper to use first names in introductions, it is important that those being introduced be contemporaries or on equal footing. When a very close friend or relative is introduced to a stranger, the last name must be worked into the introduction: "Mary, may I present Midshipman John Jones . . ."; then, turning to Midshipman Jones, you add, "—Miss White." Otherwise he will have no idea who "Mary" is.

You should be careful about making personal comments when introducing people. Biographical data or human interest stories that are too long may cause unease rather than establish a topic of conversation, as they were intended to do. However, a brief comment can be very helpful in breaking the ice between strangers, and may lead to a lasting friendship: "Mrs. Wilson, may I present Mrs. Smith? Her husband, as you know, served with General Wilson at Iwo Jima."

INTRODUCTIONS IN GROUPS

Introductions made in groups must be handled efficiently, with the person or persons presented *to* the group. It is impossible to introduce everyone at a large function, but do introduce all guests at gatherings of a dozen or so. A host or hostess introduces a guest into a small group upon his or her arrival, and to others later, when convenient. Otherwise, after the first introduction, guests are on their own.

To introduce a latecomer to a small group, the easiest way is to announce to all present, "This is Jane Brown." Then the names of those present are stated in rotation around the room as they stand or sit. Should part of the group be actively engaged in a game or conversation at the time, introductions are made only to those in closest proximity to you and the latecomer.

FAMILY INTRODUCTIONS

When introducing a member of your family, usually you omit the last name of the person you are introducing. A midshipman or cadet may say, "Mother, this is my roommate James Smith." If your mother has remarried, you would say, "Mother, this is my roommate James Smith"; then, turning to Midshipman (or Cadet) Smith, you would say, "—Mrs. Northrop."

When the person to whom you wish to introduce your relative seems uncertain of *your* name, then add the last name of your relative. For example: "Colonel Wilson, this is Roger Doe, my brother." After the customary courtesies are exchanged, you might add: "Colonel Wilson is my group air officer, Roger. Sir, my brother is going to Exeter and hopes to be a plebe next year."

SPOUSES

A married man refers to his wife as "my wife" to people who do not know her, and by her first name to people who do. Introduce your wife in this manner: "Mrs. Smith, may I present my wife?" If you want to encourage the friendship, you may add your wife's first name: "Mrs. Smith, may I present my wife, Ruth?"

A man introduces his wife to a man in this manner: "Ruth, this is Captain Jones . . .—my wife." *Never* refer to your wife as "Mrs." at a social occasion, except when you are going through a receiving line, when you present your wife as "Mrs. Brown." When speaking with very junior officers, enlisted personnel, and tradespeople, however, you do refer to your wife as "Mrs."

When a woman introduces her husband, she says, "Mrs. Smith, this is my husband." She refers to him as "my husband"—not as "Mr." or "the lieutenant." She only refers to him as "Mr. Brown" with tradespeople, etc.

When introducing or referring to your wife, *never* use humorous forms such as "Jim, I want you to meet the missus," or "Meet the greatest little wife in the world."

OTHER RELATIONS

A stepparent may be introduced as "My stepfather, Mr. White," but the relationship need not be mentioned unless you care to.

Half-brothers or -sisters are usually introduced as brothers and sisters, even though their last name is different from your own. You must give their names, however, when they are different from your own: "Mary, this is Cadet Smith—my sister, Miss White." Relatives such as cousins and uncles are so designated at the end of the introduction rather than in the body of the introduction.

IN-LAWS

When introducing your mother- or father-in-law, you may say "my mother-in-law" or "my father-in-law." Or say, "Mother (or whatever she is called), may I present Lieutenant John Smith?" Then, turning to Lieutenant Smith, you add, "Mrs. Woods is Mary's (or John's) mother."

FORMER IN-LAWS

Members of a family who have kept a warm relationship with former in-laws following a divorce or death are sometimes puzzled about the best way to introduce them.

A former father-in-law could say, "I want you to know Jane Doe, who was my son's wife and is now married to John Doe." If she was a widow who has remarried he would say, " . . . who is my son's widow and is now married to John Doe." She would introduce you as "Colonel Smith, my first husband's father." In-laws, past or present, should be friends.

LIVE-INS

When an unmarried couple are living together, the best way to introduce them is simply, "This is Jane Doe and John Smith." If they are newcomers, your might add, "They are living in Georgetown." You do not need to explain their relationship—this is their privilege.

When writing to them, you address them as Miss Jane Doe and Mr. John Smith. A business letter would be to Miss (or Ms.) Doe and Mr. Smith.

FORGOTTEN INTRODUCTIONS

When you are presented to someone you have met previously but who apparently has forgotten that introduction, you may say, "I believe that I met Miss Lewis at the ring dance last year," or make other reference to the place of introduction. But do not blurt out, "Oh, I've met Miss Lewis—don't you remember?" It is obvious that she does not remember, and such a remark only causes embarrassment.

The fact that a junior officer, midshipman, or cadet is not remembered by a senior officer does not imply that the junior did not make a good impression. A senior officer meets many people at many places, and the person who "never forgets a name or face" is a rarity. Introductions made at large social functions, or made long ago, are easily forgotten.

When someone momentarily forgets your name when introducing you, help him out by giving your name, "John Jones." This momentary lapse of memory sometimes happens even to your best friends, and, in reverse, to you. When someone seems to have forgotten you, you may say, "How do you do, Mrs. Smith? I'm John Jones. We met at the station Christmas party."

If a person deliberately appears to forget you were introduced previously, you should not mention having met before. But don't be too quick to take offense at a forgotten introduction. Some people are just naturally forgetful.

When a person joins a group and his last name is unknown— or you have forgotten it—it is best to say, "I'm sorry, but I have momentarily forgotten your last name," before attempting introductions.

ACKNOWLEDGMENTS

The customary answer to an introduction for both persons concerned is, "How do you do?" You may add, "So nice to see you." If you want to be certain that you understand the name correctly, say "How do you do, Mr. Smith?" Mr. Smith is *not* expected to answer, "I'm fine, how are you?"

It is good training to listen carefully when introductions are made so that it will not be necessary to have the name repeated. To acknowledge an introduction with a flip remark or with an attitude of indifference is not only improper but insulting. Introductions should always be treated with the respect they deserve; they constitute first impressions, and first impressions should be good ones.

Young people frequently say "Hello" to each other following an introduction. Although the expression "How are you?" is frowned on, it is correct and is used in certain sections of the country. The temptation is to answer the query, which makes for an awkward situation.

Some people acknowledge an introduction by saying, "It is nice to know you," which phrase the other may repeat, or merely say, "Thank you."

Always avoid such acknowledgments as "I am pleased to make your acquaintance," or "Pleased to meet you." But a hostess will cordially greet a guest's friend who is a stranger by saying, "I am so pleased you could come." And when you are introduced to someone who is an intimate friend of a friend of yours, you will probably say that you are pleased to know him!

Never use such trite phrases as "Cadet Jones, shake hands with Jim Brown," or " . . . I want you to make the acquaintance of . . . ." Embellishments on introductions can be confusing; it is best to keep introductions as simple and as direct as possible.

SELF-INTRODUCTIONS

Self-introductions are sometimes necessary, but treat them with care. Too often, the self-introduction has been used by presumptuous persons, with the result that others are wary of the custom.

There are occasions when self-introductions are necessary. For instance, when you are a stranger at a large reception or cocktail party and the host and hostess are busy elsewhere and cannot introduce you into a group—then introduce yourself. A man may shake hands with each man near him and with any woman who offers her hand first. A single woman introduces herself.

It is preferable for a lady to speak first to a gentleman. If she doesn't, he should talk about something impersonal—the decor of the room or a floral arrangement or even the weather—and then introduce himself.

When you introduce yourself at a social or nonofficial occasion, *do not use your rank or title*. Say, "My name is John (or Jane) Jones," or "I am John Jones." When your name is mispronounced and it seems advisable to correct it, say "Excuse me, my name is Jones (or John Jones)." Do not say "Lieutenant Jones" or "Mr. Jones."

When telephoning a senior, say "Colonel Brown, this is John Jones." When the call is official, state your rank or title. A woman would say to the colonel's wife, "Mrs. Brown, this is Mary Jones. My husband is Lieutenant John Jones, who is serving under Colonel Brown. . . ."

At an occasion when a junior officer is not in uniform but wishes to identify himself to a senior officer, he might say something like this: "Colonel, I'm Lieutenant Hawkins. I was the forward observer in your battalion in the Alaskan maneuver. . . ."

THE MALE OFFICER

When introduced to a man or woman, a seated man rises. He shakes hands with another man when being introduced but usually waits for a woman to extend her hand first. There is no set rule for this. If he extends his hand first, it is no breach of etiquette, since he is showing friendliness. However, he will probably feel more comfortable if he remembers to wait.

When at an inconvenient distance from a person to whom you are being introduced, you may nod or bow slightly. At a crowded table in a restaurant, you may half-rise when a person stops at your table and introductions are made. But if you are the one *making* the introductions, stand.

Outdoors, in uniform, the hand salute may be given when you are introduced to a man or a woman. In the naval services you do not remove your cap; in the other services, you may salute or remove your cap. In civilian dress, you remove your hat and leave it off, weather permitting. Should you be the only man in uniform in a mixed group, you may feel more comfortable by deferring to civilian practice, and accordingly remove your hat when introduced to a woman.

Usually, you do not lift your hat to men when women are not present. It is awkward to lift your hat and then shake hands. But if you are presented to a dignitary or very high-ranking man outdoors when in civilian dress, as a matter of courtesy remove your hat with your left hand before shaking hands.

In Europe, a man shakes hands with anyone presented to him. The gallant old custom of kissing the hand of a Continental woman is not expected of American men visiting in a country where this custom prevails—or when the woman is visiting here.

THE FEMALE OFFICER

On duty or at an *official* occasion, when you are introduced to a senior officer, male or female, you stand. Thereafter you do not rise every time the senior enters or leaves the room—but you do upon the senior's departure when nearby.

You also stand upon being introduced to a dignitary or senior civilian, man or woman.

Socially, the junior woman officer does not stand when introduced to a contemporary woman officer.

If, at an informal occasion, you are introduced to the wife of your commanding officer and she is your own age, you stand in order to show respect to your CO. Common sense will dictate what to do in a group of contemporaries when the CO's wife is also a contemporary, but it will be pointed to do the opposite of what the others in the group do.

Since the junior woman officer stands to greet her female commanding officer, she remains standing to be introduced to her CO's husband, civilian or military.

At nonmilitary functions and in everyday living, men prefer that you do not stand for introductions.

NONMILITARY WOMEN

A woman does not rise when introduced to another woman of about her own age, but she stands when introduced to an elderly woman or the wife of a senior official. She remains standing until that person is seated. A woman shakes hands with another woman, when convenient. But the younger or junior woman usually waits for the senior to offer her hand.

A woman does not rise when introduced to a man—unless he is the president, a king, or a dignitary of the church, or when she is a junior woman officer being introduced to a senior officer. When a young woman is in the presence of a very high-ranking officer or dignitary, she stands. A woman extends her hand first to a man of *any* age or rank except to heads of state or members of royal families. Children and teenagers should stand when introduced to an adult.

THE PRESIDENT OF THE UNITED STATES

If you have the good fortune to present someone to the President of the United States, stand straight, look directly at the President, and say, "Mr. President, may I present Admiral Brown?"

If you—a man or a woman—are the person being presented, you wait for the President to offer his hand, then you shake hands.

If called upon to make a formal presentation of the President at a banquet, you give his full title: "Ladies and gentlemen—the President of the United States." In conversation, you address him as "Mr. President."

The Vice President is addressed and introduced in the same way as the President. The wives of presidents and vice-presidents are introduced and addressed as "Mrs." When introduced and when in conversation, a former president is called "Mr. Doe." Although he is never so called while in office, a former president is given the courtesy title of "The Honorable."

FAREWELLS

After an introduction, the first person to move away might say, "I hope I see you again soon." The other person will probably answer "Thank you," and may wish to add a comment such as "I hope so, too."

In taking leave of a group of strangers, it makes very little difference whether a person has been introduced all around or merely included in certain conversations. The most courteous action is to nod good-bye to anyone who happens to be looking at you. No attempt should be made to attract the attention of those who are apparently unaware that you are leaving. When saying good-bye (or good night) to an acquaintance, you may say, "Good-bye, it was so nice to see you," or "I hope we meet again soon."

It is impossible to say good-bye to all guests at a large party, but you can do so to those with whom you were most recently talking. You say good-bye to all guests at a very small party, such as a dinner, and you *always* say good-bye to your host and hostess.

When saying good-bye, both men and women stand. A hostess rises to her feet when she sees that a guest is ready to leave. A woman guest of honor, or a ranking guest, makes the first move to leave, and that person's spouse or escort, if seated, immediately rises. The hostess and host shake hands with their guests on departure, just as they did on arrival.

A departing guest should make some appreciative comment to the hostess, then to the host: "It's been a very pleasant evening. Thank you so much." The hostess might answer, "Good night. I'm so glad you could be with us."

At a formal dinner, the hostess remains standing inside the living room when saying good-bye to guests, and the host walks to the door of the living room or into the hall with a high-ranking guest. The high-ranking guest is always the first to leave. In very senior quarters, an MS (mess specialist), airman, or Army aide (or a butler in a civilian home) opens the door for guests and says, "Good night, Sir (or Madam)." A guest answers, "Thank you. Good night."

At informal parties, or when the host lives in the country, the host may walk the guests to their cars—and always makes certain that everyone has a way home.

CHAPTER 8

Service & Civilian Forms of Address

WRITTEN AND SPOKEN ADDRESSES AND INTRODUCTIONS: ARMY, AIR FORCE, AND MARINE CORPS

Although the Marine Corps is an integral part of the Navy, the ranks are similar to those of the Army and Air Force and therefore are included with these services. In written correspondence, both official and social, full rank and ratings precede the name and are written out. In conversation, all generals are *General*; all colonels are *Colonel*; and all privates and sergeants are *Private* and *Sergeant*.

Written Address	*Spoken Address and Introductions*
Official:	
Brigadier General John Doe, U.S. Army	General Doe
Commandant of Cadets	*Or formal:*
United States Military Academy	Brigadier General John Doe,
West Point, New York	the Commandant of Cadets at
(with zip code, West Point, NY)	the United States Military
	Academy
Social:	
Brigadier General and Mrs. John Doe	General and Mrs. Doe
Quarters 101	
United States Military Academy	
West Point	
New York	

Written Address	*Spoken Address and Introductions*

Official:

Lieutenant Colonel John Doe, U.S. Air Force
335th Bomber Squadron
Langley Air Force Base
Virginia

Colonel Doe
Or formal:
Lieutenant Colonel Doe, of
the 335th Bomber Squadron

Social:

Lieutenant Colonel and Mrs. John Doe
Quarters M
Langley Air Force Base, Virginia

Colonel and Mrs. Doe

Official:

First Lieutenant John Doe, U.S. Marine Corps
Marine Corps Base
Camp Lejeune, North Carolina

Lieutenant Doe
Or formal:
First Lieutenant Doe, of the
Marine Corps Base, etc. (In
the Army, first and second
lieutenant are designated
"Lieutenant.")

Social:

First Lieutenant and Mrs. John Doe
1073 East Peleliu Drive
Tarawa Terrace 1
Camp Lejeune
North Carolina

Lieutenant and Mrs. Doe

Official:

Chaplain John E. Doe, U.S. Air Force
Office of the Command Chaplain
United States Air Force Academy
Colorado

Chaplain Doe
Or formal:
Chaplain Doe, a colonel in
the Air Force, is Command
Chaplain at the Air Force
Academy

Social:

Colonel and Mrs. John E. Doe
Chaplain's Quarters
United States Air Force Academy
Colorado

Informally:
Chaplain Doe

Written Address	*Spoken Address and Introductions*
Official: Cadet John (or Jane) Doe Company C, Corps of Cadets United States Military Academy West Point, New York	Cadet Doe
Social: Cadet Paul (or Jane) Doe Room 3A20, Vandenberg Hall United States Air Force Academy Colorado	Cadet Doe
Official or Social: Sergeant Major Mary Doe United States Marine Corps Marine Corps Air Station Cherry Point North Carolina	Sergeant Major Doe (The spoken address for first sergeants is "First Sergeant" and for other sergeants "Sergeant." A corporal is addressed "Corporal.")

WRITTEN AND SPOKEN ADDRESSES AND INTRODUCTIONS: NAVAL SERVICES

Full rank *precedes* the name of commissioned officers; customarily, rank may be abbreviated in official correspondence but is *written out* in social correspondence. Likewise, the names of the services are often abbreviated in official correspondence but are written out in business or social correspondence. The rank also precedes the names of warrant officers, midshipmen, Coast Guard cadets, and Merchant Marine cadet/midshipmen. When in civilian dress, a captain and a lieutenant are introduced as *of the Navy* to distinguish the rank from the Army, Marine Corps, and Air Force. In conversation, all admirals are *Admiral*. Chaplains are introduced and addressed by rank; informally, they can be called "Chaplain," "Rabbi," or "Father."

Written Address	*Spoken Address and Introductions*
Official: Rear Admiral John Jones, U.S. Navy Superintendent United States Naval Academy Annapolis, Maryland	Admiral Jones *Or formal:* Rear Admiral John Jones, Superintendent of the United States Naval Academy

Written Address	*Spoken Address and Introductions*

Social:

Rear Admiral and Mrs. John Jones
Superintendent's House
United States Naval Academy
Annapolis
Maryland

Admiral and Mrs. Jones

Official:

Lieutenant Commander John Jones, U.S. Navy
Gunnery Officer
USS *Los Angeles*
Fleet Post Office
San Francisco, California

Lieutenant Commander Jones

Social:

Lieutenant Commander and Mrs. John Jones
7100 Atherton Drive
Long Beach
California

Lieutenant Commander and
Mrs. Jones

Official:

Chief Warrant Officer John (or Jane) Jones,
   U.S. Coast Guard
USCGC *Eastwind*
Fleet Post Office
New York, New York

Chief Warrant Officer Jones

Social:

Chief Warrant Officer and Mrs. John Jones
1125 Ocean Drive
New London
Connecticut

Chief Warrant Officer and
Mrs. Jones

Official or Social:

Midshipman John (or Jane) Jones, U.S. Navy
Room 3654, Bancroft Hall
United States Naval Academy
Annapolis, Maryland

Midshipman Jones

Written Address	*Spoken Address and Introductions*

Official / Formal:
(Senior woman officer and husband)
Colonel Mary Doe, U.S. Air Force
  and Major John Doe, U.S. Air Force
Commander, 6940th Security Wing (her office)
Goodfellow Air Force Base
Texas

Colonel Doe and Major Doe

Social / Informal:
Major and Mrs. John Doe
Quarters Nine
Goodfellow Air Force Base Texas

Major and Mrs. Doe
or
Major and Colonel Doe

Note: On less formal and official addresses, the abbreviations USN, USMC, USA, etc., may be used. With these addresses, however, the rank is also abbreviated; thus, for example, LCdr. John Jones, Jr., USN, FPO San Francisco, with no state preceding the zip for overseas addresses. Today, *lieutenant commander* is often abbreviated *LCDR,* and the rank of *lieutenant colonel as LtCol* in the Marine Corps and Air Force and *LTC* in the Army.

    When the personal name and service designation are both long, *United States* (of America) is abbreviated USA.

    Women and men students at the service and maritime academies are *midshipmen* and *cadets;* these are grades of rank, not titles.

    The social address for a midshipman or cadet need not include the service after the name; for example, Midshipman John Jones, Room 3654, Bancroft Hall, United States Naval Academy, Annapolis, Maryland. A personal or business letter would abbreviate the academy: U.S. Naval Academy, or, locally, USNA, Annapolis, Md.

    Each service has its own regulations concerning correspondence, frequently in the form of memorandums, and abbreviations such as these may be used in addressing an envelope:

CH, MajGen, John Doe
HQ USAF/HC
Washington, D.C.

    While zip codes are not included in this chapter, they are used on all envelopes in all types of correspondence.

SERVICE ABBREVIATIONS

In official correspondence, rank and ratings are abbreviated and fully capitalized in the Army, Navy, and Coast Guard; they are partially capitalized in the Air Force and Marine Corps. The abbreviations for the relative ranks of commissioned officers of the U.S. armed forces, and for each branch of service, are given below, as published by the Uniformed Services Almanac, Inc./P.O. Box 4144/Falls Church, VA 22044/(703) 532-1631.

Navy and Coast Guard

Fleet Admiral (Navy only)	FADM
Admiral	ADM
Vice Admiral	VADM
Rear Admiral, upper half*	RADM
Rear Admiral, lower half**	RADM
Captain	CAPT
Commander	CDR
Lieutenant Commander	LCDR
Lieutenant	LT
Lieutenant, junior grade	LTJG
Ensign	ENS

Marine Corps

General	Gen
Lieutenant General	LtGen
Major General	MajGen
Brigadier General	BGen
Colonel	Col
Lieutenant Colonel	LtCol
Major	Maj
Captain	Capt
First Lieutenant	1stLt
Second Lieutenant	2ndLt

Warrant Officers—All Services Except Air Force

Chief Warrant Officer (CW5)	CWO
Chief Warrant Officer (CW4)	CWO
Chief Warrant Officer (CW3)	CWO
Chief Warrant Officer (CW2)	CWO
Warrant Officer (W01)	WO

Sergeants—Air Force

Chief Master Sergeant (E-9)	CMSgt
Senior Master Sergeant (E-8)	SMSgt
Master Sergeant (E-7)	MSgt
Technical Sergeant (E-6)	TSgt
Staff Sergeant	SSgt

*One wide and one narrow stripe on sleeve.
**One wide stripe.

Army

General of the Army	(No abbr.)
General	GEN
Lieutenant General	LTG
Major General	MG
Brigadier General	BG
Colonel	COL
Lieutenant Colonel	LTC
Major	MAJ
Captain	CPT
First Lieutenant	1LT
Second Lieutenant	2LT

Air Force

General of the Air Force	(No abbr.)
General	Gen
Lieutenant General	Lt Gen
Major General	Maj Gen
Brigadier General	Brig Gen
Colonel	Col
Lieutenant Colonel	Lt Col
Major	Maj
Captain	Capt
First Lieutenant	1Lt
Second Lieutenant	2Lt

Branch of Service

United States Army	USA
United States Navy	USN
United States Marine Corps	USMC
United States Coast Guard	USCG
United States Air Force	USAF
United States Merchant Marine	USMM
United States Maritime Service	USMS
National Guard	NG

Reserve Officers

Reserve officers of all the services add the letter *R* after the branch; for example, USAR, USCGR.

Reserve and National Guard officers use their titles only when on active duty.

NOTE: For the insignia of rank of all commissioned and warrant officers, see pages 52 and 53.

WRITTEN AND SPOKEN ADDRESSES AND INTRODUCTIONS: FEDERAL, STATE, AND LOCAL DIGNITARIES

The Honorable is the preferred form for addressing most American officials in office or retired; it is always written out in full on the line above and aligned with the name. The phrase is always used with the full name, and *never* with any other title; thus, *the Honorable Admiral Jones* and *the Honorable Mr. Jones* are both inappropriate. In the salutation of a letter to the President, you would write, officially or in business, *Dear Mr. President,* and, socially, *My Dear Mr. President.* In the close of the letter you would write, officially and in business, *Respectfully yours,* and, socially, *Very respectfully.* In writing to all other American officials, the official or business closing is *Very truly yours,* and, socially, *Sincerely yours.* Wives of American officials without titles of their own are addressed and introduced as *Mrs. Jones.* In the following list, the *official* form precedes the *social* form. When only one is given, it is appropriate for both occasions.

Written Address	Spoken Address	Introductions
THE PRESIDENT		
The President	Mr. President	The President
The White House		*Or formal:*
Washington		The President of the
District of Columbia*		United States
		Abroad, add:
		. . . of America
Social:		
The President		
and Mrs. Doe		
The White House		
Washington, D.C.		
THE PRESIDENT'S WIFE		
Mrs. John Doe	Mrs. Doe	Mrs. Doe
The White House		
Washington, D.C.		
THE VICE PRESIDENT		
The Vice President	Mr. Vice President	The Vice President
United States Senate	or	*Or formal:*
Washington, D.C.	Mr. Doe**	The Vice President
		of the United States
		Abroad, add:
		. . . of America

*Formally written *District of Columbia,* although the abbreviation *D.C.* is generally used, as in the remainder of this chapter.
**In continued conversation, *Mr. Doe* is used.

Written Address	*Spoken Address*	*Introductions*

Social:

The Vice President and
   Mrs. Doe
(home address)

THE VICE PRESIDENT'S WIFE

Mrs. James Doe (home address)	Mrs. Doe	Mrs. Doe

CHIEF JUSTICE OF THE SUPREME COURT

The Chief Justice of the Supreme Court Washington, D.C.	Mr. Chief Justice or Mr. Doe	The Chief Justice *Or formal:* The Honorable John Doe, Chief Justice of the Supreme Court of the United States *Abroad, add:* . . . of America

Social:

The Chief Justice
   and Mrs. Doe
(home address)

ASSOCIATE JUSTICE

Mr. Justice Doe The Supreme Court Washington, D.C.	Mr. Justice Doe or Mr. Doe	Mr. Justice Doe *Or formal:* The Honorable John Doe, Associate Justice of the Supreme Court of the United States *Abroad, add:* . . . of America

Social:

Mr. Justice Doe
   and Mrs. Doe
(home address)

Written Address	Spoken Address	Introductions

CABINET OFFICER* (man)

The Honorable John Doe Secretary of State Washington, D.C.	Mr. Secretary or Mr. Doe	The Secretary of State, Mr. Doe *Or formal:* The Honorable John Doe, Secretary of State

Social:

The Secretary of State
   and Mrs. Doe
(home address)

CABINET OFFICER* (woman)

The Honorable Jane Doe Secretary of Labor Washington, D.C.	Madam Secretary then Miss or Mrs. Doe	The Secretary of Labor, Miss (or Mrs.) Doe *Or formal:* The Honorable Jane Doe, Secretary of Labor

Social, when married:

The Secretary of Labor
   and Mr. Doe
(home address)

THE ATTORNEY GENERAL

The Honorable John Doe Attorney General Washington, D.C.	Mr. Attorney General or Mr. Doe	The Attorney General, Mr. Doe *Or formal:* The Honorable John Doe, Attorney General

SECRETARY OF DEFENSE, AND OF THE ARMY, NAVY, AND AIR FORCE (UNDER SECRETARY AND ASSISTANT SECRETARY)

The Honorable John Doe Secretary of the Air Force Washington, D.C.	Mr. Secretary or Mr. Doe	The Secretary of the Air Force, Mr. Doe *Or formal:* the Honorable John Doe, Secretary of the Air Force

---

*All cabinet officers except the Attorney General and the Postmaster General use the title of *Secretary.* Although the service secretaries do not have cabinet rank, they may be addressed and introduced as *Mr. Secretary,* or *The Secretary of the Army,* etc. The Secretary of Defense has cabinet rank.

Written Address	Spoken Address	Introductions

Social:

The Secretary of the Air
  Force and Mrs. Doe
(home address)

FORMER PRESIDENT OF THE UNITED STATES

The Honorable John Doe San Francisco, California	Mr. Doe (or any title, such as military)	The Honorable John Doe, the former President of the United States

THE ASSISTANT TO THE PRESIDENT

The Honorable John Doe Assistant to the President The White House Washington, D.C.	Mr. Doe	The Assistant to the President, Mr. John Doe *Or formal* The Honorable John Doe, Assistant to the President of the United States

Social:

The Honorable John Doe
  and Mrs. Doe
(home address)

THE SPECIAL ASSISTANT TO THE PRESIDENT WITH MILITARY RANK

Major General John Doe, U.S. Army Special Assistant to the President The White House Washington, D.C.	General Doe	The Special Assistant to the President, General John Doe, United States Army

Social:

Major General and Mrs.
  John Doe
(home address)

Written Address	Spoken Address	Introductions
THE SPEAKER OF THE HOUSE OF REPRESENTATIVES		
The Honorable John Doe Speaker of the House of Representatives The Capitol Washington, D.C.	Mr. Speaker or Mr. Doe	The Speaker, Mr. Doe *Or formal:* The Honorable John Doe, Speaker of the House of Representatives
Social: The Speaker of the House of Representatives and Mrs. Doe (home address)		
AMERICAN AMBASSADOR (man)*		
The Honorable John Doe American Ambassador London, England	Mr. Ambassador *Or on leave:* Mr. Doe *Or with military rank:* General Doe	The Honorable John Doe, the American Ambassador (When he is not at his post, the name of the country to which he is accredited must be added: . . . to England.)
Social: The American Ambassador and Mrs. Doe American Embassy London England or His Excellency The American Ambassador and Mrs. Doe London England	Your Excellency or Mr. Ambassador	His Excellency the American Ambassador
AMERICAN MINISTER (man)*		
The Honorable John Doe American Minister Dublin, Ireland	Mr. Minister or Mr. Doe	The American Minister *Or formal:* The Honorable John Doe, the American Minister *Or not at his post:* . . . to Ireland

*When a woman is a United States ambassador or minister, the word *Madam* is substituted for *Mr.* in the spoken address.

Written Address	Spoken Address	Introductions

Social:

The American Minister
   and Mrs. Doe
American Legation
Dublin
Ireland

AMERICAN CHARGÉ D'AFFAIRES OR CONSULAR OFFICER

John Doe, Esquire	Mr. Doe	Mr. Doe
American Chargé		*Or formal:*
d'Affaires		Mr. John Doe, the
(or Consul General, or		American Chargé
Vice Consul)		d'Affaires
Paris, France		

Social:

The American Chargé
  d'Affaires
  and Mrs. John Doe
(home address)

UNITED STATES SENATOR (or State Senator, with appropriate State address)

The Honorable	Senator Doe	Senator Doe
John Doe	or	*Or formal:*
United States Senate	Senator	The Honorable John Doe,
Washington, D.C.		Senator from Oklahoma

Social:

Senator and Mrs. Doe
(home address)

UNITED STATES CONGRESSMAN

The Honorable	Congressman	Congressman Doe*
John Doe	Doe	*Or formal:*
House of Representatives	or	The Honorable John Doe,
Washington, D.C.	Mr. Doe	Representative from South
		Carolina

*The title *Congressman* seems to be widely used in informal introductions by the Representatives themselves and by others when introducing them. It is not incorrect to call a Congresswoman *Congressman*. The prefix *Representative* is never used in correspondence.

Written Address	Spoken Address	Introductions

Social:

The Honorable and Mrs.
   Doe
(home address)

GOVERNOR*

The Honorable	Governor Doe	Governor Doe or
John Doe	or	The Governor
Governor of Texas	Governor	*Or formal:*
Austin, Texas		The Honorable John Doe,
		Governor of Texas, or
		. . . of the state of Texas

Social:

The Governor and
   Mrs. Doe
Or outside the state:
The Governor of Texas
   and Mrs. Doe
   or
His Excellency the Gover-
   nor and Mrs. Doe
(home address)

MAYOR

The Honorable	Mayor Doe	Mayor Doe
John Doe	or	*Or formal:*
Mayor of Boston	Mr. Mayor	The Honorable John Doe,
Boston, Massachusetts		Mayor of Boston, or
		. . . of the city of Boston

Social:

Mayor and Mrs. Doe
   or
The Honorable and Mrs.
   John Doe
(home address)

*The Governor is given the title *Excellency* in many states, but the title *Governor* is the one used by the Department of State.

Written Address	Spoken Address	Introductions

JUDGE

The Honorable	Judge Doe	Judge Doe
John Doe		*Or formal:*
Judge of District Court		The Honorable John Doe,
(or other court)		Judge of the District Court
Wheeling, West Virginia		

Social:

Judge and Mrs. Doe
   or
The Honorable and Mrs.
  Doe
(home address)

HEAD OF A FEDERAL AGENCY

The Honorable	Mr. Doe	Mr. Doe
John Doe		*Or formal:*
Administrator of (name of		The Honorable John Doe,
agency)		Administrator of (name of
Washington, D.C.		agency)

Social:

Mr. and Mrs. John Doe
   or
The Honorable and Mrs.
  John Doe
(home address)

HEAD OF A DIVISION OR BUREAU OF A DEPARTMENT

Mr. John Doe	Mr. Doe	Mr. Doe
Chief, Federal Bureau of		or
Investigation		Mr. John Doe, Chief of
Washington, D.C.		the Federal Bureau of
		Investigation

Social:

Mr. and Mrs. John Doe
(home address)

WRITTEN AND SPOKEN ADDRESSES AND INTRODUCTIONS: AMERICAN CLERGY AND CHURCH DIGNITARIES

Written Address	*Spoken Address*	*Introductions*
THE PRESIDING BISHOP OF THE PROTESTANT EPISCOPAL CHURCH IN AMERICA		
The Most Reverend John Doe, D.D., LL.D. Presiding Bishop of the Prostestant Episcopal Church in America (local address)	Bishop Doe	Bishop Doe or The Most Reverend John Doe, Presiding Bishop of the Protestant Episcopal Church in America
PROTESTANT EPISCOPAL BISHOP		
The Right Reverend John Doe, D.D., LL.D. Bishop of— (local address)	Bishop Doe	Bishop Doe or The Right Reverend John Doe, Bishop of—
ROMAN CATHOLIC CARDINAL		
His Eminence John Cardinal Doe Archbishop of New York New York, New York	Your Eminence	His Eminence or Cardinal Doe or His Eminence, Cardinal Doe
ROMAN CATHOLIC ARCHBISHOP OR BISHOP		
His Excellency, The Most Reverend John Doe, S.T.D. Archbishop (or Bishop) of Chicago Chicago, Illinois	Archbishop (or Bishop) Doe	Archbishop (or Bishop) Doe or His Excellency, The Most Reverend John Doe, Archbishop of Chicago or His Excellency, The Archbishop of Chicago
METHODIST BISHOP		
The Very Reverend John Doe, D.D., LL.D.* Bishop of Denver Denver, Colorado	Bishop Doe	Bishop Doe or The Very Reverend Bishop Doe, Methodist Bishop of Denver

Written Address	Spoken Address	Introductions
ROMAN CATHOLIC MONSIGNOR		
The Right Reverend Monsignor John Doe (local address)	Monsignor Doe	The Very Reverend (or Right Reverend) Monsignor John Doe or Monsignor Doe
PROTESTANT EPISCOPAL ARCHDEACON		
The Venerable John Doe, D.D.* Archdeacon of— Diocese of Virginia	Archdeacon Doe or Mr. Doe	Archdeacon Doe or Dr. Doe or The Venerable John Doe, Archdeacon of— in the Diocese of Virginia
DEAN OR CANON		
The Very Reverend John Doe, D.D. Dean (or Canon) of Washington Cathedral Washington, D.C.	Dean (or Canon) Doe or Dr. Doe	The Very Reverend John Doe, Dean (or Canon) of Washington Cathedral
PRIEST WHO IS ADDRESSED AS "FATHER"		
The Reverend John Doe, S.J. St. Mary's Church Washington, D.C.	Father Doe	Father Doe or The Reverend John Doe
MORMON		
Mr. John Doe President of Manti Temple Manti, Utah	Mr. Doe	Mr. John Doe, President of Manti Temple

*These protestant clergymen with a doctor of divinity degree may be addressed and introduced as *Dr. Doe* and *The Reverend Dr. Doe,* respectively. Without such a degree, they are addressed and introduced as *Sir* and *The Reverend Doe,* respectively. In conversation, say *Reverend Doe* or *Mr. Doe.*

Written Address	Spoken Address	Introductions
RABBI		
Rabbi John Doe Kneseth Israel Congregation Annapolis, Maryland	Rabbi Doe or Rabbi *Or with scholastic degree:* Dr. Doe	Rabbi Doe *Or with scholastic degree:* Dr. Doe
MOTHER SUPERIOR		

The Reverend Mother
   Mary (and the initials
   of her order)
The Convent of—
(address)
	Reverend Mother	Reverend Mother

SISTER		
Sister Mary (and initials of her order) (local address)	Sister Mary	Sister Mary
BROTHER		
The Reverend Brother John Doe Fordham University Bronx, New York	Brother John or Brother	Brother John
CANTOR		
Cantor John Doe Kneseth Israel Congregation Annapolis, Maryland	Cantor Doe	Cantor Doe

WRITTEN AND SPOKEN ADDRESSES AND INTRODUCTIONS: INDIVIDUALS

Written Address	Spoken Address	Introductions
Professor (or Assoc. Professor or Asst. Professor) John Doe	Mr. Doe or Professor Doe	Professor Doe
Or with *Doctor's Degree:* Dr. John Doe, Ph.D. Columbia University New York, New York	Dr. Doe	Dr. Doe
DIVORCÉE Mrs. Smith Doe (or Mrs. Jane Doe) (the maiden surname or given name is followed by the ex-husband's name) (local address)	Mrs. Doe	Mrs. Doe
WIDOW Mrs. John Doe (the same as when her husband was alive) (local address)	Mrs. Doe	Mrs. Doe

CHAPTER 9

The Art of Conversation

FOR MANY PEOPLE, the art of conversation is of little importance. In some walks of life this may be true—but not for you as an officer in the armed forces, or for anyone who chooses to become a professional leader of men and women.

The general public considers an officer in the services to be a person of position and so renders judgment upon this basis. You must, therefore, devote significant thought and effort to the development of proficiency in general conversation, since you are, so to speak, "on the spot."

The first thing you must do in order to be a good conversationalist is to *have something to say;* second, you *must be able to say it well.*

MANNER OF CONVERSATION

Poor grammar, rude or vulgar talk, and the persistent use of improper and uncouth phraseology are representative of careless personal habits that can be corrected if you take sufficient interest. There are officers who perform their duties acceptably—occasionally, excellently—despite their inability to express themselves clearly and in good taste. But this is the exception rather than the rule.

Errors of a gross nature in conversation are particularly noticed by officers junior to the speaker—including, paradoxically, those juniors who themselves use poor grammar.

Juniors, despite shortcomings of their own, expect high standards in their superiors, whose careless speech will inevitably result in the loss of prestige. The juniors are likely to suspect that a senior who is careless in speech may be careless in other phases of his or her official behavior. It is well that a cadet or midshipman, ROTC or OCS student, recognize this fact early and cultivate the habit of proper speech in everyday conversation.

OFFICIAL AND SOCIAL CONVERSATION

"The tongue is but three inches long, yet it can kill a man six feet high." This old Japanese proverb too often can be only too true.

In the services, the essential difference between official and social conversation is one of situation. In an *official situation* the conversationalists recognize differences in rank while carrying on their conversation. Regardless of how pleasant and congenial such talk may be, congeniality is never an excuse for taking verbal liberties.

Social conversation is general talk with no conscious recognition of rank as such. It is made up of considerable "small talk," pleasant but not important—and not at all harmful. Small talk that is fitting and proper at a dinner party is not carried on during official conversation.

In both types of conversations, the objective is the same: to create a personal relationship without tension in which thoughts and ideas may be exchanged. The tone of official conversation is generally more serious, but not necessarily so. Admirals and generals are only midshipmen and cadets grown older, and, like anyone else, they often enjoy a light conversation that does not concern career or business problems. Official business is never discussed at social gatherings—in particular not at cocktail parties.

When talking with a senior or very high-ranking officer, a junior officer allows the senior to take the lead in the conversation—but never freeze up while desperately trying to think of something brilliant to say. At a social occasion, the officer should be attentive—but not "at attention."

FAMILIARITY

There is an old military maxim that you should always remember: in the relations between seniors and juniors, the senior will never think of the difference in rank—but the junior will never forget it. This adage is true in both social and official relations. Adherence to it will lead to ease and harmony, but a violation may bring embarrassment.

Official conversations follow a basic principle: seniors may call you, the junior, by your first name, but this does not grant you the same privilege. Upon occasion, a senior may ask a junior to call him or her by first name—but it must be clearly understood that such familiarity is *not* to be used in official conversation. Neither does the privilege carry with it a "back slapping" familiarity—in fact, quite the opposite. The senior must have expected you to exercise the utmost propriety, or the bars would not have been lowered in the first place.

In talking with contemporaries in the mess or anywhere else, be on guard against telling your personal affairs. Your mess mates and station friends will become good friends in time, but they are not the same as your parents or your immediate family. When you talk "just a little" with others about your personal affairs, a "little" quickly becomes "too much," and you may find that constraint develops in your formerly easy relationship.

When on duty, conversations between seniors and juniors, and commissioned and noncommissioned officers, should be kept on the official and impersonal level. This does not mean that you should resemble Captain Hornblower, but it does mean that you avoid undue familiarity.

Enlisted personnel appreciate your consideration for their welfare and your interest in their interests, but they do not appreciate— or want—familiarity. They know that fraternization tends to cause an officer to forfeit his credibility; they distrust the officer who talks as though he or she wants to "join the gang" one moment, then issues even a minor reprimand in an official capacity. Any such occurrence hurts the sensibilities of the subordinate.

The necessity for reprimands is not frequent, but the same situation will hold when you must make even minor criticisms: their significance is clouded over by the personal element. In positions of command, "Familiarity breeds contempt."

DISSENSIONS

Be careful of dissensions! You will find that you can disagree in your mind completely, and furthermore, can express that disagreement in conversation with a group, without "leaving the sea strewn with burning wrecks." It merely takes tact. And tact, as one wit stated, is the talent for not saying that you were right in the first place. But there are those who cannot disagree with any expressed opinion without seeming to launch a personal attack on the person who stated the opinion.

An effective way to disagree with an expressed conversational opinion is to make no return comment at all, or to make a rather roundabout comment that tends to veer the conversation away from the offensive statement without being obvious about it.

Religious discussions in dissimilar groups are generally unwise because statements that are seemingly innocent to the speaker may seem offensive to a listener. This does not mean that you should refuse to state an opinion on a religious subject, or to enter into a discussion, but it does mean that you should be careful of the company in which a religious discussion is carried on. Unless the group is composed of people of good will, intelligence, and tolerance, such discussions tend to break down into heated arguments and end in wrangles.

When you feel it necessary, however, to go on record as disagreeing with something that has been said, you may do so in a number of polite ways. For example, you may say, with a pleasant smile, "I'm afraid that I don't agree with that," or "I have given the matter considerable thought and have come to an entirely different conclusion." A light but disarming remark could be, "I'm from too far south to agree with such a Yankee idea." In brief, learn how to disagree without being disagreeable.

You express disagreement by obviously changing the subject. Since this action is not in the best social taste, reserve it for situations that require drastic treatment—as when a person commences a tirade concerning another service, and you know a member of that service is present.

There may come a time when a senior officer (or anyone) states an opinion that is radically against your own convictions. Unless some action on your part is called for, you avoid comment, out of deference for your senior's greater age and experience. But if the senior then asks you to give an opinion and persists, you must state your honest opinion, or you will not be true to your own convictions and risk being labeled as a "yes man." With due respect, you may say "Sir (or Ma'am), that is a matter of opinion, but my experience has been to the contrary."

IMPORTANCE OF REMEMBERING

It is important to remember names. You do not like your own name forgotten or mispronounced, so do not forget or fumble another's. Some people have excellent memories for names and faces, others must work at remembering. Most memory courses depend upon associating the name with an object, or repeating a name over and over in your mind after an introduction. If you miss the name on first being introduced, you can quite properly ask to have the name repeated.

When you cannot remember a person's name, and yet it is your duty to make the introduction to a conversational group, it is better to admit your lapse and say, "I'm sorry, but I will have to ask you your name," or "Please tell me your name again." The question should be asked with poise and no embarrassment.

In conversations, it is complimentary to remember another's personal concerns: a birthday or wedding anniversary, or an accomplishment by a member of the family. Any pleasant occurrence—an award, or a recent promotion in grade—serves to provide a background for conversation.

WHEN YOU DON'T KNOW THE ANSWER

Does it hurt your pride to admit that you do not know something? It takes a big person to admit that he or she does not know the answer to a question that he should know, particularly when the questioner is an important person whom he would like to impress.

Can you do this? If so, it is to your credit. Always remember that even though you may be an expert on some subject, no one knows everything about every thing.

WHEN YOU DO KNOW

Have you been in a conversation—say at a party—when someone sounds off on a subject that he or she knows little about but you know a great deal about?

If you are a sensitive person you will consider the type of individual sounding off: is he making small talk, trying to keep the conversation going? If so, he could be shattered if you pointed out his lack of knowledge by giving the correct version. An inhibited person would likely withdraw, and you might even drive him into a deep shell from which he would be afraid to emerge for fear of further blundering. In such a case, the kindest thing would be to change the conversation to another subject as quickly as possible. But if the person sounding off is a show-off, then a brief correction of the statement, pleasantly stated, is in order.

THE JOKER

Some people just love to tell a joke. They must be the life of the party, and quite often they are. But when the joke discredits another person—intentionally or not—then "the insult with a smile" is not funny at all.

Sometimes the joker merely wants to show a little self-superiority by his or her cleverness. But when the joke stings or hurts another because of some social or business error that has been made, the "joke" is a put-down.

TABOOS

Controversial subjects—religion, race, and politics—and any unpleasant subject should not be discussed at social functions, and are treated carefully at all times. Examples of such subjects are death, disasters, accidents, battle losses, serious illness, and, with some people, age.

Never discuss a person's age in his or her presence. Elderly people do not enjoy being considered decrepit; young people do not want to feel immature and inadequate. Both the very young and the very old are frequently sensitive about their age.

EASY CONVERSATION

An essential part of your everyday living is the art of simple, easy conversation. A good conversationalist always has something interesting to talk about, is not overbearing, and never irritates listeners.

In general, plain words are preferable to ponderous phrases, and trite expressions are tiresome. The topics for conversations are endless: newspapers, books, magazines; television personalities and news analysts. Art, music, and concerts appeal to the artistic. Any sport event in season is of interest to many men and women.

A topic of conversation may be discussed as long as the listeners find it of interest; then new ones must be introduced. When you are talking, look at your listeners and observe their reactions. No monologue is of interest—except possibly to yourself. When you are the listener, pay attention to what is being said. It is extremely discourteous openly to show disinterest, for example, by allowing your glance to wander off to other people or things.

A good conversationalist does not interrupt or contradict another. He or she is a good listener, one who draws out the shy person by finding out his interests, then asks questions concerning that hobby or interest. When talking with a horticulturist, you could ask about his garden or the beautiful azaleas at Charleston; an author would be interested in a new book—perhaps one with controversial reviews.

When you want to start a lively conversation, ask a question that presents a challenge: "I hear Army is strong—who do you think will win the Army-Navy game?" or "Would it be better to return to the three Rs than to continue with progressive education?"

When you want a certain subject discussed without coming right out with it, bring up a related subject or experience that will open the door to the desired subject. For example, if you wish to hear a man who wears the Congressional Medal of Honor talk about his experiences, you might pave the way by saying, "Sir, how many patrols did you make during World War II?"

In order to talk intelligently on a certain subject to a person of authority, it is well to brief yourself on that subject beforehand. In this way you can converse easily with the personage about his or her work or accomplishment and at the same time increase your own store of knowledge.

In your desire to make a good accounting of yourself, however, do not be so obvious that you appear insincere. It is an insult to your seniors, or to anyone else, to express more interest than common courtesy allows.

POISE AND GOOD MANNERS

When you talk, do you keep your hands and feet quiet, or do you gesture wildly and shuffle your feet? Do you drum on a table with your fingers, or tap your feet on the floor? If you do—stop it. To shift from one foot to the other makes you appear ill at ease and detracts not only from your appearance but also from what you are saying. Finger or foot tapping draws attention to what you are *doing* and away from what you are *saying*.

It is well to reflect upon a new thought before blurting out a remark that may be regretted later. Be tolerant of others' ideas, and do not ridicule or laugh at an unfortunate remark or tell an amusing story to the discredit of anyone.

Poise in conversation includes the ability to time a conversation—to know when to talk and when to be silent. Relaxation is an essential ingredient; an incessant chatterer will soon exhaust listeners.

Sometimes two people start talking simultaneously, usually when there is a lull in a conversation, and both attempt to relieve the situation at the same time. When you are one of them, give way amiably and quickly. To fail to do so makes a person seem domineering.

A skilled conversationalist can be compared to a ship's captain; he can steer thoughts and ideas into interesting conversational channels, but when necessary, he charts the course of an unfortunate subject away from the reef to the safety of calmer seas.

TONE OF VOICE

A well-modulated voice is an asset to anyone. Words should be enunciated clearly, in a pleasant tone which is pitched neither too high nor too low. If you aren't aware of how your voice sounds to others, try speaking naturally or reading a news item into a recording machine; then play it back. Do your words run together? Do you bark them out? Are you too loud? Too high-pitched? Shrill? The range of your voice is always important; speaking in a monotone makes any topic dull.

With some effort on your part, you can control your voice by breathing from your diaphragm and developing a range in tone which will improve both your voice and your conversational appeal.

NAMES AND TITLES

Sometimes it's hard to know just what to call a person who is very junior or senior to you. A senior officer and spouse may call a junior officer and spouse by their first name in a friendly manner— but they are still "Colonel and Mrs. Smith" to you, the junior, unless you are requested to call them by their first name.

Officially, senior rank is always observed when speaking with or referring to an officer, regardless of how well you know that person. Socially, close friends call each other by their first name regardless of age or rank.

A man does not call a woman by her first name until she takes the initiative, such as calling him by his first name or asking that he call her by hers. Then, he is free to do so.

ASKING FOR FIRST DATES

Although the majority of young men at the service academies and in ROTC units are experienced in asking girls for dates, there are some who have had little time or inclination to date before entering these institutions.

Upon meeting a young lady, a rather shy young man usually "talks around" the objective of asking for a date the first time. If you are that young man you might say something like, "Do you like sports?" If she replies in the affirmative, you might mention a game you plan to attend, and in her manner will be a clue as to whether or not she would like you to ask her to accompany you.

If she seems favorably interested, then say, "How would you like to meet me after the game and go on to the mixer?"—or to the movies, etc. If you are a fourth classman, ask her to meet you at the place or occasion limited to your opportunities of meeting young ladies.

Some young men are afraid they will be turned down, and thus hesitate to ask for a date. In turn, she may be afraid to seem overeager, and what appears to be coolness on her part may be a bit of stage fright. So *ask.*

If she refuses you twice with no reasonable explanation, then you should hesitate to continue the pursuit. But do learn to take an occasional refusal with equanimity—she may have a very sound reason for being unable to accept your invitation.

In this modern age of equality, women of all ages often take the initiative in asking for dates. Then, the tables are turned.

RULES TO REMEMBER

Do:

Have something to say—and say it well. Brief amusing stories, a news item, unusual incidents, a TV personality—all are conversation starters.

Be a good listener.

Develop the art of small talk; this is pleasant talk about nothing in particular, but does *not* include official or harmful subjects.

Learn to remember names and faces; nothing will make you more popular.

Put shy persons at ease by getting them to talk about their hobbies, pets, children, or known interests.

Put yourself at ease—by thinking of the *other* person.

As a host, act as moderator and intervene in a monologue, a "dead" group, or a controversial discussion by changing the subject.

Talk in a moderate tone of voice.

Keep your eyes and ears open—and, occasionally, your mouth *shut*.

Be able to say "I don't know"—when you don't.

Do not:

Say anything about anyone that you would not want them to hear.

Talk business at a social gathering.

Substitute sarcasm or ridicule for wit.

Interrupt or contradict others.

Monopolize a conversation.

Talk over anyone's head or "talk down" to anyone.

Flatter others; insincerity is unwelcome.

Talk endlessly; silence, at times, *is* golden.

Allow a guest to be stranded with a conversational bore.

"Clam up"; a shy guest is a burden to a host, who thereupon must force conversation.

Exclude anyone from a conversational group—other than a disruptive person, such as one "under the influence."

Give the state of your health when someone says, "How are you?" This is simply a polite expression, generally used in greetings or "small talk."

Talk about a party you have been invited to when others present have not.

Be ingratiating. Deference expresses respect for authority; bootlicking does not.

CHAPTER 10

Good Manners Before an Audience

An officer must be able to speak effectively in any situation. At the service academies, public speaking is considered so important that cadets and midshipmen receive formal classroom instruction in speech and make several brief speeches during the year. A dining-in is complete with toastmaster, guest of honor, and an instructor who gives helpful criticism. The dinners are formal and are prepared under conditions approximating those which can be expected later.

After graduation from one of the academies, Officer Training Schools, Officer Candidate Schools, or ROTC units, you, the officer, will find that an important aptitude is skill in addressing a group. From the very beginning of your career, you will be called on to address a division aboard ship or a company ashore, to enter into general meetings in the wardroom or barracks, and to discuss professional matters before groups of other officers at critiques and symposiums.

Later on you will find yourself drawn into the public life of your community, to deliver speeches on patriotic occasions and to be an active member of service clubs and civic organizations.

Preparedness for such a role is one of the responsibilities that you will assume as a person in public life, where the general public expects experienced leadership from officers in the services. The responsibility for group leadership may not be something that you desire—but it may be something that you assume.

When you are asked to be president of a PTA or chairman of service night at Rotary or to speak to a professional club, you cannot plead inability to speak in public or ignorance of parliamentary procedure. The public knows better. The public knows that you had the opportunity to learn these things, and it expects to find you, if not an expert, at least well grounded in the fundamentals. The best grounding that any officer can have is an understanding of the proprieties of public speaking and the forms of courtesy to be followed when addressing a group.

In effect, public speaking is based on one's ability to win the interest of the audience and to communicate with the group with courtesy and consideration.

It is an axiom in public speaking that your first objective is to create a favorable relationship between your audience and yourself. It is necessary to reach this objective before attempting to deliver your message. The impression you leave with an audience is almost as important as the message you delivered.

Dale Carnegie recognized the relative importance of this relationship of a speaker to his audience in the title of his book on public speaking: *How to Win Friends and Influence People.* You will note that *friendship* ranks ahead of *influence.*

PREPARATION

You should not accept an invitation to talk on a subject about which you are not well informed, unless you have time to research the subject.

Any serious speech should be prepared well in advance, with all facts, dates, and names checked carefully. Thoughts should be well organized and presented in logical order. You will want to know how long you are to talk—and stay within this limit.

APPEARANCE

The *appearance* of a speaker is the first thing an audience notes; then *mannerisms* and *voice.* A speaker in uniform should be at his or her best—uniform immaculate, posture relaxed. A man in civilian dress should be conservatively dressed, tie in order, suit pressed, and hands out of pockets. A woman should make certain that her skirt hangs evenly, and that her stockings do not wrinkle. A speaker should not stand or sit stiffly, but neither should his or her hands or feet be in constant motion.

PERSONAL CONDUCT IN SPEAKING

An audience expects the speaker to recognize and address properly the leader or chairman of the meeting. It also expects the speaker to use correct forms of address when speaking to the group as a whole, or to an individual member. A speaker can be as polite—or as impolite—to a group of people as he or she can be to a single person.

Avoid both "talking down" to a group and talking "over their heads." It is insulting to an audience to address it as though you are the only one who knows anything about a given subject—even when you are an expert in that particular field. Avoid overusing the first-person pronoun: "*I* think—," "*I* know—," "*I* did—." And be careful of overusing such words and phrases as "You know," "Well—," "Uh—," and "Anyway,—."

A useful yardstick in speaking (or writing) is: Can people understand what I mean? A familiar word is better than a "show-off" word or phrase; a short word is preferable to a long one.

No audience likes to hear a speaker apologize for himself or for what he has to say. Any apology puts the speaker on the defensive. Clearing the throat, bobbing the chin up and down, straightening a tie or skirt, shifting from one foot to another—all such self-conscious gestures make an audience as uneasy as the speaker.

Although most words spoken in private conversation are just words, some of these same words may set up a chain reaction against you when used in a speech or before an audience. Experience will teach the speaker what these words and expressions are, and they should be mentally catalogued as *fighting words* and not used again. From various viewpoints, such fighting words could be: "We of the intelligentsia—," "You military dictators—," or "You civilians couldn't understand—." To the listener, such words and expressions indicate a disregard for another's feelings. The listener may merely consider you highhanded—nevertheless, you will be poorly received. And remember that a joke that is amusing to one may seem like ridicule to another.

You should be respectful of others' opinions at a meeting, and try to look at various viewpoints from all sides before making up your mind on a subject. Always be fair—but firm.

Always give credit whenever credit is due, but be careful of the timing in expressing a compliment made in public. An ill-timed compliment may embarrass the recipient as well as give an impression of fawning on him or her.

In order to achieve a feeling of communication between yourself and your audience, you may find it helpful to select someone in the audience and talk to that person as if you were having a private conversation.

THE FUNNY STORY

A brief amusing story of reminiscence, a good joke, or a good quotation are all ice-breakers at the opening of a meeting. Such stories must be *good,* however, or the speaker will lose his audience and have to try harder than ever to win it over.

The first rule in telling a story is that it must be amusing to you, the speaker, or you cannot expect it to be funny to your audience—unless you presume them to be of lower intelligence than yourself. In this case, you have played down to your audience.

The second rule is that a joke sparkles best in brevity.

The third rule is not to laugh heartily at your own joke.

You must, of course, be fully aware of the type of audience you will address when speaking before a club or organization: large or small, mixed or stag, rural or cosmopolitan. You should take into careful consideration the racial, religious, political, and age groups involved. The type of club or organization will determine the tone of your talk, and you must make certain that your material is in keeping with the spirit of the occasion.

An off-color story is a dangerous story to tell before an audience at any time. Such a story told in a locker room or in a foursome may seem hilarious—but when the same story is told at a public or private gathering, particularly before a mixed group, the one telling the story may be marked as vulgar or uncouth.

Lastly, at no time must you allow your sense of humor to desert you. A good sense of humor will protect you from a seemingly disinterested audience and also from becoming "too full of yourself."

YOUR GRAMMAR

The grammar you use when making a speech—and in everyday conversation—tells much about you. If you are unsure of your grammar, it probably will be reflected in your talk. Hesitations, too many "uhs" or "wells," will slow your train of thought and dampen the listeners' interest.

An academy professor has stated that in his opinion cadets and midshipmen have a poorer background in English grammar than in any other subject. If you are uncertain of your usage, check out a book from the library or hunt up a school grammar book that explains everything about verbs and sentence structure.

YOUR VOICE

A well-modulated voice is pleasing to your audience. If you have a tendency to talk too fast and rush your sentences, slow down. Learn to space important words and phrases; for emphasis, pause a second or so after making a very important remark.

If nature did not provide you with a pleasant speaking voice, then cultivate one. Take courses in public speaking and voice control. Practice pitching your voice down, should it be high or shrill.

Although it is better to talk slowly than to rush your words, the man or woman who talks very slowly in a droning fashion can lull an audience to sleep.

PARLIAMENTARY PROCEDURE

You will need some knowledge of parliamentary procedure, whether you are the presiding officer at a meeting or a member of an organization who sits in the back row and just listens.

The nationally recognized book on parliamentary procedure is *Robert's Rules of Order Revised.* Incidentally, this book was written by a West Pointer—Class of 1857—Brigadier General Henry Martyn Robert, who became Chief of Engineers, U.S. Army.

General Correspondence, Invitations, & Replies

CHAPTER 11

Business Correspondence

IN CONVERSATION you are judged by what you say; in correspondence, by what you write. Plain words and phrases are preferable in letter writing, just as they are in conversation. A letter difficult to compose is handled with more ease when written as though you were speaking to the person addressed.

When you choose your stationery, consider its use: for official or business correspondence, social or personal. White paper is used for all types of business correspondence in the services, but personal stationery may also be cream, gray, blue-gray, or light tan. In addition, these and other pastel colors are used by women.

Engraving is much more expensive than printing. The tremendous amount of correspondence at any large post or station, the thousands of invitations issued each year, make the cost of engraving prohibitive except for the very official or important formal occasion. And engraving costs are prohibitive for many individuals.

A process called *thermography,* which produces a raised printing, is widely used for formal as well as informal invitation cards and official or personal stationery. It is almost indistinguishable from engraving and is much less expensive, although the cost is more than for plain printing. Today this printing is acceptable for all but the most elegant occasion. Any good stationer or the PX can advise you about this.

Because all departments of the Armed Forces issue directives for military correspondence, this chapter stresses guidelines for business and nonofficial letters.

BUSINESS PAPER

Official or business stationery is white, with black or dark blue engraving or printing. The official letterhead is usually at the top center of the sheet, but it may be placed at the top left-hand side.

The sizes of business paper most frequently used are:

The traditional white bond paper, single sheet, 8 by 10 inches, with standard matching envelope of oblong shape and plain flap.
A slightly larger sheet, with or without telephone number in the letterhead, 8½ by 11 inches.
A slightly narrower sheet (for business and personal use), 7¼ by 10 ¼ inches, used for both longhand and typewriter.
A smaller business-personal sheet, 7 by 8½ inches, for business invitations.

BUSINESS LETTERS

There are several styles for official or business letters with letterheads.

The *full block* style, with everything flush left on the page: the date, the name and address, the salutation, all paragraphs and lines, the complimentary close, and the signature, all begin at the left-hand margin. Double spacing separates the single-spaced paragraphs.

The *modified block* style, with the date at the upper right: the name and address, the salutation, all paragraphs and lines, are flush left; paragraphs are separated by double spacing. The complimentary close and signature are to the right, in line with the date.

The *modified semi-block* style, with the date at the upper right: the name and address and the salutation are flush left; each paragraph is indented (5 or 10 spaces) and single spaced; paragraphs are separated by double spacing. The complimentary close and signature are to the right, in line with the date.

The dates in business letters, civilian form, may be written "May 7, 1988," but the official service form is "7 May 1988." No letter should be dated "5/7/88."

There is a colon after the salutation and a comma after the complimentary closing of a letter.

The *inside address* is written in the same way as on the envelope, with no punctuation at the end of the lines. The title may be abbreviated when it precedes the name, as "Lt. John B. Jones," but it is written in full in the salutation, as "Dear Captain Jones."

In official service correspondence, the order of address usually is: (a) administrative position; (b) station; (c) attention line when name is not used (such as: ATTN: AMCPE-GA); (d) city (when needed), state, zip code. Sometimes rank and name constitute "(a)."

In business, the order usually is: (a) title and name; (b) administrative position; (c) company name; (d) company address; (e) city, state, zip code.

The *salutation* is "Dear Mr. Jones:" or "Dear Captain Jones:". When names are unknown, "Dear Sir:" or "Gentlemen:" is used. A business woman is addressed "Dear Miss Jones:" or "Dear Mrs. Jones:"—but when it is not known whether she is married or not, use "Ms." Two or more women are addressed as "Mesdames."

Paragraphs in business letters are not numbered as they are in official correspondence, but items within paragraphs may be lettered and numbered.

The body of the letter includes all necessary information, with well-constructed sentences and no errors in spelling, punctuation, or grammar. Avoid stilted or trite phrases; be courteous. Whenever possible, write a one-page letter. A second page is labeled by "—2—" at the center top.

The *complimentary close* is the polite phrase or word (adverb) with which you end your letter. Business letters are customarily closed by the "yours" phrase, with "Very truly yours," the most formal. "Sincerely yours," or "Cordially yours," is used for a more personal business letter, and "Very respectfully yours," when writing to a superior. The complimentary close is typed *two lines* below the preceding line of typing.

Your *signature* is typed or stamped *four lines* below the complimentary close, and hand signed above the typed signature. It is incorrect to use titles such as "Mr.," "Mrs.," "Capt.," "Dr.," and "Prof." in signatures.

For an officer, the order of signature is:
1. Name in capitals
2. Rank or
3. Functional title
4. Authority line, if any

The order of signature for a business person usually is:
1. Name, not capitalized throughout
2. Functional title
3. Company name (when not in the letterhead)

Signatures on the official service letter vary from the business-form letter in these respects: (1) the rank, if any, is included; (2) the functional title is added; and (3) the authority line, if any, is expanded to include the title of the command at whose direction the letter is prepared.

The following are examples of signatures on business and official service letters.

John B. Jones
Assistant Secretary for Maritime Affairs
U.S. Department of Transportation

J. B. JONES
Brigadier General, U.S. Air Force
Director of Telecommunications

JANE B. JONES
First Lieutenant, U.S. Army
Defense Advisory Committee
   on Women in the Services

J. B. JONES
Rear Admiral, U.S. Navy
Head, Division of Administration
By Direction of the Chief of Naval Operations

J. B. JONES
Captain, U.S. Coast Guard
Commandant of Cadets

JOSEPHINE B. JONES
Deputy Chief
Directorate for Defense Information
Office of the Secretary of Defense

Men and women in business usually use the company's writing paper for all business correspondence, and important executives often have specially engraved or printed paper. Under the company's letterhead, at the *left-hand* margin, the full name is engraved, with the title of office directly underneath. For example:

Rear Admiral John E. Doe, USN (Ret.)
President

The following is an example of a military modified semi-block letter.

DEPARTMENT OF THE ARMY
OFFICE OF THE ADJUTANT GENERAL
ALEXANDRIA, VA 22331

1
2   (date)

REPLY TO
ATTENTION OF
1
2 Administrative Management
Directorate

Honorable James B. Smith
Chairman
Armed Services Appropriations Committee
United States Senate
Washington, D.C. 20510
1
2 Dear Mr. Chairman:
1
2 When a Member of Congress is a chairman or chairwoman of a committee, the greeting of "Dear Mr. Chairman:" or "Dear Madam Chairman:" is preferred. The use of addresses as chairman depends on the capacity in which the member wrote the letter. One key is the letterhead used and the title used when the member signs. When in doubt contact the office of the writer to determine the correct title and greeting to be used.

Some titles do not recognize gender (e.g., Mayor; Governor; Senator; Judge). Use as appropriate: "Dear Mayor _____:", "Dear Governor _____:", etc.
1
2   Sincerely,
1
2
3
4
5   William D. Jones
                                  Major General, U.S. Army
                                    The Adjutant General

SOURCE: *Preparing and Managing Correspondence* (Washington, D.C.: Department of the Army, March 1985).

NOTE: The numerals in the left-hand margin indicate the number of spaces between various parts of the letter.

The following is an example of a nonmilitary modified semi-block letter.

(letterhead)

(date)

Major Mary Smith, USA
Cadet Activities Officer, Women
United States Military Academy
West Point, New York 10996

Dear Major Smith:

You are cordially invited to be our guest speaker at a luncheon to be held for junior girls of Plains High School on Friday, April 5. The luncheon will be held at 12 noon in the school's new activity room, with about 100 students attending.

Many of our girls have expressed a keen interest in becoming women cadets, and we think that your being with us will give them an opportunity to learn how to achieve an appointment and what to expect in cadet life.

We hope very much to have you with us on April 5.

Very sincerely yours,

John Earl Doe
Principal
Plains High School
Plains, New York (zip)

ENVELOPES

Business envelopes usually match the paper. They range in size from 3⅞ by 8⅞ inches to 4½ by 10⅜ inches. The return address, imprinted in the top left corner, provides the title of an official or company, or the name of the command.

The letter is folded in horizontal thirds and inserted in the long envelope, or folded first in half and then in thirds for the shorter envelopes.

ADDRESSING THE ENVELOPE

Envelopes are addressed in the same manner as the accompanying letter, and are single spaced. Usually in block style, the address may also be indented. The address is typed or written in the center of the envelope. The name of the recipient is on the first line, followed by the information/attention line (when used); the command or delivery address comes next. The state is on the last line, with the zip code typed or written two spaces after the last letter in the state.

Most titles in the address are abbreviated, including "Capt." and "Lt.Col.," "Mr.," "Dr.," and "Prof."

A business or personal letter going overseas, say to an Army officer stationed in the Republic of Panama, is addressed thus:

(name)
PSC Box (number)
APO Miami 34004

ATTENTION LINE

The attention line does just that: it brings the letter to the attention of a specific person, department, or command. In the military it may be written:
Commander

or

Marine Corps Development and Educational Command
ATTN: Marine Corps Association
Quantico, Va. (zip)

On a business envelope it could be written:

World Computer, Inc.
ATTENTION: Sales Department
400 Coxe Ave.
Asheville, N.C. (zip)

CHAPTER 12

Social & Personal Correspondence

PERSONAL NOTEPAPER

Men and women officers are privileged to have their service crest or insignia embossed on their personal notepaper. The size of the paper for men is approximately 7 by 10 inches, but may be as small as 5½ by 7 inches for women. White or cream are the favored colors, but other light shades are popular.

The fold-over notepaper (card), about 4 by 6 inches, is widely used by women for brief notes and for acknowledging and issuing invitations, but men do not use fold-over cards. Cards for men are about 4 by 5 inches, or a little larger.

An officer's rank, name, and address, if retired, or insignia, are engraved or printed at the top of the card. A nonmilitary married woman's notepaper is engraved or printed "Mrs. John Doe" rather than "Mrs. Jane Doe." An unmarried woman is "Jane Doe," but "Miss" is used on the envelope; a business woman might prefer "Ms."

FLAGS/CRESTS

An admiral's or general's flag, or any military insignia of note, is used on official and personal writing paper. Insignia also are used by a married couple on wedding and formal invitations and joint cards.

However, the family coat of arms (or crest) is the exclusive property of the male members of the family, and it is *not* used by the wife or widow on her notepaper or invitations or in any personal way. Similarly, the flag or crest is not for the nonmilitary wife or widow to use.

The crest is embossed without color on engraved invitations.

INITIALS

Initials may be engraved or die-stamped in simple block form at the top center or left of the sheet. Initials are usually ³/₁₆ of an inch high, and are spaced to take up no more than ³/₄ of an inch overall. On large sheets of paper, they may be ¼ of an inch high, and cover about the same amount of space. Initials are preferable to a monogram, but an address is better than either.

HANDWRITTEN LETTERS

Certain types of informal letters may be typed, *but others must be written by hand,* in a legible manner. It is obligatory to write "bread-and-butter" and "thank-you" letters by hand, as well as letters of congratulation and condolence and notes of welcome to a prospective son- or daughter-in-law.

Invitations to small weddings (and their reply), and engagement and birth announcements, may be handwritten. Answers to formal invitations are always handwritten.

ADDRESSING THE ENVELOPE

Addresses on the envelopes of social correspondence, such as a note or letter to a friend or relative, are written by hand unless the contents are typewritten.

Write out the rank and name in full unless the envelope is small, when such abbreviations as LtCol., BrigGen., and RearAdm. are used. Write out names rather than using initials, such as "Col. and Mrs. John Lee Jones," rather than "Col. and Mrs. J. L. Jones."

When addressing a letter to a boy of twelve or under, you may use the word *Master:* Master John Jones. There is no title for him until his teens or high school age, when he is addressed "Mr. John Jones." *Messrs.* is the French abbreviation of the plural of *Mister* and may be used to address brothers but not a father and son.

A young girl is addressed "Mary Jones" until she reaches her teens, when she is addressed "Miss." When you do not know the title of a person to be addressed, such as a businesswoman, you may write "Ms." A married woman is "Mrs." unless she has a title or rank: "Dr. Mary Jones" or "Lieutenant Mary Jones, U.S. Air Force."

A man may use "Jr." after his name as long as his father is living; later it may be dropped. If his mother is living nearby he may prefer to retain the "Jr." for postal and business reasons.

A confidential letter may have the word *Personal* written above the address if addressed other than to that person's home. When you are uncertain of an address, write *Please Forward* in the lower left side, but not below the zip code.

At all times add the zip code. And write legibly.

SOCIAL AND PERSONAL LETTERS

A social or personal letter follows basic rules. A long letter has the date at the upper right-hand corner of the page. The date may also be written on the last page, near the left-hand margin but slightly below the signature, or at the bottom of the first page. Only very informal letters have abbreviated dates. The more formal the letter, the fewer the abbreviations.

The basic parts of a social or personal letter are:

1. *Date:*
Near the top right or at the lower left: "June 15th" or "June fifteenth" or "The fifteenth" (all very informal)

or   Near the top right: "June 15, 1988" (civilian form)

or   Near the top right: "15 June 1988" (service form)

or   Near the lower left: (same form)

or   Near the lower left: "Saturday" (very formal or very brief)

2. *Salutation:* Flush with the left margin, no inside address. Examples:

"Dear Mary,"

or   "My dear Mary,"

or   "Dear Mary Jones,"

3. *Body of letter:* Indented paragraphs, or one paragraph for a brief note. Avoid overuse of the pronoun *I.*

4. *Complimentary close:* Start at center of page, or start at the right, even with date line. Examples:

"Sincerely,"

or   "Sincerely yours,"

5. *Signature:* Directly under, or under and slightly to the right of, complimentary close. No title or rank. First name only for close friends—or, when the body of the letter gives no clue to the identity

of the signer, full name, "John Jones." Otherwise, write your name in full.

The conventional salutations and closings for informal or personal correspondence are:

June 15th

(*To a woman*)
    Dear Mary,

        ....
....

As ever, (or "Yours ever,")
John (or "John Jones")

(*To a man*)
    Dear George,

     ....
....

Sincerely, (or "As ever,")
John Jones

In letters to a relative or intimate friend, the closing would probably be "Affectionately," "With love," or "Devotedly," with the last name of the person writing omitted from the signature.

The date is usually written at the upper right-hand corner of the paper, with no address. On a short or very formal note, the day instead of the date may be written at the bottom left of the page, two spaces lower than the signature. On an informal note, the month is sometimes abbreviated; otherwise, it is written out.

VERY PERSONAL LETTERS

It is a wise man or woman who observes certain rules in writing very personal letters:

Never state anything that can be used against you.

Be careful of making direct promises or of stating familiarities.

Never write anything that might damage another's reputation or harm him in any way—for the person who might eventually be harmed could be you.

You should guard against writing angry or abusive letters. If you must write a letter of complaint, wait several hours or overnight, and then reread the letter before mailing it.

Letters of apology are sometimes required of even the best of us. Brief and sincere notes of explanation are always advisable when you are unable to keep an appointment, when there has been some misunderstanding, or when you have hurt someone.

THANK-YOU LETTERS

"Thank-you" letters should be written within a week after you have received a gift or a favor, or have been a houseguest or a guest of honor at some occasion. When you have been a houseguest, your thank-you note is called a "bread-and-butter" note. Although the envelope is usually (but not always) addressed to the hostess, there is no inside address, and mention should be made of the host in the letter when appropriate.

A basic form to follow in both the bread-and-butter letter and the thank-you note is:

(date)

Dear Mrs. Doe,

1. "Thank-you for . . . (the gift or occasion, etc.)."
2. A sincere comment concerning the occasion or gift; an expression of appreciation; a comment concerning something of mutual interest.
3. A looking-forward-to-seeing-you-again (soon) sentence.
4. A "thanks again," and a request to be remembered to the host and/or any other members of the family.

Sincerely,

For a bride's thank-you notes, see chapter 30.

RESERVATIONS

When you write to a hotel or motel for a reservation, give brief but full information. For example:

Quarters M
Fort Sam Houston
San Antonio, Texas (zip code)
(date)

The Manager
Hotel Thayer
West Point, New York

Dear Sir:

Please reserve a room with bath for my wife and me, from June first for one week.

If such accommodations are not available at present, let me know the earliest date you can take us.

Yours truly,
James Smith
Major, U.S. Army

A wire for advance reservations could read:

UNITED AIR LINES
DULLES INTERNATIONAL AIRPORT
CHANTILLY, VA.

PLEASE RESERVE TWO SEATS TO STOCKHOLM WIFE AND SELF FIRST AVAILABLE JUNE, REPLY COLLECT.

MAJOR JAMES SMITH (address)

For reasons of clarity, other than in telegrams, use the words *my wife and me.* Upon arrival at the hotel or motel, however, you register as "Major and Mrs. James Smith," *not* "Major James Smith and wife."

The most satisfactory way to ask for, and receive confirmation for, a hotel, motel, or plane when you are short on time is to phone. Use the toll-free 800 number when listed.

CLUB RESIGNATIONS

When you resign from a club, address your letter to the secretary and send it before the date of the next yearly dues. The letter could be worded thus:

(date)

Dear Doctor Doe:

It is with regret that I must resign from the Shenandoah Country Club. My company is transferring me to St. Louis, and I will be leaving by the end of next month.

Please present my resignation at the next board meeting, and express my regret upon leaving not only my fellow members but the best greens in the Valley.

I would like to keep in touch with the club, and will send my new address as soon as I have it.

> Sincerely,
> William (or Wilma) Smith
> Lieutenant Colonel
> United States Marines, Retired

LETTERS OF CONDOLENCE

One of the most difficult letters to write is a letter of condolence— but no letter is more appreciated than the one expressing sympathy at a time of sorrow. Respect and obligation, affection and friendship, are the grounds for writing such letters. A letter of condolence is addressed to the spouse or closest family member, and references to other members of the family are made in the letter.

The brief letter has a traditional form:

1. Salutation
2. An expression of sympathy
3. A kind comment or remembrance concerning the deceased person
4. A last word of affection and sympathy
5. The complimentary close and your signature

Always be careful of your choice of words in a message following a death that resulted from an accident, suicide, or any catastrophe.

The essentials in writing a letter of condolence are the expressions of sympathy, encouragement, and a desire to help. The following example is a letter written to a mother of a classmate killed in an accident.

Dear Mrs. Smith,

I have just heard of Dan's fatal accident, and I want you to know that you have my deepest sympathy. Our friendship began at the Academy, and continued through the years.

I am being transferred next month and plan to stop over in Atlanta en route. At that time, I want to call on you and, if possible, be of some service.

> *Sincerely,*
> *John Jones*

A wire could take this form:

OUR DEEPEST SYMPATHY.

MARY AND JOHN JONES

or

DEEPLY SHOCKED AT YOUR LOSS, ALL OUR SYMPATHY.
SINCERELY
MARY AND JOHN JONES
(or MARY AND JOHN, for very close friends)

REPLIES TO SYMPATHY MESSAGES

Letters, telegrams, and other messages of condolence, as well as floral tributes, charity contributions, and such gifts as food for the family, should be personally acknowledged by the individual to whom they were addressed. This very brief reply of thanks should be handwritten and mailed within six weeks after the message (or flowers or contribution) was received—earlier, if possible.

A sentence or two will be enough, particularly in cases of ill health or extreme grief. In these cases, it is permissible for a member of the family to write the note. Today, all-white paper or a light gray paper is used.

A reply to a message of condolence may be:

Dear Mrs. Smith,

Thank you so much for your very kind expression of sympathy.

Sincerely,
John Jones

Or, to a longtime friend, a more personal note:

Dear Mary,

Your very kind letter gave me great comfort. Thank you so much for the roses, and for writing. I will call you and Bill as soon as I can.

Very sincerely,
John Jones

In order for the bereaved to acknowledge accurately the messages of condolence, the flowers, etc., an accurate list must be kept by a close friend or a member of the bereaved family. When services take place at a funeral home, a member of the staff will collect the cards for the family.

Although letters of condolence are usually handwritten, a letter may be dictated and typed from a business office to someone related to a person the writer has known in official or business life.

MOURNING CARDS

It is correct to send engraved or printed cards of acknowledgment in response to expressions of condolence when in the hundreds or thousands. For example:

SECRETARY OF THE AIR FORCE AND MRS. DOE
ACKNOWLEDGE WITH GRATEFUL APPRECIATION
YOUR KIND EXPRESSION OF SYMPATHY

CHRISTMAS CARDS

Christmas cards are sent to close friends and acquaintances you cannot greet personally or see often. Usually cards are not sent within a service activity or base. Exceptions anywhere are shut-ins.

Envelopes for Christmas cards are always addressed to *both husband and wife*, even if you know only one or the other. A printed or engraved card without your name carries the signature at the bottom of the greeting. The rule for signatures is: the person who is signing writes the other person's name first. When cards are printed with names, the husband's name may come first, but either way is correct. Or you may sign or have the cards printed as: "The John Joneses." When the names of several members of a family are listed on the card, the father's name is written first. It is wise to place your return address in the upper left-hand corner of the envelope when you are unsure of the mailing address. In addressing the envelope to a family, you may write "The John Joneses" rather than "Mr. and Mrs. John Jones and family."

From the strictly religious point of view, Jewish people do not celebrate Christmas or send Christmas cards. However, many Jewish people observe Christmas as a national rather than a religious holiday and send out nonreligious cards as well as receive them.

LETTERS OF REFERENCE

When you are asked to write a letter of reference—for example, for someone leaving the service or your place of employment—you will want to write an honest, straightforward account of that person's ability and character. It is important that the letter be fair both to the future employer and to the employee. The letter is dated.

A letter of reference, or any letter written to an unknown reader, needs neither salutation nor closing. The letter is a statement of fact, and is attested to by the signature. The phrase "To Whom It May Concern" is outmoded. When you know to whom the letter will be addressed, use that person's name.

Letters of reference can be typewritten or written by hand. The general points covered in the typical letter are:

The name of the employee
The length of his or her service or employment
The nature of his or her service or work—and *competence*
Comments on the employee's honesty and character and loyalty to
   the service or business
Comments on the employee's sobriety
Comments on the employee's ability to get along with others
The reasons he or she is leaving the service or business; an expres-
   sion of your regret at losing the employee, if such is the case
Your willingness to answer any further questions, and an expression
   of your confidence in the employee

When you know a person has been unsatisfactory in his or her work, or when the person has a questionable reputation, you cannot shrug it off. You are under no obligation to give any reference at all. But when personally asked, you will need to remember your oath upon entering your service—an oath that lasts your lifetime.

LETTERS OF INTRODUCTION

A letter of introduction can be useful in business as well as in social matters. When you are the writer, you must use care: you are recommending someone as a potential friend, or possibly for a job.

When the letter is handed to the receiver in his or her office, it is unsealed. A business letter of introduction does not commit the receiver to anything, but he or she will talk several minutes with the stranger, and if time permits—and if the receiver is favorably impressed—an invitation for cocktails or luncheon may be extended. But even then the receiver is not committed socially.

When you write a note of introduction concerning a retired officer (or anyone) to a longtime friend in the business world, use your personal card in this manner:

> *Introducing John Smith*
>
> # Robert Edward Decatur
>
> Major General
> United States Air Force

A longer note or letter should be mailed several days before the time of arrival of the person being introduced:

Dear Mary,

A good friend of mine, John Doe, will be in Washington the week of April fifth, and I want very much for him to get acquainted with you. He is reading a paper at the Medical Center and will be doing research there.

John is a fine person, a very efficient doctor, and a specialist in his field. As a speech therapist you have much in common with him. I do hope that you can find time to get together.

> *Affectionately,*
> *Jane Smith*

BIRTH ANNOUNCEMENTS

The announcement of a new baby is made soon after the birth. Usually the choice of cards is made in advance. Fill-in cards may be purchased at the stationers, or in the greeting cards department of a store, or at the PX. Or you may want to send handwritten notes.

When cards are ordered—and they are more expensive than handwritten notes—one frequently used is a small white card, with the baby's name and birth date printed on a smaller card attached by a pink or blue ribbon to the one with the parents' names. Sometimes the card is edged in pink or blue. Such a card looks like this:

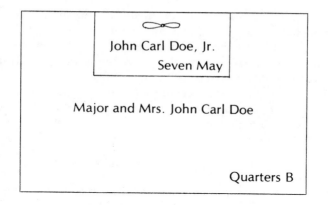

In the case of twins, both names appear on the smaller card, and when the twins are not the same sex, the ribbon bows are of both colors—pink for the girl, blue for the boy.

ADOPTION ANNOUNCEMENTS

Parents usually make public in the very beginning the fact of their adoption of a child. Announcement could be worded in this manner:

Lieutenant and Mrs. John Doe
have the pleasure of announcing
the adoption of
Mary Jane
age two months

Adopted children receive the same baby or children's gifts that biological children do.

ANNOUNCEMENTS OF A CHANGE IN NAME

Should you want to change your name—your first name, your surname, or both—this can be done legally, but select your new name with care. The new name may best be fairly similar to your old name, to avoid causing too much confusion for people you know.

Sometimes a name of Mediterranean or Slavic extraction is very long and hard to pronounce, and a citizen of this country—new or old—finds it easier to simplify it, particularly in the military or business world. But to be happy with your new name, you must *want* to change your old name, not feel that you should just because it is long and hard to pronounce and spell.

Occasionally foolish parents bestow "cute" names on their infants which they grow up to detest. A name such as "Ima Nutt" could—should—be changed to "Emma Nutt."

If you wish, you may inform your friends concerning your new name in person, by note, or by announcement. When a family prefers to send out printed announcements, on plain white cards, these could read:

> Ensign and Mrs. Konrad Mieckelmeister
> wish to inform you
> that they have adopted the names of
> Ensign and Mrs. Conrad Michaels

Or the second and third lines could read: "announce that by permission of the court/they have changed their names to" (or "they will be known as").

If you do not care to send out announcements, the change in your name may be noted on your Christmas or any seasonal card, when you would sign it "The Conrad Michaelses (formerly the Mieckelmeisters)."

A service person must send a request to his or her service Bureau of Personnel, including the court order authorizing the name change. Copies of the bureau's letter of authorization will be sent to all offices having custody of your various official records.

CHAPTER 13

Informal Invitations & Replies

THE ISSUANCE OF INVITATIONS, as well as their acknowledgment, follows definite social rules. These rules may be considered a framework within which you can extend and answer invitations with maximum advantage and minimum effort for both the guest and the host. In general, the types of invitations that you will receive are:

Informal: These may be issued in person, over the telephone, by handwritten note, by informal card, or on a personal card enclosed in a matching envelope.

Formal: These may be fully engraved, partially engraved, thermographed, telephoned, or handwritten in the same form as the fully engraved invitation. Thermography, or raised printing, is less expensive than engraving and is an effective way of simulating it.

Envelopes for both informal and formal invitations are addressed by hand.

Although most invitations are informal during the early years in the career of a midshipman, cadet, or young officer, formal invitations are issued by the superintendent or commandant at the various academies and by presidents of college ROTC units, OCS, OTS, and military schools in all states. Junior officers, as well as midshipmen and cadets, will receive formal invitations to debutante dinners and dances. Official occasions as well as informal parties are encountered during the annual summer cruises to foreign countries. Senior officers receive many invitations to state, official, and social occasions throughout their service careers.

GENERAL RULES

When invitations are extended in person or on the telephone, you must be prepared to accept or refuse without advance notice. When the invitation is one that you will enjoy accepting, there is no difficulty in expressing pleasure. But when you do not care to accept it, your feelings must be concealed.

When you refuse any invitation, your answer should be plausible. Do not fumble with generalities, such as, "Well, I may have the duty that night so I don't know whether I can come or not. . . ." Instead, say "I'm sorry, I'm not free that evening—but thank you."

When you are not sure if you are free to accept the invitation, be frank with the person extending it and say why you cannot commit yourself at the moment. If you can truthfully say that you believe you have the watch, and if a delayed reply is not inconvenient, check your schedule and let the hostess know immediately. If a delay is inconvenient, you refuse at once.

Telephone invitations and those given face to face follow the same pattern. The information concerning the time, date, and place should be repeated so no mistake is made. Write the information in an engagement book or on a pad; it is embarrassing, to say the least, if you forget or arrive at the wrong hour or day.

Oral invitations may be issued for smaller occasions, including luncheons, dinners, cocktails, teas, children's parties, christenings, picnics, and morning coffees. Invitations by card—usually the fill-in kind—are for such large occasions as cocktails and receptions, dances, and at-homes.

Remember to order matching envelopes with the cards. Personal cards used for invitations should have outer envelopes at least 3½ by 5 inches in size, in accordance with postal regulations.

Written invitations are also extended to those who cannot be reached by telephone, or when the location of the house or place of entertainment is difficult to find. Pertinent information concerning the location of the party is sometimes illustrated by charts or clever sketches either drawn or imprinted on the card.

When you receive an invitation for a time when a friend will be visiting you, state in your answer that you are sorry that you cannot accept the invitation because a houseguest will be with you at that time. Common sense will dictate whether you should do this, however, since you do not want to place the hostess in the position of *having* to invite your guest.

When it is convenient, the hostess probably will invite you to bring your houseguest with you. Otherwise, she may say something like "I'm sorry; we're only having ten guests, and the dinner isn't buffet—but perhaps another time?" As anyone will realize, when mixed guests are to be seated at the dining table, an extra guest would upset the seating arrangement.

INVITATION CARDS

For informal or formal invitations, cards are about 3½ by 5½ inches or 4 or 4½ by 6 inches in size, with matching envelopes. The card may be fully or partially engraved or printed with a crest.

At most commands, particularly large ones, the cost of engraving is prohibitive, and good printing is used almost exclusively.

The popular *fill-in* cards are white or ivory, with the crest or insignia embossed or engraved in dark blue or black at the top center. The host's name or administrative position is directly under the crest, followed by the lines: "requests the pleasure of/the company of." A few key words complete the engraving. For example:

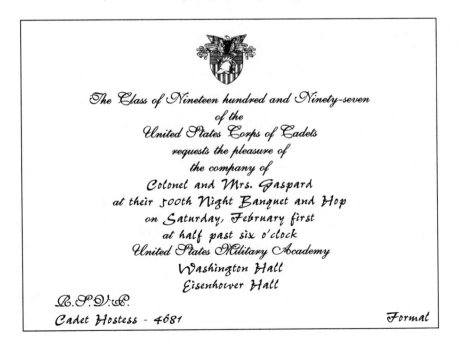

The Class of Nineteen hundred and Ninety-seven
of the
United States Corps of Cadets
requests the pleasure of
the company of
Colonel and Mrs. Gaspard
at their 500th Night Banquet and Hop
on Saturday, February first
at half past six o'clock
United States Military Academy
Washington Hall
Eisenhower Hall

R.S.V.P.
Cadet Hostess - 4681

Formal

The name of the guest and other information is written by hand in blue or black ink. The cards are used for almost any occasion: formal or informal dinners, large or small receptions, etc.

When an officer's station will not change for some time and many cards are used, or when a retired officer has a permanent address, the address may be placed in the center of the card directly under the "at . . . o'clock" line. Or the address may appear under the R.S.V.P., and the place of entertainment written by hand under the "at . . . o'clock" line.

INFORMALS

Fold-over cards are about 3 by 4 inches in size, and are frequently used for invitations to luncheons, cocktail parties, buffet suppers, etc. These cards are called informals and are of smooth, heavy paper

You are cordially invited
to attend
an informal mixer
to be given by
The Class of 1997
United States Naval Academy
Saturday, the ninth of August
Dahlgren Hall
eight to eleven in the evening

An informal invitation may be fully printed

in white or cream or pastel color with contrasting engraving or printing, and are ordered with matching envelopes. Your name is centered on the outside of the card, and the invitation written on the lower half of the inside of the card.

A single flat informal, which is about 3¼ by 4 inches in size, is often used in place of the fold-over informal. Your name is in the center—or slightly above the center—of the card, with the address in the top right-hand corner. If desired, a telephone number is in the top left-hand corner.

The message or invitation is written below the name, and an *R.s.v.p.* or *Regrets only* would be written in the lower left corner. These cards are never used for calling cards. When required, replies to invitations sent by a married couple are addressed to the hostess only.

REGRETS ONLY

It is customary for a host and/or hostess, or aides and secretaries, to write or have printed or engraved *Regrets only* in place of the *R.s.v.p.* on invitations (other than wedding and very formal invitations). This means that only those who cannot attend the party or occasion need reply. At a very large occasion this saves considerable time.

Frequently, a telephone number is listed under the *R.s.v.p.* or *Regrets only* on the invitation, for the convenience of the guest in replying—usually to an aide or social secretary, who keeps the guest list up to date.

Telephone numbers are never placed on wedding or very formal social invitations but are used on official or less formal invitations.

ENVELOPES

Matching envelopes are ordered with informals and fill-in cards, and with personal cards when they are to be used for invitations or replies, or to send with gifts.

Postal regulations require that envelopes be at least 3½ by 5 inches. When envelopes are smaller, write only the name on this envelope and enclose it in a larger envelope addressed for mailing.

REMINDER CARDS

To confirm invitations, particularly those sent to guests of honor or VIPs, and those issued verbally, reminder cards are sometimes sent out a short time before the occasion to those who have accepted.

The regular invitation may be used again, with a line drawn

through the telephone number and/or the *R.s.v.p.*, with the words *To Remind* written underneath. Such cards are not acknowledged.

A smaller fill-in card may be used, with specific information written by hand. For informal occasions, a personal or joint card may have this sentence written on it: "To remind you—Thursday 12th, 7 P.M."

INFORMAL INVITATIONS AND REPLIES

An invitation given by a married couple is usually extended by the hostess. An oral invitation, given in person or by telephone, may be stated in a simple manner: "John and I are having a few friends in for supper on Saturday at seven; we do hope that you and Bill can join us. It will be informal."

An invitation to an older couple might be in this form: "This is Mary Jones. Could you and Colonel King have supper with us next Saturday at seven?"

When the host extends the invitation, it is given in the name of the hostess: "Mary would like you to have supper with us on Saturday at seven."

An invitation written on personal notepaper is usually brief but will give full information. For example:

Quarters 15
Fort McNair
Washington, D.C.

Dear Cadet Jones,

Captain Doe and I are having as our houseguests during Christmas leave Miss Betty Hall, the daughter of an old friend, and several of her friends from Mary Baldwin College.

We are asking several midshipmen and cadets for dinner and dancing at our quarters on Saturday, the twenty-ninth, at seven o'clock. We sincerely hope that you can join us. Dress is informal.

I am sure that you will find Betty and her friends most congenial.

Cordially,
Mary Doe

Monday

Your *reply* should be written by hand and mailed within a day or two, or as soon as possible. Replies are addressed to the hostess only, and the signature is the writer's full name, without title or any other information. For example:

Room 2634, East Barracks
(date)

Dear Mrs. Doe,

    I am very pleased to accept your kind invitation for dinner at your quarters on Saturday, the twenty-ninth, at seven o'clock.
    The occasion will be of added pleasure since I met Miss Hall at the Thanksgiving Dance a few weeks ago. Thank you for including me.

Sincerely,
John Jones

When your reply is a *regret,* you explain the refusal:

Room 2634, East Barracks
(date)

Dear Mrs. Doe,

    I appreciate your invitation to dinner on Saturday, the twenty-ninth, but unfortunately I am not able to accept since I will be in Montreal during the holidays.
    It was very kind of you and Captain Doe to include me, and I regret very much that I will not have the opportunity to meet Miss Hall and her friends.

Very sincerely,
John Jones

Invitations for luncheons and dinners may be sent on *personal cards* or *informals.* When an *R.s.v.p.* or *Regrets only* is written on the cards, an answer is mandatory. Your acceptance or refusal of the invitation may be made on your personal or informal card, by brief note, or by telephone.

INVITATION ON A PERSONAL CARD

> *Dinner*
> ## Saturday, 2 March, 8 p.m.
> **Major Mary Jane Dickinson**
>
> *Army Navy Town Club*
> R. S. V. P.   **United States Air Force**

INVITATION ON A JOINT CARD

> *To meet*
> *Captain and Mrs. Henry Roy Smith*
>
> *Lieutenant and Mrs. John Doe*
> *At home*
> *Fri. May 18*   *420 East*
> *6–8*   *Douglass Valley*

INVITATION ON A FLAT INFORMAL

34 Upshur Road

Captain and Mrs. John Henry Jones

Reception
Wednesday, October tenth
after parade

(If no parade—five o'clock)

INVITATION ON A FOLD-OVER INFORMAL

(Outside)

Colonel and Mrs. Lee Adam Smith

3700 Connecticut Avenue

(Inside)

Cocktails
Wednesday, June 9th
5–7 P.M.
Regrets Only

or

Cocktails-Buffet
Wednesday, June 9th
6:30–8:30 P.M.
Regrets Only

REPLY ON A PERSONAL CARD

Will be happy to come
Saturday at eight

William Paul Ormond

Bill

Third Mate
United States Merchant Marine

It is not necessary to write your name under your engraved name on the card, but close friends do.

CHAPTER 14

Formal Invitations
& Replies

FORMAL INVITATIONS

Invitations to formal occasions may be fully engraved, partially engraved, thermographed, or handwritten on the first page of folded white or cream-colored notepaper, in the third person. They may also be telephoned. Invitations are issued between two and three weeks in advance of the occasion, but wedding invitations and other invitations for which advance notice is necessary are sent out three or four weeks in advance.

Invitations to very important functions may be fully engraved and carry the phrase "request the honor (or pleasure) of your company." Popular letterings are script and shaded antique Roman. An admission card to be shown at the door is frequently enclosed. With today's stress on the importance of economy, invitations to large or small, formal or informal, occasions may be printed, usually thermographed.

An admiral's or general's flag may be used on an invitation extended by him or her, and official seals and insignia in gold or color are often used on invitations for such occasions as inaugurations, dedications, ship christenings and commissionings, and graduation exercises. The family crest or coat of arms may be embossed without color at the top of wedding or other important invitations.

Notepaper for formal use is about 6 by 7, or 5 by 8, inches in size, and is of fine quality in a glazed or kid (velvety) finish. The crest or insignia (if used) is engraved, and the paper is always white or cream color, with matching envelopes.

A double sheet with no crest is often used in answering formal invitations, such as to weddings, dinners, receptions, etc.

WORDING OF FORMAL INVITATIONS

The following general rules should be followed:

1. Abbreviations and initials are to be avoided, but there are some established exceptions: "Mr.," "Mrs.," "Dr.," "*R.s.v.p.*" (or *R.S.V.P.*), etc. When an initial is always used in place of a first or middle name, that initial may be used: "Lieutenant J. Marshall Jones."

2. Ranks, titles, and names are written in full: "Lieutenant, junior grade," "Lieutenant Commander;" "Major General," "Lieutenant Colonel," "Vice Admiral," etc. The exception is that of "Second Lieutenant" and "First Lieutenant"; both are designated "Lieutenant" in the Army.

3. The date and hour are always spelled out, but only the day and month are capitalized: "Thursday, the seventh of January." "Half after eight o'clock" is preferable to "Eight-thirty," although the latter is also correct.

4. The person or persons issuing or acknowledging invitations refer to themselves by their full names: "Lieutenant and Mrs. John Jones, Junior." (When your name is very long, "Jr." is correct.) But their guests or hosts are designated by their last names only: "Captain and Mrs. Brown."

5. Honor guests are designated by the phrases: "In honor of . . .," which is used for very prominent persons, or "The pleasure of your company at a dining-in." The phrase "To meet . . ." is for new arrivals and houseguests.

6. "White Tie" written or engraved in the lower right-hand corner of the invitation indicates a very formal function and means full evening dress, military or civilian.

7. "Black Tie" denotes the less formal occasion and means dinner dress uniform or tuxedo.

8. *R.s.v.p.* means a reply is mandatory.

9. *Regrets only* on formal or informal invitations means that only those who cannot attend the function must reply. When many guests are invited, this keeps correspondence to a minimum. When a telephone number is included, you reply by telephone.

10. You reply as soon as possible, preferably within a few days.

THE USE OF TELEPHONE NUMBERS

At large commands where many invitations are issued, the Autovon is frequently used to verify a military guest list and to replace immediately someone who cannot accept an invitation.

It is customary to place a telephone number under the *R.s.v.p.* or *Regrets only* on the invitation for the convenience of the guest in contacting the aide or social secretary, who confirms the guest list. Such numbers are never placed on wedding or very formal social invitations, when handwritten replies are mandatory, but they are used on very important official and some formal invitations—such as those issued at the service academies.

REPLIES TO FORMAL INVITATIONS

1. Answers should be returned within 48 hours after you receive dinner or luncheon invitations. When you refuse early, a hostess will have time to invite another guest without the new guest feeling like a "fill in."

2. Replies are handwritten, in the third person, on the first page of folded white or cream-colored notepaper, or on the reply card.

3. However, when relatives or close friends reply to a formal invitation, a personal handwritten reply in the first person is a correct and warm response.

4. An *acceptance* should include your own full title and name, the title and surname of the host and hostess, and the date and time; also the place if not the host's address. The reason for this repetition is to allow the hostess to make corrections if the prospective guest has made a mistake.

5. A *regret* includes the same information, except that it makes no reference to the time or place.

6. Envelopes are addressed by hand to the host and hostess, or to an aide or social secretary if so indicated in the *R.s.v.p.* In civilian life it is customary to address the envelope to the hostess (or social secretary) even when the invitation was issued jointly with her husband.

7. A formal dinner or luncheon invitation to a married couple must be refused when either one or the other cannot accept. The rule here is: both or neither, unless the hosts insist upon one attending.

After accepting a formal invitation, you are committed to the occasion over all others (other than duty), with the exception of a White House invitation, which takes precedence over any other invitation. In such a case, you withdraw the previous acceptance. An invitation from the Chief of Mission takes precedence over all others for service attachés.

REPLY CARDS

Reply cards are usually enclosed with invitations to large official functions such as retirement ceremonies, the luncheons following graduation exercises at the service academies and colleges, ship commissionings, parades and reviews, subscription dances, and weddings. Their purpose is to facilitate the check-off guest list.

The cards, with self-addressed envelopes, are the small fill-in type, with specific information to be written by hand.

The reply card is engraved or printed in the same style as the invitation. It should be sent to a couple or individual, but it is best not to include a line requesting information about the "number to attend," or the receivers may take for granted that they can bring extra people—children or houseguests.

REPLIES AT THE SERVICE ACADEMIES

If you are a midshipman or cadet at the service or maritime academies, or are in an ROTC program, you answer a formal invitation by hand or on the reply card.

Remember to write by hand on the first page of folded notepaper (white or cream-colored), in the third person. Answer promptly and include this information in your *acceptance:*

    1. Your title and full name, without abbreviations
    2. The title and last name of your host and/or hostess
    3. The occasion
    4. The date
    5. The time
    6. The place—if other than the host's address

> *Midshipman John Ray Jones*
> *accepts with pleasure*
> *the kind invitation of*
> *Admiral and Mrs. Lee*
> *to dinner*
> *on Saturday, the seventh of April*
> *at seven-thirty o'clock*

If you are requested to give the name of your date, his or her name is added as follows:

> *Midshipman John Ray Jones*
> *Miss Mary Jane Smith*
> *accept with pleasure*
> etc.

If you are requested to furnish the address as well as the name of your date, you write your formal acceptance without adding his or her name. Instead, you write the name and address on the aide's or flag lieutenant's *reply card,* which is enclosed with the invitation.

A *regret* would be as follows:

> *Cadet Mary Anne Smith*
> *regrets that because of official duties*
> *she will be unable to accept*
> *the kind invitation of*
> *General and Mrs. Williams*
> *for Saturday, the twelfth of May*

Other reasons for declining include "because of illness" and "because of a previous engagement."

ADDRESSING THE REPLY ENVELOPE

After writing your reply, address the envelope to the person (or office) indicated in the lower left-hand corner of the invitation, or to the person (or office) whose name appears on the *reply card* enclosed in the invitation.

When you are replying to a formal invitation issued by an officer and spouse, such as a dinner to be held in their quarters, address the envelope to both. For a less formal or an informal dinner, address the envelope to the hostess. For example:

> *Mrs. John Levis Doe*
> *Quarters 9*
> *United States Military Academy*
> *West Point, New York 10996*

INVITATIONS FOR MARRIED WOMEN OFFICERS

There are variations in addressing invitations for married women officers whose rank exceeds that of their officer husbands; for commissioned officers who are married to noncommissioned officers; for women officers who are married to civilian men; and for married women who have retained their maiden name.

There are differences in addressing invitations for official and nonofficial or social occasions. The important thing to remember is that the recognition is to the office, not to the individual, man or woman.

OFFICIAL INVITATIONS FOR WOMEN OFFICERS

When a woman officer and her husband are invited to an official occasion and her rank exceeds his, the invitation is addressed to her. On both the envelope and the invitation his name will follow hers. The envelope would be written in this way, with the second line indented three spaces:

> *Captain Jane Doe, U.S. Coast Guard Reserve**
> *Commander John Doe, U.S. Coast Guard*
> *Office of the Commandant*
> *U.S. Coast Guard Headquarters*
> *(address)*

The handwritten names on the invitation would be Captain Doe and Commander Doe.

The invitation is sent to her office. When addressed to a junior officer, it is sent to her quarters.

When a woman officer is married to a civilian or noncommissioned officer, his name with title or grade is on the second line of the envelope, and the invitation would read: "Lieutenant Doe and Dr. Doe," or (if he is, for example, a sergeant in the Army) "Lieutenant Doe and Mr. Doe."

Should the married couple have the same rank and serve in the same service—and she has not retained her maiden name—the official invitation envelope could be addressed to "The Captains John Doe," and, inside, "The Captains Doe."

When a married woman officer has retained her maiden name, the envelope could be addressed in this manner:

---

*For a formal/official occasion, neither the service nor the word *Retired* is abbreviated on the invitation or envelope. *United States* is also spelled out.

> *Captain Jane Smith, U.S. Coast Guard Reserve*
> *and Captain John Doe, U.S. Coast Guard, Retired*
> *(her office address)*

Inside, the invitation would read: Captain Smith and Captain Doe.

When a unit is issuing invitations to an occasion such as a dining-in, and a woman officer member's husband is in another service and his rank exceeds hers, it is the name of the person in the *host service* which takes precedence on the invitation and envelope. For example:

> *Lieutenant Jane Doe, United States Army*
> *Major John Doe, United States Air Force*
> *(quarters, etc.)*

SOCIAL INVITATIONS FOR WOMEN OFFICERS

Usually, a formal or informal (nonofficial) invitation is extended to a married couple in the same way as for everyone else—Lieutenant and Mrs. John Doe—regardless of the higher rank of the woman officer. If a woman is sensitive about the matter, or if she has retained her maiden name, then address the formal invitation as you would for the official occasion, but send it to the couple's home as you do the others.

Should the social occasion be held in the officers' club, the noncommissioned officer is as welcome as any senior guest. However, when the occasion is over, the noncommissioned spouse is not at liberty to visit the officers' club unless accompanied by the commissioned spouse. An officers' club is officers' country.

INVITATIONS FOR RANKING CIVILIAN WOMEN

A civilian woman whose position and title are higher than those of her husband is addressed in the same way as the senior woman officer. A congresswoman or cabinet member is "The Honorable." Therefore, the envelope for the formal official invitation would be addressed thus:

> *The Honorable Janet Doe*
> *Colonel John Doe, United States Army**
> *United States House of Representatives*
> *Washington, District of Columbia*** 20515*

---

*A separate invitation may be sent to a spouse in a secondary but official position.
**For less formal occasions, the abbreviations *U.S.* and *D.C.* are used.

Women in high government positions have an option in how their names appear on both official and social invitations. Some prefer their husband's title on the less formal invitation: Mr. and Mrs. Doe. The official form is: The Honorable Doe and Mr. Doe.

HANDWRITTEN INVITATIONS

The formal invitation does not have to be engraved or printed, but may be written by hand, on white or cream-colored notepaper, in the third person. The wording and spacing follow the engraved form. The address or place of entertainment is usually centered underneath the line indicating the time, but it may be written at the lower right-hand side.

Colonel and Mrs. John Smith
request the pleasure of the company of
Lieutenant Jones
at dinner
on Saturday, the ninth of January
at eight o'clock

Quarters 4311D

R.s.v.p.   *Black Tie*

An acceptance would be:

Lieutenant Elizabeth Jones
accepts with pleasure
the kind invitation of
Colonel and Mrs. Smith
to dinner on Saturday, the ninth of January
at eight o'clock

A regret would say ". . . regrets that she will be unable to accept," or ". . . regrets that because of a previous engagement. . . ."

FORMAL INVITATIONS AND REPLIES

FORMAL EVENING RECEPTIONS

An invitation to a formal evening reception would be:

IN HONOR OF THE PRIME MINISTER OF PATRIA
AND
MRS. CAESAR
THE AMBASSADOR OF PATRIA AND MRS. LEGATE
REQUEST THE HONOR OF THE COMPANY OF

(handwritten names)
AT A RECEPTION
ON SATURDAY, THE FIFTH OF MAY
AT TEN O'CLOCK

R.S.V.P.
2698 CALIFORNIA STREET, N.W.

WHITE TIE
GRAND BALL ROOM, MAYFLOWER HOTEL

The acceptance would be something like this:

Major General and Mrs. James Smith
have the honor to accept
the kind invitation of
The Ambassador of Patria and Mrs. Legate
for Saturday, the fifth of May
at ten o'clock
Grand Ball Room, Mayflower Hotel

The regret would be:

Major General and Mrs. James Smith
regret that because of their absence from the city
they will be unable to have the honor of accepting
the kind invitation of
The Ambassador of Patria and Mrs. Legate
for Saturday, the fifth of May

SHIP-COMMISSIONING INVITATION AND RECEPTION CARD

THE COMMANDANT, FIRST NAVAL DISTRICT,
THE PROSPECTIVE COMMANDING OFFICER AND SHIP'S COMPANY
REQUEST THE HONOR OF YOUR PRESENCE
AT THE COMMISSIONING OF THE
USS JOHN SIDNEY MC CAIN (DL-3)
AT THE BOSTON NAVAL SHIPYARD, BOSTON, MASSACHUSETTS
ON MONDAY AFTERNOON, THE TWELFTH OF OCTOBER
AT TWO-THIRTY O'CLOCK

PLEASE PRESENT THIS CARD
AT THE HENLEY STREET GATE

CAMERAS NOT PERMITTED

THE COMMANDING OFFICER AND WARDROOM OFFICERS
OF THE USS JOHN SIDNEY MC CAIN (DL-3)
REQUEST THE PLEASURE OF YOUR COMPANY
AT A RECEPTION AT THE
COMMISSIONED OFFICERS' MESS
BUILDING 5, BOSTON NAVAL SHIPYARD
IMMEDIATELY FOLLOWING THE COMMISSIONING

R.S.V.P.
COMMANDER, BOSTON NAVAL SHIPYARD

UNIFORM CARD

A small card, stating the prescribed uniform, may be enclosed with an official reception invitation. For example:

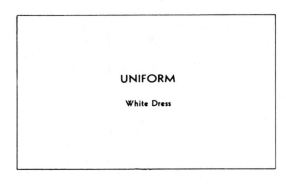

UNIFORM

White Dress

DANCE INVITATIONS

To a debutante ball:

THE COMMITTEE OF
THE CHARLESTON COTILLION
REQUEST THE HONOR OF THE PRESENCE OF
Cadet Richard Earl Doe
AT THE CHRISTMAS BALL
ON THURSDAY, THE TWENTY-SIXTH OF DECEMBER
AT HALF AFTER TEN O'CLOCK
THE FRANCIS MARION HOTEL

R.S.V.P.   WHITE TIE
387 KING STREET

The acceptance would be:

> *Cadet Richard Earl Doe*
> *accepts with pleasure*
> *the kind invitation of*
> *The Committee*
> *of the Charleston Cotillion*
> *for Thursday, the twenty-sixth of December*
> *at half after ten o'clock*
> *The Francis Marion Hotel*

The refusal could be:

> *Cadet Richard Earl Doe*
> *regrets that because of orderly duty**
> *he will be unable to accept*
> *the kind invitation of*
> *The Committee*
> *of the Charleston Cotillion*
> *for Thursday, the twenty-sixth of December*

A less formal invitation may omit the name of the guest:

> COLONEL AND MRS. JOHN SMITH, JUNIOR
> MISS MARY MARTHA SMITH
> REQUEST THE PLEASURE OF YOUR COMPANY
> *at a small dance*
> *on Saturday, the fifteenth of February*
> *at ten o'clock*
> *The Broadmoor*

R.S.V.P.
JUNIPER HILLS
COLORADO SPRINGS

When an invitation carries the names of several persons—such as co-hosts at a dinner or reception, or the names of the parents with that of their daughter written directly underneath, or the names of the sponsors of the event—all the names also appear in the reply.

A reply to an invitation to a "small dance" omits the word *small*.

---

*Or: "regrets that he is unable to accept. . . ."

The Superintendent

and the

Class of Nineteen Hundred Ninety-seven

of the

United States Military Academy

request the honor of your presence

at the Graduation Exercises

Saturday, May the thirty-first

at ten o'clock

Michie Stadium

West Point, New York

The Class of 1997

of the United States Coast Guard Academy

requests the pleasure of your company

at the

Second Class Ring Dance

on Saturday, the twenty-sixth of April

at nine o'clock

Leamy Hall   **Formal Attire**

The Superintendent
of the United States Air Force Academy
and Mrs. Stein
request the pleasure of your company
at the Superintendent's Christmas Ball
Friday, the fifth of December
at nine-thirty o'clock
Arnold Hall Ballroom

RSVP   Winter Mess Dress

REPLY CARD WITH ENVELOPE

United States Merchant Marine Academy
Graduation Exercises
(date)

I and my spouse / guest

_____ *will* _____ *will not attend*
the graduation exercises

I (We) _____ *will* _____ *will not attend*
the graduation luncheon

My name _____

Name of spouse / guest _____

Number of persons attending _____

RSVP by June 10

TELEPHONE INVITATIONS

Telephone invitations are correct for formal functions, mainly for smaller affairs, when the hostess makes the calls herself. The guest may accept at the moment, or if absent when the message was received, may reply by note or telephone.

An aide may call for his chief, or a secretary may make the call. In quarters, a maid may take the call, and the conversation could be somewhat as follows:

"Commander Smith's quarters."
"I'd like to speak to Mrs. Smith, please."
"May I ask who is calling, please?"
"I am calling for General and Mrs. Jones."
"I'm sorry, but Madam is not at home. May I take a message?"
"Would you please say that Mrs. Jones would like to know if Commander and Mrs. Smith could dine on Saturday, the fifth of March, at eight o'clock, at quarters 'M'?"

"To dine with General and Mrs. Jones on Saturday, the fifth of March at eight o'clock at quarters 'M' . . . very good. Thank you."
"Thank you."

Your reply is made in the same way: "Will you please tell General and Mrs. Jones that Commander and Mrs. Smith are happy to accept. . . ."

POSTPONING OR ADVANCING INVITATIONS

If Colonel and Mrs. Smith must postpone the dance, the announcement to that effect would follow the same form as the invitation:

COLONEL AND MRS. JOHN SMITH, JUNIOR

WISH TO ANNOUNCE

THAT THE DANCE IN HONOR OF THEIR DAUGHTER

MUST BE POSTPONED UNTIL

SATURDAY, THE TWENTY-SECOND OF FEBRUARY

PLEASE RESPOND TO
300 FIRST STREET

When it is necessary to postpone or advance the date of a formal invitation, a notice is sent out similar to the original invitation, with this information:

BECAUSE OF THE

IMMINENT DEPARTURE OF

THE CHIEF OF STAFF OF THE AIR FORCE

THE RECEPTION IN HONOR OF

GENERAL AND MRS. WARD

WILL BE ADVANCED FROM

THURSDAY EVENING, THE TWENTIETH OF JUNE

TO

FRIDAY EVENING, THE FOURTEENTH OF JUNE

AT NINE O'CLOCK

GRAND BALL ROOM, MAYFLOWER HOTEL

R.S.V.P.

WHITE HOUSE INVITATIONS

An invitation to the White House must be answered promptly—no later than 24 hours after its arrival. Should you be out of town, answer by Autovon (telephone) or by special delivery letter.

There are valid reasons why an invitation must be refused:

illness, official duty that takes you a distance from Washington, transfer of duty, a death in the family. Otherwise you accept.

Do not be late for a White House function; rather, you should be ten or so minutes early. Reception and dinner guests usually enter through the Diplomatic Entrance, where your name is posted; then an usher will direct you to the room where all guests wait for the appearance of the President and his wife. For large receptions or parties of five hundred or more, the East Gate will be used by guests.

The President and his wife will greet and shake hands with each guest. You do not sit down until they do. You address the President and Vice President as "Mr. President" and "Mr. Vice President," and their wives as "Mrs. Doe." In prolonged conversation you address the President and other male dignitaries as "Sir."

Guests are seated according to protocol at a state dinner, with the nonranking husband or wife seated in accordance with their ranking or titled spouse.

At a reception, a military aide will make the presentations, with men preceding their wives in the line.

A reply to a formal White House invitation follows the standard form; it is sent to the office as indicated in the invitation's *R.s.v.p.* line. You reply to an informal invitation in the same way that it was extended—by phone or note. The reply is addressed to the President's secretary, or his wife's secretary or office, as indicated.

WITHDRAWING AN ACCEPTANCE

There are valid reasons for withdrawing the acceptance of an invitation: serious illness, a death in the family, absence occasioned by a transfer of duty, official duty, or very important business elsewhere.

As mentioned earlier, an invitation from the White House or Chief of Mission takes precedence over all other invitations. In such cases, if you have already accepted an earlier invitation to a conflicting occasion, you would have to cancel your previous acceptance. For example:

Rear Admiral and Mrs. John Smith Hampton
regret that because of an invitation
to the White House
they must withdraw from
Captain and Mr. Jones's dinner
on the third of May

RECALLING AN INVITATION

It is better to postpone than to cancel an invitation once you have extended it, but a formal invitation may be recalled when unavoidable circumstances warrant. When the occasion was to have been small and the guests would know the reason for the withdrawing of the invitations—such as a bereavement or a serious accident—no reason need be stated:

THE INVITATIONS OF
GENERAL AND MRS. JOHN SMITH
FOR SATURDAY, THE FIFTEENTH OF MAY
ARE RECALLED

But when it is an official occasion involving guests who might not know the circumstances, the reason for recalling the invitation would be stated on printed forms, since engraving takes too long:

GENERAL AND MRS. JOHN SMITH
REGRET EXCEEDINGLY
THAT BECAUSE OF THE RECENT DEATH OF
ADMIRAL OWENS
THE INVITATIONS TO THE RECEPTION IN HONOR OF
THE SECRETARY OF DEFENSE
AND
MRS. WINGATE
MUST BE RECALLED

GUEST OF HONOR

It is contrary to custom to invite guests of higher rank than the honor guest at an official dinner or luncheon. However, when this is unavoidable and a dignitary is a guest, the following rules may be employed:

Ask the ranking guest (when not a top dignitary) to waive his or her right for the occasion in favor of the guest of honor.
Seat the guests according to precedence as protocol requires in Washington, even if it places the guest of honor well down the table. When ambassadors and very high-ranking guests are present, this plan is followed.
Make the senior guest the co-host.

When the party or dinner is informal, you may have a guest of honor of lower rank than other guests.

In extending the invitation to someone to be a guest of honor, you may say, "I would like so much to give a dinner for you"—and when the person is married, ". . . for you and your wife (or husband)," for the invitation must include both. A letter may be written in this form:

> *Dear Mrs. Jones,*
>
> *Will you and Senator Jones dine with us on either Thursday, the third of October, or Saturday, the twelfth, at eight o'clock?*
> *We want to ask some friends to meet you, and hope very much that we may be fortunate enough to find you free on one of those evenings.*
>
> > *Very sincerely,*
> > *Mary Smith*
>
> *September seventeen*

When invitations to guests are issued over the telephone, do not use the phrase "in honor of," as this phrase is used only on formal invitations. The hostess may say instead, "We are giving a dinner next Saturday, the tenth, for Senator and Mrs. Jones. . . ."

When invitation cards have been issued, reminder cards may be sent to the guest or guests of honor shortly before the occasion.

CHANGING YOUR ANSWER

When circumstances change after you have given a definite regret to an invitation, formal or informal, and you find that you can go to the occasion after all, immediately phone the host or hostess and explain your change of plans. If the occasion has a flexible guest list, such as a cocktail party, an at-home, or a reception, you will very likely be told to come ahead. But if the occasion is a seated luncheon or dinner, a theater party, or bridge luncheon, etc., another guest may have already been invited to take your place and one more would upset arrangements.

When you cannot attend an occasion after accepting, let your hosts know immediately. A matter of hours either way—accepting or refusing—can make all the difference to a hostess. Remember that hosts pay dearly for large or small catered affairs, whether guests show up or not.

SECTION V

Entertaining in the Home

CHAPTER 15

Entertaining at Dinner

TODAY'S SERVICE FAMILY is the forerunner in the American custom of adapting the best of old European traditions to present-day needs on a modest income. With the modern service family living briefly in many states and various countries all over the world, it is only natural that the best of American as well as Continental or Far Eastern customs be modified into everyday living.

The goal of any host and hostess is to serve the best food in the most pleasant surroundings to congenial guests. The service family combines the French tradition of good food with Southern expertise and a Yankee minimum of time and expense. With the general lack of household help, it is essential that modern entertaining fit today's needs—not yesterday's.

A young officer's household has little, if any, help. A higher-ranking officer's family may have a part-time maid, but permanent household help has almost vanished. The old rating of steward has vanished, currently replaced by the mess specialist (MS) in the Navy, airman aide in the Air Force, and enlisted aide in the Army. They are assigned to the quarters of high-ranking officers, such as the Chief of Naval Operations, the Chiefs of Staff of the Army and Air Force, the Commandant of the Marine Corps, and the superintendents and presidents of the various academies and military schools.

When the occasion demands, waiters are available from a cater-

195

ing service or from an officers' club. Waitresses may serve at today's formal dinner, although this was once considered incorrect.

In keeping with the times, less formal dinners are the order of the day, with the sit-down buffet favored. Buffet meals, with guests helping themselves, are popular from coast to coast.

The modern service family entertains more often, entertains more casually, and has more fun entertaining than ever before. The dining table may be in the dining room, in the family room, or on the patio. Men and women often exchange household duties that once were considered the duty of only one or the other.

It is gratifying to any host to know that friends come to his quarters because they want to—not have to. But it is not by chance that a dinner, large or small, is successful. The part that seems so easy is that way because it was planned to the last detail, long in advance, to avoid last-minute work.

Officers and members of their families will also attend many formal occasions through the years. As an officer, you will attend official, public, and state occasions, starting as a midshipman or cadet and continuing throughout your service career—and on into retired life.

You should know exactly what to do as the guest or the host at any type of dinner, formal or informal.

PREPARING FOR GUESTS

In order to save time, money, and wear and tear, and when they have no help other than members of the family, a host and/or hostess should plan a menu that requires very little last-minute preparation. The main dish should be something that can be placed in the oven before the arrival of the first guests and will finish cooking during the cocktail hour. Casseroles and roasts are favorite foods that can be prepared in advance. A variety of foods—from casseroles to desserts—can be prepared days earlier and stored in the freezer compartment.

All food should be purchased as far ahead as practical, all vegetables and fruits washed and ready to be used in salads or other dishes. The silver should be polished, the house cleaned, the flower arrangements assembled or purchased ahead of time. The dining table should be set early in the day. A detailed check-off list helps the entertainers avoid forgetting an essential.

SEATING IN-LAWS

When the parents of the host or hostess are guests in the home, the host's mother or mother-in-law is seated to his right at the table, and his father or father-in-law is to the right of the hostess.

When both sets of in-laws are on hand, the hostess's mother is seated to the host's right, and his mother is seated to his left. The host's father is seated to the hostess's right, and her father is to her left. If many in-laws should be gathered together, such as at a holiday dinner, then the rule of seniority may be followed. When children are present, alternate them and the grandparents. Teenagers may prefer to have a separate table.

CLASSIFICATIONS OF ENTERTAINING

There are three general classifications of entertaining:

Informal: The hostess serves two or three courses, at the table or buffet style. The host will assist.

Semiformal: There is service at the table, with the host and hostess helping somewhat (mostly before the meal); three or four courses.

Formal: There is full service at the table, with no assistance from the host and hostess; waiters or waitresses serve four or five courses.

INFORMAL DINNERS

MENUS FOR INFORMAL DINNERS

Two or three courses are customary. The meal includes bread or rolls and coffee and tea. The addition of dessert determines the number of courses served.

Main course (meat and vegetables), and dessert
or Casserole, green salad, dessert
or Seafood, chicken or turkey salad, etc., and dessert (summer menu)
or Main course, fruit salad, and cheese (no dessert)
or Soup, main course, and dessert

INFORMAL DINNER, WITHOUT HELP

When the host and hostess serve the meal, the dinner plates may be placed directly in front of the host, with the meat placed above the plates, along with carving knife and fork. The host places a portion of meat on each plate. which is then passed to the hostess for vegetables.

When a casserole is the main dish, it is placed on a hot pad above the stack of plates in front of the hostess. The serving fork is to the left and the serving spoon to the right of the casserole, and the hostess serves each guest. The filled salad plates would be in place above and to the left of the forks.

The hostess indicates who is to receive the plate, with the first plate going to the woman at the right of the host. Should she not so indicate, a male guest passes the plate to the woman nearest him. All persons are served in the same way, with the hostess serving herself last. When the host serves, he serves himself last.

After the plates and dishes are cleared from the table—by the hostess or someone she has asked to help—the dessert is served either from the kitchen or, when attractively prepared and easy to serve, such as a torte, from in front of the hostess's plate at the table. A simple and delicious dessert is a light sherbet placed in a large glass bowl over which freshly cut fruits and their juices have been poured. Coffee is served with or after dessert, either at the table or in the living room.

INFORMAL DINNER, WITH HELP

When a maid serves eight or ten seated guests at a three-course dinner, the hostess assists at the table while the maid is busy in the kitchen. The first course of soup or fruit cup may be in place on the table when guests sit down. Upon the removal of the first course, the main course or entrée is brought in by the maid and placed in front of the hostess for serving.

The plates are set directly in front of the hostess, and she fills each plate. The maid sets the plate in front of each guest, serving from the left. The woman at the right of the host is served first, then the woman at the left of the host and on around the table. The hostess is served next to last, and the host last.

The hostess may prefer to pass each plate directly down the table, designating the plate for the woman at the right of the host, etc. This leaves the maid free to pass the rolls or work in the kitchen.

The maid may serve the main course on a platter, with the vegetables placed by the meat. The platter is offered to the left of each guest.

After the main course is eaten, the maid removes the plates, the bread and butter plates, the relish dishes, salt and pepper shakers, bread tray, and serving platters. The dessert is served from the kitchen, or the maid places it in front of the hostess for serving.

Coffee may be served at the table with the dessert, but it is usually served in the living room. The coffee service is placed on a low table. The hostess asks each person his or her preference for cream and sugar, and the cup is handed to the guest, who comes forward to receive it, or the host or another guest may assist by handing the cups to the guests. The cream and sugar are passed on a small tray, with each guest helping himself.

THE FAMILY DINNER

The family dinner is one that you will attend most often as a guest and will most often give as the host or hostess. Since a dinner with a family is an intimate occasion, guests should consider it an honor to be invited into a home. The hostess usually extends the invitation by telephone, or perhaps by a brief note (see chapter 13). As the host, you may extend the invitation in the name of the hostess: "Mary would like you to have supper with us on Saturday, at seven." If you are the only guest, and if there are children in the family, the dinner hour may be as early as six o'clock.

If you are a guest, the hostess should precede you into the dining room and tell you where to sit. And if you are the ranking or oldest male guest, you should be seated at the right of the hostess. The senior woman is at the right of the host.

When a blessing, or grace, is said at the table, it is said before anything is touched—including the napkin. You may be asked to say the blessing. A blessing that is acceptable to all faiths is:

> For what we are about to receive,
> Lord, make us truly thankful.   Amen

The table may be simply set, with mats or a cloth, and a small bowl of flowers or a simple decoration the centerpiece. The food may already be on the table when you sit down, with the meat set in front of the host and the vegetables in front of the hostess.

If the hostess prefers, the platters and dishes of food—other than a very heavy or hot dish—may be passed in one direction around the table, with each guest serving himself. The bread tray and jellies are also passed to each person. The water glasses should be filled before the family sits down, and each salad placed to the left of and above the forks.

Dessert may be served directly from the kitchen, after all plates and dishes have been removed from the table, with the dessert silver

*Dessert silver placed Continental fashion above the plate at a less formal dinner
or semiformal luncheon*

When the main course is served first, the salad fork is placed inside the
dinner fork. The napkin may be placed to the left of the forks.

in place on the plate. When dessert is served at the table, the stack
of plates, along with the dessert and serving fork and/or spoon, is
set directly in front of the hostess, and she serves each person.
Sometimes the dessert silver is in place on the table, lengthwise above
each plate, before anyone is seated. The spoon is placed above the
fork, with the handle of the spoon to the right and the handle of the
fork to the left.

Coffee is frequently served throughout the family dinner, in
medium size cups (teacups), or with or after dessert. The coffee
service may be placed on the sideboard or nearby table, with cups
and saucers, sugar and cream. The coffee would be poured from

there and placed to the right of each person at the table, with cream and sugar passed down the table.

At a family dinner—or any informal dinner—you may take a second helping *when offered,* or even a third if your hostess insists and if you really want the food. It is flattering to your host and hostess that you enjoy the meal, and you should say so. But if you do not care for a second helping, you need not feel any obligation to take it. When passing your plate for a second helping, leave your knife and fork on your plate, the knife above and parallel across the top or at the right of the plate, the fork placed below with tines up.

Wait for the hostess to begin eating before beginning yourself (unless she asks you not to wait for her), and wait until she rises from the table before doing so yourself. When something needs to be done during the meal, or afterwards—such as bringing in the coffee service or clearing the table—you may offer to assist, but most hostesses prefer that guests not help, or want their children to have this experience. When children are too small to help, the hostess may appreciate your giving them a little time—which you should do anyway—by engaging them in conversation or a game while she does last-minute things.

After dinner, you should leave within an hour when nothing has been planned such as a game of bridge.

THE BUFFET SUPPER

The buffet supper is a way to serve a large number of guests in a small space with or without help, and is the best type of get-acquainted party.

At such a meal the table is placed so that guests may easily move around it and serve themselves. The table is usually covered with a cloth, which is placed over a silence pad. There should be a centerpiece, not too large, and several sets of salt and pepper.

The stacks of plates, napkins, rows of silver, and platters and bowls of food are placed in sequence around the table. Serving forks and spoons are near the dishes they accompany. Dinner forks may be the only silver on the table, since a wise hostess does not serve foods that are difficult to cut, but knives are placed on the table if needed.

When there is no help, everything is placed in the dining area for convenience in serving. A water pitcher and glasses, coffee service, and wine decanter and glasses may be on a sideboard or convenient table, if not on the dining table. Dessert and dessert plates and silver may also be on the sideboard, or they may be placed on the table or sideboard after the dishes for the main course have been taken away.

As a guest, you fill your plate and carry it into the living room or any other room designated by the hostess. Small tables or folding tables are frequently provided by the hostess, but if not, you take any seat and balance your plate on your knees. At very large buffet meals, you will probably eat while standing up.

When you are finished eating, you may place your plate on the sideboard or dining table, leaving the host or hostess, or the maid if there is one, to carry it into the kitchen. Or the maid may take the plate from each guest, removing two at a time. Guests may serve themselves dessert and coffee from the table or sideboard.

At buffet suppers, three courses, as well as hot buttered rolls or biscuits, are usually offered. Although soup may be a first course, it is inconvenient to serve and is usually avoided by a busy hostess.

Buffet menus are varied:

Roast beef, turkey, or ham, salad, and dessert. All three roasts may be served at very large occasions.

or   Main course of meat and vegetables, with or without salad, and dessert. Many meat dishes, such as chicken divan, can be prepared well in advance.

or   Any of the curries with innumerable side dishes, plus salad and dessert.

or   A casserole, salad, and dessert.

THE SIT-DOWN BUFFET

The sit-down buffet table is set as it would be for dinner, with the exceptions of the plates and the main course, which are placed on the sideboard for guests to serve themselves. The napkins, silver, glasses, salt and pepper, and butter plates are all in place on the table.

Place mats are usually used, and a centerpiece. If small tables—card tables—are used instead of the larger table, the centerpiece is small, to save space.

The dessert silver may be in place above the space for the plate, and butter plates are a matter of convenience. When dessert is served from the kitchen, the dessert silver is on the dessert plate.

When there is a maid, soup may be the first course, and this is in place on the place plate when guests sit down. The maid will remove used plates before guests serve themselves at the sideboard; later she will remove other plates. Coffee may be served at the table.

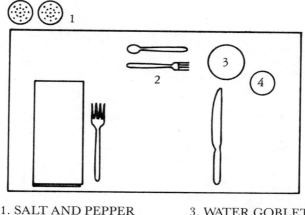

1. SALT AND PEPPER
2. DESSERT SILVER
3. WATER GOBLET
4. WINE GLASS

The sit-down buffet

At very large buffets, the coffee service, water, wine, and glasses are placed in convenient areas, with guests helping themselves.

FORMAL DINNERS

Today's formal dinner was termed semiformal in days when stewards or waiters were easily obtained. The main difference between today's formal—or semiformal—dinner and the truly formal dinner is in the service: fewer waiters will serve fewer courses to the same number of people, and black tie or its equivalent is usually worn by the men, with women in dinner dresses.

The sit-down buffet is a favorite form of less formal entertaining, when the very nicest appointments are used, with the least service. Table decorations are as elaborate as any at the most formal table.

A tablecloth of linen, damask, or lace may be used, or mats of the same materials. The silver will be either sterling or an attractive substitute; the glassware may be clear or jewel toned; and butter plates may be used. The first course of soup or seafood usually is in place on the table when guests sit down, but it is preferable that hot soup be served after the guests are seated, so that it does not get cold.

Place arrangement for a formal dinner

From the left: Meat fork, salad fork, seafood cocktail in place plate, salad knife (if needed), meat knife, soup spoon (when needed), seafood fork. The water goblet stays throughout the dinner, but wine glasses are removed with their accompanying courses with the exception of the dessert wine glass, which remains throughout the serving of demitasse. Only two wines, sherry and champagne, may be served. For the very formal table, fish forks and knives would be in place, and extra wine glasses for the courses they accompany. Individual salts and peppers are placed above the place plate, or one set may be a little below and to the right of the outer glass so that two guests may share one set.

A four-course dinner could be:

First course: Soup, usually clear, or oysters or clams on the half-shell, or shrimp or melon
Second course: Main course of meat and vegetables
Third course: Salad
Fourth course: Dessert, coffee

After-dinner coffee is served to both men and women in the living room. The ranking woman guest will make the first gesture toward going home, probably around ten-thirty when dancing or other entertainment has not been provided.

VERY FORMAL DINNERS

A very formal dinner is always a dignified occasion, but it should not be a cold and formidable affair. Although most very formal entertaining has disappeared in the services, there are official and state functions that high-ranking officers must give and attend.

At such dinners the most delicious food is served with the utmost efficiency at a table set with the most beautiful appointments. Full service, preferably by male waiters, is required at the truly formal table.

Men wear black tie, unless white tie is indicated on the invitation, or the uniform equivalent, and women wear formal attire or the uniform equivalent. Place cards are used, and protocol is followed in the seating arrangement, with due regard for congeniality of guests. When an equal number of men and women are at the table, care must be taken that men do not sit by other men or women by other women.

The formal table is set with sterling silver; a damask, linen, or lace cloth or mats; fine china; and crystal glassware. There will be a centerpiece of flowers flanked by silver candlesticks or candelabra. Customs have changed in recent years concerning the number of courses served, with four or five the usual number; six is the maximum.

The high-ranking man is seated to the right of the hostess, and the high-ranking woman to the right of the host. The host and hostess may be seated at opposite ends of the table, or they may sit opposite each other at a round table or at the center of a very long table.

WHEN GUESTS ARRIVE

If you are a guest, you should arrive at the designated time, usually eight or half-past eight in the evening. Be on time. In quarters of officers of high rank, a mess management specialist (MS)—or the service equivalent—will open the door for you and direct you to the coatroom. In homes of civilians with considerable means, a butler usually is at the door. Or a butler and other help will be hired for the occasion.

Male guests may find a small envelope in a tray on a hall table, with the name of their dinner partner enclosed. A table diagram will be displayed to enable the men to check the seating arrangement. At large dinners, a small folded card with the man's name on the outside and his partner's name on the inside on a small diagram will show the seating positions at the table. Such cards are frequently used instead of the usual card and envelope.

Your hostess stands just inside the living room door to greet guests, and the host is nearby. Guests greet the hostess first, and then the host, before greeting other guests. A guest, or guests, of honor will be with the host and hostess. When the guest of honor is a dignitary, an aide to the host will meet the guest at the gate of the station or base and escort the guest to the host's quarters. The host will be waiting in the hall to greet the honored guest, and to present other guests to him.

It is the duty of the host to see that each guest meets his or her dinner partner before going into the dining room. At large official dinners, aides introduce dinner partners when necessary; at times, the host may ask a friend to make necessary introductions.

Your host, or an aide, introduces you into a group; then it is up to you to meet and talk with the other guests. A choice of one or two cocktails, as well as sherry and fruit or vegetable juice, will be offered before dinner. It is wise not to have more than two drinks.

When a married woman officer of high rank is the hostess and her husband is of lesser rank or a civilian with or without title, he is in all respects the host. When the woman officer of high rank is single, an aide will meet the dignitary at the gate and assist in introducing guests throughout the evening.

ENTERING THE DINING ROOM

When dinner is announced, the hostess turns to the ranking male guest and says, "Shall we go in to dinner?" *But it is the host who offers his arm to the high-ranking woman guest and leads the way into the dining room.* When a guest other than the honor guest or guests is late, the general rule is to wait no more than 10 or 15 minutes after the cocktail hour before going in to dinner.

When the guest of honor is a man of *very* high position, or a dignitary of note, the hostess and guest of honor will enter the dining room first, with the host and ranking woman following. All other guests follow in pairs, in no order of precedence.

Place cards are laid flat on the napkin in the place plate or stood at the head of each plate. Names are handwritten (calligraphy is very nice), with titles and last names only: "Mrs. Smith," "Captain Jones," "The Ambassador of Thailand," or "The Secretary of the Army." The last two are addressed as "Mr. Ambassador" and "Mr. Secretary" (see chapter 22).

SEATING

Women are seated as soon as they enter the dining room. They usually are seated from the left by their dinner partner, who assists with the chair. Men remain standing until the hostess takes her place, with the male guest of honor on her right seating her *after* he has first seated the woman to his right. If there is a butler, he seats the hostess.

When seating a woman, the man steps behind her chair and draws it back carefully; then, as she starts to sit down from the left, he slides the chair forward.

SERVICE

The number one waiter will be standing behind the hostess's chair, directing the service. As soon as all guests are seated, the first course is placed in the place plate, which is on the table when guests sit down. There will always be a plate before you until dessert is served.

The service begins with the woman at the right of the host (see chapter 18). The number one waiter pours the wine as soon as the first course is served, and will serve other wines with the courses they accompany. If there are toasts, guests need the wine whether it is drunk or not.

At dinners held in homes, and at small formal dinners anywhere, you start eating as soon as the hostess begins (or the host, at a stag luncheon or dinner). At large formal dinners or banquets, you start eating as soon as those near you have been served.

DINNER COURSES

Menus for formal dinners are varied. The following menus may be changed to three-, four-, or five-course menus by omitting certain courses. In this country, soup is traditionally the first course, although it may be preceded by seafood, such as oysters. In foreign countries, several more courses may be offered, and dinner may start at 9:00 or 9:30 P.M.

Sequence of Courses	*Accompanying Wines*
Shrimp cocktail, oysters or clams on the half-shell, fruit cup, or	white Burgundy, dry*
Soup (usually clear)	sherry
Fish, hot or cold	white Rhine, lighter*
Main course of meat and vegetables, or	claret, red
Main course of game and vegetables	Burgundy red, heavier
Salad	no new wine
Dessert (ice cream, sherbet, etc.), or	champagne*
Fresh fruit (pears, grapes, etc.)	champagne*

Five-course dinner: Soup, fish, main course, salad, dessert
Four-course dinner: Soup, main course, salad, dessert
Three-course dinner: Soup, main course (asparagus instead of salad), dessert

Rolls and after-dinner coffee are always served. Mints are frequently served after the final course, but not necessarily.

Although the use of butter plates is now condoned on the formal dinner table, their use depends upon the amount of space at the table, since crowding is always to be avoided.

Cigarettes may be offered at formal dinners, but hosts may prefer that there be no smoking at the table. Individual ashtrays, when used, are placed between each two guests at the table.

An outmoded custom is the serving of demitasse and liqueurs in the living room to the women, and at the table or in the library to the men. Today, they are served in the living room to both men and women. When not going on to some other function, guests form into conversational groups. The high-ranking person should make the first move to leave when the time for departure comes, usually within an hour after the dinner is over.

Upon departure, you shake hands with your host and hostess and thank them for their hospitality. The hostess rises when guests rise to leave, but she does not leave the living room. The host, however, may walk to the door with guests.

Although it is impossible to tell each guest good-bye at a large dinner, you should speak to your dinner partner before leaving, as well as to others with whom you were just talking. The MS or butler will open the door for you and say, "Good night, Sir (or Madam)." You answer, "Good night and thank you."

*Serve chilled; serve others at room temperature.

THE LATE GUEST

When a guest is late a hostess may delay serving dinner after cocktails have been served about 15 minutes; then she must proceed. The latecomer goes to his or her place upon arrival. The hostess remains seated—otherwise all the gentlemen at the table would also have to rise. Only the man to the right of a late lady guest rises to seat her. The latecomer should briefly say, "I am very sorry to be late. It was unavoidable." He or she should give an explanation to the hostess later.

RÉSUMÉ

INFORMAL DINNER RULES

When the invitation states *informal,* a man wears a dark or light business suit, in season, and a woman wears afternoon dress. *Informal* means coat and tie after 6:00 P.M.

For a *casual* occasion—say a barbecue or a supper around the swimming pool—sports attire is worn. The hostess must be certain that guests are informed whether the occasion is informal or casual—and know the difference herself.

Two or three courses are served, probably by the host and hostess.

The hostess is not served first by a servant unless she is the only woman at the table. The hostess serves herself last.

One or two wines may be served. The bottle or decanter may be set on the table, with guests serving themselves.

When nothing has been planned afterwards, such as bridge, guests may leave within an hour.

Guests write a thank-you note to the hostess, or telephone. It's the hospitality of the hosts that guests are thanking them for.

FORMAL DINNER RULES

Invitations are extended by telephone, by handwritten note, or by the fill-in card. Those receiving invitations answer promptly in the same manner, except that the fill-in invitation is answered by hand, or by phone when a number is listed.

The time is usually 8:00 P.M., and men wear black tie or the military equivalent. Women wear dinner dress or the military equivalent.

Four courses are customary.

The dinner may be a sit-down buffet.

Butter plates may be on the table.

Small tables seating four, six, or eight are frequently used for seated
   dinners; tables for eight offer wider conversational range for
   guests. A no-host table is a little more intimate.
Appointments and place mats or tablecloth are the same for formal
   and very formal dinners. The most beautiful centerpiece and
   the nicest china, crystal, and sterling are used.
Guests may leave about 10:30 P.M. when nothing is planned
   afterwards.
Guests write a thank you note, or telephone the hostess.

VERY FORMAL DINNER RULES

Invitations are handwritten, engraved, or printed (frequently the
   fill-in card) in the third person, and those invited reply
   promptly in the third person on white or cream-colored notepaper. Invitations are also issued and replied to by telephone.
The time is 8:00 or 8:30 P.M. (later in Europe), and guests must be
   on time.
Men wear white tie for state or very formal occasions, or as indicated on the invitation. In telephoned invitations, the hostess,
   aide, or secretary will indicate whether black or white tie is to
   be worn. Women wear long dress. Military men and women
   wear the equivalent uniform.
There is full service at the table, with four or five courses served
   (but never more than six).
Butter plates are now used on the formal table.
"Turning the table" means co-operating with the hostess midway
   through the meal by talking with the person at one's left as
   well as the person at one's right.
Other guests do not leave unless absolutely necessary until after the
   high-ranking guests leave, 30 to 60 minutes after the dinner is
   over.
The ranking lady makes the first move to leave—other than a dignitary such as the President. She must not keep everyone waiting when it is time to go.
Courtesy requires that guests write the hostess a note of thanks
   within two or three days. Or they may telephone.

CHAPTER 16

Luncheons & Lighter Repasts

OFFICIAL LUNCHEONS

Most luncheons that the officer will attend will be official occasions, frequently held in the officers' club. They may be in honor of a dignitary who is a visitor to the base or station. These luncheons are often stag, but when a male guest of honor's wife and servicewomen attend, other women may be invited. Everyone should be on time.

The table arrangements and service for an official/formal luncheon are about the same as those for a less formal dinner. Three courses are customary, four at the most. An informal luncheon may have only two courses, since the food served at midday is lighter than that at evening meals.

Place cards are a matter of convenience, and are used for as few as eight or so guests. The table probably will be covered with a white cloth, but mats may be used. There should be a centerpiece, but when candles are part of the decorations, they are not lighted. Butter plates are in place, and the first course is on the table when everyone sits down. Each course is served by waiters or waitresses.

Cocktails are offered about 30 minutes before the meal, with wine poured at the table.

INFORMAL LUNCHEONS

When a hostess does not have help, a buffet luncheon is the easiest and most pleasant way to entertain a group of friends. The food may be arranged on a sideboard, and the guests serve themselves and sit at the dining table or at card tables already set up. After the used plates and dishes have been removed to the kitchen, the hostess places the dessert, coffee, and tea on the sideboard for guests to help themselves, or she serves each guest.

In this weight-conscious era, menus are much simpler. A casserole with green salad in winter would be sufficient, salads and sandwiches in warm weather. Fruit is always a good dessert.

The distinction between the words *lunch* and *luncheon* should be observed. When speaking of the noon meal, you refer to it as "lunch." You would say, "Yesterday I lunched with your classmate Bob Smith." A hostess should say, "Luncheon is served" or "Shall we go in to lunch?"

TIME

Luncheons usually start at noon or 1:00 P.M., depending upon duty hours. You stay about half an hour afterwards, unless you must return to your station. You wear the uniform of the day at official luncheons. Nonmilitary women wear afternoon dress or suits.

The high-ranking person must keep in mind that others may be on a tight time schedule, and he or she should not linger unduly.

INVITATIONS

Luncheon invitations may be given in person or by telephone, letter, informals, personal cards, or fill-in cards. You answer all but the fill-in card invitation in the same manner—unless a telephone number is listed on an official invitation, when you may telephone your reply.

GUEST OF HONOR

At a stag luncheon, the guest of honor or guest with the highest rank will be seated to the right of the host, with the second-ranking guest to his left.

At a mixed luncheon, guests are seated in the same way as at a dinner: the ranking lady to the right of the host, and the ranking man to the right of the hostess.

At a women's luncheon, say an officers' wives club luncheon, the senior officer's wife is seated to the right of the club president.

When there is an honored guest, she sits to the right of the club president, and the wife of the high-ranking officer sits to the club president's left.

MENUS

Menus for luncheons are varied. A two-course summer luncheon could be fruit or seafood salad and dessert, a two-course winter luncheon, casserole with green salad, and dessert.

Three-course luncheons:

Soup, main course, dessert
or Main course, salad, dessert
or Fruit (melon or grapefruit), main course, dessert
or Casserole, salad, dessert
or Soufflé, salad, dessert

Coffee, tea, and rolls are offered.

A formal luncheon consists of no more than four courses. For example: soup, main course, salad, dessert.

Soup is usually in place on the table when guests sit down. A two-handled cup, with matching plate, is called a bouillon cup. After the bouillon or clear soup has cooled, the cup may be lifted with both hands, and the soup drunk. When soup is served at the informal table, the hostess may serve from a tureen placed in front of her.

Sherry often accompanies the soup course and may be the only wine served. A white or red wine, or both, may be offered at formal luncheons. Iced tea is in place on a coaster on the summer table when guests sit down. The iced tea spoon is at the right of the knives, or above the plate at an informal meal; after the spoon is used, the bowl of the spoon is placed on the coaster. When hot tea is served, the service is the same as for coffee.

Second portions are not offered at a formal luncheon.

RÉSUMÉ

The time is noon or 1:00 P.M. You are expected to be on time.

There are *no* luncheon partners when entering the dining room. You walk into the room with the person you were talking to when luncheon was announced. A man does *not* offer his arm to a woman when entering the dining room.

One wine is customarily served at the table, but two may be offered. Lighter wines are served at luncheons than at dinners.

BREAKFASTS

Breakfast is usually a simple meal, except for such occasions as wedding breakfasts and hunt breakfasts. A small bowl of flowers or fruit may be on the table, and the table is bare or mats are used.

The silver at each place is usually a fork, knife, and cereal spoon. The coffee cup will be at the right of the knife, the spoon on the saucer at the right of the cup handle.

Jam is served in a dish set on a small plate, with the spoon on the plate. After you have served yourself, you leave the spoon in the dish. Fruit is on the breakfast plate, or a juice glass is set at the right of the water glass (when water is on the table).

Plates are arranged in the kitchen, or the food is set on the table and passed. Food can be kept hot on a hotplate set on the sideboard, along with the coffee and toast, with people serving themselves.

At a family breakfast, the food is set on the table for convenience. When guests are present and time is not important, a leisurely breakfast may be served by the hostess. Then, fruit or fruit juice will be in place on the table, with dry cereal in bowls set above the plate. Hot cereal and other food will be served from the kitchen or from the sideboard.

THE WEDDING BREAKFAST

Following a formal morning wedding, a sit-down breakfast is served the guests. (Wedding breakfasts are discussed in chapter 29.)

OTHER LIGHT REPASTS

COFFEES

A "coffee" is an informal type of entertaining that is popular for wives of a unit or command, usually held on a weekday between 10:00 and 11:30 A.M. Dress is informal.

The menu consists of coffee, tea, sweet rolls, biscuits, small sausages, and the like.

BRUNCHES

A brunch starts a little later than a coffee; it is usually held between 11:00 A.M. and 1:00 P.M. There will be a more elaborate menu than at a coffee, since brunch is a combination of breakfast and lunch. Hot muffins, scones, ham, sweet rolls, pastries, and fruit juice, as well as coffee and tea, may be served.

The brunch may be held in a home, on the patio or terrace, or in a club. Men as well as women are invited to a weekend brunch. Dress is informal.

Invitations to coffees and brunches are extended by telephone or cards.

TEAS

Teas, for a few or many guests, usually start at 4:00 P.M., and frequently are given to introduce someone: a newcomer, a house-guest, or a very special person. Guests should arrive no later than half an hour before the last hour indicated in the invitation.

In a home, a tea is held in the dining area, the table covered with a lace or elaborate cloth. The plates of food, the stacks of little tea plates, the napkins, cups, and saucers, are arranged in a balanced pattern in relation to the floral centerpiece and to the two trays—one for the tea service and one for the coffee service—which are placed at opposite ends of the table. The cups and saucers are close to the tea and coffee services.

The food at teas is varied, but will include thin sandwiches and small cakes. There may be small rolls or biscuits filled with hot creamed chicken, seafood, or ham, tarts, pastries, cake, nuts, and mints, as well as tea and coffee with lemon, cream, and sugar. The serving of tea starts as soon as the first guests arrive, with the hostess greeting each guest upon arrival. Friends of the hostess, including the CO's wife, are asked to pour.

Invitations are often extended by telephone, and replies are made in the same way. Afternoon dress is worn, but not hats or gloves as in former years.

When guests depart, the conventional remark is, "I must be going; thank you so much." The hostess may answer, "Good-bye. I'm so pleased you were able to come." The hostess may accompany a guest to the door of the living room, or a high-ranking guest or a much older guest to the front door.

CO-HOSTESSES

Frequently, two or more junior officers' wives hostess a large brunch, coffee, or tea together in repayment for luncheons or informal social obligations. In the services, as elsewhere, obligations are repaid in keeping with one's budget, not dollar for dollar. Junior officers' quarters are usually as small as their budgets, and getting together in the officers' club for a large occasion can be a nice time for all.

Men are often invited to the brunch, which spans the luncheon hour, and a convenient place for the brunch is the officers' club.

CHAPTER 17

Setting the Table

A BASIC RULE in setting any table, formal or informal, is that crowding must be avoided; there should be at least 24 inches of table space for each person. Another rule is that everything on the table must balance. The centerpiece in the middle of the table is balanced by any other decorations placed around it, unless the table is against a wall, such as at a large buffet, when space is needed. In that case, the centerpiece is closer to the wall.

The traditional table arrangements for 6, 8, and 18 guests shown here may be adapted for various numbers of guests.

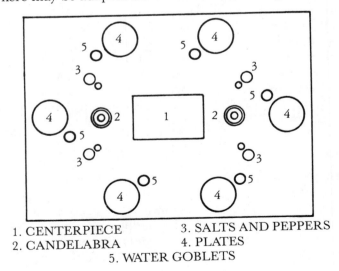

1. CENTERPIECE
2. CANDELABRA
3. SALTS AND PEPPERS
4. PLATES
5. WATER GOBLETS

A table set for six

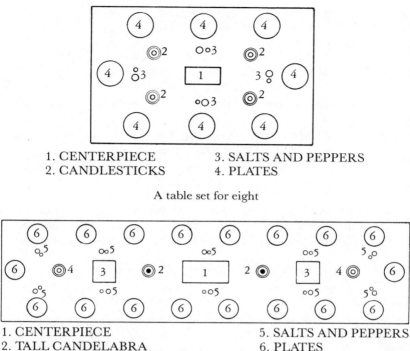

1. CENTERPIECE   3. SALTS AND PEPPERS
2. CANDLESTICKS   4. PLATES

A table set for eight

1. CENTERPIECE   5. SALTS AND PEPPERS
2. TALL CANDELABRA   6. PLATES
3. MATCHING FLOWERS OR FRUITS
4. CANDLESTICKS OR SMALL CANDELABRA

A table set for eighteen

THE MODERN TABLE

It is well for midshipmen, cadets, OCS and OTS students, and single officers to know what is correct in furnishings for the home, since they will have the opportunity to buy beautiful articles at prices lower than those in this country when they are on a practice cruise or overseas air cruise, and when they have duty abroad. Furthermore, such articles make excellent Christmas, wedding, birthday, and anniversary gifts, as well as hostess gifts, when the officer is a weekend guest.

Today's modern table is one of utility as well as beauty. Mats have replaced the tablecloth on most tables—even the more formal table. Harmony in color and design, and balance of table appointments and decorations, are the main rules in setting any table, formal or informal.

The type of entertaining determines the formality of the service. Table linens may be found in every color of the artist's palette and in a wide range of fabrics.

Fine bone china, or any of the serviceable potteries or earthenwares, is the choice of the hostess; glassware is usually crystal—clear or colored, plain or etched. When possible, sterling silver is preferable for the more formal occasion, but silver plate is equally acceptable. Sterling or silver plate, porcelain or pottery, fine table service is never mixed with coarse accessories, any more than fine evening accessories would be mixed with sports attire.

TABLE LINEN

The traditional formal dinner table is covered with a white or ivory-colored damask tablecloth, still used for such special occasions as anniversaries and holiday entertaining. However, the modern white or pastel-colored cloth of lace, linen, or polyester (no-iron) is more frequently used, as well as place mats of the same materials.

The tablecloth should never overhang the table by more than 18 inches, or by less than 12 inches. A silence pad should fit the top of the table, with the tablecloth placed over the pad.

Matching napkins are between 18 and 22 inches square—or 24 inches square for the very formal dinner table.

A lace or linen tablecloth for the formal luncheon or dinner table must not overhang the table; mats are frequently used.

Luncheon napkins are from 14 to 16 inches square and match the tablecloth or mats.

Cocktail napkins, used before the luncheon or dinner, are one-third smaller than luncheon napkins. They are of cloth or, for informal occasions, paper.

NAPKINS

Large napkins are used at formal dinners or banquets. There are two customary ways of folding them: (1) Loosely fold the napkin once in each direction, then fold the square into thirds. Place on the place plate. (2) Fold the napkin into a square, fold opposite corners together to form a triangle, and then cross the two matching points at the back to form the five-sided napkin as illustrated. Place on place plate. Some napkins are monogrammed. The order of three initials of equal size is either the order of the hostess's name (Mary Senn Fisher would read "MSF") or first name, last name, middle name: "mFs." A single initial is that of the last name, capitalized.

Informal napkins are from 14 to 16 inches square, and are used for breakfasts, luncheons, teas, informal dinners, and buffet suppers. They are usually placed to the left of the forks, one inch from the edge of the table, on a line with the place plate and table silver. The open edges may be placed toward the plate and the table edge, or toward the left.

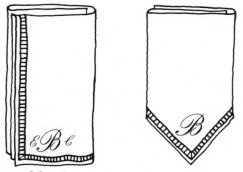

Most frequently used napkin folds

For the informal table, napkins may be folded in one of two ways: (1) Fold the napkin into a square, then fold it in half again. (2) Fold a smaller napkin from corner to opposite corner to form a triangle, and place it beside the plate with the triangle pointing *out* from the plate. For buffet suppers, fold the napkins in triangles or rectangles and place them near the stack of plates, or fold them in rectangles and place silver for each guest on each napkin. At an informal occasion, napkins may be placed on the place plate when a first course is not on the plate.

TABLE CHINA

There are three main types of plates used daily: breakfast, luncheon, and dinner. In setting the table, the plate is placed one inch from the edge of the table, as are the silver and napkin.

Other pieces are necessary in daily living and for special occasions, including coffee and tea cups, serving dishes, and salts and peppers. Various-sized plates are needed for the soup cup or bowl, the butter, the salad, and other foods. Place plates (or service plates) are the plates that are on the formal table when guests sit down.

Although all china used throughout the meal need not match, it is a rule that all plates used together at the same time should match; that is, all dinner plates used in the main course must be alike, all dessert plates alike, and so on.

There are three sizes of cups most frequently used: the after-dinner (demitasse) or small coffee cup for formal and semiformal meals; the teacup or medium size coffee cup at luncheons and less formal meals; and the large coffee cup for breakfasts and informal meals.

The sizes of the most frequently used plates are:

The plate for the main course (the dinner plate): about 10 inches in diameter.

The luncheon plate: 9 inches.

The flat dessert or salad plate: about 8 inches.

The flat bread and butter plate: between 4 and 6 inches.

The soup plate, between 9 and 10 inches across, is a broad bowl about 1 inch deep with a broad, flat rim; it is used at formal dinners. The smaller, handled, cream soup or bouillon cup, with plate, is used at luncheons and less formal dinners.

SERVING DISHES

A complete set of serving dishes is necessary to serve each 6 or 8 guests. At a meal for 12 to 16 guests, a second set would be needed. Serving dishes may match the china service, or they may be silver. They should blend with the china if they do not match exactly. There are many shapes and sizes, with oblong or oval dishes having broad flat bottoms and deep sides the most useful.

Two pairs of vegetable dishes are needed if you entertain often, with a smaller pair for everyday use and a larger pair for serving many persons.

The customary sizes of serving dishes are:

Vegetables dishes, 12 to 14 inches, one or two pairs.

A bowl 5 or 6 inches deep, for soft foods, etc.

A shallow bowl, about 10 inches in diameter and 2 or 3 inches deep, for serving fruits, desserts, etc., or used as a centerpiece.

A bread tray or basket, which may be of various sizes and materials. A smaller tray may be used for serving asparagus, celery, carrot sticks.

Sauceboat or gravy boat.

The customary sizes of platters are:

A small oval platter, 15 inches long, for meat or fish for a few persons.

A large oval platter, 18 inches long, for large roasts and cold meats; particularly useful at buffet meals.

A round platter, 12 inches in diameter, for serving pies, cakes, canapés, cookies, etc.

GLASSES

WATER AND WINE GLASSES

The stemmed water goblet is used on the more formal luncheon or dinner table, and is placed above the knives. The goblets are filled with water before guests sit down. Smaller (and sometimes stemless) water glasses are used at the less formal table, and after or between meals. Goblets and glasses come in a variety of shapes and sizes, and in many different qualities of crystal or glass.

Wine glasses are placed on the table in several ways, but customarily to the right and forward of the water goblet in the order of their use. They are filled immediately after the course they accompany has been served. Sherry glasses are filled almost to the top; wine glasses no more than two-thirds full.

Long-stemmed water and wine glasses are held by the thumb and first two fingers at the base of the bowl. Small-stemmed glasses are held by the stems, and tumblers near the base. Brandy snifters are held in the palms of both hands to warm the brandy.

Hold a glass of chilled wine by the stem so that your fingers do not warm the glass, and thus the wine.

TABLE GLASSES

The most frequently used glasses are the ones illustrated. The dessert/champagne glass may be used for either, and the iced beverage glass may also be used for highballs.

From the left: Dessert/champagne glass, wine glass, water goblet, and iced beverage glass

FLATWARE

Silver flatware is always placed on the table *in the order of use,* starting from the outside and working in toward the plate. Although some of the following rules have been mentioned elsewhere, they are worth repeating:

The silver, napkin, and plate are lined up *one inch* from the edge of the table.

Forks are placed to the left of the plate, with the exception of the seafood fork, which is to the right of the spoon, tines up.

There are never more than three forks in place on the table at any one time. If more forks are needed, they will be brought in with the course they accompany.

When salad is served following the main course, the salad fork is placed next to the plate. When salad is served first, the salad fork is outside the dinner fork.

Knives and spoons are to the right of the plate, with the blade of the knife facing in toward the plate.

Teaspoons or place spoons on the informal luncheon or dinner table are used for soup served in cups or for fruit. Teaspoons on the breakfast table are for grapefruits, cereals, etc.

Spoons for tea and coffee are placed on the saucers, at the right of the handles, before service.

Dessert spoons and/or forks are usually brought in on the dessert plate, with the fork at the left, the spoon at the right.

At informal meals, dessert spoons and/or forks may be placed on the table above the plate. The spoon will be above, with the handle to the right, and the fork will be directly below the spoon, the handle to the left. This is a European, not an American, custom.

The iced beverage spoon, used mainly at luncheons, is placed on the table to the right of the soup spoon, or it may be laid above the plate, with the handle of the spoon to the right.

The individual butter knife is laid across the top of the butter plate, parallel with the edge of the table. The handle of the knife is at the right, the blade facing toward the edge of the table. The knife may be placed on the right side of the plate, parallel to the other table silver.

The steak knife is in lieu of the regular knife.

TABLE DECORATIONS

The center of interest on the luncheon or dinner table is the centerpiece. The size depends upon the size and shape of the table, but it should not be so tall or large that guests cannot see over it. When candles are used, the flame must be either above or below eye level.

The basic formal table centerpiece is a china, silver, or porcelain bowl or tureen, filled with flowers, flanked by silver candelabra or four candlesticks. A long table will have slightly smaller matching replicas of the centerpiece placed midway down each side of the table—and both sides of the table must be alike.

In addition to the candelabra on the long table, four or more candlesticks with white or colored candles may be placed in a rectangle around the centerpiece. When two candlesticks are shorter than the others, they are placed at the ends of the table.

A single candelabrum, or a small bowl of flowers artistically arranged, is on the less formal table. Flowers are on any type of table. Modern tables include use of almost any material in good taste: fruit, vegetables, figurines; antique containers are silver, china, porcelain, or crystal.

CANDY DISHES

Candy is served less frequently today than in former years. Candy dishes are considered a part of the table decorations, and may be placed between the candelabra and the place plates at each end of the formal table.

At a long table, candy dishes would be spaced at equal distances midway down the sides, to be passed by the hostess or waiter.

OTHER COMPONENTS OF THE MODERN TABLE

ASHTRAYS

Ashtrays are rarely placed on the formal or informal table today, as in former years, because of the health hazards from smoking.

When used, ashtrays, either individual or for every two guests, are in place on the table when guests sit down.

FINGER BOWLS

Finger bowls are not a part of everyday living, but the officer should know how to use them. It is not necessary for finger bowls to match the glass at the table.

The bowl is brought to the table in one of two ways: (1) On the dessert plate, with the dessert spoon at the right and the dessert fork at the left of the plate. The bowl is taken off the plate by the guest, who sets it on the table above and to the left of the plate. The guest places the dessert silver on the table, with the fork at the left and the spoon at the right of the plate. When a lace doily is under the finger bowl, this is also removed from the plate and is placed on the table under the finger bowl. (2) On the fruit plate, when fruit is the final course. The bowl and fruit knife and fork are removed from the plate by the guest, and are placed on the table in the same manner. When the bowl is brought in with no silver, no other course will be served.

The bowls may be brought in at any meal but usually are offered at formal meals or after the serving of food that is greasy or that must be handled. They are three-quarters filled with warm water.

SALTS AND PEPPERS

One salt and pepper set may be placed on the informal table and passed around the table when needed. Antique condiment sets add interest to a table.

On the formal table, an individual set may be placed directly above the place plate, or one set is placed to the right of the line of glasses of a guest and is shared by two guests. Sets may be placed in a rectangle around the centerpiece, with the pepper above and the salt below.

Open salts and peppers require a very small sterling or glass spoon.

TABLE LISTS

A young couple just starting out may begin the table service with a starter set for 2 or 4. With *open-stock* china, silver, or glassware, extra pieces or sets are available for purchase. Choosing established patterns is advisable.

CHINA

Sets of china for 4 or 8 are preferable for a young couple, with service for 12 the average in most households. When purchasing a service for 6, it is well to know that when the number of *dinner and salad plates* and *coffee cups* is doubled, the same list will take care of 12 guests at a two-course luncheon or dinner.

The sizes of plates most frequently used are: dinner, 10½ inches; luncheon, 9 inches; dessert or salad, 8 inches. The place plates used at formal meals are approximately 9 or 10 inches in diameter.

In the average household, the medium size cup, or teacup, is used more often than any other cup.

A five-piece place setting includes the dinner plate, salad plate, bread and butter plate, teacup, and saucer.

Service for six:
 6 Dinner plates
 6 Bread and butter plates
 6 Salad or dessert plates
 6 Teacups and saucers
 2 Large coffee cups, family use
 1 Sugar bowl
 1 Cream pitcher
 6 Soup bowls
Extra pieces:
 6 Demitasse (after-dinner cups) and saucers
 6 Luncheon plates
Serving dishes:
 Platters, small, medium, or large
 Platter, round buffet
 Vegetable, open or closed
 Sauceboat

Useful pieces:
> Casserole
> Water pitcher of silver, glass, or pottery
> Salad bowl
> Individual salad bowls
> Cereal bowls
> Butter dish, china or silver
> Tea and coffee service, silver or china

GLASSWARE

Thin crystal, plain or etched, is for formal occasions. Modern glassware comes in all qualities, colors, and designs, and is used for almost any occasion. Water goblets and wine glasses that do not match should harmonize in color, quality, and design.

A desirable list that can be added to through the years is:

6 Water goblets, stemmed, holding about 10 ounces (formal)
6 Water glasses for family or informal use
6 Wine glasses, stemmed, holding from 3 to 5 ounces
12 Cocktail glasses, 3 to 4 ounces (cocktail and wine glasses may be interchanged if the wine glass is not too large)
12 Highball glasses, also used for iced tea or fruit juices, soft drinks, etc., 12 to 14 ounces, no stems
6 Fruit or vegetable juice glasses, no stems, 4 to 5 ounces
6 Champagne/dessert glasses

SILVER FLATWARE

Your silver flatware pattern should be selected for a lifetime. Since there is considerable difference in the cost of sterling, semi-sterling, silverplate, gold electroplate, pewter, and stainless steel, a discussion of the differences between these kinds of flatware is included here to help you select your pattern.

Sterling silver flatware not only lasts a lifetime but is passed down through the generations. Sterling silver is a classic symbol of prestige and good taste; it is used for every occasion and becomes more beautiful through the years.

Since pure silver is too soft to be used as flatware, copper is added for strength; by federal law the proportions are 925 parts pure silver and 75 parts copper. Sterling flatware is the most expensive.

Semi-sterling combines sterling silver handles with stainless steel knife blades, spoon bowls, and fork tines. It is dishwasher safe, and costs about half the price of traditional sterling.

Silverplate is made by electroplating a layer of pure silver over a base metal, with an extra layer of silver at points of wear. It is dishwasher safe and costs a fraction of the price of sterling.

Pewter flatware has a heritage that dates from the early days of this country. Pewter is an alloy of several lead-free metals, with a satin finish. It is nontarnishing and dishwasher safe. It is safe for use with foods, unlike some of the early pewter, which contained lead. The handles are pure pewter, the knife blades, spoon bowls, and fork tines of stainless steel. The price is moderate.

Gold electroplate flatware is flatware electroplated with 24-karat gold; the finish is nontarnishing and is carefree. But you will have to like it, since it is bright. The price is in keeping with the gold karat.

Stainless steel flatware has come into its own in recent years, the patterns both attractive and serviceable. It is low-care, dishwasher safe, reasonable in price, and used for almost any occasion other than the strictly formal.

PLACE SETTINGS

The minimum place setting is the teaspoon, place knife, place fork, and salad or dessert fork.

Starter sets for 4 or 6 place settings may be increased to 8 or 12 as needed. When you have place settings for 4 or 6, you should consider adding extra teaspoons, forks, and salad forks before other pieces, since these are the most frequently used.

SERVING PIECES

A variety of multi-purpose serving pieces complement the place settings. Certain ones are the essentials. The others are nice to have when possible.

A salad serving fork and spoon are very nice to have in your silver pattern, and they may also be used for casseroles and larger dishes of vegetables or desserts. They are available in a variety of patterns of wood or glass to blend with the salad bowl. A carving set for slicing and serving large roasts, hams, and poultry, and/or a steak set for smaller roasts as well as for steaks will soon be on the needed list. Sugar tongs are a change from the regular sugar spoon.

Bon bon or nut spoon. Also for canapés.

* *Butter knife.* For butter service on the butter dish.
  For cheeses and hors d'oeuvres.

* *Cheese server.* For cutting and serving solid cheeses
  and spreads. Also for molded jellies.

* *Cold meat or buffet fork.* For meat, fish, salads served
  on platters.

Cream or sauce ladle. Also for mayonnaise.

Flat server. For hard-to-balance foods like broccoli,
  asparagus, sliced tomatoes, pancakes.

* *Gravy ladle.* For stews, soups, creamed dishes, and
  dessert sauces, too.

* *Jelly server.* Also for cutting and serving cheeses and
  relishes.

Lemon fork. And for serving olives, pickles, and butter pats.

Lemon, olive, or pickle fork. Doubles as a butter pick.

Pie or cake server. For pastries, frozen desserts, fish,
  and aspics, as well.

* *Salad or serving spoon.* Larger than a tablespoon. For
  vegetables, berries, salads, puddings, and
  casseroles.

* *Sugar spoon.* Also great for thick sauces and relishes.

Sugar tongs. Go in the small ice bucket or on the
  candy dish, too.

* *Tablespoon.* The indispensable, multipurpose spoon.

* *Pierced tablespoon.* For fruits and vegetables served
  in their juices.

* *Roast carving set.* For slicing and serving large
  roasts, hams, and poultry.

Steak set. Slightly smaller. For steaks, small roasts,
  and poultry.

COURTESY INTERNATIONAL STERLING.

*Most frequently used pieces.

TEA AND COFFEE SERVICE

A tea set includes a teapot (usually with an alcohol burner and stand), a cream pitcher, a sugar bowl, a tea caddy, and a bowl into which dregs of the teacups may be emptied. Sugar tongs or a spoon and a small fork for serving lemon are placed on a tray.

A coffee set includes a coffeepot, a cream pitcher, and a sugar bowl with sugar spoon placed on a tray large enough to avoid crowding.

A tea and coffee set are usually combined, with the same sugar bowl and cream pitcher, sugar tongs, spoon, and tray being used with each service.

The coffee service usually is silver (silverplate), with a matching teapot and accessories. However, many lovely teapots, sugars, and creamers are china, and both services may be of pewter or the less expensive stainless steel.

There are three sizes of trays most useful in a household:

1. Eight-inch tray for serving one or two glasses of water or drinks.

2. Medium size (13-inch) tray for iced beverages, cocktails at small dinners and luncheons, liqueurs at larger dinners, etc.

3. Large tray (approximately 16 to 24 inches) for tea and coffee service. Useful for serving sandwiches and cakes. At informal parties, may be placed in a room with decanter and glasses or food for guests to serve themselves.

CHAPTER 18

Rules of Serving at the Table

DUE TO THE general lack of help in the service household, the informal dinner is the norm, and the formal seated dinner more for senior officers and those who are attached to government agencies here or abroad. However, junior officers are promoted through the years and someday will be host or hostess to dignitaries.

Today, four or five courses are served at the formal dinner; at the most elaborate, six courses. Occasionally, when guests are going on to an official or social occasion such as a reception, lecture, or service ball, only three courses are served. Food may be catered and waiters hired for the occasion.

For a formal dinner, two waiters or waitresses are needed to serve 10 to 12 guests. Two complete services (sets of serving dishes) are necessary. At a very formal dinner, one waiter or waitress serves each 4 guests. Almost twice the number of guests may be served with the same amount of help at a sit-down buffet, when the very nicest table appointments are used.

A waiter or waitress can serve 8 guests at a seated dinner of three courses in a home, but a hostess assists in serving at the table for a luncheon or dinner for 10 or 12 when there is help in the kitchen.

Many a versatile hostess serves a buffet supper for a dozen guests with no help; this takes advance planning and food preparation and an uncomplicated menu. Guests do not want to see their hosts in an exhausted condition—and no host wants to appear in such a condition. The hosts should enjoy their own party.

ESSENTIALS OF SERVICE

The service at the formal table must be efficient, quiet, and unobtrusive. Guests should not be rushed in eating, and there should be no long waits between courses.

Nothing is ever taken directly from the waiter's or waitress's hand. Everything served—even a glass of water—must be brought on a tray, with the tray held in the server's left hand, his right hand at his side.

Waiters and waitresses address the host and male guests as "Sir" and the hostess and female guests as "Madam."

The waiter wears a white coat, the waitress a dark or conservatively colored uniform with white apron.

The woman at the right of the host is served first and offered an untouched dish.

Everything is served at the formal luncheon or dinner; nothing is passed by the guests.

RULES OF SERVICE

The rule of *formal* service is: serve left, remove from the left.

The rule of *informal* service is: serve left, remove from the right, except for the butter plate, which is removed from the left.

A waiter or waitress (server) places one plate at a time at a formal luncheon or dinner. He or she places the plate in front of the guest, serving from the left, and never reaches in front of a guest.

A server places two plates at a time at an informal dinner. He places one plate with his left hand to the left of the guest, then the other with the right hand to the left of the next guest.

The serving dish is offered to the left of each guest at a comfortable level for serving. Dishes are held in the server's left hand, his right hand held at his side or slightly behind his back. If the dish is heavy it is held with both hands.

The dish or platter rests on a folded napkin placed on the flat of the server's hand. At no time should he grasp the dish or platter by its rim.

A large serving spoon and fork are with each serving dish, face down, the handles toward the guest.

At less formal meals, a server may carry a serving dish in each hand, offering first the dish in his left hand, then the dish in his right hand. Or the dishes may be on a tray and served to each guest, the tray held in the left hand of the server. A vegetable (usually potatoes) may be on the meat platter.

Plates are removed after each course at luncheons or dinners when *all* guests have finished eating. They are removed at very large dinners or banquets after each guest has finished eating.

At a formal luncheon or dinner, the server holds the freshly filled plate in his *right* hand while removing the used plate from the left of the guest with his left hand. The fresh plate is set down at the left of the guest.

At less formal meals, to speed service, the server removes two plates at a time. After removing a used plate and a butter plate (or two used plates if butter plates are not used), he brings back two fresh plates, placing one with the right hand to the left of a guest and the other plate with the left hand to the left of the next guest.

Two servers may work as a team in removing used plates, with the first removing the used plate from the left and placing it on the large tray carried by the second. The first server takes a fresh plate from the tray and places it before the guest, from the left side.

The table is cleared of crumbs before dessert, with the server holding a tray below the edge of the table, at the left of the guest. Crumbs, place cards, etc., are brushed into the tray with a folded napkin or table brush.

The order of removal at an informal luncheon or dinner is: plates, butter plates, serving dishes and platter, pepper, salt, bread tray, and crumbs.

ORDER OF SERVICE

At a dinner with *one service* (complete set of serving dishes) for 6 or 8 guests, the woman at the right of the host is served first, then the host, then the woman at his left, and on clockwise around the table.

Depending upon the placement of the table and the location of the kitchen, the service may be counterclockwise, always starting with the woman at the right of the host, then around the table, with the host served last.

At a dinner with *two services,* and from 12 to 16 guests, the *first* service should start with the woman at the right of the host, and the *second* service with the woman seated to the right of the man at the right of the hostess.

When a very important man is guest of honor at the dinner, the second service may be started with the guest of honor at the right of the hostess.

When there are *three services,* and 18 to 22 guests, the *first* service goes to the woman at the right of the host, then clockwise; the *second* starts where the first leaves off (or after six servings); and the *third* takes up where the second leaves off. However, all services must be synchronized so that food is offered at about the same time.

At times it may be better to start one of the services (never the first) with a man. When there are 14 people, the man at the right of the hostess may be the first to be served at that end of the table, and when there are 20 persons, a service may start with the man at the left of the hostess.

A custom that is not practiced very often in this country but is observed in some foreign countries, including Latin America, is the serving of all women before the men. This is customary at very formal dinners and in most service messes. In this case, the woman on the right of the host is served first, then the woman on his left, and so on, ending with the hostess. Then the men are served in the same way, ending with the host.

COFFEE SERVICE

INFORMAL SERVICE

Coffee is served in several ways at informal luncheons and dinners. There are three main sizes of coffee cups: demitasse or small cups, used mainly after formal dinners; teacup or medium size, used at most meals; and large cups, for breakfast or family meals.

Coffee is frequently served at the informal table with, or following, dessert. At a family meal, with or without guests, coffee may be served throughout the meal. The coffee is prepared in advance, ready to be poured whenever needed. The tray may be set on the sideboard, or the hostess may place the service on the table at her place, and serve each person. The cups are passed down the table after they are prepared with cream and sugar, or the cream and sugar are passed, with people helping themselves.

When there is help, the coffee service may be placed before the hostess, who will pour and prepare each cup for the server to place at each person's right. Or the server places the coffeepot on a small tray with a cup, sugar, and cream. The server stands at each guest's right and asks his or her preference concerning sugar and cream, then places the cup at the right of the plate. Or the server may stand at the left of each guest, with the guest helping himself to sugar and cream. Additional cups will be on the sideboard, convenient for serving.

The hostess may pour coffee in the living room, from a tray placed on a low table in front of her. She asks guests their preference for cream and sugar, and hands each a cup. The host or guests may assist.

Before the coffee is served, the spoon is always placed on the saucer to the right of the cup handle.

FORMAL SERVICE

After-dinner coffee (demitasse) is served in the living room to both men and women after formal or informal dinners in a home.

There are a number of ways of doing this at formal occasions:

Two servers work as a team, the first holding a small tray with a coffeepot, sugar and cream, and one cup. The second server follows with a large tray filled with cups and saucers. The first server asks each guest his preference for cream and sugar, then offers the cup on his small tray. Or the guest may help himself to cream and sugar.

The server has several cups on a tray, with cream and sugar, and stands before each guest, who helps himself.

At large occasions the tray is brought in with filled cups, cream, and sugar, and guests help themselves.

TEA SERVICE

The serving of hot tea at the luncheon or dinner table is similar to the service for coffee. Although coffee is always offered after luncheons and dinners, tea should be served to those who prefer it.

The server may place the tea service in front of the hostess; the hostess places the service on the table herself when there is no help. She asks each guest his or her preference for lemon, cream, or sugar, then passes the cup down the table. The first cup goes to the woman at the right of the host.

When only one or two guests care for tea, and when there is no help, the hostess may arrange a small tray and have the water hot before the meal, then quickly prepare the tea and serve it when needed.

Teaspoons are always placed on the saucer to the right of the cup handle before the tea is served.

COCKTAILS BEFORE MEALS

Cocktails may be offered before luncheons and dinner parties. Sherry, and fruit juice or tomato juice for the nondrinker, are offered on separate trays, the glasses filled before they are brought into the room.

There are several ways to serve cocktails before meals:

At formal or less formal occasions, the server brings a large tray into the room with filled shakers and unfilled glasses. He stands in front of each guest and asks what he or she would like, then pours it. The guest takes the glass from the tray.

At more formal occasions, two servers work as a team. The first holds a tray with the shakers, and the second follows with a tray with glasses for all drinks. The first server asks each guest what he or she wants, and then offers the drink on the small tray.

At large dinners, a tray of filled glasses is brought from the kitchen by the server and offered to each guest.

When there is no help, the host mixes the cocktails in advance and places the tray with shakers and glasses in a convenient place in the room before guests arrive. The ice and canapés (cocktail food) are brought in after the arrival of the first guests.

The host may prefer to place all ingredients on a large tray and mix each drink upon the arrival of the guests. (This is time consuming, and he may ask a friend to take over.)

SERVICE FOR WINES

Wines are served at meals with the courses they accompany. The first wine is poured after all guests have been seated. One wine is customary at an informal meal, but two may be offered. Several wines may be served at the very formal dinner, usually two or three. After the serving of sherry, champagne may be the only wine served throughout the formal dinner.

The server stands to the right of each person at the table and pours until the wine glass is one-half or two-thirds full, according to the type of wine. An old custom is that a tablespoonful is poured first in the host's glass, so he may determine the quality and clearness of the wine. Then the woman at the right of the host is served first, then the woman at his left, and clockwise around the table. The glass of the host is filled last.

Wine glasses may remain on the table throughout the meal, except when several wines are to be served. In that case, the sherry glass is removed after the salad course. Glasses are refilled whenever empty.

Wines served at luncheons are lighter than those at dinners. Sherry may be the only wine served at luncheons, or a white or red wine—sometimes both. Usually, red wines are decanted and the white wines are left in the bottle.

One bottle or decanter will serve each 5 or 6 guests at informal meals, and a bottle or decanter may be placed at each end of the table for 10 or 12 guests. The host fills the glass for the woman at his right and at his left; then the bottle is passed around the table to his left.

Champagne may be served in the living room after a very formal dinner, or at a home wedding reception or dance. The bottles and unfilled glasses are placed on a tray, with a server pouring the champagne and serving each guest.

SERVICE FOR LIQUEURS

Liqueurs are served after dinners but not after luncheons. They are offered after formal and informal meals, following the serving of coffee.

The service for liqueurs is similar to that for cocktails at a formal dinner, with two servers working as a team, the first holding a small tray and taking the liqueur and glass from a tray held by the second.

At informal meals, the host or hostess serves liqueurs from a tray arranged beforehand with bottles and glasses.

CHAPTER 19

Duties of the Host & Hostess

THE HOSTS

The "rule of thumb" at any party, formal or informal, is: good food, good conversation, and good company. The primary responsibility of the host and hostess is to see that guests enjoy the occasion. Not only must the food excel, but the guests must be congenial. An air of cold formality is to be avoided—even if the occasion is formal.

The host and hostess should be in the living (or club) room ten minutes before the luncheon or dinner hour, relaxed and ready to greet the guests, warmly but not effusively.

When incompatible personalities are brought together, a pleasant evening may be ruined. If it is unavoidable to have two such personalities at the same party, place them as far apart at a dining table as possible.

When a high-ranking person or dignitary is your guest, he or she must not be lionized to the extent that other guests feel neglected. Special respect is due guests in high position, but each guest must feel welcome.

As the host, you talk with all guests during the course of the evening. You move from group to group and make a special effort to introduce newcomers or a single or shy individual into small groups. Bring persons of less rank or position to meet the person of high rank, or the guest of honor.

A good host will "hear all and see all." You should notice when a guest is left out of a group, or when he or she seems bored. You should be careful of interrupting a group that is obviously congenial, but you do interrupt when the conversation becomes controversial, particularly if the discussion is to the discredit of another guest or person.

A good host tries to anticipate his guests' needs but is never overanxious or overly casual. Do not insist that a guest have another drink or more food when he refuses. You may offer again, but allow a little time to elapse. Never urge a guest to have "just one more drink," and if that person does not drink at all, never make a joke of it or point it out to other guests. Instead, offer any soft drinks that you have without comment.

When something goes wrong—when the food is burned or when you run out of ginger ale—do not apologize profusely. Never apologize because your quarters are small and the food not elaborate. Don't discredit your hospitality by belittling it. Guests should not feel forced to reassure their hosts that the evening is wonderful and the food superb.

At a buffet meal, when plates must be balanced in guests' laps, avoid serving food that must be cut with a knife.

Before the party, the host and hostess plan what guests will do following the meal. Bridge, charades, or dancing are frequently enjoyed, but hosts often prefer that guests continue in conversational groups.

THE GUESTS

As a guest, you owe it to your hosts to be congenial and to mix and talk with other guests at any social occasion. Upon arrival and departure, shake hands with your host and hostess.

During any party, large or small, you talk with your hosts for a brief period, but you do not monopolize their time. A congenial guest moves from group to group, conversing with as many other guests as possible.

When your luncheon or dinner partner is a stranger to you, there are many agreeable subjects with which to initiate and maintain a conversation: current plays, a bestseller, a TV program. If your partner is in one of the services, you can always discuss the merits of a recent duty station. However, each guest must carry his or her share of the conversation with some "small talk" which does not include business or "shop."

If it is your misfortune to be seated alongside someone whom you do not particularly care for, you must conceal your feelings. You are expected to talk with your partner at your right, but do not forget the person at your left.

THE LATE GUEST

The hostess must decide how long to wait for a late dinner or luncheon guest when something is being served that may be spoiled by waiting. Also, the hosts may be planning on going to a lecture or dance, and then it would be impossible to wait longer than 15 minutes past the set time.

THE OBNOXIOUS GUEST

Although the host and hostess do everything within reason to make their guests comfortable, their hospitality should not be taken advantage of by a rude or unthinking guest. It is always difficult for the host to handle a situation in which a guest makes himself undesirable by coarse conversation or by drinking too much or by insulting another guest. In consideration of the other guests, this cannot be tolerated. You may tactfully introduce another subject of conversation or suggest to the insulting guest that you show him or her something in another room, and thus draw him away from the group where he is not desired.

You may have to ask a trusted friend to drive the unwise drinker home.

Since you are responsible for whatever happens within your home, no guest should be made to feel embarrassed about anything. You do not discuss any such unpleasant incident with others—but you must think twice about inviting such a guest into your home again.

As host, you may have to speed on their way the guests who stay too long. You can sometimes accomplish this by mentioning an early-morning golf game, the next day's heavy duty, or an important conference. And again you may have to disentangle yourself from the guest who opens a new—and lengthy—conversation at the door after already saying good-bye.

Concerning the friend who habitually drops in around cocktail or mealtime, you should feel no obligation to ask him or her to stay at times when this is inconvenient. You may say, "We have already made plans for the evening or I'd ask you to join us. . . . Perhaps some other time."

BREAKING AN ENGAGEMENT

A person should not break a social engagement unless an emergency arises, such as illness or a change of orders. A sudden decision not to go because "you don't want to" or because a better invitation has been received is no excuse at all after you have previously accepted an invitation.

An acceptance or refusal should be made as soon as possible. Immediately check your calendar and make certain that you have no other commitment on that date. An early reply gives the hostess time to call another person without making him or her feel like a last-minute replacement, although a person should not mind being a replacement—occasionally. When you refuse an invitation, explain why.

EXTENDING INVITATIONS

An invitation is *not* extended by saying, "You must come to dinner with us sometime," but by setting the date.

Junior officers are not expected to repay the hospitality of their seniors in the same style; rather, they should entertain in a way that they can afford. Hospitality is not weighed by the dollar.

RÉSUMÉ

Some of the following tips have been mentioned elsewhere, but they are important enough to bear repeating.

A thoughtful guest will offer assistance to the host or hostess when assistance seems needed, particularly in a house without help, but do not insist. If your offer is accepted, go about your task quietly and efficiently. You never "do the honors" in another person's house.

A thoughtless guest is one who asks the hostess at the last minute if a friend may come along—thus upsetting the seating plan at a more formal table.

No one wants to make an error in the use of silver at the table, but do not worry about it if you do. And when you spill something, do not overapologize and make everyone uncomfortable.

If you, the guest, break anything of value, try to replace it as soon as possible. Do not buy a coffee cup in another pattern—it will be of little use to the hostess and a waste of money. You may, instead, send flowers and a note of apology to the hostess. The note should be brief, with an expression of regret concerning the mishap—which, at some time in some way, has happened to everyone.

A guest should accept no more than one or two cocktails before dinner, and no more than one or two liqueurs after dinner. The guest who overindulges in drink is a problem to a host—and a nuisance to everyone else.

Do not take a lighted cigarette to the dining table, and *never* use a saucer or plate as an ashtray. The host or hostess may prefer no smoking at the table, and therefore smoking is not appropriate until after dinner—or at all.

When a single woman is a guest, she is responsible for her own transportation and any taxi fare. Should the hosts live in the suburbs, where most people arrive by car, it is considerate of them to ask a person living in her area to offer a ride. But guests of all ages and numbers take care of their own conveyance.

It goes without saying that guests never call attention to poor service or poor food, or discuss such things with other guests.

SECTION VI

Your Table Manners

CHAPTER 20

Good Table Manners

GOOD TABLE MANNERS in the services are good table manners anywhere. Customs may vary abroad and in various parts of the United States, but good fundamentals in eating are generally the same. The proper use of table silver should be as easy and as familiar to you as the proper use of any mechanical device you consider important to your career.

Mealtime is the time for enjoyment of not only foods but also the company of others. Pleasant conversation, coupled with the relaxation that comes with knowing what to do, will mean pleasure in dining anyplace—in a luxurious hotel, in the mess, or at an embassy.

Good manners are not turned on or off in accordance with the importance of the occasion or the individual, yet neither are they marked by rigid formality. The desirable attitude at even the most formal occasion is *relaxed politeness*. The ability to make interesting "small talk" is always desirable.

But it takes everyday practice before manners at the table become easy and automatic. Poor manners at home will invariably mean poor manners in the mess or the commandant's quarters.

TABLE TRADITIONS

The modern-day use of table silver goes back to A.D. 1100, when the wife of an Italian nobleman introduced the two-tined fork into table usage in Venice because she did not like to pick up meat with her fingers.

The use of forks was not entirely satisfactory, and their use spread but slowly, even in Italy, where they had the blessing of the nobility. Complete acceptance of the fork came only with the Renaissance, which also ushered in the use of the table knife to displace the common hunting knife which every freeman carried at all times on his belt and used at the table for cutting.

France and England were slower in accepting these customs, and it was not until the mid-1600s that English craftsmen commenced the manufacture of table knives and forks, and then spoons. These utensils were made of silver and were still rare.

As a result of the scarcity of table silver, it fell to the English gentry to formulate the table manners of the land. It is from them that Americans inherit their table manners, modified somewhat by native American thought and customs.

The first table napkins made their appearance in Reims, France, in the court of Charles VII. They were used exclusively in the palaces of kings and princes, and from the early part of the fifteenth century they were trimmed in lace and intricate embroidery.

Later, in the seventeenth century, napkins became an important decorative element in table setting. They were folded and pleated to represent flowers, birds, fans. Ornate foldings are still used occasionally in Europe, and there reputedly are 400 ways of folding napkins. In this country, however, a few simple methods of folding are preferred.

MEALS

Dinner is the main meal of the day in the United States, when, except on Sundays and holidays, it is the evening meal. Luncheon is the everyday noon meal, and a light or informal evening meal is usually called "supper." (In certain sections of this country, dinner is the noon meal and supper the evening meal.)

Suppers are also held after formal occasions, such as weddings, dances, and receptions, and may be served very late. Buffet meals in the evening are referred to as *suppers,* never *dinners*—even when guests are in evening attire.

When abroad, remember that dinner in many countries is not served until 9:00 or 9:30 in the evening.

EATING CUSTOMS

FLATWARE

You may use the American or Continental way of eating, but the favored American custom is to hold the dinner fork in your left hand to pin down the food for cutting, and then to transfer the fork, tines up, to the right hand for the purpose of eating. The Continental, or European, custom of eating is to transfer the food to the mouth from the fork while it is still held in the left hand, tines down. Either fashion is correct.

In the United States, the *knife* is always held in the right hand, with the handle in your palm and your index finger along the back of the blade. After using the knife, never put it down on the table. Place the knife across the upper half of the plate, or on the right side of the plate, with the blade facing in.

The *fork* is held in the left hand while being used with the knife to cut food. The handle of the fork will rest in your palm, with your index finger extending along the back.

Basic table setting

At all other times, the fork is preferably held in the right hand, tines up, with the handle controlled by your thumb and first two fingers in a manner similar to holding a pencil. The end of the handle should extend out between your thumb and index finger.

After using the fork, put it on the plate below the knife, or at the left of the plate and parallel to the knife, with the handle at the right and the tines up.

The *spoon* is held in the right hand in the same manner as the fork. Strictly speaking, the only spoon to appear on the table at the beginning of a meal—except breakfast—is a soup spoon. However, a modern hostess places the teaspoon or place spoon at the right of the knife at an informal or family meal.

The most commonly used spoon is the *teaspoon*. It is used at informal meals for dessert, tea, coffee, cereal, grapefruit, etc. The multipurpose *place spoon* is slightly larger than the teaspoon and is used for dessert and cereal as well as for soup served in a soup bowl or bouillon cup at less formal meals and luncheons.

The *coffee spoon* is laid on its saucer after being used. When coffee is served in a mug and there is a tablecloth or mat that would stain, the bowl of the spoon may be rested, tip down, on the rim of the butter or dinner plate.

The place knife, fork, and spoon are the most frequently used utensils.

The individual *butter knife* (sometimes called a *butter spreader*) is usually laid across the top of the butter plate, with the handle at the right, the blade facing the edge of the table. The individual butter knife is used only to spread butter on a piece of bread. It is not used to take butter from the butter plate. A knife for that purpose is placed on the butter dish—when such a dish is used. The individual butter knife is much smaller than a dinner knife.

The *salad fork* is shorter than the luncheon or dinner fork and may be used for either a salad or a dessert course. The placement of the fork depends upon when the salad course will be served. When the salad is served after the main course, the fork is placed next to the plate on the left-hand side, and inside the place fork. When salad is served as a first course, the salad fork is placed outside the luncheon or dinner fork. When there is no separate salad course and the fork is to be used for dessert, the fork is usually placed on the dessert plate.

A *seafood fork,* or oyster fork, is much shorter and slimmer than the salad fork, and is placed at the right or outside of the spoon. Sometimes the tines of the seafood fork rest in the bowl of the spoon, with the handle of the fork placed even with the handle of the spoon.

The *dessert spoon* is longer than a teaspoon and is placed on the dessert plate at formal meals as well as at informal meals. But the place spoon and/or fork, most frequently used for dessert, may be on the table at the beginning of an informal meal. The place spoon may also be used for cereal or soup—but not for cream soup.

The *iced beverage spoon* (iced tea spoon) is a long-handled spoon. After the spoon is used, the bowl of the spoon is laid on the small service plate or coaster which should be placed under the iced beverage glass. However, when no such plate or coaster has been provided, and if this is not a luncheon where you could rest the spoon on the rim of your butter or luncheon plate, as you would with a spoon for the coffee mug, then leave the spoon in the glass and drink with the handle held against the far side with your finger. Then leave the spoon in the glass. This is awkward—but correct.

Soup spoons are longer than the dessert spoon or teaspoon, and they have oval bowls. In using a soup spoon, dip the spoon *away* from you and avoid scraping the bottom of the soup bowl. After the spoon is used, it is placed on the soup plate on the right-hand side.

Demitasse (coffee) spoons are used with small cups of after-dinner coffee. They are about four inches long, and are placed on the saucer when coffee is served.

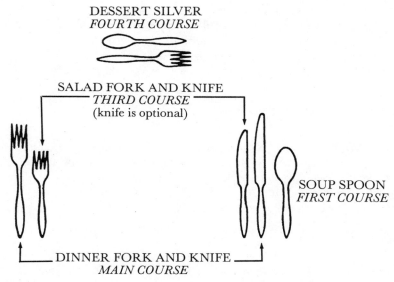

DESSERT SILVER
FOURTH COURSE

SALAD FORK AND KNIFE
THIRD COURSE
(knife is optional)

SOUP SPOON
FIRST COURSE

DINNER FORK AND KNIFE
MAIN COURSE

Flatware in place for a four-course meal, one inch from the edge of the table

When salad is served first, the salad fork is placed outside the dinner fork.

The *serving fork and spoon* are placed on the platter or in the vegetable dish. These pieces are larger than other forks and spoons. In serving yourself, you hold these like other forks and spoons, with the fork in your left hand, the spoon in your right hand. Slip the spoon under a portion of food, and, while holding the food in place with the fork, transfer the food to your plate. Meats are usually portioned before serving, but if not, you cut the food—meat loaf, for example—with the spoon and transfer it to your plate with the fork and spoon. A pierced serving spoon permits liquids to drain from such vegetables as peas and corn.

Remember to use *table silver* (or *flatware,* as it is called) beginning from the outside and working in toward the plate. There should not be more than three knives and three forks placed on the most formal table at any time. If more silver is needed, it should be brought in with the courses it accompanies.

NAPKINS

Napkins are placed at the left of the forks at luncheons and informal meals, and on the place plate at formal meals. After you sit down at the table—and after grace has been said—place your napkin, half unfolded, in your lap as soon as your hostess takes up her napkin. To place the napkin smoothly, pick it up by the right top corners and spread in one motion across your lap.

At the end of the meal, replace the napkin *unfolded* at the left of your plate. At formal dinners, the napkin may be laid at the right of the plate. When paper napkins are used at informal meals, they are laid at the left of the plate. Never crush or roll them into a ball.

HOW TO EAT VARIOUS FOODS

Artichokes: Pull off each leaf, dip the base of the leaf in a sauce, and eat. When down to the heart, scrape or cut off the fuzz with a knife, cut and eat the heart. Leaves are piled on the plate or butter plate.

Avocados: When halved, with a spoon. When peeled and served in a salad, with a fork.

Bacon: With a fork.

Cake: With a fork when served as a dessert.

Caviar: On small pieces of toast with cocktails, or in a bowl before dinner or at buffet suppers.

Cheese: With the salad course, or with fruit and coffee as the final course, with a fork.

Chicken: Broiled or fried, hold with the fork in the plate, strip the meat off the bones with your knife. Or, at home, hold the chicken in your left hand against the plate, strip the meat off with the fork. At picnics, family meals, etc., fried chicken is eaten in the fingers.

Corn on the Cob: Serve only at informal meals. Hold with the hands or by small spears inserted in each end. Salt, pepper, and butter are sometimes mixed in small pats or balls before the meal, or mix on the dinner plate before eating. Butter a few rows of kernels at a time.

Cream Puffs or Eclairs: With a fork when served at the table.

Fish: When not boned, hold in the plate with the fork, slit with tip of the knife from head to tail. Insert tip of knife under the end of the backbone and lift out the skeleton. Lay skeleton and bones on the side of the plate. *Fillet* means "without bones."

Fresh Fruits (except citrus fruit): At the table, either the American or Continental way. Continental is to skin the fruit, halve and stone it, then cut into small pieces and eat with the fork. The American way is to halve, quarter, and stone the fruit with the knife and fork, but not skin it (except peaches); eat the quarters with a fork. At a formal dinner, fruit is served with a fruit knife and fork. Fresh grapes and cherries are eaten whole; remove pits with the fingers; place on side of plate.

Frog Legs: In the same manner as chicken.

Fruit Compote (fruit cocktail): Served in juice, with a spoon. Without juice, as in a salad, with a fork.

Grapefruit and Oranges: Served in halves, with a fruit spoon or a teaspoon. Do not squeeze the fruit for juice.

Honey: With a twisting motion of the serving spoon, catch any drops, then transfer the spoonful to the butter plate.

Ice Cream: With a fork and/or spoon; the fork is for the solid part, the spoon for the soft. With a spoon when served in a sherbet glass.

Lobster and Hard-Shelled Crabs: Boiled or broiled, break shells, remove meat with seafood fork. The major part of the meat is in the stomach cavity and the tail or claws. The best crab meat is in the large claws and the main body.

Olives: Hold in the fingers; place stones on butter plate. Small stuffed olives are eaten whole.

Onion Rings: With a fork.

Oranges and Tangerines: Other than at the table, peel and hold in the fingers; eat segments by hand. At the table, peeled in their juices, with a spoon.

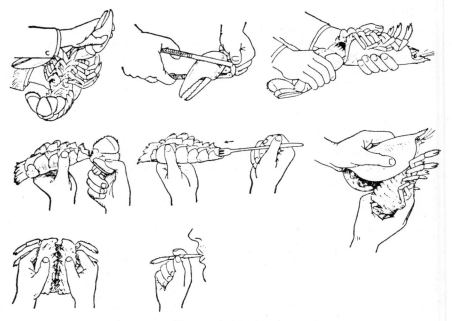

How to eat lobster

Courtesy State of Maine Department of Economic Development.

Oysters and Clams on the Half Shell: Eat raw with oyster fork. Lift
whole from shell, sprinkle with lemon juice or dip in cocktail
sauce, eat in a single mouthful. As a first course, the half shells
come to the table in cracked ice. Regardless of size, do not cut
oysters or clams with fork before eating. Clams are usually
served steamed, until the shell has opened. If not fully open,
bend the shell back with fingers, hold in left hand over the
dish, lift out clam by neck with right hand. Pull body of the
clam out and discard neck sheath. Hold clam in right hand,
dip in melted butter or broth, or both, eat in one bite. Place
empty shells on plate provided for that purpose. Fried clams,
eat with fork. Clam broth is drunk in a bouillon cup or small
bowl.

Pâté de Foie Gras: Imported paste of goose livers, served on toast at
cocktail parties, or with cocktails before dinner. Or in its
earthenware crock on a tray with a knife at a buffet supper.

Pickles: With a fork when served with meat at a table.

Potato Chips: With the fingers.

Potatoes: French fried, with the fork after being cut in shorter lengths. Do not spear with the fork.

Salad: Cut and eat with a fork. Iceberg lettuce is cut with a knife and fork, then eaten with fork.

Sandwiches: By hand. The large or double-decker sandwiches are cut in half, then in quarter pieces. Open-face sandwiches, with a fork.

Shrimp, Oysters, Scallops: With seafood fork. Hold French-fried shrimp by the tail, dip in sauce, eat to the tail. Unshelled shrimp (never served with heads on), hold in fingers, shell, eat whole except for end of tail.

Shrimp Cocktail: When very large, cut in half with side of seafood fork; hold stem of glass with one hand while cutting shrimp.

Spaghetti: Twisted around the fork, cocoon fashion, eat from fork tip; or cut with side of fork before winding. Never bite off.

Tortillas (thin Mexican corncakes): Laid flat on plate, fill with frijoles (beans) or special sauce, roll and eat from end with fingers.

Turkey (or poultry): Carved at table, eat like chicken.

HOW TO CARVE

Everyone should know how to carve a roast or a turkey. Midshipmen, cadets, and junior officers should learn early how to carve—not knowing how could one day prove embarrassing.

Roast Beef may be carved at the table by the host, or partially carved in the kitchen beforehand.

Rib Roast:

Turkey or Other Fowl:

Ham:

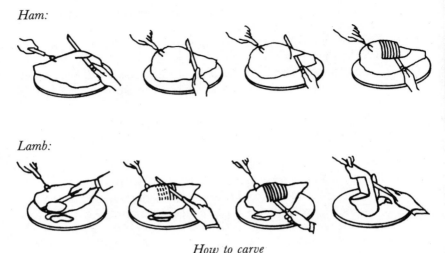

Lamb:

How to carve

COURTESY STATE OF MAINE DEPARTMENT OF ECONOMIC DEVELOPMENT.

AT THE TABLE

There are many simple rules in eating that may seem elementary, but they are the rules by which you are judged. The difference between good or crude manners is the way you observe the following rules.

Do *not* talk with food in your mouth, make noises while eating or swallowing, chew food with your mouth open, or blow on hot liquids to cool them.

Avoid such unattractive eating habits as smacking your lips or taking overly large mouthfuls from food piled high on your fork. Use your napkin before drinking from a glass of water in order not to leave traces of food on the glass. Never lick your fingers after they have been in contact with food—use your napkin.

If something is out of reach at the table, do not rise out of your seat to obtain it; ask for it to be passed. However, you may reach for anything you conveniently can without bothering your dinner partner.

Avoid curling your little finger on a cup handle—and be sure to remove the spoon from the cup after stirring and before drinking. Remember to place the spoon in the saucer, at the right of the cup handle, and not on the tablecloth. If the liquid seems hot, test it by sipping a spoonful—but do not continue drinking by spoonfuls.

You may tilt a soup plate away from you when the plate is almost empty; remember to dip the spoon in the bowl *away* from you. Clear soup served in a cup or bowl with handles may be drunk. You must not place the bowl of the spoon in your mouth, but sip somewhat from the side. Leave the spoon in the soup plate, *never* in the bouillon cup or cream soup bowl.

Bread and rolls are broken in half, and then into smaller pieces with the fingers. Do not cut breads with a knife. If butter is served, you butter each piece of bread before eating.

Jams and condiments go onto the butter plate, not directly onto the bread.

Do not place your elbows on the table while eating. Between courses, you may momentarily place your forearms on the table—if you do not turn your back on your dinner partner.

You should keep your elbows at your sides when cutting food; they move as easily up and down as sideways and, if held in, cannot hit your partner.

Do not slump at the table, but do not sit "at attention," either. Avoid twisting your feet around the chair legs or extending your legs under the table.

When finished eating, don't push back your plate—leave it where it was placed. Lay your unfolded napkin at the left side of the plate, not in it.

Whenever you use your napkin, pat your lips—don't rub them.

TABLE TALK

Loud talk and laughter at the table are disturbing to others. A monopolized or too-intimate conversation between partners is equally impolite.

Be careful of controversial or unpleasant subjects, such as politics, religion, or death, and avoid talking "shop." Always remember not to discuss personal affairs or the opposite sex at the table, or before groups anywhere. Also, never criticize a senior in the mess or at any table.

Small talk—the pleasant, unofficial, interesting things in everyday living, such as a play, a bestseller, or your trip to Disney World—is always safe and noncontroversial.

DROPPED SILVERWARE

As a guest in a restaurant or home, when you drop a fork or spoon at the table, do not pick it up. When you need another, ask the server for it, or the hostess, if she hasn't noticed your mishap. Do not apologize for the mistake. The less the incident is noticed, the better.

UNEXPECTED SITUATIONS

Common sense will dictate what to do in unexpected situations, such as coughing or sneezing, or when you need to blow your nose or you take a foreign object into your mouth.

When a sip of water does not help a fit of coughing, then leave the table. If you must sneeze, use your handkerchief or your napkin.

Although it is better not to attend a dinner or any occasion when you have a cold—colds are highly contagious—sometimes it is necessary that you attend unless you are quite ill, particularly an official occasion. If you must use a handkerchief at the table, do so as unobtrusively as possible. If your cold is a serious one, it may be better momentarily to leave the table.

Upon returning to the table, you need not apologize profusely, if at all. You may murmur "Sorry" to the hostess, or in the general direction of the hostess at a long table. By apologizing or acting embarrassed over such a situation, you only draw attention to an incident that is best ignored.

Whenever possible, stay home and don't spread the germs.

CHOKING

When a person is choking on a piece of food—or anything else—he needs help *immediately.* From the moment that something is lodged in the windpipe and cuts off oxygen, the victim has no more than four minutes to live. You do not have time to call a doctor. Such mishaps kill at least eight Americans a day.

A choking victim while conscious—and he is conscious only a very short time—cannot speak and is in distress; he can nod his head when asked if he is choking. The symptoms of choking are similar to those of a heart attack: an inability to breathe; growing pale, then turning blue; then becoming unconscious.

The Heimlich Maneuver

A "bear hug" technique for stopping someone from choking, called the Heimlich maneuver after the Cincinnati surgeon who devised it, has been endorsed by the American Medical Association. The following procedures should be memorized:

When the victim is standing or sitting. Stand behind him, wrap your arms around his waist, then make a fist with one of your hands and place it, thumb-side in, above the victim's navel but just below the rib cage. You grasp the fist with your other hand and press with a quick, upward thrust. Repeat several times, if necessary. Because there is always residual air trapped in the lungs, the sudden pressure forces the air upward, and the obstruction is expelled.

When the victim is on the floor, unconscious: Place him face up and kneel astride his hips. With one of your hands on top of the other, place the heel of the bottom hand above the navel and below the rib cage and give the quick upward thrust.

When you are alone and choking: Press into a table or a sink—try anything that applies force just below your diaphragm. Or use your own fist.

When the victim is an infant: Although the maneuver is used on older children, care must be taken when using it on an infant. You place the infant on a firm surface, or on your lap facing away from you, then make a cushion of your fingers while using both hands to make the upward thrust.

CHAPTER 21

Dining in Public Places

SELECTING A RESTAURANT

Restaurants in the United States vary in as many ways as American ingenuity can express itself. They range from the milkshake-and-hamburger spots to expensive supper clubs. Hotel dining rooms and coffee shops cater to the most particular gourmet as well as the person who eats and runs.

You should learn something about a restaurant before entering. In a strange city or in a foreign country, guide books will give much information. You can always ask a bell captain in a reputable hotel—regardless of whether you are staying there—about a good place to eat, and the approximate cost. You can mention the type of place you have in mind, inquire if there is music and dancing, and state that you like seafood or Italian food, etc. When money is an important consideration, you had better find out in advance whether or not a supper club has a cover charge.

Quick information concerning good eating places can be found in inexpensive books or pamphlets sold in almost any drug store, or in travel guides put out by chain hotels and motels.

In order to make sure you get a table at a well-patronized eating place, you need to make a reservation in advance.

BEING SEATED

You may check your coat and hat or a package at a restaurant, hotel, or supper club, but women may prefer to wear their coats into the dining room and lay them across the backs of their chairs. Wait at the entrance of the dining room until the headwaiter or hostess comes up, and then ask, "Have you a table for two? (or the desired number)." It is a wise host or hostess who confirms a reservation in advance.

Women precede men and follow the headwaiter to the table. When there is no headwaiter or hostess, a man goes first to find a table. In a mixed group of several couples, the women are given the seats facing the room at large or any view that is offered. At tables in an open space, women sit opposite each other; at banquettes or wall tables, they usually sit in the wall or inboard seats. At a small table for two, the man sits across from the woman, or by her at a banquette. A handicapped person is given an outside seat.

A man should help a woman with her coat by laying it over the chair back, or stand by while the waiter does this.

ORDERING

In most restaurants there are two methods of ordering a dinner: *table d'hôte* and *à la carte*. The first method means paying a single price for the complete meal as outlined on the menu. The second method involves paying a specific price for each item ordered. If a complete dinner is desired, it is more economical to order *table d'hôte*. Ordering *à la carte* is always more expensive, but also more selective: you get what you want.

The host or hostess will perhaps make suggestions to the guest or guests concerning the ordering of the dinner, such as "I understand that the chicken tetrazzini is excellent here," or "Seafood is their specialty. Do you care for lobster?" Regardless of suggestions, the host always asks guests, "What would you like?"

When a man takes a lady out to lunch or dinner, she may tell him what she wants, and then he places both orders. When you are host to a group, your guests will tell the waiter or waitress what they want, and sometimes how they wish certain dishes prepared: steaks well done or rare, for example. Dessert and coffee are usually ordered following the main course, when the waiter again brings menus for everyone to study.

Depending upon the part of the country you are in, the size of the city, and the type of restaurant, the menu may list local dishes, or be entirely in French, or list foods that are completely disguised. When you do not recognize the name of a dish, ask the waiter or waitress what it is.

Most menus for a complete dinner include soup, tomato or fruit juice, or shrimp or fruit cocktail; a main course (or entrée) of meat and two vegetables; salad; dessert; and coffee. When a date accompanies a male junior officer, it is to be hoped that she is aware of his financial status, but no one who is not solvent asks someone to dinner in an unknown restaurant.

When you are host to a large group at dinner or luncheon, it is best to order in advance. You may always telephone, but when you have time, talk with the headwaiter personally.

WAITERS AND WAITRESSES

A good waiter or waitress will give a couple or a group time to study the menu and determine what they care to order. But remember that every waiter and waitress is a human being, and a little consideration toward them may prove the difference between good and indifferent service.

You address a waiter as "Waiter," not "Hey you!" or "Boy," and a waitress as "Waitress," or "Miss" (but you *never* address a waiter as "Sir"). In speaking to the waiter, a man refers to his guest as "the lady." When the waiter or waitress is busy, do not attract his or her attention by clapping your hands, drumming on the table with silverware, or hissing. When a waiter passes within hearing distance but fails to notice you, you may call "Waiter!" in a clear tone—but don't bark an order for attention.

The host should make any complaints to the manager concerning improperly prepared or served food, or when a mistake of any consequence has been made in the order. A very small error is not worth mentioning, but when anything of importance needs correcting, you do so quietly, but with firmness. Mistakes do happen, but they may not be the fault of the waiter who serves the food but does not prepare it.

If the waiter assigned to your table disappears continuously, or takes too long to serve you, this may be mentioned to the headwaiter. But do not lose your temper and create a scene.

SHOULD YOU STAY?

After you have been seated at a table in a restaurant and you look at the menu and see that what you want is not listed or that you cannot afford the prices, you may get up and leave *if* you have not used any of the flatware or touched the water goblet or napkin or disarranged anything. Should the water goblet have been filled and bread or crackers placed on the table, you should leave a small tip, explain to the waiter why you are not staying, and go.

But if you have taken a sip of water or used the napkin, then order the least expensive item on the menu—and look more carefully next time, and be sure that you have enough money.

When you have invited someone as a guest, or when plans have been made to meet someone at a restaurant at a given time and place, and that person does not show up, how long should you wait? Only for as long as you can. First, phone that person and try to find out what has happened—whether he or she has forgotten the appointment or something important has caused a delay. When there is no answer, wait for perhaps 30 minutes, then either go ahead with your lunch or dinner, or leave. If you decide to leave without ordering, then leave a good tip for tying up the table.

Whenever you need to cancel a reservation, immediately phone the restaurant and say so.

PAYING THE BILL

When it is time to leave, you say to the waiter or waitress, "The check, please." He or she may bring the check on a small tray, with the check face down, and set the tray by the host or whoever did the ordering. In a small eating place, the check may be laid on the table face down. The host or hostess will look at the bill long enough to see if it is correct, and then place the money or credit card on the tray. The waiter or waitress will take the tray to the cashier and return any change; you usually leave this for the tip, deducting or adding to the sum as necessary.

In small eating places where the bill states "Please pay the cashier," the host or hostess takes the check directly to the cashier and pays there. In this case, leave a suitable tip on the table for your waiter or waitress.

Tips are 15 *percent* of the entire check at the average restaurant. It is better to avoid quantities of small change.

If you should find an error in the check (other than a few cents), call this to the attention of your waiter or waitress. If he or she insists that the bill is correct and you are certain that it is not, discuss this matter with the headwaiter, the cashier, or the manager. After all, it is your money that is involved.

When a stag or mixed group goes "Dutch treat," one person may be designated beforehand to pay the check, with others in the party settling up later. This avoids the clutter of paying at the dinner table, but it is inexcusable for anyone to forget to settle accounts immediately afterward with the one who paid.

If you are a guest at a dinner in a hotel or restaurant, do not offer to help your host or hostess pay the bill. Instead, repay such hospitality later with a dinner or similar social occasion of your own.

Although most good restaurants and hotels across the country accept credit cards, some don't. In case of doubt, phone first and find out.

RESTAURANT MANNERS

A man may try to rise to his feet when a woman stops to chat at his table, but this can be awkward as well as inconsiderate of others at a crowded table. He need not rise completely in crowded conditions, even when introductions are underway. A half-rise, or a brief attempt to rise, is acceptable. Ladies seated at the table may give a slight inclination of their heads, accompanied by a smile. Servicewomen do not rise when a senior momentarily stops by.

It is thoughtless of anyone to stop and talk at a table when hot or very cold food is before those eating. It is better just to nod or speak and then go on your way; later you can talk briefly with your friends during a lull in the service, or over coffee. When someone stops at your table, you need not ask him to sit down unless you and your guests so desire.

Do not rise when the restaurant hostess stops at the table to inquire about the service and the quality of your food. Hers is a courteous business gesture, not a social gesture.

In any public eating place, you never wipe the silver with your napkin; if it appears unclean, ask the waiter or waitress for fresh silver. When you drop a piece of silver or a napkin, leave it alone and ask for another. Do not write or chart a course on the tablecloth, and avoid cluttering up the floor space with your feet or bundles.

When it is time to leave—or long past time—call for the check.

THE SINGLE WOMAN HOSTESS

Today, a man should not hesitate when a woman invites him to dine with her in a restaurant and makes it clear that *she* is the hostess and will pay the check.

If she knows him well, she might suggest giving him the money for the check before they enter the restaurant. He would, of course, return any money left over.

An easy way to pay for the dinner is with a credit card acceptable to the restaurant. But if she prefers to pay cash, she can find out how much the dinner will probably cost when she makes the reservation.

Should the check be paid at the table, then she should have large bills handy in her purse, and place them on the plate that the waiter or waitress brings.

When a married couple are invited by a single woman for dinner in a restaurant, they should understand that she is the hostess and they are *her* guests. Should the man offer to pay the check or, worse, insist upon it (and this is very poor manners on his part, since he knows who is hostess and is making too much of the money angle), then she must be firm and point out, "This was my invitation and you are my guests."

A single executive or military woman may correctly invite a male senior executive or officer, single or married, to lunch—but not to dinner unless the spouse is also invited.

When women dine together, it is best to go "Dutch" and ask the waiter or waitress for separate checks when ordering. This will save considerable time and confusion, but in a crowded restaurant, when the waiter is very busy, he may not have time to write separate checks.

The easiest way for a group to settle up is for someone to use a small calculator that can be carried in a purse or wallet. Also available in gift shops and stores is a small plastic card showing the 15 percent tip table from $1 to $100.

SECTION VII

Protocol

CHAPTER 22

Seating Plans & Precedence

PROTOCOL IS THE code of etiquette in ceremonies of nation and state, the code prescribing "the deference to rank and strict adherence to correct procedure as in diplomatic exchange and ceremonies, and in the military."*

Customs differ in each nation, but by and large these international rules of etiquette are observed by everyone. Otherwise, there would be chaos in receiving lines at state receptions, seating at official dinners, and the procedures during military reviews and other such occasions. At all times, anywhere, tact and diplomacy, as well as knowledge of another nation's customs, are required.

SEATING ARRANGEMENTS

It is customary at mixed dinners and luncheons for the high-ranking man to be seated at the right of the hostess, and his wife at the right of the host. But at occasions governed by protocol, the high-ranking man is seated at the right of the hostess and the high-ranking woman at the right of the host. The high-ranking woman may be a congress-

---

*This definition of the term *protocol* and the charts showing seating arrangements at the formal luncheon and dinner tables are from the *Social Usage and Protocol Handbook* (Washington, D.C., Office of the Chief of Naval Operations, Department of the Navy).

woman or an admiral or general, a scientist or an astronaut, and not the wife of the high-ranking man.

The second-ranking man is seated to the left of the hostess, and the second-ranking woman is to the host's left. The third-ranking woman sits at the right of the man of highest rank, the fourth woman is at the left of the man of second rank. Under this arrangement a hostess may find that a man would be seated alongside his wife, and since this is not done, the wife is seated elsewhere.

Unless they are officers or hold an official position of higher rank or title, women are seated according to the rank of their husbands.

Dinners for 6 or 10, 14 or 18, etc., are easily arranged, with the hosts sitting opposite each other and with married partners sitting by other guests.

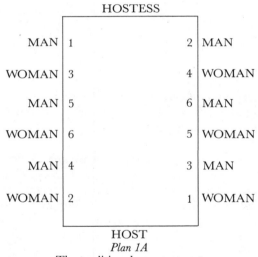

Plan 1A
The traditional arrangement

MULTIPLES OF FOUR

At tables for any multiple of four—8, 12, 16, etc.—the host and hostess cannot sit opposite each other without having to place two men or two women together when there is an equal number of each sex present. To avoid this, the hostess may relinquish her position at the end of the oblong or oval table and move one seat to the left, which places the male guest of honor opposite the host. When all couples are married, follow Plan 2A. When one couple is unmarried and seated together, use Plan 2B.

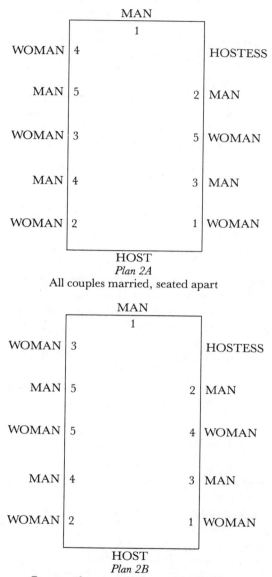

MAN
1

WOMAN	4			HOSTESS
MAN	5		2	MAN
WOMAN	3		5	WOMAN
MAN	4		3	MAN
WOMAN	2		1	WOMAN

HOST
Plan 2A
All couples married, seated apart

MAN
1

WOMAN	3			HOSTESS
MAN	5		2	MAN
WOMAN	5		4	WOMAN
MAN	4		3	MAN
WOMAN	2		1	WOMAN

HOST
Plan 2B
One couple unmarried, seated together

THE ROUND TABLE

The round table is popular for both formal and informal luncheons
and dinners. Although care must be exercised to ensure that women
are not seated by each other at the more formal table, the problem

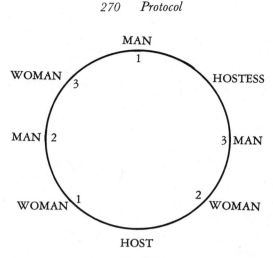

Plan 2C
Round table for multiples of four, all couples married

of women having to sit at the ends of a table never arises. There is a friendliness about a round table that appeals to young and old.

Hostesses have found that several round tables may be arranged for 6 or 8 guests each, with the host at one table, the hostess at another, and co-hosts designated at any others. When protocol must be observed, some hostesses have ranking guests act as hosts at the various tables.

Smaller round or oblong tables are usually set up in a banquet room, in addition to the head table for VIPs.

THE SINGLE HOST OR HOSTESS

A single host or hostess may choose from several seating arrangements, depending upon the number of guests, their rank, etc. The high-ranking guests will be seated to the right of the host or hostess.

At a mixed luncheon or dinner, the host may ask a woman guest to act as hostess to balance the table when the number is not divided by four. In this case, Plan 1A may be followed, with the ranking male guest seated at the right of the guest hostess.

The host may prefer to ask the ranking male guest to sit opposite him, when Plan 3A may be used. Plan 3B may be used when the ranking man and woman are not married to each other and the bachelor host does not want a hostess or co-host at a dinner divisible by four.

When a woman entertains alone, the seating roles for women and men are exchanged in Plans 3A and 3B.

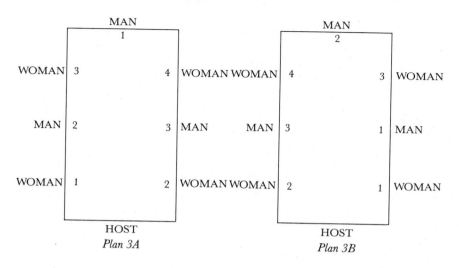

Plan 3A

Plan 3B

STAG DINNERS AND LUNCHEONS

A co-host is frequently appointed to assist the official host at a large stag dinner or luncheon in order to balance the rank at the official table.

The co-host may be the next ranking guest after the guest of honor. If there are guests from foreign countries as well as from the United States, the ranking United States guest could be appointed co-host. Foreign guests should be seated between guests of the host country.

Usually, the host and co-host sit opposite each other at the center of a long table. When there is no co-host, or when the dinner or luncheon is small, the host sits at the head of the table and the junior at the foot.

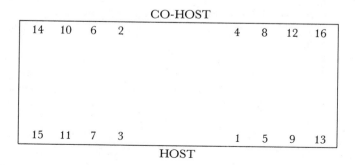

BANQUETS

SPEAKER'S TABLE

Utmost tact is required in seating toastmaster and speakers at a banquet or dining-in (for the dining-in, see chapter 44). The host, hostess, or chairman will be seated at the center of the head table, with the guest of honor to his or her right and the second-ranking guest to his or her left. The toastmaster is customarily at the left of the second-ranking guest.

When distinguished nonmilitary guests are present, they may be seated between the guests of official rank after the guest of honor and second official guest are seated.

When the occasion is not stag, and the speaker or guest of honor is a very important person (number 1), the spouse of the official host or hostess is seated in the number 3 position, and the spouse of the VIP is seated to the left of the official host or hostess, in the number 2 chair. If the speaker or VIP is a lady, she is seated to the right of the official host, hostess, or chairman, with the ranking person to the left.

Should the main speaker or a guest of honor be outranked by others present, he or she need not be seated in seat 1, but it is correct to place him or her to the left of the official host in seat 2, or possibly in seat 3.

Although guests are seated according to protocol at official and formal occasions, every effort must be made to place them with congenial persons. Juniors are at the ends of the table, "with the salts and peppers."

5	
3	
1	Guest of Honor or Speaker
	HOST or CHAIRMAN
2	Second Ranking Guest
4	Toastmaster
6	

The customary banquet table

7	Air Force General
5	U.S. Delegate to U.N.
3	Civic Leader
1	Former President
	HOST
2	Foreign Ambassador
4	Red Cross Official
6	Congressman
8	Protestant Bishop

The seating of distinguished guests

CADET OR MIDSHIPMAN HOST

At the academies, when cadets or midshipmen are the official hosts or hostesses, and high-ranking officers and their spouses are guests, there may be variations in seating arrangements. For example, at the formal ring banquet at West Point, where there always is a guest speaker, the chairman of the ring and crest committee (cadet) is host. When the cadet chairman is a male, seated to his right may be the superintendent's wife (1); the speaker (3); the dean's wife (5); the commandant (7). To his left are his date (2); the superintendent (4); the speaker's wife (6); the dean (8); the commandant's wife (9); and a nondating cadet member of the ring committee, which ensures no woman is seated at the end of the table. When the cadet chairman is a female, the seating arrangements are reversed. The number of guests at the table is increased or decreased as needed.

It is desirable at all academies and colleges for young people to learn how to be hosts. The Black, Gold, and Gray Room in Washington Hall at West Point is available to any group of cadets for organizational dinners, dining-ins, or special occasions. The tables are round, the chairs have academy crests, and table service includes silver flatware, Lenox china, and crystal wine and water goblets. The white plates with a black border are centered with a gold emblem.

THE HORSESHOE-SHAPED TABLE

When horseshoe-shaped tables are used at large official banquets, the host and hostess will sit with their honor guests on the outside of the curving center. The other guests will sit down the sides.

When places are set both inside and outside the curving ends, the inside seats begin at the lower third section of the table, with the seats inside but nearer the host ranking those farther away on the outside. When the horseshoe has a prong, the junior ranking guests are seated on each side of it.

FORFEITURE OF POSITIONS

A host and hostess, with the exception of the President of the United States and the First Lady, relinquish their positions at the head and the end of their luncheon or dinner table when their guest is a president or head of any country, or a king or queen. In that case, the reigning king or queen sits at the head of the table, and his or her spouse sits at the other end of the table.

In order not to "give honor to themselves," the host and hostess sit to the *left* of the president or royalty and their spouses, with the

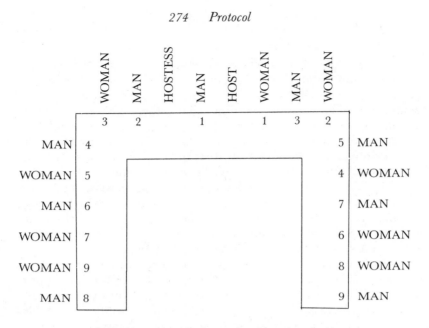

A plan for seating couples at a horseshoe-shaped table

This arrangement of couples 8 and 9 avoids placing a woman at the end of the table.

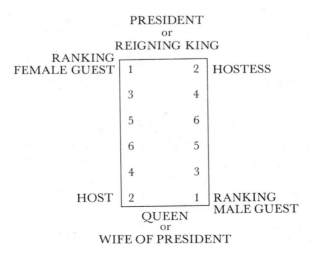

high-ranking man and woman guests sitting at the *right* of the honored guests. This will place the high-ranking guests in the traditional guests of honor position.

CLUB OFFICERS

At a men's or women's club luncheon or dinner, the ranking guests and club officers would be seated as follows:

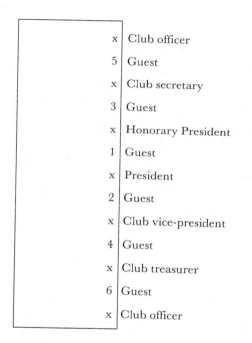

x	Club officer
5	Guest
x	Club secretary
3	Guest
x	Honorary President
1	Guest
x	President
2	Guest
x	Club vice-president
4	Guest
x	Club treasurer
6	Guest
x	Club officer

PLACE CARDS

Place cards are often used at the luncheon or dinner table, formal or informal, as a matter of convenience in seating guests without confusion or according to protocol. Cards are of heavy plain white or cream-colored paper, with plain, gold, or silver beveled edges.

The cards are about 1½ by 2 inches, or 2 by 3 inches, in size. The flag of an admiral or general, the seal of a ship or an embassy, or a family crest may be embossed or stamped in the top center or the upper left corner of the card.

The cards are placed on top of the napkin in the place plate, or laid flat on the table above the plate.

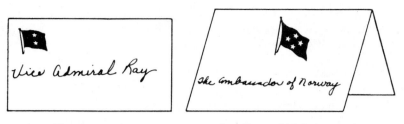

Flat place card   Standing or folded place card

Folded place cards are about 3 by 3¼ inches in size, and are folded in half, with the name written across the lower half of the card. They usually stand directly above the place plate.

Names are written by hand on the cards in black or dark blue ink. For formal occasions, names may be written in script: "Mrs. Jones," "Colonel Smith," "The Ambassador of Norway," "The Secretary of the Army." At informal occasions first names are often used, and are also written: "Marion," "Allan"—except when there are others with the same name, then "Marion Smith" and "Marion Jones." Calligraphy is very nice for formal and informal cards.

MENU CARDS

Menu cards may be used at official dinners, at state and public occasions, and occasionally in a home—such as for an anniversary dinner. A crest or coat of arms may be embossed at the top center of the card, which is of heavy white or cream-colored paper. An admiral's or general's flag or a seal is customarily used.

The card is about 4 by 5½ or 6 inches, with a gilded or silvered beveled edge, and is placed in a stand or laid on the table. In homes, the cards may be placed in front of the host and hostess, and one for each three guests down each side of the formal table, about 6 inches above the plate.

The word *Menu* is written by hand in black ink beneath the crest, and one dish is written on each line centered directly underneath. The first letter on each line is capitalized and each course is separated by a space or asterisks.

Appetizers, bread, relishes, jellies, candy, and coffee are not written on the menu as they are on hotel menus. Menus for formal dinners are engraved or printed in French, but on naval ships and in Army and Air Force messes—for instance, at formal dinners in flag messes—they are printed, embossed, or handwritten in English.

Menu cards are considered souvenirs, especially those from an inaugural luncheon or the Christmas dinners given annually at the academies.

PRECEDENCE IN ENTERTAINING

An officer of high rank or one who serves with high-ranking officials, such as an attaché, must be well versed in local customs both at home and abroad. When serving abroad, consult the protocol section of the American Embassy. In Washington, get advice on protocol in the foreign liaison section of the office of your service.

At nonofficial occasions, precedence at a dinner or luncheon is determined by the prominence of the guests, their age, and degree of friendship. In civilian life, age receives deference, as do professional and scholastic achievement.

In official life, strict protocol governs government, ecclesiastical, and diplomatic precedence, which has been established by international agreement. A younger official will precede an older official if the office of the former is in a higher echelon.

Although a person is the guest of honor at a dinner or luncheon, he or she may not be seated in the ranking position at the table unless rank justifies it, or the higher-ranking guest concedes his or her position. When ambassadors and very high-ranking guests are present, they are seated according to precedence—and the guest of honor may be seated down the table.

When you have to invite someone higher in rank than the guest of honor, you have these choices:

Ask the ranking guest to waive his or her right for the occasion in favor of the guest of honor

Seat the guests according to precedence—although the guest or guests of honor are well down the table

Have the senior guest co-host the party

When nonranking guests are present at an official dinner or luncheon, their places at the table are determined by age, prominence, linguistic ability (when foreigners are present), and congeniality. After the guests of honor and top officials have been seated, these nonranking guests are placed between those of official rank in the most congenial way for all concerned.

There are various ways in which a host and hostess may determine the equal seating of a number of high-ranking guests. For example, at a state dinner at the White House, three tables were arranged side by side; the President was the host at one table, with the Chief Justice seated across from him; the First Lady was hostess at the second table, with the Speaker of the House beside her; and the Vice President was host at the third table.

THE UNMARRIED COUPLE

In Washington, when guests at a state dinner will include a member of the diplomatic corps, the Cabinet, or the Senate—or any dignitary of church or state—the question arises: Should the live-in partner of a high-ranking guest be invited?

In the past, protocol recognized only the married couple, and in some countries this is still the rule. (In a few distant countries where multiple wives are recognized, only the number one wife is invited.)

In the United States, times are changing. When the unmarried partner is invited to an official occasion, he or she will not be seated with the spouses of other guests of equal rank, but much farther down the table—unless this person has title or rank of his or her own. Then he or she is seated accordingly.

CHAPTER 23

Order of Precedence

THE OFFICIAL GOVERNMENT position of a man or woman is determined by election or appointment to the office, and the length of time served; in the military it is determined by promotion within the rank structure. Comparable rank and the date of its attainment is the basis for precedence among officers in all services, both here and in foreign countries.

MILITARY PRECEDENCE

A younger military officer of either sex precedes an older military officer when the former's rank is higher.

Active duty officers precede reserve officers of the same rank.

Retired officers rank with but after active duty Reserve officers of the same rank.

The ranking of military men and women is the same in all services.

DIPLOMATIC PRECEDENCE

The precedence established in diplomatic life is the result of international agreement. The precedence of chiefs of missions depends upon the length of their service. An ambassador accredited in June precedes another appointed in October. An ambassador always precedes a minister who heads a legation.

Below the post of chargé d'affaires, the position of the mission is the base for precedence; this, in turn, is determined by the ranking of the mission's ambassador. A change of ambassador or minister of legation changes the relative positions of the entire staff.

Military (naval, air) attachés take precedence among themselves according to their respective grades and seniority of service. They rank after the counselors of embassy or legation; at a post where the Department of State has not assigned a counselor, they rank after the senior secretary. Assistant military attachés come after the lowest-ranking second secretary.

Precedence is not always hand-in-glove with the individual. When an ambassador is on leave, or on a trip home, he or she does not hold the same status as when on post. When invited to a function that he or she cannot attend, the ambassador may send a representative; this person cannot expect to be accorded the senior's place of precedence.

PLANNING FOR THE VIP

The aide or officer who is designated to take care of local arrangements for the visit of a dignitary must carefully plan all details in advance. Sometimes a small detail is overlooked, to the consternation of all concerned. All plans should be made as early as possible. Information concerning the dignitary and, if a foreign VIP, his or her country, should be studied, and notes taken for future reference.

The following suggestions should be followed:

1. Obtain any reservations at hotels and restaurants in writing.

2. The dignitary should be met upon arrival, and also be accompanied to his or her place of departure. A flag officer should be present at the arrival and departure of another flag officer.

3. Have a map of the area, and know the roads well. Make certain that all drivers of the official party are briefed on their schedules and know exactly where they are going, how to return, and just what to do should a car become separated from others in the party.

4. Allow time for any delays, such as travel to and from an airport, and baggage transfer.

5. Whenever possible, billeting should be provided for the local escort officer in the same building as that of the dignitary. Otherwise, he or she will need transportation.

6. If the schedule is a busy one, try to allow for breaks—time for a short rest, or a visit to historic sites.

7. Provide transportation, meals, and recreation for the aide or aides who accompany the dignitary. Usually they are officers of high rank, destined for positions of authority in their country.

8. Aides are usually lodged in the BOQs, where room assignments must be made well in advance. The rooms should be in keeping with the aides' standing as members of a dignitary's party.

9. When spouses accompany the dignitaries, particularly those from foreign countries, plans for their pleasure must be made in advance.

10. When persons of esteem in such fields as science, the arts, and literature are invited to a state or official dinner, they are seated in consideration of their prominence—in accordance with those of rank or title.

THE OFFICIAL ORDER OF PRECEDENCE

The President
The Vice President
Governor of a state (when in his or her own state)
The Speaker of the House of Representatives
The Chief Justice of the Supreme Court
Former Presidents of the United States
The Secretary of State
Ambassadors of foreign countries accredited to the United States (in order of the presentation of credentials)
Ministers of foreign countries accredited to the United States (only those ministers who are chiefs of diplomatic missions; in order of the presentation of credentials)
Associate Justices of the Supreme Court (by date of appointment)
The Cabinet (other than the Secretary of State)
The Secretary of the Treasury
The Secretary of Defense
The Attorney General
The Secretary of the Interior
The Secretary of Agriculture
The Secretary of Commerce
The Secretary of Labor
The Secretary of Health and Human Services
The Secretary of Housing and Urban Development

The Secretary of Transportation
The Secretary of Energy
The Secretary of Education
The President Pro Tempore of the Senate
Former Governors
Senators (according to the number of years they have served)
Governors of states (when outside their own state; relative precedence determined by their state's date of admission to the Union, or alphabetically by state)
Acting heads of executive departments (e.g., Acting Secretary of Defense)
Former Vice Presidents of the United States
Congressmen (according to the length of continuous service; if this is the same, arrange by date of their state's admission to the Union, or alphabetically by state)
Delegates of territories (Puerto Rico, Guam)
Chargé d'Affaires of foreign countries
Former Secretaries of State
Deputy and Under Secretaries of executive departments (e.g., the Deputy Secretary of Defense)
Secretaries of the military departments (Army, Navy, Air Force, in that order)
Chairman, Joint Chiefs of Staff
Retired Chairman, Joint Chiefs of Staff
Members, Joint Chiefs of Staff (Army, Air Force, and Navy and Marine Corps, by date of appointment to JCS)
Retired Service Chiefs
Five-Star Generals and Admirals
Director, Central Intelligence Agency
Commandant of the Coast Guard
U.S. Ambassadors accompanying foreign chiefs of state on a state visit
U.S. Ambassadors on assignment within the United States
Assistant Secretaries of executive departments (by date of appointment)
Judges of the U.S. Court of Military Appeals
Under Secretaries of the military departments (Army, Navy, Air Force, in that order)
Governors of territories
Generals and Admirals (four-star grade)
Assistant Secretaries of military establishments (Army, Navy, Air Force, by date of appointment within each service)

The Special Assistant to the Secretary and Deputy Secretary of Defense

Assistants to the Secretary of Defense

General Counsels of military departments

Deputy Under Secretaries of Defense (by date of appointment)

Three-Star military

Principal Deputy Assistant Secretaries of Defense and Deputy General Counsel of the Department of Defense (by date of appointment)

Former foreign Ambassadors

Former U.S. Ambassadors and Ministers of foreign countries

Ministers of foreign powers (not accredited heads of missions)

Deputy Assistant Secretaries of executive departments and deputy counsels

Deputy Under Secretaries of the Army, Navy, and Air Force (by date of appointment within each service)

Counselors of foreign embassies

Consuls General of foreign powers

GS-18

Two-Star military (Rear Admiral, upper half)

Deputy Assistant Secretaries of military departments (by date of appointment)

Heads of offices, Office of the Secretary of Defense

GS-17

One-Star military (Rear Admiral, lower half, and Commodore)

Heads of offices of military departments

Foreign consuls

GS-16

Captains and Colonels

GS-15

THE ARMED FORCES ORDER OF PRECEDENCE

The following is the order of precedence* of members of the armed forces when in formation:

Cadets, United States Military Academy
Midshipmen, United States Naval Academy
Cadets, United States Air Force Academy
Cadets, United States Coast Guard Academy

*Established by the Department of Defense.

Midshipmen, United States Merchant Marine Academy
United States Army
United States Marine Corps
United States Navy
United States Air Force
United States Coast Guard
Army National Guard of the United States
Army Reserve
Marine Corps Reserve
Naval Reserve
Air National Guard of the United States
Air Force Reserve
Coast Guard Reserve
Other training organizations of the Army, Marine Corps, Navy, Air
    Force, and Coast Guard, in that order

When the Coast Guard operates as part of the Navy in times of war, the cadets, Coast Guard Academy, the Coast Guard, and the Coast Guard Reserve take precedence after the midshipmen of the Naval Academy, the Navy, and the Naval Reserve, respectively.

CHAPTER 24

Toasts

THE CUSTOM OF "TOASTING" goes back to ancient times, when a piece of toast was placed in the goblet with the mead, or any alcoholic brew. When it became saturated, the toast sank to the bottom of the goblet, and after someone challenged "Toast!" it was necessary to drain the goblet in order to get to the toast.

Nowadays, one does not drain a glass of champagne or wine—the favorites for toasts. On the contrary, you take only a sip or two so there will be plenty of wine left for other toasts. Upon informal occasions, almost any liquid at hand may be used when making a toast: it is the love or appreciation or respect that is shown the person toasted which is important.

It is disrespectful for anyone not to participate in a toast. A teetotaler need only go through the motions of holding the wine glass to his lips.

Toasts are given upon various occasions: at wedding receptions, bachelor dinners, birthday parties, christenings, engagement parties, dinners, anniversaries, dining-ins, and wetting-down parties. A dining-in is a formal dinner given by a wing or unit or a military organization. A wetting-down is an informal party held in celebration of an advancement in rank in the services.

THE MECHANICS OF A TOAST

When you are presenting a toast, you stand. When you are the one receiving the toast at a table, you remain seated while everyone else stands, and you do not sip your drink—or you will be drinking to yourself. After everyone else sits down, you may rise and thank them and offer a toast in return. A woman may respond with a toast or she may remain seated, smile at the person who toasted her, and raise her glass in a gesture of "Thanks, and here's to you."

At formal occasions a toastmaster will propose the toasts. At a dining-in, it will be "Mr. Vice (or Madam)." A very high-ranking officer or a dignitary of church or state does not always return a toast; he may make a slight bow in recognition of the honor and remain seated while others stand. At less formal occasions anyone can propose a toast.

Toasts are generally given at the end of a meal, during or after dessert as soon as the wine or champagne is served and before any speeches are made. They last about a minute.

When you are the one making the toasts at a formal occasion, be well prepared. You must have advance information about the person or persons to be toasted so that your remarks are pertinent and related to the individual and are accurate. If he or she is a close friend you may make a more personal remark.

When you tell an amusing story or joke, don't laugh at it yourself—allow your audience to appreciate it. Unless you are adept at dialects, avoid them.

Never tell a story or joke which may reflect adversely upon the person toasted, intentionally or otherwise. Anything that gibes another is out. Always, a toast must be brief. A toast is not a speech.

KINDS OF TOASTS

At an *engagement party* given by the parents of the engaged woman (or a close member of her family if her parents are not living), the father proposes a toast to his daughter after all guests have arrived and have been served champagne or another wine. He calls for attention and raises his glass, saying words to this effect: "To my daughter, Susan, and my future son-in-law, William Smith. Let's drink to their happiness." Or, "I would like to have you join me in welcoming a new member to our family. To Susan and her fiancé, William Smith." The couple smile and, if seated, remain seated. Then the future bridegroom proposes a toast to his fiancée's family: "To Susan and her very wonderful parents."

At a *wedding reception,* the first toast is always offered by the best man and is always a toast to the bride and groom. For example: "I propose a toast to the bride and groom. Congratulations and best wishes." The couple accept the toast by smiling and remaining seated.

When the bridegroom makes a toast to his bride he might say, "I want you to join me in this toast to Mary, who has just made me the happiest man in the world."

At a reception where all guests are seated at tables, the third toast at the bride's table may be proposed by the groom to the bride's parents. Other toasts may be to the bridesmaids, but there should not be too many toasts.

At a reception where everyone stands, the bride and groom cut the cake and eat the first piece; then everybody else has a piece of cake, and the toasts begin.

At a *bachelor dinner* given by a groom for his ushers (see chapter 25), the groom's toast to the bride traditionally is, "To the bride." He will rise to his feet when giving the toast, and all others at the table will also rise to their feet.

At a *small dinner* a toast may be proposed by anyone as soon as the first wine has been served, and guests stand only if the person giving the toast stands. More than one toast may be drunk with the same glass of wine, and you may say, "To your health," or "Your health." You might say "Many happy returns" at a birthday party.

At a *child's baptism,* the toast to the child's heath and prosperity is given during the reception, luncheon, or tea which usually follows the baptismal ceremony. The toast is proposed by the child's godfather.

Toasts may be drunk anywhere with soft drinks, tea, sake, etc. The important thing is to return the toast.

THE ARMY TOAST

The traditional old Army toast "How" in drinking to one's health is equivalent to "Cheers." One story has it that during the Seminole War in Florida in 1841, Chief Coacoochee tried to imitate the officers' toasts by shouting "How!" Officers of the 8th Infantry and the 2nd Dragoons picked it up, and thus the custom spread throughout the Army.

CEREMONIAL TOASTS

All American officers should be familiar with the international customs observed when toasts are exchanged on foreign stations, on board foreign ships or in messes ashore, at official dinners, and at luncheons given in honor of visiting dignitaries.

On these occasions, toward the end of the meal, the host—or the highest official of his country present—proposes a standing toast to the head of state (sovereign or president) of the guest's country. This toast is customarily followed by the national anthem of the country concerned. The highest-ranking foreign guest then responds with a toast to the ruler of the host country, followed by that country's anthem.

The preliminary ceremonial toasts may be succeeded by toasts to the countries or services represented. The order and subjects of all toasts should be previously agreed upon so that the host and guests know what is expected of them. All present drink to a ruler or country, but they do not drink toasts proposed to themselves or to their own services.

When the guests represent more than one nation, the host proposes a collective toast to the heads of their several states, naming them in the order of the seniority of the representatives present.

To this collective toast the highest-ranking foreign officer present will respond on behalf of all guests by proposing a toast to the health of the head of state of the host.

When you know you will be going overseas, find out about the smoking customs in the countries you will visit. There may be less smoking at meals than in this country. At a formal occasion held in England, there is no smoking before the "Queen's toast."

TOASTS IN FOREIGN COUNTRIES

BRITISH CUSTOMS

At an official dinner given by a British officer to an American officer, the British officer rises during or after dessert to toast the President of the United States, and then the orchestra plays "The Star-Spangled Banner." After the guests are seated, the American officer rises to toast "Her Majesty, Queen Elizabeth II," and the orchestra plays "God Save the Queen." These toasts are sometimes followed by short speeches and toasts to the services represented.

At regular mess dinners in the British armed services, the senior member of the mess proposes the toast, "The Queen," and all members in a low voice repeat "The Queen," and sip the toast. If an American officer should be a personal dinner guest in a mess where a toast to the Queen is drunk every night, the mess president might propose a toast to the corresponding U.S. service after the usual toast to the Queen.

The proper reply by the American officer then would be a toast to the corresponding British service. At official dinners, the British officer would toast "The President of the United States," and the senior American would reply with a toast "To Her Majesty, Queen Elizabeth II."

Officers of the Royal Navy have the unique and traditional privilege of remaining seated when toasting their sovereign at mess, although those serving in the royal yacht choose to rise.

FRENCH AND ITALIAN CUSTOMS

Officers of these services are more likely to begin a toast with the phrase, "I have the honor, etc." At a dinner for a senior American officer, the French host would probably say, "I have the honor to propose a toast to the President of the United States," and the American officer might reply with the toast, "It is my great honor to propose a toast to the President of the Republic of France."

SCANDINAVIAN CUSTOMS

In the Scandinavian countries ceremonial toasts are not customary; instead the host "skoals" (toasts) each individual guest. No one drinks any wine at the table until after the host has made a general skoal welcoming all the guests. Then skoaling proceeds all during the meal, and women in particular must be on the alert to respond to individual skoals from the men.

Each man is supposed to skoal the woman sitting at his right at least once. The procedure is for him to raise his glass slightly from the table, and looking straight into his partner's eyes draw the glass down and toward his body, bow slightly, say "Skoal" and drink— not forgetting to salute again with his glass before putting it down. This skoal must be returned a few minutes later.

During the dinner the host and hostess are supposed to skoal everyone around the table, but guests do not toast them immediately. At the end of the meal, the guest of honor (seated at the left of the hostess in Scandinavian countries) makes a little speech of thanks, and skoals the host and hostess on behalf of all the guests, who join in this skoal.

JAPANESE CUSTOMS

At a Japanese dinner the customary procedure is all but reversed. The host, before dinner is begun, welcomes and toasts the guests from a seated position. The senior guest replies and thanks the host. Throughout the dinner, individual toasts are given. One person will pick up his cup, catch the eye of the one he is toasting, and both will drink but remain seated.

"TO YOUR HEALTH"

It is well to know the most simple form of toasting when abroad. The following are translations of "To Your Health":

French—A votre santé
German—Prosit
Spanish—Salud
Swedish—Skoal
Hebrew—L'Chaim ("To life")
Greek—Is tin egian sou

SECTION VIII

All About Weddings

CHAPTER 25

Planning the Wedding

THROUGHOUT THE COURSE of your service career you will be called upon to take part in weddings. You may be an usher or the best man, the maid or matron of honor. Perhaps the wedding will be your own. It is difficult, sometimes, for officers at sea or at a remote base, post, or station to obtain the correct and detailed information concerning wedding ceremonies and what is expected of the ushers or bridesmaids.

The military wedding is like other weddings, except that the officers in the bridal party are in uniform, and the bride and groom usually leave the chapel or church under the traditional arch of swords (sabers). The groom's sword is used by the bride to cut the first piece of cake at the wedding reception.

The wedding ceremony is not a military service but a religious one.

The uniform worn is in accordance with the kind of wedding planned—formal or informal—and with the season of the year. Evening dress uniform may be worn at the very formal wedding, and dinner or mess dress uniform at the less formal. Dress blues or whites are worn at informal weddings. A boutonniere is never worn with uniform.

The arch of swords takes place immediately following the ceremony, preferably when the couple leaves the chapel or church, on the steps or walk. Ushers' swords (sabers) are usually unbuckled and left in a side room until after the religious ceremony, when they are buckled on in preparation for the arch of swords.

Since a church is a sanctuary, the arch is formed *with permission* inside chapels and churches. In case of bad weather; the arch may be formed in the vestibule at a small wedding, or after the reception as the bride and groom are walking outside under a canopy.

Only commissioned servicemen and servicewomen participate in the arch of swords or sabers.

THE ENGAGEMENT ANNOUNCEMENT

A formal engagement is announced by the bride-elect's parents or closest relative, usually between six weeks and one year before the wedding date (military orders may determine the length of the engagement). Such an announcement is frequently made at a reception, tea, or other social occasion.

The parents of the bridegroom-elect should call on the family of the bride-to-be before the engagement is announced. If the family lives in a distant city, a note should be written or a phone call made to them. The bride-elect should, by note or voice, be cordially welcomed into the family. And the bridegroom-to-be into the bride's family.

In order to inform friends in a widespread area—particularly service personnel, who are constantly being transferred and whose new duty stations may not immediately be known—it is helpful to have the engagement announcement published in a newspaper.

When the announcement is sent to a newspaper to be printed by a certain date—but not before that date—state the date of release at the top left of the announcement: FOR RELEASE MONDAY, MARCH 15. The account should be signed by the mother or closest relative, for purposes of authenticity, and could read:

> Capt. John James Smith, USN (Ret.), and Mrs. Smith of Baltimore, Md., announce the engagement of their daughter, Mary Ann, to Ens. Donald James Adams, USN, son of Mr. and Mrs. William Claton Adams of St. Louis, Mo.
>
> Miss Smith was graduated from Wellesley College. Ensign Adams attended Wake Forest and was graduated from the U.S. Naval Academy, class of 1997. He is in flight training in Pensacola, Fla. The wedding will take place in December.

THE ENGAGEMENT RING

A man wants to give his prospective bride the nicest engagement ring he can afford—but he should not go heavily in debt and take months paying for it. A midshipman or cadet frequently gives his fiancée a miniature of his class ring, and ROTC college men give miniatures of their fraternity rings. Often a man will give a ring to his fiancée that has been in the family as a treasured keepsake; the ring can be sized or the stone remounted if necessary.

A woman wears the engagement ring on her left hand, third finger. Following the wedding ceremony, the wedding ring is worn first, closest to the heart.

When an engagement is broken the ring is returned to the man. In case of the death of the fiancé before marriage, the woman keeps the ring. But if the ring is a treasured family heirloom, it should be returned to the family.

Usually the divorcée does not continue to wear her engagement ring, but will have it reset or redesigned into another piece of jewelry. Should she continue to wear it, it should not be worn on the traditional finger but may be worn on the little or middle finger of the left or right hand.

Upon remarriage, the widow or divorceée should no longer wear the engagement ring from the first marriage. She may wish to give the ring to an adult son or daughter, or have it restyled.

ESSENTIALS OF A WEDDING

The essentials of a wedding are: (1) religious ceremony; (2) a father (brother, uncle, or any male relative of age) to give the bride away; (3) a best man for the groom; (4) an attendant for the bride; (5) a bouquet or corsage for the bride; (6) rings for the bride and groom (when he desires one); (7) a reception, even if no more than a wedding cake and champagne or punch, tea, or coffee; (8) a wedding trip.

The most important thing to remember in planning a wedding is that the day belongs to the couple. The wedding should be what they truly desire, large or small, in a chapel or garden. Although the couple gives every consideration to the suggestions of the parents and others taking part in it, the decisions are primarily theirs.

The invitations should be ordered *at least six weeks* in advance of the wedding date, and mailed by the bride's family *three to four weeks* before the wedding day. Marriage announcements are mailed *after* the wedding takes place to those to whom invitations were not sent.

Usually, the bridegroom's parents and relatives have to travel to get to the wedding, and it is up to the bride's family to find lodging for them. Relatives and friends usually accommodate as many as possible; otherwise, rooms must be reserved in nearby motels or hotels. Unless they are hard up financially, those who use the rooms pay for them.

It is up to the bridegroom's mother to let the bride's mother know how many will be arriving, and this should be done several weeks in advance. Usually, luncheons and dinners are given by the bride's family or friends during the out-of-town guests' stay.

THE CHAPLAIN

It is important that the engaged couple consult their chaplain or clergyman before the wedding—as early as possible. When they are of mixed faith, or when the bride has been married previously, these facts must be brought to the attention of the chaplain or clergyman before the couple continue with their wedding plans.

He will advise the couple concerning such legal requirements as medical tests, obtaining the marriage license, and signing the Marriage Register.

Although chaplains officiate at ceremonies held in the chapel to which they are assigned, a clergyman from the couple's home church may assist at the ceremony if this is acceptable to the chaplain and is arranged beforehand. The chaplain, like the clergyman, is bound by his ordination vows to uphold the laws and regulations of his particular church regarding marriage.

Service chaplains are of many faiths, and as commissioned officers, they are subject to transfer. Therefore, what is customary in one chapel may not be in another, and customs change in the chapels.

Chaplains on active duty are paid by the service they represent, and will not accept a fee, but a donation to the chapel fund is welcome. However, it is customary to offer any assisting civilian clergyman an honorarium, which the bridegroom pays. Since the amount varies, the prospective bridegroom should contact the office of the chaplain to determine such fees as well as those for an organist or soloist, if used.

CIVILIAN CLERGY

When a clergyman (minister, rabbi, priest) officiates at a wedding in his own church, he receives an honorarium. This is handed to him by the best man in a sealed envelope before the ceremony, and is given by the bridegroom or by his or the bride's parents.

Fees vary throughout the country in accordance with local custom, the formality of the wedding, and the area. The average is $150, but in a large city or rural area the fee may be considerably more or less. An assisting minister would receive much less.

There are some faiths that do not permit their clergymen to accept fees, and this must be determined beforehand by the bridegroom or best man. In such a case, remember that checks are written out to the chapel or church fund; when clergymen accept fees, checks are written directly to them (see page 344).

COUNSELING

Preparation for marriage includes much more than arranging for the ceremony. A chaplain or clergyman will want to spend time in counseling the couple—in uniform or in civilian life—before the wedding takes place. Some denominations have special requirements related to preparation and counseling.

THE DATE AND TIME

The date and time of the wedding are set by the couple and their parents, but in the services this may be a matter of convenience for the bride- and groom-elect.

A couple should try to set a date that will not conflict with plans of their families or close friends, particularly not their attendants. These plans might be a transfer, the graduation from college of a family member, a planned vacation, a reunion, or a busy holiday season that might keep loved ones at home.

However, an active duty military couple must set the date in keeping with any expected change of orders that will take them to a distant post or base. When orders have been changed, often the wedding date must also be changed.

Because May and June are the most favored months for marriage, it is important to reserve time at a chapel or church as far in advance as possible of a wedding planned for one of these months.

The favored hour for a church or home wedding differs in

different sections of the country, with evening weddings perhaps held more frequently in the southern and southwestern states (probably due to the weather), often at eight, half-past eight, or nine o'clock. The most formal wedding is one held in a church or chapel, but a formal wedding may also be held at home. Weddings—formal or informal—are at almost any convenient hour of the day or evening.

Couples of various religious faiths should always discuss the time, day, and hour of weddings with their chaplains or clergymen, priests, or rabbis, with particular concern for the Lenten season and holy days.

Generally, weddings at the service academy chapels are permitted Monday through Saturday, from noon through 4:00 P.M. on the hour. Dates are scheduled at the offices of the command chaplains.

WEDDINGS AT THE MILITARY CHAPEL

The chapel is reserved on a first-come, first-served basis. Permission for its use should be obtained as soon as possible, in order to secure the desired date and hour for your wedding. Whenever possible, applications should be made in writing to the chaplain's office months in advance of the event.

There is no charge for the use of the service chapel or the officiating chaplain, but a donation to the chapel fund is customary. The fund is for candles, flowers, marriage books, music, and many other services provided by the chapel staff. No one is asked to donate to the fund, but the cost of a week's wedding decorations in the academy chapels is between $100 and $150.

When a donation is made by check, it should be made out to The Chapel Religious Offering Fund, *not* to the chaplain. How much the bridegroom gives is determined by his circumstances.

GRADUATION WEEK WEDDINGS

Following graduation from the service academies in mid- to late May, the first chapel weddings for the new ensigns and second lieutenants will be held on the hour starting at 1:00 P.M. For the next several days only, they will start at 10:00 A.M. and continue until 8:00 P.M.

Rice and confetti are prohibited inside or outside the chapels at all times. Wedding receptions are never held in the chapels, and no arrangements for them are made by the chapel staff.

Each chapel has its own regulations concerning photographers, but generally they are permitted to take pictures before the wedding in designated areas, outside the chapel, and during the processional and recessional, with flashes permitted. Flashes are not permitted during the ceremony.

In order to schedule these numerous weddings, forms are sent early in the year to all members of the first class who wish to be married in the chapel. They will be filled out and returned to the chaplain's office. Drawings are made for the scheduling.

All service academies have more than one chapel. At the Air Force Academy Cadet Chapel, there are Protestant, Catholic, and Jewish chapels located on two separate levels, each having its own entrance; services are held simultaneously without interfering with one another.

Rooms for last-minute preparation are available for the bride and groom and their attendants, but there are no dressing rooms for either group.

ELIGIBILITY

Those eligible to be married in the chapel at any of the service academies are graduates, active or retired, or one of the following: a dependent; an officer or enlisted person assigned to the academy complex, or his or her dependents; a faculty or staff member, active or retired, or his or her dependents who regularly attend chapel services.

THE MUSIC

Wedding ceremonies are religious ceremonies, and the organist plays traditional wedding music and selections from the library of sacred music available in the chapel or church. The couple selects the music after consultation with the music director and chaplain.

It is customary but by no means obligatory for the bridal chorus from Wagner's *Lohengrin* and the wedding march from Mendelssohn's *Midsummer Night's Dream* to be played for the processional and recessional.

Less traditional music may be played in some churches, and a wide range is permitted in a few—but variations must be approved by the church organist or music director. No matter how modern the couple may be, some contemporary music is unsuitable for what should be a dignified occasion.

In the case of service weddings, when the organist is attached to the station, he receives no fee. At other chapels, such as the Navy Chapel in Washington, D.C., the organist is a civilian and receives a fee for the wedding, and an additional fee when attending the rehearsal. If the organist accompanies a soloist, there is an additional fee. Solos, if any, are usually presented before the ceremony begins.

It is not necessary for the organist and soloist to attend the wedding rehearsal, unless the couple so desires. The fees should be given to them at the rehearsal or at some other convenient time prior to the wedding. The bride's family or the person in charge of the wedding expenses pays these fees.

THE FLOWERS AND DECORATIONS

Rules for decorating military chapels vary throughout the nation. At the academy chapels, flowers, candelabra, and white hangings are furnished by the Chapel Altar Guild and are the same for all weddings. Two vases of altar flowers are usually permitted. The altar flowers may be the only flowers used—where decorating the altar is permitted—at both informal and formal weddings. Sometimes the aisle posts or reserved pews are decorated; greenery alone may be used in some churches and chapels.

Some chapels and churches do not furnish decorations, and if desired, they are arranged for by the bride's family. Any decorations that require alterations to the chapel or church (for example, those fastened to the pews or walls) may only be used with the chaplain's or clergyman's approval.

For chapel weddings held during holiday seasons, such as Christmas and Easter, flowers and decorations are furnished by the chaplain's office.

Flowers for the wedding party are the responsibility of the bride's parents, and should be delivered to the bride's room in the chapel in plenty of time for the ceremony. At a church wedding, they may be delivered either to the church or to the place where the bridal attendants are dressing.

WEDDING EXPENSES

A wedding and reception can cost anywhere from a few hundred to several thousand dollars. The cost depends upon the type of wedding (formal or informal); the number of guests and bridal attendants; the place of reception and the kind of food and drinks served; the type of invitations; the photographer's fees; the cost of the bridal gown and parents' clothes; the cost of the flowers; any fees for an organist, vocalist, or clergyman; any expenses for housing or transportation of guests.

A wedding should not burden anyone, parents or participants. Therefore, plan a wedding that does not take forever to pay for. A beautiful, meaningful wedding, formal or informal, can be one of simplicity but in good taste. Some couples prefer a less expensive wedding. With the money they save, they can furnish their new quarters.

The expenses of a second wedding may or may not be paid by the parents. If they gave a large first wedding and paid for an expensive reception, they are not required to pay for the second, but may if they want to. The expenses may be shared by the couple and the bride's parents—or the couple may prefer to pay all expenses themselves.

An older couple pay for their own wedding and reception.

THE MODERN WAY

There are several ways wedding expenses can be met. First, the prospective bride and bridegroom pay all expenses themselves. When both are working they may earn more than their parents. Second, the couple splits expenses with one, or both, sets of parents. Third, one or both sets of parents pay for everything. Fourth, other relatives, say affluent grandparents or godparents, take care of everything.

When you, the military couple, plan your wedding and will pay for it, it is important that you keep in touch with your parents, who may feel slighted, particularly when they are not affluent. When the wedding date has been moved up, or the guest list cut, you might need to explain that this is necessary because there has been a change of orders for one or the other of you, or because the best man or maid of honor is being transferred earlier than expected.

When parents help, you should talk freely with them about how much of the expense they can assume and how many guests can be invited. Wedding expenses today are much higher than they were in the past. In addition, there is considerable difference between a sit-down supper for a couple of hundred guests, with open bar and strolling musicians, and the traditional champagne and cake and finger-food offered at an afternoon reception for the same number of people.

One of the hazards in planning a wedding is the over-use of credit cards. It is easy to charge far more than is needed for this special occasion, but when the bills arrive, they can be hard to pay.

EXPENSES OF THE BRIDE'S FAMILY

Traditionally, the bride's family pays for most of the expenses of the wedding—up to the moment the bride leaves the reception. This includes the wedding invitations and/or announcements; wedding photographs before and during the event (at least one is given to the bridegroom's family; if they want more, they should pay for them); trousseau; flowers for the church and reception and any other decorations not furnished by the chapel or church; fees for the organist, soloist, sexton, if any; bridesmaids' bouquets and presents (the latter are all alike, are presented by the bride, and may be jewelry, such as a bracelet); the bridegroom's ring, if he wants one; reception expenses; and the hotel bills for out-of-town bridal attendants when they are not affluent and cannot be accommodated in the parents' home or the homes of relatives or friends.

The bridal gown and accessories (but *not* the gowns of the bridal attendants) are paid for by the bride's parents, and they usually give the bride a nice gift for the new household.

The considerate bride-elect will not select a gown to be worn by her bridesmaids whose cost is beyond what their budget allows, or someone may be forced to withdraw.

THE DIVORCED FATHER'S RESPONSIBILITY

When parents are divorced, the question arises about the bride's father's contribution—if any—toward the wedding expenses.

When the daughter and any other children live with the mother, the father almost always pays alimony and child support.

However, when he is financially able, a father may want to help with the wedding expenses, and he should discuss with his daughter what he might do. Perhaps he can pay for the wedding gown or the flowers or the reception. Otherwise, he might give the couple a special wedding present which they desire, or a check as large as he is able (or chooses) to give.

EXPENSES OF THE GROOM AND HIS FAMILY

Traditionally, the expenses of the groom and his family include the bride's engagement and wedding rings; the marriage license; the bride's bouquet (which she selects; the center of the bouquet may be removable and used for the going-away corsage); the corsages for both mothers; the ties and gloves for the best man and ushers, and mementos for each. Also, the clergyman's fee, if any, and the wedding trip.

If the ushers and the best man are in civilian dress, the groom pays for their boutonnieres as well as boutonnieres for the fathers. Other than their ties and gloves, the ushers and best man pay for their own clothes (or rental charges) and for their transportation to and from the city or place of the wedding. The groom, or members of his or the bride's family, should try to find places for the groom's attendants to stay; otherwise the groom usually pays for any hotel bills incurred by his attendants.

The groom usually gives his bride a gift on, or just before, the wedding day. The gift is something lasting, usually jewelry. He pays for his bachelor dinner, if he has one, and it is held a few days before the wedding (preferably *not* the night before). His gifts to his attendants are alike.

A gift of substance is given to the couple by his parents when possible. Their main contribution is hosting the wedding rehearsal dinner.

THE WEDDING RING OR RINGS

The prospective bridegroom and his fiancée should go to the jeweler in plenty of time to select and order the wedding ring—or rings, if he also wants one. (This would be a good time to look at silver and china patterns.)

A wedding ring has little space inside for engraving, so it is customary to inscribe only the initials and date, the bride's initials usually coming first: "A.B.S. and M.W.J. 7 June 1997"; the man's initials may be inscribed first: "M.W.J. to A.B.S." The rings may simply be inscribed "A.B.S.-M.W.J." When the wedding band is wide and you desire an inscription, any personal phrase may be used.

After the ring is selected, the bride-elect does not see it again until it is placed on her finger during the ceremony. The bridegroom pays for her ring, and it will be delivered to him.

When the groom also wants a wedding ring (in the double ring ceremony), his should be a little wider and heavier than a woman's ring. He wears it on the third finger of his left hand, just as the bride does, and not on his little finger. His ring is a gift from the bride. She pays for it, and it is engraved in a way similar to her own.

VARIANCES IN WEARING RINGS

A man or woman who has been married before never uses the wedding ring worn during the first marriage.

A woman does not have to have an engagement ring but legally she must have a wedding ring.

A *divorcée* usually removes the wedding ring except when she has children—and nowadays she may remove it, regardless.

A *widow* or *widower* wears her or his wedding ring until remarriage. A wedding ring is customarily interred with a person.

THE REHEARSAL AND REHEARSAL DINNER

In order that a wedding ceremony proceed smoothly, it is customary for a rehearsal to be held in the chapel or church at least a day before the wedding—but not immediately after a cocktail party.

When the rehearsal is scheduled the night before the wedding, hold the rehearsal *before* the dinner for the bridal party.

The hour of rehearsal is set with the chaplain or clergyman at the convenience of all members of the bridal party, *who are expected to attend.* No words of the ceremony are spoken during the rehearsal, but the chaplain or clergyman will indicate each person's role. The actual wedding rings are not used, but the motion of placing the ring on the bride's and groom's finger is practiced.

The rehearsal dinner usually is given by the groom's parents; otherwise, by the bride's parents or an intimate friend or relative of either family. The guests should include the members of the bridal party, the chaplain or clergyman and spouse, and the spouses of attendants. Other close relatives and friends of the couple may be invited if desired. At a large dinner, the fiancé or fiancée of a member of the bridal party may be included.

BRIDAL ATTENDANTS

The bride and groom may have only one attendant each: a best man and maid or matron of honor. Usually there are a maid or matron of honor, a best man, and from two to six bridesmaids and ushers.

The bride asks a sister or very close relative, or an intimate friend, to be her maid or matron of honor. The bridesmaids are close friends of the bride and usually include a sister or relative of the bridegroom. They pay for their own clothes.

Ushers and bridesmaids may be married or single. However, it is *not* necessary to ask both husband and wife to be a member of the wedding party when only one is a close friend of the bride or groom. The husband or wife not included in the wedding party would be included in any prenuptial parties, but need not be invited to sit at the bridal table at the reception unless the bride and groom so desire.

At a very large wedding, there may be both a maid and matron of honor and as many as eight or ten bridesmaids and a corresponding number of ushers, or more, as well as junior bridesmaids (10 to 14 years of age), flower girl (4 to 7), pages, train bearers, and a ring bearer (4 or 5 years old). The ring bearer wears a white or a dark suit and white shirt, never a miniature tux or tails.

Frequently, the bride gives a dinner for her bridesmaids on the night the groom gives his bachelor dinner. When such a dinner is given, this is the time for the bride to give the bridesmaids their presents.

Several days before the wedding, preferably after they have all arrived, the bridesmaids and maid or matron of honor may give a joint shower or party for the bride-elect. Individual presents, or a joint present, or both, are given to her.

THE BEST MAN

The groom chooses his best man and ushers from among his closest friends and relatives. His best man may be a brother or intimate friend, and occasionally is his father.

The best man is the bridegroom's aide. It is his duty to carry on, regardless of what arises. In order to instill calmness in members of the bridal party, he must maintain it himself.

Before the ceremony, the best man checks on the groom's clothes, gloves (if worn), the marriage license, and the bride's wedding ring. If the ceremony is held in a church, he delivers the clergyman's fee (paid by the groom), which is enclosed in a sealed envelope. He checks to see what has to be signed, and if everything is in order. He notifies the ushers to be at the chapel or church at least 20 minutes before the ceremony, and he arrives with the groom to be sure that the latter is not late and that he is properly dressed. During the ceremony, he produces the ring at the chaplain's (clergyman's) request.

Following the couple's vows, the best man joins in the recessional, in which he escorts the maid or matron of honor. Afterwards, he may wish to hurry on to the place of reception and check on details—such as stowing the bridal luggage in the going-away car. He does not stand in the receiving line at the reception, but is near the groom to be of further help. His is the first toast to the bride and groom at the bridal table.

THE USHERS

The ushers represent not only the groom but the families of the bride and groom as well. They act as unofficial hosts, greeting the guests in a pleasant manner, and are escorts to the bridesmaids. Ushers individually give the couple gifts, or they give a major gift together.

The number of ushers depends on the size of the wedding. An average-sized chapel wedding may be well handled by four to six ushers, with more serving at a large formal wedding. When the wedding is very small, no ushers may be needed. It is not necessary to have an equal number of ushers and bridesmaids. Usually, there are more ushers than bridesmaids, since ushers have definite duties to perform.

The main duty of the ushers is to seat guests in the chapel, church, or home. In accordance with the chaplain's faith at a military wedding, ushers may or may not wear swords while ushering. If not, the swords are left at a place convenient for the arch of swords (sabers) ceremony. It is preferable that six ushers in uniform perform this ceremony, although more may take part. Ushers may be in the uniform of one or more service.

When there are ushers who are nonmilitary and are wearing suits, they should be paired. For the arch of swords (sabers) ceremony, when held in the chancel area, the nonuniformed ushers unobtrusively step to the side following the wedding vows; or, when the arch is held outdoors, they step to the side following the recessional.

Ushers do not stand in the receiving line at the reception. They should make themselves useful in talking with the guests and as dancing partners when dancing is held.

WHAT THE GROOM AND USHERS WEAR

At a military wedding, officers wear the uniform in accordance with the formality of the wedding and seasonal regulations. *Evening dress uniform* conforms to civilian *white tie and tails. Dinner* or *mess dress uniform* is in accordance with *black tie. Service blues* or *whites* are comparable to a dark blue or conservative business suit or a cutaway. Any male member of a bridal party not in uniform dresses accordingly.

The groom, best man, and ushers wear the uniform of their services. Should the father of the bride be a retired officer, he may wear his uniform.

In civilian ceremonies, the groom and best man should be

dressed alike, and the ushers dressed like the groom and best man, with slight differences in shirts and ties. Suits and accessories may be rented. The fathers usually dress like the groom, except that their ties need not match.

At service weddings, formal or informal, the groom and best man do not wear gloves because of the necessity of handling the ring or rings. The ushers wear white gloves throughout the ceremony. At civilian weddings, the groom and best man carry gloves if they so desire, but gloves need not be carried at informal weddings.

THE WOMAN OFFICER'S WEDDING

A woman officer may wear a traditional bridal gown, or she may be married in uniform. Her bridal attendants will dress in accordance with her uniform or bridal gown. When the bridegroom is an officer, he should dress in accordance with the type of gown or uniform his bride will be wearing. The formality of the wedding determines the uniform worn.

When the military bride-elect is serving at a station where she has many responsibilities and free time is scarce, she must carefully weigh which type of wedding is best. If her home town is at a distance and the wedding will take place in the station chapel, her parents may not be able to help to any extent with the plans—they may not even be able to attend. In such a case she would have to make her own arrangements, which she may prefer to do; but even with the help of friends, a woman officer has less time than the average woman for planning a wedding.

A military wedding is usually scheduled during leave, or at a time when a change of orders gives the couple an opportunity to drive to the new duty station or to have a longer wedding trip in a locale of their choice. The date for the wedding can be made as soon as the leave or the date of the change of orders is determined, with the wedding probably held in the chapel and the reception in the officers' club.

When the bride chooses to wear the traditional wedding gown, she will save time by making an appointment with a marriage consultant at any reputable store who can coordinate her gown and those of the bridesmaids, as well as help with accessories.

Like the civilian career woman, the military woman can plan a large or small, formal or informal, wedding within her budget. At any type of wedding, the commanding officers and their spouses and all or some of the staff officers in the couple's office or staff (and their wives or husbands)—depending upon the size of the station—should be invited.

OFFICIAL MARRIED STATUS

When a woman officer marries, it is mandatory that she notify the personnel department of her service concerning her married status. If she prefers, she may officially retain her maiden name, or she may use her married name. The following forms are applicable to any service; the head of office of the service to whom it is directed is the only change required.

> From: Lieutenant Janet J. DOE, USN, 123-45-6789/1100
> To: Chief of Naval Personnel
> Via: (Commanding Officer)
> Subj: Marriage; notification of
> Ref: (a) BUPERSMAN 5010240
> Encl: (1) Photocopy of marriage certificate
>
> 1. In accordance with reference (a), the Chief of Naval Personnel is hereby notified of my marriage. Enclosure (1) is forwarded as proof of the marriage.
>
> 2. I do not desire to have my official records changed to indicate my married name.
>
> JANET J. DOE

> From: Lieutenant Janet J. DOE, USN, 123-45-6789/1100
> To: Chief of Naval Personnel
> Via: (Commanding Officer)
> Subj: Change of name; request for
> Ref: (a) BUPERSMAN 5010240
> Encl: (1) Photocopy of marriage certificate
>
> 1. In accordance with reference (a), it is requested that my name be changed in the official records from Janet Joyce Doe to Janet Doe Jones due to my marriage. Enclosure (1) is forwarded as proof of the marriage.
>
> JANET J. DOE*

*The new name cannot be used on any official forms until official change has been approved by the Chief of Naval Personnel (or the corresponding office of your service). The Chief of Naval Personnel acknowledges change of name in writing to the officer concerned.

MISS, MRS., OR MS.

The marriage vow is a contract, a covenant between a man and a woman. The modern bride may choose to take the last name of her husband, or she may legally retain her maiden name.

A military bride often continues to use her maiden name, as registered upon entering the service, although she is now Mrs. John Doe, the wife of (for example) Major Doe, USA.

The military or professional wife can, if she chooses, add her new husband's last name to her own maiden name: Lieutenant Jane Smith-Doe, USA. This form shows equality by recognizing both family names.

The civilian wife may prefer to be known professionally as Dr. or Senator Jane Doe, but socially and in private life as Mrs. John Doe, the wife of Mr. Doe.

How you sign your name is your choice: with rank or with Miss, Mrs., or Ms.

CIVILIAN WEDDINGS

When you are a member of a civilian wedding party, you need to know the general dress for formal and informal, daytime and evening, ceremonies:

VERY FORMAL DAYTIME (BEFORE 6:00 P.M.)

Bride: long white dress, train, veil, white shoes, gloves (optional, but worn when the sleeves of the gown are short), a white bridal bouquet or white flowers on a white prayer book.

Bride's attendants: long dresses, headpiece, matching shoes, gloves (optional); carry flowers.

Groom, his attendants, bride's father: cutaway, gray gloves, black shoes, ascots, and boutonnieres.

Mothers of the couple: long dresses with sleeves, small hat or head covering, gloves, corsage.

FORMAL DAYTIME (BEFORE 6:00 P.M.)

The same as for very formal daytime, except that the groom and his attendants and the bride's father wear sack coats and the mothers wear shorter or mid-calf dresses.

INFORMAL DAYTIME (BEFORE 6:00 P.M.)

Bride and her attendants: afternoon dress, or suit. Mothers of couple dress accordingly. Corsages.

Groom and his attendants: dark suits in winter; in summer, dark trousers and white or light-colored jacket or white trousers with charcoal or navy jacket; in hot weather, white suit. Boutonnieres.

VERY FORMAL EVENING (AFTER 6:00 P.M.)

Bride and her attendants: same as for formal daytime; the bride's train may be longer.

Groom and his attendants: white tie—black tailcoat and starched shirt, wing collar, white tie, boutonnieres, black dress shoes and socks.

Mothers of the couple: long evening or dinner dresses with sleeves or jacket, small headdress, gloves, corsage.

FORMAL EVENING (AFTER 6:00 P.M.)

Dress is the same as for very formal evening, except that men in the bridal party wear tuxedos (black tie); in summer, white jackets.

SEMIFORMAL EVENING (AFTER 6:00 P.M.)

Bride: long white dress and shorter veil, bouquet.

Bride's attendants: long dresses, corsages.

Groom and his attendants: black tie, with white or dark jacket when bride wears long dress; dark suit when bride wears simplified dress; black shoes and socks. Boutonnieres.

Mothers of the couple: short dresses or dressy suits, corsages.

INFORMAL EVENING (AFTER 6:00 P.M.)

Dress is the same as for informal daytime.

The dress described is for the traditional wedding. There is considerable leeway in color and design for both men and women for the less formal and informal wedding. The fathers of the couple wear boutonnieres, and the mothers wear corsages.

GUESTS

Officers wear service blues or whites at an informal wedding, or a dark blue or gray business suit or any conservative suit according to the season. The same type of business suit or dress blues or whites is worn at a formal daytime wedding, since cutaways are not often worn except by the men in the more formal wedding party.

At a formal evening wedding, you wear dinner or mess dress uniform or a dinner jacket, or evening dress uniform. Men may wear black tie at any formal evening wedding, and dark business suits at less formal or informal weddings.

Women wear long or short evening dresses with a jacket, or a dinner dress with sleeves for the formal evening wedding. For a less formal ceremony, you may wear a cocktail dress with a matching jacket or coat; gloves are optional. An afternoon dress or a dressy suit is worn to a morning wedding, and an afternoon dress or cocktail suit to an afternoon wedding. You do not wear all white—dress, shoes, and bag—at an informal or formal wedding, but an all-white dress is acceptable when worn with colored accessories.

Children wear their best party clothes, but they do not attend the wedding unless their names have been included in the invitation.

SECOND MARRIAGES

A second marriage for a man does not affect the ceremony. Formerly, a second marriage for a woman meant a small and informal wedding. Not so today. She may wear the traditional white wedding gown, but a veil and train are not appropriate. A combination of white with pastel is in good taste. Or a light-colored dress, long or short. The reception is as large as desired.

MIXED MARRIAGES

There is a rise today in interfaith marriages, long called a "source of family strife" or a "model of religious tolerance." According to statistics, about half of all Catholics are choosing non-Catholic spouses, and one-third of all Jews marry gentiles.*

Due to the rulings of the Second Vatican Council of 1962–65, which emphasized religious tolerance, the Protestant or Jewish spouse of a Catholic no longer signs an agreement to raise any children Catholic. And the wedding ceremony now may be held in a Catholic or Protestant church or a synagogue, with a minister or rabbi presiding.

* Sociologists Dean Hoge of Catholic University and Egon Mayer of Brooklyn College, quoted in *U.S. News and World Report,* 1986.

THE PUBLISHED WEDDING ANNOUNCEMENT

Wedding accounts for publication in metropolitan newspapers should be sent to the women's section editor as soon as possible. When pictures are used, either candid or those taken by a professional photographer, glossy prints are best for newspaper reproduction.

The account should include the pertinent information from the engagement announcement, as well as the date and place of the wedding, the name of the officiating chaplain or clergyman, the church or chapel, and the duty station of the bridegroom and/or bride. When either one is from a very old or distinguished family, the family connection may be included in the account. How much of the account will be used is determined by the policy of the paper.

A home-town paper may include additional information: the names and home towns of the entire bridal party, as well as a description of the bridal gown.

When space permits, a newspaper may publish the names of distinguished or out-of-town guests, but a complete list of guests is never published. You may wish to send a brief notice to your alumni magazine if such news is published.

MARRIAGE FINANCES

The groom should have his financial house in order before marriage, including money to cover the wedding trip. A wedding trip may follow the route to a new duty station, and in this case motel or hotel reservations are made in advance.

Although the groom must have enough money to cover the costs of the new household, today's bride may be in the military or in the civilian work force; then, finances may be of no immediate concern.

When the town or base of destination is unfamiliar, and quarters are not assigned, a classmate or friend stationed there can be of assistance in helping the couple find housing.

Sometimes the family of the bride or the groom give the young couple a check as a wedding gift, and financial problems are of no immediate concern. But a young couple should work as a team in household finances, fully understanding the limitations of a paycheck.

Since an officer is subject to duty in remote areas, someone must handle the household and other financial obligations while he or she is gone. The spouse can contribute much to the success of a new marriage by developing an ability to handle these obligations.

A household budget should be worked out and thoroughly understood by *both* of you before the serviceperson departs.

WHAT TO CALL IN-LAWS

Should a bride and groom call their new in-laws "Father" and "Mother" when this is what they call their own parents? This is a difficult question and must be answered by the individuals themselves. Perhaps the parents will suggest that their new daughter- or son-in-law call them "Mom" and "Dad" or use their first names, "Ruth" and "Bill."

To end the worry, when nothing has been suggested, the young couple should ask their in-laws what they wish to be called. Until then, you may call them "Mr." and "Mrs." or "Colonel" and "Mrs.," both of which show respect if not warmth.

ACCEPTING AN HONOR—OR NOT

It is an honor to be asked to be a bridesmaid or groomsman for a close friend—perhaps a roommate or relative. But there is considerable expense and time involved.

When you are financially burdened, when the association has not been close, or when new orders place miles or oceans between you, then you need not accept. But you do need a logical and honest reason for your refusal, particularly when the bride or groom is close to you. A sincere note or phone call is then in order.

Bridesmaids pay for their own gowns and accessories, and groomsmen pay for their cutaway or business suit (usually rented) when not in uniform. You pay for your transportation to the city where the wedding is to be held.

A thoughtful bride-elect will consider her bridesmaids' ability to pay for their gowns and narrow the choice to two or three gowns that won't be too costly and could be used again. She will then let them choose.

CHAPTER 26

Wedding Invitations, Announcements, & Replies

TODAY, A BRIDE-ELECT has the choice of selecting contemporary wedding invitations or the traditional invitations of white or ivory-colored paper with engraved lettering—a choice that a few years ago was not possible within the realm of good taste. The traditional invitation is always beautiful, and always will be. Contemporary stylings can be beautiful when wordings are not faddish or eccentric and pastel colors are used with discrimination. Your good taste and the type of wedding you are having—formal or informal—should determine your selection.

TRADITIONAL WEDDING INVITATIONS

The traditional wedding invitation is engraved on white or ivory vellum or kid-finish paper. This may be a double sheet, about 5½ by 7½ inches, which is folded and enclosed in the inner of one of two envelopes. A smaller invitation, about 4½ by 6 inches in size, is not folded and is placed sideways in the envelope.

When invitations have double envelopes, the *inner* one has the guest's rank or title and last name written on it in black or dark blue ink (for example, "Colonel and Mrs. Smith"), with active or retired status *not* used. The tissue protecting the engraving on the invitation is not removed before placing the invitation in the envelope.

Although black engraving has been mandatory in past years—and is desirable—a good quality of raised printing is available today and is much less expensive. There are many lettering styles to choose from, but shaded Roman, antique Roman, and script are always in good taste.

Abbreviations, initials, and numerals are to be avoided whenever possible in wedding invitations. The hour is always written out in full. However, Roman numerals may denote a second or third generation: John Paul Truxtun II or III. The designation "Junior" applies to the next in direct line of descent. The numbers "II," etc., indicate the sequence in the use of the name. A man usually does not continue to add "Junior" or "Jr." after his name following the death of his father, but he may if his mother is still living.

LETTERING STYLES

Thermography is a very good substitute for engraving, and is a good idea when the expense of the invitations must be considered. The photo-letter techniques have script lettering and details usually associated with hand engraving.

Before you decide on the paper and lettering, look at the stationer's or printer's samples. There is considerable difference in price between engraving and the raised or thermograph lettering frequently used today.

SERVICE RANK

Commissioned officers of the rank of commander and up in the Navy and Coast Guard, and of captain and up in the Army, Air Force, and Marine Corps, use their titles before their names on the invitation. The ranks of junior grade and company grade officers are placed beneath their names. The grades of second and first lieutenant, U.S. Army, are designated lieutenant. The ranks of first and second lieutenant, lieutenant commander, lieutenant colonel, vice admiral, and so on are spelled out.

Retired officers of the ranks of commander and lieutenant colonel and up usually keep their titles in civilian life and use their titles on wedding invitations.

When issuing a wedding invitation with his or her spouse, the retired officer does not use the word *Retired*. But if he or she is a widower or widow, or if he or she is the groom or bride, then the word *Retired* is used as follows:

Colonel John (or Jane) Doe
United States Air Force, Retired

Reserve officers on active duty only use their titles on wedding invitations or announcements. High-ranking officers who are retired but who keep their titles in civilian life use their titles.

Noncommissioned officers and enlisted men or women use their names with the branch of service immediately below.

THE GUEST LIST

The groom sends a list of his friends' names and addresses to his mother, who in turn will send his list with her own to the mother of the bride. If his mother is dead, he will send the list. If all guests are not to be invited to the reception or breakfast following the wedding, this should be designated on the list by an R for reception and C for ceremony. The bride's mother should keep an alphabetical check list for acceptances and regrets.

ISSUING INVITATIONS

Invitations are mailed at least three or four weeks before the event. Even though they know "all about it," don't neglect to send invitations to the bridegroom's parents and to members of the bridal party; these invitations are treasured mementos. If the parents of the bride are deceased, the invitations are issued by a close or older relative, a brother or grandparent. In the case of divorced parents, they would be issued in the name of the one with whom the bride has been living. Or she sends them herself.

When a card is included with the invitation inviting you to the reception or breakfast following the ceremony, and the card has an R.S.V.P., it must be answered. A "Regrets only" is *not* used. Invitations to some church weddings are announced by the pastor as including the entire congregation; these do not require a reply.

The home address of the bride's family is usually engraved on the reception or wedding breakfast card, so that replies will be sent to that address and *not* to the place of the wedding.

Small self-addressed and stamped (or unstamped) envelopes with reply cards are often included with the invitations. Although replies may be handwritten, the changing times have brought acceptance of this easy way to ensure replies.

Wedding invitations are always sent to a married couple, even though you know only one or the other.

Brigadier General and Mrs. John Henry Doe

request the honour of your presence

at the marriage of their daughter

Ann Carol

to

James Paul Smith

Lieutenant, United States Army

on Thursday, the ninth of June

at half after four o'clock

Cadet Chapel

West Point, New York

Traditional formal invitation

"Second" Lieutenant or "First" Lieutenant is designated in the Air Force and Marine Corps. The Navy uses the designation "Lieutenant, junior grade." The word *Retired* is not used by a retired senior officer and his or her spouse, but it is used by a single officer, divorced or widowed.

ADDRESSING ENVELOPES

A formal engraved wedding invitation has two envelopes: the *outside,* gummed, which bears the full name and address of the guest or guests, and the *inside,* ungummed, envelope, which has only the rank or title and the surname and holds the invitation or announcement. The inside envelope is faced toward the back of the outside envelope when inserted, so that the names will be face up when the envelope is opened.

All envelopes are addressed by hand, in black or dark blue ink. Order extra envelopes to allow for mistakes, and have plenty of stamps on hand.

The *outside* envelope will be fully addressed without abbreviations, initials, or commas:

Major and Mrs. James Paul Doe
7618 Van Noy Court
Argonne Hills
Fort George G. Meade
Maryland 20755

The *inner* envelope is addressed: *Major and Mrs. Doe.*

Other adult members of the family, such as a grandmother or mother-in-law, receive separate invitations. For a close relative, you write *Grandmother,* etc., on the inner envelope.

You may write the name or names of teen-age children of the family directly under the parents' names on the outer envelope, and *Miss* or *Misses Doe* on the inner envelope. The outer envelope would be:

Major and Mrs. James Paul Doe
Miss Susan Doe
(address)

Or, when the children are under age, simply write: *Susan, Mary, and John* on the inside envelope under the parents' names.

Invitations may be addressed to brothers 12 years of age or younger as "The Messrs. Doe." But *Messrs.* is used only for brothers, not for a father and son. A girl of any age may be addressed "Miss," and teen-age and high school boys are "Mr."

When a woman's service rank or civilian title exceeds that of her husband, for an informal occasion, including a wedding, her rank or title need not be used on the envelope, which is addressed to *Mr. and Mrs. John Earl Doe,* with the inside envelope addressed to *Mr. and Mrs. Doe.* (For formal and official invitations, her rank or title is used. See chapter 14.)

The *inner envelope,* as stated elsewhere, has only the rank or title and surname of the invited guest or guests: *Major and Mrs. Doe.* An adult member of the family or other close relative would be addressed *Grandmother,* etc. A single person would be *Captain Jones* or *Mr. Smith.* In case of a married couple with the same rank and service, they would be the *Captains Doe;* in a different service, different ranks, they would be: *Captain Doe, Major Smith*—when she has retained her maiden name—and *Captain and Major Doe,* when she has not.

RETURN ADDRESS

It is sensible to have a legible return address on the wedding invitation envelope, and the style of the address should be determined at the time envelopes are ordered. Usually the return address is embossed on the flap of the envelope, but for the sake of clarity, raised printing could be used.

The return address lets a person know where to send a wedding gift. Also, should the person to whom the invitation is sent have moved without leaving an address, the invitation will not be lost.

THE SERVICEWOMAN'S WEDDING INVITATION

When the bride is a member of the armed forces, she uses her title with the branch of service (see Service Rank, page 315). For example:

LIEUTENANT GENERAL AND MRS. WILSON JOHN DOE
REQUEST THE HONOUR OF YOUR PRESENCE
AT THE MARRIAGE OF THEIR DAUGHTER
CAPTAIN ELIZABETH ANNE DOE
UNITED STATES MARINE CORPS
TO
MAJOR JAMES LEE SMITH
UNITED STATES ARMY
SATURDAY, THE NINTH OF JANUARY
AT FOUR O'CLOCK
THE MARINE CORPS MEMORIAL CHAPEL
MARINE CORPS BASE
QUANTICO, VIRGINIA

When the wedding will be private and only close friends and relatives invited, or when the bride is a divorcée but a large reception will be held, the wedding invitation could be oral or handwritten, and the printed *reception invitations* worded in this manner:

LIEUTENANT GENERAL AND MRS. WILSON JOHN DOE
REQUEST THE PLEASURE OF YOUR COMPANY
AT THE WEDDING RECEPTION
OF THEIR DAUGHTER
CAPTAIN ELIZABETH ANNE DOE
UNITED STATES MARINE CORPS
AND
MAJOR JAMES LEE SMITH
UNITED STATES ARMY
SATURDAY, THE NINTH OF JANUARY
AT HALF AFTER FOUR O'CLOCK
QUARTERS ONE
MARINE CORPS BASE
QUANTICO, VIRGINIA

VARIATIONS IN WORDINGS

There are many variations in the wording of parts of the invitation:

1. When the bride's parents are deceased and a relative is sending the invitations:

MR. GEORGE OLIVER SMITH
REQUESTS THE HONOR OF YOUR PRESENCE
AT THE MARRIAGE OF HIS SISTER
MARY MARTHA

2. When the bride's parents are divorced and the mother has not remarried, she uses her maiden surname with her former husband's name: Mrs. Brown Smith. When the divorce is "friendly," both names may be on the invitation; the mother's name appears first:

MRS. BROWN SMITH
AND
COMMANDER JOHN JAMES SMITH
UNITED STATES NAVY, RETIRED
REQUEST THE HONOR OF YOUR PRESENCE
AT THE MARRIAGE OF THEIR DAUGHTER

3. When the mother has remarried and is widowed or divorced from her second husband, her name is placed first on the invitation, with the bride's father's name on the following line (when agreeable with all parties):

MRS. SMITH DOE
AND
COMMANDER JOHN JAMES SMITH
UNITED STATES NAVY, RETIRED
REQUEST THE HONOR OF YOUR PRESENCE
AT THE MARRIAGE OF THEIR DAUGHTER

Regardless of the number of times the parents have remarried, the bride is still *their* daughter.

4. When the bride's father is dead, or her parents are divorced, and her mother has remarried:

MR. AND MRS. PAUL LEWIS DORN
REQUEST THE HONOR OF YOUR PRESENCE
AT THE MARRIAGE OF HER* DAUGHTER
MARY MARTHA SMITH

5. Or the invitations may be issued in the mother's name only:

MRS. PAUL LEWIS DORN
REQUESTS THE HONOR OF YOUR PRESENCE
AT THE MARRIAGE OF HER DAUGHTER
MARY MARTHA SMITH

6. Or issued in the father's name only:

COLONEL PAUL LEWIS DORN
UNITED STATES AIR FORCE, RETIRED
REQUESTS THE HONOR OF YOUR PRESENCE
AT THE MARRIAGE OF HIS DAUGHTER

7. If the bride's mother is dead and the father has married again, the form usually is:

COMMANDER AND MRS. JOHN JAMES SMITH
REQUEST THE HONOR OF YOUR PRESENCE
AT THE MARRIAGE OF HIS* DAUGHTER
MARY MARTHA

When a widow or widower who has not remarried is issuing the invitations, her or his name appears alone.

8. When a young widow is married, the married name of the widow is given, and the form is:

*When the relationship between the stepparent and the bride is close, *their* would be used instead of *his* or *her.*

BRIGADIER GENERAL AND MRS. JOHN JAMES SMITH
REQUEST THE HONOR OF YOUR PRESENCE
AT THE MARRIAGE OF THEIR DAUGHTER
MARY MARTHA ADAMS
TO
JOHN DOE BLANK
SECOND LIEUTENANT, UNITED STATES AIR FORCE
ON SATURDAY, THE FOURTH OF JUNE
AT SEVEN O'CLOCK
RANDOLPH AIR FORCE BASE CHAPEL
TEXAS

When an older widow gives her own wedding, it is usually informal, and handwritten invitations are sent. But when engraved or printed invitations are used, the form is:

THE HONOR OF YOUR PRESENCE
IS REQUESTED AT THE MARRIAGE OF
MRS. DONALD JAMES ADAMS
TO
JOHN DOE BLANK

9. These forms may be used by the divorcée, except that her given name and maiden name are used with the last name of her former husband: "Martha Smith Adams." For an older woman: "Mrs. Smith Adams."

10. When sisters are married at a double wedding, the name of the older sister is given first:

COMMANDER AND MRS. JOHN JAMES SMITH
REQUEST THE HONOR OF YOUR PRESENCE
AT THE MARRIAGE OF THEIR DAUGHTERS
MARY MARTHA
TO
CAPTAIN DONALD JAMES ADAMS
UNITED STATES MARINE CORPS
AND
SARAH JANE
TO
FRED PERRY HAAS
ENSIGN, UNITED STATES COAST GUARD
ON MONDAY, THE SIXTH OF JUNE
AT FOUR O'CLOCK
CHRIST EPISCOPAL CHURCH, GEORGETOWN
WASHINGTON, DISTRICT OF COLUMBIA

11. When there are no close relatives or friends, or should she be an orphan, the bride may send out her own invitations, with the wording as follows:

THE HONOR OF YOUR PRESENCE
IS REQUESTED AT THE MARRIAGE OF
MISS MARY MARTHA SMITH
TO
DONALD JAMES ADAMS

12. At a double wedding when the brides and bridegrooms are very close friends but are not related, the invitations may be written according to the rank of the fathers or bridegrooms, or in alphabetical order.

13. When the bride's parents are separated but not divorced, the fact of the separation is frequently ignored, and the invitations are engraved in the customary form.

14. When the bride-elect is adopted, there is no need to mention this fact. When her name is different and it is necessary to use it, both the engagement announcement and the wedding invitation could use the words *adopted daughter.*

CONTEMPORARY WORDINGS

Once, it was unheard of to change the wording of a formal wedding invitation. Although the traditional is unchanged for the truly formal wedding, there are variations in expressions of religious faith and other sentiments that are meaningful and beautiful.

When personal wordings are preferred for informal invitations, caution must be observed so that self-expression does not become overly sentimental or extreme.

WEDDINGS GIVEN BY BOTH SETS OF PARENTS

Less customary but becoming more frequent today is the informal or semiformal wedding that is given by both sets of parents. The wedding invitations are issued in the names of both sets of parents, and the reception is given jointly (and paid for jointly).

The parents of both the bride and the groom would stand in the receiving line, or the fathers would be in the line briefly or not at all. In such a case the number of bridesmaids is kept to a minimum; otherwise, the line would be very long.

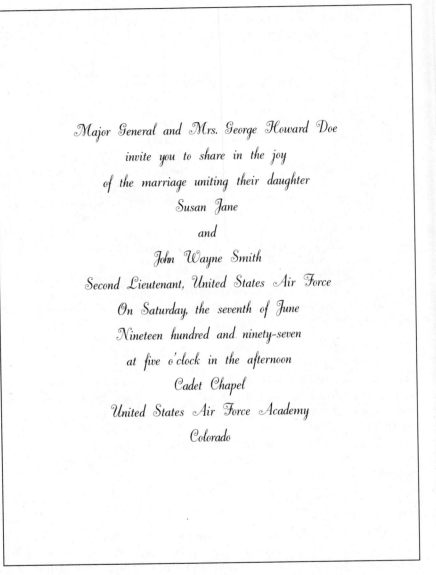

Major General and Mrs. George Howard Doe
invite you to share in the joy
of the marriage uniting their daughter
Susan Jane
and
John Wayne Smith
Second Lieutenant, United States Air Force
On Saturday, the seventh of June
Nineteen hundred and ninety-seven
at five o'clock in the afternoon
Cadet Chapel
United States Air Force Academy
Colorado

Contemporary formal invitation
Inclusion of the year is optional.

INVITATIONS FOR INFORMAL WEDDINGS

A small, informal wedding does not require engraved invitations. The mother of the bride may write short notes of invitation, or she may telegraph or telephone the relatives and friends who are to be invited to the ceremony or to the reception, or to both.

The notes are written on conservative notepaper, white or cream color, giving the time and place of the ceremony. If the invitation is only for the reception, the time and place of the reception are all that is necessary. Informal invitations may be sent on short notice when, for instance, a change of orders is imminent:

1052 Douglass Valley

Dear Mary,

Janet is being married in our quarters to Second Lieutenant John Wayne Smith, USAF, who was graduated from the Air Force Academy last week.

The wedding will take place Thursday the sixteenth of June at four-thirty. We do hope you will be with us and stay for the reception afterwards.

As ever,

Bess Doe

Replies to invitations to small weddings, including those sent by phone or telegram, are made by letter—if you have time. A brief, sincere note on your personal notepaper is correct.

RECEPTION INVITATIONS

There are several ways of extending an invitation for a wedding reception.

1. If the wedding takes place in the morning or early afternoon—but no later than one o'clock—a *wedding breakfast* card is enclosed. A small card about 3 by 4 inches, engraved on the same type paper as the wedding invitation, is included along with the invitation. There is no crest or coat of arms on the card, and the protecting tissue (when provided) is not removed before mailing. The phrase "pleasure of your company" is used, since this is now a social occasion:

COLONEL AND MRS. JOHN JAMES SMITH
REQUEST THE PLEASURE OF YOUR COMPANY
AT THE WEDDING BREAKFAST
FOLLOWING THE CEREMONY
AT
DOGWOOD HILLS
ARLINGTON

R.S.V.P.

2. If the wedding is to be in the late afternoon or evening, a *reception invitation* card is enclosed with the wedding invitation:

Reception

immediately following the ceremony

Officers' Club, Bolling Air Force Base

The favour of a reply is requested
3909 Connecticut Avenue, Northwest
Washington, District of Columbia

3. When a wedding is very small, with *no* wedding invitations to be issued, but with a large reception planned afterwards, the *reception invitations* are engraved on paper about the same size as the traditional wedding invitation:

COLONEL AND MRS. JOHN JAMES SMITH
REQUEST THE PLEASURE OF YOUR COMPANY
AT THE WEDDING RECEPTION OF THEIR DAUGHTER
MARY MARTHA
AND
DONALD JAMES ADAMS
LIEUTENANT, UNITED STATES NAVAL RESERVE
ON MONDAY, THE SIXTH OF JUNE
AT FOUR O'CLOCK
DOGWOOD HILLS
ARLINGTON, VIRGINIA

R.S.V.P.

4. The invitation to the reception may be included in the wedding invitation when *all* guests are invited to *both* the wedding and reception. The following information is added to the bottom of the wedding invitation, following the name and address of the church:

AND AFTERWARDS AT
DOGWOOD HILLS
ARLINGTON, VIRGINIA

R.S.V.P.

ACCEPTANCES AND REFUSALS

When you are invited to the ceremony and to the reception, or to the reception alone, the R.S.V.P. is usually requested and *must* be answered. Your reply will follow the form of the engraved invitation, or of the informal letter. You will write in longhand, on cream-colored or white notepaper, and the form for the acceptance or regret is similar, except for the lines of acceptance or regret.

Your reply is addressed to the bride-elect's mother, unless she is deceased; then you address it to the person who issued the invitation. If you received a reply card, just fill it in.

A simple and desirable form of answering the invitation to the wedding, to both the wedding and the reception, or to the reception only, is:

Lieutenant and Mrs. Willian Blank
accept with pleasure
the kind invitation of
Colonel and Mrs. Smith
for
Monday, the sixth of June
at four o'clock

The same general form is used to regret as to accept an invitation. You will remember that in all refusals, the hour of the occasion and the address are always omitted. When the refusal is for an invitation from a close friend, the reason is frequently added in the second and third lines, such as: "regret that their absence from the city prevents their accepting."

A more detailed form for answering the invitation is shown in the following regret for a reception only:

*Lieutenant and Mrs. William Blank
regret that they are unable to accept
the very kind invitation of
Colonel and Mrs. Smith
to the wedding reception of their daughter
Mary Martha
and
Donald James Adams
on Monday, the sixth of June*

When either the husband or wife cannot accept the invitation, the person accepting may write the reply as follows:

*Mrs. William Blank
accepts with pleasure
the kind invitation of
Colonel and Mrs. Smith
for
Monday, the sixth of June
at four o'clock
Lieutenant William Blank
regrets exceedingly
that he will be unable to accept*

A reply to a small or informal wedding invitation is usually sent in the same form in which it was received. Telephone and telegram invitations may be answered in kind. When time allows, it is preferable that reply be made by a handwritten note. An acceptance could read:

Monday

Dear Mrs. Smith,

I am very happy about your daughter's forthcoming marriage to my classmate, Dick Brown, and am pleased to be in the States and able to attend. I'll fly in and will be staying with friends.

Sincerely,

John Jones

CHILDREN AS GUESTS

An invitation to a wedding is only for those persons whose names are written on the envelopes, unless the envelope reads "and guest" or "and family." Parents with older children whose names *are* on the envelope and who *will* attend the wedding do *not* bring their baby or small child, no matter how good they think he or she is. This is the bridal couple's day, and they do not need a crying child in the middle of the service or reception, which may be long and tiring to a child.

Invitations are sent out early enough for the parents to make arrangements for a baby-sitter at home or in another room of the chapel or church. So don't put the bride-elect on the spot by asking her, even if she is your sister or best friend, if you may bring the baby along. And if you do ask, don't be offended when she says no.

MARRIAGE ANNOUNCEMENTS

Engraved or printed marriage announcements are issued on the same type of paper used for wedding invitations, and are sent out *after* the marriage has taken place. The announcements are sent by the bride's parents or by a person designated to do this.

Wedding announcements are sent to less intimate friends and acquaintances who were not invited to the wedding, or to all friends and acquaintances following a ceremony when no guests were invited. In wedding announcements, the year is customarily written out, the name of the church may or may not be included, and the hour of the wedding is not specified:

CAPTAIN AND MRS. JOHN JONES SMITH
HAVE THE HONOR OF ANNOUNCING
THE MARRIAGE OF THEIR DAUGHTER
MARY ANN
TO
MR. GEORGE CARL WILSON
ON SATURDAY, THE SEVENTH OF JUNE
NINETEEN HUNDRED AND NINETY-SEVEN
TREASURE ISLAND CHAPEL
SAN FRANCISCO, CALIFORNIA

When the bride's parents do not approve the wedding, which may have been an elopement with a civil ceremony, or when the bride's parents are deceased and there are no close relatives, or when she is an orphan, the couple may announce their own marriage. When a civil ceremony was held, the name of the city or town, but not where the wedding took place, is mentioned:

MISS JANE ELLEN DOE
AND
WILLIAM JOHN SMITH, JUNIOR
ENSIGN, UNITED STATES COAST GUARD
ANNOUNCE THEIR MARRIAGE
ON SATURDAY, THE SEVENTH OF JUNE
ONE THOUSAND NINE HUNDRED AND NINETY-SEVEN
AT MYSTIC, CONNECTICUT

RECALLING WEDDING INVITATIONS

Because of illness, a change of orders, or a change of mind, wedding invitations may have to be recalled after they have been issued. Notices must then be sent to all those who received invitations. The best form for recalling the invitation is:

DR. AND MRS. WILLIAM SMITH
ANNOUNCE THAT THE MARRIAGE OF THEIR DAUGHTER
MARY ELLEN
TO
ENSIGN JOHN LEE JONES
WILL NOT TAKE PLACE

When the wedding invitation is recalled because of a bereavement in the family, the engraved or printed card may state the reason:

DR. AND MRS. WILLIAM SMITH
REGRET EXCEEDINGLY
THAT BECAUSE OF THE RECENT DEATH OF
THE FATHER OF ENSIGN JONES
THE INVITATIONS TO THE MARRIAGE OF THEIR DAUGHTER
MARY ELLEN
TO
ENSIGN JOHN LEE JONES
MUST BE RECALLED

or

MRS. WILLIAM SMITH
REGRETS THAT THE DEATH OF
DR. SMITH
OBLIGES HER TO RECALL THE INVITATIONS
TO THE WEDDING OF HER DAUGHTER

The recalling of the invitations in case of a death in the immediate family does not always mean that the wedding may not take place on the scheduled day. If the families agree, a very quiet ceremony may be held on the original day of the wedding, with perhaps only one attendant each for the bride and groom.

When members of the bridal party have already arrived, and some have come from a distance, or when the bride or groom is in the service and has only a few days' leave or has a new duty that will take her or him some distance, the wedding may be held as scheduled, but with no guests other than members of the families and the bridal party, and a few very close friends.

POSTPONING THE WEDDING

When it is necessary to postpone a wedding, a form similar to this may be followed:

CAPTAIN AND MRS. JOHN JONES SMITH
ANNOUNCE THAT THE MARRIAGE OF THEIR DAUGHTER
MARY ANN
TO
MR. GEORGE CARL WILSON
HAS BEEN POSTPONED FROM
SATURDAY, THE FOURTH OF JUNE
UNTIL
SATURDAY, THE TWENTY-FIFTH OF JUNE
AT FOUR O'CLOCK
TREASURE ISLAND CHAPEL
SAN FRANCISCO, CALIFORNIA

AT-HOME CARDS

When you want friends to know your new address, and when you know where you will be living long enough to make the cards worthwhile, at-home cards may be enclosed in the same envelope with the wedding announcement.

The cards may be similar in size to a couple's joint card—about 3 by 4 inches—and are the same color as the wedding announcement. One form is:

LIEUTENANT AND MRS. JOHN CARL SMITH

9 COLUMBINE VISTA

AFTER THE FIRST OF JUNE   COLORADO SPRINGS, COLORADO

Or smaller cards, about the size of a personal card, may be used:

AFTER JUNE 4TH
9 COLUMBINE VISTA
COLORADO SPRINGS, COLORADO

WEDDING ANNIVERSARIES

For announcements of wedding anniversaries, the year of the wedding and the year in which the invitation is issued are customarily stamped or engraved at the top of the anniversary invitation or announcement. The couple's initials or monogram, coat of arms, or a seal may be engraved in gold or silver, or in black or dark blue ink. Such invitations may be sent out by the couple or by their children. An example in the first case would be:

1947   1997
MAJOR GENERAL AND MRS. JOHN JAMES SMITH
REQUEST THE PLEASURE OF
Colonel and Mrs. George Ballou's
COMPANY ON THE FIFTIETH ANNIVERSARY
OF THEIR MARRIAGE
ON FRIDAY EVENING, MAY THE NINTH
FROM SEVEN UNTIL NINE O'CLOCK
THE BROADMOOR
COLORADO SPRINGS, COLORADO

or

1947–1997
MAJOR GENERAL AND MRS. JOHN JAMES SMITH
AT HOME
FRIDAY, THE NINTH OF MAY
FROM FIVE UNTIL SEVEN O'CLOCK
237 MOUNTAIN VIEW ROAD
COLORADO SPRINGS, COLORADO

CHAPTER 27

Military & Civilian Weddings

ON TIME!

Everyone is expected to be on time at a wedding. The bride and her party should arrive at the chapel or church 30 minutes before the designated hour, and go directly to the room made available for making final preparations. *It is inexcusable for the bridal party to be late.*

The groom, best man, and ushers also arrive at the chapel or church at least 30 minutes before the time of the ceremony; ushers must be on hand to seat early guests.

All guests should be seated before the time designated for the ceremony to begin. When there is a soloist, guests wait quietly at the rear of the chapel until the conclusion of the song before being seated.

CHAPEL OR CHURCH PEWS

When the center aisle of the chapel is banked by candelabra, two ushers will light the candles some 15 minutes before the hour of the

333

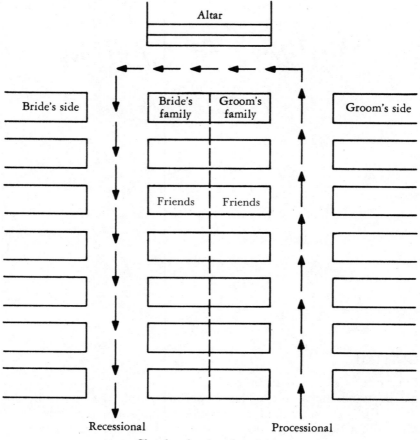

Chapel or church with two aisles

The center section may be divided by a white ribbon or rope, with the bride's family seated in the left-side pews facing the altar, and the groom's family on the right. However, a warm and friendly way is not to use a dividing ribbon or rope, but for the families to sit in the first pews together but on "their" side. At a very large wedding, friends of the bride would sit at the far left, the groom's friends at the far right, as well as behind the families in the center section.

ceremony. They proceed to the front of the chapel; each usher lights the candles on his side with the aid of a taper. Reserved pews are frequently decorated with ribbons or sprays of flowers at the ends.

Runners are infrequently used in service chapels. If they are used, two ushers march in step to the front of the chapel or church, where they grasp the runner; facing the back, they walk until the runner is stretched as far as it will go.

TWO AISLES

When the chapel or church does not have a single central aisle, but has two aisles, you may select one aisle and plan the wedding as though that were the only one. Or you may use one aisle for the processional and the other aisle for the recessional. The bride's family would be seated in the front pews on the left side of the center section, and the bridegroom's family in the front right-side pews.

USHERING

When guests arrive at the chapel (church or home), ushers ask if they want to be seated on the bride's side or on the groom's side, or they may ask, "Are you a relative (or friend) of the bride or groom?" Guests are seated accordingly: on the *left* of the chapel facing the altar for the bride's friends, on the *right* for the groom's. An usher always offers his *right arm* to a lady when escorting her down the aisle.

However, when one side of the church is filling rapidly while the other side remains almost empty—as may happen when the groom's relatives and friends live at a distance—then the ushers may ask late-arriving guests to sit on the less full side of the church.

A woman who arrives with her husband or other male guest often is escorted to the proper pew, with the usher asking the man to follow. Today, however, it is not unusual for an usher to escort both the husband and the wife, walking together, to a pew, rather than having the husband (or male escort) trailing along behind. Children follow their parents. A man attending alone walks beside the usher—who does not offer his arm.

Traditionally, each woman is escorted to a pew separately, unless there are many guests waiting to be escorted. Then, the usher may offer the senior woman his right arm and ask the others in the party to follow. He may make appropriate remarks while escorting, but quietly, and in keeping with the dignity and reverence accorded a sanctuary. Guests should not be hurried to their seats, but the seating must be done with a minimum of delay; guests are never seated during a solo.

Guests who arrive first are given the choice aisle seats, and later arrivals take the inner seats. At a large wedding, the head usher may be given a typed alphabetical list of guests and the seating arrangement.

The commanding officer of the bride or groom, and his wife or her husband, may be invited to sit in the front pew if the parents are unable to attend. When the parents are in attendance, the commanding officer's party may be accorded the courtesy of being seated near or with immediate family.

Flag and general officers, the couple's commanding officers, and dignitaries may be seated just behind the families, but protocol is not adhered to at weddings.

The head ushers are so designated by the groom. One usher escorts the groom's mother to her pew on the right. Just before the ceremony is to start, the head usher escorts the bride's mother to her pew on the left—and she is the *last* person to be seated. The chapel doors are then closed, but if they are not locked the latecomer may seat himself in the back of the chapel. *But guests are not expected to be late.*

THE WEDDING CEREMONY

THE PROCESSIONAL

A wedding in an academy chapel follows the procedure explained here. In general, this same procedure may be used or adapted in any chapel or church.

The procession forms upon the completion of the ushers' duties, with the ushers taking their places at the head of the procession in the vestibule.

The first note of the wedding march is the signal that the ceremony is about to begin, and the bride's mother rises to her feet. Or, she may ask the chaplain beforehand to say: "Will everyone please stand?" By this time, everything is in order, and everyone in his or her place. The order of procedure is as follows.

A. The chaplain enters from a side door, faces the altar in a quiet moment of prayer, then turns left and advances toward the congregation.

B. The groom enters, followed at about two paces by the best man, and both are in the same marching step as paced by the chaplain. As they approach the altar area, they pause in a moment of prayer, then turn left and face the congregation and the direction from which the bride will enter.

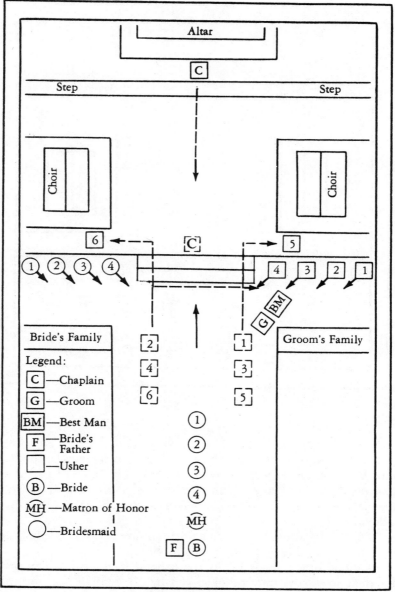

The wedding procession

An alternate plan from the one shown here is for the bridesmaids and ushers to continue to the altar, and then take positions before the steps, to the left for the bridesmaids, to the right for the ushers.

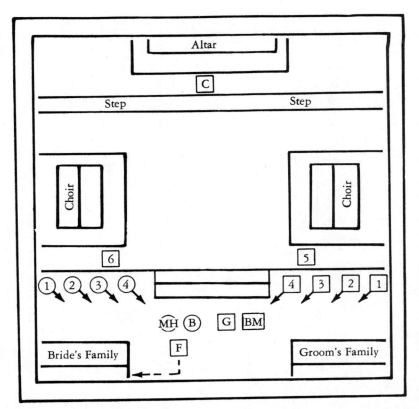

When the bridesmaids are in position, the chaplain will advance toward the bride and groom.

C. Simultaneously with the appearance of the groom and best man, the first ushers start forward *in pairs*. The pairs of ushers are separated by *six pew spaces*. Ushers are paired so that the shorter ones precede the taller. (In some chapels and churches the ushers may walk singly.)

D. The ushers face the altar until all are in position, then they turn together and face the approaching bride.

E. The bridesmaids follow the ushers, walking *singly* in order that their loveliness may be observed by all guests. They are also approximately *six pew spaces apart*. The bridesmaids face the altar until the arrival of the maid of honor. (The bridesmaids may also walk in pairs.)

F. The maid or matron of honor is *eight pew spaces* behind the

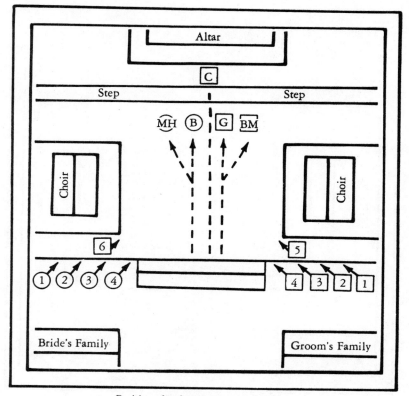

Positions for the ceremony at the altar

bridesmaids. She also faces the altar, then she and the bridesmaids *together turn right* and face the bride.

G. When there are a ring bearer and flower girl (in that order), they walk *ten pew spaces* between the maid or matron of honor and the bride—five pew spaces behind the maid or matron of honor, and five pew spaces in front of the bride. (A ring bearer and flower girl may walk singly or together. They are not used as frequently as in former years.)

H. The bride approaches on the *right* arm of her father, although it is also correct for her to be on his left arm. In the latter way, after he answers the question "Who giveth this woman to be married to this man?" he can place the bride's right hand in the hand of the groom without having to cross in front of her. The members of the bridal party and the congregation are now facing the altar.

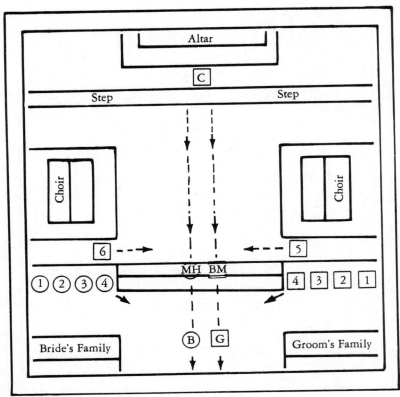

Plan A

The bride and groom are the first to leave the chancel

I. When the bride reaches a point between the groom and the maid of honor, she pauses about three paces from the groom, and the groom advances to meet her, at which time her father pauses, and she takes the *groom's* left arm.

J. Before the ceremony, the bride should tell the chaplain whether she would like the guests to be seated or to remain standing throughout the ceremony. When guests are to be seated, the chaplain says, "At the request of the bride, all guests will now be seated." The father of the bride then gives his daughter in marriage and goes to his seat.

When the bride and her parents so desire, at the point in the ceremony when the chaplain asks, "Who giveth this woman to be married?" her father may answer, "Her mother and I do."

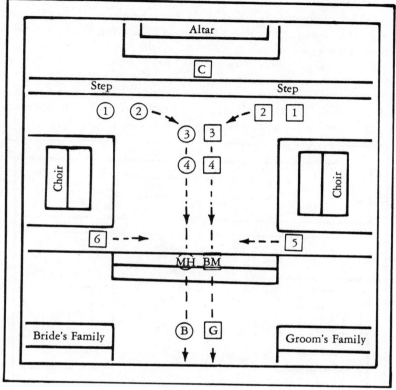

Plan B

The bride and groom are the first to leave the chancel

K. The chaplain leads the way to the altar, and the wedding ceremony takes place. Upon reaching the altar steps, the bride hands her bouquet or prayer book to the maid or matron of honor, and at the appropriate time the best man gives the groom the wedding ring. If the groom is also going to wear a wedding ring, the bride at the same time receives it from the maid or matron of honor.

L. At the conclusion of the ceremony, the bride and groom are congratulated by the chaplain, and the groom may now kiss his bride. She receives her bridal bouquet or prayer book from the maid or matron of honor, and holds it in her right arm ready for the recessional.

M. When the arch of swords ceremony takes place inside the chapel, it will be at this time—when the bride and groom rise from their kneeling position after the benediction.

THE RECESSIONAL

The bride and groom are the first to leave the chancel, with the bride on the *right arm* of the groom. The maid or matron of honor and the best man walk out together, followed by the bridesmaids and ushers in pairs. Ushers 5 and 6 escort the bride's and groom's mother, followed by the chaplain, from the chapel before others leave.

When there are not two more ushers than bridesmaids, two head ushers will be designated to act as escorts to the bride's mother and the groom's mother, who leave in that order.

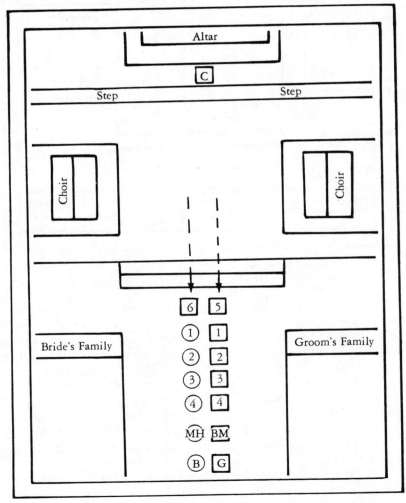

The recessional

There is no effort made to keep step with the music during the recessional, but everyone walks with a natural, smooth gait—neither hurried nor slow. Following the families' departure, the guests leave in no precedence of departure.

It is important, when a wedding reception follows elsewhere, that the bride and groom go immediately to an anteroom, or any secluded area, after they reach the vestibule, so that they are not immediately extended congratulations and best wishes by the guests.

At a military ceremony, it is the duty of the ushers (in fair weather) to see that all guests go outdoors immediately after the wedding for the arch of swords cermony. An usher may clearly—and courteously—request that guests "Please proceed to the chapel steps."

Members of the bridal party usually stand at either or both sides of the outer door of the chapel, with guests standing at any convenient place along the steps or walk.

When the ushers have taken their positions on the steps or walk, the best man will notify the bride and groom that the arch of swords/sabers ceremony can proceed.

THE ARCH OF SWORDS/SABERS CEREMONY

The ushers, when they are commissioned officers, usually act as sword bearers, but other officers may be designated for the arch of swords/sabers ceremony following the wedding vows. Customarily, six or eight ushers (or designated sword bearers) take part in the ceremony. The chaplain's office will furnish swords or sabers. At West Point the cadets furnish their own white belts, gloves, and breastplates.

If the ushers have removed their swords, they now hook them on. In an outdoor ceremony, they proceed down the steps of the chapel and form, facing each other in equal numbers.

In the *naval service,* the head usher gives the command, "Officers, *draw swords,*" which is done in one continuous motion, tips touching. The bride and groom pass under the arch—*and only they may do so*—then they pause for a moment. The head usher gives the command "Officers, *return* (swords brought to the position of 'present arms') *swords.*"

Swords are returned to the scabbard for all but about *three or four inches* of their length. The final inches of travel are completed in unison, the swords returning home with a single click.

When permission is received from the chaplain to hold the arch of swords ceremony indoors, it takes place just as the couple rises after receiving the blessing. All members of the bridal party wait until the ushers' swords are returned to their scabbards before the recessional proceeds.

In the *Army* and *Air Force,* the *arch of sabers* is carried out in this way: when the bride and groom rise from their kneeling position after the benediction, the senior saber bearer gives the command *"Center face."* This command moves the saber bearers into position facing each other. The next command is *"Arch sabers,"* wherein each saber bearer raises his right arm with the saber, rotating it in a clockwise direction, so that the cutting edge of the saber will be on top, thus forming a true arch with his opposite across the aisle.

After the bride and groom pass under the arched sabers, the command is *"Carry sabers,"* followed almost immediately by *"Rear face,"* with the saber bearers facing away from the altar, thus enabling them to march down the side aisle. They form again with arched sabers on the steps of the chapel.

It is to be remembered that only commissioned servicemen and servicewomen participate in the arch of swords or sabers.

CHURCH EXPENSES

Members of a church are not charged for use of the sanctuary for their wedding ceremony, but nonmembers donate about $200, which includes the custodian's fee ($25). There is an additional fee for special arrangements such as a candlelight service.

There is considerable expense in opening a church during weekdays or nights: heating or air-conditioning, lighting, cleaning before and afterwards, preparing a room for a reception, and special arrangements.

As early as possible before the wedding, the bride-elect should confer with the organist and the soloist about the wedding music. They both receive fees.

CHAPTER 28

Special Weddings

THE HOME WEDDING

A couple may be married at home, and the wedding can be as elaborate as a chapel wedding.

A large room far from the door is usually the best place for the ceremony. A screen can be placed in front of a fireplace, and vases of white flowers effectively used. At a long, narrow table or altar placed in front of the screen is where the bride and groom stand. The altar should be arranged according to the direction of the chaplain or clergyman. The room is emptied of as much heavy furniture as possible, with chairs and sofas placed along the walls. Other chairs should be placed to form an aisle, but crowding is to be avoided.

The immediate families of the bride and groom sit in the first rows of chairs placed to the left and right, respectively, of the aisle. The first chair at the left side is for the bride's father, or whoever gives her away. The ushers stand near the front door and direct guests.

As soon as all the guests have arrived, the groom's mother goes up the aisle with her husband. The bride's mother is the last to be seated; she is escorted by a male relative or the head usher.

The chaplain or clergyman, the groom and best man, take their places as they would in church. The groom and best man stand near the altar, at the right side of the aisle, with the best man just behind and to the right of the groom. The bride's mother rises at the first note of the wedding march, and the procession follows the same form as in the chapel or church, except that ushers are *not* included.

The bridesmaids enter the room first, then the bride and her father. When the ceremony is over, the bride and groom usually remain at the altar, with guests coming up to extend their best wishes and congratulations.

The couple go directly to the room where the reception is to be held, with the guests following. There is usually no seated bride's table, and the reception is as elaborate or simple as desired.

At a small afternoon wedding at home, with only members of the immediate families and intimate friends attending, the bride may wear a long bridal gown or a pastel-colored or white afternoon dress or suit, with a corsage. A military woman wears either her uniform or bridal dress.

The bride and groom and their parents stand a little apart to greet guests. A buffet tea may be served, with a wedding cake at the center of the table. Punch, tea, and sandwiches should be placed in convenient sequence around the table. Invitations to a small wedding may be handwritten, with wedding announcements sent out after the ceremony.

At a formal evening wedding (usually at eight or half after eight) the members of the bridal party may be in full evening dress, with men in dinner or mess dress or evening dress uniform, but more often in black tie. The bride wears the traditional long white bridal gown, and her attendants also wear long gowns. The mothers of the bride and groom, as well as the women guests, wear long dresses.

At less formal weddings, men wear business suits and women wear cocktail-style dress.

THE DOUBLE WEDDING

At a double wedding, when two sisters are being married, the older takes precedence over the younger throughout the ceremony. The older sister walks up the aisle with her father, and the second sister walks with a brother, uncle, or other male relative or friend of the family. The father gives both daughters away—the older daughter first, then the younger.

The bridegrooms stand at the head of the aisle, with their best men behind them, the bridegroom of the older sister nearer the congregation. The older sister is at the left and the younger at the right during the ceremony, with the vows repeated separately. The older sister goes down the aisle first when the ceremony is over.

Usually, the sisters have the same bridesmaids, half of whom each sister selects. The ushers are also divided in this way, but each bride should have her own maid or matron of honor, and each groom his own best man. In the wedding procession, the maids or matrons of honor directly precede each bride, with the ushers and bridesmaids preceding the entire bridal party.

The families of both grooms may share the first pew at the right of the chapel or church, or the family of the groom of the older sister may sit in the first pew, and the family of the groom of the second sister in the second.

In the receiving line at the wedding reception the older sister stands before the younger sister, with the traditional order followed thereon. The mother of the brides stands at the door to greet guests, with the mother of the older daughter's husband next to her, then the mother of the other groom.

When the brides are not sisters at a double wedding, the older girl, or the higher-ranking of the brides' fathers, or the higher-ranking bride or bridegroom, may decide the question of which bride goes down the aisle first. Sometimes the question is settled by alphabetical order of the brides' names. The same precedence follows at the reception.

VARIABLES

WHO GIVES THE BRIDE AWAY?

Questions often arise about the propriety of the bride walking unescorted down the aisle. Also whether it is proper for the mother to escort the bride and give her in marriage.

Both procedures are correct.

Some brides prefer to walk alone, perhaps after their father's death when they do not want to replace him, or after a divorce when he has become nearly a stranger.

When the bride's father is confined to a wheelchair he may prefer not to have a role in the processional. If the bride and he are willing, he could wheel himself (or be wheeled when he cannot do this himself) to the altar and wait for his daughter as she walks up the aisle. Then he would have the pleasure of giving her in marriage.

THE COUPLE WHO LIVE TOGETHER

Many parents worry about their son or daughter who wants to be married in a church and have a reception with all the trimmings after living with the prospective bride or groom for months or years.

What caring parents do is to forget their personal feelings and allow the couple to enjoy a church wedding and reception.

It is important that the couple talk with the chaplain or minister before the wedding about their relationship. Counseling is required by many chaplains and ministers in various faiths, as a means of better preparing the couple for their life together.

ESTRANGED PARENTS

Some of the most difficult problems to solve concern estranged parents when there is bitterness between them. Although divorced parents do not share the same pew at the wedding, there can be trauma when one or the other insists upon bringing his or her live-in friend or the disliked second spouse.

Traditionally, the mother sits in the first pew with other members of her family, and the father sits a row or two behind them with his second wife or friend. When the friend or second spouse has not been invited to the wedding, this is evident on the wedding invitation envelope, which has written on it only the father or mother's name, as the case may be.

When both parents are seated at the bridal reception table, they should be at opposite ends, next to compatible friends or persons.

When excessive bitterness exists between the estranged parents, the bride (or groom) may choose not to invite one or the other to the wedding or reception.

VARIATIONS IN PROCEDURE

Variations in the traditional wedding procedures arise from such circumstances as the bride's parents are divorced, one or the other of the parents has remarried, or the bride's father or mother is dead. When the bride is a divorcée or a widow, the wedding and reception may be as large and formal as desired, unlike in former years, when a small, quiet wedding was considered appropriate.

When the *bride's parents are divorced,* the parent with whom she has been living usually gives the wedding and the reception. The bride's father may give her in marriage, but he may—or may not— go to the wedding reception alone when his new wife is not accepted. On the day of the wedding, the father calls for the bride just before the ceremony.

At the chapel or church, he sits in the second pew during the ceremony; if he has remarried, he may sit in the third pew on the left with his present wife, if she attends. If the relationship is congenial, the father and his present wife attend the reception.

When the bride's mother has remarried, and she is in charge of the wedding, her present husband sits with her during the ceremony in the first pew at the left of the aisle. At the wedding reception, he acts as host. When the relationship with a stepfather has been a happy one, and the father of the bride is at a distance or cannot attend the ceremony, or when she prefers, the stepfather may give the bride in marriage.

When the *bride's father is deceased,* a brother, uncle, cousin, or male relative of suitable age may give the bride away. Or a classmate of the father's, or close friend—perhaps the bride's or bridegroom's commanding officer—may be asked to give the bride in marriage. It is not improper, but it is unusual, for a mother to give her daughter in marriage, in which case she would escort the bride down the aisle to the altar, or remain standing at the end of the first pew on the left, and at the correct time say "I do."

When the *bride's mother is deceased* and the father has remarried, the stepmother may be in charge of the wedding plans. If the bride prefers, an aunt, grandmother, or close friend of the family may act in this capacity.

When the *bride's parents are deceased*—or when they are living at a considerable distance from the place of the wedding, or when they cannot give the wedding for financial reasons or will not for reasons of religious or personal differences—the parents of the bridegroom may offer to give the wedding and/or the reception. The couple may prefer to marry quietly in the bride's parish, with members of the families and very close friends attending.

When a couple *elopes,* a civil marriage usually follows in a registrar's office or by a justice of the peace. When parents give their blessings, they may send out wedding announcements and give the couple a wedding reception, with close friends and relatives attending. Only the name of the city or town appears in the announcement; the fact that it was a civil ceremony is not included.

SECOND MARRIAGES

There is little difference between the marriage of a widow and widower and the marriage of a woman and man who are divorced from their former spouses.

As with any less formal wedding—and a second wedding often

is less formal—invitations are extended by word of mouth or by handwritten note; for the larger occasion, they may be engraved or printed.

The couple may want only two attendants, both contemporaries, or a daughter may be the maid or matron of honor and a son the best man. A younger couple could have daughters as junior attendants, or a small child as a flower girl or ring bearer. But whatever the age of the couple, their children, if any, are the most important guests at the wedding.

The *mature* bride should choose a pastel-colored dress (more flattering than white), *never* black, while the younger bride may wear white, but neither the mature woman nor the divorcée wears the traditional wedding gown and veil, and the flowers should be either a corsage or a small bouquet. The mature groom wears a business suit in keeping with the season.

The second wedding may be smaller than a first wedding, with only close friends and relatives attending, but the trend today is for larger weddings and receptions. Most couples want everyone who attends the ceremony to enjoy the reception also.

Although the weddings of a divorcée and a widow are similar, the widow usually waits a year before marrying again, partly out of respect for her deceased partner and partly to make certain she isn't marrying just to overcome loneliness. It is no longer mandatory to wait. The divorcée, however, can remarry as soon as her divorce becomes final. The same rules apply for the widower and the divorced man.

THE CIVIL CEREMONY

When a couple cannot be married in a church (in cases of divorce), or when the couple has no religious affiliation or convictions, or when there is no time to plan a wedding (such as when imminent orders arrive for an officer), the wedding may be held in a judge's chambers or in a magistrate's office. There must be two witnesses, preferably close friends or relatives who will be maid or matron of honor and best man. The witnesses may be complete strangers to the couple but known to the officiating magistrate—probably members of the office staff.

The bridegroom should wear a business suit or service uniform and the bride her uniform or a daytime dress, or suit, with a corsage. They may go on to a place of reception, most likely to a restaurant or club for luncheon or dinner. The time to order a cake and champagne is when reservations are made.

When there is no best man to take care of the fee, the bride-groom should do this at a convenient time before the wedding. The amount depends upon the place and the person officiating.

When the wedding is held in a private home or a wedding chapel, the rules are about the same, except that in a home, should the officiating person be a high-ranking official who is a friend of the family's such as a judge of the Supreme Court or a mayor, you may consider sending a gift later, instead of a fee, with a note of thanks.

Frequently a couple who were married in a civil service without friends or relatives, or a couple who eloped, wish to remarry in a religious ceremony. When a reception was not held after the civil service, it can be planned like any other. If several years have elapsed after the civil cermony, then only close friends and relatives should be invited, since the religious aspect of the wedding is being stressed. The bride should not wear a veil, but she may wear white.

DIFFERENCES IN RELIGIOUS CEREMONIES

The various religious marriage ceremonies are essentially the same. There are differences between Protestant ceremonies; there are sim-ilarities in the Christian and Jewish ceremonies; today the Roman Catholic Church permits interfaith mariages, and with the special consent of the bishop a nuptial mass may be solemnized between Catholics and non-Catholics who have been baptized.

In cases of interfaith marriages, or when one or both persons has been widowed or divorced, the restrictions of any church or synagogue with strict procedural rules must be learned in advance and discussed with the officiating clergyman, rabbi, or priest. Pre-nuptial instruction is required by most churches.

In a *Roman Catholic* ceremony, weddings with a nuptial mass by custom are held in the morning between eight and noon, but today, nuptial mass may be held in the afternoon. Without a mass, wed-dings may be held at almost any hour, with the couple taking com-munion together earlier in the day. A ceremony with a nuptial mass is longer than without it, and the bridal party is seated.

The father of the bride does not give her away. He escorts her up the aisle and at the moment he turns to enter his pew the bride-groom meets her and together they go to the altar. The ring may be received from the acolyte or the best man, and it is blessed by the priest before being handed to the groom.

Whether only the bride and groom enter the sanctuary for this blessing of the ring, or the couple and the best man and maid or matron of honor—or the entire bridal party—is determined by church custom.

A couple has a choice in the wording of vows (the traditional "To have and to hold" or a more modern version) and in whether to repeat the vows after the priest or recite the vows to each other. The couple may choose selections from the Old or the New Testament.

In the *Jewish* faith, weddings may be Orthodox (traditional), Conservative (moderate), or Reform (most lenient). Weddings are not held between sundown Friday and sundown Saturday. Most weddings take place late on Saturday evening or on Sunday. On holy days, and many days between the second day of Passover and the holidays of Shabuoth, weddings are not held.

Jewish weddings usually take place in synagogues, but both weddings and receptions may be held in clubs, halls, hotels. Before the ceremony, guests may be received by the bride and her attendants

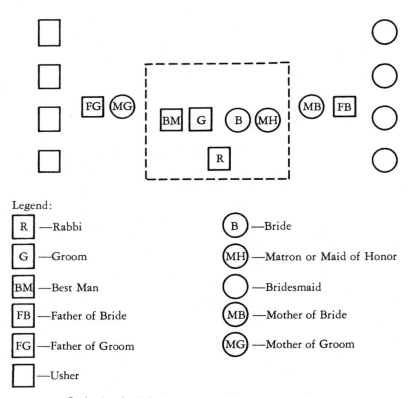

Legend:

R —Rabbi

G —Groom

BM —Best Man

FB —Father of Bride

FG —Father of Groom

—Usher

B —Bride

MH —Matron or Maid of Honor

—Bridesmaid

MB —Mother of Bride

MG —Mother of Groom

Orthodox Jewish ceremony under canopy at altar

in a private room. Fathers do not "give their daughters away," but in the Reform ceremony the father escorts his daughter up the aisle to meet the groom, then he turns and sits in the pew.

In Orthodox and Conservative ceremonies, the fathers and mothers of both the bride and groom walk with them to the canopy at the altar. The ceremony is conducted under the canopy, where the rabbi stands beside a table holding two glasses of wine. Although the parents may stand under the canopy with the bride and groom and maid or matron of honor and best man when there is room, they usually stand just on the outside. The service is in Aramaic, with the rabbi's address to the couple in Hebrew or in the language of the couple or congregation. In a Reform wedding most of the service is in English.

All men wear yarmulkes—skull caps—or hats at Orthodox and Conservative ceremonies, and married women wear a hat or headdress. Skull caps are available in the vestibule. It is optional but desirable that single women wear a headdress. Men do not wear hats at a Reform service. Otherwise, dress is the same as for a Protestant wedding.

The Betrothal Benedictions open the Orthodox ceremony, followed by the ring ceremony, then the reading of the marriage contract, "Kesubah." After the wine is blessed, the rabbi hands one glass of wine to the groom, who takes a sip then passes it to his bride. The ritual in drinking the second glass of wine by both bride and groom is completed with the crushing of a glass under the shoe of the groom, which is an admonition that regardless of the happiness of this occasion, the congregation should remember and work for the rebuilding of Zion.

In the Reform ceremony only one glass of wine is used, it is not crushed, and the canopy is not required.

The *Eastern Orthodox* ceremony is celebrated without mass and is held in the afternoon or evening. The ceremony takes place at a table set near the front of the sanctuary but not at the altar. Guests and participants stand or kneel throughout the service. Vocal music is all that is permitted, and the bride enters the room as wedding hymns are sung by the choir. The bride is given in marriage by her father, who then returns to the side of his wife.

Prior to the wedding, the bride and groom fast, make confessions, and take communion. Although the ceremonial forms are similar to those of Catholicism, members of the church do not acknowledge the pope as their spiritual leader. The Holy Trinity has deep significance, and after the final blessing the choir chants "Many Years" three times.

CHAPTER 29

Wedding Receptions

PLANS FOR A RECEPTION should take into account the type of wedding, the time of day or night the wedding will take place, and where the reception will be held, as well as the number of guests to be invited.

A reception may be held in the home or garden, at an officers' or private club, at a hotel, or in a church parlor. When the reception is not held at home, reservations for the use of the reception room or rooms should be made well in advance of the wedding date.

THE RECEIVING LINE

At a large reception, such as one held at an officers' or private club, the mother of the bride stands just inside the door of the reception room, with the groom's mother next to her. The bride's mother greets the guests and introduces them to the groom's mother; then each guest moves on to greet the newlyweds, the maid or matron of honor, and the bridesmaids.

The fathers of the bride and groom may stand with the mothers for a brief time, but usually they mix with the guests. The best man and ushers *never* stand in the line; the best man should be near the groom, however, ready to help in any way possible, while the ushers act as unofficial hosts.

If the mother of the bride is not living, her father may receive the guests, or he may wish to ask a close relative, such as a grandmother or aunt, to receive with him. He stands just inside the door and introduces the guests in this manner: "This is Anne's grandmother, Mrs. Smith . . . Mother, Colonel James."

The bride and groom always stand together, and *the bride is always on the groom's right*. Next in order is the maid or matron of honor, then the bridesmaids. If a flower girl stands in the line for a while (she usually is age 7 or younger), she should stand on the groom's left. Since she is very young she need not be in the line at all, or only for a short time. When sisters are bridesmaids, the older sister precedes the younger. The line remains intact until all guests have been greeted.

If you are a guest at a reception and there is no one to announce you as you approach the line, you announce yourself. You say to the bride's mother (who will extend her hand first), "I'm John Jones, Mrs. Smith. Such a lovely wedding." You shake hands briefly, but do not linger in the line, even if you are a longtime friend.

When you greet the bridal party, you offer *best wishes to the bride* and *congratulations to the bridegroom*. You *never* congratulate the bride. You may say a few words to the groom about how lovely his bride is, and he may answer, "Thank you so much," and agree that she is lovely as he passes you along. Usually, you have little more time than enough to say "How do you do?"

The simplest form of reception is one where the bride's mother and father greet the guests and introduce them to the groom's parents. Then the guests go over to the bride and groom standing together and wish them well.

At a small reception, the mothers of the bride and groom may stand in a continuous line with the bride and groom and the maid or matron of honor.

At a large reception, the receiving line may be in this order: half the bridesmaids, the maid or matron of honor, the bride, the groom, the flower girl, and the rest of the bridesmaids. The mothers of the bride and groom stand in the customary position near the door to the reception room. At some weddings the bridesmaids do not stand in the line, and this speeds up the flow of guests. The line does not disband until all guests have been received, with the mother of the bride making the move to leave.

Women in the receiving line may wear gloves, but take them off as soon as the line is disbanded. However, when the bride's gown has long sleeves, she does not wear gloves. It is optional for women guests to wear gloves.

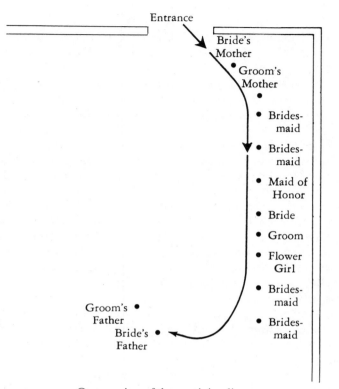

One version of the receiving line

When a small reception is planned to which it is impossible to invite all the guests who may come to the wedding, a very short receiving line may be held in the foyer of the chapel or church immediately after the recessional, if permission has been obtained from the chaplain or minister.

This is a friendly and thoughtful way of receiving the congratulations of the congregation. Guests who have come from a distance will have the opportunity to speak to the bride and groom and to wish them happiness.

When such a receiving line is formed, the same procedure is followed as at the small reception.

NO RECEIVING LINE

When the bride's or the bridegroom's mother—or both—is unable to receive guests in the traditional receiving line (due to illness or death), it is correct to have no line at all.

Guests will go up to members of the bridal party (who move about in the reception room), introduce themselves, and engage in conversation—something one does not have time to do in the formal line.

This is a very friendly and easy way to talk with everyone at the formal as well as the informal reception.

VARIATIONS

When the *bride's parents are divorced* and the daughter has been living with her mother, it is the mother who customarily gives the wedding and the reception. Then, she is the hostess and will stand first in the receiving line.

When the father gives the wedding and the reception and he has remarried, his *present* wife acts as hostess; if his former wife (the bride's mother) attends, she attends as an important guest.

If the father and the mother have not remarried and have a friendly relationship, he may ask her to stand in the receiving line with him at the reception—but, since he is the host, he will be first in line, unless he prefers that she be first. Although this procedure has been frowned on in past years, the bride is *their* daughter; when she wants very much for them all to be together on this important day, then this variance is acceptable. The increase in divorces in this country has necessitated many changes in social mores.

When the father has not remarried and the mother has, and the father is host, he may receive guests by himself, or he may ask his mother or sister or an older daughter to assist.

When the bride's mother has remarried, she alone or she and the stepfather will receive guests where they give the reception. When the bride has not had a very close or friendly relationship with her stepfather, he mingles with the guests.

Sometimes the mother gives the wedding and the father gives the reception, or vice versa. The one who gives the reception is considered the host.

When divorced parents are not on good terms, it is better that the one who does not give the wedding and reception stay away from the reception. On this occasion, personal feelings must be laid aside, their daughter's happiness their only consideration.

When the *bride's parents are deceased*—or when they are ill or are living at a distance and cannot attend the wedding, or when the wedding is in the home town of the bridegroom's parents—then the bridegroom's parents may offer to give the wedding and/or the reception.

When her parents are deceased or incapacitated, the bride may ask a grandmother, aunt, older sister, godmother, or very close older friend, or the bridegroom's mother, to receive guests.

At a *double wedding reception* the older sister and her husband stand in line before the younger sister and her bridegroom; when bridal attendants serve both brides, the usual procedure is followed. When both brides have their own attendants, then there could be two lines, with the mother of the older bride receiving in the first line with that bridegroom's mother, and the mother of the bridegroom of the younger daughter receiving in the second line.

RECEPTION FOOD

There are three main types of food served at wedding receptions: a light buffet tea at small and informal receptions, with more elaborate food at the formal afternoon reception; a wedding breakfast, which follows morning or noon weddings; and a buffet or completely served supper following evening ceremonies.

The type of drinks served depends upon the wishes of the bride and groom, although in some communities liquor is not served. At large weddings in most cities, an open bar is usual. Usually champagne is offered, along with fruit punch for nondrinkers. On a cold day coffee and tea are welcome.

At a very small reception, a wedding cake and punch with which to toast the bride are all that need be offered. It is customary at an afternoon reception, however, for a buffet to include tea and coffee, thin sandwiches, small cakes, and fruit punch and/or champagne. At any reception, there is always a wedding cake.

At a late afternoon reception, the menu could be seafood salad (shrimp, lobster, crab), ice cream molds, tea, coffee, and cakes. By adding a hot or cold soup, the menu could be used for a buffet breakfast. Creamed sweetbreads and peas, or baked ham and salads, little cakes (petits fours), demitasse, champagne, and/or punch are frequently served.

A menu served to guests who eat standing up may be creamed chicken in pastry shells, salad, ice cream molds or meringues, cakes, coffee, and champagne or punch. This is good for afternoon or evening receptions.

The buffet menu may be seafood, roast turkey, ham, or beef— or all of them, if the reception is very large. Any wedding breakfast or supper may be served to guests seated at tables, but more often it is buffet style, with guests serving themselves and eating standing up.

Food for a large reception held at home is usually catered.

SEATING ARRANGEMENTS

At a seated wedding breakfast or supper, there may be two tables, one for the bride and groom and bridal party, the other for the parents and their intimate friends. The bride's table is always covered with a white cloth, and the wedding cake may be placed in the center of the table. At a large table white flowers may be placed on either side of the cake.

The bride and groom sit together at one end or at the center of the table, with the bride on the groom's right. The best man sits to the right of the bride, and the maid or matron of honor is at the left of the groom. The bridesmaids and ushers alternate around the table.

The parents' table is set with a white cloth and flowers, and the parents of the bride sit across from each other as they would in their own home.

The father of the groom sits at the right of the bride's mother, and the chaplain or clergyman is at her left. The mother of the groom is at the right of the bride's father, and the wife of the chaplain or clergyman at his left. Members of both immediate families and intimate friends are at the table. All other guests may be seated at small tables for four or six each, or they may not be served at tables but eat standing up.

At smaller weddings, the bride's table and the parents' table are combined.

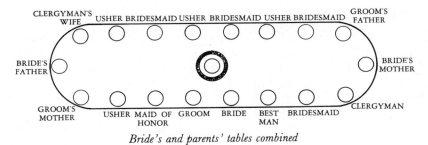

Bride's and parents' tables combined

THE STAND-UP BUFFET

At a stand-up buffet at a large reception (or cocktails-buffet or any reception), guests serve themselves and eat standing up. The reception food is placed on a long table covered with a white cloth, in convenient sequence with stacks of plates, rows of silver, and napkins. The bride's cake may be placed on a smaller table, with guests coming to the table to watch the bridal couple cut the first piece of cake and then receive a serving.

Champagne and glasses will be on a smaller table, except at a small wedding, when they may be set on the main buffet table. A nonalcoholic drink usually is served in addition to the champagne or punch.

CHAMPAGNE AND TOASTS

At the seated bridal table, champagne is poured as soon as all guests are seated, with the bride served first. At any reception, however, the first toast is proposed by the best man to the bride and groom. The groom responds by proposing a toast to his bride, who may give a short one of her own to her new husband. Then there will be other toasts, to the bridesmaids, the parents, and so on. Toasts should be brief, however, and there should not be too many of them (see chapter 24).

CUTTING THE CAKE

At a military wedding reception, the groom unsheaths his sword and hands it to his bride, who is standing to his right. She cuts the first piece of cake with his hand over hers. At a civilian wedding reception, the bride and groom cut the wedding cake in the same manner, with a silver knife, usually decorated with a white ribbon.

THE GUEST BOOK

The wedding guests will sign the bride's guest book either before or after going through the receiving line at the reception. A relative or friend of the bride will be in charge of the book at a small table convenient to the guests but out of the line of traffic.

DANCING

When dancing follows the reception, the bride and groom have the first dance together, perhaps a waltz. Then the father of the bride dances with the groom's mother, and the bride's mother with the groom's father. After the first dance, the bride dances with her father-in-law and the groom dances with his mother-in-law; then the bride dances with her father, the best man, and the ushers, while the groom dances with his mother, the maid or matron of honor, and the bridesmaids. When the attendants join in, other guests also participate. The dancing may continue for an hour or so. Music is usually provided by a trio, unless the wedding is very large, when more musicians would be needed.

GOING AWAY

It is a tradition for the bride near the closing hour of the reception to throw her bouquet, from either a staircase or a doorway, to her bridesmaids. The bride and groom then change into traveling clothes while the guests wait to see the couple off.

The parents tell the bride and groom good-bye in private, then the couple go outdoors to a car that is waiting while the guests throw confetti or rice or rose petals on the couple. Birdseed may also be used, and then cleanup is not a problem, as it is with confetti and rice, which are prohibited at many chapels and churches. The destination of the wedding trip, and its duration, are strictly up to the couple—and the length of time the bride and groom may have on leave, between duty stations, or from their jobs.

CHAPTER 30

Gifts for Weddings, Anniversaries, & Showers

WHEN YOU RECEIVE an invitation to a wedding and reception, and accept, you send a gift. When you receive an invitation to the wedding only, or when you receive a wedding announcement, you are not obligated to send a gift, but may if you so choose. When you are invited to a double wedding but know only one of the couples, you need only send a gift to that one couple.

Following an elopement or a civil marriage, when there was no reception, you send a gift when you know the couple well and want to. Quite often the ones who do not have a reception, perhaps because they cannot afford it, are the ones who most appreciate a gift.

Although most gifts are sent to the bride-elect before the wedding, there are times when they must be sent afterwards, and then they are addressed to the couple at their new address.

Make certain that the mailed package is wrapped carefully and insured against breakage. If the gift is damaged in the mail, the bride must save the wrapping showing the insurance stamp for proof of mishandling and for the insurance claim.

WHAT TO GIVE

When you buy a gift, the old rule of "getting something that you would like for yourself" rarely holds true. The other person's taste may be completely different from yours, and the bride may be hoping to fill in a set of china or bed linens with a different color and design than the ones you had in mind. Pictures in good taste are not given very often, and are always needed.

Don't buy more than you can afford to give. Some of the loveliest and most treasured gifts are those that a person makes or hands down in the family: a patchwork quilt or crocheted bedspread, a piece of needlepoint, a wild-flower picture, an old Spode dish.

What you give is a wedding present that you know the couple needs or wants. It may be beautiful, something to be cherished through the years, or it may be practical and used every day. It is always better to give something small but choice rather than a large, showy present. One or two cups and saucers or plates in the bride's china pattern, a single piece of sterling flatware, or a crystal goblet are always appreciated.

Sterling silver, which constantly increases in value, will last the couple's lifetime and can be passed down to future generations. Good linens are another item of beauty and durability, but sizes of bed sheets, blankets, bedspreads, and tablecloths must be learned beforehand. No-iron bed and table linens are a must for a bride. Place mats are used for all types of entertaining.

Brides will list their silver, crystal, and china patterns at stores that have gift registers. Sometimes they list only their silver pattern, because sterling is very expensive. Also, service-oriented couples know that crystal and china may be purchased when officers have foreign duty or cruises, and prefer to have less expensive china and glassware during the years when they will be moving frequently, when things are easily broken. Brides often select brightly colored or patterned china to use with plain-colored mats—or the reverse.

Many couples prefer practical gifts for everyday living, such as a vacuum cleaner, an ironing board and iron, and kitchen utensils (skillet, pots, pans). Others, particularly those who have been married before or who have set up a home on their own, may have a surplus of practical things and want something beautiful, something to treasure through the years. Try to find out beforehand what is truly desired.

Before making certain selections—those involving color and size, particularly—ask the bride's mother what her daughter could use and prefers. In case of duplication, a bride should feel free to exchange any present.

GIFTS TO EACH OTHER

The bride and groom exchange gifts with each other just before the wedding day. These gifts should be meaningful. The groom's parents may have a piece of jewelry that they would like his bride to have; or he may have found something on a cruise or foreign duty that would please her. A string of pearls from Japan—cultured or any grade within his financial circumstances—makes a desirable gift.

In turn, the bride selects something that he does not have and would enjoy through the years—possibly her bridal picture in a silver frame, small enough that he could take it with him, later on. Perhaps it would be a fitted leather traveling case, or monogrammed gold or silver cuff links. Or a photo album both will enjoy through the years.

MONEY GIFTS

Many young couples starting out on a shoestring need money more than a present. Before the wedding, a check could be sent to the bride's address, written in her name or in the name of both. Afterwards, the check should be made out to them as a couple: "Lieutenant and Mrs. John E. Doe," or "Mary and John Doe." Bonds or stocks are also a welcome gift. The dividends are always helpful.

It is customary for certain ethnic groups to give money as a wedding gift. A number of Jewish and Italian people retain this tradition. The money should be in the form of a check, made out to the bride-elect or to her and her fiancé, and it is sometimes handed to one or the other at the reception. Otherwise, mail the check to the bride-elect at her home or deliver it in person, or send it to the couple after the wedding.

GIFTS FOR SECOND MARRIAGES

When you are invited to the wedding and reception of an older couple, one or both of whom were married before, and you are a close friend or relative, you will probably want to send a present, but you are not obligated to. Frequently they have a surplus of possessions. It is thoughtful to send flowers or, later, take the couple out to dinner.

GIFTS FOR COUPLES WHO ELOPE

Your affection for the bride and groom, and their families, will determine whether or not you send the couple a gift after their return home, or after a marriage announcement has been sent out. When you care, *do*.

SHOWER GIFTS

Friends of the bride-elect—but not immediate members of her family—usually give her a shower or two before the wedding. It is customary for the bridesmaids and maid or matron of honor to give a joint shower within the week of the wedding, after any out-of-towners have arrived.

Shower presents are taken, not delivered by a store, to the home of the hostess, and each one is opened by the bride-to-be, who thanks the giver then and there. It is not necessary for her to write thank-you notes except to the hostess and anyone who sent a gift but could not attend. Always enclose a card with your gift.

The hostess should ask someone to keep a record of who gave what, and gifts should be in accordance with the type of shower stated in the invitation: linen, miscellaneous, kitchen. The latter can be very original as well as useful, such as a sturdy wastepaper basket filled with goodies or small kitchen gadgets.

A MUST FOR THE BRIDE

It takes time to write the many thank-you notes, which all brides must do when they receive wedding presents. They are handwritten, with a mention of the gift, not just "thank you for the lovely present. . . ."

Such a note might read:

Dear Mrs. Smith,

It was thoughtful of you and Colonel Smith to send us such a needed picture. The temple rubbing is now hanging over our fireplace mantel, and it is beautiful.

Thank you very much.

Very sincerely,
Jane Doe

For a belated present you might write:

Dear Grandmother,

John and I are delighted with your check. It will make all the difference in our being able to decorate our new quarters as we really want to.

We plan to buy an oil painting of the Rampart Range which we have long admired, and when you feel better we hope that you will come and see it. We are sure that you will like it, too. Thank you.

With love,
Jane

As many thank-you notes as possible should be written before the wedding. Afterwards, you will have about two months to get them off. If you wait longer than three or four months, the sender will wonder if the gift was received; it is embarrassing to hear from someone who asks if it arrived safely—when it has.

A *gift-register* book is the best way to keep a list of the gifts as they arrive. Such books are available at stationery or other stores, or you may use a lined notebook and make the headings yourself. This book can be a memento of the wedding, but it is essential to keep a clear account of who gave what.

The headings and an entry might be:

No.	Sent By	Article	Sender's Address	Date Rec'd	Thanks Sent
14	Dr. and Mrs. G. W. Doe	Silver spoons (2)	1130 Conn. Ave. D.C.	8/5	8/7

There will be sheets of numbered stickers with the book that you buy—or you can make your own—and one sticker is placed on the bottom of each gift, or a set or pair, after it is opened. The corresponding number is written in the book, and this cross-check will ensure that the gift does not get mixed up.

DISPLAYING THE GIFTS

This not only gives the bride-elect pleasure but shows appreciation for the gifts. A room in the home may be set aside, with tables set up and covered with white tablecloths or sheets. Unnecessary furniture is moved out of the room, to enable people to walk around easily. Gifts are never displayed at a club or hotel where the reception is held. Out-of-town guests, especially, should be invited to drop by at a convenient time.

Gifts should be displayed to their best advantage. Sometimes silver is placed on one table, china on another; sterling and pewter might show up to better advantage separated but not "hidden." The donor's cards usually are placed with the gifts, but not necessarily. When checks are displayed, arrange them so that the amounts are concealed but not the signatures.

RETURNING PRESENTS

When a wedding is cancelled or annulled, gifts are returned. When an engagement is broken, gifts are also returned. But when a marriage breaks up almost immediately, gifts are not returned but are divided between the ex-partners.

The briefest of notes should be included with the returned gift, stating that the engagement or marriage is over but not stating why.

WEDDING ANNIVERSARY GIFTS

Any happy couple wants to observe their wedding anniversary, maybe with a small party for close friends, perhaps at a dinner together in a special restaurant, or, when years have gone by, with a more formal party, dinner, or at-home.

When a couple observes their twenty-fifth or fiftieth anniversary, they may want to make a special occasion of it and send out invitations engraved or printed in silver or gold. Sometimes they will request that no gifts be given, and this request, of course, should be honored.

Sometimes a money tree is given in lieu of unwanted presents when someone other than the couple gives the party. Then, the "tree," which may be a real branch, is sprayed with white, silver, or gold paint, and dollar bills are taped to it. No one gives more than a few.

Since an older couple may be a little touchy about receiving money (even if they need it), a little tact can be employed, and the invitation, either oral or written (but never in a newspaper account), could state "Gifts for a money tree are welcome."

But when gifts are not wanted, the invitation should so state.

The following types of gifts are suitable for the various anniversaries:

	Traditional	*Modern*
First	Paper	Clocks
Second	Cotton	China
Third	Leather	Crystal, glass
Fourth	Fruit, flowers	Appliances
Fifth	Wood	Silverware
Sixth	Iron, candy	Wood
Seventh	Wool, copper	Desk sets
Eighth	Bronze	Linen, laces
Ninth	Pottery	Leather
Tenth	Tin, aluminum	Diamond jewelry
Eleventh	Steel	Costume jewelry
Twelfth	Silk, linen	Pearls

	Traditional	*Modern*
Thirteenth	Lace	Furs, textiles
Fourteenth	Ivory	Gold jewelry
Fifteenth	Crystal, glass	Watches
Twentieth	China	Platinum
Twenty-fifth	Silver	Silver, pewter
Thirtieth	Pearl	Diamond
Thirty-fifth	Coral	Jade
Fortieth	Ruby	Ruby
Forty-fifth	Sapphire	Sapphire
Fiftieth	Gold	Gold
Fifty-fifth	Emerald	Emerald
Sixtieth	Diamond	Diamond

RÉSUMÉ

When you have been invited to a wedding, you should be aware of the customary rules for giving presents. These are as follows:

Send presents to friends and relatives when they are close to you. You are not obligated to send a present to everyone who sends you a wedding invitation or announcement.

When you receive an invitation to a wedding reception, send a gift if you accept, but you need not if you regret.

Do not send more than you can afford—and always remember that quality is superior to quantity.

When you receive many invitations (such as the innumerable Graduation Week weddings at the service academies), send presents only to those classmates or friends close to you, whether you attend the ceremony or not.

When you are invited to the wedding but not the reception, you are not obligated to send a present, but you may, if you so desire.

Do not take a wedding present to the reception unless absolutely necessary, with the exception of a gift of a check, which can be handed to the bride or groom in an envelope. A service couple en route to a new station with only a few days' leave might find a bulky gift difficult to handle.

When there are no invitations or announcements, nor any reception, after a civil ceremony, you send a present to the couple according to your friendship with them. Every young couple enjoys a wedding present and will always treasure it. If you prefer, you may take or send the couple a house-warming present.

The couple needs to be aware of these rules regarding gifts:

In case of a broken engagement or cancelled or annulled marriage, the woman returns the gifts to the sender with a brief but tactful note. She does not explain the break.

When a marriage is dissolved shortly after it has taken place, presents need not be returned. Meaningful ones should be retained by each ex-partner, particularly those given by relatives and close friends.

A bride *must* write thank-you notes for wedding presents. If the givers can find the time to shop for the present, wrap it, and send it to her, then she can find time to thank them in writing (not ordinary "thank-you" cards), and the sooner, the better. She can get her bridegroom to help! It is better to be late than not to write at all.

SECTION IX

On the Go

CHAPTER 31

The Traveler

SERVICE PEOPLE are traveling people, and for those making their own plans for a trip during leave, the following suggestions may prove helpful. As you know, when being transferred to a new station or post in the United States or abroad, all necessary information is made available to you.

On your own, you attend to the basics, such as making your reservations early enough to get what you want when you want it. Passports are necessary when going abroad, and visas and vaccinations are needed for travel to certain countries. Your doctor will give you the necessary shots, and health certificates for retired military personnel and other civilians usually are available at the county health department. Applications for passports should be made early; summer months are the busiest time for travel, and getting a passport takes longer in that season. You will need three small pictures and your birth certificate for your first passport (two pictures later on), so have them ready. You can get more information about passports at any post office.

Do research the foreign countries to be visited and learn what to expect in the way of climate and what clothing will be needed. A good language booklet and guidebook are helpful; your travel agent frequently can help you, and information can be found in the library. You should consider purchasing travel insurance before departure.

Have a check-off list of all the things that must be done before departure. In order to secure a house, make certain that lights are turned off, water taps closed, newspaper and mail delivery stopped, pets taken to a kennel, and plans made for having the grass cut and houseplants watered. Should you be leaving small children at home while you are away, be absolutely certain that the person in charge is reliable. Always leave a copy of your itinerary with a member of the family or nearby friend.

By departure time, have everything in order: credit cards that are accepted abroad, such as MasterCard or American Express; traveler's checks; small change; your passport; and such necessities as contacts or eyeglasses, medicines, and a small flashlight. Pack a toothbrush and toothpaste, comb, brush, and kleenex; although these can be purchased in any airport or almost anyplace, it is a nuisance to have to do so. Should you be bothered with travel sickness, take a motion-sickness tablet half an hour before departure and carry a supply of them throughout the trip. Have everything laid out or hanging in a section of the clothes closet where nothing will be overlooked; on the night preceding an early-morning departure, pack your bag (preferably only one plus a tote). Fold everything carefully, placing the heavier things in the bottom of the bag. Then recheck your passport folder, traveler's checks, medicines, eyeglasses—things you always carry in your handbag or pockets, never in your checked-through bags. Expensive jewelry, if brought along, is carried with you, but it is best left at home or in a safety deposit box.

An experienced traveler takes extra money, medicine, and eyeglasses, "just in case."

LUGGAGE

Travel light! This includes your luggage as well as what is inside it. You need strong but not heavy luggage in several sizes. A small bag—a carry-on or carryall—can be carried on board the plane, where it is stowed under the seat or in the overhead compartment.

The regular size carryall has staggered hangars, and large flat pockets for holding shirts, blouses, and underwear. It will hold up to three suits or six dresses, six shirts or blouses, and six sets of underwear and socks or stockings and pajamas. There is room for your dress shoes (you should wear your walking shoes) and for a nonbulky robe and soft or folding slippers.

Your razor or cosmetic kit will fit into the carryall or in the carry-under bag, which fits under the plane seat; many women like the tote bag with shoulder strap. Your folding umbrella, camera, film, scarf, and other small items, as well as small purchases, will also fit into any of these bags.

When traveling abroad, you may need an adapter for electrical appliances such as razor, hair-dryer, and heating pad, since the voltage is different from that in this country. Adapters can be purchased in a hardware store; some better European hotels will rent them and refund the money upon departure—but you cannot count on this.

Another necessity to put in the carry-under or tote bag is a small box or plastic bag of soap granules for washing your drip-dry clothes; something washed out during the evening is usually dry by morning. Cleaning and laundry services are both slow and expensive abroad and in this country.

WEIGHT LIMITS AND SECURITY CHECK

The weight limitation for your luggage in flight is variable. Two pieces may be checked through and one small bag carried on at no additional expense. But don't stuff the largest bags you own, or you will be charged for excess weight. Airport rules have been tightened, so do not attempt to lug on board too many, too large, or too heavy packages. What you carry with you, such as an all-purpose coat and camera, is not weighed.

Security in airports requires that the things you carry, including your handbag, be X-rayed before you are permitted to board the plane. A special envelope has been designed for the protection of film, which otherwise may be ruined.

FARES

First-class seats cost more than the economy class; first class offers more comfort (the seats and aisles are roomier), and cocktails are free. But you pay for the comfort. Charter (tour) groups are the least expensive of all, but they are scheduled at certain times for a definite length of time, with set date for departure and return. Meals and soft drinks are included in all fares on a long trip. Economy class and charter groups pay for their own cocktails.

Off-season trips are much less expensive than those taken during a regular season as far as fares and hotel accommodations are concerned.

WHAT TO TAKE

Proper clothing for a trip depends upon where you are going and for how long. A smart traveler takes drip-dry clothing that can be laundered and worn time and again; this way, fewer things need be taken. In the old days, when trips—particularly those aboard ship— demanded formal dress (which had to be dry cleaned), traveling involved packing and carrying many more pieces of luggage.

Today, slacks (or pantsuits) are worn by women all over the civilized world, including the Ginza in Tokyo, where older generation Japanese women in their kimonos and obis walk side by side with the younger generation in jeans. For any kind of travel, pantsuits are the most popular attire for women of all ages because they are the most comfortable.

Generally, women will need an extra pair of slacks and a blouse or two; an afternoon dress or costume (jacket) dress which can be worn just about anywhere; possibly a long skirt, not fancy, but noncrushable, and a blouse or top to go with it. A pair of dress shoes, a scarf, an all-purpose coat—or, in a warm climate, a lightweight sweater—a folding umbrella, and a few underthings should complete the list. Plan to wear your most comfortable walking shoes while traveling.

A man needs one good basic suit, either dark or a little lighter in color, according to the destination; slacks and shirts; underwear and socks; a pair of dress shoes—these are the basics. If big business is being combined with pleasure, the basic business suit is a must. Slacks and sports jacket or a suit are the usual attire on the flight. In cooler climates, you may need an all-purpose coat—otherwise forget it. It's easily lost and a bother to carry, and a sweater is much easier to pack.

All travelers should keep a list of what they need to pack.

TEMPERATURES

Some like it hot, some like it cold, but everyone wants to know what sort of weather to expect in the area to be visited. Weather can be temperamental, but generally the average day and night temperatures in these cities are as follows:

Daytime and Nighttime Temperatures at Home and Abroad

U.S. Eastern Cities

		(*Day-Night*)			
	JAN FEB	MAR APR	MAY JUNE	JULY AUG	SEP OCT	NOV DEC
Boston	36 20	49 33	70 53	92 62	66 50	44 30
Miami	75 61	79 65	85 73	86 76	85 73	77 64
New York	38 24	50 36	70 57	86 66	69 54	46 33
Philadelphia	40 25	52 38	75 58	86 67	71 53	48 34
Wash., D.C.	42 27	58 39	79 59	85 67	73 53	50 33

U.S. Central Cities

		(*Day-Night*)			
	JAN FEB	MAR APR	MAY JUNE	JULY AUG	SEP OCT	NOV DEC
Chicago	33 19	49 35	70 55	80 66	67 53	42 29
Cleveland	35 23	57 38	76 54	87 67	71 51	41 26
Detroit	33 19	50 32	75 52	83 62	68 48	40 27
Kansas City	41 23	60 40	80 61	90 70	84 55	48 30
Pittsburgh	37 21	60 37	74 53	85 65	70 49	41 26
St. Louis	41 25	59 41	80 62	87 70	74 56	48 32

NOTE: For these cities, pack your basic city wardrobe: tailored suits and dinner dresses. Chicago will probably live up to its nickname ("Windy City") in the winter, so be prepared with slim skirts, hats you can anchor firmly, and a very warm coat. In the summer it gets hot, so bring cottons.

U.S. Western Cities

		(*Day-Night*)			
	JAN FEB	MAR APR	MAY JUNE	JULY AUG	SEP OCT	NOV DEC
Denver	44 20	55 31	75 49	85 56	71 44	49 24
Las Vegas	58 36	73 46	93 69	104 75	89 60	63 37
Los Angeles	65 47	69 50	74 55	82 60	78 57	70 50
Phoenix	67 41	78 50	96 64	102 77	91 62	70 44
San Francisco	57 46	61 49	65 52	65 58	68 59	60 49

Europe

		(*Day-Night*)			
	JAN FEB	MAR APR	MAY JUNE	JULY AUG	SEP OCT	NOV DEC
Athens	55 42	64 49	81 64	90 72	79 63	61 49
Berlin	36 27	49 34	68 50	73 55	62 46	40 32
Copenhagen	35 29	43 34	61 49	67 56	56 48	41 26
Dublin	47 35	51 36	61 45	66 51	59 44	49 37
Frankfurt	37 27	45 34	69 49	73 55	61 45	41 32
Geneva	34 28	48 36	64 54	70 60	58 47	39 32
Lisbon	55 47	61 53	72 61	76 66	66 61	60 50
London	44 35	52 38	65 48	71 54	61 47	47 38
Madrid	50 34	60 40	76 53	87 62	71 51	51 38

Europe *(Continued)*

	JAN FEB	MAR APR	*(Day-Night)* MAY JUNE	JULY AUG	SEP OCT	NOV DEC
Milan	44 34	55 42	70 56	78 63	66 52	48 38
Paris	44 33	55 38	70 49	76 55	65 47	47 36
Rome	54 39	63 47	77 58	87 66	75 58	57 43
Zurich	34 28	48 36	64 54	70 60	58 47	39 32

Near East and Africa

	JAN FEB	MAR APR	*(Day-Night)* MAY JUNE	JULY AUG	SEP OCT	NOV DEC
Addis Ababa	76 45	77 49	76 49	69 50	74 47	73 42
Cairo	69 46	80 54	92 65	95 71	87 65	74 53
Capetown	79 60	75 55	66 47	64 45	68 50	75 56
Dar es Salaam	88 77	87 74	85 69	83 66	84 68	87 73
Johannesburg	78 58	74 52	64 41	66 41	75 50	78 56
Kampala/ Entebbe	80 64	79 65	77 64	77 62	79 62	79 63
Nairobi	78 54	76 57	71 54	70 51	76 53	74 55
Tel Aviv	64 47	71 50	81 59	85 69	84 61	76 50
Tunis	60 43	68 49	80 59	91 68	82 62	64 47
Tripoli	62 48	70 54	79 64	86 71	83 68	69 53

Far East

	JAN FEB	MAR APR	*(Day-Night)* MAY JUNE	JULY AUG	SEP OCT	NOV DEC
Bangkok	93 68	96 74	94 76	92 76	91 75	89 69
Bombay	93 56	98 64	97 73	94 72	93 71	94 60
Hong Kong	64 55	70 63	83 75	87 78	83 75	70 61
Tokyo	47 30	58 41	73 58	84 70	76 60	55 38

Courtesy TWA.

SPACE AVAILABLE

Space available means just that: surplus space aboard a military aircraft in scheduled and nonscheduled domestic and overseas flights. Those eligible are active duty, reserve, and retired service personnel. Eligible dependents are those with armed forces ID cards—spouses and children under 21.

There are no reservations for Space A flights, but you do go on a waiting list, with retirees last on the list. On a nonofficial flight, you will stand by at the Military Airlift Command (MAC) terminal. In heavily traveled areas this may involve a long wait, so wear comfortable civilian clothing. All services require military members on active duty, including ROTC personnel, to be in uniform while traveling on military airplanes.

You will be bumped at any terminal to provide space for active duty passengers—those on emergency leave, annual leave, or temporary additional duty (TAD)—and for college students in military families on their allotted once-a-year round trip to and from schools in the States.

Seats are issued after all official duty passengers are assigned. It is important for all Space A passengers to sign in as early as possible, since seats are meted out on a first come, first served, basis. Retirees should apply about 45 days before the date of the desired leavetaking, and remember that traveling during off-peak times of the year—from January to March and from September to November—will improve your chances for a timely departure. When you arrive at the terminal, check in immediately in order to be placed near the top of the waiting list.

Have everything ready before the day of departure: passports, visas, records of shots and immunization (when necessary), and traveler's checks.

The following are the military and commercial gateways from which Space A travelers receive travel information for home and overseas. (FAX numbers are in bold type.)

MILITARY AND COMMERCIAL GATEWAYS

	Telephone Number	Fax Number	Area Served
Andrews AFB, MD	(301) 981-1854;	**(301) 981-4241**	—Europe, Caribbean, and South America
Charleston AFB, SC	(803) 566-3082;	**(803) 566-3845**	—Caribbean and South America
Charleston IAP, SC	(803) 767-0588;	**(803) 566-4309**	—Panama and Europe
Dover AFB, DE	(302) 677-2854/4088;	**(302) 677-2953**	—Europe
Elmendorf AFB, AK	(907) 552-2912		—Pacific
Hickam AFB, HI	(808) 479-7494		—Pacific
Los Angeles IAP	(213) 363-0715/6;	**(213) 216-2670**	—Pacific
McGuire AFB, NJ	(609) 724-3078;	**(609) 724-5026**	—Europe, Lajes Field, Greenland and Iceland
McChord AFB, WA	(206) 984-1110;	**(206) 984-3110**	—Alaska and the Pacific
Norfolk NAS, VA	(804) 444-4148;	**(804) 444-6578**	—Europe, Caribbean, Iceland
Philadelphia IAP	(215) 897-5642;	**(215) 897-5627**	—Europe and Iceland
St. Louis IAP	(314) 263-6269/6260;	**(314) 263-6247**	—Europe/Pacific
Scott AFB, IL	(618) 256-4042;	**(618) 256-3066**	—Europe/Pacific

SHIP TRAVEL

TRANSOCEANIC LINER

On a transoceanic liner crossing, dress is modified nowadays for first-class passengers, with men wearing business suits and women in cocktail dress for most of the dressy occasions. In any case, evening dress is not worn on the first and last nights aboard ship, due to the hustle and bustle. Tourist-class passengers are much more relaxed in dress.

Customarily, the captain will host one cocktail party for first-class passengers, and another for the tourist class. He usually gives smaller parties for VIPs on board, to which you may be invited; or you may be asked to have dinner at the captain's table. You should accept.

Bathing suits, with capes or kaftans out of the water, may be worn throughout the day, when shuffleboard and other games are enjoyed, as well as when swimming.

Although the number of bags that you take on board ship, and their weight, is no problem while at sea, you must think about their handling when going ashore. Then, your luggage leaves the ship when you do.

CRUISE SHIP

Dress on board a cruise ship is casual except on the night of the captain's party, when guests dress up—or there may be a costume party. You wear leisure clothes befitting the climate. Colorful but simple daytime or cocktail dresses are worn in the evening by the ladies, with men in lightweight suits. Slacks or shorts may be worn during the day. Everyone wears sandals, and dark glasses are a necessity. Even in warm climates the nights may turn cool, so take along a lightweight sweater.

It is always best to travel light, although your luggage is left on board while you are in port.

BON VOYAGE PARTY

At a bon voyage party, your friends see you off on your trip. You should schedule the party at least one hour before departure. Friends may bring champagne as a going-away gift, and their own bottle, but you arrange with the steward for soft drinks and hors d'oeuvres. You bring your own liquor on board, since liquor cannot be served by the steward or purchased at the bar until the ship sails.

Regardless of the fact that the party is in your honor, you pay for whatever is ordered during the party.

YOUTH TRIPS

Many high schools throughout the country organize trips for students to various foreign countries in the early spring (when rates are low), usually for a week or ten days. Teachers or parents act as leaders, with at least two for a group of twenty. Rooms in second-class hotels are clean and adequate, but there probably will be only one bathroom for several rooms.

Students are asked to travel light (one piece plus a tote), because they will have to handle their own luggage most of the time. They should take along enough underclothing for the trip, since it may not be possible to wash out things. They should also take a small plastic bag or box of soap granules, to be used whenever possible.

Slacks and jeans, shirts and tops, a jacket, are worn by both boys and girls. Mix and match clothing is desirable; a girl can wear the same blouse with a skirt or jeans.

Many high school and college students and other young people of that age set off for a summer's travel abroad with knapsacks on their backs and no place in particular to stay, although a list of inexpensive youth hostels, which exist all over Europe, is carried as a guide. A list of hostels also should be left at home, in case of emergency.

These young people should have confirmed return reservations and tickets with a reputable airline before leaving home, since reservations are hard to come by in the tourist season. Without reservations, they might not be able to return home when they want to—usually when their money runs out.

A youth hostel is operating in Washington, D.C., which caters to young people but is available to anyone who doesn't mind dormitory quarters. To stay there, or in any of the 5,000 hostels around the globe, you must first purchase a pass for $10 to $30, depending on your age; a night's lodging costs an additional $10. For details, write: American Youth Hostel, P.O. Box 37,613, Washington, D.C. 20013.

SPENDING MONEY

All students should be advised by their leaders and parents not to spend too much money on souvenirs or "junk" gifts, but to save money for one or two nicer presents. It is up to the leaders to see that the most interesting museums and tourist attractions are visited, and not to leave the students "on their own" too much, since it is sometimes difficult for them to find their way to these places alone.

TRAVELING ABROAD

THE WC

All travelers should be aware of some of the differences in customs in other countries. Fortunately, English is spoken by someone almost everyplace you go. In any language, *WC* stands for water closet, or toilet. There may be a separate WC for men and women, with a drawing of a man or a woman above the door of each, or with *men* or *women* written in the language of the country. Or only one WC may be provided for everyone. Public water closets usually charge a small fee.

First-class hotels in any country are about the same as those at home. In small hotels in Europe and various countries, one bathroom may be used by occupants of several rooms, or the whole floor, with a washbasin or a pitcher of water and a bowl provided in each room.

PUSH-BUTTON SERVICE

In some European hotels, particularly older ones, there may be no telephone in the room. Instead, there may be a panel with a system of push buttons, with a figure of a maid or waiter or valet above each, indicating which button is to be pushed for service.

MEDICAL HELP ABROAD

A free directory of recommended English-speaking doctors around the word is available by writing: IAMAT, 736 Center Street, Lewiston, NY 14092. This is the International Association for Medical Assistance to Travelers, which tells you to whom you can turn in case of illness while vacationing overseas.

CHILDREN TRAVELING ALONE

When young children must fly alone, parents or guardians should reserve a nonstop flight whenever possible, and inform the reservations agent that their child, or children, will be unaccompanied.

Most airlines will not be responsible for children under age 5, but they will schedule youngsters between 8 and 11. A fee of about $20 is charged for this service, money well spent—and earned— when there are flight changes. For minors under 18 traveling alone, airline officials near the departure gate will send dispatches concerning flight numbers and/or changes in airlines ahead to all scheduled stops.

All airline officials must be informed that a responsible person will meet the children when they reach their destination.

Children who are to travel alone should be taken to the airport well ahead of the time of departure so they may become acquainted with surroundings that may seem frightening at first. Some airlines have supervised lounges for waiting children.

Parents must make certain that unaccompanied children keep their tickets in a safe place and not carry them in their hands; tickets that are lost or stolen are negotiable. A name tag with the child's full name, address, and phone number, and that of the person meeting the child, also must be secured. In case of an emergency or a mix-up, the child should have enough change for phone calls and some folding money.

TRANSPORTING PETS

When a new assignment takes your service family overseas, check with the nearest consulate or its embassy in Washington, D.C., to find out whether you are permitted to bring your pet. Several countries do not permit this.

A two-week to six-month quarantine is enforced in Australia, Barbados, Hong Kong, Ireland, Japan, South Korea, Panama, Scotland, and the United Kingdom.

Almost all U.S. states have laws governing the entry of animals from other states, with interstate health certificates and rabies inoculations required for dogs and horses. Hawaii has a 120-day quarantine for all entering pets.

By air, you can ship your pet as excess baggage in the baggage compartment, or as air freight. A shipping crate may be ordered from the airline, or you may make it yourself. Your local Humane Society can give you advice on requirements for the crate. Or airline personnel will pick up your pet and deliver it—for a price.

Be sure that the rabies tag, as well as your name, telephone number, and address, is on the animal's collar.

CHAPTER 32

Hotel & Motel Manners

UNLESS YOU ARE an experienced traveler, you may have a moment of unease when you step up to the desk clerk in a hotel or motel to register. A newly married man may wonder about the best way to sign his name—and his wife's—and how much, and whom, he should tip.

Before you start your trip, you should obtain information concerning hotels and motels. There are a number of reliable sources of information about places to stay in each state, such as the AAA, Tour Aids, or any local travel agency.

When you know where and when you will be arriving, write or phone the selected hotel or motel for a reservation, and ask that it be confirmed. You ask the price of the room and state the number of people who will be occupying it and the expected length of your stay. All large motel chains have a service whereby reservations are made instantaneously, toll free.

When your request is confirmed, be sure that you do not lose the confirmation slip; this little piece of paper can be very important when a busy clerk has bungled your reservation.

HOTELS

Any first-class hotel in any city in any country has a doorman who greets guests upon their arrival. When you are a guest and are arriving by car, tell the doorman that you would like a porter to come for your bags—unless you travel light and can carry your bag yourself.

If you plan to use the hotel's garage, the doorman will arrange to have your car taken there. If you are not using the hotel garage, ask where you can park your car. Unless he performs some special service for you, it is not necessary to tip the doorman at this time. If you arrive at the hotel by taxi, the doorman will open the taxi door, but, again, no tip is required.

When you do not travel light and the porter has taken your bags to the lobby, he will direct you to the desk. The usual tip for a heavy bag is $1, and twice that for several pieces of luggage. Give the desk clerk your name and say that you have a reservation.

When you do not have a reservation, say what you would like— a single or double—and ask if such a room is available.

You will want to know what the price of the room will be, so ask. If the price is more than you can pay, ask the clerk if he has something less expensive. When there is nothing else—you stay or you leave.

REGISTERING

If the room is satisfactory, you sign the register. It is necessary in all states and in all countries that you sign the hotel or motel register, writing your name and your home town or your ship or station. Usually the desk clerk asks for a street address (and, at a motel, your car license number).

When you sign, write "Lieutenant John (or Jane) Smith, Washington, D.C." In the case of married couples, you sign "Lieutenant and Mrs. John Smith, Washington, D.C.," *never* "Lieutenant John Smith and wife." A divorcée is "Mrs. Jones Smith" or "Mrs. Jane Smith." An unmarried woman is "Miss Jane Smith" or "Ensign Jane Smith."

After you have registered, the bellman will precede you to your room with the key. After he has deposited your luggage, turned on the lights, and asked if there is anything else that you need, you are expected to tip him $1 for opening the room and $1 for each heavy bag he carried. Your tip may be more at an expensive hotel and less in a rural area, but the norm is $1.

SPECIAL SERVICES

All hotels offer many personal services, and these services are usually spelled out somewhere in the room, along with the prices. In a big hotel, it may be difficult to determine who you should make your request to. The easiest way is to pick up the phone and ask for room service, and tell them what it is that you want. Sometimes you will be referred to the valet (pronounced "val-lay"), in which case you ask for valet service. Large hotels will have one number for all services and will tell you whom to call, or else will take your order directly.

For any special services, you pay at the time they are received, or you can have the charge put on your bill by signing the check that accompanies the service. Should you need extra towels or blankets, call the housekeeper. She will have a maid bring you the necessary items, but you must be specific in what you need. If you need one blanket and three towels, say so. In most hotels, the housekeeper also is in charge of lost and found articles.

Should the luxury of having breakfast in bed appeal to you, remember that food served in the room is always subject to a substantial service charge, and you pay the 15 percent tip for each meal. If you must be economical, the coffee shop in most hotels will have the fastest service at about half the cost.

ROOMS WITH—OR WITHOUT—MEALS

European plan means that the price of the room does not include any meals. Some hotels furnish instant coffee (which you prepare) along with croissants or sweet rolls for breakfast. *American plan* means that the price of the room includes all meals. The latter plan is usually found in resort hotels, and has one disadvantage: You take all your meals at the hotel or you will lose money. If you want to eat when and where the fancy strikes you, select a hotel that does not operate under the American plan.

There is also a *modified American plan* at many resort hotels, where you have breakfast and either lunch or dinner at the hotel but are free to take the other meal anywhere you choose. These popular plans vary a great deal in different areas, so find out what is included in the price.

When you choose the American plan, you may be given a specific table in the hotel dining room which you will occupy at each meal—if the table meets with your approval—during your entire stay. In Europe, this same system is practiced at some small hotels under the title of *pension*. When you register at a resort hotel, it is a good idea to inquire into the practice of serving meals.

HOTEL MANNERS

As a guest, be considerate of employees but be impersonal. When a guest appears uncertain or ill at ease, some hotel employees become careless with that guest's requests. Therefore, be firm when making requests but make none that is unreasonable.

You should tip in accordance with your income, the hotel's reputation, and the service rendered. If the service has been poor, you tip accordingly. While you may not want to undertip, it is just as bad taste to overtip—particularly when you cannot afford it.

MOTELS

Motels are a boon to those traveling by car. The average motel differs basically from a hotel in that there are almost no services provided, no garage problems, and almost no tipping. There is little fuss and bother; you arrive and leave without delay. Accredited motels are approved by various qualified organizations and inspected at regular intervals.

A motor lodge may be a large, several-storied complex with coffee shops and restaurants, and offer services similar to those in a hotel. In such a place you tip for services, when used, as you would in a hotel.

Before you register or pay out any money at a nondescript motel, ask the manager to show you the room that he expects you to occupy. The first-hand inspection gives you the opportunity to make sure that the room is clean and in order. If it is not, ask to see another room—or go on your way.

Most motels require that you pay in advance in order to facilitate early-morning checkouts, so be ready to pay promptly upon registering. Credit cards and traveler's checks are a must for the traveler. You do not need to carry much cash.

CROSS-COUNTRY TRAVEL

When you are driving cross-country and know where you will be the following day or night, it is advisable to make advance reservations. In the summer months and in resort areas, motel rooms should be reserved well in advance.

When you find a motel chain that you like, you may want to stay with it on your entire trip. Advance reservations are made by computer, free of charge, in a matter of minutes.

SOUVENIRS

Although you are paying for the motel room, you should treat it with the same respect that you would the home of another person. Before taking ashtrays and towels as souvenirs, stop and consider how much it would cost you if guests in *your* home carried off ashtrays and towels.

For tipping customs in hotels and motels, see the following chapter.

BED AND BREAKFAST

Many travelers find that accommodations in a private home are a delightful, and often a more economical, alternative to motels and hotels.

A room with a private bath can cost between $30 and $40 a night and generally includes breakfast. (Prices vary, and they are much higher in resort areas or in historic old homes.) The hosts are usually more than willing to give their guests inside information as to the area's better restaurants and interesting attractions.

CHAPTER 33

Tipping

IN AMERICA

It's easy to trip over tips, particularly since tipping varies in different sections of this country, as well as abroad. Like death and taxes, tipping is always with us.

Originally, tips were given to individuals for services better or beyond those expected. Nowadays, tips are expected for almost any kind of service, but you never tip a person for inefficient or discourteous service; neither do you allow yourself to be bullied into leaving too large a tip by a scornful attendant.

Never overtip—that is considered flashy—but it is cheap to undertip. Learn at the start what a fair tip is—and then stick to your system.

If a crafty waiter brings you only large denominations of folding money after you have paid the bill, simply ask him to bring you some smaller change.

When you tip for good service, say "Thank you."

It is a wise person who carries a quantity of small change for small tips.

WHEN NOT TO TIP

While it is important to know when to tip, it is equally important to know when not to tip. If you make a mistake and offer a tip to someone who should not be tipped, you will discover your error when it is waved away. In such a case you simply repocket your money.

You do not tip professional people, including nurses, ship or airplane officers, government employees, lawyers, doctors, stenographers, department store workers, owners or managers of places of business, or postal service deliverymen.

You don't tip ushers in theaters. You may give presents at Christmas time to any person who provides a service throughout the year: a newspaper boy or girl, garage attendant, or garbage collector. They may prefer a present of folding money.

Do not tip nurses or doctors, but you may tip maids and attendants at a hospital for special services. In a private or semi-private room, you may give a dollar or two to each attendant; you do not tip in wards.

If you would like to give something to your nurse upon departure or at Christmas time, give fruit, candy, or a box of cookies. The gift should be left at the desk nearest the patient's room, and there should be enough for all the staff who cared for the patient. A note could state, "This is for the staff on Wing A who have been so nice to my son."

WINE AND DINE

Fifteen percent of the total bill is the general rule for tipping waiters and waitresses in the average restaurant anywhere. At a luxury hotel or restaurant you tip 20 percent; do not tip the headwaiter or maître d' unless he has made special arrangements for a dinner party; then tip between $5 and $10, depending upon the size of your party and the extras. You hand him this tip upon departure.

You tip the wine steward 15 percent of the dinner wine bill; the bartender at any bar receives the same percentage of the bar bill.

At a lunch counter the tip is between 10 and 15 percent of the check; do not tip less than 10¢ for coffee or a soft drink, or less than 25¢ for a snack. At a cafeteria where you wait on yourself, do not tip.

When you check your coat or hat, the attendant receives $1 (75¢ for the service, 25¢ tip); the washroom attendant is tipped 50¢ for a service. The garage attendant is given $1 for parking and returning your car.

The 15 percent tip for a restaurant dinner costing these amounts would be:

$ 6 check—$ .90	$ 40 check—$ 6.00
$12 check—$1.80	$ 50 check—$ 7.50
$20 check—$3.00	$ 84 check—$12.60
$33 check—$4.95 or $5	$100 check—$15.00

CREDIT CARDS

When you pay for your dinner or lunch with a credit card, you sign the charge slip brought by the waiter after quickly looking it over to see that there is no error.

Sometimes the tip is included in the total dinner bill. When it is not, you have the option of adding it on the credit card slip or leaving it in cash on the table. Cash tips are placed in the small tray brought by the waiter with the bill.

HOTELS AND MOTELS

In an urban area you tip the bellman who opens your hotel room and carries your bag $1.50; when you carry your own bag, give him $1; for more than one bag you tip him $1 for each. In a small town you probably tip less.

You do not tip the chambermaid for an overnight stay, but for several days or a week you give her from $3 to $5 in a moderate hotel and from $5 to $10 in a luxury or resort hotel. Do not tip the valet for pressing your clothes; the charge is added to your hotel bill.

You do not tip the doorman unless he performs some service, such as helping with the luggage. When your stay is for a week and he has called taxis or helped in some way, tip him a couple of dollars.

At a motel you park your own car and carry in your own bags. You tip at the bar or in the dining area the same as at a restaurant.

TAXIS

The minimum tip for a fare up to $1.50 is a quarter. Otherwise, it is the standard 15 percent. Should you run into a rude driver, give no tip.

AMTRAK

Dining-car waiters are tipped the same as in a restaurant: 15 percent of the bill. Do not tip less than a quarter for a cup of coffee and snack. Tipping is the same in the bar car or club car, and the sleeping-car porter is tipped $2 a night for extra services.

BUS TOURS

When guides or driver-guides are provided on a longer trip—not a brief sightseeing excursion—the "hat" (or an envelope) is generally (but not necessarily) passed among the passengers, and 50¢ to $1 per person is given for this service. On a long trip, and a pleasant one, tips are from $5 to $10 each for the driver and guide.

LUXURY LINERS AND CRUISE SHIPS

Transoceanic crossings are expensive for first-class passengers, who are expected to prorate 15 percent of the cost of passage among the service crew; the cabin and dining-room stewards receive about half the total tip. The remainder is divided among the other stewards in proportion to their services. Lounge and bar stewards receive 15 percent of the bill at the time of service.

Fares, and thus tips, are considerably less for cabin- or second-class passengers, about 10 percent.

Some lines include gratuities in the fare, and then tips are not given except for special services. Ship's officers are never tipped.

AIRLINES

There is no tipping of flight personnel: stewards or stewardesses or flight officers. Airline reservation clerks are not tipped. Skycaps receive the usual $1.00 a bag, or $2 for a loaded baggage cart.

GROOMING

In a barber shop you tip 50¢ for a haircut in a small city, $1 in an urban area. For a shave, shampoo, and manicure, tip $2.

In a beauty parlor you tip 15 percent of the bill when one person does it all; otherwise, 10 percent for the hair stylist, and 10 percent for anyone else who helped. For facials and manicures, tip is 15 percent.

The owner-operator is not tipped as a rule. But you may give a Christmas present.

SERVICES

You do not tip the letter carrier—it is against United States postal regulations—but you may give a Christmas gift. When you use the services of a commercial messenger on a regular basis, you may give him or her money.

When you have live-in or regular household help, you will want to give an extra $5 or $10 for special help after an occasion such as a cocktail party or a large dinner, or a larger amount at Christmas time.

Guests in a home never tip household help after such an occasion. But a weekend guest may want to give that person something, a small present or from $3 to $5 for a single helper or couple.

Apartment dwellers give building employees a gift at Christmas for special services, the amount ranging from $10 to $25, according to the services rendered.

CLUBS

It is customary for members of private clubs to contribute to a Christmas fund for employees, with additional tips for the various attendants.

Golf caddies receive 15 percent of the regular club charge for 9 or 18 holes. Golf pros are never tipped, nor are instructors in sports and health clubs.

OVERSEAS

No matter where you go when abroad, do not tip in American money. Before leaving the United States you should obtain about $50 in the currency of the first country on your itinerary for tips, taxis, and small purchases. TIP PACs of specific foreign currencies are available at your local AAA office. For example, for $50 you'll receive 250 French one-franc notes or 5 fifty-franc notes; for $55 you'll receive 70 German marks or 7 ten-mark notes.

It is helpful to carry a currency converter with you until you become familiar with the currency of the country.

Wallet- or purse-size booklets are available at many airport newsstands or at travel agencies. Public libraries have a wide range of books on travel in almost any country.

In some hotels throughout Europe and in countries such as Japan, a 15-percent service charge will be prorated and added to your bill, so you do not need to tip. In other countries, however—France, for one—you are expected to tip. Therefore, be sure to look at the check before paying it. Extra tips are for such services as shoeshining and carrying luggage. When there is no service charge you prorate the customary 15 percent among those who help you, in accordance with custom and services rendered.

Many working people depend on tips to make ends meet; they receive small or no wages and must rely on tips. The washroom attendant, for example, counts on the 25¢ or 50¢, or equivalent, that you give. You tip the attendant at bath houses in the Orient and at the saunas in the Scandinavian countries. You bathe in private or public bath houses or saunas in these countries.

Guides are always tipped in Europe. If there is no fixed fee for the guide, then your tip will depend on the length of the tour. If there is a fixed fee, tip 15 percent of that amount. The gas station attendant—especially in Germany, Italy, and France—should receive a small tip when he does more than fill the gas tank. And the porter who shines the shoes you leave outside the door of your hotel room should receive a small tip.

When in doubt about who to tip, and how much, do as you would at home—but in the currency of the country you are visiting.

TRAVEL TIPS

Be sure the date on your passport has not expired. If it has, apply for a new one long before the date of departure for your next trip abroad. You should allow a minimum of two weeks prior to departure for getting any vaccinations required by your country of destination.

To secure a passport, you'll need proof of U.S. citizenship (a birth certificate, naturalization papers, or your old passport). You must submit two 2-by-2-inch photographs along with your application. Passports are valid for 10 years and cost $55.

Should you need a doctor while you're abroad (and you are not fluent in the language[s] spoken), contact the nearest American embassy or consulate for advice. It is wisest, though, to get hold of a directory of English-speaking doctors abroad before you leave. Phone the International Association for Medical Assistance to Travelers at (716) 754-4883 for more information.

If you lose your passport or credit cards while abroad—or if they are stolen—immediately contact the issuer or an embassy or consulate for help. Purse snatchers are everywhere, so don't be careless. You can buy a plastic ID bracelet for about $2 upon which you can write with a waterproof ballpoint pen such important facts as your name, your station, and passport and credit card numbers.

Have some local currency on you when you arrive at your destination. You can, of course, exchange your traveler's checks at the airport or a hotel, but when you must deal with jet lag and long waiting lines, you'll wish you were prepared.

CHAPTER 34

Places of Entertainment & Private Clubs

MOVIES

Too often there is a lack of common courtesy among movie-goers. There is the peanut and popcorn eater, the paper rattler, the loud whisperer. There is the person who passes back and forth in front of you, and the character who lolls in his seat and overflows on the arm of yours.

If you are a man escorting a woman, take her into the lobby, where she can wait while you buy the tickets. If the line is long and the weather pleasant, she may prefer to stand outside and talk with you.

After you have bought the tickets, take off any outer coat in the lobby. A woman usually prefers to leave her coat on until she sits down.

Before going down the aisle, ask your guest where she would like to sit—in front, near the center—then walk ahead of her when there is no usher, step aside, and allow her to precede you into the row.

If your seats are in the center of a section, be careful of the people you are passing. Face the screen as you go by. Say "Excuse me" in a low tone. Watch out for the coat you are carrying; it may sweep the heads of people in the row in front of you.

THE THEATER

At the theater, you are expected to be on time, and curtain time is usually 8:00 P.M. for an evening performance. You may check your hat and coat, or take them to your seat. You need not buy a program, since the management issues a playbill. If you want a more detailed program, one is enough for two or more persons.

There are ushers at theaters, and you wait for one to show you to your seat. During intermission, you may want to go to the lobby, but when the lights are dimmed or when a bell rings, the management is signaling that the next act is about to begin and you return to your seat immediately. Don't linger and then be forced to stumble over someone's feet in a darkened theater.

If for some good reason you are late at curtain time, you should stand in the back of the theater until the first intermission.

CONCERTS, THE OPERA, AND THE BALLET

Operas, concerts, and the ballet are other forms of entertainment that you will encounter through the years. Although the opera once was a full-dress affair, you will see only a few men in black tie—most wear dark business suits. Frequently, a formal dinner precedes the theater when formal dress is worn.

At concerts, the conductor of a symphony orchestra will turn around and face the audience at the end of a number—and you do not begin applauding until he does so. At a piano recital, do not applaud between the movements of a sonata or a similar piece of work, even though the pianist momentarily stops playing.

If you should have the misfortune to develop a coughing fit, leave the room or auditorium, since any noise is disturbing to an artist. Intermissions are plainly marked on the program, and that is the only time you leave the auditorium, if at all possible.

Encore numbers are often played or sung after the artist has received a number of curtain calls, or after much applause. He or she will indicate that there will be an encore, and this cue stops further applause.

If the music at an opera or concert is too classical for an uneducated ear, or the ballet beyond appreciation, never fidget or show signs of boredom. Other people will be enjoying themselves, and it is discourteous to interrupt their pleasure. By attending as many performances in the fine arts as possible, you may find that boredom turns to enjoyment.

PAYING FOR TICKETS

When you are host or hostess at a theater, concert, or movie party, or when you invite just one guest, you pay for the tickets. When you are a guest, do not insist on paying, or helping to pay, for tickets.

When a woman asks a man to buy the tickets in advance and gives him the money for them, he should not offer to pay or feel any hesitancy in taking the money.

If a group decides on the spur of the moment to attend a performance, then couples go "Dutch treat." Usually the men pay for their dates' tickets, but women may want to pay for their own—particularly if their dates are academy or college students on a limited allowance.

PRIVATE CLUBS

Private clubs, in one form or another, exist all over the country. The types most familiar are the country clubs and the officers' clubs at military installations.

A country club has a club house, golf course, swimming pool, and tennis courts. Membership is by invitation, and there probably will be a large initiation fee and sizable monthly club dues. A member pays his bills on time. Failure to do so may lead to expulsion from the club. If you cannot afford to stay in, resign before your debts accumulate.

When you are invited to be a guest at such a club, you should look upon the invitation in somewhat the same manner as being asked into a home, and take part in whatever activity is offered. On the golf course, you are not expected to pay for anything other than your caddy fee, although if you are invited by the same member more than once, you should offer to pay your greens fee as well as your host's.

As a guest, you must remember that your host has accepted the responsibility of introducing you into his club and to his friends, so do not turn this responsibility into a liability. In brief, do not embarrass your host. A man should not barge up to a woman and say he is Bill Jones's guest—Bill Jones may not know her, either! If he does know her, he will make the proper introduction, just as he would at home.

Sometimes, when you are stationed in an area where friends of your family or friends of your own are members of a private club, you may be given a guest card for a limited time. The card will be given to you by your friend, or it may be mailed to you by the club. This card must be handled with discretion.

A guest card means that you enjoy the privileges of the club, and that you pay for these privileges: food, drinks, and any fee for the use of the swimming pool or golf course. Sometimes these fees are printed on the card, but if not, inquire at the club's business office concerning fees. There is usually a moderate charge to the member for each guest card he obtains.

When you accept the guest membership, take the card to the office, where your name is placed on the guest list. Leave the address where bills are to be sent, and, upon receiving the bill, pay it *immediately*. When you don't pay, your bill is placed on the account of your sponsor—and you may lose a friend. A guest card does not give you the right to nominate anyone else for a card, nor does it give you the privilege of taking guests to the club for meals, etc.

Private clubs other than country clubs are usually located in the city proper, and generally have rooms for entertaining. There are dining rooms, a library, a lounge, and a bar, in addition to bedrooms where members live, or rooms where out-of-town members may stay briefly, and some clubs have indoor athletic facilities, as well. The atmosphere of such clubs is more like home than that at a country club, and there will be fewer members. These members are usually friends of long standing. As a guest, your behavior must be circumspect.

The issue of money is the same here as at the country club— you cannot pay for privileges. If you are given guest privileges for a limited period of time, you are charged for them. Although the private town club is more intimate, you must not presume to intimacy with the members.

Older members of private clubs have many little privileges; certain chairs in certain parts of a room may be "theirs." A table by a window at one side of the dining room may always be occupied by a certain man or group at a given hour. It is well to respect these privileges.

Before or just after leaving the area, be sure to write a note to whoever extended you guest privileges (to the member, if this was the case), *and* to the club president, mentioning any individual who showed you special courtesies.

Some private clubs—including country clubs—do not permit tipping of club personnel. However, the locker-room attendant at either may be tipped for some special service. Ask your host what the usual tip is for such services in his club.

OFFICERS/ALL-RANKS CLUBS

With the deep cutbacks in military personnel and funding, a growing number of officers clubs, both at home and abroad, are now open to civilians and noncommissioned service personnel. At the Army's 100th Area Support Group at Grafenwohr, Germany, for example, the former club is now called the Community Club, and at West Point it is the West Point Club. Club members are billed at the end of every month; prompt payment is expected.

These clubs are usually located on the station or post and offer one or more dining rooms and lounges and a bar. Each club has its own house rules, including dress requirements. If you plan on visiting a club at another station or a different military branch, find out in advance if there are differences in their rules. In general, things are more informal today than in former years.

Overdrinking is frowned on in the services just at it is everywhere else, and abuse of alcohol can affect your career as well as your health. Consequently, happy hour is deemphasized in many of these clubs.

WIVES' ACTIVITIES

Off station as well as on, the service wife is often called on to speak in public. Many women choose to show colored slides as they talk to various groups about their family's experiences living around the world, moving "at the drop of a hat."

Service wives are also often invited, when eligible, to join women's groups connected with various civic organizations. These may include the University or Panhellenic Clubs or garden and crafts clubs. Some of their projects are to benefit charities, others just for your own enjoyment.

CIVIC ORGANIZATIONS

Retired as well as active duty officers are frequently asked to join a civic or service organization that has a large membership, with civic improvement and national and international good will their goal. Examples of such organizations are the Rotary, the Chamber of Commerce, and the Military Order of World Wars (MOWW).

Active duty officers have little time for such membership but join whenever time allows. Later, upon retirement, you will have a nucleus of friends almost anywhere you choose to live. But active or retired, when you are invited to be a member or to attend as a guest speaker, you are an ambassador of your service.

COLLEGE FRATERNITIES AND SORORITIES

Men's fraternities and women's sororities are not clubs but national organizations owning their own houses on or near the campuses of colleges and universities throughout the country. Anywhere from forty to one hundred members make these houses their homes during the academic year, and a housemother is assigned to each.

Membership is by invitation, and the houses are governed by strict rules of conduct. Infractions of rules cause the member to be fined, and a serious infraction may result in the failure of a pledge to be accepted or the expulsion of someone who is already a member.

As a guest, a midshipman or cadet must observe the house rules, particularly those concerning drinking and gambling. At many colleges and universities, drinking and gambling have as heavy a penalty as at a service academy.

Sororities and fraternities are closed organizations with private weekly meetings, and a guest should not ask questions concerning these meetings. Questions about the history or activities of such an organization are in order, but not about its business.

At a sorority house, the housemother is more in evidence than at a fraternity, and respect is always shown her. Most sororities have a curfew, and a man must be careful to get his date back to her house on time. You will not be permitted to stay on at the house after curfew, so don't try. As a rule, most sorority houses do not have guests for casual meals, but you will probably be invited for more formal dinners.

CHAPTER 35

The Houseguest

THROUGHOUT YOUR LIFE, you will frequently extend and receive invitations to visit. As the guest, you may be invited to stay with friends when you are passing through their city. A midshipman or cadet is often asked to spend the holidays with a roommate, or is invited for a casual weekend. Usually, your friends are in about the same circumstances as you are, and you act in their home as you would in your own. As the host, you expect a houseguest to be congenial and courteous.

THE WEEKEND GUEST

The weekend guest is probably the most frequent type of guest. The invitation is extended in person, by telephone, or by letter. As the guest, you answer immediately, and your reply must be definite.

When accepting the invitation, make it clear when you expect to arrive and how. If you need to be met, your time of arrival is important. When refusing the invitation, always say *why*.

Your hosts will inform you concerning the weekend, so that you will know what to bring. When something special is planned—a formal dance, a boating trip, golf, etc.—any necessary clothes or sports equipment should be mentioned beforehand by the hosts. If nothing special was mentioned, take it for granted that the weekend is informal—but it is better to *ask* than to be caught unprepared.

A guest is always concerned about how much luggage to take. Most guests bring too much rather than too little, which is cumbersome to all hands. The proper amount is frequently decided by the method of travel, but a carryall that holds everything including a shaving or cosmetic kit should take care of an average weekend. Although luggage is expensive, you will need it for the rest of your life, since you will be traveling a great deal in the service. It is wise to invest in good quality luggage.

WHAT TO TAKE

In this day of drip-dry clothing, you can take less and pack it more easily than ever before. What you will need depends upon where you visit—the climate and type of community (a summer colony or a city apartment)—but no matter where you go, travel light.

Usually, a man needs a conservative suit, dress shoes, a sports jacket and slacks—which he will probably wear on the trip—an extra pair of slacks, one pair of pajamas, two changes of shirts a day, socks, changes of underwear, and house slippers (soft and crushable ones that will take little room in a bag). For an informal weekend, he may need more sports shirts, a sweater, tennis shorts, an extra pair of slacks, and swimming trunks, rather than dress clothes.

A woman wears a pantsuit or slacks and walking shoes on the trip, and packs a cocktail dress if a party is planned. She will also need a daytime dress or skirt and blouse for luncheon or casual wear, sports clothes for whatever activities her hosts told her about, and dress shoes. More casual clothes may be needed for a summer weekend. Also needed will be a robe, pajamas, and house slippers.

When your hosts plan a special occasion such as deep-sea fishing, you need not worry about gear; they have all the necessary equipment, or they would not plan such an occasion.

When formal entertaining is planned, a man will need his dinner jacket. If you do not own one, take your blue dress uniform (or service equivalent) with black bow tie, or your summer whites or blues. A servicewoman would probably prefer a long dress to her uniform.

After you have packed everything you need, recheck your luggage. Persons who travel on short notice should have a checklist taped to the inside of the shaving or cosmetic kit, or some convenient spot. Include in your list such items as toothpaste, Aspirin, medicines, comb and brush.

DUTIES OF GUESTS

The duty of any guest is to be congenial. When you are an overnight or houseguest, do not be hard to please. When you take part in a game, join in the spirit of it.

It is important that you be on time for meals. Your hostess usually tells you at what time meals will be served—so be there. The importance of being on time holds for any activity in which you may engage: a boat trip, a golf game, or any other planned event. If anything, be a little ahead of time.

The breakfast hour may be a minor problem in a household; the host may go to work early, the family may be early or late risers, the children may get off to school in the usual early-morning confusion. A hostess may find it easier to send a tray to your room when you want to sleep late, or, if she doesn't mind, you could fix your own breakfast.

A considerate guest will be alert to the household routine, particularly in small quarters. If you sleep on the sofa in the living room, that part of the house cannot be occupied until you are dressed. It is helpful if you make your own bed. On the day of departure, take off the sheets and place them in the clothes hamper, unless your hostess tells you not to bother.

When one bathroom is shared by the family and guests, be careful not to overstay your fair time or use all the hot water. Try to leave the bathroom as neat as it was when you entered it. Don't leave damp towels on the floor, nylons on the towel rack, or a razor in the wash basin. Always hang up your clothes, and do not leave things lying around on the furniture.

You should offer to help your hosts when there are no servants, but do not insist if your hostess says no. Try to be helpful, but don't get in the way.

A thoughtful guest may take a small gift to his or her hosts, but the old standby of a box of candy may not be appreciated by diet-conscious hosts. It is a wise traveler who buys several inexpensive gifts while in foreign countries—small items that cost a few dollars there, but more in this country—to use as gifts on such occasions.

An overnight guest may choose to take something to the children in the family rather than to the hostess. In this case, candy, a book, or an inexpensive toy is a good choice. When you do not take a gift along, you send something after your departure. Upon any occasion, flowers are in good taste. The rule of thumb concerning gifts is: they should never be expensive, but must always be of *good quality.*

Now, one more don't: *don't* be so anxious *not* to get in the way that you freeze up and aren't much fun!

OVERSTEPPING HOSPITALITY

When visiting in a town or community where you have other friends, you must be careful not to use the house where you are staying as a springboard for renewing these other acquaintanceships. Your hosts may urge you to have your friends visit you in their home, and you are free to do so, but guard against overstepping their hospitality. It might be better to visit your friends at times when your hosts have other obligations—or to save such visits until your stay is over.

As a guest, you must remember not to talk endlessly on the telephone and to pay for all toll charges, including tax.

A houseguest does not arbitrarily bring along a classmate or friend "because there was room in the car" or "because Joe used to live here and wants to see the place." No one should bring along an unexpected guest, be he relative or friend, without first inquiring if this is convenient. And discretion must be used as to whether the question is raised at all.

PETS

Everyone loves his own cat, dog, or bird, and sometimes the other fellow's, but when visiting or going on leave the question of what to do with the family pet arises.

You can take the pet with you, leave it with a friend, or take it to the vet, for a fee. If you can afford a vacation trip, you should be able to afford the fee.

When you are to be a houseguest, you must make absolutely certain that your hosts are willing for you to bring your pet. Otherwise, they may not only object to your bringing it but also have no place or provisions for it. Remember, too, that some people are allergic to animals. And some people just plain don't like them.

Sometimes friends have an agreement to exchange pet sitting. But never force your pet on anyone. If a person asks to keep him, fine. Some people have a hard time saying no and seethe after they accept such a responsibility—in which case you might lose a friend.

For an overnight, a responsible neighborhood youngster can

feed and water your pet and check on its welfare for a reasonable amount. On the road, when staying in motels, you should check beforehand as to their provision for pets.

When traveling by car and taking the cat or dog with you, keep the pet on a leash when he needs to run. Otherwise he might take off and not be able to find his way back to you.

And *never* leave a pet in a locked car with windows closed in hot weather; he can suffocate or die from the heat in a very short time.

ACCIDENTS IN HOMES

When something unexpected happens—such as you break a valuable object or suddenly become ill—common sense will tell you what to do. If you broke something that you can replace, you do so at your earliest convenience. If you cannot replace it, send a gift that you feel your hostess will enjoy, such as flowers, a nice potted plant, or a book, which can give pleasure for some time.

Say how sorry you are for such a mishap at the time of the accident, and after your departure briefly state on your personal card, enclosed with the gift, that you regret the incident.

If you should become ill while on your visit, let your hosts know, and call a doctor. Any host would be distressed to learn that a guest was ill but said nothing about it. Of course, the guest pays all doctor fees and for all medicines.

DEPARTURE

When you leave after a visit, be sure that you have not forgotten anything. A checklist is handy in preventing this. It is a bother for your host to wrap and mail your eyeglasses or some other object, so don't leave anything behind.

When you have said that you plan to leave at a given time, do so. Don't be persuaded to take a later bus or flight; your hosts may be sincere when they urge you to stay longer, but usually a family has other plans or obligations. In any case, it's *time to leave!*

As soon as you are home or at your station, write a note of thanks to your hosts, addressed to the hostess. Express your appreciation for their hospitality, and mention some special incident. Your letter should be on its way within a few days after your visit (see chapter 12).

THE HOST'S RESPONSIBILITY

When you have houseguests, can you accept an invitation to another party? Not often. The problem is that if you mention to the prospective hosts that you have guests, they may feel impelled to invite them also. When they are not invited, should you stay home when you really want to go?

Such questions are worrisome.

For certain kinds of parties—cocktails, receptions, or a club dance—another guest or two may not make any difference, but at a seated dinner or luncheon they would, and you should not expect your houseguests to be invited, although they may be.

When your houseguests are with you for an extended visit, you should occasionally feel free to accept another party—certainly an official affair such as one given by your commanding officer. Then you explain to your guests why you need to go and that you are not at liberty to take guests, and make plans for their pleasure during the time you are gone. Or they may want to make plans of their own.

UNEXPECTED GUESTS

Service people are in a constant state of change, due to new duty stations. Therefore, they frequently are "on the road." Although it is pleasant and convenient for longtime friends to stay overnight or a few days with classmates while en route to new stations, do not take advantage of your friends or descend on near-strangers just because they were classmates.

You always telephone would-be hosts (or write, when you have time), either at their office or at their home, before going to visit, regardless of how well you know them. Then you will know if it is convenient for you to stop by for a meal or overnight. There may be illness in the family, they may have other guests, or they may have plans for the very time you would be stopping.

It is no excuse that you need to stay with someone because you are short of funds. Other than an emergency trip, you know in advance when you will be leaving your station, and an *adult* saves for emergencies.

VISITS TO CIVILIAN COLLEGES

In visiting a civilian college, a midshipman or cadet should not be too surprised at the differences—particularly the lack of regimentation of the students. Every college campus has its rules and conventions, however, and you will discover that these actually differ little in spirit from those to which you are accustomed.

Informality of dress is the rule at colleges, just as regulation of dress is stressed at the academies. You will find that there are a few special rules by which the college community lives, and by learning them, you will establish a friendship with people whose purposes in life are surprisingly similar to your own.

You may be a guest on a college campus, either as a member of an athletic team or as a social guest for the weekend. In either case, your academy will be judged by your actions. A midshipman or cadet member of an athletic squad should follow the special instructions of the officer sport representative and the coach during his or her stay on campus.

When you are a social guest, the normal rules for a weekend guest apply. You must be alert to the local ground rules, and follow them conscientiously. At all times be congenial.

The rules for a man visiting a women's college may be a little more strict, but you will have a good time if you are a good sport and observe certain regulations, such as:

Do not violate drinking rules on or off campus.

Get the arrangements straight concerning the time of your arrival and departure, transportation, clothes, etc. (You will be facing the same problem every date faces when coming to your academy or college.)

Remember that you have a hostess—your date—and do not play up to the entire campus.

Your hostess may reserve and pay for your room, and sometimes your meals, during your stay, but you pay for the extras and share some of the expenses.

For more information on visits to colleges, see chapter 4.

CHAPTER 36

Good Sportsmanship

GOOD MANNERS at sports contests are synonymous with good sportsmanship. Every officer has taken part in athletics at some time in his or her past, either as a player in the game or as an observer, and undoubtedly will do so many times in the future.

In the world of sports, there is a saying: "If you want to find out what kind of man he is, play golf with him when he is off his game, or go fishing with him when they aren't biting."

Good sportsmanship embodies the ideals of fairness, self-control, support of the team, and performing to the best of one's ability and honor. These qualities should be displayed by everyone, at every age—and it is best to learn them early.

It is good sportsmanship for midshipmen and cadets to cheer when it is announced that another service academy is winning a game. You want the other academy to win every game—except, of course, the one they are playing against your own team!

Although no one likes to lose, a good loser will compliment the winner on his skill, and a good winner commiserates with the loser's bad luck.

There are many places to show good sportsmanship other than on the golf greens or at a sports contest. A good sport is the person who can take the various setbacks of life without complaining.

OFFICIALS

The spectator is very much a part of any game. The player reacts to the roar of the crowd as much as the fan thrills to the exploits of the player. An official of the contest is also aware of the spectators and must always be on the lookout for the person who attempts to interfere with the rules of the game, or who tries to intimidate him or her by heckling.

An official is empowered to remove a player from a team for unsportsmanlike conduct as well as for an infraction of a rule. And he may eject from the stands anyone who abuses the rules of the game, or stop the contest when discourteous actions continue after due warnings. Should the game be forfeited, the rowdy spectators can consider themselves responsible for the loss of the game by their favorite team.

Officials of amateur or professional contests are selected after passing examinations in a particular sport. Their decisions are matters of judgment made according to vantage point and interpretation of rules. And, like it or not, you abide by their decisions.

BOOING

The American baseball fan displays a peculiar blend of intense loyalty to and intense criticism of the home team. He knows better than the manager when to bunt, hit, and run. The bum of the previous inning may become the hero of the day by a timely hit. The fan seems to be a maze of contradictions, and is consistent only in his inconsistencies.

Baiting officials at any sports contest is very poor manners. Throwing debris on the field or at the players and officials can be injurious. Running onto the field of play and using abusive or profane language are flagrant displays of ill temper.

While enthusiastic cheering for your favorite athlete or team is expected, booing a decision or play that goes against your team is not only childish but unsportsmanlike.

SPORTSMANSHIP

The most common breaches of good manners at sports events are excessive noises made by spectators or players in an effort to divert the opponent. This interference includes shouting, whistling, and clapping hands at critical moments.

The sports program at the service academies covers the proper behavior of midshipmen and cadets, as both participants and spectators, at all events. At least twenty sports have team competition. Among the rules of courtesy are those of keeping quiet when an opponent or a member of your own team is attempting a free throw in basketball, a putt in golf, a spare in bowling, or a rally in tennis. Any game of skill demands concentration by the player.

Displays of temper defeat the purpose of the game. Spectators should conduct themselves in such a manner as not to reflect discredit upon their academy or college during liberty periods following the game as well as at the game itself. This is particularly important for uniformed personnel, as the entire service may be labeled as rowdy through the isolated indiscretions of a few individuals.

Many football games are played during inclement weather, which creates a conflict between personal comfort and good manners. An umbrella may keep the rain from your head—but it may also block the view of someone behind you. Also, jumping up with an umbrella during an exciting play is not without its hazards for those sitting nearby.

Football games are frequently played in very cold weather, and this is used as an excuse for consuming alcoholic berverages in the stands. This not only is illegal in many stadiums, but is a reflection upon the individual and his or her service.

In golf matches, no one should move, talk, or stand close to or directly behind the ball or hole when a player is making a stroke. Attention is paid to the casting of shadows between the hole and a ball about to be played. Players should leave the putting green immediately upon determining the result of a hole.

When a ball is lost, or when your twosome or foursome is taking excessive time to play, you should signal players behind you to go through, then wait until this group has played past you and is out of range before continuing play.

A woman is responsible for her own golf bag. Presumably, she is in good health and able to care for her own bag, or she wouldn't be on the course.

The fast-moving game of tennis requires good manners by the spectators, in that players are distracted by moving objects in their range of vision. A tennis ball in flight moves with great speed, and any unexpected movement, particularly at the opposite end of the court, can throw a player off his game.

If you should be sitting in a stand that faces more than one court, do not move from one match to another until play is over except on the odd games when the players change courts. You do not applaud during a rally, but you may when the point has been played out. An error such as a shot that goes out of the court or into the net should not be applauded, even if it gives the point to your favorite player. Only express approval for *good* strokes.

A number of specific sports have not been mentioned, not because they are less important, but because behavior at other sports is similar to behavior at those discussed. The basis of the rules in any sport is fair play. The line between the rules and good manners is a fine one. The distinction might be made in this manner: the rules prescribe penalties to be invoked when there is a violation, whereas there generally is no penalty for a breach of good sportsmanship—except the censure of your neighbors or the public.

YOUR ALMA MATER

Every academy or college man or woman is proud to hear the song of his or her alma mater played or sung. Midshipmen and cadets stand at attention when their own alma mater is played or sung; therefore, it is good manners to stand when the opponent's alma mater is played or sung.

PAYING A WOMAN'S WAY

It was once considered gentlemanly for a man to offer to pay for a woman's expenses, no matter what. Today, when a single woman is included in a group that is going on a fishing trip, a ski weekend, a hunting trip, or a sports event of some kind, she pays for her transportation and her share of the expenses involved, unless, of course, she has been specifically invited as a guest. In either case, it should be clearly understood in advance what she will and will not pay for.

When people find themselves traveling together to the same destination, by chance or by pre-arrangement, a man does not pay a woman's expenses, other than for trifles if he wishes.

Older men whose wives have never worked or earned their own money are often uncomfortable when women insist on paying their own way. Although a man should not insist on paying a woman's way, a woman's discretion should guide the decision.

PAYING YOUR OWN WAY

A good sport pays for his or her share of expenses when a group gets together on the golf course, at a theater party, or for drinks in the officers' club. It is an old custom for a couple or group to go no-host or "Dutch treat," with expenses evenly divided. But a nondrinker should not be expected to share the expenses of those having "just one more drink."

When you go sailing with friends, you may volunteer to split the expenses or to bring drinks and some food. There must be an understanding beforehand; otherwise you might show up with provisions that duplicate your host's.

In fishing, the host always offers to divide the catch, regardless of who caught the fish. In the case of an accident, you replace any lost tackle as soon as possible.

Deep-sea fishing is luxury fishing at its best, and is expensive. The no-host situation is customary, with a small group chartering a boat and splitting expenses. Prices vary for charter boats at different ports, with three or four persons going out at a time. In party-boat fishing, when many people go out for a day or a half-day, expenses are much lower.

The problems encountered with a skiing party are slightly akin to those of a safari—you usually travel a distance to get to your destination, and stay a weekend at least. When unmarried women are in the no-host group, dormitory-style lodging is customary, and they pay for their own lodging. Tipping is similar to that in any hotel.

On a hunting trip, guests are expected to bring their own gear, guns, and ammunition—unless the host specifically states that he has equipment for all hands.

When you are a guest at a private game preserve or hunting camp, you may be assigned a guide. You tip the guide depending upon the length of your stay and the services received. This tip is in addition to the share of the guide's wages which courtesy or custom would assign to you.

When invited as a guest to play on the golf course at a country club, you pay your own way whenever you can. Usually, your invitation is a privilege extended to you by a member, and you should be prepared to pay all other costs—or as many as your host will permit. Such expenses include greens fees, caddies, food and drink.

When everything is paid for in cash, the guest has no problem; when the member host signs you in, have your greens fee ready. If your host insists that he take care of the fees, accept and thank him, then pay for both caddies, if you use them. When everything is paid through chit service, you return your host's hospitality by inviting him to your ship or station, or to some special occasion.

SECTION X

The Military Family

In the home circle it is the correct thing to be as courteous,
considerate, affable and entertaining at home as in society.

JOSEPHINE STAFFORD, PRACTICAL ETIQUETTE (1903)

CHAPTER 37

The Service Spouse

EVERYONE WANTS to lead a happy, worthwhile life. To achieve this goal—which must be earned—it is important that nonmilitary spouses understand the customs of the service in everyday living. A newcomer who has always lived in a civilian community may at first be bewildered by the regulations and traditions of the service.

In many ways there is no difference between living on post or base and living in Little Rock. You have friends in for pot-luck supper, probably are a member of the church and the PTA, have joined a garden club, and play golf or another sport. There are churches and garden clubs and golf greens just about everywhere. Wherever you live there are certain things expected of you: congeniality, friendship, a sharing of your time and effort through participation in community affairs.

One of the main differences between service and civilian life is that a service family is always on the go. Every few years—or less—a change of orders means a change in friendships, schools, and activities, which may give family members a sense of shallow roots. The good thing about the moves is the opportunity they provide to make friends and to extend knowledge through travel in various areas of this country as well as overseas.

FAMILY SUPPORT PROGRAMS

As a means of helping people adjust to service life, a family support program has been established at posts and stations throughout the country. New spouses and family members of all ages are invited to attend the free classes sponsored by the station.

In recent years, all services have placed greater emphasis on the military family and how its well-being affects readiness and retention. The Air Force has Family Support Centers; there are Navy and Marine Corps Family Service Centers, Army Community Service Centers (as well as a Family Liaison Office in the Pentagon), and Coast Guard Work-Life Centers.

Symposiums are held on many subjects: the rank and rate structures; the various benefits such as health and retirement programs; financial and legal issues; pay and allowance; and crisis assistance. Solutions are offered for such problems as what to do when beds, linens, pots and pans have not been delivered during a move.

A newcomer to the station receives a letter or folder with maps and charts of the base or post as well as of the surrounding areas, including historic places of interest and good eating places. There are telephone numbers for the most frequently used facilities and the area's civic, fraternal, and service clubs. Information is provided about schools and their entrance requirements, where to apply for a driver's license, the base nursery, thrift shops, aerobic fitness classes, and the housing referral office.

For times of stress, there are care and prayer chains as well as hotlines for drugs or child and spouse abuse.

THE PX

You will need your ID card when you shop in the commissary or post exchange (PX) or in other government-run stores. Your ID card bears your photograph and signature. If you should have the misfortune of losing the card, report the loss to the station officials immediately, and the card will be replaced.

A service spouse can save money at the commissary, where groceries are purchased, and in the post exchange, where you can buy anything from clothing to bicycles. There are discounts on gas and services at the filling station and garage. Each PX operates within the Armed Services Exchange Regulations, and it is illegal to sell to unauthorized persons—so it behooves you or any dependent to buy only for your own use or as a bona fide gift. There are commissaries and exchanges both in this country and overseas, and members of one service may purchase in the post exchange and commissary of another service.

NEWCOMERS

A priority for any newcomer to a station (or base or post) is to get acquainted with others as soon as possible. There will be others new to the station—you will not be alone. The commanding officer (CO) customarily gives a "newcomers reception" or a "hail and farewell"— no hats, gloves, or calling cards. If the CO is a married woman, she and her husband probably will entertain at one of these types of receptions. Since social calls are a thing of the past, most commanding officers consider such receptions "calls made and paid."

Frequently, the wife of the CO or the president of the officers' or community women's club affiliated with the station will give a brunch, coffee, or tea for the wives. Since most women's clubs have a number of activities, the newcomer will have the opportunity to join a group with the same interests as hers, which might be antiques, drama, or gourmet cooking.

Although social calls are no longer made—there simply isn't time for them on busy stations—greatly appreciated is a telephone call that welcomes the newcomer to the station. Or an invitation to join a bowling group. Or an inquiry about when it will be convenient to stop by and say hello.

And after a year or so, when you are the old-timer and newcomers arrive at the station, *you* extend the welcome.

THE CO'S WIFE

The wife of any officer wants to take an active part in the social and group activities of the station. But unlike in years long past, the modern CO's wife—and many other station wives—may have a full-time job. As a result, responsibilities as a host or group chairwoman will fall to someone with more time.

The CO's wife of today may be the honorary or advisory member of a group, and she will take part in activities only as time permits. She may host a welcome-aboard luncheon or honors brunch on a given weekend; she will also try to continue the custom of hosting at-homes and dinners in the family's quarters.

SPOUSES AND PROMOTIONS

According to congressional instructions in the fiscal 1988 and 1989 National Defense Authorization Act, "officer and enlisted efficiency or evaluation reports may not contain any information about the military member's marital status or spouse."

In short, today the wife of a serviceman may join the work force without affecting her husband's chance for promotion or top assignment. (And vice versa!)

VOLUNTEERS

There are a number of organizations connected with the station which need volunteer help: the hospital, chapel guild, thrift and gift shops, nursery, Young Life, Boy and Girl Scouts, the Red Cross. Your time—as much as you can give—is important to their success. A station newsletter will print information about such work, and the officer in charge of station activities is always helpful.

The widespread work of the Relief and Aid Societies of each service augments that of the Red Cross. In Washington, D.C., where the headquarters of the Military Wives Association, Inc., is located, wives from all services work for the legislative well-being of the military family, both active and retired. They are particularly concerned for the service widow and the benefits to which she is entitled.

Many parents cooperate in babysitting and car pools, taking turns in caring for others' children as well as their own, and in driving to meetings.

HOUSING

The Armed Forces Hostess Association, located in the Pentagon, Washington, D.C., has an extensive file on worldwide housing for service personnel. The office is staffed by volunteer workers who are members of service families in the area. Information is available on clothing needs, travel, schools, churches, commissaries, climate, etc. When you write for information, make certain that your questions are specific. You should give your full name and grade; service; base, post, or station. Include a self-addressed and stamped return envelope.

The office in the Pentagon handles housing requests for service personnel transferred to the Washington area, and will help you in renting or buying a house and give advice on schools, shopping, and transportation systems. There is no charge for these services.

The Joint Armed Forces Housing Referral Office, with headquarters at Fort Myer, Virginia, helps personnel in all services with off-base housing in the area. All stations have referral offices with approved lists of off-base rental housing. A separate service is the family housing office, where eligible families are assigned government housing.

RELIEF/AID SOCIETIES

A number of service organizations give emergency assistance to service personnel and their families. Each organization has auxiliaries, sections, or branches throughout the United States as well as overseas. They are not connected with the American Red Cross, but may work in cooperation with that organization.

Financial assistance is given for such needs as nonreceipt of pay or family allowances; expenses incidental to emergency leave; medical, dental, and hospital expenses; funeral expenses; emergency food supplies; unpaid rent and eviction notices; training dependents in order to make them self-supporting; assistance with educational or vocational training for service children above the high school level.

Some of these organizations are the Army Emergency Relief (AER); the Navy–Marine Corps Relief Society, the Coast Guard Mutual Assistance, and the Air Force Aid Society. All have headquarters in Washington, D.C.

Funding is by membership dues and fund-raising campaigns by officers' and NCO clubs and servicewomen's clubs, as well as proceeds from balls, special shows, and sports events.

ALONE AND LONELY

When an officer has overseas duty or goes to sea and the family remains at home, a problem sometimes arises for the spouse: loneliness. Too often loneliness leads to depression or to a drinking problem. On the bright side, a spouse now has the time to accomplish something formerly only dreamed of: continuing education, pursuing a hobby, doing volunteer work. If there are children, most spouses keep busy with them and the housework. Raising children is one of the most demanding and rewarding of jobs.

There are good preschool facilities for the part-time care of children, but investigate all facilities before sending your children to any of them.

When there are no children, or if they are in school, a part- or full-time job will not only take your mind off yourself but give you extra income. A savings account will allow you and your spouse, when he or she returns, the opportunity to finance something that otherwise you could not afford—perhaps a second honeymoon!

PROTECTING YOURSELF

If you are living alone, or must drive through isolated areas or for some distance, you must take safety precautions. Nine times out of ten, nothing will happen—but you must think about that tenth time that could prove harmful. Even in the daytime you should keep the doors of your house locked, with a chain on. The wrong sort of person is on the alert for an empty house or apartment, or one occupied by someone who is defenseless.

Automatic night lights, set to go on and off at definite times, are helpful when you are gone overnight or for any length of time. When you will be gone only for a night or two, ask a neighbor's child to pick up the mail and newspaper; payment of a dollar or a small gift will make them happy.

If you plan to be gone a longer length of time, have the newspaper delivery stopped until your return; when requested to, the post office will hold your mail for a stated time. And hire someone to cut the grass during your absence.

When you must drive somewhere alone, always check the gas gauge and make certain that the tires are properly inflated before starting out. Lock the car doors to prevent someone from jumping into the car while you are stopped at a red light. Avoid poorly lit or isolated parking lots, and lock your car when you leave it. Should you forget to lock the car, look in the backseat before getting in.

ASSAULT

In case of assault or attempted assault, scream. Fight with anything at hand, and with your fists and feet. If you have time—should this be a drunken or retarded person—try to talk him out of it. No one wants to be fatally injured, and a lethal weapon in the intruder's hand precludes making much resistance, but statistics indicate that less than 5 percent of women who resist are killed.

There are ways for a woman to help herself; some women submit in fear of their lives or become hypnotized with fear. When you can, fight. Yell "Fire!" People will come running when the dreaded word *fire* is shouted, but few will intercede otherwise, either thinking this is a family fight or simply not wanting to get involved.

In a lonely or crime-ridden area, car doors should be kept locked. A can of Mace or a shrill whistle can scare off a wrongdoer. There are a few basic rules anyone should follow:

Keep out of lonely areas day or night, but particularly after dark in parking lots and shopping malls.

Keep the chain on your door when you are at home.

Have your house key in your hand and ready for use when returning home so that you do not waste time hunting for it—time that gives an assaulter the chance to grab it and get inside the house.

Do not permit your children, boy or girl, to hitchhike, and explain
why: that "sick" people might hurt them.
And never pick up hitchhikers yourself.

Officials* in crime detection and prevention state that most
sexual assaults on women and children are planned; that only a few
are spur-of-the-moment acts. The individual may be a person you
know, or someone who has seen you somewhere. Any assault should
be reported to authorities in person or anonymously. You need not
press charges, but in order to help prevent such attacks on others,
you must give a description of the attacker. Such information is kept
confidential.

Some women take karate lessons to learn how to protect themselves. There are classes given by various organizations, such as the
YWCA and YMCA, which will instruct you in self-defense. For
example, it is good to know that the heel of your shoe can be a handy
weapon, and that your thumbs pushed into an assailant's eyes or
your sharply raised knee to the groin or stomach can gain you
valuable time.

Today, many assaults are made to obtain money for drugs.
Purse or wallet snatching can happen anyplace, and in broad day-
light. A drug addict is a dangerous person, and may be a teenager.
Such acts must be reported to authorities.

In this country, remember that the phone number 911 brings
instant help from police, fire department, or an ambulance.

YOUR CHILDREN

A spouse is father, mother, and the protector of the family when the
service wife or husband is away. Children should be given a set of
rules to go by, in the house as well as out. Small children must be
told never to accept goodies from a stranger, or to get into his or
her car, or to talk with any unknown adult either on the school
ground or on the sidewalk. A parent should always know where the
children are—and the children should know where the parent is.
There is little more disturbing to most children than to return to an
empty or unlighted house.

Teenagers can be almost as unsuspecting as young children of
a wrong-doer's intentions, because teens are in a questioning and
learning stage of life. Parents should know about their teen's
friends—without seeming to be inquisitive—and this means show-

*The Sex Offense Squad and the Rape Crisis Center in Washington, D.C.

ing patience and understanding, even when they run thin. Rules should be made for hours to come home, household chores, allowances. But a teenager needs time for privacy.

CHILD AND SPOUSE ABUSE

There is child and spouse abuse in the military family just as there is in the civilian family, in towns and cities and in the country. A child can be scarred for life by abuse from family members or anyone; a spouse may be so intimidated that he or she will not discuss the problem until too late. Mental abuse—the domination of one person over another—can be as damaging as physical abuse.

When a family member needs help, the station chaplain or counselor can advise you concerning the specialist needed for adult or child. All stations and most cities have hotline numbers for help, whether the problem is a runaway, physical abuse, or drugs.

There is a precaution you must take concerning young children: never leave them unattended anywhere. In malls and stores, at state parks, and at filling stations along highways, accompany small children to public restrooms. Teenagers should use caution in such places, as well.

FAMILY SECURITY

As soon as you, a service spouse, learn that new orders do not allow for your family to accompany you, you must discuss all household affairs with the partner to be left behind.

When there is important business to attend to, there may be need for a power of attorney to be obtained for the one making the decisions, paying the bills, balancing the budget, keeping the car in condition, and disciplining the children. That person must have ready access to important family records and understand them. He or she may have had little experience in handling financial affairs before marriage, so a little time should be spent in explaining their importance. However, the departing officer may also have had little financial experience, so it may be wise to seek outside advice.

Records are usually kept in a safety deposit box in a bank or trust company vault. These papers should include a copy of your service record, and insurance premium statements for car, house, and life. You may choose to have such premiums paid out of your monthly paycheck, but this must be arranged beforehand by your local disbursing office or by writing to the Finance Center of your service: Cleveland for the Navy, Indianapolis for the Army, Denver for the Air Force, and Kansas City for the Marines. Since it takes about eight weeks for the center to process the request, it must be made as soon as possible.

Other important papers include: a statement of medical benefits; an up-to-date will (the station legal officer can help with this); marriage and birth certificates; bank and savings accounts statements; records of investments such as stocks and bonds; real estate records, including an estimate of present value; a power of attorney; family death records; and burial site information.

Also included should be the names, addresses, and telephone numbers of persons or organizations to be contacted in case of emergency: your commanding officer and duty station; the Aid or Relief Society of your service; the national headquarters or local chapter of the American Red Cross; the legal assistance officer; the nearest military hospital; and the chaplain or minister in your area. Keep copies of all records in a lockbox at home for ready access.

DEPENDENTS' DENTAL PLAN

Spouses and children of active-duty personnel in the Army, Navy, Air Force, Marine Corps, Coast Guard, National Oceanic and Atmospheric Administration, and Public Health Service are eligible for enrollment in the Tricare Active Duty Family Dental Plan (ADFDP), a DoD managed-care program that started in 1987 as the Delta Dental Plan.

A dependent child is defined as one up to 21 years of age unless he or she is in college and relies on financial assistance or he or she was disabled before their 21st birthday. Adopted children and step-children are eligible.

The plan provides broad dental coverage by accredited civilian dentists throughout the country who voluntarily participate in ADFDP. A licensed health benefits advisor in your area will advise you concerning eligibility, costs, coverage, and locations of participating dentists, and they can supply you with claim forms. For further information, write or phone ADFDP at:

West of the Mississippi River—Tricare ADFDP/P.O. Box 269023 (claims only)/P.O. Box 269024 (correspondence & inquiries)/ Sacramento, CA 95826-9023/(916) 381-9368 (active-duty families only)/(916) 381-9369 (dental care providers only).

East of the Mississippi River—Tricare ADFDP/P.O. Box 9086/ Farmington Hills, MI 48333-9086/(313) 489-2240.

INCOME

BASE PAY

The monthly paycheck of each service member is mailed to that person by the Finance Center of the service. The amount is based on rank and ratings and is the same for all services. It is subject to federal income tax.

ALLOWANCES

Extra allowances, allowances that are not taxable, make things a little easier for service men and women. Every active duty officer receives a *subsistence allowance* each month. For officers who are not assigned government-furnished quarters on base but must find housing in a nearby town or community, a *basic allowance* for quarters is issued each month, with a little more for those with dependents. There is *proficiency pay* for those with various job skills, and an *incentive bonus* for doctors in specialized medical fields.

When an officer goes overseas or has sea duty, there is *family separation allowance* and *travel allowance*. When you move, you will have professional packers and movers—all you need to do is have things clean and ready to pack, guard the inventory list, and keep your children, your pets, and yourself out of the way.

ALLOTMENTS

An allotment is that portion of a service person's paycheck which is allotted to any individual, business, or agent during his or her absence. An individual can arrange for an allotment by writing to the Finance Center to direct how much of the check is to be sent where.

The allotment may be charged by the officer at any time through written instructions. Otherwise it will stay in effect until an emergency decrees a change (when he or she is known to be a prisoner of war or missing in action and the family needs financial aid), or until that person's death.

When authorized by the officer in writing, the Finance Center will purchase government bonds and hold them in safekeeping until his or her return, or will withhold a designated amount from the paycheck, which will earn good interest.

LEAVE

Leave is the authorized absence of a serviceman or servicewoman from duty. In the civilian world, it is vacation time. Leave is chargeable against his or her leave account, with 30 days granted each year. This amounts to about two and a half days for each month of duty.

You can take your leave all at one time, or a few days or a week or so at a time. Or you may not take it at all. Earned leave can accumulate to 60 days, except in combat areas, where 90 days can accumulate.

For the good of all concerned, talk with your CO about the best time to take leave, and do so well in advance of when you would like to take it.

PROMOTIONS

The system of promotions is based on the years of experience and qualifications of the service person. Second lieutenants in the Army, Air Force, and Marines, and ensigns in the Navy and Coast Guard, are automatically promoted to the next grade. But after that their records are scrutinized by members of the selection board where promotions are being considered. The board of about six senior officers meets annually to pass on the records of all officers in the promotion zone.

As rank increases, selections become tighter. Each officer's record or "jacket" includes his or her fitness report, which is sent in by the commanding officer each year, or whenever the officer is transferred. This report includes performance of duty, any disciplinary action, and the CO's overall evaluation.

A spot promotion is made when a service person has shown exceptional ability and the commanding officer promotes him or her on the spot.

A deep selection is made before the regular time for being promoted. This usually occurs when certain specialties (outstanding) are needed in a specific command.

Congress sets the numerical strength of the armed forces, and the need for officers in each service changes constantly. In times of war the number is greatly enlarged; in times of peace it is sharply reduced.

It is important that the military family be aware of the many facets of service life, and the roadblocks which may affect their loved one's career. When the officer fails to be promoted or is retired early for physical disability, the family may be called on to provide sympathy and moral support more than at any other time.

PASSED OVER

After an officer of any rank has failed to be promoted, he or she is said to have been passed over. There is no greater trauma for a dedicated officer than to be passed over. Too often there is a deep sense of rejection: *Why me?*

When a large number of officers are being considered and only a few can be picked up, the deciding factor may be that one has only a slightly higher "number" than another. A service academy graduate has a permanent number based on his or her academic standing and aptitude; when two officers have equal ability and only one can be chosen, the number may make the difference. Every serviceman and servicewoman has a lineal number; upon retirement the name is placed on the retired list, and upon death it is removed.

By law, junior officers who have twice been passed over are separated from the service with severance pay. Reserve officers with at least 5 years of active duty and 25 years of Reserve service receive benefits.

Once an officer attains the rank of lieutenant colonel in the Army, Air Force, and Marines, and commander in the Navy and Coast Guard, he or she may remain on active duty for 20 years. The higher the rank the longer the officer stays in. A captain in the Navy who is not selected for rear admiral, or the Army colonel who does not make brigadier general, must retire after completing 30 years of active duty.

SEPARATED

A service person of any rank may be separated involuntarily from the service due to a courtmartial, misconduct, mismanagement of personnel or government affairs, or financial irresponsibility. A separation may occur when he or she is considered tempermentally unsuited to the service. Individuals so separated have the right to state their side of the case before a Board of Inquiry.

Individuals receiving honorable and general discharges are entitled to all benefits afforded by law for military retirees, Regular or Reserve. About 75 percent are for reasons of health and quality of service. A punitive discharge, with punishment or penalties, deprives the service person of virtually all benefits.

RESIGNATION

When an officer resigns his or her commission, there will be no retirement pay or other benefits, and he or she will be unable to use the commissaries, post exchanges, or officers' clubs. A resignation is a voluntary act by the officer and is considered an "unqualified resignation."

A "qualified resignation" is given a member of the armed forces for several reasons, for example, for a violation of honor, or for "the good of the service"—a serious charge.

RETIREMENT

Many officers retire after 20 years of service. Some stay in for 30 or so years and achieve flag rank. A handful become four-star generals and admirals. With congressional accord, five-star rank is held by each service commander during times of war: Generals of the Army and Air Force, and Fleet Admirals of the Navy.

After retiring, military persons receive a monthly retirement check for the rest of their lives. The amount of the check is based on their rank at the time of retirement and the number of years served. They will be entitled to many benefits, and use of the facilities of the officers' club.

Very important is the opportunity to enter into a low-cost Survivor Benefit Plan (SBP) for military retirees which will give the officer's family financial protection in case of his or her death—when the retirement checks stop. The Uniformed Services Health Benefits Program (USHBP), including the Civilian Health and Medical Program of the Uniformed Services (CHAMPUS), offers service families care or assistance at a civilian hospital or facility at government expense. (For more about an officer's retirement, see chapter 45.)

MIA AND POW

In times of war military persons are declared missing in action (MIA) when their fate is not known during or after their assigned duty. They remain on the missing in action list until found or officially declared dead. The pay of someone missing in action is held and credited to his or her account until the legal status is determined.

Allowances and allotments continue as set up, but when an allotment was not made, the spouse or next of kin may request through the MIA's service that one be set up for financial need.

When it is determined that the missing have been captured by the enemy, they are declared prisoners of war (POW), and the families are immediately notified. A family assistance program is available.

POW HOTLINE

Former POWs may call a toll-free number in Washington, D.C. (800-821-8139), which offers service 24 hours a day. This hotline augments the local Veterans Administration medical centers and regional offices, and helps former POWs with questions concerning benefits or any problem that may arise.

PERSIAN GULF HOTLINE

Persian Gulf War veterans may call a toll-free number for information on disability and medical care benefits. The service is handled by the VA regional office in St. Louis: 1-800-749-8387. This is part of their outreach program to help veterans suffering from illnesses arising from their service in the 1991 gulf war, or for the two years thereafter.

VETERANS ADMINISTRATION

When applying for VA benefits, write, phone, or visit the office nearest you in any state. Phone numbers are listed under United States Government, Veterans Administration, in the phone book. Calls are toll-free, and no record is kept of calls.

DEATH BENEFITS

When an officer dies on active duty, his or her survivors will receive a substantial check for immediate expenses. The deceased may be buried in a national cemetery of the family's choice with provision made for expenses. Transportation is furnished.

Within a year of death, transportation is also furnished families moving to another house, in another state if necessary, or the household goods may be stored up to six months. If you are in quarters, you will be given time to move out, but the quarters will soon be needed for others reporting in.

There is Dependency and Indemnity Compensation (DIC) for the spouse, with payments based on the pay grade of the deceased and the number and age of children in the family. If the spouse remarries, spousal payments stop but payments will continue for eligible children (see chapter 40).

FINANCIAL HELP

The legal assistance officer at any station will give you referral information for the preparation of papers for Social Security, indemnity compensation, and any other benefits to which you are entitled. In a civilian community, consult a lawyer.

There are several agencies that can tell you how to obtain a loan or grant for study or training. The aid or relief societies of your spouse's service can help, and information may be obtained from the Military Family Association in Washington, D.C., and the family support programs of the deceased's service. The National Society of Military Widows is another organization that can be of great assistance. Contact them at 5535 Hempstead Way/Springfield, VA 22151-4094.

THE BEREAVED

At first, a widow or widower may not care to go to large or lively affairs and should not be urged to do so. There is no set time for mourning as there was in former years. Black or somber dress is rarely worn, other than to the funeral service.

A psychiatrist has stated that loneliness is the mother of depression. When bereaved persons grieve to the extent that they become recluse from friends and family, when self-pity overwhelms them, these are signs of depression. Their chaplain and friends are the ones who can help the most during this time of stress.

HELP YOURSELF

In time, you, the bereaved, must help yourself. At first you may want to talk about your loss, to reminisce about the happy times in your married life. And your friends should be sympathetic listeners.

But to dwell on one's unhappiness too long will eventually drive even the best friend away, at least for a while. The sooner you mix with others, take a trip, or play golf, the better off you will be. The best therapy of all may be a part- or full-time job or volunteer work.

PERSONAL HELP

When an emergency or serious problem arises, you should seek the advice of the station legal officer. Your problem, no matter how grave, will be held in confidence. The legal officer cannot represent service personnel in civilian courts, but he or she can give you names and addresses of civilian counsel.

When a person needs help on such problems as alcoholism, child abuse, depression, or serious mental disturbances with possible threats of suicide or drug addiction, help is obtained from commissioned medical professionals. The earlier you seek help, the sooner the problem can be corrected.

FAMILY SUPPORT CENTERS

Family centers on military installations offer a wide range of information and assistance for service personnel and their families. These are: Army Community Service Centers, Air Force Family Support Centers, Navy and Marine Corps Family Service Centers, and Coast Guard Work-Life Centers. Large installations have a 24-hour hot line.

Family support covers a wide range of issues: crisis assistance, disability, family separation, neglect, child and spouse abuse, and financial and personal problems.

IN CASE OF ACCIDENT

In case of an accident or sudden illness, call the doctor and/or take the person stricken to the emergency room of the nearest hospital. The name, telephone number, and address of your doctor and hospital should be in your wallet or handbag.

People who have a history of heart disease or diabetes, or who have an allergy to any medication, must keep a notice of that information with them at all times, particularly when traveling.

There should be a first-aid kit in the car and in the home, out of reach of children but in an easily accessible place. It is the wise parent who is well versed in first-aid procedures and has a *First Aid Guide*.

Children should also memorize the emergency number 911. Time is precious in cases of accidents, burns, drug overdose, or suspected poisoning.

BENEFITS

The quickest, most accurate response concerning the many benefits offered to military personnel is obtained by contacting the Family Support Center or Family Service Center at the military installation nearest you. Your Social Security number or serial number will be needed. The Veterans Administration publishes a manual titled "What Every Veteran Should Know," which covers just about everything. The National Association of Uniformed Services puts out almanacs for active and retired military personnel, Reserve forces, and the National Guard. Their address is: P.O. Box 4144/Falls Church, VA 22044.

CHAPTER 38

The Family

LITTLE PEOPLE

Children are people. Little people with big feelings that can be hurt just like your own.

Some parents constantly scold small children in an effort to make them be polite. Of course, parents want their children to shake hands politely, to smile and say "Hello." But frequently a shy child or a goaded child will balk. Children who hold back, or cry, need a little special understanding, not nagging and shaking. In their own good time, they will surprise you by demonstrating their good manners.

It is desirable for children to use the words *Sir* or *Ma'am* when speaking to seniors, but the words—like seasoning—should not be overused. And a little girl's curtsy is outmoded.

It is also desirable that parents not permit (or insist) that their children call them by their given names: "Bob" and "Mary." Given names are used by people on an equal footing. Children show their respect to their elders by calling them "Mr. Smith," "Mrs. Smith," or "Captain Smith"—unless they are "Uncle Bill" and "Aunt Mame."

Parents who use vulgar or uncouth language at home and scream at their children should not be surprised to hear the same in return.

TABLE MANNERS

When your child is old enough to sit at the family table, he or she should learn a few everyday manners—slowly—so that they become a habit; to be clean when he comes to the table (especially his hands), to close his mouth when he chews food, and to talk only after the food is swallowed. He should not play with his food or smack his lips. Eventually he must learn not to interrupt others, but this takes time, because children talk spontaneously.

A child must learn to ask for food and not to grab for it. When he finishes eating, he should ask if he may be excused to leave the table though others are still eating.

WHEN SMALL CHILDREN STAY HOME

It's fun to take your children along whenever you can. But there are times when they should stay home for everyone's sake, including their own. For instance, young children may be keyed up after the splendor of the wedding, and become noisy, bothersome, or weary at the reception—or all three!

Children should not be taken with you to any social affair *unless specifically invited.* Your friends know that you have children, so when your children are not included in an invitation, you should not take them along.

Should you be the hosts and others ask if they may bring their children, be frank when it is inconvenient. You know who is apt to do this, so when extending the invitation say, "I'm not having any children this time, and I want to give you plenty of time to get a sitter." To offset the possibility of any problem, suggest the name of a trusted sitter.

It is becoming more common for the host and hostess at a large party, particularly when many young parents are invited, to provide sitters, either in a separate area of their home or at another location.

GODPARENTS

Following the birth of a child, parents choose godparents from among close friends or relatives. The child's godparents will keep in contact with the child throughout the years.

When the child is christened, the godparents attend whenever possible but they can accept by proxy. Godparents give the child a christening present, perhaps a silver cup with the baby's name engraved on it; older godparents may want to start a college fund with a savings account, or give a bond in the child's name. You should not accept the honor of being a godparent when you feel that the responsibility is too great.

OLDER CHILDREN

Good manners do not appear suddenly as adulthood approaches—they are acquired when children are still small. The child who is permitted to interrupt anyone, anywhere, at will, will do so when grown up. Conversely, when children are taught to say "Thank you" and "Excuse me," they grow up automatically expressing thanks and observing other social amenities.

Teenagers need to be told *why* they cannot do something that seems logical to them but not to their parents. In order to make a house regulation hold, explain why they cannot do what Tom, Dick, and Mary are doing. Don't arbitrarily say, "Because I say so, that's why."

It takes patience for parents to pull through the teen years, but the pattern of their children's lives may be set during these years. Parents often do not understand teenagers very well because the teens don't understand themselves. This is a growing, a learning, stage of life. And teenagers spend time dreaming, time when everyone else is excluded.

Teens need friends, as everyone does, and parents should make certain that through the years their children's friends are welcome in the home. Letting teens have a hand in planning and carrying out their own informal parties or special occasions is always a good idea.

It is easy for parents to become too involved with their children, or to expect too much family participation from them at certain ages. The youngster who had a wonderful time on the family trip last summer may flatly refuse to go this summer, preferring to stay home and cut grass, deliver papers, baby-sit, or go to the swimming pool.

Teen-age sloppiness seems endless; therefore, house rules should be established for teens about keeping their room in order, taking baths, and shampooing—habits that should be established early in life.

The matter of allowances is something that parents and children have to work out together, depending on the needs of the youngsters and how they carry out their household chores, as well as the financial status of the parents. Regardless of the parents' financial status, it is better for teenagers to have too little than too much, to earn money on their own and find out that it can be hard to come by. Otherwise they might have trouble, later, dealing with the school of hard knocks. But parents should try to avoid being too rigid or too lax. Common sense must be used.

THE BABY SITTER

When you leave the children with a sitter, or when your own child is the sitter, a little advance planning will be helpful for all concerned.

First, tell the children ahead of time that a sitter will be staying with them and who that person is. Ask a new sitter to come ten or fifteen minutes early so that you can show the sitter around the house and he or she can get acquainted with the children.

Second, explain to the sitter all rules for the children: their bedtime; television programs to be viewed or not viewed, and how long they may watch; snacks, if any, that are permitted before bedtime. Also go over the "specials" that a small child finds necessary for contentment, such as a particular blanket or teddy bear.

Third, leave the telephone number as well as the name of the person or place you are visiting, and the telephone number of the doctor, close neighbor, or friend the sitter can call for help. The emergency number (911) should be posted in a conspicuous place.

Fourth, explain all house rules: that the doors are to be kept locked and no unknown person is to be admitted—not even someone who claims to be a friend or relative; that the sitter is not to have a guest—unless you give permission; that a small child is never to be left alone in a bathtub—not even when the phone rings; that small children are not to be unattended while the sitter watches TV or does homework; that the volume of the TV or radio must be set at low so the sitter will be able to hear the cry of a child.

IN-LAWS

Relatives should be friends. You can't choose your relatives like you choose your friends, but you should try to get along together in harmony regardless of differences in age and opinions.

In-laws can be your very best friends. Often, parents-in-law and a young couple immediately develop a warm relationship that lasts a lifetime. Other times, problems arise almost immediately. In-law problems, according to some marriage counselors, rank almost even with financial woes as difficulties for young couples.

In-laws should not interfere. They should not give advice unless asked to, and should refrain from giving more advice than they have been asked for.

Whenever possible, parents and their married children should not live together. Should it be necessary for the parents to live in the younger couple's home, the parents should have a room of their own and stay in it at certain times in order to give the younger couple privacy and time to talk things over and make plans together. But they should not be expected to stay in their room for long periods of time, or be shushed up like small children—this is unkind. Of course, the same holds true for single parents living with their children and married children living with their parents.

An older parent (or parents) in good health and without financial problems should under no circumstances visit his or her children for a few days or weeks, and then stay on for months or years. Loneliness, the "poor me" syndrome, is no excuse. In good health, anyone can do something worthwhile other than "visiting."

Too often a parent looks upon a child as a possession—my house, my car, my daughter, my son—but a child is on loan to a parent only until adulthood; then the child is on his or her own. When parents realize this, they can make plans of their own—travel, do volunteer work, work part time, develop a hobby or new interest (in addition to their grandchildren).

On the other hand, some young people ignore an older parent, frequently out of thoughtlessness, but sometimes deliberately. When there is friendship between in-laws and their children, annoying or troublesome problems can be aired and talked over. Then, hard feelings are not apt to occur.

THE ELDERLY

All too often, the elderly are overlooked in today's bustling world. Persons old and infirm appreciate a little attention more than anyone else other than small children. Usually, they are the last to get it.

To someone confined to home, or a nursing home or hospital, a few minutes of your time will give more pleasure than any gift that you can offer. When the aged cannot get out, it becomes very important who comes in.

If distance or time does not permit a visit, then a brief phone call (a receiver grows heavy in a weak hand), a pleasant newsy note, or an anniversary card helps to brighten a long day.

When the elderly feel like getting out, it is thoughtful of you to invite them for a ride on a nice day, or to take them to lunch in a tearoom with a handicapped entrance, if one is needed.

Should you ever have to place someone in a nursing home, make absolutely certain that it is well recommended and clean, that the attendants and nursing staff are efficient and kind, and that a qualified doctor is in attendance. Do not stop in the lobby when you check the home out, but visit the kitchen and the dining and recreation areas as well.

If their physical condition permits, talk with the ill or elderly on several different occasions, when staff members are not around, and ascertain how contented they are.

THE UNMARRIED COUPLE

Today, some people live together who are not married. Such couples are accepted in a number of places—more frequently in larger cities and college campuses. Within families, there may be heartbreak, embarrassment, a strain on the family ties. Therefore, deciding to live with someone is not as simple as "living my own life and not hurting anyone else."

The unmarried couple cannot expect parents (or other relatives or friends, usually seniors) to accept their way of life and let them share a room in the parents' home. When someone wants to bring home his or her roommate for the weekend, and that roommate is of the opposite sex, the relationship between them should first be explained if they expect to stay together in the same room. Otherwise, when they know that a parent or parents (relatives or friends) would object, they should agree to stay in separate rooms. This is not old fashioned of the parents or friends; it reflects differences in social mores, moral standards, and religious convictions.

When introducing an unmarried couple who may be visiting in your home—or anywhere—simply say, "This is Mary Smith (or "Mary," if she is a relative) and John Doe."

GIVING GIFTS

Everyone likes receiving a present, but a conscientious person does not want gifts from those he or she does not know well—or too many gifts from friends or relatives. Some people, mainly young marrieds, with little to spend for gifts make a rule—and announce it early to friends and relatives (with the probable exception of parents and children)—that they wish to give presents once a year, at Christmas or birthdays, and that cards and notes will be sent upon other occasions. They also request that others do likewise in regard to them.

When you consider that the average person (and double this for married couples) has parents, grandparents, sisters, brothers, aunts, uncles, nieces, and nephews, as well as in-laws, godparents, and close friends to remember—the gift list can become very long as well as expensive.

In selecting a present, it is better to give a thoughtful though inexpensive gift in good taste than a showy though costly one. Something you make yourself may be treasured.

GIFTS FOR OLDER PEOPLE

Many older people can buy whatever they want within reason—or already have everything they want—and prefer a phone call or a long, newsy letter if they live at a distance. For those who live nearby, gifts can be a problem.

When older people have only a small income, there is no problem. Try to find out if they want or can use what you plan to give. A radio gives pleasure throughout a sleepless night. House slippers such as backless mules that you simply slide your feet into, or a robe, will keep them comfortable.

A nice gift is fruit. Oranges, grapefruit, pears, and apples are shipped from a number of reliable growers in this country directly to one's door—no packing, no wrapping, no mailing. For those who entertain or have friends drop in frequently, cheese, smoked ham or turkey, jellies, cookies, flowers, or a potted plant may give much pleasure. A number of good nurseries will package and mail bulbs, such as amaryllis, to any state.

GIFTS FOR YOUNG PEOPLE

It is difficult sometimes for an older person to find the right gift for a young person: child, teenager, or newlywed. Styles change rapidly, fads come and go; if possible, it is better to find out ahead of time what is needed or wanted, and the exact size or color if clothing is indicated.

Although a check may not be as much fun to send, there comes a time when shopping in crowds—or shopping at all—becomes difficult, or when you haven't a clue as to what to send. Then a check is in order

Quite often a check is a blessing and is the nicest gift of all. Then, the child can choose her own cuddly robe, the teenager can afford something the sender never heard of, and the college student or graduate has a little nest egg. It's a lovely feeling to have some money to spend exactly as you please.

JOINT PRESENTS

There are times when a joint present is much more desirable than individual ones. An office staff or an organization may contribute to a single expensive present which an engaged or newly married couple might not otherwise be able to have. For example, a starter set of sterling flatware; or, if the couple wants something of a practical nature, a stainless steel set of kitchen utensils or a vacuum cleaner. A few dollars given by each person to the office "kitty" goes a long way toward a gift that will last a lifetime.

A joint gift is often given to a retiring or detached officer upon his or her departure, or to someone who is promoted in rank and honored at a wetting-down party. A new baby is the recipient of a unit's joint gift, and a group of office workers often go in on a shower gift together. Children may all chip in for a single lovely present for their parents' wedding anniversary.

NO GIFTS

When an invitation states "No gifts," please honor the request. When you go ahead and show up at a party bearing a gift, everyone feels uncomfortable, including the recipient.

If you are a close friend of the guest of honor at a no-gift party, you could take or send something to him or her at home beforehand. Flowers are always acceptable.

WEDDING PRESENTS

Probably the most meaningful gift of all is a wedding present. The gift should be selected with consideration to the needs and desires of the couple receiving it, and be as nice as you can afford, since it will be used and enjoyed for the duration of the marriage. A very nice gift is something that the couple might not be able to afford for a long time, if ever. (For more information, see chapter 30.)

ACKNOWLEDGING GIFTS

It is obligatory that all gifts be acknowledged by the recipient, young or old. If a person can spend time and money to send you a gift, you can take the time to say thank you. A note should be written (or sometimes a phone call made) within a day or two of receiving the gift.

PURCHASING GIFTS WHILE ON FOREIGN DUTY

Service personnel have a golden opportunity to buy unusual and beautiful gifts while on foreign duty. Although prices are higher than in former years, and the dollar has depreciated in some countries, a good shopper can find many a bargain and gifts of lasting interest.

Do learn everything possible about the country before arriving; then you can save money by doing some comparative shopping after you reach the station or port. Small objects that can be easily mailed, or packed and later used for gifts, should be an important part of your shopping.

GEMS AND FLOWERS

Each month has a gem and a flower, and you may want to take that into consideration when selecting a gift.

	Birthstones	*Flowers*
January	Garnet	Carnation or snowdrop
February	Amethyst	Violet
March	Bloodstone or aquamarine	Jonquil or daffodil
April	Diamond	Sweet pea
May	Emerald	Lily of the valley
June	Pearl or moonstone	Rose or honeysuckle
July	Ruby	Larkspur
August	Sardonyx or peridot	Gladiolus or poppy
September	Sapphire	Aster or morning glory
October	Opal or tourmaline	Calendula or cosmos
November	Topaz	Chrysanthemum
December	Turquoise or lapis lazuli	Narcissus or holly

COURTESY OLYMPICARD.

SECTION XI

The Serious Side of Life

CHAPTER 39

Your Religion

Oh, Great Spirit, grant that
I may never find fault
with my neighbor until I
have walked the trail of life
in his moccasins.

Cherokee Prayer

THE RELIGIOUS BELIEFS of people have much in common, regardless of formal religious affiliations. Notwithstanding the many different religious denominations and the great variety of individual attitudes toward religion, the student of theology is generally impressed by the similarities, rather than the differences, in the basic teachings of all religions.

When you understand these similarities, it becomes apparent how ill mannered and foolish it is for any person to make light of another's beliefs, or to make derogatory remarks about the faith of another. A person who does so is violating a fundamental of both his own and the other person's religion: *to love thy neighbor.*

It is not enough for an officer simply to understand and respect the beliefs of others. There are many occasions when individuals of different religions are brought together to participate in the social observances of religious ceremonials. It is necessary that you know the proper behavior and procedures for such occasions.

As you go about your daily social and official life, you will be called upon to take part in numerous religious ceremonies, in either an active or a passive role. In most cases, you will do no more than stand quietly, uncovered, and with bowed head until the ceremony is concluded. On other occasions you will be asked to take an active part in a religious ceremony such as a funeral, wedding, baptism, or service of thanksgiving. Members of a wedding party or a funeral cortege need to learn everything possible about their responsibilities before the ceremony from the rabbi, chaplain, or clergyman of that particular faith.

During benedictions by a chaplain in an outdoor ceremony, you uncover and follow the motions of the chaplain. Ceremonies in a church or chapel require specific knowledge of procedure.

BLESSINGS AT THE TABLE

As a guest at a meal, you may be called upon to take part in a simple family observance of religious custom. These expressions of thanksgiving may help you:

Catholic: "Bless us, O Lord, and these, Thy gifts, which we are about to receive from Thy bounty. Through Christ our Lord. Amen."

Jewish: "Lift up your hands toward the sanctuary and bless the Lord. Blessed art Thou, O Lord our God, King of the universe, who bringest forth bread from the earth. Amen."

Protestant: "Bless, O Lord, this food to our use, and us to Thy service, and make us ever mindful of the needs of others, in Jesus' name. Amen."

When you are a guest in a home of another religious affiliation and are asked to pray, do not attempt to use a blessing of the host's religion unless you are familiar with it. Instead, use your own favorite grace and say it in your own sincere way.

SILENT PRAYER

When you dine out with another couple and want to offer a silent prayer of thanks before the meal, you may ask: "May we have a moment of silent thanks?" Or you may briefly say your private thanks, without asking.

CHILD'S BAPTISM

The baptism of an infant is usually held in a chapel or church. A Protestant child may be baptized within the first year of life, preferably when two to six months old, during or following the regular Sunday morning service.

A Catholic infant is baptized at age two weeks to one month, and the ceremony is frequently held at an early hour on Sunday afternoon.

In the Jewish faith, a ceremony for male infants (known as *brith milah* in Hebrew and *brit* in Yiddish) is held in a synagogue, home, or hospital eight days after birth. The naming of female infants takes place the week following birth, during services at the synagogue.

The parents issue invitations by note or telephone and host a reception, tea, or luncheon following the religious ceremony. The party is usually held at the home of the parents, and guests are close friends and relatives of the families.

A white cake and wine, or fruit punch, may be served at the reception. Toasts to the child's health and prosperity are proposed by a godfather, if there is one, when dessert is served at a luncheon, or later on at the reception or tea.

Officers of the parents' immediate service unit may present the child with a gift, such as a silver christening cup, which can be engraved with the child's name, the date of christening, and the title of the service unit of the donors.

RELIGION IN THE ARMED FORCES

Military personnel have the opportunity to attend church services, since armed forces regulations require that all commanding officers provide for the free exercise of religion. Services may be attended on weekdays by those whose faiths call for services during the week.

Protestant, Catholic, and Jewish services are held at all major installations, and usually one or two are held at the smallest base or post. Those of other faiths are provided services whenever possible, either in nearby houses of worship or by visiting clergy.

Chaplains hold military rank and are in uniform. They have been trained at seminaries and ordained, as are all other clergymen, before entering the service.

Cadets and midshipmen attend church services on a voluntary basis at their academy chapels or in a church in the community. Each academy has one or more chapels. All academies have Bible study classes, prayer groups, and retreats, also attended on a voluntary basis. The cadets and midshipmen assist the chaplains in various ways: as ushers at church services and choir programs, and as teachers of Sunday School classes for family members of service personnel.

At the service academy chapels, all-faith rooms provide a neutral place of worship for small groups of other denominations. An altar is available which can be adapted to several types of service, including Buddhist.

As a member of a given church, the chaplain must follow his

denomination's teachings. Therefore he works within the boundaries of his denomination: he answers first to the church. When a chaplain tells a couple that they must be counseled before their wedding, or that he cannot marry non-members of the church or divorced persons, they should not be offended: he cannot, due to his conscience and his church.

ADDRESSING THE CHAPLAIN

It is always correct to address a chaplain as "Chaplain," regardless of rank, although the naval service customarily introduces and addresses a chaplain by rank.

In the Air Force and Army a chaplain is addressed "Chaplain." As an Air Force officer in the Office of the Chief of Chaplains in Washington, D.C., said, "Primarily the word *chaplain* is used to help bridge the gap between rank and the ministry."

CHAPTER 40

Emergency & Death

EMERGENCY

When an active duty officer has been seriously injured or killed while on leave or en route to a base, post, or station, this information is telephoned as soon as possible to the commanding officer of the nearest armed forces activity. The following information should be given: the officer's full name, rank, and service number; where the death, accident, or illness took place; the extent of the injury and present condition; the name, address, and telephone number of the physician in charge, and of the hospital or place where the patient or deceased is at that time; where the person giving the information can be reached.

A military officer will be assigned to check on the accident or illness, and to assist in every way possible. In case of an automobile accident, it is necessary to have verification that the accident was not the fault of the deceased or injured, and that no negligence or carelessness was involved—otherwise the family may not receive all forthcoming benefits.

Service personnel, officer and enlisted, receive emergency medical treatment at any government hospital or, when none is available, at a civilian hospital at government expense. A survivor assistance officer of the armed forces activity and its chaplain will aid the deceased or injured officer's or enlisted man's family.

DEATH

You will need help at this most devastating of times—the death of a loved one. A relative or close friend, a member of the Relief or Aid Society or the Family Support Program of your service, and the Red Cross are some of the people who can help with details such as: contacting the funeral director in a nonmilitary area, or the survivor assistance officer of the nearest military installation; notifying the newspapers in which the obituary notice will be published and compiling accurate information; phoning the chaplain or clergyman and relatives or friends who live at a distance. If the officer was retired and in a second career, his or her employer must be notified.

Arrangements must be made for the funeral: the money for a private or civilian interment; clothing to be sent to the funeral director; clothing to be worn by the family; flowers to be sent by the family for the service; transportation for other than active duty personnel. Then there will be legal business that must be attended to: the reading of the will, and the accounting of personal property, taxes, insurance, benefits.

The retirement plan that was taken—or not taken—may determine the survivor's new way of life. There are many informative books available about probating wills, and how to avoid probate, which a wise person will read before death, so that the heirs have as little difficulty and expense as possible at this time.

Many spouses are shocked to learn that unless the checking or savings account was in both names (a joint account), they will be unable to draw funds until legal matters are determined—and this may take time. A spouse whose husband or wife was on active duty will receive compensation; the amount will depend on such factors as the length of time in the service and the place of interment. But the retirement checks for a retired officer stop immediately after death. When the family car was registered in the name of the deceased, in most states the car can be driven by the spouse or next of kin upon showing the death certificate.

NOTIFICATION OF DEATH OR EMERGENCY

A notification of death, with a copy of the death certificate, is sent to the military department of the deceased person's service. Retired and reserve officers' spouses (or next of kin) should promptly notify the nearest military installation in order to set in motion the annuities that will be payable to the family.

When a member of the family of a service person dies, this information is given to the local Red Cross, which in turn notifies the Red Cross on the military base or post, which verifies the service person's emergency leave. When overseas, the person receives emergency leave and immediate military transportation to the place of emergency. There is no cut in pay or allowance, and the best government hospital and medical services are given the ill or injured.

INTERMENT IN A NATIONAL CEMETERY

Active duty and retired members of the armed forces and their dependents are entitled to burial in a national cemetery. Due to the population expansion throughout the United States, however, space is not always available in a desired cemetery, and grave sites cannot be reserved in advance.

There are 130 national cemeteries in 38 states and Puerto Rico. Fifty-eight Veterans Administration regional offices (with at least one in each state) arrange for 60,000 burials each year. A headstone, marker, or urn, and an American flag are provided. Permission for burial and information on military procedures can be obtained from the superintendent of the cemetery where the burial will take place. In state cemeteries, honors are usually rendered by the nearest military installation or local veterans organization.

Arrangements for burial at sea are made through the Naval District Commandant, which has written instructions for the ceremony. Availability of this service depends upon the ships' schedules.

MILITARY FUNERAL EXPENSES

The active duty serviceman or servicewoman who dies is entitled to interment in a national cemetery and transportation costs for his or her family. Household furnishings may be stored up to six months, and then moved to any location within a year at government expense. The next of kin receives a death gratuity equivalent to six months' base pay, which is for immediate expenditures.

Death compensation from the Veterans Administration up to $1,500 is not subject to tax or seizure except for property purchased in part or entirely out of the payments. The Social Security Administration pays a lump sum of $255 to the survivors.

NONMILITARY FUNERAL EXPENSES

When interment will not be in a national cemetery, a plot at a private cemetery can be purchased at any time and the deed placed with your will. The average cost of a funeral is between $5,000 and $7,500, depending on the state and whether the cemetery is in an urban or a rural area. These figures include the cost of the plot, a vault, and a marker. Embalmment, or cremation, a hearse or limousine, chapel rental, a minister's fees, and flowers are additional.

Active duty and retired persons would do well to consider various plans for burial of themselves and their family members. One way is to set up a trust fund in a bank in the area where you want to be buried, allowing interest to accrue to cover funeral expenses. Pre-plans for perpetual care are also offered in certain cemeteries. The contract of purchase is guaranteed at any future time, whether you live in or out of state or the country, with no future expenses. (The money you pay will accrue through the years to defray any such costs.)

Don't hesitate to consult with several cemetery directors to compare costs and services, which vary. And make certain that your purchase is guaranteed in writing, and send a copy to your lawyer.

Note that cremation expenses are less than the costs for embalming and interment in a coffin.

RETIRED COMPENSATION

For retired personnel, the Veterans Administration pays $450 when death occurred in a veteran's hospital and interment is in a national cemetery in a non-service-connected death. When the cause of death was service connected, there is an allowance up to $1,500 in lieu of other burial benefits. Also, Social Security provides $255 to the next of kin when the deceased was eligible.

The cost of transporting the deceased, when a retired service person, is not paid. The VA will pay the cost of transporting the remains of any veteran who was hospitalized or in a contract nursing home, or was in transit to or from the hospital or facility.

CREMATION

The services for those cremated are the same as for those buried. Since a minister includes the burial prayers in the funeral service, the family need not go to the crematorium. When they wish to do so, a very brief service will be held there.

The ashes will later be delivered to the family, who may dispose of them in any legal way. The urn is usually deposited in a section of the churchyard or cemetery set aside for this purpose.

MEMORIAL SERVICES

A memorial service may be held for a number of reasons, frequently at the prior request of the deceased. Such a service is held when it is necessary to wait a length of time after the death, such as when death occurred at a distant place or verification was delayed; when a serviceman or servicewoman was lost at sea or in battle and never recovered; or following cremation.

The mourners meet in a chapel or a church or at graveside and a brief eulogy is given by the chaplain or a clergyman or close friend. There usually is a period of meditation and a hymn or organ music. Friends attending should not send flowers.

PRIVATE SERVICES

When the funeral is private, you go to the services only when notified to do so. Only the family and closest friends go to the grave site. When the announcement states *services and interment private,* you do not go to either, unless notified. When a published account does not mention "private," you may go to the services but not to the grave site.

Out-of-town relatives and friends should find their own place to stay overnight and take meals, unless the family tells them otherwise. This is no time to add an extra burden to the family, particularly if the bereaved is elderly or ill. Should there be room in the house or quarters, or in the home of a friend, the family will tell you so.

CIVILIAN FUNERALS

The services may be held in a church, chapel, home, or funeral home. More services are being held in the funeral home than in past years, with the funeral director in charge of arrangements.

IN A CHURCH

The family sits in the first few pews of the church, on the right side of a center aisle when the waiting room is on that side, with the pallbearers on the left. The casket is usually covered with a blanket or spray of flowers from the family, and is closed by Catholic and Jewish custom and by the wishes of Protestant families.

Those attending the services sit wherever they choose; women wear street dress, not necessarily dark. Older women in the immediate family usually wear black; younger women wear dark or subdued dress, and young children their Sunday School dress. Men in the family wear dark suits, others wear conservative suits.

Frequently, there is no processional, with the family entering through a door nearest the pews where they will be sitting. If there is a processional, it forms in the vestibule. The clergymen and choir, if any, enter from the rear, then the honorary pallbearers in pairs; then the casket, followed by the family. The widow or widower walks with a member of the family, the widow escorted by the eldest male relative—a son, brother, or uncle; the widower with his oldest daughter, perhaps. Other members of the family walk in pairs directly behind.

The procession leaves in the same order as it entered, except that the choir stays in place. The family follows the hearse to the cemetery in the first car or cars, followed by the pallbearers, ushers, clergyman, and close friends to the graveside.

AT THE HOUSE

For a funeral service at home, the living room or the largest room would be used. The casket rests on a stand furnished by the funeral director, who also furnishes extra chairs. The service is a little simpler, with more privacy offered for those who need or desire it.

IN A FUNERAL HOME

In a funeral home (or parlor or chapel), where the casket remains until the day of the funeral, members of the family often receive friends at specified times before the service. Such hours are stated in a published obituary; if they are not so published, no receiving hours are planned.

There will be a register furnished by the funeral parlor in which friends attending write their names. This will later be given to the family. When signing the register in a funeral home, a married couple signs on one line, "Lieutenant and Mrs. John Doe." Should they visit the funeral home at different times, they would sign separately as "Mrs. John Doe" and "Lieutenant John Doe." A single person signs his or her name in full, such as "Major James Smith" or "Captain Mary Ann Brown."

You need stay only a brief time after extending your sympathy, and the bereaved need only say, "Thank you for coming," or make some more personal remark.

Services held in the funeral chapel are the same as those in a church. The clergyman is paid a fee (between $50 and $100—whatever is customary in the community), which is handed to him by a member of the family in an envelope before the services.

The flowers sent by friends will be placed throughout the room or rooms, then taken to the grave site.

DIVORCED PARTNERS

A divorced man or woman may want to pay respect to the former wife or husband. The divorced person may go to the funeral parlor for a short time, but he or she does not sit with the bereaved family at the services or go to the cemetery, unless invited by the family to do so.

When there has been unpleasantness after the divorce, the ex-spouse may prefer to send flowers or a charity contribution with a brief note of condolence and not go to the funeral parlor or attend the services.

The death of a former spouse does not make a divorced man or woman a widower or widow.

Today, an obituary notice frequently includes the names of divorced spouses.

AFTER THE FUNERAL

You should find out beforehand if the bereaved want relatives and guests to be with them after the funeral, or not. Some people want to get their minds off their sorrow for a while and find it beneficial to be with others. Some prefer to be quietly alone.

In many areas of the country, it is customary for friends and neighbors, or members of a church group or organization, to prepare food and have it on the table, buffet style, when the family returns from the services with their close friends.

In this way, people from out of town who may not have seen the family for some time will have the opportunity, though briefly, to talk with them.

MESSAGES OF CONDOLENCE

Whether or not you are able to attend the funeral, it is important that you send a message of condolence. The purpose of the message is to express your sympathy to the closest member, or members, of the deceased person's family. The brief note, letter, telegram, or telephone call should be taken care of immediately after you learn of the death.

You may find a letter of condolence difficult to write—many persons do. But it is very important for the bereaved person or persons to receive a message of sympathy, *to know that you care,* and you should send this message immediately.

Address a written message to the nearest living relative, whether you know him or her, or not. On the death of a male friend, for example, send the message to his wife, if he was married, or to his parents, if he was single. If there are no surviving parents the message should be addressed to a brother or sister, or any relative.

Letters of condolence are always written by hand, usually on plain white paper of the more formal type. Your letter should be short and simple, but sincere. Since you desire to express comfort to the bereaved, do not dwell on the illness or manner of death. (For the form of a letter of condolence, and its reply, see chapter 12.)

The recipient of a condolence note will likely be comforted if you mention a favorite remembrance of the deceased. The bereaved will be encouraged by hearing that the person who has died has left a pleasant mark on those still living.

FLOWERS OR CHARITY CONTRIBUTIONS

When sending flowers to a funeral, *never send them in the name of the deceased.* If the services are to be held in a home, the flowers should be sent to the nearest relative. When services are to be held in a chapel, church, or funeral home, the florist will send them there, addressed to "The funeral of Mr. Smith Jones." Write your full name on the plain white card enclosed with the flowers. If the relationship with the bereaved was a close one, then sign your name "John Doe" or "Ann and John Doe." Do not write "Ann and John," since there may be many Anns and Johns. You may sign "Captain and Mrs. John Doe" or enclose your personal card or joint card.

When the obituary notice states "Please omit flowers," then do so. If the notice states that contributions may be sent to a charity (or church) in lieu of flowers, include in your note to the charity that the check is in memory of the deceased.

You send your personal card to the family saying that you have done this, but never mention the amount. The charity notifies the bereaved family upon the receipt of the contribution.

Later, the widow or widower or a member of the family (or, in case of illness, a close friend) will acknowledge the flowers, contributions to charity, and telegrams and letters of condolence in brief handwritten notes. A note should be sent to the chaplain (or officiating clergyman), thanking him for his help.

CALLS ON THE BEREAVED

When you are a close friend or relative of the bereaved, you will want to call on them. The purpose of such a call is to give them comfort and sympathy. When speaking to them, you may say, "I'm sorry," and briefly but warmly hold their hand. You do not ply them with questions; if they want to talk to you, you listen sympathetically.

Whether you can be of assistance or are invading a family's privacy depends upon how well you know the bereaved. Your own good sense should give you the answer. When you cannot be of assistance, a call is brief.

In some cases, a family may urgently need assistance—as well as sympathy—whether you know them well or not. Such a case may follow an accident and death, which are always a shock to a family.

Of great help is taking care of any children in the bereaved family for a day or two. Perhaps you can best help by wiring or telephoning friends of the family who are at a distance. Someone is usually needed in the home of the bereaved to answer telephone calls and do other necessary tasks. Prepared food may be urgently needed. Whenever possible, send the food in a disposable container, so the recipient need not worry about returning it.

You never take offense if you call on a bereaved family and are told by whoever answers the door that the family is not receiving visitors. (Such calls, of course, are never returned.) You may leave your personal card with the phrase "Deepest sympathy" written across it.

When calls are received at the funeral chapel, a member of the family or a representative should be present during the afternoon or evening when calls are expected to be made.

When making a call, try not to become overemotional, for you may add to the distress of the bereaved rather than comforting them. Friends who are not very close to the family call at the funeral home rather than at the house.

IN MOURNING

In recent years, there have been many changes in the conventions of mourning, particularly in the matter of dress. Most people feel that grief is a private thing, and that the public appearance of an individual *after the funeral* is not determined by set rules but by necessity and personal feelings.

Members of the family wear mourning at the funeral, with

women dressed in all black or white, according to the season, navy blue and other dark shades, or whatever they feel is appropriate. Servicemen and servicewomen wear the prescribed uniform. Retired officers and civilian men wear dark suits and ties. It is no longer customary for men to wear black arm bands or mourning badges, although you may do so if desired, or if required by uniform regulations.

Mourning clothes are not worn for any length of time following the funeral, if at all. How long a person stays in social seclusion following a death in the family is a personal matter. It is proper for the bereaved to attend the theater, a concert, movies, and small, quiet gatherings not too long after the loss. A bereaved person should not stay in seclusion.

Wedding invitations may be sent to those in mourning, and it is correct for the bereaved to accept such an invitation if they choose. Previously scheduled weddings may take place during a time of mourning, usually a small wedding for members of the immediate families.

Generally, the gaiety of the occasion will determine whether a bereaved person attends a few weeks or months after a death in the immediate family. A widow or widower usually does not go to certain functions, such as dances and balls, for several months.

DONATING YOUR BODY

Should you want to donate your body, or parts of it, after death for scientific research or to help (through kidney or eye transplants, for example) a living person who is ill, first explain this wish to your family, then inform your doctor. After that, notify any hospital or research institution to this effect, or sign an organ donor card that conveys to an institution certain rights for this purpose. Any organ intended for transplant must be immediately taken to that institution.

Some states provide an opportunity for any person 18 years of age or older to designate on his or her driver's license that upon death he wishes to donate his body for purpose of transplantation, therapy, medical research, or education. Other states, in a legalized anatomical gift act, furnish cards that are signed before witnesses and are to be carried in a wallet.

For organ donor information contact your doctor or a local medical facility.

CHAPTER 41

The Military Funeral

THE MILITARY FUNERAL CEREMONY is based on customs and traditions that have developed through the years. The ceremony demonstrates the nation's recognition of the debt it owes for the services and sacrifices of the members of the armed forces.

The casket is covered with the American flag. It is usually transported to the cemetery on a caisson, and is carried from the caisson to the grave by six military body bearers. In addition to the body bearers, honorary pallbearers, when designated, march to the cemetery alongside or behind the caisson.

At the cemetery, the casket is placed over the grave and the body bearers hold the flag-pall waist high over the casket. After the committal service is read by the chaplain, a firing party fires three volleys. A bugler sounds "Taps," and the military funeral is completed. The body bearers then fold the flag, and it is presented to the next of kin.

These basic elements are the foundation of all military funerals, whether last rites are being conducted for a private or seaman, or final honors are being paid at the grave of an admiral or general.

Military funerals are divided into three classes:

With chapel service, followed by the march to the grave or place of local disposition with the prescribed escort.

Without chapel service, the funeral procession forming at the entrance (or at a point within reasonable distance) of the cemetery. With graveside services only.

FUNERAL WITH CHAPEL SERVICE

Before the service begins, the funeral escort is formed in line facing the chapel. The band forms on the flank toward the direction of march.

Members of the immediate family, relatives, and friends of the deceased are seated in the chapel before the casket is taken in. Chapel ushers ensure that a sufficient number of front seats on the right side of the chapel facing the altar are reserved for the immediate family. The two front pews on the left are reserved for the honorary pallbearers. If body bearers are used to carry the casket into position inside the chapel, seats are reserved for them at the rear of the chapel.

The conveyance bearing the remains to the chapel should arrive a short time before the hour set for the service. Since the casket normally is covered with the national colors, the escort is called to attention and the escort commander salutes as the conveyance arrives.

When all is in readiness to move the casket into the chapel, the escort commander brings the escort to *present arms*. At the first note of the hymn, the casket is removed from the conveyance by the body bearers and carried between the ranks of the honorary pallbearers, if any, into the chapel. The escort is then brought to order and given *at ease*.

At the conclusion of the chapel service, the body bearers follow the honorary pallbearers, or, if there are none, the body bearers follow the chaplain in a column of twos as they carry the casket to the entrance of the chapel. When honorary pallbearers are present, they form an aisle from the entrance of the chapel to the conveyance (caisson or hearse) and uncover or salute as prescribed.

FUNERAL WITHOUT CHAPEL SERVICE

When the funeral is without chapel service, the escort usually forms at or near the entrance to the cemetery. The officer in charge supervises the transfer of the casket from the hearse to the caisson or makes provision for the hearse to be included in the procession from the point of origin to the grave site.

While the casket is being transferred, the escort is brought to *present arms.* The family and friends remain in their cars during the transfer of the casket.

GRAVESIDE SERVICE

The military elements (chaplain, body bearers, firing squad, and bugler) participating in a graveside service are in position before the arrival of the remains.

The leader of the firing squad gives the appropriate orders for the firing of three volleys, and the bugler sounds "Taps" immediately upon completion of the last volley. The senior body bearer gives the order to march off after the flag has been presented to the next of kin.

CREMATION

For all phases of the funeral where the receptacle containing the cremated remains is carried by hand, one body bearer will be designated to do so. Four men detailed as flagbearers will follow the receptacle when it is carried from the conveyance into the chapel, from the chapel to the conveyance, or from the conveyance to the grave. The flag is folded and is carried by the leading flagbearer on the right.

When the receptacle has been placed on a stand before the chancel of the chapel or in the conveyance, the folded flag is placed beside the receptacle. If the caisson is equipped with a casket container for the receptacle, the open flag is laid upon the container as prescribed for a casket.

CANNON SALUTE

The funeral of a flag or general officer (active or retired) which takes place at or near a military installation will be marked with the number of minute guns to which the officer was entitled. These will be fired at noon on the day of the funeral.

The cannon salute corresponding to the grade of the deceased will be fired immediately after the benediction, followed by three volleys of artillery, guns firing simultaneously, or three volleys of musketry.

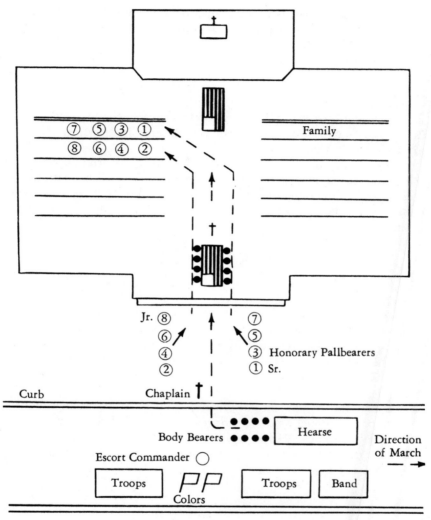

Entering the chapel

Honorary pallbearers salute while honors are being rendered; then they fall in
behind the casket to enter the chapel.

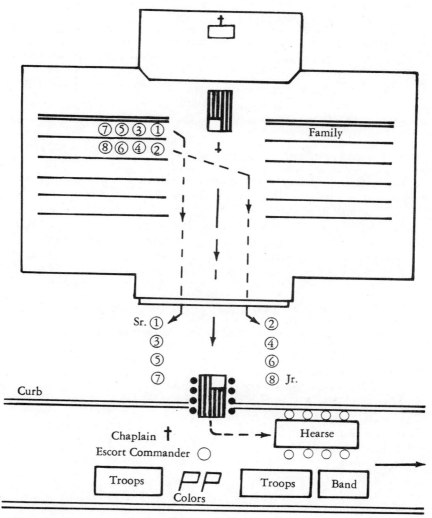

Leaving the chapel

Honorary pallbearers precede the casket out of the chapel and take positions in reverse of the ones they took before the service, as indicated. They salute while escort renders honors and hold the salute until the band ceases playing; then they take positions on either side of the hearse or caisson. (If riding, they proceed to cars ahead of the chaplain's car.)

AVIATION PARTICIPATION

When there is aviation participation in a military funeral, it is timed so that the airplanes appear over the procession while the remains are being taken to the grave.

When the funeral is that of an aviator, it is customary for the airplanes to fly in a normal tactical formation less one aircraft, indicating the vacancy resulting from the loss of the deceased.

FRATERNAL OR PATRIOTIC ORGANIZATIONS

A fraternal or military organization of which the deceased was a member may take part in the funeral service with the consent of the immediate family of the deceased.

When the ritual is military or semi-military, the rites begin immediately upon the conclusion of the military religious service. If the ritual contains the firing of three volleys and the sounding of "Taps," the military firing bugler plays at the appropriate time.

SPECIAL MILITARY FUNERAL

A special military funeral is held for the following dignitaries:

Commander in Chief
Secretary of Defense
Deputy and former Secretary of Defense
Secretaries of the Army, Navy, and Air Force
Chairman, Joint Chiefs of Staff
Five-Star Generals and Admirals
Chief of Staff, U.S. Army
Chief of Staff, U.S. Air Force
Chief of Naval Operations
Commandant, U.S. Marine Corps
Commandant, U.S. Coast Guard
Other personages specifically designated by the Secretary of Defense
Foreign military personnel when designated by the President

In each service, the commanding officer of the military or naval command or district in which the death occurs is the designated representative of the Secretary of Defense to make the necessary arrangements for the special funeral. Upon request, the Commandant of the U.S. Marine Corps or the Commandant of the U.S. Coast Guard will perform this function for deceased personnel of their services.

When the death of a dignitary occurs in Washington, D.C., the remains are moved to a selected place of repose, attended by a Guard of Honor composed of members of all the armed services. When death occurs outside the city, the remains are transported to Washington for final honors; they are met at the point of arrival by a reception party and escorted to the place of repose.

After three days, the remains are escorted from the place of repose to the Amphitheater, Washington Cathedral, or the church where the funeral service will be held.

When burial is to be outside Washington, the remains are escorted to the point of departure, where honors are accorded.

FOLDING THE FLAG

The flag that covers the casket symbolizes the service of the deceased in the armed forces of the United States. The three volleys fired, according to ancient belief, scare away evil spirits. The playing of "Taps" over the grave marks the beginning of the last sleep and expresses confidence in an ultimate reveille to come.

The flag is folded immediately after the sounding of "Taps." The body bearers hold the flag at the pall over the grave and fold the flag in the accustomed manner. The senior body bearer hands it to the chaplain or the officer in charge, who in turn presents it to the next of kin or a representative of the family.

DUTIES OF PALLBEARERS

Active pallbearers, called body bearers, are six to eight men who carry the casket whenever necessary. At a military funeral, they are service personnel appointed by the command.

Honorary pallbearers are persons who have no duties to perform other than rendering appropriate honors to the deceased. They may be few, or more, in number, usually six or eight. They are appointed by the family of the deceased, usually from among the close friends or honored acquaintances of the deceased, or, at the request of the family, they may be appointed by the commanding officer.

The officer in charge of the funeral arrangements should give detailed information to the active and honorary pallbearers in advance of the funeral, including the uniform to be worn.

RULES TO REMEMBER

1. Mourning Flag: The colors are hoisted to the peak of the flagpole or staff, and then lowered halfway. Before the flag is removed, it is again raised to the peak. Where flags cannot be flown at half-staff, they should carry a black streamer from the spearhead halfway down the flag.

2. A casket is carried foot first, except that of a clergyman, which is carried head first.

3. When the flag is draped over the casket, the blue field is over the left shoulder of the deceased.

4. The cap and sword of the deceased are never displayed on the flag-draped casket, but may be placed under it.

5. The bearer of the personal flag of a deceased general or flag officer marches in front of the hearse or caisson.

6. The national ensign is never dipped at a funeral, but a unit or battalion flag is dipped when appropriate.

7. The word *pall* denotes the flag held at waist level, stretched taut, and kept even at all points while being held.

8. Military funerals are rarely postponed on account of bad weather.

9. The distinction between *grave site* and *graveside* is: grave site is the section of the cemetery where the funeral will take place; graveside is the lot in which the burial takes place.

10. At a military funeral, service personnel wear the prescribed uniform with mourning sleeve bands. At a nonmilitary funeral, men wear dark business suits; mourning bands are no longer customary.

11. A chaplain at a military post or base is never given a fee for his services, but a note of appreciation for his help may be written by a member of the family.

12. A fee of $50 to $100 for an average funeral is given to a civilian clergyman. The fee is enclosed in a letter of appreciation and handed to him before the services.

SECTION XII

Strictly Service

CHAPTER 42

Salutes

CUSTOMS CONCERNING salutes are covered in the regulations of each service, as well as in regulations of the service academies, and the reserve and officer-training programs.

All servicemen and servicewomen should know the regulations not only of their own service, but of all services. The rules for military etiquette are founded on custom and tradition, and their strict observance is an important factor in the maintenance of discipline, which must be observed equally by all officers and enlisted personnel. The responsibility is a mutual one in which the junior accepts the role of initiating the act of courtesy.

ORIGIN OF THE SALUTE

There are various schools of thought on the origin of the salute, one tracing the custom to the days of chivalry, when knights in armor raised their visors to friends for the purpose of identification. The junior was required to make the first gesture.

Another possible origin of the salute goes back to the days of the Borgias, when assassinations by dagger were not uncommon and it was customary for men to approach each other with raised hand, palm to the front, to prove that no dagger was concealed.

However, from the earliest days of military organization, the junior uncovered when meeting or addressing a senior; gradually the act of uncovering was simplified into touching the cap and, finally, into the present-day salute, which means "I greet you."

THE HAND SALUTE

The hand salute is required on naval and military installations both on and off duty. At other places and times, it may be suspended by regulations or local order.

You always salute the commanding officer (or any flag or general officer) any time you meet him or her during the day. You salute other seniors the first time you meet them each day. Remember "Precept and Example"; those of less rank will imitate you, for better or for worse.

MANNER OF SALUTING

The hand salute is executed by raising your right hand smartly until the tip of your forefinger touches the lower part of your headgear, slightly to the right of your right eye.

The upper arm is parallel to the ground, thumb and fingers are extended and joined, the palm is down, and there is a straight line from the tip of the middle finger to the elbow.

The salute is concluded by dropping your hand down to your side in one clean motion. Avoid slapping your side as you do so.

In the Army and Air Force, your forefinger touches your right eyebrow when you are uncovered.

It is important that you keep your head and eyes turned toward the saluted person. And *never* hold anything in your right hand while saluting.

SALUTING DISTANCE

Saluting distance is that distance at which recognition is easy—not over *thirty paces*. The first position of the hand salute is rendered when the person to be saluted is *six to twelve paces* distant. Hold the first position of the salute until the person has passed or the salute is returned, then execute the second movement of the hand salute.

A salute is rendered only at a halt or a walk. If running, you slow to quick-time before saluting.

When overtaking a senior whom the junior must pass, the salute is given when the junior is abreast of the senior. The junior asks, "By your leave, Sir (or Ma'am)?" Not until the senior replies "Carry on" does the junior proceed.

GREETINGS

Salutes are usually accompanied by an exchange of greetings, determined by the time of day, such as: "Good morning, Sir (or Ma'am)" or "Good evening, Colonel Blank."

From early morning until noon: "Good morning—."
From noon to evening meal: "Good afternoon—."
From evening meal until turning in: "Good evening—."

COVERED—AND UNCOVERED

In the *Army* and *Air Force,* you salute when covered or uncovered.

In the *naval services,* protocol does not call for saluting when uncovered except for the return of uncovered salutes rendered first by Army and Air Force personnel. The exception in this case follows the general rule that *"Social customs or military courtesy should always be interpreted so as to prevent awkward situations."* Therefore, the Navy establishes an exception whereby any uncovered salute may be returned. When uncovered, the Navy initiates salutes by coming to a position of attention.

Individuals *under arms* uncover only when:

Seated as a member of or in attendance on a court or board
Entering places of worship
Indoors and not on duty
In attendance at an official reception
Entering messing facilities during meal hours

In certain public places—a church, theater, or hotel dining room—servicewomen leave on their hats or caps when men do not. In such instances, women are technically "uncovered" and do not salute.

WHEN TO SALUTE

The salute is rendered but *once* if the senior remains in the immediate vicinity and no conversation takes place. If a conversation does take place, the junior again salutes the senior on departing or when the senior leaves.

In making reports, the person making the report salutes first, regardless of rank; for example, a regimental commander making a report to the brigade adjutant during a ceremony or a head of department commander making a report to an officer of the deck lieutenant.

When men or women officers are of the same rank, they salute more or less simultaneously and exchange greetings.

The saluting requirement varies upon certain occasions, such as:

If you, the senior, are in the company of a junior or company grade officer and a field grade officer approaches, the salute will be initiated by the field grade officer who salutes you, the ranking officer. When you return the salute, the junior or company grade officer will salute simultaneously with you.

If you are conversing with a senior officer and a junior approaches, you salute at the same time as the senior. If the senior is unaware of the junior's salute, do not interrupt him by rendering your salute to the junior.

When encountering an encumbered senior officer, you salute and can expect a verbal greeting in return. When both junior and senior officers are encumbered, oral greetings are rendered instead of the salute.

REPORTING TO AN OFFICER

The salute is always rendered by the junior on reporting to a senior. Juniors are expected to rise and stand at attention whenever a senior officer enters their room or office, and remain standing until the senior gives permission to *carry on* or *at ease*.

A junior stands at attention when addressed by a senior. If covered, the junior salutes when first addressed and again upon the conclusion of the conversation. The junior stands at attention unless otherwise directed.

Midshipmen, cadets, and other officer candidates are subject to local regulations, which generally require that when addressing an officer, during the salute, and before entering upon any conversation, they give their names; for instance, "Midshipman Doe, Sir," or "Cadet Thomas reports to Captain Brown, Ma'am." The salute is held during the report until returned by the officer.

The word *Sir* or *Ma'am* is added to statements by the very junior; thus, "I report for duty, Sir." The "Sir" or "Ma'am" is a military expression used in connection with "yes" or "no" whenever conversing with senior men and women officers.

Reporting indoors unarmed. When reporting to an officer in his or her office, a junior not wearing arms removes his or her headgear and any outer garment such as an overcoat, knocks, and enters when told to do so. You, the junior, approach to about two paces from the officer, salute, and report. While standing, a salutation such as "Good morning, Sir, I wish to make the magazine report," is given. When the business is over, take one step back, salute, face about, and depart.

Reporting indoors, under arms. Ordinarily, reports are not made indoors under arms except in rare cases. In carrying a rifle, a junior enters with the rifle at the trail, halts, and renders the rifle salute at *order arms*. When wearing sidearms or duty belt, the hand salute is given and headgear kept on.

Reporting outdoors. The procedure outdoors is the same as described in the foregoing two paragraphs. Headgear is never removed outdoors, and the junior armed with the rifle may, in approaching the senior, carry it at the trail or at right shoulder arms. The rifle salute is executed at the order or at right shoulder arms.

It is improper to change the rifle position when addressing or being addressed by a senior except during a formal inspection. For example, if at right shoulder arms upon approaching or being approached by a senior, you render the salute at the position held. This avoids the awkwardness that would result if the junior approached the senior at right shoulder arms, then came to the order—and then rendered the salute.

The term *outdoors* is construed to include such buildings as armories, gymnasiums, and other huge-roofed enclosures used for drills. Theater canopies, covered walks, and other shelters open on the sides to the weather are also considered outdoors. *Indoors* includes offices, corridors, etc.

The expression *under arms* means carrying the arms, or having them attached to the person by sling, holster, or other means. In the absence of arms, it refers to the equipment pertaining directly to the arms, such as cartridge belt, pistol holder, sword belt, or automatic rifle belt.

SALUTING IN GROUPS

In formation. Individuals in formation do not salute or return salutes except at the command "Present Arms." The individual in charge will salute and acknowledge salutes for the entire formation. Commanders of organizations or detachments which are not a part of a larger formation salute officers of higher grades by bringing the organization or detachment to attention before saluting.

A formation *at ease* or *at rest* comes to attention when one (or more) of the formation is addressed by a person superior in rank. The group will remain at attention until directed by the senior

"Carry on," or "At ease," but will continue to be aware of the senior's presence during the time he or she is in conversation with members of the group or conducts other business.

Not in formation. On the approach of an officer of higher rank, a group of individuals not in formation is called to attention by the first person noticing the senior officer, and all in the group come to attention and salute. Individuals participating in games, and members of details at work, do not salute. The individual in charge of a work detail, if not actively engaged, salutes or acknowledges salutes for the whole detail. A unit resting alongside a road does not come to attention upon the approach of an officer.

However, if the officer addresses a group (or an individual), the group come to attention and remain at attention (unless otherwise ordered) until the termination of the conversation, at which time they salute the officer.

PIPING A VIP ABOARD SHIP

When a very important person is piped aboard ship, all hands stand at attention, with those in the quarterdeck area holding the salute for the duration of the pipe, ruffles, or music. The VIP faces aft, salutes the colors, and turns; all hands hold the salute until the end of the sideboys or of the music.

The VIP says to the officer of the deck, "Sir, I request permission to come aboard." Upon departure he requests permission to leave the ship. Again the VIP and all hands hold salute while facing the national colors; then the visitor goes down the gangway.

SALUTING ON FLIGHT LINES

Rules for saluting on an aircraft flight line may differ from base to base, but generally saluting is required around the Base Operations building, the passenger terminal, and similar locations.

You usually do not salute at an aircraft parking or cantonment area, an aircraft alert hangar area, or an aircraft maintenance area. However, when in doubt, salute.

SALUTING IN AUTOMOBILES

A senior officer passing in an automobile is entitled to a salute, which will be returned when conditions permit. If driving, he or she will not return a salute when safety is involved or it is otherwise impractical.

In some cases, it may be awkward for the senior officer to

return the salute properly, and recognition is by a modified salute or a slight nod of the head.

Juniors must be alert to the passing of automobiles from which the flag of a high-ranking dignitary is displayed and, when such a flag is observed, be punctilious in saluting the occupant of the car. These salutes should be rendered at all times, day or night, on all occasions, whether the flag officer or high-ranking dignitary is covered or not.

Remember that officers of high rank, civilian leaders of state and federal governments, and foreign dignitaries have the insignia of the highest-ranking passenger displayed on the automobile in either flag or plate form.

COURTESIES TO INDIVIDUALS

When an officer enters a room, midshipmen, cadets, and other juniors present will come to attention until the officer directs otherwise or leaves the room. When more than one person is present, the first to see the officer commands "Attention!"

When an officer enters a room used as an office, workshop, or recreation room, those at work or play therein are not required to come to attention unless addressed by him. A junior, when addressed by a senior, comes to attention—except in the transaction of routine business between individuals at work.

A junior always answers "Sir" or "Ma'am" when his or her name is called by an officer. When encountering persons known by name, it is courteous to say, "Good morning, Major Jones," instead of "Sir" or "Ma'am." When the senior knows the junior's name, the response is, "Good morning, Cadet Smith."

Junior male officers escorting young ladies will, on meeting their senior officers, render the customary salute. If seated, they rise and salute. Nonmilitary dates remain seated.

Civilians may be saluted by persons in uniform, but the uniform hat or cap is not raised as a form of salutation. In turn, the civilian gentleman will tip or raise his hat, when worn, and verbally acknowledge the salute.

Midshipmen or cadets are expected to salute their contemporaries on duty when addressed by or addressing them officially, and may salute the professors at the various academies and colleges.

Always remember that personal likes and dislikes have nothing to do with salutes. You salute whenever necessary, without discrimination.

WHOM TO SALUTE

As a member of a service you salute all individuals who are senior to you in rank in any of the armed forces of the United States or of friendly foreign governments, as well as officers of the Coast and Geodetic Survey and of the Public Health Service who are serving with the armed forces of the United States.

In addition, some appointed and elected civilian members of both national and state governments are so honored:

President of the United States
Vice President of the United States
State Governors
Secretary of Defense
Deputy Secretary of Defense
Secretaries of the Army, Navy, and Air Force

Also these members of friendly governments:

Heads of State
Ambassadors
Ministers of Defense or other civilian leaders of defense establishments and their assistants at or above the level of the Assistant Secretary of the Army, Navy, and Air Force
Officers, male or female, in any of the armed forces

WHEN NOT TO SALUTE

In general, do *not* salute when:

Engaged in routine work if the salute would interfere
Indoors, except when reporting to a senior or on duty as a sentinel or guard
Carrying articles with both hands or so occupied as to make saluting impracticable
A prisoner (the guard does the saluting for the prisoner)
Working as a member of a detail, or engaged in sports or social functions
Driving a moving automobile and saluting is not practicable
In public places such as theaters or churches, and in public conveyances
In the ranks of a formation; when at ease in a formation, come to attention when addressed by a senior

CHAPTER 43

Flag Etiquette

A MILITARY MAN or woman is expected to be something of an expert on the national flag, including its history and the customs and conventions which govern its display and handling. Every loyal American citizen, in uniform or not, should know the history of our country's flag, what to do when the flag passes in parade or when the flag is passed in a car, and what is expected of someone asked to review a parade.

HISTORY

With the onset of the American Revolution each of the 13 colonies created its own flag—many colonies several of them. The flags were symbolic of the country and the struggle for independence and carried a tree, anchor, rattlesnake, or beaver and a motto such as "HOPE," "LIBERTY," or "AN APPEAL TO HEAVEN." One bore a coiled rattlesnake and the motto "DON'T TREAD ON ME." Each regiment had its own colors, and the naval vessels and privateers fitted out by each colony flew distinctive flags.

Eventually, standardization became necessary. On 2 December 1775, the Continental Congress approved the design of a flag which was first hoisted aboard the *Alfred* by Lieutenant John Paul Jones. It consisted of 13 red and white stripes and, on a canton, the British Union Jack with its crosses of St. George and St. Andrew.

On 1 January 1776, the day the Continental Army came into being, these flags were displayed in the lines of the colonial forces besieging Boston. This famous flag has been called the Continental flag and, later, the Grand Union flag. After the Declaration of Independence, continued use of the British Union Jack became inappropriate, and a new flag was created. The first Act of Congress establishing the Stars and Stripes, 14 June 1777, ordained the present arrangement of stripes and stated that the 13 white stars would represent "a new constellation" on a union of blue.

The Continental Army adopted a design in which the 13 stars were arranged in a circle so that no colony would take precedence. The first Navy version of the Stars and Stripes had the stars arranged in a staggered formation of alternate lines and rows of threes and twos, on a blue field. Variations in the stripes continued, and privateers continued to use the superseded flag with its British Union Jack. But eventually order emerged from what must have been a chaotic situation.

Both stars and stripes continued to be added; after the admission of Kentucky and Vermont, a resolution that provided for the addition of a stripe and a star for each new state was adopted by Congress on 1 May 1795, giving the flag 15 stars and 15 stripes. This flag flew over Fort McHenry on the occasion of its bombardment by a British fleet and inspired Francis Scott Key to write "The Star-Spangled Banner."

Realizing that the flag would soon become unwieldy, Captain Samuel C. Reid, U.S. Navy, who commanded the *General Armstrong* during the War of 1812, suggested to Congress that the stripes be fixed at 13 in number to represent the original 13 colonies that had struggled to found the nation and had become its first states, and that a star be added to the blue field for every state coming into the Union. This suggestion became the text of a resolution by Congress, effective 18 April 1818, whereby the flag should contain 13 alternate red and white stripes representing the 13 original states, with a new star added for each new state on 4 July following its admission. The flag next ordered had 20 stars.

During the Mexican War the Stars and Stripes had 28 and 29 stars; during the Civil War, 33, 34, and 35, no stars being removed because 11 states seceded. In the Spanish-American War it had 45 stars. During the first and second world wars and the Korean conflict there were the familiar 48 stars. With the admission of Alaska as a state on 3 January 1959, and Hawaii on 21 August 1959, the forty-ninth and fiftieth stars were added.

The *jack,* a nautical flag, corresponds in design to the blue field and its stars. It is flown from the jackstaff (in the bow) on government vessels while at anchor, provided that the national flag is being displayed. Another American flag frequently seen is the yachting ensign, displayed by privately owned craft, which consists of the 13 red and white stripes and a blue field with 13 stars arranged in a circle about a white foul anchor.

HOW TO DISPLAY THE FLAG

The national flag is raised and lowered by hand. It should be displayed only from sunrise to sunset, or between such hours as may be designated by proper authority. Do not raise the flag while it is furled. Unfurl it, then hoist it quickly to the top of the staff. In lowering it, however, do so slowly and with dignity. Place no objects on or over the flag. For instance, various articles are sometimes placed on a speaker's table covered with the flag. This practice should be avoided.

When displayed in the chancel or on a platform in a church, the flag should be placed on a staff at the clergyman's right, and all other flags at his left. If displayed in the body of the church, the flag should be at the congregation's right as they face the clergyman.

Other rules are:

When displayed over the middle of the street, the flag should be suspended vertically, with the union—the cluster of white stars on the blue field representing the fifty states—to the north in an east-west street, or to the east in a north-south street.

When displayed with another flag, from crossed staffs, the flag of the United States of America should be on the right (the flag's own right), with its staff in front of the staff of the other flag.

When flown at half-mast, the flag should be hoisted to the peak of the staff for an instant, then lowered to the half-mast position; before being lowered for the day, it should again be raised to the peak. "Half-mast" means hauling down the flag to one-half the distance between the top and the bottom of the staff. On Memorial Day the flag is displayed at half-mast until noon, then hoisted to the top of the staff for the rest of the day.

When flags of states or cities or pennants of societies are displayed on separate halyards, but from the same pole on which the flag of the United States of America is being flown, the U.S. flag should always be hoisted first and lowered last.

When the flag is suspended over a sidewalk from a rope, extending from house to pole at the edge of the sidewalk, it should be hoisted out from the building, toward the pole, union first.

When the flag is displayed from a staff projecting horizontally or at any angle from the window sill, balcony, or front of a building, the union of the flag should go to the peak of the staff (unless the flag is to be displayed at half-mast).

When the flag is used to cover a casket at funerals or ceremonies honoring a person deceased, it should be so placed that the union is at the head and over the left shoulder. The flag is *not* lowered into the grave or allowed to touch the ground.

When the flag is displayed in a manner other than by being flown from a staff, it should be flat, indoors or out. When the flag is displayed either horizontally or vertically against a wall, the union should be uppermost and to the flag's own right; that is, to the observer's left. When displayed in a window, the flag should be situated in the same way—with the union or blue field to the left of the observer in the street. When festoons, rosettes, or drapings in the national colors are desired, bunting of blue, white, and red should be used, but *never* the flag itself.

In this country or in any parade of U.S. troops, when carried in a procession with another flag or flags, the Stars and Stripes should have the place of honor at the right; or, when there is a line of other flags, our national flag may be *in front* of the center of that line.

International usage forbids the display of the flag of one nation above that of another nation in time of peace.

When the flags of two or more nations are displayed, they should be flown from separate staffs of the same height, and the flags should be of approximately equal size.

A federal law provides that a trademark cannot be registered which consists of, or comprises, among other things, "the flag, coat-of-arms, or other insignia of the United States, or any simulation thereof."

At all times, every precaution should be taken to prevent the flag from becoming soiled. It should not be allowed to touch the ground or floor, or to brush against objects.

When the flag is used at the unveiling of a statue or monument, do not use it as a covering of the object to be unveiled. If displayed on such occasions, it must not be allowed to fall to the ground, but is hung aloft to form a feature of the ceremony.

PLEDGE OF ALLEGIANCE

I pledge allegiance to the flag of the United States of America and to the republic for which it stands, one nation under God, indivisible, with liberty and justice for all.

APPROVED FLAG CUSTOMS

Laws have been written to govern the use of the flag and to ensure a proper respect for the Stars and Stripes. Custom has decreed certain other observances in regard to its use.

All services have precise regulations regarding the display of the national flag—when, where, and how it shall be hoisted or lowered. When naval vessels are at anchor; the national ensign and the Union Jack are flown from the flagstaff and the jackstaff, respectively, from 8:00 A.M. to sunset. When other vessels are entering or leaving port, the flag is flown prior to 8:00 A.M. and after sunset.

When the ship is getting under way or coming to anchor, cruising near land, falling in with other ships, or engaged in battle, the national ensign is flown during the daylight from the gaff, or as directed.

It is the custom at all bases, posts, and stations to raise the flag every morning at eight o'clock, and it remains flying until sunset or retreat.

Only one flag may be flown above the Stars and Stripes, and that is the Church Pennant, a dark blue cross on a white background. Code signal books of the Navy, which date back to the early 1860s, state: "The Church Pennant will be hoisted immediately above the ensign at the peak or flagstaff at the time of commencing and kept hoisted during the continuance of divine service on board all vessels of the Navy."

A chaplain's flag may be displayed at the place of divine worship or in his office, and it may be flown from the chaplain's car.

Civilian dignitaries of the federal and state governments, as well as flag and general officers, are entitled to individual flags which indicate their title or grade. They also have automobile flags which are attached to a staff on official cars.

The national flag may be displayed on all days when the weather permits, but it should especially be displayed on New Year's Day; Martin Luther King Day; Inauguration Day, 20 January; Presidents' Day; Armed Forces Day, third Saturday in May; Memorial Day (half-staff until noon); Flag Day, 14 June; Independence Day, 4 July; Labor

Day, first Monday in September; Columbus Day; Veterans Day; Thanksgiving Day, third or fourth Thursday in November; Christmas Day, 25 December; and such other days as may be proclaimed national holidays by the President of the United States, as well as on the birthdays of states (the dates of their admission into the Union), and on state holidays. (By state and national law, the dates of some of these holidays vary; therefore, no dates are given for them.)

FOR FUNERALS

If a serviceman or servicewoman dies while on active duty, the flag for the funeral ceremonies is provided by the service to which he or she belonged. For an honorably discharged veteran, the flag is provided by the Veterans Administration, Washington, D.C., and may be procured from the nearest post office.

In filling out the application, the person signing for the flag must indicate kinship. The flag is presented to the next of kin at the proper time during the burial service. If the deceased had no relatives or if a relative cannot be located, the flag must be returned to the Veterans Administration in the franked container provided for that purpose.

Postmasters require proof of honorable discharge of a deceased service member before issuing the flag for use at funeral ceremonies, but upon receipt of proof, a flag is issued promptly.

When the national flag is worn out, it should be disposed of with due reverence. According to an approved custom, the union is first cut from the flag, and then the two pieces, which now no longer form a flag, are cremated.

UNITED NATIONS FLAG REGULATIONS

The United Nations flag code prescribes that the United Nations flag may be displayed as follows:

With one or more other flags, all flags should be displayed on the same level and be of approximately equal size.

On no occasion may any flag so displayed be larger than the UN flag.

On either side of any flag without being considered to be subordinated to any other flag.

Normally only on buildings and on stationary flagstaffs from sunrise to sunset.

The UN flag should not be displayed on days when the weather is inclement.

The UN flag should never be carried flat or horizontal, but always aloft and free. It should never be used as a drapery of any sort, festooned, drawn back, or up in folds, but always allowed to fall free.

The United Nations flag may be displayed on the following occasions:

On all national and official holidays
On United Nations Day, 24 October
On the occasion of any official event honoring the United Nations

FLAG DESIGNATIONS

When the flag is carried by dismounted units it is known as the *colors*. When flown from ships and boats, the flag is an *ensign*. When carried by tank, car, truck, or on horseback, the flag is the *standard*.

HONORS TO THE NATIONAL ANTHEM

Reveille signifies the start of the military day; *morning colors* is the daily ceremony of raising the national flag. *Evening colors* or *retreat* is the ceremony of lowering the flag and putting it away for safekeeping. During bad weather or when a band is not present for the ceremony, a bugle call, "To the Colors," is played instead of the national anthem.

Outdoors. The following rules are customarily observed whenever and wherever the national anthem or "To the Colors" is played (not in formation):

At the first note, all dismounted personnel face the music, stand at attention, and render the prescribed salute; except at the "Escort of the Colors" or at "Retreat," they face toward the color or flag. The position of salute will be retained until the last note of the music is sounded.

Vehicles in motion should be brought to a halt. Military persons riding in a passenger car or on a motorcycle dismount and salute if practicable; otherwise they remain seated at attention. Tank or armored car commanders salute from the vehicle.

During *colors*, a Navy boat under way within sight or hearing of the ceremony either lies to or proceeds at the slowest safe speed.

The boat officer (or, in his absence, the coxswain) stands and salutes, except when dangerous to do so. All other persons in the boat remain seated or standing, and do not salute.

The above marks of respect are shown the national anthem of any friendly country when played upon official occasions.

Indoors. When the national anthem is played indoors at a formal gathering, individuals will stand at attention and face the flag, if one is present; otherwise, they face the music. They do not salute, unless covered or under arms.

IN CIVILIAN DRESS

Outdoors. When facing the flag or music all men in civilian dress remove their hats or caps and hold them with their right hand over their heart. Ladies stand quietly.

Indoors. All men and women stand quietly, facing the flag or music, their hands over their hearts. Civilian women may stand quietly, hands at their sides.

THE REVIEW

A review (or honors ceremony) is held during a parade. When troops are ceremoniously marched onto the field, a person of distinction is on hand to take the review. (In olden days, the dress parade was intended to impress visiting emissaries with the strength of the monarch's troops rather than to honor the visitor.) While a parade is in progress, those attending stand quietly and do not smoke or talk.

When a dignitary or one or more individuals is to be honored during a parade, certain formalities are followed. At the service academies (for example, at a Cadet Wing Parade), a senior government official, or one or more officers or senior professors who may be retiring, may be asked to take the review.

The honored guest (or guests) is invited by the superintendent by formal invitation, which includes the guest's spouse for both the parade and the reception that follows in the superintendent's quarters. Other guests are invited to sit in the superintendent's section on the parade ground and to attend the reception. Various officers and their spouses from the station are also invited, and others, including the general public, may attend and sit in the stands.

After the cadets or midshipmen have marched by companies or squadrons onto the parade ground—each company with its own flag (guidon), and with all companies preceded by the Color

Guard—the Brigade or Corps or Wing Commander gives the "Order arms" and "Parade rest."

The reviewing party will have already walked forward and taken a position facing the regimental officers, and an announcer will make the appropriate remarks about the honored guest. The Brigade or Wing or Corps Commander brings the companies to attention and announces, "Sir, the Brigade of Midshipmen (or Corps of Cadets or Cadet Wing)." The "Pass in Review" is spoken by the superintendent, and as each company marches by with flags momentarily dipped in salute to the honored guest and others in the reviewing group and stand, the salutes are returned by the honored guest and reviewing party.

Everyone stands during the review. Officers in uniform salute, but those out of uniform and civilian men face the flag, their right hand (with or without a hat) over their heart. Civilian men and retired officers as well as officers out of uniform wear business suits. Civilian women guests stand quietly facing the flag; they wear suits or afternoon dress.

OTHER HONORS

To colors. Military personnel passing an uncased color (standard) salute at a distance of six paces and hold the salute until they have passed six paces beyond it. Similarly, when an uncased color passes by, military personnel salute when it is six paces away and hold the salute until it has passed six paces beyond. Small flags carried by individuals are not saluted.

Personal honors. When personal honors are rendered, military personnel salute at the first note of the music and hold the salute until the completion of the ruffles, flourishes, and march.

When a gun salute is rendered, military personnel being saluted and other persons in the ceremonial party render the hand salute throughout the firing of the gun salute. Others in the vicinity of the ceremonial party stand at attention.

Acknowledgment by persons in civilian dress may be made by standing at attention. A gun salute to the national flag requires no individual action. In addition to standing at attention during dress parades—say, on the parade field at a service academy—all officers under the canopy are considered to be in the ceremonial party, and salute accordingly.

Military funerals. Military personnel salute during the passing of a caisson or hearse in a funeral procession. You salute whenever honors are rendered: when the body is removed from the hearse to the chapel, from the chapel to the hearse or caisson, and from the hearse or caisson to the grave. You salute when volleys are fired and when "Taps" is sounded. In civilian dress, men stand at attention, uncovered (see chapter 41).

MOURNING FLAG

The colors are hoisted to the peak of the flagpole or staff, and then lowered halfway. When the flag is removed, it is again raised to the peak before being lowered. Where flags cannot be flown at half-staff, they should have a black streamer from the spearhead halfway down the flag. Flags hung horizontally or perpendicularly bear a black bunting border of appropriate width.

INCLEMENT WEATHER

Flags are not usually flown at night or in inclement weather. A code of display adopted by Congress on 22 June 1942 states: "It is the universal custom to display the flag only from sunrise to sunset on buildings and on stationary flagstaffs in the open. However, the flag may be displayed at night upon special occasions when it is desired to produce a patriotic effect."

DESECRATION OF THE FLAG

The American flag symbolizes the sacrifices made by millions of Americans to protect life, liberty, and justice for all. When the flag is burned or desecrated in any way, this shows complete disrespect to the nation and all it stands for.

CHAPTER 44

The Dining-In &
Dining-Out

A DINING-IN is a formal dinner given by members of a military wing, unit, or organization. It may honor a departing officer or welcome a new one, or give recognition to a dignitary or to individual and unit achievements. Or this may simply be a pleasant way for officers to get better acquainted. The only women included are military women on the station. When nonmilitary women are invited, the occasion is called a dining-out.

The term *dining-in* derives from a Viking tradition of celebrating great battles and feats of heroes by formal ceremony. This tradition spread to the monasteries and early-day universities, and to the military when the officers' mess was established.

Medals are worn by all members of the mess and the military guests, including retired officers. A civilian guest wears black tie or the dress indicated in the invitation, and officers wear the prescribed uniform.

There are two officers of the mess: the president, who usually is the commanding officer of the station, and the vice, called "Mr. (or Madam) Vice." He or she is a junior officer in the command, chosen for his or her ability to speak well and handle innumerable details. All others in the unit (organization, etc.) are expected to attend a dining-in, but a written request to be excused may be accepted by the president.

GUESTS

Mess officers should arrive at least ten minutes before the hour of invitation in order to meet and talk with the guests of honor and get acquainted with others. Officers do not leave until the guests have departed unless they have been excused beforehand for a good reason.

Official guests are guests of the mess as a whole; their expenses are shared. The expenses of personal guests are paid by the one who invited them. This includes bar expenses. Cocktails are usually served about 45 minutes before dinner; the cocktail time should be stated on the invitation.

THE PRESIDENT AND MR. OR MADAM VICE

The *president* sets the date and place of the dining-in, arranges for the speaker, military or civilian, arranges for a chaplain to give the invocation, and greets all guests before dinner and all members of the mess if possible. He or she introduces the guest speaker and other honored guests to the mess. The president's duties include the appointment of Mr. or Madam Vice and various committees.

The *vice,* usually called Mr. (or Madam) Vice, is the first to arrive and the last to leave the mess. He makes the appropriate toasts, and should be prepared to make others if called upon. He sounds the dinner chimes at the designated time. Long before the night of the dining-in he should have checked on the reservations, musicians, and music; kept in touch with the mess manager concerning the menu and the cleaning of unit silver; attended to the collection of any paintings or photographs to be shown; and made certain that all colors and standards to be used were in good order. The national and organizational colors are placed behind the president's chair.

The president appoints other mess officers as committee chairmen. Examples of committees are *table arrangements* (place cards, seating, centerpiece, silver, crystal, and china) and *dining room arrangements* (menu, serving time, public address system, awards, flags, trophies, photographer, payment of mess and bar charges).

The seating arrangement for the mess usually is posted in the cocktail lounge so all hands know where they will be seated.

Hosts are appointed to contact the invited guests in advance and inform them as to mess customs, dress, the agenda, and the time allowed for speeches; hosts also arrange for transportation and quarters when needed.

A *protocol* committee prepares invitations for the president's signature, provides biographical sketches, briefs the hosts when necessary, and has a thank-you letter ready for the president's signature, to be sent to the guest of honor following the dining-in.

PLANNING THE DINING-IN

Start early. Two weeks to a month before the time set for the dinner, send out invitations to the guests who are not members of the mess. The fill-in card is often used for the invitations, or invitations may be handwritten or printed. Since this is a formal occasion, formal wording is used. For example, the wording for very high-ranking guests includes the phrase "the honor (or honour) of the presence of . . . ," but "the pleasure of the company of . . ." or ". . . your company" is more frequently used.

Invitations must state the type of uniform to be worn. It is correct to write "Military Evening Dress, if convenient" in the lower right-hand corner of the invitation for a retired officer who may not own the evening dress uniform. Mess officers wear the prescribed uniform. At a dining-out, nonmilitary women wear long dinner dresses.

The menu consists of four or five courses, with roast prime ribs of beef and Yorkshire pudding traditional but not a must. Wines may be served in decanters by waiters, or placed on the table and passed around, from left to right counterclockwise.

SEATING

At a dining-in, the guest of honor, usually the speaker, sits to the right of the president at the head table, with the next ranking guest on the president's left. Other guests are seated throughout the mess. The members of the mess are seated according to protocol, with Mr. (or Madam) Vice at the foot of the table.

At a dining-out, the spouse of the president is seated to the right of the guest speaker, and the spouse of the guest speaker is seated to the left of the president. (For variations in seating, see chapter 22.)

The tables should be set up in the manner most suitable to the dining area. The head table usually is a long, single table, but side tables may be placed down each end in a modified E—with no seats off-center. No one should be seated across from those at the head

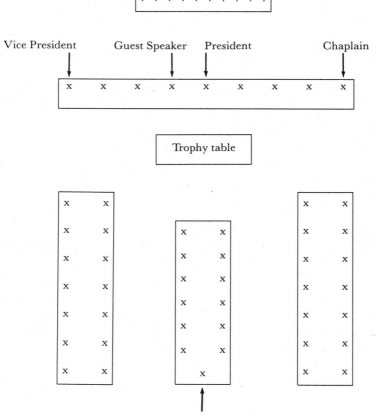

Air Force plan for table and seating arrangements

table. It is important that tables not be crowded, with everyone having plenty of elbow room.

SMOKING AND TOASTING

The table is cleared following dessert and coffee, with port—or the wine used—poured. But you do not drink the wine or smoke until the president announces, "Ladies and gentlemen, the smoking lamp is lighted." *Now* you may smoke. Mr. (or Madam) Vice will light the smoking lamp, when there is one, which is passed to the president, who lights the guest of honor's cigar, if he smokes.

The president stands and proposes a toast to the Commander in Chief of the United States (when foreign guests are present, their head of state is toasted first), and each officer stands with raised glass. Other toasts will continue, but you must remember not to drain your glass on each toast. Only on the final, traditional, toast are glasses bottoms-up. And you do not stand or drink a toast when you are the one toasted (see chapter 24).

AIR FORCE JOC DINING-IN/OUT AGENDA

Date
Place

1900   Members and guests arrive.
1940   The bar closes. Members take their positions at the tables. (All remain standing.) The after burner is off—no smoking.
1945   President calls mess to order with one rap of the gavel.
1946   President requests the flags. Colors are posted by the honor guard.
1950   Invocation.
1952   President proposes a toast to the Commander in Chief.
President: "To the President of the United States."
Members: "To President—."
Mr. (or Madam) Vice proposes a toast to the Secretary of the Air Force.
Mr. Vice: "To the Secretary of the Air Force."
Members: "To Secretary—."
Mr. Vice proposes a toast to the Chief of Staff, United States Air Force.
Mr. Vice: "To the Chief of Staff, United States Air Force."
Members: "To the Chief of Staff."
1955   President seats the mess.
1956   Welcoming remarks by the president of the mess.
1958   The president introduces each guest and spouse at the head table. (Hold your applause, as an appropriate toast will be rendered.)
1959   Mr. Vice proposes a toast. (Members stand, guests and spouses remain seated.)
Mr. Vice: "To our distinguished guests."
Members: "Hear, hear."

2000 President seats the mess.

2001 Dinner is served. (Begin eating immediately.)
Dinner music is provided.

2040 President calls for a break with two raps of the gavel. Members adjourn to the bar.

2055 Members return to the mess and remain standing. President will seat the mess with one rap of the gavel. (Dessert is brought in to the sound of music.)

2100 Smoking lamp is lit.

2121 President introduces the distinguished speaker.

2122 Speech by Senator Doe.

2145 Mr. Vice proposes a toast to the distinguished speaker. Everyone rises and picks up his wine glass.
Mr. Vice: "To our distinguished speaker."
Members: "Hear, hear."

2146 President calls for the retiring of the colors.

2147 President/commander renders closing remarks.

2148 President adjourns the mess with two raps of the gavel. (Members remain standing behind their chairs until the guests have left.)

2150 Dancing commences, with music provided.

CHAPTER 45

When You Retire

A SERVICEMAN or servicewoman nearing retirement age has had plenty of time to decide what to do before the day of retirement arrives. The officer who must retire before the mandatory age, perhaps because he or she has been passed over or unexpectedly retired for physical disability, may not have had much time to plan for it.

PHYSICAL DISABILITY

Officers may be retired at any time, at any age, for physical disability. At first, you may be retired temporarily, and be examined regularly by doctors until the extent of the illness or injury is determined.

During this time you will receive disability retirement pay and other benefits of regular retirement. After the extent of the disability is known, you will be returned to active duty or retired permanently with benefits.

While ill or disabled, you will receive medical care at the nearest military hospital. For extended or specialized care, patients may be taken to the National Medical Center at Bethesda, Maryland. Military hospitals have trained personnel to assist members of the family through legal or everyday counseling, or they may refer the family to other sources of aid.

POST-RETIREMENT EMPLOYMENT

PLANNING AHEAD

A thoughtful man or woman will make plans for the future long before the necessity arises. When you are stationed in an area with a university or college nearby, you may take night classes and perhaps earn a master's degree or a doctorate. Business administration courses will help earn you entry into the business world. With your military background and specialized training, your future should be secure—if you stay clear of conflict-of-interest jobs.

THE RÉSUMÉ

After you retire and want a job, you may need to send out résumés to prospective employers. With the résumé—which may be one or two pages in length and photocopied—send a one-page cover letter— which must be the original, *not* photocopied. The department head and president of the company to whom you send the résumé will not want to read through a lengthy cover letter *and* résumé; they want to be able to go through the whole thing quickly, catch the gist of it immediately, feel that you truly want to work for them, know that you are qualified for their particular needs, and make an on-the-spot evaluation. When interested, they will thoroughly scrutinize your application, and then ask you in for an interview.

Make your cover letter positive and concise. State why you want to work for their firm and mention any special abilities that make you eligible for this particular job. Do not use military terms that are not relevant to the business. This cover letter is your personal advertisement. And like any good ad, it should be brief and to the point. Although you send original letters to each prospective employer, you can use the same format for all the letters.

In writing the résumé, employ the standard newspaper trick of writing the most important thing first, then the next most important, and so on. But remember that the most important thing is what the prospective employer is interested in, not what you may personally believe was the acme of your military career. Also remember that any employer (in a large firm particularly) wants only those who can get along with others and can take orders as well as give them. If you have had leadership training or experience in a special program, be sure that you add this. Getting along with people is an art.

It is very important that all names and titles, including the name of the firm and the address, be correct. Do your homework before sending out the application; learn as much about the business as possible. When called in for an interview, you must be prepared for any question. It is best not to offer references until they are requested or to mention salary before the employer does. Look your best, pay particular attention to your grooming, and be on time.

You should send out letters and résumés to various firms, regardless of whether or not they need new people at that time. A position might open unexpectedly, and a check of the firm's files would turn up your application.

One of the best ways to learn about new jobs is through classmates and friends who are already employed. Word of mouth frequently discloses a line on a new job that is just what you want.

RESTRICTED EMPLOYMENT

A retired officer must be aware of what qualifies as conflict-of-interest employment, which he or she cannot undertake without the risk of losing retired pay or being prosecuted.

If you have any doubt concerning such restrictions you should write for an opinion to the office of the Judge Advocate General of your service in Washington, D.C. Some restrictions apply to regular retired officers, others to all retired personnel.

In your letter, give complete information about the type of work you are interested in, the duties you will be expected to carry out, and any special provisions, as well as your retired status.

WEARING THE UNIFORM

Retired, reserve, and separated personnel are authorized to wear the uniform upon many occasions. You may wear it to memorial services, military weddings or funerals, military balls, and inaugurals. A separated person wears a uniform of the highest grade held during war service.

You may wear your uniform for such patriotic occasions as parades, national holidays, or ceremonies when any active or reserve U.S. military unit is taking part.

Other occasions are meetings or functions of associations established for military purposes, or when the membership of a group is mainly or entirely made up of honorably discharged or retired veterans of the armed forces or of reserve personnel. The uniform may be worn when traveling to and from the place of the ceremony on the day of the occasion or within 24 hours of the time of the scheduled function.

Retired officers wear a uniform when engaged in a military

activity, such as military instruction, or when responsible for military discipline at an educational institution.

You do not wear your uniform when you are visiting or living in a foreign country, except at a formal ceremony or social occasion as required in the invitation or the regulations or customs of the country.

You do not wear the uniform when conducting personal or business matters, or in any demonstration or activity of a political, economic, or religious nature—except upon bona fide authority.

Retired members may wear civilian clothing when riding in military aircraft, but their attire must reflect favorably on the military service.

MILITARY TITLES

You retain your military title following retirement, subject to certain restrictions. These restrictions are in connection with commercial enterprises when such use, intentionally or not, gives rise to any appearance of sanction, endorsement, sponsorship, or approval by any service department or the Department of Defense.

You do not use your official service title when making public appearances outside of this country unless authorized by the appropriate overseas commander.

RETIRED DESIGNATIONS

The word *Retired* (or the abbreviation *Ret.*) is used by all regular and reserve personnel who retired because of age or physical disability, including those on the temporary disability retired list.

For example, when you retire from the Army or Army Reserve, you would write "USA, Retired" or "USAR Ret." On a business envelope this could be Colonel John E. Doe, USA (Ret.). Informally, *Colonel* would be abbreviated to *Col.*

DESIGNATIONS ON SOCIAL INVITATIONS, CARDS

Some people are unsure of the correct way to address or extend invitations to, or as, retired personnel. There is a misunderstanding, sometimes, in the wording of a formal wedding invitation.

There is no difference between the wording for active and that for retired *couples*. For example, the traditional wording is:

COLONEL AND MRS. JOHN EARL DOE
REQUEST THE HONOUR OF THE PRESENCE OF

In addressing the envelope you write "Colonel and Mrs. John Earl Doe," never adding "U.S. Army, Retired." The civilian wife is not included in his military designation.

But when a divorced or widowed officer sends the invitation in his or her name only, the wording includes the word *Retired* after his or her name:

COLONEL JOHN EARL DOE

UNITED STATES ARMY, RETIRED

REQUESTS THE HONOUR OF THE PRESENCE OF

On personal cards, the retired status is used in the same way as on the wedding invitation. But on joint cards, as with the wedding invitation, the word *Retired* is not included. On joint cards only, rank abbreviations or a middle initial may be used with very long names.

LOOKING AHEAD

There is no excuse for any officer to leave his or her family in poor financial circumstances after his or her death. No one wants to face the fact of death, but this is no reason for putting off making a plan that ensures the security of the family. Upon retirement, each member of the armed forces has the opportunity to participate in this plan when they take reduced retirement pay to provide an annuity for eligible beneficiaries.

The *Survivor Benefit Plan* (SBP) will provide up to 55 percent of a retired member's pay to the surviving widow or widower; an additional plan includes dependent children. A third plan provides for children only (if the spouse is deceased or divorced); when there is no spouse and there are no children, an alternate plan provides for another person with an insurable interest in the retiree.

As you know, retired pay stops on the day a retiree dies. To ease the problem of service families without adequate income, Congress signed into law the SBP in 1972, with members automatically enrolled in the plan with maximum coverage if they have spouses or dependent children at retirement, *unless* they choose a lesser coverage in writing or decline participation. It is available to any Reserve or Regular retiree, and starts when the service member reaches the twenty-year mark.

RETIREMENT BENEFITS

Most officers retire between their twentieth and thirtieth years of service—or when they are a little over 40 or 50 years of age. In case of war or national emergency, a retired officer may be recalled to active duty. Otherwise he or she may start a second career.

As a retired officer, you will receive a retirement check for as long as you live. If you retire after 20 years, the amount is about half of your base pay at the time of retirement.

You receive a number of benefits upon retirement, including the continued use of the PX, commissary, the military hospitals and medical services, the officers' club, and recreational facilities; you also will retain your ID card. In addition, there are Social Security and Veterans Administration benefits. And there is space available in military aircraft for travel (see chapter 31).

SERVICEMEN'S GROUP LIFE INSURANCE (SGLI)

All members of the uniformed services—including cadets and midshipmen of the service academies, commissioned officers of the Public Health Service and NOAA, and eligible Army and Air National Guard Reservists—are insured for $100,000 under Servicemen's Group Life Insurance (SGLI). Members may purchase an additional $100,000 (for a maximum total of $200,000) for approximately $18 per month.

SGLI and Veterans Group Life Insurance (VGLI) are supervised by the Veterans Administration. Call the Department of Veterans Affairs on their toll-free hot line—1-800-669-8477—for VGLI information. Their main office is in Philadelphia, and they have a number of regional offices throughout the states.

SOCIAL SECURITY

Since January 1957, members of the armed forces have contributed to Social Security and are eligible to receive benefits in the same manner as civilian employees in various occupations. The amount of the benefit depends upon the contributor's average earnings over a specified time. No one can be fully insured who has credit for less than one and a half years of work. Any questions should be directed to the nearest office of the Social Security Administration.

For an application for a Social Security card, a Personal Earnings and Benefit Estimate statement, proof of your current benefit, or directions to your local field office call 1-800-772-1213 from 7 A.M. to 7 P.M. business days. It is best to phone late in the week and month. Automated services are available 24 hours a day all week long.

CHAMPUS AND USHBP

Congress in 1966 authorized a supplementary health-care program using civilian facilities to meet the needs of service families living at a distance from military facilities.

The Civilian Health and Medical Program of the Uniformed Services (CHAMPUS) is the portion of the Uniformed Services Health Benefits Program (USHBP) that ensures the availability of medical and health facilities and services that cannot be obtained from a military hospital or facility, on a low-cost, cost-sharing basis.

TRICARE

DoD's support care program, Tricare, works in conjunction with CHAMPUS to furnish and finance quality medical services and benefits to all uniformed services personnel and their families, as well as staff of the Public Health Service and NOAA.

Tricare is available to active duty and retired military personnel at regional clinics and hospitals throughout the nation. Their main objectives are lower costs for medical care and easier access to medical facilities and benefits in both remote and crowded areas.

You have three plan options: prime, extra, and standard; fees vary according to plan. For further information, contact your local medical clinic or phone or write to: CHAMPUS/Public Affairs Branch/Aurora, CO 80045-6900/(303) 361-1126.

Remember to keep a copy of all claims you send to CHAMPUS, as well as all other medical and Medicare records, in case of an error or a lost claim.

CHAMPVA is the Department of Veterans Affairs' version of the DoD program, which aids families of disabled veterans. Apply to CHAMPVA Registration Center/4500 Cherry Creek Drive South/Box 64/Denver, CO 80222, or call 1-800-733-8387.

YOUR ASSETS

Make a list of your assets and keep these records and all important papers in a safe place accessible to a member of your family or your lawyer. These records must be updated as the need arises due to cost of living changes, bonuses, new investments. Keep any record of a financial setback (such as a loss in bond or stock sales) which may be deducted in the profit-loss evaluation of your taxes. There should be car, life, fire, and property insurance records, and your all-important military records; any citizenship papers or change-of-name records; mortgages, abstracts, stocks or bonds, birth and death certificates of all members of the family, burial instructions, and your will.

This list must be discussed with your spouse. Both partners should agree on what can or cannot be done later on. Some men, usually those of an older generation, have "protected" their wives from some of the realities of life—and this has done her no favor. When she cannot carry on by herself, then someone has to do it for her or help on matters that she probably wishes she knew how to do herself.

PROOF OF AGE

Anyone who has lost a birth certificate, or who never received one, can apply for proof of age from the U.S. Bureau of the Census. When the bureau finds that the person's age was recorded during a certain year, a document will be sent showing the proper age. This can be used to get a delayed birth certificate from state officials. And it can also be used as a substitute that is now accepted by state or federal agencies and private industry. A small fee is charged.

When you need proof for Social Security, get an application at a local Social Security office. Otherwise, write to: Personal Census Service Branch, Bureau of the Census, Pittsburg, KS 66762.

YOUR WILL

A well-thought-out will is one of the most important legal papers you will ever write. It must be witnessed. Your will gives you, the testator, the right to leave your property to whomever you wish.

When a person dies without a will, he is said to die intestate. This means that any property will be distributed in accordance with the laws of your state, with the court appointing an administrator for this purpose. This is both expensive and time consuming.

Some husbands and wives have joint wills, leaving their estate to each other. If you think that you do not need to make out a will—possibly having no children or great riches—then consider the fact that if you and your spouse were killed in an accident, your property would be disposed of by law in the line of descendancy, perhaps going to someone you may not know very well or care for.

When you make out a will before you retire, the legal assistance officer can help you. When you write it after retirement and live at a distance from a military installation, you may write to your military department, which furnishes retirees with handbooks on this and many other subjects. Otherwise, a civilian attorney can help you; he will be knowledgeable about the laws of your state.

In drawing up a will you name an executor or executrix (usually your spouse) to carry out its provisions. The will must be kept in a safe place known to the executor, your lawyer, or the person charged with this responsibility. In cases of emergency, say on a battlefield or following an accident, a will can be written and witnessed by those nearby. One or more witnesses are required; the number depends upon the laws of your state—of which you should be aware.

When the time comes, the will is probated. The executor or person named files the will in the office of the Clerk of the Probate Court, Orphans Court, or Register of Wills, as the office is called in various parts of the country.

POWER OF ATTORNEY

A power of attorney is a legal document whereby you give another person the power to act for you either in a single transaction or in all transactions. That person is known as your "attorney in fact." To grant this power is something to consider carefully.

Occasions when you might need to appoint a power of attorney are when you will be out of the state or country for a time and business must be attended to; in cases of serious illness, senility, blindness; or when you are living temporarily or permanently in a nursing home and are unable to handle business affairs.

Although almost all cases in connection with a power of attorney are honorable transactions, it is possible in extreme cases of abuse for your name to be pledged to loans or mortgages and your property sold for any amount, regardless of its worth. Therefore, it is very important that you be careful in granting this power; when able, you should first discuss this with a legal assistance officer or civilian attorney.

THE LIVING WILL

The *Living Will*—the right to die with dignity—is a document that you may sign, stating that you do not want to have your life prolonged artificially after a physician decides that there is no hope for recovery. Members of your family, your doctor, and your lawyer should have copies.

Such a document does *not* give anyone the right to end the life of another in a "mercy killing," but it does give permission to a doctor to stop using any artificial means, such as a machine attached to an electrical outlet, or medications, to prolong life.

When a terminally ill patient is mentally or physically incapable of making a choice—when he or she is brain-dead or suffering great pain—a member of the family, or the attending physicians, may have to make the decision to withdraw artificial means of life support.

The issue of the right to die has serious ethical impact on family members and physicians. The living will is not a document of suicide and should be written while you are of sound mind and in good health. For it to be valid, the document must be signed in the presence of a witness not related to the patient. For a copy of a living will, contact your lawyer or doctor.

SCAMS

The lonely, the kind-hearted, and the elderly are prime targets for scam artists who phone, write, or appear on their doorstep. They all bear the same news: you've won big money or a prize—a cruise, jewelry, a car, property—and all you have to do is give them a downpayment in cash or with a check to secure the prize. Chances are you will never hear from them again, or you will receive a piece of junk. Beware of requests for unknown charities and fabulous sweepstakes. Also be on the alert for staged car "accidents," which are often followed up with lawsuits for false damages or physical injuries.

SECTION XIII

Service Organization

CHAPTER 46

The Armed Forces

As A SERVICEMAN or servicewoman, you are thoroughly indoctrinated in the structure and customs and traditions of your own service. You know the general structure of the armed forces, and a great deal about the other services, since all service personnel work together as a team for the security of this country. For those who have been out of uniform for some time, and for members of service families, the following should prove informative.

THE CHIEF EXECUTIVE

As the Chief Executive, the President of the United States is the Commander in Chief of the armed forces. In matters of national security he is advised by the Secretary of Defense, the Joint Chiefs of Staff, and the National Security Council.

THE DEPARTMENT OF DEFENSE (DoD)

The Department of Defense, as it has been titled since 1949, was created in 1947 as the National Military Establishment. DoD is headed by the President's chief advisor on defense matters, the Secretary of Defense, who is a civilian of cabinet rank appointed by the President. The department has a Deputy Secretary of Defense, a number of Under Secretaries and Assistant Secretaries, a General Consul, an Advisor, and various agencies.

The three military Departments—the Army, the Navy, and the Air Force—and sixteen defense agencies are answerable to the DoD. The Navy Department includes the Marine Corps and, in times of war, the Coast Guard. During peacetime the Coast Guard is under the jurisdiction of the Department of Transportation.

Each military department has a civilian Secretary responsible for the personnel, equipment, and training of its forces. Operational control rests with one of the unified or specified commands. A unified command has components from two or more services, and has a broad mission under a single commander, whereas a specified command is composed of forces from one service. In the chain of command, both commands are under authority of the Joint Chiefs of Staff.

UNIFIED COMMANDS

U.S. Atlantic Command, Norfolk, Virginia
U.S. Central Command, MacDill AFB, Florida
U.S. European Command, Stuttgart-Vaihingen, Germany
U.S. Pacific Command, Honolulu, Hawaii
U.S. Special Operations Command, MacDill AFB, Florida
U.S. Southern Command, Quarry Heights, Republic of Panama
U.S. Space Command, Peterson AFB, Colorado
U.S. Strategic Command, Offutt AFB, Nebraska
U.S. Transportation Command, Scott AFB, Illinois

THE NATIONAL SECURITY ACT

The National Security Act of 1947 was enacted after World War II for the purpose of reorganizing the military establishment of the United States, which was facing worldwide responsibilities following the war.

The Department of Defense Reorganization Act of 1958 moved the military department out of the chain of command, which now flows from the President to the Secretary of Defense through the Joint Chiefs to commanders of the unified and specified commands.

THE JOINT CHIEFS OF STAFF (JCS)

The group to be called the Joint Chiefs of Staff came into being shortly after Pearl Harbor. President Franklin D. Roosevelt and Prime Minister Winston Churchill made the decision to establish a supreme Anglo-American military body for the strategic direction of World War II. The American chiefs of staff needed to discuss procedures among themselves before meeting with the British officers, and they met regularly though informally. Soon the group became known as the "Joint Chiefs of Staff."

The JCS is composed of the Chairman, the Vice Chairman, the Chiefs of Staff of the Army, the Marine Corps, and the Air Force, and the Chief of Naval Operations.

The Chairman of the Joint Chiefs of Staff is appointed by the President on a rotating basis among the services. Each service Chief is responsible for keeping the Secretary of his military department fully informed about the activities of the JCS.

DACOWITS

The Defense Advisory Committee on Women in the Services (DACOWITS) was created in 1951. The Chairman and members are appointed by the Secretary of Defense from among civilian professional women and women civic leaders in the United States.

The Secretariat is headed by an executive officer in the Army, Navy, Air Force, or Marine Corps, on a rotating basis.

SPECIALIZED TRAINING

Service personnel have the opportunity for advanced study and specialized training at a number of universities and bases throughout the country.

DEFENSE SCHOOLS

Defense Equal Opportunity Management Institute, Patrick AFB, Florida
Defense Foreign Language Institute, Presidio of Monterey, California
Defense Information School, Fort Meade, Maryland
Joint Military Intelligence College, Bolling AFB, District of Columbia
Joint Military Intelligence Training Center, Bolling AFB, District of Columbia
National Cryptologic School, Fort Meade, Maryland
Defense Polygraph School, Fort McClellan, Alabama
Department of Defense Security Institute, Richmond, Virginia
Defense Systems Management College, Fort Belvoir, Virginia
Defense Mapping School, Fort Belvoir, Virginia
Defense Resources Management Education Center, Monterey, California
Uniformed Services University of the Health Sciences, Bethesda, Maryland
Defense Business Management University, Southbridge, Massachusetts
Joint Military Intelligence Training Center, Bolling AFB, District of Columbia
Information Resources Management College, Fort McNair, District of Columbia

SERVICE WAR COLLEGES AND OFFICERS SCHOOLS

Air Command and Staff College, Maxwell AFB, Alabama
Air War College, Maxwell AFB, Alabama
Army Command and General Staff College, Fort Leavenworth, Kansas
Army War College, Carlisle Barracks, Pennsylvania
College of Naval Command and Staff, Newport, Rhode Island
Marine Corps Command and Staff College, Quantico, Virginia
Naval War College, Newport, Rhode Island

SERVICE ACADEMIES

There are four service academies for the training of young men and women as midshipmen and cadets:

The United States Air Force Academy, Colorado Springs, Colorado
The United States Coast Guard Academy, New London, Connecticut
The United States Military Academy, West Point, New York
The United States Naval Academy, Annapolis, Maryland

By congressional order, no more than 1,800 students are accepted for the fourth class (freshman) year. Appointments depend upon physical and academic tests and age: fourth classmen must be between the ages of 17 and 22. At the Coast Guard Academy, applicants are considered on a nationwide competitive basis.

Upon graduation, the cadets and midshipmen are awarded the degree of Bachelor of Science and commissioned second lieutenants and ensigns, respectively, with a minimum requirement to serve six years in their chosen branch of the armed forces.

COMMISSIONED OFFICERS

	ARMY	NAVY	MARINE CORPS	AIR FORCE	TOTAL DOD
ACADEMY	1,024	799	125	1,022	2,970
ROTC SCHOLARSHIP	1,557	993	158	1,321	4,029
ROTC OTHER	1,923	60	—	486	2,469
OCS	379	709	598	893	2,579
DIRECT APPOINTMENT	1,782	1,313	5	1,287	4,387
OTHER	1	519	565	41	1,126
UNKNOWN	24	37	—	—	61
TOTAL	**6,690**	**4,430**	**1,451**	**5,050**	**17,621**

COMMISSIONING PROGRAMS

There are several ways for men and women to acquire a commission in the armed forces: by attending one of the service academies; by joining an ROTC program in a college or university; by attending one of the various officer candidate schools which are open to college graduates and qualified enlisted personnel; and by direct appointment—usually offered to highly trained professionals in the medical and allied health sciences and legal or religious fields.

The Marine Corps has no ROTC program but participates in the Navy ROTC option programs for Marines. (Postgraduate work is at the Command and Staff College, Quantico, Virginia.)

WOMEN IN THE SERVICES

It took a very long time for women to be accepted in the armed forces, and a long time for them to be integrated into the services, as they are today, with opportunity for advancement in rank and for commands once available only to men. Assignments are the same, with the exception of those in direct combat or close to combat areas. The assignment of military women to combat zones is being studied by Congress.

Today's servicewomen are an important part of the work force in the Department of Defense. There are approximately 200,000 women serving in the four military services, of whom more than 30,000 are officers.

In 1968 women officers first became eligible to attend the senior service colleges, and now attend command and staff colleges as well.

In 1976 women were admitted to the service academies. The first women cadets to attend the maritime academies entered Kings Point in 1974.

MEMORIAL

Currently under construction is the Women in Military Service for America Memorial at Arlington National Cemetery. The memorial will honor the 1.8 million women who have served in the armed forces since the Revolutionary War.

Privately funded, the $25 million memorial was authorized by Congress in 1986 and should be dedicated within two years.

BASE CLOSINGS

Midnight, December 31, 1995, brought to an end the Defense Base Closure and Realignment Commission, established by Congress, that voted to close 243 domestic military bases. The shutdown started in 1988 and will continue for the next several years. It has greatly affected the civilian population as well as the military infrastructure.

Future major base closures and realignments are as follows:

ARMY

Fort McClellan, Alabama	September 1999
Fort Chaffee, Arkansas	September 1997
Oakland Army Base, California	July 2001
Fitzsimmons Army Medical Center, Colorado	September 2000
Savannah Army Depot Activity, Illinois	July 2001
Fort Holabird, Maryland	September 1996
Fort Ritchie, Maryland	October 1998
Bayonne Military Ocean Terminal, New Jersey	July 2001
Seneca Army Depot, New York	July 2001
Fort Indiantown Gap, Pennsylvania	September 1998
Fort Pickett, Virginia	September 1997

NAVY

Naval Air Facility, Adak, Alaska	January 1998
Fleet Industrial Supply Center, Oakland, California	September 1998
Naval Shipyard, Long Beach, California	September 1997
Ship Repair Facility, Guam	September 1997
Naval Air Warfare Center, Aircraft Division Detachment, Indianapolis, Indiana	September 2000
Naval Air Warfare Center, Aircraft Division Detachment, Louisville, Kentucky	September 1997
Naval Surface Warfare Center, Dahlgren Division Detachment, White Oak, Maryland	July 1997
Naval Air Station, South Weymouth, Massachusetts	September 1997
Naval Air Warfare Center, Aircraft Division, Warminster, Pennsylvania	March 1997

AIR FORCE

McClellan Air Force Base, California	July 2001
Ontario IAP Air Guard Station, California	September 1997
Roslyn Air Guard Station, New York	September 1997
Bergstrom Air Reserve Base, Texas	September 1997
Reese Air Force Base, Texas	September 1997

Note: All dates are subject to change.

CHAPTER 47

The U.S. Army

THE CONTINENTAL ARMY was established on 14 June 1775, more than one year before the Declaration of Independence was signed. The Continental Congress appointed Colonel George Washington as Commander in Chief of the Regular Army and the volunteer militia. Farmers, merchants, and craftsmen were the first volunteers, carrying a variety of hunting weapons and family firearms.

From those first 10 companies of untrained fighting men to today's global strength on the battlefield, there are such troops as those at Fort Knox, Kentucky, trained in the use of high-tech M1A2 Abrams tanks and command-and-control vehicles. The Army is capable of airborne deployment to any location in the world within a matter of hours, with the most sophisticated equipment for infantry, airborne, mechanized, and amphibious operations.

DEPARTMENT OF THE ARMY

The Secretary of the Army is responsible for the Army establishment. There is an Under Secretary, various Assistant Secretaries, and a Sergeant Major of the Army. The principal advisor is the Army Chief of Staff, who is a member of the Joint Chiefs of Staff.

The Army division is the basic unit of ground combat power.

There are five types: Infantry, Armor, Mechanized, Airborne, and Air Assault.

MAJOR U.S. ARMY COMMANDS

Army Materiel Command, Alexandria, Virginia
Corps of Engineers, Washington, D.C.
Criminal Investigation Command, Fort Belvoir, Virginia
Eighth U.S. Army, Seoul, Korea
Forces Command, Fort McPherson, Georgia
Medical Command, Fort Sam Houston, Texas
Information Systems Command, Fort Huachuca, Arizona
Intelligence and Security Command, Fort Belvoir, Virginia
Military District of Washington, Fort McNair, Washington, D.C.
Military Traffic Management Command, Falls Church, Virginia
Special Operations Command, Fort Bragg, North Carolina
Training and Doctrine Command, Fort Monroe, Virginia
U.S. Army Europe and Seventh Army, Heidelberg, Germany
U.S. Army Pacific, Fort Shafter, Hawaii
U.S. Army South, Fort Clayton, Panama

THE U.S. MILITARY ACADEMY

On 4 July 1802, ten young men enrolled as cadets at the U.S. Military Academy at West Point, New York, established by an act of Congress signed by President Jefferson the preceding March. Almost three decades earlier, the strategic importance of the location of West Point on the Hudson River had led General George Washington to place a garrison of American Revolutionary troops there to thwart British efforts to control river navigation.

Today, approximately 4,000 young men and women compose the Corps of Cadets (women entered the Academy for the first time in July 1976). Upon completion of the four-year course, the graduates are commissioned second lieutenants in the U.S. Army.

The Academy's colors are black, gold, and gray; the motto is *Duty, Honor, Country.* The official song is "Alma Mater," and the mascot is the Army mule. The reservation encompasses 16,000 acres.

The fourth classmen (Plebes) have a continuous indoctrination course during their first year. By year's end the new third class (Yearlings) leaves the reservation immediately after Graduation Week and then returns to spend two months at Camp Buckner just outside West Point. There the cadets are introduced to the modern Army and practice the unit tactics that have been taught.

Second classmen (Cows) undergo an intensive summer training program, with some cadets spending three weeks at Airborne School at Fort Benning, Georgia, which qualifies them as parachutists. Others enter Range School at Fort Benning, or attend Flight School at Fort Rucker, Alabama. Still others attend Jungle School in Alaska. A month is spent in the Army Orientation Program with active army units in the continental United States, Alaska, Hawaii, Europe, and Panama.

The first class of cadets take over a number of responsibilities during their final summer. Some help in the training of the plebes, while others aid in the training of the third class at Camp Buckner. The year brings to a conclusion the intensive courses of study in the sciences and humanities, with leadership stressed.

WOMEN IN THE ARMY

On 14 May 1942, Congress enacted a law establishing the Women's Army Auxiliary Corps because of the shortage of manpower in the Army. By a subsequent act, the name was changed to Women's Army Corps, the members called "Wacs."

During World War II, more than 140,000 women served in the Corps in this country, Europe, Africa, the Southwest Pacific, China, India, Hawaii, the Philippines, and Alaska.

At the end of the war, the Army was faced with the loss of its women soldiers and asked Congress to make the WAC a permanent part of the military establishment. By Public Law 625, the Women's Army Corps became a component of the regular Army and Army Reserve of the United States in 1947.

Twenty years later, restrictions that earlier had been imposed on strength, promotion, and length of service for retirement were removed, and women were permitted to enter the National Guard. In 1972 the AROTC programs were opened to women.

A "FIRST"

The first women to serve unofficially near the fields of battle were volunteer nurses in the Civil War. Among them were Dorothy Dix and Clara Barton, whose work later led to the founding of the American Red Cross.

In 1901 Congress recognized the services of the nurses by establishing the Army Nurse Corps within the Medical Department of the Army, without rank, officer status, equal pay, retirement, or veterans benefits. During World War I, and particularly during World War

II, the demands for manpower created the opportunity for women to do work other than nursing; the men they relieved became available for combat. Today, ranks for women include that of general.

MEDAL OF HONOR

The only woman to receive the Congressional Medal of Honor was Dr. Mary Edwards Walker, who served as a nurse and a physician in the Union Army during the Civil War.

At age 22 she was the sole woman in the 1855 graduating class at Syracuse Medical College. Dr. Walker applied for an appointment as a surgeon at the onset of the Civil War. She was rejected, but undeterred. She became a volunteer nurse at a makeshift hospital in the U.S. Patent Office in Washington, D.C., and also worked in Virginia and Tennessee.

In September 1864 her round-the-clock work was duly noted, and she was appointed assistant surgeon of the 52nd Ohio Infantry. While making a medical round, she was taken prisoner and interned at Castle Thunder in Richmond. After several months as a prisoner of war Dr. Walker was exchanged for a Confederate surgeon and placed in charge of a women's prison hospital in Louisville, where the staff and inmates accused her of undue severity. Transferred to Clarksville, Tennessee, she was head of an orphans' asylum at war's end.

In June 1865 President Andrew Johnson awarded Dr. Mary E. Walker the Medal of Honor for meritorious service. The Medal of Honor Board of 1907 redesigned the medal and sent her a replacement. Ten years later, however, her name was struck from the list of recipients because she had not been a member of the armed services and had served without military rank. Dr. Walker did not return the medals, though, and wore both until her death in 1919.

CHAPTER 48

The U.S. Navy

A LITTLE-KNOWN GROUP of ships called "Washington's Navy" preceded the founding of the Continental Navy on 13 October 1775. General Washington was concerned with the need for supplies and ammunition to continue the siege of the British in Boston. By using funds provided for his Army, the future first President assembled a fleet of eight vessels to capture some urgently needed supplies.

After the Continental Congress authorized a Navy, a naval committee was ordered to fit out a number of ships, and the 24-gun ship *Alfred* and the 20-gun *Columbus* were ready in late December. The first Commander in Chief of the eight-ship fleet was Esek Hopkins, who put to sea in February 1776. Serving as first lieutenant aboard the flagship *Alfred* was John Paul Jones. In all, the Continental Navy never numbered more than 3,000 men at any one time, and had a total of 123 officers.

Today's electronic, supersonic, and nuclear Navy has come a long way from yesterday's sloops of war and ironclads. The USS *Nimitz* can accommodate more than 6,000 men—twice the number who served at any one time in the Continental Navy.

DEPARTMENT OF THE NAVY

The Secretary of the Navy heads the naval establishment. In his immediate office are the Under Secretary and various Assistant Secretaries.

The Chief of Naval Operations (CNO) is the principal naval adviser to the Secretary of the Navy; he is a member of the Joint Chiefs of Staff. The office of the CNO includes the Vice Chief and various Deputy CNOs, a Master Chief Petty Officer, and a Sergeant Major of the Marine Corps.

Command flows down from the Chief of Naval Operations through the Fleet Commanders to all bases and ships of the Fleet, and from the Commandant of the Marine Corps to the various forces and commands. The Marine Corps is an integral part of the U.S. Navy, and in times of war the U.S. Coast Guard comes under naval jurisdiction. The ranking officer is the Commandant of the Coast Guard.

OPERATING FORCES

Atlantic Fleet, embraces the Second Fleet, Norfolk, Virginia
Pacific Fleet, inclusive of the Third and Seventh Fleets, Pearl Harbor, Hawaii, San Diego, California, and Yokosuka, Japan
U.S. Naval Forces, Europe, London, England, and *Sixth Fleet,* Gaeta, Italy
Military Sealift Command, Washington, D.C.
Mine Warfare Command, Ingleside, Texas
Naval Forces Central Command, Fifth Fleet, Manama, Bahrain
Naval Forces Southern Command, Rodman, Panama
Naval Reserve Force, New Orleans, Louisiana
Operational Test and Evaluation Force, Norfolk, Virginia
Naval Special Warfare Command, Coronado, California

SHORE ESTABLISHMENTS

Bureau of Medicine and Surgery, Washington, D.C.
Naval Air Systems Command, Washington, D.C.
Naval Data Automation Command, Washington, D.C.
Naval Education and Training Command, Pensacola, Florida
Naval Facilities Engineering Command, Alexandria, Virginia
Naval Intelligence Command, Washington, D.C.
Naval Legal Service Command, Alexandria, Virginia
Naval Doctrine Command, Norfolk, Virginia
Bureau of Naval Personnel, Washington, D.C.
Naval Meteorology and Oceanography Command, Bay St. Louis, Mississippi
Naval Sea Systems Command, Washington, D.C.
Naval Security and Investigative Command, Washington, D.C.
Naval Security Group Command, Washington, D.C.

Naval Space Command, Dahlgren, Virginia
Naval Supply Systems Command, Washington, D.C.
Naval Telecommunications Command, Washington, D.C.
Space and Naval Warfare Systems Command, Washington, D.C.
Office of Naval Intelligence, Washington, D.C.

THE U.S. NAVAL ACADEMY

The U.S. Naval Academy was founded as the Naval School in 1845 at Annapolis, Maryland. The 10-acre site along the Severn River was a nearly abandoned Army post, Old Fort Severn. In 1850 the school received its present name, and a four-year course of study with summer cruises replaced the five-year program in which one year was spent at sea. During the Civil War the northern midshipmen were quartered at Newport, Rhode Island, and again the Academy compound was used by the Army. (In 1863 the Confederate States Naval Academy officially started the training of southern midshipmen in the CSS *Patrick Henry,* anchored in the James River. The ship was burned upon the evacuation of Richmond in April 1865.)

Today, on 322 acres (including considerable landfill), about 4,000 young men and women comprise the Brigade of Midshipmen. The first women to enter arrived in July 1976. The Academy colors are navy blue and gold, and the mascot is Bill the Goat. The official song is "Navy Blue and Gold."

The fourth classmen, or Plebes, undergo an indoctrination program their first year; the third class, or Youngsters, have six to eight weeks' sea training with the Fleet their first summer. Second classmen receive professional training in and familiarization with warfare specialties through visits to the Submarine School at New London, Connecticut, the Surface Warfare School at Newport, Rhode Island, and the air facility at Pensacola, Florida. Introduction to amphibious assault is provided by the Marines. During their last summer at the Academy, midshipmen perform the duties of junior officers with the fleet.

Graduates are commissioned either ensigns in the Navy or second lieutenants in the Marine Corps. The majority of ensigns are line officers, with duty in aircraft carriers, cruisers, destroyers, nuclear power programs, or flight or submarine training.

WOMEN IN THE NAVY

At the height of World War II, some 86,000 women were serving in the Navy as Women Accepted for Volunteer Emergency Service—WAVES. The term is inappropriate, since women are a part of the regular Navy and not "accepted for volunteer service." However, the term remains popular if not official.

In 1942, congressional legislation authorized the enlistment and commissioning of women in the Naval Reserve, and two years later women were permitted to serve in Hawaii and Alaska. Since the Women's Armed Forces Integration Act of 1948, women have served not as a separate corps but as an integral part of the naval establishment. Legislation in 1967 repealed the restrictions on rank.

In World War I, by act of 29 August 1916 which set up the Naval Reserve Force, Navy and Coast Guard women were designated Yeoman (F), called "Yeomanette," and Marine (F), called "Marinette." They served in clerical and administrative duties as draftsmen, fingerprint experts, and recruiters.

Women are interchangeable with men in most shore and overseas assignments, and by congressional order they now serve in combat ships. Several officers completed the first flight training as female naval aviators in 1973.

SHIP'S LAUNCHING

There are three ceremonial occasions during the construction and fitting out of a ship authorized by Congress: the keel laying, the launch and christening, and the commissioning.

The construction of a large warship requires about three years from keel laying to launching. The name of the ship and its sponsors are chosen by the Secretary of the Navy upon the recommendation of the Chief of Naval Operations. There are more than 125 types of ships the sources of whose names are not set by law but have been standardized by tradition and approved by the Navy.

Although a ship is assigned a name long before she is launched, the ship does not receive her name until she is christened. Since mariners facing the unknown perils of the sea place their faith not only in a stout ship but in an unseen guiding spirit, the religious part of the christening ceremony is important.

Carriers are usually named for famous men, ships of the Old Navy, or historic battles; *cruisers* for cities; *submarines* for fish and other creatures of the sea and also for famous men; and *destroyers* for American heroes and Secretaries of the Navy.

Aircraft carriers are usually sponsored by the wives of naval personnel associated with aviation, and submarines are sponsored by wives of personnel in that specialty. Sponsors for vessels named in honor of particular persons are usually the nearest female relative of the honored person. Although women are sponsors today, in early years men performed this honor. The first recorded christening of a U.S. ship is that of the frigate *Constitution* on 21 October 1797 by Captain James Sever, USN. One person usually christens a ship, but a co-sponsor may be named.

THE SHIP'S CAPTAIN

Guests attending any function aboard a navy ship should remember to address the ship's captain as "Captain" regardless of the rank that he or she has attained. A lieutenant commander, for example, would be called "Captain."

CHAPTER 49

The U.S. Marine Corps

Prior to the American Revolution able-bodied men from the colonies had been serving as Marines in America—but in support of British operations. Four colonial battalions were raised in 1740 to fight in England's war with Spain. During the Seven Years' War (French and Indian War), the colonials again served as Marines in support of the British against the French.

In October 1775, the Continental Congress directed General George Washington to secure two armed vessels from Massachusetts, place them on the "Continental risque and pay," and use them to capture ammunition. He was also to give orders for the "proper encouragement to the Marines and seamen" who served in the vessels. Records indicate that this was the first time Congress mentioned "Marines."

Throughout the Revolution, three types of Marines fought for their country: the Continental or Regular Marines, Marines of the state navies, and Marines of the privateers. But it was the Continental Marines who were officially charged by Congress with fulfilling a military role in the fight for independence. This came about on 10 November 1775 by a resolution formally establishing two battalions of Marines to be distinguished by the name "American Marines."

Thus the Marine Corps was born almost eight months before the Declaration of Independence was signed. Then, as now, they were charged ". . . to serve to advantage by Sea when required. . . ." Some 173,000 men and women are on active duty today.

ORGANIZATION

The National Security Act reaffirmed the Marine Corps as a separate service within the Navy Department. The Commandant of the Marine Corps is a member of the Joint Chiefs of Staff on matters pertaining to the Marines. Marine Corps Headquarters is in Washington, D.C.

There is an Assistant Commandant; a Chief of Staff; a Sergeant Major; and a number of Deputy Chiefs of Staff and directors.

MAJOR COMMANDS

Fleet Marine Force, Atlantic, Camp Lejeune, North Carolina
Fleet Marine Force, Pacific, Camp H. M. Smith, Hawaii
I *Marine Amphibious Force,* Camp Pendleton, California
II *Marine Amphibious Force,* Camp Lejeune, North Carolina
III *Marine Expeditionary Force,* Camp Butler, Okinawa
Marine Corps Air Ground Combat Center, Twenty-nine Palms, California
Marine Corps Combat Development Command, Quantico, Virginia
Marine Corps Systems Command, Quantico, Virginia
Marine Reserve Forces, New Orleans, Louisiana

OFFICER CANDIDATE PROGRAMS

Commissions in the Marine Corps may be acquired through these avenues:

1. *Marine Corps Officer Candidate Class* (OCC). For men and women college graduates. Qualified enlisted personnel are eligible.

2. *Marine Platoon Leaders Class.* For undergraduate college students.

3. *Naval Reserve Officer Training Corps* (NROTC). For undergraduate students at various colleges and universities, with options for Marines.

4. *U.S. Naval Academy.* A limited number of midshipmen (16.6 percent of the graduating class) may elect to go into the Marine Corps upon graduation.

College graduates who want to be aviators or ground officers are eligible for a reserve commission after completing a 12-week training and screening course, followed by advanced flight training. Undergraduates may take the naval aviator or naval flight officer program open to both Navy and Marine candidates.

The Marine Corps Combat Development Command at Quantico, Virginia, includes the Development Center, the Marine Corps Education Center, and Long Range Study Panel. All new Marine officers, both men and women, receive basic training there.

WOMEN IN THE MARINES

More than 300 Reservists (Female), called "Marinettes," served during World War I, mainly in clerical jobs at Marine Headquarters and at the Navy Department. Some were assigned to Marine recruiting. About 20,000 women served in World War II, when, as now, they shared the name Marine with the men. Currently almost 10,000 women are an integral part of the Corps. Of this number, more than 690 are officers.

Officers and enlisted women are now eligible for assignments once available to men only. This came about after a successful pilot program was conducted at 1st Marine Division, Camp Pendleton, California, and the 2nd Marine Aircraft Wing at Cherry Point, North Carolina.

Women Marines are assigned to stateside divisions, aircraft wings, force service regiments, and force troops headquarters in rear echelon billets. They serve overseas in many countries.

Ever-increasing numbers are assigned to such nontraditional areas for women as engineering and electronics, with a captain currently serving as a military judge and a lieutenant commanding a military police platoon. The majority of women Marines continue to serve in positions of administration, communications, supply, and disbursing.

THE U.S. MARINE BAND

Traditionally referred to as "The President's Own," the United States Marine Band officially came into existence in 1798, when President John Adams signed a bill creating the Marine "Musicians."

However, the band dates its beginning from 10 November 1775, the birthday of the Marine Corps, when the fife and drum were played as Marines were on the march, and two drummers and one fifer were assigned to the Marine Guard in ships of the Navy. In 1801 the band first played in the White House at a New Year's Day reception given by President Adams, and it has played at every presidential inauguration since Thomas Jefferson's day.

The band is quartered at Marine Barracks, Washington, D.C., the oldest post of the Marine Corps. It was here that John Philip Sousa, while leader of the band, wrote many of his marches.

SILENT DRILL PLATOON

The precise military drills and maneuvers called the Silent Drill Platoon is a part of the Ceremonial Guard Company at Marine Barracks, Washington, D.C., with performances held during summer months.

The silent drill by 24 selected Marines is carried out without any verbal command and with intricate movements in strict military cadence set by the crack of rifles being exchanged among the Marines. The Marines perform on Friday evenings at 9 P.M. at the weekly "Moonlight Parades," and at 7:30 P.M. at the Marine Memorial Ceremony conducted on the grounds of the Iwo Jima Statue in Arlington, Virginia.

CHAPTER 50

The U.S. Air Force

THE U.S. AIR FORCE is the youngest armed force. The need for such a force was proven during World War II, when the air offense and defense were major factors in the war's successful conclusion. About 400,000 men and women are now on active duty.

The Air Force started within the U.S. Army in August 1907, when one officer and two enlisted men were assigned to the newly established Aeronautical Division in the Office of the Chief Signal Officer. The division underwent a number of changes before being formally designated in 1920 as the Air Service, a combatant arm of the Army. Six years later the service formally became the Army Air Corps.

Early in World War II, the corps became the Army Air Forces, with General H. H. Arnold the commanding general. Following the war, President Harry S. Truman signed the National Security Act of 1947, which established not only a new defense organization—the Department of Defense—but a separate Department of the Air Force which was on an equal footing with the Army and Navy. Thus were established separate military departments for land, sea, and air.

DEPARTMENT OF THE AIR FORCE

The Secretary of the Air Force is responsible for the affairs of the Department of the Air Force. His chief assistants are the Under

Secretary and the Assistant Secretaries. There is also a Chief Master Sergeant of the Air Force.

The *Air Staff* consists of a Chief of Staff, a Vice Chief of Staff, Deputy Chiefs of Staff, and other military and civilian specialists.

The basic Air Force structure is: Flight (the lowest tactical echelon), Squadron, Group, Wing (the basic unit), Air Division, Numbered Air Force, and Major Command.

MAJOR COMMANDS

Air Mobility Command, Scott AFB, Illinois

Air Force Materiel Command, Wright-Patterson AFB, Ohio; provides supplies around the world

Air Education and Training Command, Randolph AFB, San Antonio, Texas

Pacific Air Forces, Hickam AFB, Hawaii

Air Force Space Command, Peterson Air Force Base, Colorado; includes most of the missions of the deactivated Aerospace Defense Command (others are assigned to the North American Air Defense Command [NORAD] components in the continental United States, Canada, and Alaska)

Strategic Air Command, Offutt AFB, Nebraska

Air Combat Command, Langley AFB, Virginia

U.S. Air Forces Europe, Ramstein AFB, Germany

Air Force Special Operations Command, Hurlburt Field, Florida

THE U.S. AIR FORCE ACADEMY

The Air Force Academy is located 10 miles north of Colorado Springs on 18,000 acres bordered on the west by the Rocky Mountains. The Cadet Wing is composed of approximately 4,000 young men and women; the first women cadets entered in June 1976. Graduates are commissioned second lieutenants in the Air Force.

The Academy was established in Congress on 1 April 1954. The first class (306 cadets) was sworn in on 11 July 1955 at Lowry Air Force Base, Denver, while new buildings were under construction at Colorado Springs. On 29 August 1958, cadets moved into their new quarters, and the first class (206 members) graduated the following year.

The fourth class, Doolies, have an indoctrination period upon entering the academy. Third classmen have survival, resistance, and escape training. Instruction in parachuting, lightplane flying, underwater demolition, and scuba training is given during the final two years.

The Academy has a planetarium and an observatory and its own airstrip, which serves the lightplane, sailplane, and parachuting activities. There are pilot and navigator indoctrination programs.

Academy colors are blue and silver, and the official song is "The Air Force Song." The falcon is the mascot.

SPACE

Today, the Air Force Academy has a continuing role in the preparation for space, with graduates in the forefront as astronauts, engineers, and mission support specialists.

Since 1965, a space physics major in the Physics Department has been available to the cadets. This major focuses on environmental problems in space. Several faculty members, as well as the cadets, are conducting space-related research in such areas as solar astrophysics, the structural design of space hardware, and the directional control of satellites.

Cadets developed the first completely successful student experiments on a space shuttle mission, carried on the *Challenger*'s first flight in 1983.

THE AIR UNIVERSITY

The Air University is a vast complex responsible for the professional education and research in specific fields for Air Force officers. The major units are at Maxwell AFB, Montgomery, Alabama, the site of the Wright brothers' early flying school.

Some of the university's schools are the Air War College, the Air Command and Staff College, the Squadron Officer School, the Air University Institute for Professional Development, and the Air Force Institute of Technology. The Air Force Senior Noncommissioned Officer Academy at Gunter AFB prepares chief and senior master sergeants for positions of greater responsibility.

WOMEN IN THE AIR FORCE

During World War II, before the U.S. Air Force was established, approximately 40,000 women served with the Army Air Force as Air-Wacs. More than 1,000 Women Air Service Pilots (WASPS) ferried aircraft, towed targets, and taught flying during the war.

The women's Armed Forces Integration Act of 18 June 1949 not only recognized the contributions of women in the services but separated the Air-Wacs from the Army by creating the Women in the Air Force as a part of the new U.S. Air Force.

Women officers lead units comprised of both sexes, and are eligible for assignment as wing commander and recruiting group commander. They are assigned to such posts as space systems, nuclear research, and computer technology, and are serving as instructors at the Air Force Academy. As in the other services, Air Force women are now assigned to combat areas.

CHAPTER 51

The U.S. Coast Guard

THE U.S. COAST GUARD is a branch of the armed forces of the United States. It is also the principal federal peacetime agency for maritime safety and law enforcement. It has a dual role: in peacetime the Coast Guard operates in the Department of Transportation; during times of war or when directed by the President it is part of the Navy. But in war or in peace, the Coast Guard remains an armed force at all times.

The history of the Coast Guard goes back to the beginning of this country, when colonists settled along the coasts and constructed lighthouses for the safety of men and their boats. The oldest recorded lighthouse is the Boston Light, built in 1716.

In terms of continuous service, the Coast Guard is the oldest of the nation's seagoing armed forces. Smuggling was widespread in the early days of the nation, and Alexander Hamilton, the first Secretary of the Treasury, asked Congress for a fleet of armed revenue cutters for the collection of tonnage dues and import duties from ships entering American waters.

Hamilton, who is called the founder of the Coast Guard, requested "that there be ten boats, two for the coasts of Massachusetts and New Hampshire; one for Long Island Sound; one for New York; one for the Bay of Delaware; two for the Chesapeake; one for North

Carolina; one for South Carolina; and one for Georgia." The bill was passed on 4 August 1790; each of the ten heavy-keeled schooners and sloops cost between $1,000 and $1,500. The service was called the "system of cutters."

For nearly eight years this fleet of cutters was the young nation's only navy. Then, in 1798, the regular Navy was organized. The following year, due to hostilities with French privateers, Congress ordained that "Revenue Cutters shall, whenever the President of the United States shall so direct, cooperate with the Navy of the United States."

Thus began the early association of the Coast Guard and the United States Navy.

In these early years the Coast Guard was known as the "Revenue Marine," the "Revenue-Marine Service," and the "Revenue Service." In 1863 the title became the Revenue Cutter Service. By 1915 the Life Saving Service had merged with the Revenue Cutter Service to form the U.S. Coast Guard.

By 1939, the Bureau of Lighthouses was transferred to the Coast Guard; a few years later the Bureau of Marine Inspection and Navigation became a part of the service. About 35,000 men and women are on active duty; some 15,000 of them are in the Coast Guard and Reserve.

ORGANIZATION

Coast Guard Headquarters is located in Washington, D.C. During peacetime the Commandant of the Coast Guard is responsible to the Secretary of Transportation. On 1 April 1967, after 177 years, the Coast Guard was transferred from the Treasury Department to the newly established Department of Transportation.

In times of national emergency the Commandant is responsible to the Secretary of the Navy. The Secretaries of Transportation and of the Navy are authorized to make available to each other such personnel, vessels, and equipment as are advisable.

The Commandant is assisted by a Vice Commandant, a Chief of Staff, several heads of offices, and a Master Chief Petty Officer. Besides enforcing federal laws on shore and at sea the Coast Guard maintains constant readiness for times of emergency. The marine safety of American vessels, including their construction and inspection, is a major responsibility of the service. Lifesaving operations have been in effect since 1731.

MAJOR COMMANDS

Coast Guard Headquarters, Washington, D.C.
Atlantic Area, New York, New York
Pacific Area, San Francisco, California

In addition, there are 10 districts in the United States.

THE U.S. COAST GUARD ACADEMY

The U.S. Coast Guard Academy, founded in 1876, is located on a 110-acre site along the Thames River at New London, Connecticut. The first "school of instruction" in 1877 had nine cadets quartered in the old refitted schooner *Dobbin.* The following year the bark *Chase* was built as a cadet ship; when the *Chase* put into winter quarters at New Bedford, Massachusetts, the school continued in a sail loft.

A few years later the *Chase* was winter quartered at Arundel Cove in Curtis Bay, Maryland, and a two-story wooden school was built in the repair yard. In 1910 the school moved into an old Army coastal defense post, Fort Trumbull, at New London.

The Corps of Cadets is composed of approximately 750 young men and women. The first women were admitted in July 1976. The Academy motto is *Scientiae Cedit Mare* (The Sea Yields to Knowledge). Colors are royal blue and white. The song is "Coast Guard Fore'er."

During summer months the cadets train in the three-masted auxiliary bark *Eagle,* and in cutters. The *Eagle* was one of the many tall ships that took part in the 1976 Bicentennial celebration, and in the summer of 1986 the *Eagle* led the procession of tall ships at the Statue of Liberty's centennial celebration in New York Harbor.

Upon graduation the cadets receive a Bachelor of Science degree and are commissioned ensigns in the U.S. Coast Guard, with a five-year service commitment. Appointments to the Academy are made on the basis of an annual nationwide competitive examination; there are no congressional appointments.

WOMEN IN THE COAST GUARD

Coast Guard women served with Navy women as "Yeomanettes" during World War I. Not until World War II did Coast Guard women come into their own. Then, 15 officers and 153 enlisted Navy women were trained at the Coast Guard Academy, making up the first contingent of SPARS.

In December 1973, legislation abolished the restriction that women could only serve in the Coast Guard Reserve, and a new program for enlistment and commissioning in the regular Coast Guard was begun.

Since 1974, the designation SPARS has gone out of official existence, but it will not soon be forgotten. The designation was coined from the initial letters of the Coast Guard motto: *Semper Paratus*—Always Ready.

Women are eligible for assignment to all Coast Guard units and ratings. They are serving in all capacities ashore and at sea, including those of commanding officers of cutters, and are among the first women from any service to be assigned to flight school at Pensacola, Florida. Upon completion of this training they are assigned to any operational aviation command in an unrestricted flying status.

CHAPTER 52

The Reserves

Fighting in the American Revolution lasted six years. After independence was won, the Army and Navy were so reduced that for a time the Continental Army had a strength of only 80 men and a few officers to guard the military supplies at West Point and Fort Pitt. The Navy fared no better.

Today, the safety and defense of America depends upon its army, air, and naval strength. In order to be prepared for any emergency at any time, and to ensure national and international security, the armed forces must have a backup force of personnel trained for military duty.

RESERVE STRENGTH

The major source of manpower augmenting the active forces is the Ready Reserve, which includes Selected Reserve units whose pretrained members perform a wartime mission. Reservists include the Inactive National Guard (ING) and Individual Ready Reserve (IRR).

The Standby Reserve is composed of men and women who have completed their six-year obligation and are mobilized by authority of Congress when needed.

Currently, about 3,600,000 men and women serve in the Army,

Navy, Marine Corps, Air Force, Coast Guard, and the Army and Air National Guard branches of Reserves, not counting the Standby Reserve force of 28,000.

Young men and women without prior military service may enlist in a Reserve program by applying at any local organized Reserve unit of the service of their choice. All programs require an enlistee to serve some time on active duty for training, and upon completion of this basic training he or she returns to the local unit and attends training assemblies or drills throughout the year. There are a minimum of 48 assemblies or drills a year, usually held on weekends or evenings; one weekend is the equivalent of four training drills; also a two-week summer refresher program is required. National Guard and Reserve pay is based on the armed forces pay scale for the grade and length of service.

THE NATIONAL GUARD

The Army and Air National Guards are volunteer military organizations within each state whose members train part time for local and national protection. There are nearly 5,000 Guard units located in this country and in Puerto Rico and the Virgin Islands.

The National Guard has a dual status: as members of a state organization, Guard personnel can be ordered to active duty in times of local emergencies or disasters; as members of Reserve components of the U.S. Army and U.S. Air Force, they can be sent into active federal service as needed. Age limits for men and women are 17 to 34, and 17 to 35, respectively. Women may enter any Air or Army Guard unit that is not directly related to combat.

Areas of intensive training—and, later, performance—include infantry, air defense, medical, and ordnance for the Army Guard; and air defense, air refueling, tactical fighter, and global training for the Air Guard. Officer candidates attend the ANG Academy of Military Science or the Army Guard OCS program.

COMMISSIONING PROGRAMS

There are several avenues leading to commissions in the services other than the federal maritime (Merchant Marine) or service academies. Among them are the Officer Candidate Schools (OCS) for the Army, Navy, and Coast Guard; the Officer Training School (OTS) for the Air Force; the Marine Corps Officer Candidate Class (OCC); and Aviation Officer Candidate (AOC) and Platoon Leaders Class (PLC) programs.

The Reserve Officers Training Corps (ROTC) programs, available at colleges and universities since 1916, provide both regular and reserve officers. In 1972 the programs were opened to women. For the freshman and sophomore years, ROTC training is the same for the Navy and Marine Corps branches; beginning in the junior year, Marine Corps courses are taught for the young men and women pursuing that service.

Currently, the ROTC consists of 500 Army, Navy, and Air Force units, with instruction taken in the Science or Aerospace departments in colleges, universities, and military and private schools in this country. Students in the program take two to five hours of military instruction each week while pursuing an academic course leading to a baccalaureate degree. The cadets and midshipmen must be between 17 and 21 years of age, are subsidized, and wear uniforms in drills and at other military occasions.

Various programs are offered, both obligated and nonobligated. Students may compete nationally for a four-year scholarship, but there are also one-, two-, and three-year scholarships. The four-year program consists of a basic course for the first two years, and an advanced course for the junior and senior years. The purpose of the two-year course is to make eligible the transfer students from junior colleges or institutions where ROTC programs were not given. Then, the student may take a six-week summer training course in order to qualify for the advanced course.

Scholarship students are obligated to serve four years on active duty. Seniors may take flight training and go into the aviation program furnished by the service; upon graduation they serve three years. Nonobligated graduates serve three to six months on active duty, then join their Reserve unit.

Junior ROTC programs are available for high school students, and those in military schools at the secondary level. All services with the exception of the Coast Guard have student programs, with boys and girls required to be at least 14 years old and to complete at least 96 hours of training and study each year.

The Junior ROTC course is an elective one. Students are instructed in history, government, and current events. At least once a week they dress in uniforms and practice marching, an activity that teaches leadership. Enrollment has tripled during the past few years.

THE CITADEL

It is not possible to list the many colleges and universities that have ROTC programs, but as an example, one college that has programs for all services is The Citadel, the Military College of South Carolina, at Charleston.

The Citadel was founded in 1842 and derived its name from the old fortress in which it was first quartered. The fortress was first garrisoned by federal troops, then by state troops until they were replaced by the 20 students who made up the first Corps of Cadets and who served as arsenal guards while pursuing their studies.

Citadel men have served in all wars since the college's founding. During World War II, over 99 percent of the approximately 4,000 undergraduates who attended the college during the war years served in the armed forces.

The Citadel is a liberal arts as well as a military college. All cadets take four years of ROTC training—a requirement for graduation. To be eligible for a commission, the cadet must complete the basic course and then accept a contract during the third and fourth years. This contract is an agreement to serve on active duty up to two years or longer in the chosen service. Cadets who major in chemistry, physics, or other highly specialized fields may receive a direct appointment.

In 1996, by congressional order, women were accepted for training.

WOMEN IN THE ROTC

The Air Force was the first to open the door to women in the ROTC, in 1956. The many restrictions led to a low enrollment, however, and the program ended in 1961.

Eight years later, the AFROTC again started a program for women, with fewer restrictions—for example, marriage and pregnancy are no longer causes for disqualification. Also, there were opportunities for more challenging jobs. One of the first women to enter the program when it opened at the University of Tennessee became a communications electronics engineer with the AF Communications Service at Richards-Gebaur AFB, Missouri. Since then, women have participated in all programs, including four-year scholarships.

CHAPTER 53

The U.S. Merchant Marine

MERCHANT SHIPS have plied the oceans of the world since long before organized navies were founded. During America's years of growth between the Revolutionary and Civil wars, much of the country's wealth was in its shipping and commerce. American ships were so numerous that England's supremacy of the sea was being challenged.

But the Civil War reversed this growth. At the end of the war the merchant fleet, including coastwise shipping, was 60 percent of its prewar size. Only 29 percent of imports and exports were carried in American ships. Shipping had gone to foreign fleets, and American seamen were unprotected from exploitation by U.S. laws. For a long time the merchant marine was in the doldrums.

In a broad sense, the U.S. Merchant Marine is composed of all privately owned American flag vessels—both oceangoing and the smaller craft engaged in local river, harbor, and coastal work—and their personnel. At peace or in war, a strong Merchant Marine is vital for successful competition in international commerce and for support of military forces which may be stationed throughout the world. During World War II and the Korean and Vietnam conflicts, more than 98 percent of the troops and supplies reached the combat zone in ships—many of them merchant ships. The peak of participation was reached during World War II in the Murmansk run, when shipping lanes to Russia were cut off by the Germans, and

American convoys were exposed to constant attack while carrying millions of tons across the oceans.

Currently, studies continue under the Maritime Security Act of 1995, H.R. 1350, a panel of the House National Security Committee that has bipartisan support in both houses of Congress. Their aim is to ensure enough sealift ships for any future crisis and adequate trained personnel to handle them.

On 6 September 1996, President Bill Clinton announced a plan to terminate the National Oceanic and Atmospheric Administration's commissioned corps of scientists whose mission it is to sustain national environmental security.

MERCHANT MARINE OFFICERS

The responsibility for the safe operation of merchant vessels rests with the officers who are licensed in their specific capacity by the U.S. Coast Guard. A license is issued only after training or experience requirements are met and a written examination is passed.

After receiving his or her license, the new third mate or third assistant engineer may join a ship as a qualified junior officer. The third mate will progress by a licensing procedure to second mate, then to ship's master. The third assistant engineer will be promoted to second assistant engineer, then to chief engineer.

THE MARITIME SERVICE

The U.S. Maritime Service comes under the jurisdiction of the Department of Transportation. There is an Assistant Secretary of Transportation for Maritime Affairs, U.S. Maritime Administration, and a Deputy Assistant Secretary, with headquarters in Washington, D.C.

This service was a voluntary civilian training organization established in 1938 pursuant to the Merchant Marine Act of 1936, as amended, for the purpose of training licensed and unlicensed personnel for service in American merchant vessels. Although personnel were assigned ranks and ratings like members of the U.S. Coast Guard, they were not, and are not, members of the armed forces.

At the present time the last vestiges of this program are the U.S. Merchant Marine Academy and the six State Maritime Academies. All academies combine formal academic studies with programs leading to careers as officers in the American Merchant Marine or career officers in the U.S. Navy and Coast Guard, or to shore careers as admiralty lawyers, naval architects, marine insurance underwriters, or oceanographers. At the conclusion of his or her training, a graduating midshipman or cadet receives a merchant marine license certifying his or her qualifications as a third mate, a third assistant engineer, or, in the case of a Dual License candidate, both. In addition, a graduate receives a Bachelor of Science degree and a commission as ensign in the U.S. Naval Reserve.

Specific Navy interest in maritime training stems from the national defense requirement that Merchant Marine officers be trained in naval procedures so they can work with the Navy in times of war—a "fourth arm of defense." The Navy provides naval science courses, the equivalent of the NROTC courses in colleges and universities. Federal authority and financial aid for the academies date from the Act of Congress of 1874.

THE MARITIME ACADEMIES

THE STATE UNIVERSITY OF NEW YORK (SUNY) MARITIME COLLEGE

The New York Maritime College, located at Fort Schuyler, Bronx, New York, is the oldest of the maritime academies. Founded in 1875 as the Nautical School, it became so successful that the states of Massachusetts, California, Maine, Texas, and finally Michigan founded their own academies.

This, the first maritime academy, was founded due to the actions of a group of New York citizens. Alarmed at the worsening condition of the maritime service following the Civil War, these citizens appealed to the New York State legislature. The first class of 26 young men (aged 15 to 19) boarded the sloop of war USS *St. Mary's*, berthed in the East River. The schoolship was later replaced by the USS *Newport,* also on loan from the Navy by Act of Congress.

Not until 1934 was a shore facility acquired, at the present site, which once was a pentagon-shaped Army post (the Pentagon in Washington, D.C., was patterned after it). During World War II, the college was the training site for Naval Reserve officers and Merchant Marine cadets.

The Maritime College is one of 32 specialized colleges of the State University of New York. Most of the men and women students are enrolled in the four-year course as cadets in the Maritime Service program, with others in the NROTC unit that was established in 1974. A master's degree is available in transportation management or engineering. The curriculum includes courses in meteorology, oceanography, nuclear science, and naval architecture. A multi-million-dollar modernization program has been completed.

Cadets wear uniforms, participate in intercollegiate sports and in the intramural program, and have the advantage of proximity to cultural activities in New York City. On-the-job summer training is in the schoolship TS *Empire State*.

THE MASSACHUSETTS MARITIME ACADEMY

The second oldest of the maritime academies is the Massachusetts Maritime Academy, founded in 1891 as the Massachusetts Nautical Training School, located at Boston. In 1942 the school was moved to Buzzards Bay and given its present name. In 1964, legislation placed the academy within the Massachusetts State College system.

The first training ship was the USS *Enterprise,* loaned to the Commonwealth by the federal government in 1892, with the first class of 40 cadets going on board the following year.

The Corps of Cadets engage in varsity athletics and an intramural program. A new building program has been completed, and the enrollment has tripled in recent years. In 1975 the Academy was designated as a Commonwealth Marine Sciences Center. Cadets have summer training in TS *Bay State*.

THE CALIFORNIA MARITIME ACADEMY

In 1929 the California Maritime Academy was established as the California Nautical School. Located on the shores of the Carquinez Strait, the Academy has the advantage of being in the San Francisco Bay area with its cultural activities *and* its access to the sea, so midshipmen are afforded the opportunity to make trips in oceangoing vessels.

The Corps of Midshipmen includes women, and a four-year program leads to a baccalaureate degree and licensing. There are two core curricula—nautical industrial technology and marine engineering technology—as well as special schools and certification in such fields as Navy firefighting and damage-control. Midshipmen can also be certified as Coast Guard lifeboatmen or able seamen. The annual summer cruise is in TS *Golden Bear.*

THE MAINE MARITIME ACADEMY

The Maine Maritime Academy was founded in 1941 on the shores of Penobscot Bay at Castine, with the first class composed of 28 midshipmen. The Regiment of Midshipmen includes both men and women.

Following World War II the curriculum was expanded from 18 months to the present four-year program. Upon completion of the sophomore year, students in the nautical science and marine engineering programs may be assigned aboard merchant ships as cadets for a 60-day training period.

The midshipmen take part in team sports and such extracurricular activities as the scuba club, the propeller club, the precision drill team, and the "Singing Mariners," who make an annual fall tour. Members of the faculty and the midshipmen, over a three-year period, built a tanker simulator for training in tanker operations, the only one of its kind in existence. This provides for the loading and discharging of liquid cargo under simulated shipboard conditions.

THE TEXAS MARITIME ACADEMY

The Texas Maritime Academy was established at Galveston in 1962. Since 1971 it has operated academically as a division of Moody College of Marine Sciences and Maritime Resources of Texas A&M University. Classes are held on Mitchell campus at Pelican Island as well as at Fort Crockett on Galveston Island.

The TS *Texas Clipper* serves uniformed cadets as classroom and dormitory both ashore and at sea. The converted cargo-passenger liner is berthed at Pelican Island during the regular school year and is manned by cadets each summer on a nine-week training cruise. The four-year course is coeducational, and high school graduates who are entering the university may earn six college semester hours aboard the clipper during the summer cruise.

Moody College of Marine Sciences and Maritime Resources offers only marine-related degree programs. Its two divisions, the Texas Maritime Academy and the Department of Marine Sciences, lead to a bachelor's degree in marine sciences. A third component is the research Galveston Coastal Zone Laboratory. All programs lead to a Bachelor of Science degree from Texas A&M.

Students meeting Coast Guard requirements may take examinations for licensing.

GREAT LAKES MARITIME ACADEMY
OF NORTHWESTERN MICHIGAN COLLEGE

The youngest of the maritime academies is the Great Lakes Maritime Academy located at Traverse City, Michigan. This academy prepares young men to serve as officers aboard Great Lakes ships, and it is the only maritime academy to operate on fresh water. It was founded in 1969.

Cadets are part of the student body at NMC, live in the residence halls with other students, and wear uniforms only in marine classes, on cruises, or on other military occasions.

The Academy is a division of a community college that offers the Associate of Science Degree and qualifies cadets to be examined under Coast Guard regulations for either a first-class pilot license (Great Lakes) or a third assistant engineer's license. Included in the three-year program is a minimum of nine months' training in basic seamanship and engine mechanics sailing in Great Lakes ships.

THE U.S. MERCHANT MARINE ACADEMY

The U.S. Merchant Marine Cadet Corps was established in March 1938, with training for the midshipmen held aboard merchant ships and, later, at temporary shore establishments. In 1942, permanent facilities were set up on the former Walter P. Chrysler estate at Kings Point, New York, overlooking Long Island Sound. Dedication services were held on the 68-acre campus in September 1943, when the Academy's present name was established. Recently, an additional 8-acre tract was acquired. In 1971 the National Maritime Research Center was located on the grounds.

During World War II the enrollment was increased, but the course of instruction reduced to two years. By the end of the war the four-year course as originally planned was instituted. During the war years the Academy graduated 6,634 officers.

Kings Point, as the Academy is referred to, was the first of the maritime or service academies to accept women—in 1974—with approximately 40 currently enrolled.

Midshipmen can choose from three basic curricula: Nautical Science, for the preparation of deck officers who will receive a U.S. Coast Guard license; Marine Engineering, for those who will become licensed as third assistant engineers; and a combined curriculum, the Dual License Program, which leads to licenses in both specialties. Commissions are in the U.S. Naval Reserve.

Sea training is a special feature of the Kings Point program, with each midshipman assigned with a fellow student to an operating vessel of the merchant fleet for two half-year intervals. A Bachelor of Science degree is granted to all graduates.

Due to the school's proximity to New York City, varied cultural programs are available. There is a full varsity and intramural program, and the sailing squadron frequently participates in races on Long Island Sound. The Academy yachts take part in the Marblehead to Halifax race, the Annapolis to Newport race, and several other ocean races.

Index

Italicized page numbers indicate illustrations.